Linear Algebra and Its Applications

Gilbert Strang

CENGAGE Learning

Australia • Brazil • Japan • Korea • Mexico • Singapore • Spain • United Kingdom • United States

CENGAGE Learning

Linear Algebra and Its Applications

Executive Editors:
Maureen Staudt
Michael Stranz

Senior Project Development Manager:
Linda deStefano

Marketing Specialist:
Courtney Sheldon

Senior Production/Manufacturing Manager:
Donna M. Brown

PreMedia Manager:
Joel Brennecke

Sr. Rights Acquisition Account Manager:
Todd Osborne

Cover Image: stock.xchng

Linear Algebra and Its Applications, 4th Edition
Gilbert Strang

Library of Congress Control Number: 2005923623

ISBN-13: 978-1-133-44289-9

ISBN-10: 1-133-44289-7

Cengage Learning
5191 Natorp Boulevard
Mason, Ohio 45040
USA

Cengage Learning is a leading provider of customized learning solutions with office locations around the globe, including Singapore, the United Kingdom, Australia, Mexico, Brazil, and Japan. Locate your local office at:
international.cengage.com/region.

Cengage Learning products are represented in Canada by Nelson Education, Ltd.
For your lifelong learning solutions, visit **www.cengage.com/custom.**
Visit our corporate website at **www.cengage.com.**

Printed in the United States of America

Table of Contents

Preface

Revising this textbook has been a special challenge, for a very nice reason. So many people have read this book, and taught from it, and even loved it. The spirit of the book could never change. This text was written to help our teaching of linear algebra keep up with the enormous importance of this subject—which just continues to grow.

One step was certainly possible and desirable—*to add new problems*. Teaching for all these years required hundreds of new exam questions (especially with quizzes going onto the web). I think you will approve of the extended choice of problems. The questions are still a mixture of *explain* and *compute*—the two complementary approaches to learning this beautiful subject.

I personally believe that many more people need linear algebra than calculus. Isaac Newton might not agree ! But he isn't teaching mathematics in the 21st century (and maybe he wasn't a great teacher, but we will give him the benefit of the doubt). Certainly the laws of physics are well expressed by differential equations. Newton needed calculus—quite right. But the scope of science and engineering and management (and life) is now so much wider, and linear algebra has moved into a central place.

May I say a little more, because many universities have not yet adjusted the balance toward linear algebra. Working with curved lines and curved surfaces, the first step is always to *linearize*. Replace the curve by its tangent line, fit the surface by a plane, and the problem becomes linear. The power of this subject comes when you have ten variables, or 1000 variables, instead of two.

You might think I am exaggerating to use the word "beautiful" for a basic course in mathematics. Not at all. This subject begins with two vectors v and w, pointing in different directions. The key step is to *take their linear combinations*. We multiply to get $3v$ and $4w$, and we add to get the particular combination $3v + 4w$. That new vector is in the *same plane* as v and w. When we take all combinations, we are filling in the whole plane. If I draw v and w on this page, their combinations $cv + dw$ fill the page (and beyond), but they *don't go up* from the page.

In the language of linear equations, I can solve $cv + dw = b$ exactly when the vector b lies in the same plane as v and w.

Matrices

I will keep going a little more to convert combinations of three-dimensional vectors into linear algebra. If the vectors are $v = (1, 2, 3)$ and $w = (1, 3, 4)$, put them into the **columns of a matrix**:

$$\textbf{matrix} = \begin{bmatrix} 1 & 1 \\ 2 & 3 \\ 3 & 4 \end{bmatrix}.$$

To find combinations of those columns, "**multiply**" the matrix by a vector (c, d):

$$\textbf{Linear combinations } c\boldsymbol{v} + d\boldsymbol{w} \qquad \begin{bmatrix} 1 & 1 \\ 2 & 3 \\ 3 & 4 \end{bmatrix} \begin{bmatrix} c \\ d \end{bmatrix} = c \begin{bmatrix} 1 \\ 2 \\ 3 \end{bmatrix} + d \begin{bmatrix} 1 \\ 3 \\ 4 \end{bmatrix}.$$

Those combinations fill a *vector space*. We call it the **column space** of the matrix. (For these two columns, that space is a plane.) To decide if $b = (2, 5, 7)$ is on that plane, we have three components to get right. So we have three equations to solve:

$$\begin{bmatrix} 1 & 1 \\ 2 & 3 \\ 3 & 4 \end{bmatrix} \begin{bmatrix} c \\ d \end{bmatrix} = \begin{bmatrix} 2 \\ 5 \\ 7 \end{bmatrix} \quad \text{means} \quad \begin{aligned} c + \ d &= 2 \\ 2c + 3d &= 5 \\ 3c + 4d &= 7. \end{aligned}$$

I leave the solution to you. The vector $b = (2, 5, 7)$ does lie in the plane of v and w. If the 7 changes to any other number, then b won't lie in the plane—it will *not* be a combination of v and w, and the three equations will have no solution.

Now I can describe the first part of the book, about linear equations $Ax = b$. The matrix A has n columns and m rows. *Linear algebra moves steadily to n vectors in m-dimensional space.* We still want combinations of the columns (in the column space). We still get m equations to produce b (one for each row). Those equations may or may not have a solution. They always have a least-squares solution.

The interplay of columns and rows is the heart of linear algebra. It's not totally easy, but it's not too hard. Here are four of the central ideas:

1. The **column space** (all combinations of the columns).
2. The **row space** (all combinations of the rows).
3. The **rank** (the number of independent columns) (or rows).
4. **Elimination** (the good way to find the rank of a matrix).

I will stop here, so you can start the course.

Web Pages

It may be helpful to mention the web pages connected to this book. So many messages come back with suggestions and encouragement, and I hope you will make free use of everything. You can directly access *http://web.mit.edu/18.06*, which is continually updated for the course that is taught every semester. Linear algebra is also on MIT's OpenCourseWare site *http://ocw.mit.edu*, where 18.06 became exceptional by including videos of the lectures (which you definitely don't have to watch...). Here is a part of what is available on the web:

1. Lecture schedule and current homeworks and exams with solutions.
2. The goals of the course, and conceptual questions.
3. Interactive Java demos (audio is now included for eigenvalues).
4. Linear Algebra Teaching Codes and MATLAB problems.
5. Videos of the complete course (taught in a real classroom).

The course page has become a valuable link to the class, and a resource for the students. I am very optimistic about the potential for graphics with sound. The bandwidth for voiceover is low, and FlashPlayer is freely available. This offers a *quick review* (with active experiment), and the full lectures can be downloaded. I hope professors and students worldwide will find these web pages helpful. My goal is to make this book as useful as possible with all the course material I can provide.

Other Supporting Materials

Student Solutions Manual 0-495-01325-0 The Student Solutions Manual provides solutions to the odd-numbered problems in the text.

Instructor's Solutions Manual 0-030-10568-4 The Instructor's Solutions Manual has teaching notes for each chapter and solutions to all of the problems in the text.

Structure of the Course

The two fundamental problems are $Ax = b$ and $Ax = \lambda x$ for square matrices A. The first problem $Ax = b$ has a solution when A has *independent columns*. The second problem $Ax = \lambda x$ looks for *independent eigenvectors*. A crucial part of this course is to learn what "independence" means.

I believe that most of us learn first from examples. You can see that

$$A = \begin{bmatrix} 1 & 1 & 2 \\ 1 & 2 & 3 \\ 1 & 3 & 4 \end{bmatrix} \qquad \textbf{does } \textbf{\textit{not}} \textbf{ have independent columns}.$$

Column 1 plus column 2 equals column 3. A wonderful theorem of linear algebra says that the three rows are not independent either. The third row must lie in the same plane as the first two rows. Some combination of rows 1 and 2 will produce row 3. You might find that combination quickly (I didn't). In the end I had to use elimination to discover that the right combination uses 2 times row 2, minus row 1.

Elimination is the simple and natural way to understand a matrix by producing a lot of zero entries. So the course starts there. But don't stay there too long! You have to get from combinations of the rows, to independence of the rows, to "dimension of the row space." That is a key goal, to see whole spaces of vectors: the ***row space*** and the ***column space*** and the ***nullspace.***

A further goal is to understand how the matrix *acts*. When A multiplies x it produces the new vector Ax. The whole space of vectors moves—it is "transformed" by A. Special transformations come from particular matrices, and those are the foundation stones of linear algebra: diagonal matrices, orthogonal matrices, triangular matrices, symmetric matrices.

The eigenvalues of those matrices are special too. I think 2 by 2 matrices provide terrific examples of the information that eigenvalues λ can give. Sections 5.1 and 5.2 are worth careful reading, to see how $Ax = \lambda x$ is useful. Here is a case in which small matrices allow tremendous insight.

Overall, the beauty of linear algebra is seen in so many different ways:

1. **Visualization.** Combinations of vectors. Spaces of vectors. Rotation and reflection and projection of vectors. Perpendicular vectors. Four fundamental subspaces.

2. Abstraction. Independence of vectors. Basis and dimension of a vector space. Linear transformations. Singular value decomposition and the best basis.

3. Computation. Elimination to produce zero entries. Gram–Schmidt to produce orthogonal vectors. Eigenvalues to solve differential and difference equations.

4. Applications. Least-squares solution when $Ax = b$ has too many equations. Difference equations approximating differential equations. Markov probability matrices (the basis for Google!). Orthogonal eigenvectors as principal axes (and more . . .).

To go further with those applications, may I mention the books published by Wellesley-Cambridge Press. They are all linear algebra in disguise, applied to signal processing and partial differential equations and scientific computing (and even GPS). If you look at *http://www.wellesleycambridge.com*, you will see part of the reason that linear algebra is so widely used.

After this preface, the book will speak for itself. You will see the spirit right away. The emphasis is on understanding—*I try to explain rather than to deduce*. This is a book about real mathematics, not endless drill. In class, I am constantly working with examples to teach what students need.

Acknowledgments

I enjoyed writing this book, and I certainly hope you enjoy reading it. A big part of the pleasure comes from working with friends. I had wonderful help from Brett Coonley and Cordula Robinson and Erin Maneri. They created the LaTeX files and drew all the figures. Without Brett's steady support I would never have completed this new edition.

Earlier help with the Teaching Codes came from Steven Lee and Cleve Moler. Those follow the steps described in the book; MATLAB and Maple and Mathematica are faster for large matrices. All can be used (*optionally*) in this course. I could have added "Factorization" to that list above, as a fifth avenue to the understanding of matrices:

[L,U,P] = lu(A) for linear equations
[Q,R] = qr(A) to make the columns orthogonal
[S,E] = eig(A) to find eigenvectors and eigenvalues.

In giving thanks, I never forget the first dedication of this textbook, years ago. That was a special chance to thank my parents for so many unselfish gifts. Their example is an inspiration for my life.

And I thank the reader too, hoping you like this book.

Gilbert Strang

Chapter 1

Matrices and Gaussian Elimination

1.1 INTRODUCTION

This book begins with the central problem of linear algebra: *solving linear equations.* The most important case, and the simplest, is when the number of unknowns equals the number of equations. We have ***n equations in n unknowns***, starting with $n = 2$:

$$\begin{array}{ll} \textbf{Two equations} & 1x + 2y = 3 \\ \textbf{Two unknowns} & 4x + 5y = 6. \end{array} \qquad (1)$$

The unknowns are x and y. I want to describe two ways, *elimination* and *determinants*, to solve these equations. Certainly x and y are determined by the numbers 1, 2, 3, 4, 5, 6. The question is how to use those six numbers to solve the system.

1. Elimination Subtract 4 times the first equation from the second equation. This eliminates x from the second equation, and it leaves one equation for y:

$$\textbf{(equation 2)} - \textbf{4(equation 1)} \qquad -3y = -6. \qquad (2)$$

Immediately we know $y = 2$. Then x comes from the first equation $1x + 2y = 3$:

$$\textbf{Back-substitution} \qquad 1x + 2(2) = 3 \quad \text{gives} \quad x = -1. \qquad (3)$$

Proceeding carefully, we check that x and y also solve the second equation. This should work and it does: 4 times $(x = -1)$ plus 5 times $(y = 2)$ equals 6.

2. Determinants The solution $y = 2$ depends completely on those six numbers in the equations. There must be a formula for y (and also x). It is a "ratio of determinants" and I hope you will allow me to write it down directly:

$$y = \frac{\begin{vmatrix} 1 & 3 \\ 4 & 6 \end{vmatrix}}{\begin{vmatrix} 1 & 2 \\ 4 & 5 \end{vmatrix}} = \frac{1 \cdot 6 - 3 \cdot 4}{1 \cdot 5 - 2 \cdot 4} = \frac{-6}{-3} = 2. \qquad (4)$$

That could seem a little mysterious, unless you already know about 2 by 2 determinants. They gave the same answer $y = 2$, coming from the same ratio of -6 to -3. If we stay with determinants (which we don't plan to do), there will be a similar formula to compute the other unknown, x:

$$x = \frac{\begin{vmatrix} 3 & 2 \\ 6 & 5 \end{vmatrix}}{\begin{vmatrix} 1 & 2 \\ 4 & 5 \end{vmatrix}} = \frac{3 \cdot 5 - 2 \cdot 6}{1 \cdot 5 - 2 \cdot 4} = \frac{3}{-3} = -1. \tag{5}$$

Let me compare those two approaches, looking ahead to real problems when n is much larger ($n = 1000$ is a very moderate size in scientific computing). The truth is that direct use of the determinant formula for 1000 equations would be a total disaster. It would use the million numbers on the left sides correctly, but not efficiently. We will find that formula (Cramer's Rule) in Chapter 4, but we want a good method to solve 1000 equations in Chapter 1.

That good method is ***Gaussian Elimination***. This is the algorithm that is constantly used to solve large systems of equations. From the examples in a textbook ($n = 3$ is close to the upper limit on the patience of the author and reader) you might not see much difference. Equations (2) and (4) used essentially the same steps to find $y = 2$. Certainly x came faster by the back-substitution in equation (3) than the ratio in (5). For larger n there is absolutely no question. Elimination wins (and this is even the best way to compute determinants).

The idea of elimination is deceptively simple—you will master it after a few examples. It will become the basis for half of this book, simplifying a matrix so that we can understand it. Together with the mechanics of the algorithm, we want to explain four deeper aspects in this chapter. They are:

1. Linear equations lead to ***geometry of planes***. It is not easy to visualize a nine-dimensional plane in ten-dimensional space. It is harder to see ten of those planes, intersecting at the solution to ten equations—but somehow this is almost possible. Our example has two lines in Figure 1.1, meeting at the point $(x, y) = (-1, 2)$. Linear algebra moves that picture into ten dimensions, where the intuition has to imagine the geometry (and gets it right).
2. We move to ***matrix notation***, writing the n unknowns as a vector x and the n equations as $Ax = b$. We multiply A by "elimination matrices" to reach an upper triangular matrix U. Those steps factor A into L *times* U, where L is lower

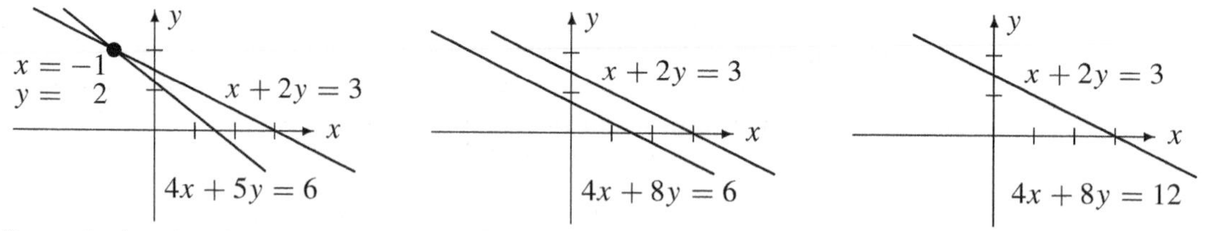

One solution $(x, y) = (-1, 2)$ **Parallel: No solution** **Whole line of solutions**

Figure 1.1 The example has one solution. Singular cases have none or too many.

triangular. I will write down A and its factors for our example, and explain them at the right time:

$$\textbf{Factorization} \qquad A = \begin{bmatrix} 1 & 2 \\ 4 & 5 \end{bmatrix} = \begin{bmatrix} 1 & 0 \\ 4 & 1 \end{bmatrix} \begin{bmatrix} 1 & 2 \\ 0 & -3 \end{bmatrix} = L \textit{ times } U. \qquad (6)$$

First we have to introduce matrices and vectors and the rules for multiplication. Every matrix has a ***transpose*** A^{T}. This matrix has an ***inverse*** A^{-1}.

3. In most cases elimination goes forward without difficulties. The matrix has an inverse and the system $Ax = b$ has one solution. In exceptional cases the method will *break down*—either the equations were written in the wrong order, which is easily fixed by exchanging them, or the equations don't have a unique solution.

   That ***singular case*** will appear if 8 replaces 5 in our example:

$$\begin{array}{lrcrcr} \textbf{Singular case} & 1x & + & 2y & = & 3 \\ \textbf{Two parallel lines} & 4x & + & \mathbf{8}y & = & 6. \end{array} \qquad (7)$$

   Elimination still innocently subtracts 4 times the first equation from the second. But look at the result!

$$\textbf{(equation 2)} - \textbf{4(equation 1)} \qquad 0 = -6.$$

   This singular case has ***no solution***. Other singular cases have ***infinitely many solutions***. (Change 6 to 12 in the example, and elimination will lead to $0 = 0$. Now y can have *any value*.) When elimination breaks down, we want to find every possible solution.

4. We need a rough count of the ***number of elimination steps*** required to solve a system of size n. The computing cost often determines the accuracy in the model. A hundred equations require a third of a million steps (multiplications and subtractions). The computer can do those quickly, but not many trillions. And already after a million steps, roundoff error could be significant. (Some problems are sensitive; others are not.) Without trying for full detail, we want to see large systems that arise in practice, and how they are actually solved.

The final result of this chapter will be an elimination algorithm that is about as efficient as possible. It is essentially the algorithm that is in constant use in a tremendous variety of applications. And at the same time, understanding it in terms of *matrices*—the coefficient matrix A, the matrices E for elimination and P for row exchanges, and the final factors L and U—is an essential foundation for the theory. I hope you will enjoy this book and this course.

1.2 THE GEOMETRY OF LINEAR EQUATIONS

The way to understand this subject is by example. We begin with two extremely humble equations, recognizing that you could solve them without a course in linear algebra. Nevertheless I hope you will give Gauss a chance:

$$\begin{aligned} 2x - y &= 1 \\ x + y &= 5. \end{aligned}$$

We can look at that system *by rows or by columns*. We want to see them both.

The first approach concentrates on the separate equations (the ***rows***). That is the most familiar, and in two dimensions we can do it quickly. The equation $2x - y = 1$ is represented by a *straight line* in the x-y plane. The line goes through the points $x = 1$, $y = 1$ and $x = \frac{1}{2}$, $y = 0$ (and also through $(2, 3)$ and all intermediate points). The second equation $x + y = 5$ produces a second line (Figure 1.2a). Its slope is $dy/dx = -1$ and it crosses the first line at the solution.

The point of intersection lies on both lines. It is the only solution to both equations. That point $x = 2$ and $y = 3$ will soon be found by "elimination."

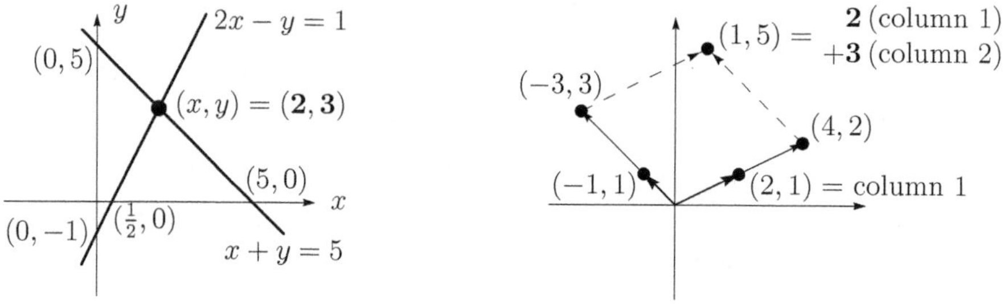

(a) **Lines meet at $x = 2, y = 3$** (b) **Columns combine with 2 and 3**

Figure 1.2 Row picture (two lines) and column picture (combine columns).

The second approach looks at the ***columns*** of the linear system. The two separate equations are really ***one vector equation***:

$$\textbf{Column form} \qquad x\begin{bmatrix}2\\1\end{bmatrix} + y\begin{bmatrix}-1\\1\end{bmatrix} = \begin{bmatrix}1\\5\end{bmatrix}.$$

The problem is ***to find the combination of the column vectors on the left side that produces the vector on the right side.*** Those vectors $(2, 1)$ and $(-1, 1)$ are represented by the bold lines in Figure 1.2b. The unknowns are the numbers x and y that multiply the column vectors. The whole idea can be seen in that figure, where 2 times column 1 is added to 3 times column 2. Geometrically this produces a famous parallelogram. Algebraically it produces the correct vector $(1, 5)$, on the right side of our equations. The column picture confirms that $x = 2$ and $y = 3$.

More time could be spent on that example, but I would rather move forward to $n = 3$. Three equations are still manageable, and they have much more variety:

$$\textbf{Three planes} \qquad \begin{aligned} 2u + v + w &= 5 \\ 4u - 6v &= -2 \\ -2u + 7v + 2w &= 9. \end{aligned} \tag{1}$$

Again we can study the rows or the columns, and we start with the rows. Each equation describes a ***plane*** in three dimensions. The first plane is $2u + v + w = 5$, and it is sketched in Figure 1.3. It contains the points $(\frac{5}{2}, 0, 0)$ and $(0, 5, 0)$ and $(0, 0, 5)$. It is determined by any three of its points—provided they do not lie on a line.

Changing 5 *to* 10, *the plane* $2u + v + w = 10$ *would be parallel to this one.* It contains $(5, 0, 0)$ and $(0, 10, 0)$ and $(0, 0, 10)$, twice as far from the origin—which is

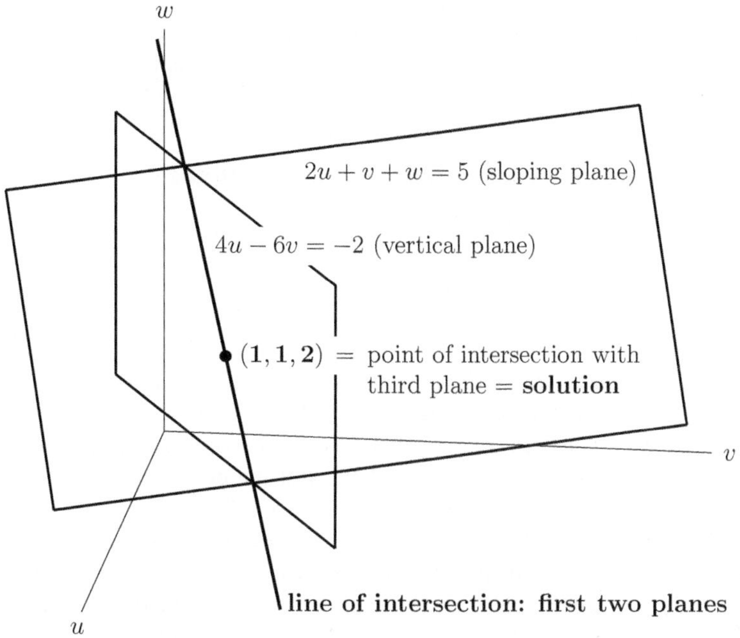

Figure 1.3 The row picture: three intersecting planes from three linear equations.

the center point $u = 0$, $v = 0$, $w = 0$. Changing the right side moves the plane parallel to itself, and the plane $2u + v + w = 0$ goes through the origin.

The second plane is $4u - 6v = -2$. It is drawn vertically, because w can take any value. The coefficient of w is zero, but this remains a plane in 3-space. (The equation $4u = 3$, or even the extreme case $u = 0$, would still describe a plane.) The figure shows the intersection of the second plane with the first. That intersection is a line. *In three dimensions a line requires two equations*; in n dimensions it will require $n - 1$.

Finally the third plane intersects this line in a point. The plane (not drawn) represents the third equation $-2u + 7v + 2w = 9$, and it crosses the line at $u = 1$, $v = 1$, $w = 2$. That triple intersection point $(1, 1, 2)$ solves the linear system.

How does this row picture extend into n dimensions? The n equations will contain n unknowns. The first equation still determines a "plane." It is no longer a two-dimensional plane in 3-space; somehow it has "dimension" $n - 1$. It must be flat and extremely thin within n-dimensional space, although it would look solid to us.

If time is the fourth dimension, then the plane $t = 0$ cuts through four-dimensional space and produces the three-dimensional universe we live in (or rather, the universe as it was at $t = 0$). Another plane is $z = 0$, which is also three-dimensional; it is the ordinary x-y plane taken over all time. Those three-dimensional planes will intersect! They share the ordinary x-y plane at $t = 0$. We are down to two dimensions, and the next plane leaves a line. Finally a fourth plane leaves a single point. It is the intersection point of 4 planes in 4 dimensions, and it solves the 4 underlying equations.

I will be in trouble if that example from relativity goes any further. The point is that linear algebra can operate with any number of equations. The first equation produces an $(n - 1)$-dimensional plane in n dimensions. The second plane intersects it (we hope) in a smaller set of "dimension $n-2$." Assuming all goes well, every new plane (every new equation) reduces the dimension by one. At the end, when all n planes are accounted for, the intersection has dimension zero. It is a *point*, it lies on all the planes, and its coordinates satisfy all n equations. It is the solution!

Column Vectors and Linear Combinations

We turn to the columns. This time the vector equation (the same equation as (1)) is

$$\textbf{Column form} \qquad u\begin{bmatrix}2\\4\\-2\end{bmatrix}+v\begin{bmatrix}1\\-6\\7\end{bmatrix}+w\begin{bmatrix}1\\0\\2\end{bmatrix}=\begin{bmatrix}5\\-2\\9\end{bmatrix}=b. \tag{2}$$

Those are *three-dimensional column vectors*. ***The vector b is identified with the point whose coordinates are* 5, −2, 9**. Every point in three-dimensional space is matched to a vector, and vice versa. That was the idea of Descartes, who turned geometry into algebra by working with the coordinates of the point. We can write the vector in a column, or we can list its components as $b=(5,-2,9)$, or we can represent it geometrically by an arrow from the origin. You can choose *the arrow*, or *the point*, or *the three numbers*. In six dimensions it is probably easiest to choose the six numbers.

We use parentheses and commas when the components are listed horizontally, and square brackets (with no commas) when a column vector is printed vertically. What really matters is ***addition of vectors*** and ***multiplication by a scalar*** (a number). In Figure 1.4a you see a vector addition, component by component:

$$\textbf{Vector addition} \qquad \begin{bmatrix}5\\0\\0\end{bmatrix}+\begin{bmatrix}0\\-2\\0\end{bmatrix}+\begin{bmatrix}0\\0\\9\end{bmatrix}=\begin{bmatrix}5\\-2\\9\end{bmatrix}.$$

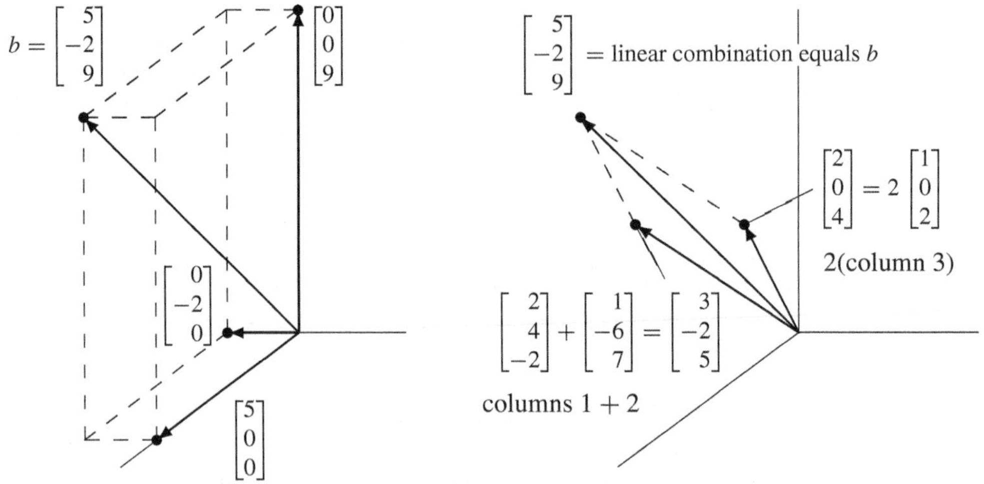

(a) **Add vectors along axes** (b) **Add columns 1 + 2 + (3 + 3)**

Figure 1.4 The column picture: linear combination of columns equals b.

In the right-hand figure there is a multiplication by 2 (and if it had been -2 the vector would have gone in the reverse direction):

$$\textbf{Multiplication by scalars} \qquad 2\begin{bmatrix}1\\0\\2\end{bmatrix} = \begin{bmatrix}2\\0\\4\end{bmatrix}, \qquad -2\begin{bmatrix}1\\0\\2\end{bmatrix} = \begin{bmatrix}-2\\0\\-4\end{bmatrix}.$$

Also in the right-hand figure is one of the central ideas of linear algebra. It uses *both* of the basic operations; vectors are *multiplied by numbers and then added.* The result is called a ***linear combination***, and this combination solves our equation:

$$\textbf{Linear combination} \qquad \mathbf{1}\begin{bmatrix}2\\4\\-2\end{bmatrix} + \mathbf{1}\begin{bmatrix}1\\-6\\7\end{bmatrix} + \mathbf{2}\begin{bmatrix}1\\0\\2\end{bmatrix} = \begin{bmatrix}5\\-2\\9\end{bmatrix}.$$

Equation (2) asked for multipliers u, v, w that produce the right side b. Those numbers are $u = \mathbf{1}$, $v = \mathbf{1}$, $w = \mathbf{2}$. They give the correct combination of the columns. They also gave the point $(1, 1, 2)$ in the row picture (where the three planes intersect).

Our true goal is to look beyond two or three dimensions into n dimensions. With n equations in n unknowns, there are n planes in the row picture. There are n vectors in the column picture, plus a vector b on the right side. The equations ask for a ***linear combination of the n columns that equals b***. For certain equations that will be impossible. Paradoxically, the way to understand the good case is to study the bad one. Therefore we look at the geometry exactly when it breaks down, in the **singular case**.

Row picture: Intersection of planes	***Column picture***: Combination of columns

The Singular Case

Suppose we are again in three dimensions, and the three planes in the row picture *do not intersect*. What can go wrong? One possibility is that two planes may be parallel. The equations $2u + v + w = 5$ and $4u + 2v + 2w = 11$ are inconsistent—and parallel planes give no solution (Figure 1.5a shows an end view). In two dimensions, parallel lines are the only possibility for breakdown. But three planes in three dimensions can be in trouble without being parallel.

The most common difficulty is shown in Figure 1.5b. From the end view the planes form a triangle. Every pair of planes intersects in a line, and those lines are parallel. The

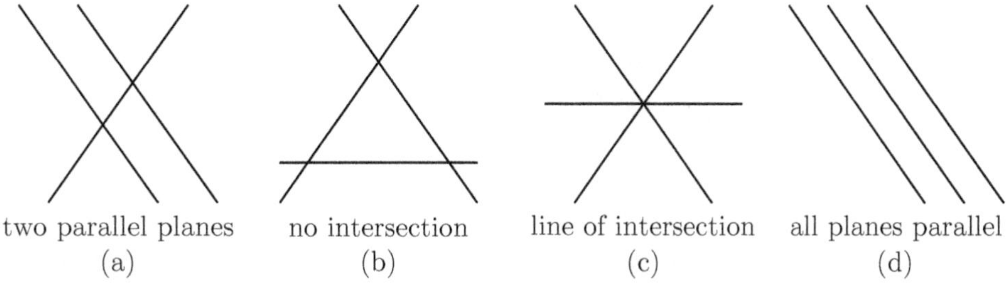

Figure 1.5 Singular cases: no solution for (a), (b), or (d), an infinity of solutions for (c).

third plane is not parallel to the other planes, but it is parallel to their line of intersection. This corresponds to a singular system with $b = (2, 5, 6)$:

$$\textbf{No solution, as in Figure 1.5b} \qquad \begin{aligned} u + v + w &= 2 \\ 2u + 3w &= 5 \\ 3u + v + 4w &= 6. \end{aligned} \tag{3}$$

The first two left sides add up to the third. On the right side that fails: $2 + 5 \neq 6$. Equation 1 plus equation 2 minus equation 3 is the impossible statement $0 = 1$. Thus the equations are ***inconsistent***, as Gaussian elimination will systematically discover.

Another singular system, close to this one, has an **infinity of solutions**. When the 6 in the last equation becomes 7, the three equations combine to give $0 = 0$. Now the third equation is the sum of the first two. In that case the three planes have a whole *line in common* (Figure 1.5c). Changing the right sides will move the planes in Figure 1.5b parallel to themselves, and for $b = (2, 5, 7)$ the figure is suddenly different. The lowest plane moved up to meet the others, and there is a line of solutions. Problem 1.5c is still singular, but now it suffers from ***too many solutions*** instead of too few.

The extreme case is three parallel planes. For most right sides there is no solution (Figure 1.5d). For special right sides (like $b = (0, 0, 0)$!) there is a whole plane of solutions—because the three parallel planes move over to become the same.

What happens to the ***column picture*** when the system is singular? It has to go wrong; the question is how. There are still three columns on the left side of the equations, and we try to combine them to produce b. Stay with equation (3):

Singular case: Column picture
Three columns in the same plane
Solvable only for b in that plane

$$u \begin{bmatrix} 1 \\ 2 \\ 3 \end{bmatrix} + v \begin{bmatrix} 1 \\ 0 \\ 1 \end{bmatrix} + w \begin{bmatrix} 1 \\ 3 \\ 4 \end{bmatrix} = b. \tag{4}$$

For $b = (2, 5, 7)$ this was possible; for $b = (2, 5, 6)$ it was not. The reason is that ***those three columns lie in a plane***. Then every combination is also in the plane (which goes through the origin). If the vector b is not in that plane, no solution is possible (Figure 1.6). That is by far the most likely event; a singular system generally has no solution. But

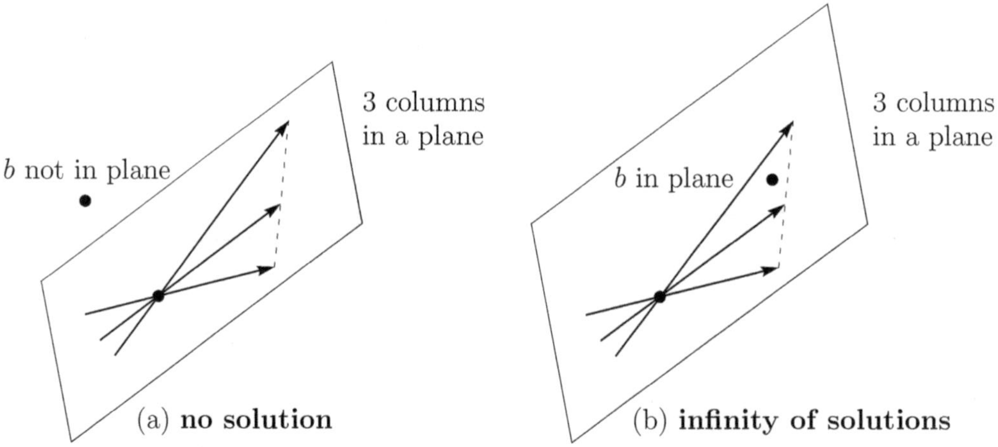

Figure 1.6 Singular cases: b outside or inside the plane with all three columns.

there is a chance that b *does* lie in the plane of the columns. In that case there are too many solutions; the three columns can be combined in *infinitely many ways* to produce b. That column picture in Figure 1.6b corresponds to the row picture in Figure 1.5c.

How do we know that the three columns lie in the same plane? One answer is to find a combination of the columns that adds to zero. After some calculation, it is $u = 3$, $v = -1$, $w = -2$. Three times column 1 equals column 2 plus twice column 3. Column 1 is in the plane of columns 2 and 3. Only two columns are independent.

The vector $b = (2, 5, 7)$ is in that plane of the columns—it is column 1 plus column 3—so $(1, 0, 1)$ is a solution. *We can add any multiple of the combination* $(3, -1, -2)$ *that gives* $b = 0$. So there is a whole line of solutions—as we know from the row picture.

The truth is that we *knew* the columns would combine to give zero, because the rows did. That is a fact of mathematics, not of computation—and it remains true in dimension n. ***If the n planes have no point in common, or infinitely many points, then the n columns lie in the same plane.***

If the row picture breaks down, so does the column picture. That brings out the difference between Chapter 1 and Chapter 2. This chapter studies the most important problem—the *nonsingular* case—where there is one solution and it has to be found. Chapter 2 studies the general case, where there may be many solutions or none. In both cases we cannot continue without a decent notation (*matrix notation*) and a decent algorithm (*elimination*). After the exercises, we start with elimination.

Problem Set 1.2

1. For the equations $x + y = 4$, $2x - 2y = 4$, draw the row picture (two intersecting lines) and the column picture (combination of two columns equal to the column vector $(4, 4)$ on the right side).

2. Solve to find a combination of the columns that equals b:

Triangular system
$$\begin{aligned} u - v - w &= b_1 \\ v + w &= b_2 \\ w &= b_3. \end{aligned}$$

3. (Recommended) Describe the intersection of the three planes $u + v + w + z = 6$ and $u + w + z = 4$ and $u + w = 2$ (all in four-dimensional space). Is it a line or a point or an empty set? What is the intersection if the fourth plane $u = -1$ is included? Find a fourth equation that leaves us with no solution.

4. Sketch these three lines and decide if the equations are solvable:

3 by 2 system
$$\begin{aligned} x + 2y &= 2 \\ x - y &= 2 \\ y &= 1. \end{aligned}$$

What happens if all right-hand sides are zero? Is there any nonzero choice of right-hand sides that allows the three lines to intersect at the same point?

5. Find two points on the line of intersection of the three planes $t = 0$ and $z = 0$ and $x + y + z + t = 1$ in four-dimensional space.

6. When $b = (2, 5, 7)$, find a solution (u, v, w) to equation (4) different from the solution $(1, 0, 1)$ mentioned in the text.

7. Give two more right-hand sides in addition to $b = (2, 5, 7)$ for which equation (4) can be solved. Give two more right-hand sides in addition to $b = (2, 5, 6)$ for which it cannot be solved.

8. Explain why the system

$$\begin{aligned} u + v + w &= 2 \\ u + 2v + 3w &= 1 \\ v + 2w &= 0 \end{aligned}$$

is singular by finding a combination of the three equations that adds up to $0 = 1$. What value should replace the last zero on the right side to allow the equations to have solutions—and what is one of the solutions?

9. The column picture for the previous exercise (singular system) is

$$u \begin{bmatrix} 1 \\ 1 \\ 0 \end{bmatrix} + v \begin{bmatrix} 1 \\ 2 \\ 1 \end{bmatrix} + w \begin{bmatrix} 1 \\ 3 \\ 2 \end{bmatrix} = b.$$

Show that the three columns on the left lie in the same plane by expressing the third column as a combination of the first two. What are all the solutions (u, v, w) if b is the zero vector $(0, 0, 0)$?

10. (Recommended) Under what condition on y_1, y_2, y_3 do the points $(0, y_1)$, $(1, y_2)$, $(2, y_3)$ lie on a straight line?

11. These equations are certain to have the solution $x = y = 0$. For which values of a is there a whole line of solutions?

$$\begin{aligned} ax + 2y &= 0 \\ 2x + ay &= 0 \end{aligned}$$

12. Starting with $x + 4y = 7$, find the equation for the parallel line through $x = 0$, $y = 0$. Find the equation of another line that meets the first at $x = 3$, $y = 1$.

Problems 13–15 are a review of the row and column pictures.

13. Draw the two pictures in two planes for the equations $x - 2y = 0$, $x + y = 6$.

14. For two linear equations in three unknowns x, y, z, the row picture will show (2 or 3) (lines or planes) in (two or three)-dimensional space. The column picture is in (two or three)-dimensional space. The solutions normally lie on a ______.

15. For four linear equations in two unknowns x and y, the row picture shows four ______. The column picture is in ______-dimensional space. The equations have no solution unless the vector on the right-hand side is a combination of ______.

16. Find a point with $z = 2$ on the intersection line of the planes $x + y + 3z = 6$ and $x - y + z = 4$. Find the point with $z = 0$ and a third point halfway between.

17. The first of these equations plus the second equals the third:

$$\begin{aligned} x + \ y + \ z &= 2 \\ x + 2y + \ z &= 3 \\ 2x + 3y + 2z &= 5. \end{aligned}$$

The first two planes meet along a line. The third plane contains that line, because if x, y, z satisfy the first two equations then they also ______. The equations have infinitely many solutions (the whole line **L**). Find three solutions.

18. Move the third plane in Problem 17 to a parallel plane $2x + 3y + 2z = 9$. Now the three equations have no solution—*why not*? The first two planes meet along the line **L**, but the third plane doesn't ______ that line.

19. In Problem 17 the columns are $(1, 1, 2)$ and $(1, 2, 3)$ and $(1, 1, 2)$. This is a "singular case" because the third column is ______. Find two combinations of the columns that give $b = (2, 3, 5)$. This is only possible for $b = (4, 6, c)$ if $c =$ ______.

20. Normally 4 "planes" in four-dimensional space meet at a ______. Normally 4 column vectors in four-dimensional space can combine to produce b. What combination of $(1, 0, 0, 0)$, $(1, 1, 0, 0)$, $(1, 1, 1, 0)$, $(1, 1, 1, 1)$ produces $b = (3, 3, 3, 2)$? What 4 equations for x, y, z, t are you solving?

21. When equation 1 is added to equation 2, which of these are changed: the planes in the row picture, the column picture, the coefficient matrix, the solution?

22. If (a, b) is a multiple of (c, d) with $abcd \neq 0$, *show that* (a, c) *is a multiple of* (b, d). This is surprisingly important: call it a challenge question. You could use numbers first to see how a, b, c, and d are related. The question will lead to:

$$\text{If } A = \begin{bmatrix} a & b \\ c & d \end{bmatrix} \text{ has dependent rows then it has dependent columns.}$$

23. In these equations, the third column (multiplying w) is the *same* as the right side b. The column form of the equations *immediately* gives what solution for (u, v, w)?

$$\begin{aligned} 6u + 7v + 8w &= 8 \\ 4u + 5v + 9w &= 9 \\ 2u - 2v + 7w &= 7. \end{aligned}$$

1.3 AN EXAMPLE OF GAUSSIAN ELIMINATION

The way to understand elimination is by example. We begin in three dimensions:

$$\textbf{Original system} \qquad \begin{aligned} 2u + \ v + \ w &= \ \ 5 \\ 4u - 6v \qquad &= -2 \\ -2u + 7v + 2w &= \ \ 9. \end{aligned} \tag{1}$$

The problem is to find the unknown values of u, v, and w, and we shall apply Gaussian elimination. (Gauss is recognized as the greatest of all mathematicians, but certainly not because of this invention, which probably took him ten minutes. Ironically, it is the most frequently used of all the ideas that bear his name.) The method starts by ***subtracting multiples of the first equation from the other equations***. The goal is to *eliminate u from the last two equations*. This requires that we

(a) subtract 2 times the first equation from the second
(b) subtract −1 times the first equation from the third.

$$\textbf{Equivalent system}\qquad \begin{aligned} \mathbf{2}u + v + w &= 5\\ -\mathbf{8}v - 2w &= -12\\ 8v + 3w &= 14. \end{aligned} \tag{2}$$

The coefficient 2 is the ***first pivot***. Elimination is constantly dividing the pivot into the numbers underneath it, to find out the right multipliers.

The pivot for **the second stage of elimination** is −8. We now ignore the first equation. A multiple of the second equation will be subtracted from the remaining equations (in this case there is only the third one) so as to eliminate v. We add the second equation to the third or, in other words, we

(c) subtract −1 times the second equation from the third.

The elimination process is now complete, at least in the "forward" direction:

$$\textbf{Triangular system}\qquad \begin{aligned} \mathbf{2}u + v + w &= 5\\ -\mathbf{8}v - 2w &= -12\\ \mathbf{1}w &= 2. \end{aligned} \tag{3}$$

This system is solved backward, bottom to top. The last equation gives $w = 2$. Substituting into the second equation, we find $v = 1$. Then the first equation gives $u = 1$. This process is called ***back-substitution***.

To repeat: Forward elimination produced the pivots 2, −8, 1. It subtracted multiples of each row from the rows beneath. It reached the "triangular" system (3), which is solved in reverse order: Substitute each newly computed value into the equations that are waiting.

Remark One good way to write down the forward elimination steps is to include the right-hand side as an extra column. There is no need to copy u and v and w and = at every step, so we are left with the bare minimum:

$$\begin{bmatrix} 2 & 1 & 1 & 5\\ 4 & -6 & 0 & -2\\ -2 & 7 & 2 & 9 \end{bmatrix} \rightarrow \begin{bmatrix} 2 & 1 & 1 & 5\\ 0 & -8 & -2 & -12\\ 0 & 8 & 3 & 14 \end{bmatrix} \rightarrow \begin{bmatrix} 2 & 1 & 1 & 5\\ 0 & -8 & -2 & -12\\ 0 & 0 & 1 & 2 \end{bmatrix}.$$

At the end is the triangular system, ready for back-substitution. You may prefer this arrangement, which guarantees that operations on the left-hand side of the equations are also done on the right-hand side—because *both sides are there together.*

In a larger problem, forward elimination takes most of the effort. We use multiples of the first equation to produce zeros below the first pivot. Then the second column is cleared out below the second pivot. The forward step is finished when the system is triangular; equation n contains only the last unknown multiplied by the last pivot.

Back-substitution yields the complete solution in the opposite order—beginning with the last unknown, then solving for the next to last, and eventually for the first.

By definition, ***pivots cannot be zero***. We need to divide by them.

The Breakdown of Elimination

Under what circumstances could the process break down? Something *must* go wrong in the singular case, and something *might* go wrong in the nonsingular case. This may seem a little premature—after all, we have barely got the algorithm working. But the possibility of breakdown sheds light on the method itself.

The answer is: With a full set of n pivots, there is only one solution. The system is nonsingular, and it is solved by forward elimination and back-substitution. But ***if a zero appears*** in a pivot position, elimination has to stop—either temporarily or permanently. The system might or might not be singular.

If the first coefficient is zero, in the upper left corner, the elimination of u from the other equations will be impossible. The same is true at every intermediate stage. Notice that a zero can appear in a pivot position, even if the original coefficient in that place was not zero. Roughly speaking, ***we do not know whether a zero will appear until we try***, by actually going through the elimination process.

In many cases this problem can be cured, and elimination can proceed. Such a system still counts as nonsingular; it is only the algorithm that needs repair. In other cases a breakdown is unavoidable. Those incurable systems are singular, they have no solution or else infinitely many, and a full set of pivots cannot be found.

Example 1 Nonsingular (cured by exchanging equations 2 and 3)

$$\begin{aligned} u + v + w &= \_\_ \\ 2u + 2v + 5w &= \_\_ \\ 4u + 6v + 8w &= \_\_ \end{aligned} \quad \longrightarrow \quad \begin{aligned} u + v + w &= \_\_ \\ 3w &= \_\_ \\ 2v + 4w &= \_\_ \end{aligned} \quad \longrightarrow \quad \begin{aligned} u + v + w &= \_\_ \\ 2v + 4w &= \_\_ \\ 3w &= \_\_ \end{aligned}$$

The system is now triangular, and back-substitution will solve it.

Example 2 Singular (incurable)

$$\begin{aligned} u + v + w &= \_\_ \\ 2u + 2v + 5w &= \_\_ \\ 4u + 4v + 8w &= \_\_ \end{aligned} \quad \longrightarrow \quad \begin{aligned} u + v + w &= \_\_ \\ 3w &= \_\_ \\ 4w &= \_\_ \end{aligned}$$

There is no exchange of equations that can avoid zero in the second pivot position. The equations themselves may be solvable or unsolvable. If the last two equations are $3w = 6$ and $4w = 7$, there is no solution. If those two equations happen to be consistent—as in $3w = 6$ and $4w = 8$—then this singular case has an infinity of solutions. We know that $w = 2$, but the first equation cannot decide both u and v.

Section 1.5 will discuss row exchanges when the system is not singular. Then the exchanges produce a full set of pivots. Chapter 2 admits the singular case, and limps forward with elimination. The $3w$ can still eliminate the $4w$, and we will call 3 the second pivot. (There won't be a third pivot.) For the present we trust all n pivot entries to be nonzero, without changing the order of the equations. That is the best case, with which we continue.

The Cost of Elimination

Our other question is very practical. *How many separate arithmetical operations does elimination require, for n equations in n unknowns?* If n is large, a computer is going to take our place in carrying out the elimination. Since all the steps are known, we should be able to predict the number of operations.

For the moment, ignore the right-hand sides of the equations, and count only the operations on the left. These operations are of two kinds. We divide by the pivot to find out what multiple (say ℓ) of the pivot equation is to be subtracted. When we do this subtraction, we continually meet a "multiply–subtract" combination; the terms in the pivot equation are multiplied by ℓ, and then subtracted from another equation.

Suppose we call each division, and each multiplication–subtraction, one operation. In column 1, *it takes n operations for every zero we achieve*—one to find the multiple ℓ, and the other to find the new entries along the row. There are $n-1$ rows underneath the first one, so the first stage of elimination needs $n(n-1) = n^2 - n$ operations. (Another approach to $n^2 - n$ is this: *All n^2 entries need to be changed, except the n in the first row.*) Later stages are faster because the equations are shorter.

When the elimination is down to k equations, only $k^2 - k$ operations are needed to clear out the column below the pivot—by the same reasoning that applied to the first stage, when k equaled n. Altogether, the total number of operations is the sum of $k^2 - k$ over all values of k from 1 to n:

$$\textbf{Left side} \qquad (1^2 + \cdots + n^2) - (1 + \cdots + n) = \frac{n(n+1)(2n+1)}{6} - \frac{n(n+1)}{2} = \frac{n^3 - n}{3}.$$

Those are standard formulas for the sums of the first n numbers and the first n squares. Substituting $n = 1$ and $n = 2$ and $n = 100$ into the formula $\frac{1}{3}(n^3 - n)$, forward elimination can take no steps or two steps or about a third of a million steps:

> If n is at all large, ***a good estimate for the number of operations is $\frac{1}{3}n^3$***.

If the size is doubled, and few of the coefficients are zero, the cost is multiplied by 8.

Back-substitution is considerably faster. The last unknown is found in only one operation (a division by the last pivot). The second to last unknown requires two operations, and so on. Then the total for back-substitution is $1 + 2 + \cdots + n$.

Forward elimination also acts on the right-hand side (subtracting the same multiples as on the left to maintain correct equations). This starts with $n-1$ subtractions of the first equation. Altogether ***the right-hand side is responsible for n^2 operations***—much less than the $n^3/3$ on the left. The total for forward and back is

$$\textbf{Right side} \qquad [(n-1) + (n-2) + \cdots + 1] + [1 + 2 + \cdots + n] = n^2.$$

Thirty years ago, almost every mathematician would have guessed that a general system of order n could not be solved with much fewer than $n^3/3$ multiplications. (There were even theorems to demonstrate it, but they did not allow for all possible methods.) Astonishingly, that guess has been proved wrong. *There now exists a method that requires only $Cn^{\log_2 7}$ multiplications*! It depends on a simple fact: Two combinations of two vectors in two-dimensional space would seem to take 8 multiplications, but they can be done in 7. That lowered the exponent from $\log_2 8$, which is 3, to $\log_2 7 \approx 2.8$. This discovery produced tremendous activity to find the smallest possible power of n. The exponent finally fell (at IBM) below 2.376. Fortunately for elimination, the constant C is so large and the coding is so awkward that the new method is largely (or entirely) of theoretical interest. The newest problem is the cost with *many processors in parallel*.

Problem Set 1.3

Problems 1–9 are about elimination on 2 by 2 systems.

1. What multiple ℓ of equation 1 should be subtracted from equation 2?

$$\begin{aligned} 2x + 3y &= 1 \\ 10x + 9y &= 11. \end{aligned}$$

After this elimination step, write down the upper triangular system and circle the two pivots. The numbers 1 and 11 have no influence on those pivots.

2. Solve the triangular system of Problem 1 by back-substitution, y before x. Verify that x times $(2, 10)$ plus y times $(3, 9)$ equals $(1, 11)$. If the right-hand side changes to $(4, 44)$, what is the new solution?

3. What multiple of equation 2 should be *subtracted* from equation 3?

$$\begin{aligned} 2x - 4y &= 6 \\ -x + 5y &= 0. \end{aligned}$$

After this elimination step, solve the triangular system. If the right-hand side changes to $(-6, 0)$, what is the new solution?

4. What multiple ℓ of equation 1 should be subtracted from equation 2?

$$\begin{aligned} ax + by &= f \\ cx + dy &= g. \end{aligned}$$

The first pivot is a (assumed nonzero). Elimination produces what formula for the second pivot? What is y? The second pivot is missing when $ad = bc$.

5. Choose a right-hand side which gives no solution and another right-hand side which gives infinitely many solutions. What are two of those solutions?

$$\begin{aligned} 3x + 2y &= 10 \\ 6x + 4y &= \underline{\quad}. \end{aligned}$$

6. Choose a coefficient b that makes this system singular. Then choose a right-hand side g that makes it solvable. Find two solutions in that singular case.

$$\begin{aligned} 2x + by &= 16 \\ 4x + 8y &= g. \end{aligned}$$

7. For which numbers a does elimination break down (a) permanently, and (b) temporarily?

$$\begin{aligned} ax + 3y &= -3 \\ 4x + 6y &= 6. \end{aligned}$$

Solve for x and y after fixing the second breakdown by a row exchange.

8. For which three numbers k does elimination break down? Which is fixed by a row exchange? In each case, is the number of solutions 0 or 1 or ∞?

$$\begin{aligned} kx + 3y &= 6 \\ 3x + ky &= -6. \end{aligned}$$

9. What test on b_1 and b_2 decides whether these two equations allow a solution? How many solutions will they have? Draw the column picture.

$$\begin{aligned} 3x - 2y &= b_1 \\ 6x - 4y &= b_2. \end{aligned}$$

Problems 10–19 study elimination on 3 by 3 systems (and possible failure).

10. Reduce this system to upper triangular form by two row operations:

$$\begin{aligned} 2x + 3y + z &= 8 \\ 4x + 7y + 5z &= 20 \\ - 2y + 2z &= 0. \end{aligned}$$

Circle the pivots. Solve by back-substitution for z, y, x.

11. Apply elimination (circle the pivots) and back-substitution to solve

$$\begin{aligned} 2x - 3y \phantom{{}+ 3z} &= 3 \\ 4x - 5y + z &= 7 \\ 2x - y - 3z &= 5. \end{aligned}$$

List the three row operations: Subtract ___ times row ___ from row ___.

12. Which number d forces a row exchange, and what is the triangular system (not singular) for that d? Which d makes this system singular (no third pivot)?

$$\begin{aligned} 2x + 5y + z &= 0 \\ 4x + dy + z &= 2 \\ y - z &= 3. \end{aligned}$$

13. Which number b leads later to a row exchange? Which b leads to a missing pivot? In that singular case find a nonzero solution x, y, z.

$$\begin{aligned} x + by \phantom{{}- z} &= 0 \\ x - 2y - z &= 0 \\ y + z &= 0. \end{aligned}$$

14. (a) Construct a 3 by 3 system that needs two row exchanges to reach a triangular form and a solution.

(b) Construct a 3 by 3 system that needs a row exchange to keep going, but breaks down later.

15. If rows 1 and 2 are the same, how far can you get with elimination (allowing row exchange)? If columns 1 and 2 are the same, which pivot is missing?

$$\begin{aligned} 2x - y + z &= 0 \\ 2x - y + z &= 0 \\ 4x + y + z &= 2 \end{aligned} \qquad \begin{aligned} 2x + 2y + z &= 0 \\ 4x + 4y + z &= 0 \\ 6x + 6y + z &= 2. \end{aligned}$$

16. Construct a 3 by 3 example that has 9 different coefficients on the left-hand side, but rows 2 and 3 become zero in elimination. How many solutions to your system with $b = (1, 10, 100)$ and how many with $b = (0, 0, 0)$?

17. Which number q makes this system singular and which right-hand side t gives it infinitely many solutions? Find the solution that has $z = 1$.

$$\begin{aligned} x + 4y - 2z &= 1 \\ x + 7y - 6z &= 6 \\ 3y + qz &= t. \end{aligned}$$

18. (Recommended) It is impossible for a system of linear equations to have exactly two solutions. *Explain why.*

(a) If (x, y, z) and (X, Y, Z) are two solutions, what is another one?

(b) If 25 planes meet at two points, where else do they meet?

19. Three planes can fail to have an intersection point, when no two planes are parallel. The system is singular if row 3 of A is a ______ of the first two rows. Find a third equation that can't be solved if $x + y + z = 0$ and $x - 2y - z = 1$.

Problems 20–22 move up to 4 by 4 and n by n.

20. Find the pivots and the solution for these four equations:

$$\begin{aligned} 2x + y \qquad\qquad &= 0 \\ x + 2y + z \qquad &= 0 \\ y + 2z + t &= 0 \\ z + 2t &= 5. \end{aligned}$$

21. If you extend Problem 20 following the 1, 2, 1 pattern or the $-1, 2, -1$ pattern, what is the fifth pivot? What is the nth pivot?

22. Apply elimination and back-substitution to solve

$$\begin{aligned} 2u + 3v \qquad &= 0 \\ 4u + 5v + w &= 3 \\ 2u - v - 3w &= 5. \end{aligned}$$

What are the pivots? List the three operations in which a multiple of one row is subtracted from another.

23. For the system

$$\begin{aligned} u + v + w &= 2 \\ u + 3v + 3w &= 0 \\ u + 3v + 5w &= 2, \end{aligned}$$

what is the triangular system after forward elimination, and what is the solution?

24. Solve the system and find the pivots when

$$\begin{aligned} 2u - v &= 0 \\ -u + 2v - w &= 0 \\ - v + 2w - z &= 0 \\ - w + 2z &= 5. \end{aligned}$$

You may carry the right-hand side as a fifth column (and omit writing u, v, w, z until the solution at the end).

25. Apply elimination to the system

$$\begin{aligned} u + v + w &= -2 \\ 3u + 3v - w &= 6 \\ u - v + w &= -1. \end{aligned}$$

When a zero arises in the pivot position, exchange that equation for the one below it and proceed. What coefficient of v in the third equation, in place of the present -1, would make it impossible to proceed—and force elimination to break down?

26. Solve by elimination the system of two equations

$$\begin{aligned} x - y &= 0 \\ 3x + 6y &= 18. \end{aligned}$$

Draw a graph representing each equation as a straight line in the x-y plane; the lines intersect at the solution. Also, add one more line—the graph of the new second equation which arises after elimination.

27. Find three values of a for which elimination breaks down, temporarily or permanently, in

$$\begin{aligned} au + v &= 1 \\ 4u + av &= 2. \end{aligned}$$

Breakdown at the first step can be fixed by exchanging rows—but not breakdown at the last step.

28. True or false:

(a) If the third equation starts with a zero coefficient (it begins with $0u$) then no multiple of equation 1 will be subtracted from equation 3.

(b) If the third equation has zero as its second coefficient (it contains $0v$) then no multiple of equation 2 will be subtracted from equation 3.

(c) If the third equation contains $0u$ *and* $0v$, then no multiple of equation 1 or equation 2 will be subtracted from equation 3.

29. (Very optional) Normally the multiplication of two complex numbers

$$(a+ib)(c+id) = (ac-bd) + i(bc+ad)$$

involves the four separate multiplications ac, bd, bc, ad. Ignoring i, can you compute $ac-bd$ and $bc+ad$ with only three multiplications? (You may do additions, such as forming $a+b$ before multiplying, without any penalty.)

30. Use elimination to solve

$$\begin{aligned} u + v + w &= 6 \\ u + 2v + 2w &= 11 \\ 2u + 3v - 4w &= 3 \end{aligned} \qquad \text{and} \qquad \begin{aligned} u + v + w &= 7 \\ u + 2v + 2w &= 10 \\ 2u + 3v - 4w &= 3. \end{aligned}$$

31. For which three numbers a will elimination fail to give three pivots?

$$\begin{aligned} ax + 2y + 3z &= b_1 \\ ax + ay + 4z &= b_2 \\ ax + ay + az &= b_3. \end{aligned}$$

32. Find experimentally the average size (absolute value) of the first and second and third pivots for MATLAB's lu(rand(3, 3)). The average of the first pivot from abs($A(1, 1)$) should be 0.5.

1.4 MATRIX NOTATION AND MATRIX MULTIPLICATION

With our 3 by 3 example, we are able to write out all the equations in full. We can list the elimination steps, which subtract a multiple of one equation from another and reach a triangular matrix. For a large system, this way of keeping track of elimination would be hopeless; a much more concise record is needed.

We now introduce **matrix notation** to describe the original system, and **matrix multiplication** to describe the operations that make it simpler. Notice that three different types of quantities appear in our example:

$$\begin{array}{ll} \textbf{Nine coefficients} & 2u + v + w = 5 \\ \textbf{Three unknowns} & 4u - 6v = -2 \\ \textbf{Three right-hand sides} & -2u + 7v + 2w = 9 \end{array} \qquad (1)$$

On the right-hand side is the column vector b. On the left-hand side are the unknowns u, v, w. Also on the left-hand side are nine coefficients (one of which happens to be zero). It is natural to represent the three unknowns by a vector:

$$\text{The unknown is } x = \begin{bmatrix} u \\ v \\ w \end{bmatrix} \qquad \text{The solution is } x = \begin{bmatrix} 1 \\ 1 \\ 2 \end{bmatrix}.$$

The nine coefficients fall into three rows and three columns, producing a ***3 by 3 matrix***:

$$\textbf{Coefficient matrix} \qquad A = \begin{bmatrix} 2 & 1 & 1 \\ 4 & -6 & 0 \\ -2 & 7 & 2 \end{bmatrix}.$$

A is a *square* matrix, because the number of equations equals the number of unknowns. If there are n equations in n unknowns, we have a square n by n matrix. More generally, we might have m equations and n unknowns. Then A is *rectangular*, with m rows and n columns. It will be an "m by n matrix."

Matrices are added to each other, or multiplied by numerical constants, exactly as vectors are—one entry at a time. In fact we may regard vectors as special cases of matrices; *they are matrices with only one column*. As with vectors, two matrices can be added only if they have the same shape:

Addition $A + B$
Multiplication $2A$

$$\begin{bmatrix} 2 & 1 \\ 3 & 0 \\ 0 & 4 \end{bmatrix} + \begin{bmatrix} 1 & 2 \\ -3 & 1 \\ 1 & 2 \end{bmatrix} = \begin{bmatrix} 3 & 3 \\ 0 & 1 \\ 1 & 6 \end{bmatrix} \qquad 2\begin{bmatrix} 2 & 1 \\ 3 & 0 \\ 0 & 4 \end{bmatrix} = \begin{bmatrix} 4 & 2 \\ 6 & 0 \\ 0 & 8 \end{bmatrix}.$$

Multiplication of a Matrix and a Vector

We want to rewrite the three equations with three unknowns u, v, w in the simplified matrix form $Ax = b$. Written out in full, matrix times vector equals vector:

Matrix form $Ax = b$

$$\begin{bmatrix} 2 & 1 & 1 \\ 4 & -6 & 0 \\ -2 & 7 & 2 \end{bmatrix} \begin{bmatrix} u \\ v \\ w \end{bmatrix} = \begin{bmatrix} 5 \\ -2 \\ 9 \end{bmatrix}. \qquad (2)$$

The right-hand side b is the column vector of "inhomogeneous terms." **The left-hand side is A times x.** This multiplication will be defined *exactly so as to reproduce the original system*. The first component of Ax comes from "multiplying" the first row of A into the column vector x:

Row times column

$$\begin{bmatrix} 2 & 1 & 1 \end{bmatrix} \begin{bmatrix} u \\ v \\ w \end{bmatrix} = \begin{bmatrix} 2u + v + w \end{bmatrix} = \begin{bmatrix} 5 \end{bmatrix}. \qquad (3)$$

The second component of the product Ax is $4u - 6v + 0w$, from the second row of A. The matrix equation $Ax = b$ is equivalent to the three simultaneous equations in equation (1).

Row times column is fundamental to all matrix multiplications. From two vectors it produces a single number. This number is called the ***inner product*** of the two vectors. In other words, the product of a 1 by n matrix (a *row vector*) and an n by 1 matrix (a *column vector*) is a 1 by 1 matrix:

Inner product

$$\begin{bmatrix} 2 & 1 & 1 \end{bmatrix} \begin{bmatrix} 1 \\ 1 \\ 2 \end{bmatrix} = \begin{bmatrix} 2 \cdot 1 + 1 \cdot 1 + 1 \cdot 2 \end{bmatrix} = \begin{bmatrix} 5 \end{bmatrix}.$$

This confirms that the proposed solution $x = (1, 1, 2)$ does satisfy the first equation.

There are two ways to multiply a matrix A and a vector x. One way is *a row at a time*. Each row of A combines with x to give a component of Ax. There are three inner products when A has three rows:

Ax by rows

$$\begin{bmatrix} 1 & 1 & 6 \\ 3 & 0 & 1 \\ 1 & 1 & 4 \end{bmatrix} \begin{bmatrix} 2 \\ 5 \\ 0 \end{bmatrix} = \begin{bmatrix} 1 \cdot 2 + 1 \cdot 5 + 6 \cdot 0 \\ 3 \cdot 2 + 0 \cdot 5 + 3 \cdot 0 \\ 1 \cdot 2 + 1 \cdot 5 + 4 \cdot 0 \end{bmatrix} = \begin{bmatrix} 7 \\ 6 \\ 7 \end{bmatrix}. \qquad (4)$$

That is how Ax is usually explained, but the second way is equally important. In fact it is more important! It does the multiplication *a column at a time*. The product Ax is found all at once, as ***a combination of the three columns of A***:

$$\textbf{Ax by columns} \qquad 2\begin{bmatrix}1\\3\\1\end{bmatrix} + 5\begin{bmatrix}1\\0\\1\end{bmatrix} + 0\begin{bmatrix}6\\3\\4\end{bmatrix} = \begin{bmatrix}7\\6\\7\end{bmatrix}. \tag{5}$$

The answer is twice column 1 plus 5 times column 2. It corresponds to the "column picture" of linear equations. If the right-hand side b has components 7, 6, 7, then the solution has components 2, 5, 0. Of course the row picture agrees with that (and we eventually have to do the same multiplications).

The column rule will be used over and over, and we repeat it for emphasis:

1A Every product Ax can be found using whole columns as in equation (5). Therefore Ax is ***a combination of the columns of A***. The coefficients are the components of x.

To multiply A times x in n dimensions, we need a notation for the individual entries in A. *The entry in the ith row and jth column is always denoted by a_{ij}*. The first subscript gives the row number, and the second subscript indicates the column. (In equation (4), a_{21} is 3 and a_{13} is 6.) If A is an m by n matrix, then the index i goes from 1 to m—there are m rows—and the index j goes from 1 to n. Altogether the matrix has mn entries, and a_{mn} is in the lower right corner.

One subscript is enough for a vector. The jth component of x is denoted by x_j. (The multiplication above had $x_1 = 2$, $x_2 = 5$, $x_3 = 0$.) Normally x is written as a column vector—like an n by 1 matrix. But sometimes it is printed on a line, as in $x = (2, 5, 0)$. The parentheses and commas emphasize that it is not a 1 by 3 matrix. It is a column vector, and it is just temporarily lying down.

To describe the product Ax, we use the "*sigma*" symbol Σ for summation:

$$\textbf{Sigma notation} \qquad \text{The } i\text{th component of } Ax \text{ is } \sum_{j=1}^{n} a_{ij}x_j.$$

This sum takes us along the ith row of A. The column index j takes each value from 1 to n and we add up the results—the sum is $a_{i1}x_1 + a_{i2}x_2 + \cdots + a_{in}x_n$.

We see again that the length of the rows (the number of columns in A) must match the length of x. **An m by n matrix multiplies an n-dimensional vector** (and produces an m-dimensional vector). Summations are simpler than writing everything out in full, but matrix notation is better. (Einstein used "tensor notation," in which a repeated index automatically means summation. He wrote $a_{ij}x_j$ or even $a_i^j x_j$, without the Σ. Not being Einstein, we keep the Σ.)

The Matrix Form of One Elimination Step

So far we have a convenient shorthand $Ax = b$ for the original system of equations. What about the operations that are carried out during elimination? In our example, the first step subtracted 2 times the first equation from the second. On the right-hand side, 2 times the first component of b was subtracted from the second component. *The same result is achieved if we multiply b by this elementary matrix* (or *elimination matrix*):

$$\textbf{Elementary matrix} \qquad E = \begin{bmatrix} 1 & 0 & 0 \\ \mathbf{-2} & 1 & 0 \\ 0 & 0 & 1 \end{bmatrix}.$$

This is verified just by obeying the rule for multiplying a matrix and a vector:

$$Eb = \begin{bmatrix} 1 & 0 & 0 \\ \mathbf{-2} & 1 & 0 \\ 0 & 0 & 1 \end{bmatrix} \begin{bmatrix} 5 \\ -2 \\ 9 \end{bmatrix} = \begin{bmatrix} 5 \\ \mathbf{-12} \\ 9 \end{bmatrix}.$$

The components 5 and 9 stay the same (because of the 1, 0, 0 and 0, 0, 1 in the rows of E). The new second component -12 appeared after the first elimination step.

It is easy to describe the matrices like E, which carry out the separate elimination steps. We also notice the "identity matrix," which does nothing at all.

1B The ***identity matrix I***, with 1s on the diagonal and 0s everywhere else, leaves every vector unchanged. The ***elementary matrix*** $\boldsymbol{E_{ij}}$ subtracts ℓ times row j from row i. This E_{ij} includes $-\ell$ in row i, column j.

$$I = \begin{bmatrix} 1 & 0 & 0 \\ 0 & 1 & 0 \\ 0 & 0 & 1 \end{bmatrix} \text{ has } Ib = b \qquad E_{31} = \begin{bmatrix} 1 & 0 & 0 \\ 0 & 1 & 0 \\ -\ell & 0 & 1 \end{bmatrix} \text{ has } E_{31}b = \begin{bmatrix} b_1 \\ b_2 \\ b_3 - \ell b_1 \end{bmatrix}.$$

$Ib = b$ is the matrix analogue of multiplying by 1. A typical elimination step multiplies by E_{31}. The important question is: What happens to A on the left-hand side?

To maintain equality, we must apply the same operation to both sides of $Ax = b$. In other words, we must also multiply the vector Ax by the matrix E. Our original matrix E subtracts 2 times the first component from the second. After this step the new and simpler system (equivalent to the old) is just $E(Ax) = Eb$. It is simpler because of the zero that was created below the first pivot. It is equivalent because we can recover the original system (by adding 2 times the first equation back to the second). So the two systems have exactly the same solution x.

Matrix Multiplication

Now we come to the most important question: *How do we multiply two matrices*? There is a partial clue from Gaussian elimination: We know the original coefficient matrix A, we know the elimination matrix E, and we know the result EA after the elimination step. We hope and expect that

$$E = \begin{bmatrix} 1 & 0 & 0 \\ -2 & 1 & 0 \\ 0 & 0 & 1 \end{bmatrix} \text{ times } A = \begin{bmatrix} 2 & 1 & 1 \\ 4 & -6 & 0 \\ -2 & 7 & 2 \end{bmatrix} \text{ gives } EA = \begin{bmatrix} 2 & 1 & 1 \\ 0 & -8 & -2 \\ -2 & 7 & 2 \end{bmatrix}.$$

Twice the first row of A has been subtracted from the second row. Matrix multiplication is consistent with the row operations of elimination. We can write the result either as $E(Ax) = Eb$, applying E to both sides of our equation, or as $(EA)x = Eb$. The matrix EA is constructed exactly so that these equations agree, and we don't need parentheses:

Matrix multiplication (EA times x) equals (E times Ax). We just write EAx.

This is the whole point of an "associative law" like $2 \times (3 \times 4) = (2 \times 3) \times 4$. The law seems so obvious that it is hard to imagine it could be false. But the same could be said of the "commutative law" $2 \times 3 = 3 \times 2$—and for matrices EA is not AE.

There is another requirement on matrix multiplication. We know how to multiply Ax, a matrix and a vector. The new definition should be consistent with that one. When a matrix B contains only a single column x, the matrix–matrix product AB should be identical with the matrix–vector product Ax. *More than that*: When B contains several columns b_1, b_2, b_3, the columns of AB should be Ab_1, Ab_2, Ab_3!

Multiplication by columns $AB = A \begin{bmatrix} b_1 & b_2 & b_3 \end{bmatrix} = \begin{bmatrix} Ab_1 & Ab_2 & Ab_3 \end{bmatrix}$.

Our first requirement had to do with rows, and this one is concerned with columns. A third approach is to describe each individual entry in AB and hope for the best. In fact, there is only one possible rule, and I am not sure who discovered it. It makes everything work. It does not allow us to multiply every pair of matrices. If they are square, they must have the same size. If they are rectangular, they must *not* have the same shape; ***the number of columns in A has to equal the number of rows in B***. Then A can be multiplied into each column of B.

If A is m by n, and B is n by p, then multiplication is possible. *The product AB will be m by p*. We now find the entry in row i and column j of AB.

1C The i, j entry of AB is the inner product of the ith row of A and the jth column of B. In Figure 1.7, the 3, 2 entry of AB comes from row 3 and column 2:

$$(AB)_{32} = a_{31}b_{12} + a_{32}b_{22} + a_{33}b_{32} + a_{34}b_{42}. \tag{6}$$

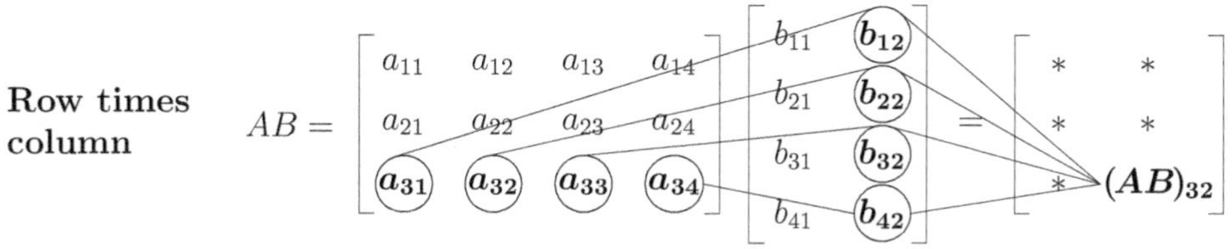

Figure 1.7 A 3 by 4 matrix A times a 4 by 2 matrix B is a 3 by 2 matrix AB.

Note We write AB when the matrices have nothing special to do with elimination. Our earlier example was EA, because of the elementary matrix E. Later we have PA, or LU, or even LDU. The rule for matrix multiplication stays the same.

Example 1

$$AB = \begin{bmatrix} 2 & 3 \\ 4 & 0 \end{bmatrix} \begin{bmatrix} 1 & 2 & 0 \\ 5 & -1 & 0 \end{bmatrix} = \begin{bmatrix} 17 & 1 & 0 \\ 4 & 8 & 0 \end{bmatrix}.$$

The entry 17 is $(2)(1) + (3)(5)$, the inner product of the first row of A and first column of B. The entry 8 is $(4)(2) + (0)(-1)$, from the second row and second column.

The third column is zero in B, so it is zero in AB. B consists of three columns side by side, and A multiplies each column separately. ***Every column of AB is a combination of the columns of A***. Just as in a matrix–vector multiplication, the columns of A are multiplied by the entries in B.

Example 2

$$\textbf{Row exchange matrix} \qquad \begin{bmatrix} 0 & 1 \\ 1 & 0 \end{bmatrix} \begin{bmatrix} 2 & 3 \\ 7 & 8 \end{bmatrix} = \begin{bmatrix} 7 & 8 \\ 2 & 3 \end{bmatrix}.$$

Example 3 The 1s in the identity matrix I leave every matrix unchanged:

$$\textbf{Identity matrix} \qquad IA = A \qquad \text{and} \qquad BI = B.$$

Important: The multiplication AB can also be done *a row at a time*. In Example 1, the first row of AB uses the numbers 2 and 3 from the first row of A. Those numbers give $2\begin{bmatrix}\text{row } 1\end{bmatrix} + 3\begin{bmatrix}\text{row } 2\end{bmatrix} = \begin{bmatrix}17 & 1 & 0\end{bmatrix}$. Exactly as in elimination, where all this started, each row of AB is a ***combination of the rows of B***.

We summarize these three different ways to look at matrix multiplication.

1D (i) Each entry of AB is the product of a ***row*** and a ***column***:

$$(AB)_{ij} = (\text{row } i \text{ of } A) \text{ times } (\text{column } j \text{ of } B)$$

(ii) Each column of AB is the product of a ***matrix*** and a ***column***:

$$\text{column } j \text{ of } AB = A \text{ times } (\text{column } j \text{ of } B)$$

(iii) Each row of AB is the product of a ***row*** and a ***matrix***:

$$\text{row } i \text{ of } AB = (\text{row } i \text{ of } A) \text{ times } B.$$

This leads back to a key property of matrix multiplication. Suppose the shapes of three matrices A, B, C (possibly rectangular) permit them to be multiplied. The rows in A and B multiply the columns in B and C. Then the key property is this:

1E Matrix multiplication is associative: $(AB)C = A(BC)$. Just write ABC.

AB times C equals A times BC. If C happens to be just a vector (a matrix with only one column) this is the requirement $(EA)x = E(Ax)$ mentioned earlier. It is the whole basis for the laws of matrix multiplication. And if C has several columns, we have only to think of them placed side by side, and apply the same rule several times. Parentheses are not needed when we multiply several matrices.

There are two more properties to mention—one property that matrix multiplication has, and another which it *does not have*. The property that it does possess is:

1F Matrix operations are distributive:

$$A(B+C) = AB + AC \quad \text{and} \quad (B+C)D = BD + CD.$$

Of course the shapes of these matrices must match properly—B and C have the same shape, so they can be added, and A and D are the right size for premultiplication and postmultiplication. The proof of this law is too boring for words.

The property that fails to hold is a little more interesting:

1G Matrix multiplication is not commutative: Usually $FE \neq EF$.

Example 4 Suppose E subtracts twice the first equation from the second. Suppose F is the matrix for the next step, *to add row* 1 *to row* 3:

$$E = \begin{bmatrix} 1 & 0 & 0 \\ \mathbf{-2} & 1 & 0 \\ 0 & 0 & 1 \end{bmatrix} \quad \text{and} \quad F = \begin{bmatrix} 1 & 0 & 0 \\ 0 & 1 & 0 \\ \mathbf{1} & 0 & 1 \end{bmatrix}.$$

These two matrices do commute and the product does both steps at once:

$$EF = \begin{bmatrix} 1 & 0 & 0 \\ \mathbf{-2} & 1 & 0 \\ \mathbf{1} & 0 & 1 \end{bmatrix} = FE.$$

In either order, EF or FE, this changes rows 2 and 3 using row 1.

Example 5 Suppose E is the same but G *adds row* 2 *to row* 3. Now the order makes a difference. When we apply E and then G, the second row is altered *before* it affects the third. If E comes *after* G, then the third equation feels no effect from the first. You will see a zero in the (3, 1) entry of EG, where there is a -2 in GE:

$$GE = \begin{bmatrix} 1 & 0 & 0 \\ 0 & 1 & 0 \\ 0 & \mathbf{1} & 1 \end{bmatrix} \begin{bmatrix} 1 & 0 & 0 \\ \mathbf{-2} & 1 & 0 \\ 0 & 0 & 1 \end{bmatrix} = \begin{bmatrix} 1 & 0 & 0 \\ -2 & 1 & 0 \\ \mathbf{-2} & 1 & 1 \end{bmatrix} \quad \text{but} \quad EG = \begin{bmatrix} 1 & 0 & 0 \\ -2 & 1 & 0 \\ \mathbf{0} & 1 & 1 \end{bmatrix}.$$

Thus $EG \neq GE$. A random example would show the same thing—most matrices don't commute. Here the matrices have meaning. There was a reason for $EF = FE$, and a reason for $EG \neq GE$. It is worth taking one more step, to see what happens with *all three elimination matrices at once*:

$$GFE = \begin{bmatrix} 1 & 0 & 0 \\ -2 & 1 & 0 \\ \mathbf{-1} & 1 & 1 \end{bmatrix} \quad \text{and} \quad EFG = \begin{bmatrix} 1 & 0 & 0 \\ -2 & 1 & 0 \\ \mathbf{1} & 1 & 1 \end{bmatrix}.$$

The product GFE is the true order of elimination. *It is the matrix that takes the original A to the upper triangular U.* We will see it again in the next section.

The other matrix EFG is nicer. In that order, the numbers -2 from E and 1 from F and G were not disturbed. They went straight into the product. It is the wrong order for elimination. But fortunately *it is the right order for reversing the elimination steps*—which also comes in the next section.

Notice that the product of lower triangular matrices is again lower triangular.

Problem Set 1.4

1. Compute the products

$$\begin{bmatrix}4&0&1\\0&1&0\\4&0&1\end{bmatrix}\begin{bmatrix}3\\4\\5\end{bmatrix} \text{ and } \begin{bmatrix}1&0&0\\0&1&0\\0&0&1\end{bmatrix}\begin{bmatrix}5\\-2\\3\end{bmatrix} \text{ and } \begin{bmatrix}2&0\\1&3\end{bmatrix}\begin{bmatrix}1\\1\end{bmatrix}.$$

For the third one, draw the column vectors $(2, 1)$ and $(0, 3)$. Multiplying by $(1, 1)$ just adds the vectors (do it graphically).

2. Working a column at a time, compute the products

$$\begin{bmatrix}4&1\\5&1\\6&1\end{bmatrix}\begin{bmatrix}1\\3\end{bmatrix} \text{ and } \begin{bmatrix}1&2&3\\4&5&6\\7&8&9\end{bmatrix}\begin{bmatrix}0\\1\\0\end{bmatrix} \text{ and } \begin{bmatrix}4&3\\6&6\\8&9\end{bmatrix}\begin{bmatrix}\frac{1}{2}\\\frac{1}{3}\end{bmatrix}.$$

3. Find two inner products and a matrix product:

$$\begin{bmatrix}1&-2&7\end{bmatrix}\begin{bmatrix}1\\-2\\7\end{bmatrix} \text{ and } \begin{bmatrix}1&-2&7\end{bmatrix}\begin{bmatrix}3\\5\\1\end{bmatrix} \text{ and } \begin{bmatrix}1\\-2\\7\end{bmatrix}\begin{bmatrix}3&5&1\end{bmatrix}.$$

The first gives the length of the vector (squared).

4. If an m by n matrix A multiplies an n-dimensional vector x, how many separate multiplications are involved? What if A multiplies an n by p matrix B?

5. Multiply Ax to find a solution vector x to the system $Ax =$ *zero vector*. Can you find more solutions to $Ax = 0$?

$$Ax = \begin{bmatrix}3&-6&0\\0&2&-2\\1&-1&-1\end{bmatrix}\begin{bmatrix}2\\1\\1\end{bmatrix}.$$

6. Write down the 2 by 2 matrices A and B that have entries $a_{ij} = i + j$ and $b_{ij} = (-1)^{i+j}$. Multiply them to find AB and BA.

7. Give 3 by 3 examples (not just the zero matrix) of

(a) a diagonal matrix: $a_{ij} = 0$ if $i \neq j$.
(b) a symmetric matrix: $a_{ij} = a_{ji}$ for all i and j.
(c) an upper triangular matrix: $a_{ij} = 0$ if $i > j$.
(d) a skew-symmetric matrix: $a_{ij} = -a_{ji}$ for all i and j.

8. Do these subroutines multiply Ax *by rows or columns*? Start with $B(I) = 0$:

```
   DO 10 I = 1,N                  DO 10 J = 1,N
   DO 10 J = 1,N                  DO 10 I = 1,N
10 B(I) = B(I) + A(I,J) * X(J) 10 B(I) = B(I) + A(I,J) * X(J)
```

The outputs $Bx = Ax$ are the same. The second code is slightly more efficient in FORTRAN and much more efficient on a vector machine (the first changes single entries $B(I)$, the second can update whole vectors).

9. If the entries of A are a_{ij}, use subscript notation to write

(a) the first pivot.
(b) the multiplier ℓ_{i1} of row 1 to be subtracted from row i.
(c) the new entry that replaces a_{ij} after that subtraction.
(d) the second pivot.

10. True or false? Give a specific counterexample when false.

(a) If columns 1 and 3 of B are the same, so are columns 1 and 3 of AB.
(b) If rows 1 and 3 of B are the same, so are rows 1 and 3 of AB.
(c) If rows 1 and 3 of A are the same, so are rows 1 and 3 of AB.
(d) $(AB)^2 = A^2B^2$.

11. The first row of AB is a linear combination of all the rows of B. What are the coefficients in this combination, and what is the first row of AB, if

$$A = \begin{bmatrix} 2 & 1 & 4 \\ 0 & -1 & 1 \end{bmatrix} \quad \text{and} \quad B = \begin{bmatrix} 1 & 1 \\ 0 & 1 \\ 1 & 0 \end{bmatrix}?$$

12. The product of two lower triangular matrices is again lower triangular (all its entries above the main diagonal are zero). Confirm this with a 3 by 3 example, and then explain how it follows from the laws of matrix multiplication.

13. By trial and error find examples of 2 by 2 matrices such that

(a) $A^2 = -I$, A having only real entries.
(b) $B^2 = 0$, although $B \neq 0$.
(c) $CD = -DC$, not allowing the case $CD = 0$.
(d) $EF = 0$, although no entries of E or F are zero.

14. Describe the rows of EA and the *columns* of AE if

$$E = \begin{bmatrix} 1 & 7 \\ 0 & 1 \end{bmatrix}.$$

15. Suppose A commutes with every 2 by 2 matrix ($AB = BA$), and in particular

$$A = \begin{bmatrix} a & b \\ c & d \end{bmatrix} \quad \text{commutes with} \quad B_1 = \begin{bmatrix} 1 & 0 \\ 0 & 0 \end{bmatrix} \quad \text{and} \quad B_2 = \begin{bmatrix} 0 & 1 \\ 0 & 0 \end{bmatrix}.$$

Show that $a = d$ and $b = c = 0$. If $AB = BA$ for all matrices B, then A is a multiple of the identity.

16. Let x be the column vector $(1, 0, \ldots, 0)$. Show that the rule $(AB)x = A(Bx)$ forces the first column of AB to equal A times the first column of B.

17. Which of the following matrices are guaranteed to equal $(A + B)^2$?

$$A^2 + 2AB + B^2, \quad A(A + B) + B(A + B), \quad (A + B)(B + A), \quad A^2 + AB + BA + B^2.$$

18. If A and B are n by n matrices with all entries equal to 1, find $(AB)_{ij}$. Summation notation turns the product AB, and the law $(AB)C = A(BC)$, into

$$(AB)_{ij} = \sum_k a_{ik}b_{kj} \qquad \sum_j \left(\sum_k a_{ik}b_{kj}\right) c_{jl} = \sum_k a_{ik} \left(\sum_j b_{kj}c_{jl}\right).$$

Compute both sides if C is also n by n, with every $c_{jl} = 2$.

19. *A fourth way to multiply matrices is* ***columns of A times rows of B***:

$$AB = (\text{column } 1)(\text{row } 1) + \cdots + (\text{column } n)(\text{row } n) = \text{sum of simple matrices.}$$

Give a 2 by 2 example of this important rule for matrix multiplication.

20. The matrix that rotates the x-y plane by an angle θ is

$$A(\theta) = \begin{bmatrix} \cos\theta & -\sin\theta \\ \sin\theta & \cos\theta \end{bmatrix}.$$

Verify that $A(\theta_1)A(\theta_2) = A(\theta_1 + \theta_2)$ from the identities for $\cos(\theta_1 + \theta_2)$ and $\sin(\theta_1 + \theta_2)$. What is $A(\theta)$ times $A(-\theta)$?

21. Find the powers A^2, A^3 (A^2 times A), and B^2, B^3, C^2, C^3. What are A^k, B^k, and C^k?

$$A = \begin{bmatrix} \frac{1}{2} & \frac{1}{2} \\ \frac{1}{2} & \frac{1}{2} \end{bmatrix} \quad \text{and} \quad B = \begin{bmatrix} 1 & 0 \\ 0 & -1 \end{bmatrix} \quad \text{and} \quad C = AB = \begin{bmatrix} \frac{1}{2} & -\frac{1}{2} \\ \frac{1}{2} & -\frac{1}{2} \end{bmatrix}$$

Problems 22–31 are about elimination matrices.

22. Write down the 3 by 3 matrices that produce these elimination steps:

(a) E_{21} subtracts 5 times row 1 from row 2.
(b) E_{32} subtracts -7 times row 2 from row 3.
(c) P exchanges rows 1 and 2, then rows 2 and 3.

23. In Problem 22, applying E_{21} and then E_{32} to the column $b = (1, 0, 0)$ gives $E_{32}E_{21}b =$ ___. Applying E_{32} before E_{21} gives $E_{21}E_{32}b =$ ___. When E_{32} comes first, row ___ feels no effect from row ___.

24. Which three matrices E_{21}, E_{31}, E_{32} put A into triangular form U?

$$A = \begin{bmatrix} 1 & 1 & 0 \\ 4 & 6 & 1 \\ -2 & 2 & 0 \end{bmatrix} \quad \text{and} \quad E_{32}E_{31}E_{21}A = U.$$

Multiply those E's to get one matrix M that does elimination: $MA = U$.

25. Suppose $a_{33} = 7$ and the third pivot is 5. If you change a_{33} to 11, the third pivot is ___. If you change a_{33} to ___, there is zero in the pivot position.

26. If every column of A is a multiple of $(1, 1, 1)$, then Ax is always a multiple of $(1, 1, 1)$. Do a 3 by 3 example. How many pivots are produced by elimination?

27. What matrix E_{31} subtracts 7 times row 1 from row 3? To reverse that step, R_{31} should ______ 7 times row ___ to row ___. Multiply E_{31} by R_{31}.

28. (a) E_{21} subtracts row 1 from row 2 and then P_{23} exchanges rows 2 and 3. What matrix $M = P_{23}E_{21}$ does both steps at once?

(b) P_{23} exchanges rows 2 and 3 and then E_{31} subtracts row 1 from row 3. What matrix $M = E_{31}P_{23}$ does both steps at once? Explain why the M's are the same but the E's are different.

29. (a) What 3 by 3 matrix E_{13} will add row 3 to row 1?

(b) What matrix adds row 1 to row 3 and *at the same time* adds row 3 to row 1?

(c) What matrix adds row 1 to row 3 and *then* adds row 3 to row 1?

30. Multiply these matrices:

$$\begin{bmatrix} 0 & 0 & 1 \\ 0 & 1 & 0 \\ 1 & 0 & 0 \end{bmatrix} \begin{bmatrix} 1 & 2 & 3 \\ 4 & 5 & 6 \\ 7 & 8 & 9 \end{bmatrix} \begin{bmatrix} 0 & 0 & 1 \\ 0 & 1 & 0 \\ 1 & 0 & 0 \end{bmatrix} \quad \text{and} \quad \begin{bmatrix} 1 & 0 & 0 \\ -1 & 1 & 0 \\ -1 & 0 & 1 \end{bmatrix} \begin{bmatrix} 1 & 2 & 3 \\ 1 & 3 & 1 \\ 1 & 4 & 0 \end{bmatrix}.$$

31. This 4 by 4 matrix needs which elimination matrices E_{21} and E_{32} and E_{43}?

$$A = \begin{bmatrix} 2 & -1 & 0 & 0 \\ -1 & 2 & -1 & 0 \\ 0 & -1 & 2 & -1 \\ 0 & 0 & -1 & 2 \end{bmatrix}.$$

Problems 32–44 are about creating and multiplying matrices.

32. Write these ancient problems in a 2 by 2 matrix form $Ax = b$ and solve them:

(a) X is twice as old as Y and their ages add to 39.

(b) $(x, y) = (2, 5)$ and $(3, 7)$ lie on the line $y = mx + c$. Find m and c.

33. The parabola $y = a + bx + cx^2$ goes through the points $(x, y) = (1, 4)$ and $(2, 8)$ and $(3, 14)$. Find and solve a matrix equation for the unknowns (a, b, c).

34. Multiply these matrices in the orders EF and FE and E^2:

$$E = \begin{bmatrix} 1 & 0 & 0 \\ a & 1 & 0 \\ b & 0 & 1 \end{bmatrix} \qquad F = \begin{bmatrix} 1 & 0 & 0 \\ 0 & 1 & 0 \\ 0 & c & 1 \end{bmatrix}.$$

35. (a) Suppose all columns of B are the same. Then all columns of EB are the same, because each one is E times _______.

(b) Suppose all rows of B are $[1\ \ 2\ \ 4]$. Show by example that all rows of EB are *not* $[1\ \ 2\ \ 4]$. It is true that those rows are _______.

36. If E adds row 1 to row 2 and F adds row 2 to row 1, does EF equal FE?

37. The first component of Ax is $\sum a_{1j}x_j = a_{11}x_1 + \cdots + a_{1n}x_n$. Write formulas for the third component of Ax and the (1, 1) entry of A^2.

38. If $AB = I$ and $BC = I$, use the associative law to prove $A = C$.

39. A is 3 by 5, B is 5 by 3, C is 5 by 1, and D is 3 by 1. *All entries are* 1. Which of these matrix operations are allowed, and what are the results?

$$BA \qquad AB \qquad ABD \qquad DBA \qquad A(B + C).$$

40. What rows or columns or matrices do you multiply to find

(a) the third column of AB?
(b) the first row of AB?
(c) the entry in row 3, column 4 of AB?
(d) the entry in row 1, column 1 of CDE?

41. (3 by 3 matrices) Choose the only B so that for every matrix A,

(a) $BA = 4A$.
(b) $BA = 4B$.
(c) BA has rows 1 and 3 of A reversed and row 2 unchanged.
(d) All rows of BA are the same as row 1 of A.

42. True or false?

(a) If A^2 is defined then A is necessarily square.
(b) If AB and BA are defined then A and B are square.
(c) If AB and BA are defined then AB and BA are square.
(d) If $AB = B$ then $A = I$.

43. If A is m by n, how many separate multiplications are involved when

(a) A multiplies a vector x with n components?
(b) A multiplies an n by p matrix B? Then AB is m by p.
(c) A multiplies itself to produce A^2? Here $m = n$.

44. To prove that $(AB)C = A(BC)$, use the column vectors $b_1, \dots, b_n$ of B. First suppose that C has only one column c with entries $c_1, \dots, c_n$:

AB has columns $Ab_1, \dots, Ab_n$ and Bc has one column $c_1b_1 + \cdots + c_nb_n$.

Then $(AB)c = c_1Ab_1 + \cdots + c_nAb_n$ equals $A(c_1b_1 + \cdots + c_nb_n) = A(Bc)$.

Linearity gives equality of those two sums, and $(AB)c = A(Bc)$. The same is true for all other ___ of C. Therefore $(AB)C = A(BC)$.

Problems 45–49 use column–row multiplication and block multiplication.

45. Multiply AB using columns times rows:

$$AB = \begin{bmatrix} 1 & 0 \\ 2 & 4 \\ 2 & 1 \end{bmatrix} \begin{bmatrix} 3 & 3 & 0 \\ 1 & 2 & 1 \end{bmatrix} = \begin{bmatrix} 1 \\ 2 \\ 2 \end{bmatrix} \begin{bmatrix} 3 & 3 & 0 \end{bmatrix} + \underline{\qquad} = \underline{\qquad}.$$

46. ***Block multiplication*** separates matrices into blocks (submatrices). If their shapes make block multiplication possible, then it is allowed. Replace these x's by numbers and confirm that block multiplication succeeds.

$$\begin{bmatrix} A & B \end{bmatrix} \begin{bmatrix} C \\ D \end{bmatrix} = \begin{bmatrix} AC + BD \end{bmatrix} \quad \text{and} \quad \left[\begin{array}{cc|c} x & x & x \\ x & x & x \\ \hline x & x & x \end{array}\right] \left[\begin{array}{cc|c} x & x & x \\ x & x & x \\ \hline x & x & x \end{array}\right].$$

47. Draw the cuts in A and B and AB to show how each of the four multiplication rules is really a block multiplication to find AB:

(a) Matrix A times columns of B.
(b) Rows of A times matrix B.

(c) Rows of A times columns of B.
(d) Columns of A times rows of B.

48. Block multiplication says that elimination on column 1 produces

$$EA = \begin{bmatrix} 1 & \mathbf{0} \\ -\boldsymbol{c}/a & I \end{bmatrix} \begin{bmatrix} a & \boldsymbol{b} \\ \boldsymbol{c} & D \end{bmatrix} = \begin{bmatrix} a & \boldsymbol{b} \\ \mathbf{0} & \_\_ \end{bmatrix}.$$

49. *Elimination for a 2 by 2 block matrix*: When $A^{-1}A = I$, multiply the first block row by CA^{-1} and subtract from the second row, to find the "*Schur complement*" S:

$$\begin{bmatrix} I & 0 \\ -CA^{-1} & I \end{bmatrix} \begin{bmatrix} A & B \\ C & D \end{bmatrix} = \begin{bmatrix} A & B \\ 0 & S \end{bmatrix}.$$

50. With $i^2 = -1$, the product $(A + iB)(x + iy)$ is $Ax + iBx + iAy - By$. Use blocks to separate the real part from the imaginary part that multiplies i:

$$\begin{bmatrix} A & -B \\ ? & ? \end{bmatrix} \begin{bmatrix} x \\ y \end{bmatrix} = \begin{bmatrix} Ax - By \\ ? \end{bmatrix} \begin{matrix} \text{real part} \\ \text{imaginary part} \end{matrix}$$

51. Suppose you solve $Ax = b$ for three special right-hand sides b:

$$Ax_1 = \begin{bmatrix} 1 \\ 0 \\ 0 \end{bmatrix} \quad \text{and} \quad Ax_2 = \begin{bmatrix} 0 \\ 1 \\ 0 \end{bmatrix} \quad \text{and} \quad Ax_3 = \begin{bmatrix} 0 \\ 0 \\ 1 \end{bmatrix}.$$

If the solutions x_1, x_2, x_3 are the columns of a matrix X, what is AX?

52. If the three solutions in Question 51 are $x_1 = (1, 1, 1)$ and $x_2 = (0, 1, 1)$ and $x_3 = (0, 0, 1)$, solve $Ax = b$ when $b = (3, 5, 8)$. Challenge problem: What is A?

53. Find all matrices

$$A = \begin{bmatrix} a & b \\ c & d \end{bmatrix} \quad \text{that satisfy} \quad A \begin{bmatrix} 1 & 1 \\ 1 & 1 \end{bmatrix} = \begin{bmatrix} 1 & 1 \\ 1 & 1 \end{bmatrix} A.$$

54. If you multiply a *northwest matrix* A and a *southeast matrix* B, what type of matrices are AB and BA? "Northwest" and "southeast" mean zeros below and above the antidiagonal going from $(1, n)$ to $(n, 1)$.

55. Write $2x + 3y + z + 5t = 8$ as a matrix A (how many rows?) multiplying the column vector (x, y, z, t) to produce b. The solutions fill a plane in four-dimensional space. *The plane is three-dimensional with no* 4D *volume.*

56. What 2 by 2 matrix P_1 projects the vector (x, y) onto the x axis to produce $(x, 0)$? What matrix P_2 projects onto the y axis to produce $(0, y)$? If you multiply $(5, 7)$ by P_1 and then multiply by P_2, you get (______) and (______).

57. Write the inner product of $(1, 4, 5)$ and (x, y, z) as a matrix multiplication Ax. A has one row. The solutions to $Ax = 0$ lie on a ______ perpendicular to the vector ______. The columns of A are only in ______-dimensional space.

58. In MATLAB notation, write the commands that define the matrix A and the column vectors x and b. What command would test whether or not $Ax = b$?

$$A = \begin{bmatrix} 1 & 2 \\ 3 & 4 \end{bmatrix} \qquad x = \begin{bmatrix} 5 \\ -2 \end{bmatrix} \qquad b = \begin{bmatrix} 1 \\ 7 \end{bmatrix}$$

59. The MATLAB commands A = eye(3) and v = [3:5]' produce the 3 by 3 identity matrix and the column vector (3, 4, 5). What are the outputs from A * v and v' * v? (Computer not needed!) If you ask for v * A, what happens?

60. If you multiply the 4 by 4 all-ones matrix A = ones(4,4) and the column v = ones(4,1), what is A * v? (Computer not needed.) If you multiply B = eye(4) + ones(4,4) times w = zeros(4,1) + 2 * ones(4,1), what is B * w?

61. Invent a 3 by 3 **magic matrix** M with entries $1, 2, \ldots, 9$. All rows and columns and diagonals add to 15. The first row could be 8, 3, 4. What is M times $(1, 1, 1)$? What is the row vector $[1 \ \ 1 \ \ 1]$ times M?

1.5 TRIANGULAR FACTORS AND ROW EXCHANGES

We want to look again at elimination, to see what it means in terms of matrices. The starting point was the model system $Ax = b$:

$$Ax = \begin{bmatrix} 2 & 1 & 1 \\ 4 & -6 & 0 \\ -2 & 7 & 2 \end{bmatrix} \begin{bmatrix} u \\ v \\ w \end{bmatrix} = \begin{bmatrix} 5 \\ -2 \\ 9 \end{bmatrix} = b. \tag{1}$$

Then there were three elimination steps, with multipliers $2, -1, -1$:

Step 1. Subtract 2 times the first equation from the second;
Step 2. Subtract -1 times the first equation from the third;
Step 3. Subtract -1 times the second equation from the third.

The result was an equivalent system $Ux = c$, with a new coefficient matrix U:

Upper triangular $$Ux = \begin{bmatrix} 2 & 1 & 1 \\ 0 & -8 & -2 \\ 0 & 0 & 1 \end{bmatrix} \begin{bmatrix} u \\ v \\ w \end{bmatrix} = \begin{bmatrix} 5 \\ -12 \\ 2 \end{bmatrix} = c. \tag{2}$$

This matrix U is ***upper triangular***—all entries below the diagonal are zero.

The new right side c was derived from the original vector b by the same steps that took A into U. *Forward elimination* amounted to three row operations:

Start with A and b;
Apply steps 1, 2, 3 in that order;
End with U and c.

$Ux = c$ is solved by back-substitution. Here we concentrate on connecting A to U.

The matrices E for step 1, F for step 2, and G for step 3 were introduced in the previous section. They are called ***elementary matrices***, and it is easy to see how they work. To subtract a multiple ℓ of equation j from equation i, *put the number* $-\ell$ *into the* (i, j) *position*. Otherwise keep the identity matrix, with 1s on the diagonal and 0s elsewhere. Then matrix multiplication executes the row operation.

The result of all three steps is $GFEA = U$. Note that E is the first to multiply A, then F, then G. We could multiply GFE together to find the single matrix that takes A to U (and also takes b to c). It is lower triangular (zeros are omitted):

$$\textbf{From } A \textbf{ to } U \qquad GFE = \begin{bmatrix} 1 & & \\ & 1 & \\ & 1 & 1 \end{bmatrix} \begin{bmatrix} 1 & & \\ & 1 & \\ 1 & & 1 \end{bmatrix} \begin{bmatrix} 1 & & \\ -2 & 1 & \\ & & 1 \end{bmatrix} = \begin{bmatrix} 1 & & \\ -2 & 1 & \\ -1 & 1 & 1 \end{bmatrix}. \quad (3)$$

This is good, but the most important question is exactly the opposite: How would we get from U back to A? ***How can we undo the steps of Gaussian elimination?***

To undo step 1 is not hard. Instead of subtracting, we *add* twice the first row to the second. (Not twice the second row to the first!) The result of doing both the subtraction and the addition is to bring back the identity matrix:

$$\begin{matrix}\textbf{Inverse of} \\ \textbf{subtraction} \\ \textbf{is addition}\end{matrix} \qquad \begin{bmatrix} 1 & 0 & 0 \\ 2 & 1 & 0 \\ 0 & 0 & 1 \end{bmatrix} \begin{bmatrix} 1 & 0 & 0 \\ -2 & 1 & 0 \\ 0 & 0 & 1 \end{bmatrix} = \begin{bmatrix} 1 & 0 & 0 \\ 0 & 1 & 0 \\ 0 & 0 & 1 \end{bmatrix}. \quad (4)$$

One operation cancels the other. In matrix terms, one matrix is the ***inverse*** of the other. If the elementary matrix E has the number $-\ell$ in the (i, j) position, then its inverse E^{-1} has $+\ell$ in that position. Thus $E^{-1}E = I$, which is equation (4).

We can invert each step of elimination, by using E^{-1} and F^{-1} and G^{-1}. I think it's not bad to see these inverses now, before the next section. The final problem is to undo the whole process at once, and see what matrix takes U back to A.

Since step 3 was last in going from A to U, its matrix G must be the first to be inverted in the reverse direction. Inverses come in the opposite order! The second reverse step is F^{-1} and the last is E^{-1}:

$$\textbf{From } U \textbf{ back to } A \qquad E^{-1}F^{-1}G^{-1}U = A \quad \text{is} \quad LU = A. \quad (5)$$

You can substitute $GFEA$ for U, to see how the inverses knock out the original steps.

Now we recognize the matrix L that takes U back to A. It is called L, because it is *lower triangular*. And it has a special property that can be seen only by multiplying the three inverse matrices in the right order:

$$E^{-1}F^{-1}G^{-1} = \begin{bmatrix} 1 & & \\ \mathbf{2} & 1 & \\ & & 1 \end{bmatrix} \begin{bmatrix} 1 & & \\ & 1 & \\ \mathbf{-1} & & 1 \end{bmatrix} \begin{bmatrix} 1 & & \\ & 1 & \\ & \mathbf{-1} & 1 \end{bmatrix} = \begin{bmatrix} 1 & & \\ \mathbf{2} & 1 & \\ \mathbf{-1} & \mathbf{-1} & 1 \end{bmatrix} = L. \quad (6)$$

The special thing is that ***the entries below the diagonal are the multipliers*** $\ell = 2, -1$, and -1. When matrices are multiplied, there is usually no direct way to read off the answer. Here the matrices come in just the right order so that their product can be written down immediately. If the computer stores each multiplier ℓ_{ij}—the number that multiplies the pivot row j when it is subtracted from row i, and produces a zero in the i, j position—then these multipliers give a complete record of elimination.

The numbers ℓ_{ij} fit right into the matrix L that takes U back to A.

1H ***Triangular factorization $A = LU$ with no exchanges of rows.*** L is lower triangular, with 1s on the diagonal. The multipliers ℓ_{ij} (taken from elimination) are below the diagonal. U is the upper triangular matrix which appears after forward elimination. The diagonal entries of U are the pivots.

Example 1

$$A = \begin{bmatrix} 1 & 2 \\ 3 & 8 \end{bmatrix} \text{ goes to } U = \begin{bmatrix} 1 & 2 \\ 0 & 2 \end{bmatrix} \text{ with } L = \begin{bmatrix} 1 & 0 \\ 3 & 1 \end{bmatrix}. \text{ Then } LU = A.$$

Example 2 (which needs a row exchange)

$$A = \begin{bmatrix} 0 & 2 \\ 3 & 4 \end{bmatrix} \quad \text{cannot be factored into} \quad A = LU.$$

Example 3 (with all pivots and multipliers equal to 1)

$$A = \begin{bmatrix} 1 & 1 & 1 \\ 1 & 2 & 2 \\ 1 & 2 & 3 \end{bmatrix} = \begin{bmatrix} 1 & 0 & 0 \\ 1 & 1 & 0 \\ 1 & 1 & 1 \end{bmatrix} \begin{bmatrix} 1 & 1 & 1 \\ 0 & 1 & 1 \\ 0 & 0 & 1 \end{bmatrix} = LU.$$

From A to U there are subtractions of rows. From U to A there are additions of rows.

Example 4 (when U is the identity and L is the same as A)

$$\textbf{Lower triangular case} \qquad A = \begin{bmatrix} 1 & 0 & 0 \\ \ell_{21} & 1 & 0 \\ \ell_{31} & \ell_{32} & 1 \end{bmatrix}.$$

The elimination steps on this A are easy: (i) E subtracts ℓ_{21} times row 1 from row 2, (ii) F subtracts ℓ_{31} times row 1 from row 3, and (iii) G subtracts ℓ_{32} times row 2 from row 3. The result is the identity matrix $U = I$. The inverses of E, F, and G will bring back A:

> E^{-1} applied to F^{-1} applied to G^{-1} applied to I produces A.

$$\begin{bmatrix} 1 & & \\ \ell_{21} & 1 & \\ & & 1 \end{bmatrix} \text{ times } \begin{bmatrix} 1 & & \\ & 1 & \\ \ell_{31} & & 1 \end{bmatrix} \text{ times } \begin{bmatrix} 1 & & \\ & 1 & \\ & \ell_{32} & 1 \end{bmatrix} \text{ equals } \begin{bmatrix} 1 & 0 & 0 \\ \ell_{21} & 1 & 0 \\ \ell_{31} & \ell_{32} & 1 \end{bmatrix}.$$

The order is right for the ℓ's to fall into position. This always happens! Note that parentheses in $E^{-1}F^{-1}G^{-1}$ were not necessary because of the associative law.

$A = LU$: The n by n case

The factorization $A = LU$ is so important that we must say more. It used to be missing in linear algebra courses when they concentrated on the abstract side. Or maybe it was thought to be too hard—but you have got it. If the last Example 4 allows any U instead of the particular $U = I$, we can see how the rule works in general. ***The matrix L, applied to U, brings back A***:

$$\mathbf{A = LU} \qquad \begin{bmatrix} 1 & 0 & 0 \\ \ell_{21} & 1 & 0 \\ \ell_{31} & \ell_{32} & 1 \end{bmatrix} \begin{bmatrix} \text{row 1 of } U \\ \text{row 2 of } U \\ \text{row 3 of } U \end{bmatrix} = \text{original } A. \tag{7}$$

The proof is to *apply the steps of elimination.* On the right-hand side they take A to U. On the left-hand side they reduce L to I, as in Example 4. (The first step subtracts ℓ_{21} times $(1, 0, 0)$ from the second row, which removes ℓ_{21}.) Both sides of (7) end up equal to the same matrix U, and the steps to get there are all reversible. Therefore (7) is correct and $A = LU$.

$A = LU$ is so crucial, and so beautiful, that Problem 8 at the end of this section suggests a second approach. We are writing down 3 by 3 matrices, but you can see how the arguments apply to larger matrices. Here we give one more example, and then put $A = LU$ to use.

Example 5 ($A = LU$, with zeros in the empty spaces)

$$A = \begin{bmatrix} 1 & -1 & & \\ -1 & 2 & -1 & \\ & -1 & 2 & -1 \\ & & -1 & 2 \end{bmatrix} = \begin{bmatrix} 1 & & & \\ -1 & 1 & & \\ & -1 & 1 & \\ & & -1 & 1 \end{bmatrix} \begin{bmatrix} 1 & -1 & & \\ & 1 & -1 & \\ & & 1 & -1 \\ & & & 1 \end{bmatrix}.$$

That shows how a matrix A with three diagonals has factors L and U with two diagonals. This example comes from an important problem in differential equations (Section 1.7). The second difference in A is a backward difference L times a forward difference U.

One Linear System = Two Triangular Systems

There is a serious practical point about $A = LU$. It is more than just a record of elimination steps; L and U are the right matrices to solve $Ax = b$. In fact A could be thrown away! We go from b to c by forward elimination (this uses L) and we go from c to x by back-substitution (that uses U). We can and should do it without A:

$$\textbf{Splitting of } \boldsymbol{Ax = b} \qquad \textit{First} \quad Lc = b \quad \textit{and then} \quad Ux = c. \tag{8}$$

Multiply the second equation by L to give LUx = Lc, which is Ax = b. Each triangular system is quickly solved. That is exactly what a good elimination code will do:

1. ***Factor*** (from A find its factors L and U).
2. ***Solve*** (from L and U and b find the solution x).

The separation into ***Factor*** and ***Solve*** means that a series of b's can be processed. The ***Solve*** subroutine obeys equation (8): two triangular systems in $n^2/2$ steps each. **The solution for any new right-hand side b can be found in only n^2 operations.** That is far below the $n^3/3$ steps needed to factor A on the left-hand side.

Example 6 This is the previous matrix A with a right-hand side $b = (1, 1, 1, 1)$.

$$\boldsymbol{Ax = b} \qquad \begin{aligned} x_1 - x_2 \qquad\qquad &= 1 \\ -x_1 + 2x_2 - x_3 \qquad &= 1 \\ - x_2 + 2x_3 - x_4 &= 1 \\ - x_3 + 2x_4 &= 1 \end{aligned} \qquad \text{splits into } Lc = b \text{ and } Ux = c.$$

$$\boldsymbol{Lc = b} \qquad \begin{aligned} c_1 \qquad\qquad &= 1 \\ -c_1 + c_2 \qquad &= 1 \\ - c_2 + c_3 \quad &= 1 \\ - c_3 + c_4 &= 1 \end{aligned} \qquad \text{gives } \boldsymbol{c} = \begin{bmatrix} \mathbf{1} \\ \mathbf{2} \\ \mathbf{3} \\ \mathbf{4} \end{bmatrix}.$$

$$\boldsymbol{Ux = c} \qquad \begin{aligned} x_1 - x_2 \qquad\qquad &= 1 \\ x_2 - x_3 \qquad &= 2 \\ x_3 - x_4 &= 3 \\ x_4 &= 4 \end{aligned} \qquad \text{gives } \boldsymbol{x} = \begin{bmatrix} \mathbf{10} \\ \mathbf{9} \\ \mathbf{7} \\ \mathbf{4} \end{bmatrix}.$$

For these special "tridiagonal matrices," the operation count drops from n^2 to $2n$. You see how $Lc = b$ is solved *forward* (c_1 comes before c_2). This is precisely what happens during forward elimination. Then $Ux = c$ is solved backward (x_4 before x_3).

Remark 1 The LU form is "unsymmetric" on the diagonal: L has 1s where U has the pivots. This is easy to correct. **Divide out of U a diagonal pivot matrix D:**

$$\textbf{Factor out } \boldsymbol{D} \qquad U = \begin{bmatrix} d_1 & & & \\ & d_2 & & \\ & & \cdot & \\ & & & d_n \end{bmatrix} \begin{bmatrix} 1 & u_{12}/d_1 & u_{13}/d_1 & \cdot \\ & 1 & u_{23}/d_2 & \cdot \\ & & \cdot & \cdot \\ & & & 1 \end{bmatrix}. \tag{9}$$

In the last example all pivots were $d_i = 1$. In that case $D = I$. But that was very exceptional, and normally LU is different from LDU (also written LDV).

> ***The triangular factorization can be written A = LDU, where L and U have 1s on the diagonal and D is the diagonal matrix of pivots.***

Whenever you see LDU or LDV, it is understood that U or V has 1s on the diagonal—each row was divided by the pivot in D. Then L and U are treated evenly. An example of LU splitting into LDU is

$$A = \begin{bmatrix} 1 & 2 \\ 3 & 4 \end{bmatrix} = \begin{bmatrix} 1 & \\ 3 & 1 \end{bmatrix} \begin{bmatrix} 1 & 2 \\ & -2 \end{bmatrix} = \begin{bmatrix} 1 & \\ 3 & 1 \end{bmatrix} \begin{bmatrix} 1 & \\ & -2 \end{bmatrix} \begin{bmatrix} 1 & 2 \\ & 1 \end{bmatrix} = LDU.$$

That has the 1s on the diagonals of L and U, and the pivots 1 and -2 in D.

Remark 2 We may have given the impression in describing each elimination step, that the calculations must be done in that order. This is wrong. There is *some* freedom, and there is a "Crout algorithm" that arranges the calculations in a slightly different way.

There is no freedom in the final L, D, and U. That is our main point:

1I If $A = L_1D_1U_1$ and also $A = L_2D_2U_2$, where the L's are lower triangular with unit diagonal, the U's are upper triangular with unit diagonal, and the D's are diagonal matrices with no zeros on the diagonal, then $\boldsymbol{L_1 = L_2}$, $\boldsymbol{D_1 = D_2}$, $\boldsymbol{U_1 = U_2}$. The LDU factorization and the LU factorization are uniquely determined by A.

The proof is a good exercise with inverse matrices in the next section.

Row Exchanges and Permutation Matrices

We now have to face a problem that has so far been avoided: The number we expect to use as a pivot might be zero. This could occur in the middle of a calculation. It will happen at the very beginning if $a_{11} = 0$. A simple example is

$$\textbf{Zero in the pivot position} \qquad \begin{bmatrix} \mathbf{0} & 2 \\ 3 & 4 \end{bmatrix} \begin{bmatrix} u \\ v \end{bmatrix} = \begin{bmatrix} b_1 \\ b_2 \end{bmatrix}.$$

The difficulty is clear; no multiple of the first equation will remove the coefficient 3.

The remedy is equally clear. ***Exchange the two equations***, moving the entry 3 up into the pivot. In this example the matrix would become upper triangular:

$$\textbf{Exchange rows} \qquad \begin{aligned} 3u + 4v &= b_2 \\ 2v &= b_1 \end{aligned}$$

To express this in matrix terms, we need the ***permutation matrix*** P that produces the row exchange. It comes from exchanging the rows of I:

$$\textbf{Permutation} \qquad P = \begin{bmatrix} 0 & 1 \\ 1 & 0 \end{bmatrix} \quad \text{and} \quad PA = \begin{bmatrix} 0 & 1 \\ 1 & 0 \end{bmatrix} \begin{bmatrix} 0 & 2 \\ 3 & 4 \end{bmatrix} = \begin{bmatrix} 3 & 4 \\ 0 & 2 \end{bmatrix}.$$

P has the same effect on b, exchanging b_1 and b_2. *The new system is* $PAx = Pb$. The unknowns u and v are *not* reversed in a row exchange.

A permutation matrix P has the same rows as the identity (in some order). There is a single "1" in every row and column. The most common permutation matrix is $P = I$ (it exchanges nothing). The product of two permutation matrices is another permutation—the rows of I get reordered twice.

After $P = I$, the simplest permutations exchange two rows. Other permutations exchange more rows. **There are $n! = (n)(n-1)\cdots(1)$ permutations of size n**. Row 1 has n choices, then row 2 has $n - 1$ choices, and finally the last row has only one choice. We can display all 3 by 3 permutations (there are $3! = (3)(2)(1) = 6$ matrices):

$$\boldsymbol{I} = \begin{bmatrix} 1 & & \\ & 1 & \\ & & 1 \end{bmatrix} \quad \boldsymbol{P_{21}} = \begin{bmatrix} & 1 & \\ 1 & & \\ & & 1 \end{bmatrix} \quad \boldsymbol{P_{32}P_{21}} = \begin{bmatrix} & 1 & \\ & & 1 \\ 1 & & \end{bmatrix}$$

$$\boldsymbol{P_{31}} = \begin{bmatrix} & & 1 \\ & 1 & \\ 1 & & \end{bmatrix} \quad \boldsymbol{P_{32}} = \begin{bmatrix} 1 & & \\ & & 1 \\ & 1 & \end{bmatrix} \quad \boldsymbol{P_{21}P_{32}} = \begin{bmatrix} & & 1 \\ 1 & & \\ & 1 & \end{bmatrix}.$$

There will be 24 permutation matrices of order $n = 4$. There are only two permutation matrices of order 2, namely

$$\begin{bmatrix} 1 & 0 \\ 0 & 1 \end{bmatrix} \quad \text{and} \quad \begin{bmatrix} 0 & 1 \\ 1 & 0 \end{bmatrix}.$$

When we know about inverses and transposes (the next section defines A^{-1} and A^{T}), we discover an important fact: ***P^{-1} is always the same as P^{T}***.

A zero in the pivot location raises two possibilities: ***The trouble may be easy to fix, or it may be serious***. This is decided by looking *below the zero*. If there is a nonzero entry lower down in the same column, then a row exchange is carried out. The nonzero entry becomes the needed pivot, and elimination can get going again:

$$A = \begin{bmatrix} 0 & a & b \\ 0 & 0 & c \\ d & e & f \end{bmatrix} \qquad \begin{array}{lll} d = 0 & \Longrightarrow & \text{no first pivot} \\ a = 0 & \Longrightarrow & \text{no second pivot} \\ c = 0 & \Longrightarrow & \text{no third pivot.} \end{array}$$

If $d = 0$, the problem is incurable and this matrix is ***singular***. There is no hope for a unique solution to $Ax = b$. If d is *not* zero, an exchange P_{13} of rows 1 and 3 will move d into the pivot. However the next pivot position also contains a zero. The number a is now below it (the e above it is useless). If a is not zero then another row exchange P_{23} is called for:

$$P_{13} = \begin{bmatrix} 0 & 0 & 1 \\ 0 & 1 & 0 \\ 1 & 0 & 0 \end{bmatrix} \quad \text{and} \quad P_{23} = \begin{bmatrix} 1 & 0 & 0 \\ 0 & 0 & 1 \\ 0 & 1 & 0 \end{bmatrix} \quad \text{and} \quad P_{23}P_{13}A = \begin{bmatrix} \boldsymbol{d} & e & f \\ 0 & \boldsymbol{a} & b \\ 0 & 0 & \boldsymbol{c} \end{bmatrix}$$

One more point: The permutation $P_{23}P_{13}$ will do both row exchanges at once:

$$\textbf{P_{13} acts first} \qquad P_{23}P_{13} = \begin{bmatrix} 1 & 0 & 0 \\ 0 & 0 & 1 \\ 0 & 1 & 0 \end{bmatrix} \begin{bmatrix} 0 & 0 & 1 \\ 0 & 1 & 0 \\ 1 & 0 & 0 \end{bmatrix} = \begin{bmatrix} 0 & 0 & 1 \\ 1 & 0 & 0 \\ 0 & 1 & 0 \end{bmatrix} = P.$$

If we had known, we could have multiplied A by P in the first place. With the rows in the right order PA, any nonsingular matrix is ready for elimination.

Elimination in a Nutshell: $PA = LU$

The main point is this: If elimination can be completed with the help of row exchanges, then we can imagine that those exchanges are done first (by P). *The matrix PA will not need row exchanges*. In other words, PA allows the standard factorization into L times U. The theory of Gaussian elimination can be summarized in a few lines:

1J In the ***nonsingular*** case, there is a permutation matrix P that reorders the rows of A to avoid zeros in the pivot positions. Then $Ax = b$ has a *unique solution*:

With the rows reordered in advance, *PA* can be factored into *LU*.

In the ***singular*** case, no P can produce a full set of pivots: elimination fails.

In practice, we also consider a row exchange when the original pivot is *near* zero—even if it is not exactly zero. Choosing a larger pivot reduces the roundoff error.

You have to be careful with L. Suppose elimination subtracts row 1 from row 2, creating $\ell_{21} = 1$. Then suppose it exchanges rows 2 and 3. If that exchange is done in advance, the multiplier will change to $\ell_{31} = 1$ in $PA = LU$.

Example 7

$$A = \begin{bmatrix} 1 & 1 & 1 \\ 1 & 1 & 3 \\ 2 & 5 & 8 \end{bmatrix} \rightarrow \begin{bmatrix} 1 & 1 & 1 \\ 0 & \mathbf{0} & 2 \\ 0 & 3 & 6 \end{bmatrix} \rightarrow \begin{bmatrix} 1 & 1 & 1 \\ 0 & 3 & 6 \\ 0 & 0 & 2 \end{bmatrix} = U. \tag{10}$$

That row exchange recovers LU—but now $\ell_{31} = 1$ and $\ell_{21} = 2$:

$$P = \begin{bmatrix} 1 & 0 & 0 \\ 0 & 0 & 1 \\ 0 & 1 & 0 \end{bmatrix} \quad \text{and} \quad L = \begin{bmatrix} 1 & 0 & 0 \\ 2 & 1 & 0 \\ 1 & 0 & 1 \end{bmatrix} \quad \text{and} \quad PA = LU. \tag{11}$$

In MATLAB, A([r k],:) exchanges row k with row r below it (where the kth pivot has been found). We update the matrices L and P the same way. At the start, $P = I$ and sign $= +1$:

```
A([r k], : ) = A([k r], : );
L([r k],1:k–1) = L([k r],1:k–1);
P([r k], : ) = P([k r], : );
sign = –sign
```

The "**sign**" of P tells whether the number of row exchanges is even (sign $= +1$) or odd (sign $= -1$). A row exchange reverses sign. The final value of sign is the **determinant of P** and it does not depend on the order of the row exchanges.

To summarize: A good elimination code saves L and U and P. Those matrices carry the information that originally came in A—and they carry it in a more usable form. $Ax = b$ reduces to two triangular systems. This is the practical equivalent of the calculation we do next—*to find the inverse matrix* A^{-1} *and the solution* $x = A^{-1}b$.

Problem Set 1.5

1. When is an upper triangular matrix nonsingular (a full set of pivots)?

2. What multiple ℓ_{32} of row 2 of A will elimination subtract from row 3 of A? Use the factored form

$$A = \begin{bmatrix} 1 & 0 & 0 \\ 2 & 1 & 0 \\ 1 & 4 & 1 \end{bmatrix} \begin{bmatrix} 5 & 7 & 8 \\ 0 & 2 & 3 \\ 0 & 0 & 6 \end{bmatrix}.$$

What will be the pivots? Will a row exchange be required?

3. Multiply the matrix $L = E^{-1}F^{-1}G^{-1}$ in equation (6) by GFE in equation (3):

$$\begin{bmatrix} 1 & 0 & 0 \\ 2 & 1 & 0 \\ -1 & -1 & 1 \end{bmatrix} \quad \text{times} \quad \begin{bmatrix} 1 & 0 & 0 \\ -2 & 1 & 0 \\ -1 & 1 & 1 \end{bmatrix}.$$

Multiply also in the opposite order. *Why are the answers what they are?*

4. Apply elimination to produce the factors L and U for

$$A = \begin{bmatrix} 2 & 1 \\ 8 & 7 \end{bmatrix} \quad \text{and} \quad A = \begin{bmatrix} 3 & 1 & 1 \\ 1 & 3 & 1 \\ 1 & 1 & 3 \end{bmatrix} \quad \text{and} \quad A = \begin{bmatrix} 1 & 1 & 1 \\ 1 & 4 & 4 \\ 1 & 4 & 8 \end{bmatrix}.$$

5. Factor A into LU, and write down the upper triangular system $Ux = c$ which appears after elimination, for

$$Ax = \begin{bmatrix} 2 & 3 & 3 \\ 0 & 5 & 7 \\ 6 & 9 & 8 \end{bmatrix} \begin{bmatrix} u \\ v \\ w \end{bmatrix} = \begin{bmatrix} 2 \\ 2 \\ 5 \end{bmatrix}.$$

6. Find E^2 and E^8 and E^{-1} if

$$E = \begin{bmatrix} 1 & 0 \\ 6 & 1 \end{bmatrix}.$$

7. Find the products FGH and HGF if (with upper triangular zeros omitted)

$$F = \begin{bmatrix} 1 & & & \\ 2 & 1 & & \\ 0 & 0 & 1 & \\ 0 & 0 & 0 & 1 \end{bmatrix} \quad G = \begin{bmatrix} 1 & & & \\ 0 & 1 & & \\ 0 & 2 & 1 & \\ 0 & 0 & 0 & 1 \end{bmatrix} \quad H = \begin{bmatrix} 1 & & & \\ 0 & 1 & & \\ 0 & 0 & 1 & \\ 0 & 0 & 2 & 1 \end{bmatrix}.$$

8. (***Second proof of*** $\boldsymbol{A = LU}$) The third row of U comes from the third row of A by subtracting multiples of rows 1 and 2 (*of* U!):

$$\text{row 3 of } U = \text{row 3 of } A - \ell_{31}(\text{row 1 of } U) - \ell_{32}\,(\text{row 2 of } U).$$

(a) Why are rows of U subtracted off and not rows of A? Answer: Because by the time a pivot row is used, ___.

(b) The equation above is the same as

$$\text{row 3 of } A = \ell_{31}(\text{row 1 of } U) + \ell_{32}(\text{row 2 of } U) + 1\,(\text{row 3 of } U).$$

Which rule for matrix multiplication makes this row 3 of L times U?

The other rows of LU agree similarly with the rows of A.

9. (a) Under what conditions is the following product nonsingular?

$$A = \begin{bmatrix} 1 & 0 & 0 \\ -1 & 1 & 0 \\ 0 & -1 & 1 \end{bmatrix} \begin{bmatrix} d_1 & & \\ & d_2 & \\ & & d_3 \end{bmatrix} \begin{bmatrix} 1 & -1 & 0 \\ 0 & 1 & -1 \\ 0 & 0 & 1 \end{bmatrix}.$$

(b) Solve the system $Ax = b$ starting with $Lc = b$:

$$\begin{bmatrix} 1 & 0 & 0 \\ -1 & 1 & 0 \\ 0 & -1 & 1 \end{bmatrix} \begin{bmatrix} c_1 \\ c_2 \\ c_3 \end{bmatrix} = \begin{bmatrix} 0 \\ 0 \\ 1 \end{bmatrix} = b.$$

10. (a) Why does it take approximately $n^2/2$ multiplication–subtraction steps to solve each of $Lc = b$ and $Ux = c$?

(b) How many steps does elimination use in solving 10 systems with the same 60 by 60 coefficient matrix A?

11. Solve as two triangular systems, without multiplying LU to find A:

$$LUx = \begin{bmatrix} 1 & 0 & 0 \\ 1 & 1 & 0 \\ 1 & 0 & 1 \end{bmatrix} \begin{bmatrix} 2 & 4 & 4 \\ 0 & 1 & 2 \\ 0 & 0 & 1 \end{bmatrix} \begin{bmatrix} u \\ v \\ w \end{bmatrix} = \begin{bmatrix} 2 \\ 0 \\ 2 \end{bmatrix}.$$

12. How could you factor A into a product UL, upper triangular times lower triangular? Would they be the same factors as in $A = LU$?

13. Solve by elimination, exchanging rows when necessary:

$$\begin{aligned} u + 4v + 2w &= -2 \\ -2u - 8v + 3w &= 32 \\ v + w &= 1 \end{aligned} \qquad \text{and} \qquad \begin{aligned} v + w &= 0 \\ u + v &= 0 \\ u + v + w &= 1. \end{aligned}$$

Which permutation matrices are required?

14. Write down all six of the 3 by 3 permutation matrices, including $P = I$. Identify their inverses, which are also permutation matrices. The inverses satisfy $PP^{-1} = I$ and are on the same list.

15. Find the $PA = LDU$ factorizations (and check them) for

$$A = \begin{bmatrix} 0 & 1 & 1 \\ 1 & 0 & 1 \\ 2 & 3 & 4 \end{bmatrix} \qquad \text{and} \qquad A = \begin{bmatrix} 1 & 2 & 1 \\ 2 & 4 & 2 \\ 1 & 1 & 1 \end{bmatrix}.$$

16. Find a 4 by 4 permutation matrix that requires three row exchanges to reach the end of elimination (which is $U = I$).

17. The less familiar form $A = LPU$ exchanges rows only at the end:

$$A = \begin{bmatrix} 1 & 1 & 1 \\ 1 & 1 & 3 \\ 2 & 5 & 8 \end{bmatrix} \rightarrow L^{-1}A = \begin{bmatrix} 1 & 1 & 1 \\ 0 & 0 & 2 \\ 0 & 3 & 6 \end{bmatrix} = PU = \begin{bmatrix} 1 & 0 & 0 \\ 0 & 0 & 1 \\ 0 & 1 & 0 \end{bmatrix} \begin{bmatrix} 1 & 1 & 1 \\ 0 & 3 & 6 \\ 0 & 0 & 2 \end{bmatrix}.$$

What is L is this case? Comparing with $PA = LU$ in Box 1J, the multipliers now stay in place (ℓ_{21} is 1 and ℓ_{31} is 2 when $A = LPU$).

18. Decide whether the following systems are singular or nonsingular, and whether they have no solution, one solution, or infinitely many solutions:

$$\begin{aligned} v - w &= 2 \\ u - v &= 2 \\ u - w &= 2 \end{aligned} \quad \text{and} \quad \begin{aligned} v - w &= 0 \\ u - v &= 0 \\ u - w &= 0 \end{aligned} \quad \text{and} \quad \begin{aligned} v + w &= 1 \\ u + v &= 1 \\ u + w &= 1. \end{aligned}$$

19. Which numbers a, b, c lead to row exchanges? Which make the matrix singular?

$$A = \begin{bmatrix} 1 & 2 & 0 \\ a & 8 & 3 \\ 0 & b & 5 \end{bmatrix} \qquad \text{and} \qquad A = \begin{bmatrix} c & 2 \\ 6 & 4 \end{bmatrix}.$$

Problems 20–31 compute the factorization $A = LU$ (and also $A = LDU$).

20. Forward elimination changes $\begin{bmatrix}1&1\\1&2\end{bmatrix}x = b$ to a triangular $\begin{bmatrix}1&1\\0&1\end{bmatrix}x = c$:

$$\begin{matrix}x+\ y=5\\x+2y=7\end{matrix} \longrightarrow \begin{matrix}x+\ y=5\\y=2\end{matrix} \qquad \begin{bmatrix}1&1&\mathbf{5}\\1&2&\mathbf{7}\end{bmatrix} \longrightarrow \begin{bmatrix}1&1&\mathbf{5}\\0&1&\mathbf{2}\end{bmatrix}.$$

That step subtracted $\ell_{21} =$ ______ times row 1 from row 2. The reverse step *adds* ℓ_{21} times row 1 to row 2. The matrix for that reverse step is $L =$ ______. Multiply this L times the triangular system $\begin{bmatrix}1&1\\0&1\end{bmatrix}x = \begin{bmatrix}5\\2\end{bmatrix}$ to get ______ $=$ ______. In letters, L multiplies $Ux = c$ to give ______.

21. (Move to 3 by 3) Forward elimination changes $Ax = b$ to a triangular $Ux = c$:

$$\begin{matrix}x+\ y+\ z=5\\x+2y+3z=7\\x+3y+6z=11\end{matrix} \qquad \begin{matrix}x+\ y+\ z=5\\y+2z=2\\2y+5z=6\end{matrix} \qquad \begin{matrix}x+\ y+\ z=5\\y+2z=2\\z=2.\end{matrix}$$

The equation $z = 2$ in $Ux = c$ comes from the original $x + 3y + 6z = 11$ in $Ax = b$ by subtracting $\ell_{31} =$ __ times equation 1 and $\ell_{32} =$ __ times the *final* equation 2. Reverse that to recover $[1\ \ 3\ \ 6\ \ 11]$ in $[A\ \ b]$ from the final $[1\ \ 1\ \ 1\ \ 5]$ and $[0\ \ 1\ \ 2\ \ 2]$ and $[0\ \ 0\ \ 1\ \ 2]$ in $[U\ \ c]$:

$$\text{Row 3 of } \begin{bmatrix}A & b\end{bmatrix} = (\ell_{31}\text{ Row 1} + \ell_{32}\text{ Row 2} + 1\text{ Row 3}) \text{ of } \begin{bmatrix}U & c\end{bmatrix}.$$

In matrix notation this is multiplication by L. So $A = LU$ and $b = Lc$.

22. What are the 3 by 3 triangular systems $Lc = b$ and $Ux = c$ from Problem 21? Check that $c = (5, 2, 2)$ solves the first one. Which x solves the second one?

23. What two elimination matrices E_{21} and E_{32} put A into upper triangular form $E_{32}E_{21}A = U$? Multiply by E_{32}^{-1} and E_{21}^{-1} to factor A into $LU = E_{21}^{-1}E_{32}^{-1}U$:

$$A = \begin{bmatrix}1&1&1\\2&4&5\\0&4&0\end{bmatrix}.$$

24. What three elimination matrices E_{21}, E_{31}, E_{32} put A into upper triangular form $E_{32}E_{31}E_{21}A = U$? Multiply by E_{32}^{-1}, E_{31}^{-1} and E_{21}^{-1} to factor A into LU where $L = E_{21}^{-1}E_{31}^{-1}E_{32}^{-1}$. Find L and U:

$$A = \begin{bmatrix}1&0&1\\2&2&2\\3&4&5\end{bmatrix}.$$

25. When zero appears in a pivot position, $A = LU$ *is not possible*! (We need nonzero pivots d, f, i in U.) Show directly why these are both impossible:

$$\begin{bmatrix}0&1\\2&3\end{bmatrix} = \begin{bmatrix}1&0\\\ell&1\end{bmatrix}\begin{bmatrix}d&e\\0&f\end{bmatrix} \qquad \begin{bmatrix}1&1&0\\1&1&2\\1&2&1\end{bmatrix} = \begin{bmatrix}1&&\\\ell&1&\\m&n&1\end{bmatrix}\begin{bmatrix}d&e&g\\&f&h\\&&i\end{bmatrix}.$$

26. Which number c leads to zero in the second pivot position? A row exchange is needed and $A = LU$ is not possible. Which c produces zero in the third pivot position? Then a row exchange can't help and elimination fails:

$$A = \begin{bmatrix} 1 & c & 0 \\ 2 & 4 & 1 \\ 3 & 5 & 1 \end{bmatrix}.$$

27. What are L and D for this matrix A? What is U in $A = LU$ and what is the new U in $A = LDU$?

$$A = \begin{bmatrix} 2 & 4 & 8 \\ 0 & 3 & 9 \\ 0 & 0 & 7 \end{bmatrix}.$$

28. A and B are symmetric across the diagonal (because $4 = 4$). Find their triple factorizations LDU and say how U is related to L for these symmetric matrices:

$$A = \begin{bmatrix} 2 & 4 \\ 4 & 11 \end{bmatrix} \quad \text{and} \quad B = \begin{bmatrix} 1 & 4 & 0 \\ 4 & 12 & 4 \\ 0 & 4 & 0 \end{bmatrix}.$$

29. (Recommended) Compute L and U for the symmetric matrix

$$A = \begin{bmatrix} a & a & a & a \\ a & b & b & b \\ a & b & c & c \\ a & b & c & d \end{bmatrix}.$$

Find four conditions on a, b, c, d to get $A = LU$ with four pivots.

30. Find L and U for the nonsymmetric matrix

$$A = \begin{bmatrix} a & r & r & r \\ a & b & s & s \\ a & b & c & t \\ a & b & c & d \end{bmatrix}.$$

Find the four conditions on a, b, c, d, r, s, t to get $A = LU$ with four pivots.

31. *Tridiagonal matrices* have zero entries except on the main diagonal and the two adjacent diagonals. Factor these into $A = LU$ and $A = LDV$:

$$A = \begin{bmatrix} 1 & 1 & 0 \\ 1 & 2 & 1 \\ 0 & 1 & 2 \end{bmatrix} \quad \text{and} \quad A = \begin{bmatrix} a & a & 0 \\ a & a+b & b \\ 0 & b & b+c \end{bmatrix}.$$

32. Solve the triangular system $Lc = b$ to find c. Then solve $Ux = c$ to find x:

$$L = \begin{bmatrix} 1 & 0 \\ 4 & 1 \end{bmatrix} \quad \text{and} \quad U = \begin{bmatrix} 2 & 4 \\ 0 & 1 \end{bmatrix} \quad \text{and} \quad b = \begin{bmatrix} 2 \\ 11 \end{bmatrix}.$$

For safety find $A = LU$ and solve $Ax = b$ as usual. Circle c when you see it.

33. Solve $Lc = b$ to find c. Then solve $Ux = c$ to find x. What was A?

$$L = \begin{bmatrix} 1 & 0 & 0 \\ 1 & 1 & 0 \\ 1 & 1 & 1 \end{bmatrix} \quad \text{and} \quad U = \begin{bmatrix} 1 & 1 & 1 \\ 0 & 1 & 1 \\ 0 & 0 & 1 \end{bmatrix} \quad \text{and} \quad b = \begin{bmatrix} 4 \\ 5 \\ 6 \end{bmatrix}.$$

34. If A and B have nonzeros in the positions marked by x, which zeros are still zero in their factors L and U?

$$A = \begin{bmatrix} x & x & x & x \\ x & x & x & 0 \\ 0 & x & x & x \\ 0 & 0 & x & x \end{bmatrix} \quad \text{and} \quad B = \begin{bmatrix} x & x & x & 0 \\ x & x & 0 & x \\ x & 0 & x & x \\ 0 & x & x & x \end{bmatrix}.$$

35. (Important) If A has pivots $2, 7, 6$ with no row exchanges, what are the pivots for the upper left 2 by 2 submatrix B (without row 3 and column 3)? Explain why.

36. Starting from a 3 by 3 matrix A with pivots $2, 7, 6$, add a fourth row and column to produce M. What are the first three pivots for M, and why? What fourth row and column are sure to produce 9 as the fourth pivot?

37. Use chol(pascal(5)) to find the triangular factors of MATLAB's pascal(5). Row exchanges in $[L,\ U]$ = lu(pascal(5)) spoil Pascal's pattern!

38. (Review) For which numbers c is $A = LU$ impossible—with three pivots?

$$A = \begin{bmatrix} 1 & 2 & 0 \\ 3 & c & 1 \\ 0 & 1 & 1 \end{bmatrix}.$$

39. Estimate the time difference for each new right-hand side b when $n = 800$. Create A= rand(800) and b= rand(800,1) and B= rand(800,9). Compare the times from tic; $A\backslash b$; toc and tic; $A\backslash B$; toc (which solves for 9 right sides).

Problems 40–48 are about permutation matrices.

40. There are 12 "*even*" permutations of $(1, 2, 3, 4)$, with an *even number of exchanges*. Two of them are $(1, 2, 3, 4)$ with no exchanges and $(4, 3, 2, 1)$ with two exchanges. List the other ten. Instead of writing each 4 by 4 matrix, use the numbers 4, 3, 2, 1 to give the position of the 1 in each row.

41. How many exchanges will permute $(5, 4, 3, 2, 1)$ back to $(1, 2, 3, 4, 5)$? How many exchanges to change $(6, 5, 4, 3, 2, 1)$ to $(1, 2, 3, 4, 5, 6)$? One is even and the other is odd. For $(n, \ldots, 1)$ to $(1, \ldots, n)$, show that $n = 100$ and 101 are even, $n = 102$ and 103 are odd.

42. If P_1 and P_2 are permutation matrices, so is P_1P_2. This still has the rows of I in some order. Give examples with $P_1P_2 \neq P_2P_1$ and $P_3P_4 = P_4P_3$.

43. (Try this question.) Which permutation makes PA upper triangular? Which permutations make P_1AP_2 lower triangular? ***Multiplying A on the*** *right* ***by P_2 exchanges the ______ of*** *A*.

$$A = \begin{bmatrix} 0 & 0 & 6 \\ 1 & 2 & 3 \\ 0 & 4 & 5 \end{bmatrix}.$$

44. Find a 3 by 3 permutation matrix with $P^3 = I$ (but not $P = I$). Find a 4 by 4 permutation $\widehat{P}$ with $\widehat{P}^4 \neq I$.

45. If you take powers of a permutation, why is some P^k eventually equal to I? Find a 5 by 5 permutation P so that the smallest power to equal I is P^6. (This is a challenge question. Combine a 2 by 2 block with a 3 by 3 block.)

46. The matrix P that multiplies (x, y, z) to give (z, x, y) is also a rotation matrix. Find P and P^3. The rotation axis $a = (1, 1, 1)$ doesn't move, it equals Pa. What is the angle of rotation from $v = (2, 3, -5)$ to $Pv = (-5, 2, 3)$?

47. If P is any permutation matrix, find a nonzero vector x so that $(I - P)x = 0$. (This will mean that $I - P$ has no inverse, and has determinant zero.)

48. If P has 1s on the antidiagonal from $(1, n)$ to $(n, 1)$, describe PAP.

1.6 INVERSES AND TRANSPOSES

The inverse of an n by n matrix is another n by n matrix. The inverse of A is written A^{-1} (and pronounced "A inverse"). The fundamental property is simple: *If you multiply by A and then multiply by A^{-1}, you are back where you started*:

$$\textbf{Inverse matrix} \qquad \text{If} \quad b = Ax \quad \text{then} \quad A^{-1}b = x.$$

Thus $A^{-1}Ax = x$. The matrix A^{-1} times A is the identity matrix. ***Not all matrices have inverses. An inverse is impossible when Ax is zero and x is nonzero.*** Then A^{-1} would have to get back from $Ax = 0$ to x. No matrix can multiply that zero vector Ax and produce a nonzero vector x.

Our goals are to define the inverse matrix and compute it and use it, when A^{-1} exists—and then to understand which matrices don't have inverses.

1K The **inverse** of A is a matrix B such that $BA = I$ and $AB = I$. There is at most one such B, and it is denoted by A^{-1}:

$$A^{-1}A = I \quad \text{and} \quad AA^{-1} = I. \tag{1}$$

Note 1 ***The inverse exists if and only if elimination produces n pivots*** (row exchanges allowed). Elimination solves $Ax = b$ without explicitly finding A^{-1}.

Note 2 The matrix A cannot have two different inverses. Suppose $BA = I$ and also $AC = I$. Then $B = C$, according to this "proof by parentheses":

$$B(AC) = (BA)C \quad \text{gives} \quad BI = IC \quad \text{which is} \quad B = C. \tag{2}$$

This shows that a *left-inverse* B (multiplying from the left) and a *right-inverse* C (multiplying A from the right to give $AC = I$) must be the *same matrix.*

Note 3 If A is invertible, the one and only solution to $Ax = b$ is $x = A^{-1}b$:

$$\textit{\textbf{Multiply}} \quad \boldsymbol{Ax = b} \quad \textit{\textbf{by}} \quad \boldsymbol{A^{-1}}. \quad \textit{\textbf{Then}} \quad \boldsymbol{x = A^{-1}Ax = A^{-1}b}.$$

Note 4 (Important) ***Suppose there is a nonzero vector x such that $Ax = 0$.*** *Then A cannot have an inverse.* To repeat: No matrix can bring 0 back to x.

If A is invertible, then $Ax = 0$ can only have the zero solution $x = 0$.

Note 5 A 2 by 2 matrix is invertible if and only if $ad - bc$ is not zero:

$$\textbf{2 by 2 inverse} \qquad \begin{bmatrix} a & b \\ c & d \end{bmatrix}^{-1} = \frac{1}{ad - bc} \begin{bmatrix} d & -b \\ -c & a \end{bmatrix}. \qquad (3)$$

This number $ad - bc$ is the *determinant* of A. A matrix is invertible if its determinant is not zero (Chapter 4). In MATLAB, the invertibility test is *to find n nonzero pivots*. Elimination produces those pivots before the determinant appears.

Note 6 A diagonal matrix has an inverse provided no diagonal entries are zero:

$$\text{If} \quad A = \begin{bmatrix} d_1 & & \\ & \ddots & \\ & & d_n \end{bmatrix} \quad \text{then} \quad A^{-1} = \begin{bmatrix} 1/d_1 & & \\ & \ddots & \\ & & 1/d_n \end{bmatrix} \quad \text{and} \quad AA^{-1} = I.$$

When two matrices are involved, not much can be done about the inverse of $A + B$. The sum might or might not be invertible. Instead, it is the inverse of their *product* AB which is the key formula in matrix computations. Ordinary numbers are the same: $(a + b)^{-1}$ is hard to simplify, while $1/ab$ splits into $1/a$ times $1/b$. But for matrices *the order of multiplication must be correct*—if $ABx = y$ then $Bx = A^{-1}y$ and $x = B^{-1}A^{-1}y$. **The inverses come in reverse order.**

1L A product AB of invertible matrices is inverted by $B^{-1}A^{-1}$:

$$\textbf{Inverse of } \boldsymbol{AB} \qquad (AB)^{-1} = B^{-1}A^{-1}. \qquad (4)$$

Proof To show that $B^{-1}A^{-1}$ is the inverse of AB, we multiply them and use the associative law to remove parentheses. Notice how B sits next to B^{-1}:

$$(AB)(B^{-1}A^{-1}) = ABB^{-1}A^{-1} = AIA^{-1} = AA^{-1} = I$$
$$(B^{-1}A^{-1})(AB) = B^{-1}A^{-1}AB = B^{-1}IB = B^{-1}B = I. \qquad \blacksquare$$

A similar rule holds with three or more matrices:

$$\textbf{Inverse of } \boldsymbol{ABC} \qquad (ABC)^{-1} = C^{-1}B^{-1}A^{-1}.$$

We saw this change of order when the elimination matrices E, F, G were inverted to come back from U to A. In the forward direction, $GFEA$ was U. In the backward direction, $L = E^{-1}F^{-1}G^{-1}$ was the product of the inverses. *Since G came last, G^{-1} comes first.* Please check that A^{-1} would be $U^{-1}GFE$.

The Calculation of A^{-1}: The Gauss–Jordan Method

Consider the equation $AA^{-1} = I$. If it is taken ***a column at a time***, that equation determines each column of A^{-1}. The first column of A^{-1} is multiplied by A, to yield the first column of the identity: $Ax_1 = e_1$. Similarly $Ax_2 = e_2$ and $Ax_3 = e_3$; the e's are the columns of I. In a 3 by 3 example, A times A^{-1} is I:

$$\boldsymbol{Ax_i = e_i} \qquad \begin{bmatrix} 2 & 1 & 1 \\ 4 & -6 & 0 \\ -2 & 7 & 2 \end{bmatrix} \begin{bmatrix} x_1 & x_2 & x_3 \end{bmatrix} = \begin{bmatrix} e_1 & e_2 & e_3 \end{bmatrix} = \begin{bmatrix} 1 & 0 & 0 \\ 0 & 1 & 0 \\ 0 & 0 & 1 \end{bmatrix}. \qquad (5)$$

Thus we have three systems of equations (or n systems). They all have the same coefficient matrix A. The right-hand sides e_1, e_2, e_3 are different, but elimination is possible *on all systems simultaneously*. This is the ***Gauss–Jordan method***. Instead of stopping at U and switching to back-substitution, it continues by subtracting multiples of a row *from the rows above*. This produces zeros above the diagonal as well as below. When it reaches the identity matrix we have found A^{-1}.

The example keeps all three columns e_1, e_2, e_3, and operates on rows of length six:

Example 1 Using the Gauss–Jordan Method to Find A^{-1}

$$\begin{bmatrix} A & e_1 & e_2 & e_3 \end{bmatrix} = \begin{bmatrix} \mathbf{2} & \mathbf{1} & \mathbf{1} & 1 & 0 & 0 \\ \mathbf{4} & \mathbf{-6} & \mathbf{0} & 0 & 1 & 0 \\ \mathbf{-2} & \mathbf{7} & \mathbf{2} & 0 & 0 & 1 \end{bmatrix}$$

$$\textbf{pivot} = \mathbf{2} \rightarrow \begin{bmatrix} \mathbf{2} & \mathbf{1} & \mathbf{1} & 1 & 0 & 0 \\ \mathbf{0} & \mathbf{-8} & \mathbf{-2} & -2 & 1 & 0 \\ \mathbf{0} & \mathbf{8} & \mathbf{3} & 1 & 0 & 1 \end{bmatrix}$$

$$\textbf{pivot} = \mathbf{-8} \rightarrow \begin{bmatrix} \mathbf{2} & \mathbf{1} & \mathbf{1} & 1 & 0 & 0 \\ \mathbf{0} & \mathbf{-8} & \mathbf{-2} & -2 & 1 & 0 \\ \mathbf{0} & \mathbf{0} & \mathbf{1} & -1 & 1 & 1 \end{bmatrix} = \begin{bmatrix} \boldsymbol{U} & L^{-1} \end{bmatrix}.$$

This completes the first half—forward elimination. The upper triangular U appears in the first three columns. The other three columns are the same as L^{-1}. (This is the effect of applying the elementary operations GFE to the identity matrix.) Now the second half will go from U to I (multiplying by U^{-1}). That takes L^{-1} to $U^{-1}L^{-1}$ which is A^{-1}. **Creating zeros *above* the pivots, we reach A^{-1}:**

$$\textbf{Second half} \quad \begin{bmatrix} U & L^{-1} \end{bmatrix} \rightarrow \begin{bmatrix} 2 & 1 & \mathbf{0} & 2 & -1 & -1 \\ 0 & -8 & \mathbf{0} & -4 & 3 & 2 \\ 0 & 0 & 1 & -1 & 1 & 1 \end{bmatrix}$$

$$\textbf{zeros above pivots} \rightarrow \begin{bmatrix} 2 & \mathbf{0} & \mathbf{0} & \frac{12}{8} & -\frac{5}{8} & -\frac{6}{8} \\ 0 & -8 & \mathbf{0} & -4 & 3 & 2 \\ 0 & 0 & 1 & -1 & 1 & 1 \end{bmatrix}$$

$$\textbf{divide by pivots} \rightarrow \begin{bmatrix} 1 & 0 & 0 & \mathbf{\frac{12}{16}} & -\mathbf{\frac{5}{16}} & -\mathbf{\frac{6}{16}} \\ 0 & 1 & 0 & \mathbf{\frac{4}{8}} & -\mathbf{\frac{3}{8}} & -\mathbf{\frac{2}{8}} \\ 0 & 0 & 1 & \mathbf{-1} & \mathbf{1} & \mathbf{1} \end{bmatrix} = \begin{bmatrix} I & A^{-1} \end{bmatrix}.$$

At the last step, we divided the rows by their pivots 2 and -8 and 1. The coefficient matrix in the left-hand half became the identity. Since A went to I, the same operations on the right-hand half must have carried I into A^{-1}. Therefore we have computed the inverse.

A note for the future: You can see the determinant -16 appearing in the denominators of A^{-1}. **The determinant is the product of the pivots $(2)(-8)(1)$**. It enters at the end when the rows are divided by the pivots.

Remark 1 In spite of this brilliant success in computing A^{-1}, I don't recommend it. I admit that A^{-1} solves $Ax = b$ in one step. Two triangular steps are better:

$$x = A^{-1}b \quad \text{separates into} \quad Lc = b \quad \text{and} \quad Ux = c.$$

We could write $c = L^{-1}b$ and then $x = U^{-1}c = U^{-1}L^{-1}b$. But note that we did not explicitly form, and in actual computation *should not form*, these matrices L^{-1} and U^{-1}. It would be a waste of time, since we only need back-substitution for x (and forward substitution produced c).

A similar remark applies to A^{-1}; the multiplication $A^{-1}b$ would still take n^2 steps. ***It is the solution that we want, and not all the entries in the inverse.***

Remark 2 Purely out of curiosity, we might count the number of operations required to find A^{-1}. The normal count for each new right-hand side is n^2, half in the forward direction and half in back-substitution. With n right-hand sides $e_1, \ldots, e_n$ this makes n^3. After including the $n^3/3$ operations on A itself, the total seems to be $4n^3/3$.

This result is a little too high because of the zeros in the e_j. Forward elimination changes only the zeros below the 1. This part has only $n - j$ components, so the count for e_j is effectively changed to $(n - j)^2/2$. Summing over all j, the total for forward elimination is $n^3/6$. This is to be combined with the usual $n^3/3$ operations that are applied to A, and the $n(n^2/2)$ back-substitution steps that finally produce the columns x_j of A^{-1}. *The final count of multiplications for computing A^{-1} is n^3:*

$$\textbf{Operation count} \qquad \frac{n^3}{6} + \frac{n^3}{3} + n\left(\frac{n^2}{2}\right) = n^3.$$

This count is remarkably low. Since matrix multiplication already takes n^3 steps, it requires as many operations to compute A^2 as it does to compute A^{-1}! That fact seems almost unbelievable (and computing A^3 requires twice as many, as far as we can see). Nevertheless, if A^{-1} is not needed, it should not be computed.

Remark 3 In the Gauss–Jordan calculation we went all the way forward to U, before starting backward to produce zeros above the pivots. That is like Gaussian elimination, but other orders are possible. We could have used the second pivot when we were there earlier, to create a zero above it as well as below it. This is not smart. At that time the second row is virtually full, whereas near the end it has zeros from the upward row operations that have already taken place.

Invertible = Nonsingular (n pivots)

Ultimately we want to know which matrices are invertible and which are not. This question is so important that it has many answers. *See the last page of the book!*

Each of the first five chapters will give a different (but equivalent) test for invertibility. Sometimes the tests extend to rectangular matrices and one-sided inverses: Chapter 2 looks for independent rows and independent columns, Chapter 3 inverts AA^{T} or $A^{\mathrm{T}}A$. The other chapters look for ***nonzero determinants*** or ***nonzero eigenvalues*** or ***nonzero pivots***. This last test is the one we meet through Gaussian elimination. We want to show (in a few theoretical paragraphs) that the pivot test succeeds.

Suppose A has a full set of n pivots. $AA^{-1} = I$ gives n separate systems $Ax_i = e_i$ for the columns of A^{-1}. They can be solved by elimination or by Gauss–Jordan. Row exchanges may be needed, but the columns of A^{-1} are determined.

Strictly speaking, we have to show that the matrix A^{-1} with those columns is also a *left*-inverse. Solving $AA^{-1} = I$ has at the same time solved $A^{-1}A = I$, but why? **A 1-sided inverse of a square matrix is automatically a 2-sided inverse**. To see why, notice that *every Gauss–Jordan step is a multiplication on the left by an elementary matrix*. We are allowing three types of elementary matrices:

1. E_{ij} to subtract a multiple ℓ of row j from row i
2. P_{ij} to exchange rows i and j
3. D (or D^{-1}) to divide all rows by their pivots.

The Gauss–Jordan process is really a giant sequence of matrix multiplications:

$$(D^{-1} \cdots E \cdots P \cdots E)A = I. \tag{6}$$

That matrix in parentheses, to the left of A, is evidently a left-inverse! It exists, it equals the right-inverse by Note 2, so ***every nonsingular matrix is invertible***.

The converse is also true: ***If A is invertible, it has n pivots***. In an extreme case that is clear: A cannot have a whole column of zeros. The inverse could never multiply a column of zeros to produce a column of I. In a less extreme case, suppose elimination starts on an invertible matrix A but breaks down at column 3:

Breakdown
No pivot in column 3
$$A' = \begin{bmatrix} d_1 & x & x & x \\ 0 & d_2 & x & x \\ 0 & 0 & 0 & x \\ 0 & 0 & 0 & x \end{bmatrix}.$$

This matrix cannot have an inverse, no matter what the x's are. One proof is to use column operations (for the first time?) to make the whole third column zero. By subtracting multiples of column 2 and then of column 1, we reach a matrix that is certainly not invertible. Therefore the original A was not invertible. Elimination gives a complete test: *An n by n matrix is invertible if and only if it has n pivots.*

The Transpose Matrix

We need one more matrix, and fortunately it is much simpler than the inverse. The ***transpose*** of A is denoted by A^{T}. Its columns are taken directly from the rows of A—*the ith row of A becomes the ith column of* A^{T}:

Transpose $\quad$ If $A = \begin{bmatrix} 2 & 1 & 4 \\ 0 & 0 & 3 \end{bmatrix}$ then $A^{\mathrm{T}} = \begin{bmatrix} 2 & 0 \\ 1 & 0 \\ 4 & 3 \end{bmatrix}$.

At the same time the columns of A become the rows of A^{T}. If A is an m by n matrix, then A^{T} is n by m. The final effect is to flip the matrix across its main diagonal, and the entry in row i, column j of A^{T} comes from row j, column i of A:

Entries of A^{T}
$$(A^{\mathrm{T}})_{ij} = A_{ji}. \tag{7}$$

The transpose of a lower triangular matrix is upper triangular. The transpose of A^{T} brings us back to A.

If we add two matrices and then transpose, the result is the same as first transposing and then adding: $(A+B)^{\mathrm{T}}$ is the same as $A^{\mathrm{T}}+B^{\mathrm{T}}$. But what is the transpose of a product AB or an inverse A^{-1}? Those are the essential formulas of this section:

1M (i) The transpose of AB is $(AB)^{\mathrm{T}} = B^{\mathrm{T}}A^{\mathrm{T}}$.
(ii) The transpose of A^{-1} is $(A^{-1})^{\mathrm{T}} = (A^{\mathrm{T}})^{-1}$.

Notice how the formula for $(AB)^{\mathrm{T}}$ resembles the one for $(AB)^{-1}$. In both cases we reverse the order, giving $B^{\mathrm{T}}A^{\mathrm{T}}$ and $B^{-1}A^{-1}$. The proof for the inverse was easy, but this one requires an unnatural patience with matrix multiplication. The first row of $(AB)^{\mathrm{T}}$ is the first column of AB. So the columns of A are weighted by the first column of B. This amounts to the rows of A^{T} weighted by the first row of B^{T}. That is exactly the first row of $B^{\mathrm{T}}A^{\mathrm{T}}$. The other rows of $(AB)^{\mathrm{T}}$ and $B^{\mathrm{T}}A^{\mathrm{T}}$ also agree.

$$\textbf{Start from} \qquad AB = \begin{bmatrix} 1 & 0 \\ 1 & 1 \end{bmatrix} \begin{bmatrix} 3 & 3 & 3 \\ 2 & 2 & 2 \end{bmatrix} = \begin{bmatrix} 3 & 3 & 3 \\ 5 & 5 & 5 \end{bmatrix}$$

$$\textbf{Transpose to} \qquad B^{\mathrm{T}}A^{\mathrm{T}} = \begin{bmatrix} 3 & 2 \\ 3 & 2 \\ 3 & 2 \end{bmatrix} \begin{bmatrix} 1 & 1 \\ 0 & 1 \end{bmatrix} = \begin{bmatrix} 3 & 5 \\ 3 & 5 \\ 3 & 5 \end{bmatrix}.$$

To establish the formula for $(A^{-1})^{\mathrm{T}}$, start from $AA^{-1} = I$ and $A^{-1}A = I$ and take transposes. On one side, $I^{\mathrm{T}} = I$. On the other side, we know from part (i) the transpose of a product. You see how $(A^{-1})^{\mathrm{T}}$ is the inverse of A^{T}, proving (ii):

$$\textbf{Inverse of } \boldsymbol{A^{\mathrm{T}}} = \textbf{Transpose of } \boldsymbol{A^{-1}} \qquad (A^{-1})^{\mathrm{T}}A^{\mathrm{T}} = I. \tag{8}$$

Symmetric Matrices

With these rules established, we can introduce a special class of matrices, probably the most important class of all. ***A symmetric matrix is a matrix that equals its own transpose***: $\boldsymbol{A^{\mathrm{T}} = A}$. The matrix is necessarily square. Each entry on one side of the diagonal equals its "mirror image" on the other side: $a_{ij} = a_{ji}$. Two simple examples are A and D (and also A^{-1}):

$$\textbf{Symmetric matrices} \qquad A = \begin{bmatrix} 1 & 2 \\ 2 & 8 \end{bmatrix} \text{ and } D = \begin{bmatrix} 1 & 0 \\ 0 & 4 \end{bmatrix} \text{ and } A^{-1} = \frac{1}{4}\begin{bmatrix} 8 & -2 \\ -2 & 1 \end{bmatrix}.$$

A symmetric matrix need not be invertible; it could even be a matrix of zeros. *But if A^{-1} exists it is also symmetric*. From formula (ii) above, the transpose of A^{-1} always equals $(A^{\mathrm{T}})^{-1}$; for a symmetric matrix this is just A^{-1}. A^{-1} equals its own transpose; it is symmetric whenever A is. Now we show that ***multiplying any matrix R by*** $\boldsymbol{R^{\mathrm{T}}}$ ***gives a symmetric matrix***.

Symmetric Products $R^T R$, $R R^T$, and LDL^T

Choose any matrix R, probably rectangular. Multiply R^T times R. Then the product $R^T R$ is automatically a square symmetric matrix:

$$\textbf{\textit{The transpose of}} \quad R^T R \quad \textbf{\textit{is}} \quad R^T (R^T)^T, \quad \textbf{\textit{which is}} \quad R^T R. \tag{9}$$

That is a quick proof of symmetry for $R^T R$. Its i, j entry is the inner product of row i of R^T (column i of R) with column j of R. The (j, i) entry is the same inner product, column j with column i. So $R^T R$ is symmetric.

$R R^T$ is also symmetric, but it is different from $R^T R$. In my experience, most scientific problems that start with a rectangular matrix R end up with $R^T R$ or $R R^T$ or both.

Example 2 $R = \begin{bmatrix} 1 & 2 \end{bmatrix}$ and $R^T = \begin{bmatrix} 1 \\ 2 \end{bmatrix}$ produce $R^T R = \begin{bmatrix} 1 & 2 \\ 2 & 4 \end{bmatrix}$ and $R R^T = \begin{bmatrix} 5 \end{bmatrix}$.

The product $R^T R$ is n by n. In the opposite order, $R R^T$ is m by m. Even if $m = n$, it is not very likely that $R^T R = R R^T$. Equality can happen, but it's not normal.

Symmetric matrices appear in every subject whose laws are fair. "Each action has an equal and opposite reaction." The entry a_{ij} that gives the action of i onto j is matched by a_{ji}. We will see this symmetry in the next section, for differential equations. Here, LU misses the symmetry but LDL^T captures it perfectly.

1N Suppose $A = A^T$ can be factored into $A = LDU$ without row exchanges. Then U is the transpose of L. ***The symmetric factorization becomes*** $\boldsymbol{A = LDL^T}$.

The transpose of $A = LDU$ gives $A^T = U^T D^T L^T$. Since $A = A^T$, we now have two factorizations of A into lower triangular times diagonal times upper triangular. (L^T is upper triangular with ones on the diagonal, exactly like U.) Since the factorization is unique (see Problem 17), L^T must be identical to U.

$$\boldsymbol{L^T = U \text{ and } A = LDL^T} \qquad \begin{bmatrix} 1 & 2 \\ 2 & 8 \end{bmatrix} = \begin{bmatrix} \mathbf{1} & \mathbf{0} \\ \mathbf{2} & \mathbf{1} \end{bmatrix} \begin{bmatrix} 1 & 0 \\ 0 & 4 \end{bmatrix} \begin{bmatrix} \mathbf{1} & \mathbf{2} \\ \mathbf{0} & \mathbf{1} \end{bmatrix} = LDL^T.$$

When elimination is applied to a symmetric matrix, $A^T = A$ is an advantage. The smaller matrices stay symmetric as elimination proceeds, and we can work with half the matrix! The lower right-hand corner remains symmetric:

$$\begin{bmatrix} a & b & c \\ b & d & e \\ c & e & f \end{bmatrix} \to \begin{bmatrix} a & b & c \\ 0 & d - \dfrac{b^2}{a} & e - \dfrac{\boldsymbol{bc}}{\boldsymbol{a}} \\ 0 & e - \dfrac{\boldsymbol{bc}}{\boldsymbol{a}} & f - \dfrac{c^2}{a} \end{bmatrix}.$$

The work of elimination is reduced from $n^3/3$ to $n^3/6$. There is no need to store entries from both sides of the diagonal, or to store both L and U.

Problem Set 1.6

1. Find the inverses (no special system required) of

$$A_1 = \begin{bmatrix} 0 & 2 \\ 3 & 0 \end{bmatrix}, \quad A_2 = \begin{bmatrix} 2 & 0 \\ 4 & 2 \end{bmatrix}, \quad A_3 = \begin{bmatrix} \cos\theta & -\sin\theta \\ \sin\theta & \cos\theta \end{bmatrix}.$$

2. (a) Find the inverses of the permutation matrices

$$P = \begin{bmatrix} 0 & 0 & 1 \\ 0 & 1 & 0 \\ 1 & 0 & 0 \end{bmatrix} \quad \text{and} \quad P = \begin{bmatrix} 0 & 0 & 1 \\ 1 & 0 & 0 \\ 0 & 1 & 0 \end{bmatrix}.$$

(b) Explain for permutations why P^{-1} *is always the same as* P^{T}. Show that the 1s are in the right places to give $PP^{\mathrm{T}} = I$.

3. From $AB = C$ find a formula for A^{-1}. Also find A^{-1} from $PA = LU$.

4. (a) If A is invertible and $AB = AC$, prove quickly that $B = C$.
(b) If $A = \begin{bmatrix} 1 & 0 \\ 0 & 0 \end{bmatrix}$, find an example with $AB = AC$ but $B \neq C$.

5. If the inverse of A^2 is B, show that the inverse of A is AB. (Thus A is invertible whenever A^2 is invertible.)

6. Use the Gauss–Jordan method to invert

$$A_1 = \begin{bmatrix} 1 & 0 & 0 \\ 1 & 1 & 1 \\ 0 & 0 & 1 \end{bmatrix}, \quad A_2 = \begin{bmatrix} 2 & -1 & 0 \\ -1 & 2 & -1 \\ 0 & -1 & 2 \end{bmatrix}, \quad A_3 = \begin{bmatrix} 0 & 0 & 1 \\ 0 & 1 & 1 \\ 1 & 1 & 1 \end{bmatrix}.$$

7. Find three 2 by 2 matrices, other than $A = I$ and $A = -I$, that are their own inverses: $A^2 = I$.

8. Show that $A = \begin{bmatrix} 1 & 1 \\ 3 & 3 \end{bmatrix}$ has no inverse by solving $Ax = 0$, and by failing to solve

$$\begin{bmatrix} 1 & 1 \\ 3 & 3 \end{bmatrix} \begin{bmatrix} a & b \\ c & d \end{bmatrix} = \begin{bmatrix} 1 & 0 \\ 0 & 1 \end{bmatrix}.$$

9. Suppose elimination fails because there is no pivot in column 3:

$$\textbf{Missing pivot} \qquad A = \begin{bmatrix} 2 & 1 & 4 & 6 \\ 0 & 3 & 8 & 5 \\ 0 & 0 & 0 & 7 \\ 0 & 0 & 0 & 9 \end{bmatrix}.$$

Show that A cannot be invertible. The third row of A^{-1}, multiplying A, should give the third row $[0 \;\; 0 \;\; 1 \;\; 0]$ of $A^{-1}A = I$. Why is this impossible?

10. Find the inverses (in any legal way) of

$$A_1 = \begin{bmatrix} 0 & 0 & 0 & 1 \\ 0 & 0 & 2 & 0 \\ 0 & 3 & 0 & 0 \\ 4 & 0 & 0 & 0 \end{bmatrix}, \quad A_2 = \begin{bmatrix} 1 & 0 & 0 & 0 \\ -\frac{1}{2} & 1 & 0 & 0 \\ 0 & -\frac{2}{3} & 1 & 0 \\ 0 & 0 & -\frac{3}{4} & 1 \end{bmatrix}, \quad A_3 = \begin{bmatrix} a & b & 0 & 0 \\ c & d & 0 & 0 \\ 0 & 0 & a & b \\ 0 & 0 & c & d \end{bmatrix}.$$

11. Give examples of A and B such that

(a) $A + B$ is not invertible although A and B are invertible.
(b) $A + B$ is invertible although A and B are not invertible.
(c) all of A, B, and $A + B$ are invertible.

In the last case use $A^{-1}(A+B)B^{-1} = B^{-1} + A^{-1}$ to show that $C = B^{-1} + A^{-1}$ is also invertible—and find a formula for C^{-1}.

12. If A is invertible, which properties of A remain true for A^{-1}?
(a) A is triangular. (b) A is symmetric. (c) A is tridiagonal. (d) All entries are whole numbers. (e) All entries are fractions (including numbers like $\frac{3}{1}$).

13. If $A = \begin{bmatrix} 3 \\ 1 \end{bmatrix}$ and $B = \begin{bmatrix} 2 \\ 2 \end{bmatrix}$, compute $A^{\mathrm{T}}B$, $B^{\mathrm{T}}A$, AB^{T}, and BA^{T}.

14. If B is square, show that $A = B + B^{\mathrm{T}}$ is always symmetric and $K = B - B^{\mathrm{T}}$ is always *skew-symmetric*—which means that $K^{\mathrm{T}} = -K$. Find these matrices A and K when $B = \begin{bmatrix} 1 & 3 \\ 1 & 1 \end{bmatrix}$, and write B as the sum of a symmetric matrix and a skew-symmetric matrix.

15. (a) How many entries can be chosen independently in a symmetric matrix of order n?
(b) How many entries can be chosen independently in a skew-symmetric matrix ($K^{\mathrm{T}} = -K$) of order n? The diagonal of K is zero!

16. (a) If $A = LDU$, with 1s on the diagonals of L and U, what is the corresponding factorization of A^{T}? Note that A and A^{T} (square matrices with no row exchanges) share the same pivots.
(b) What triangular systems will give the solution to $A^{\mathrm{T}}y = b$?

17. If $A = L_1D_1U_1$ and $A = L_2D_2U_2$, prove that $L_1 = L_2$, $D_1 = D_2$, and $U_1 = U_2$. If A is invertible, the factorization is unique.

(a) Derive the equation $L_1^{-1}L_2D_2 = D_1U_1U_2^{-1}$, and explain why one side is lower triangular and the other side is upper triangular.
(b) Compare the main diagonals and then compare the off-diagonals.

18. Under what conditions on their entries are A and B invertible?

$$A = \begin{bmatrix} a & b & c \\ d & e & 0 \\ f & 0 & 0 \end{bmatrix} \qquad B = \begin{bmatrix} a & b & 0 \\ c & d & 0 \\ 0 & 0 & e \end{bmatrix}.$$

19. Compute the symmetric LDL^{T} factorization of

$$A = \begin{bmatrix} 1 & 3 & 5 \\ 3 & 12 & 18 \\ 5 & 18 & 30 \end{bmatrix} \quad \text{and} \quad A = \begin{bmatrix} a & b \\ b & d \end{bmatrix}.$$

20. Find the inverse of

$$A = \begin{bmatrix} 1 & 0 & 0 & 0 \\ \frac{1}{4} & 1 & 0 & 0 \\ \frac{1}{3} & \frac{1}{3} & 1 & 0 \\ \frac{1}{2} & \frac{1}{2} & \frac{1}{2} & 1 \end{bmatrix}.$$

21. (Remarkable) If A and B are square matrices, show that $I - BA$ is invertible if $I - AB$ is invertible. Start from $B(I - AB) = (I - BA)B$.

22. Find the inverses (directly or from the 2 by 2 formula) of A, B, C:

$$A = \begin{bmatrix} 0 & 3 \\ 4 & 6 \end{bmatrix} \quad \text{and} \quad B = \begin{bmatrix} a & b \\ b & 0 \end{bmatrix} \quad \text{and} \quad C = \begin{bmatrix} 3 & 4 \\ 5 & 7 \end{bmatrix}.$$

23. Solve for the columns of $A^{-1} = \begin{bmatrix} x & t \\ y & z \end{bmatrix}$:

$$\begin{bmatrix} 10 & 20 \\ 20 & 50 \end{bmatrix} \begin{bmatrix} x \\ y \end{bmatrix} = \begin{bmatrix} 1 \\ 0 \end{bmatrix} \quad \text{and} \quad \begin{bmatrix} 10 & 20 \\ 20 & 50 \end{bmatrix} \begin{bmatrix} t \\ z \end{bmatrix} = \begin{bmatrix} 0 \\ 1 \end{bmatrix}.$$

24. Show that $\begin{bmatrix} 1 & 2 \\ 3 & 6 \end{bmatrix}$ has no inverse by trying to solve for the column (x, y):

$$\begin{bmatrix} 1 & 2 \\ 3 & 6 \end{bmatrix} \begin{bmatrix} x & t \\ y & z \end{bmatrix} = \begin{bmatrix} 1 & 0 \\ 0 & 1 \end{bmatrix} \quad \text{must include} \quad \begin{bmatrix} 1 & 2 \\ 3 & 6 \end{bmatrix} \begin{bmatrix} x \\ y \end{bmatrix} = \begin{bmatrix} 1 \\ 0 \end{bmatrix}.$$

25. (Important) If A has row 1 + row 2 = row 3, show that A is not invertible:

(a) Explain why $Ax = (1, 0, 0)$ cannot have a solution.
(b) Which right-hand sides (b_1, b_2, b_3) might allow a solution to $Ax = b$?
(c) What happens to row 3 in elimination?

26. If A has column 1 + column 2 = column 3, show that A is not invertible:

(a) Find a nonzero solution x to $Ax = 0$. The matrix is 3 by 3.
(b) Elimination keeps column 1 + column 2 = column 3. Explain why there is no third pivot.

27. Suppose A is invertible and you exchange its first two rows to reach B. Is the new matrix B invertible? How would you find B^{-1} from A^{-1}?

28. If the product $M = ABC$ of three square matrices is invertible, then A, B, C are invertible. Find a formula for B^{-1} that involves M^{-1} and A and C.

29. Prove that a matrix with a column of zeros cannot have an inverse.

30. Multiply $\begin{bmatrix} a & b \\ c & d \end{bmatrix}$ times $\begin{bmatrix} d & -b \\ -c & a \end{bmatrix}$. What is the inverse of each matrix if $ad \neq bc$?

31. (a) What matrix E has the same effect as these three steps? Subtract row 1 from row 2, subtract row 1 from row 3, then subtract row 2 from row 3.
(b) What single matrix L has the same effect as these three reverse steps? Add row 2 to row 3, add row 1 to row 3, then add row 1 to row 2.

32. Find the numbers a and b that give the inverse of 5 * eye(4) − ones(4,4):

$$\begin{bmatrix} 4 & -1 & -1 & -1 \\ -1 & 4 & -1 & -1 \\ -1 & -1 & 4 & -1 \\ -1 & -1 & -1 & 4 \end{bmatrix}^{-1} = \begin{bmatrix} a & b & b & b \\ b & a & b & b \\ b & b & a & b \\ b & b & b & a \end{bmatrix}.$$

What are a and b in the inverse of 6 * eye(5) − ones(5,5)?

33. Show that $\mathsf{A} = 4 * \mathsf{eye}(4) - \mathsf{ones}(4,4)$ is *not* invertible: Multiply $\mathsf{A} * \mathsf{ones}(4,1)$.

34. There are sixteen 2 by 2 matrices whose entries are 1s and 0s. How many of them are invertible?

Problems 35–39 are about the Gauss–Jordan method for calculating A^{-1}.

35. Change I into A^{-1} as you reduce A to I (by row operations):

$$\begin{bmatrix} A & I \end{bmatrix} = \begin{bmatrix} 1 & 3 & 1 & 0 \\ 2 & 7 & 0 & 1 \end{bmatrix} \quad \text{and} \quad \begin{bmatrix} A & I \end{bmatrix} = \begin{bmatrix} 1 & 4 & 1 & 0 \\ 3 & 9 & 0 & 1 \end{bmatrix}.$$

36. Follow the 3 by 3 text example but with plus signs in A. Eliminate above and below the pivots to reduce $[A \;\; I]$ to $[I \;\; A^{-1}]$:

$$\begin{bmatrix} A & I \end{bmatrix} = \begin{bmatrix} \mathbf{2} & \mathbf{1} & \mathbf{0} & 1 & 0 & 0 \\ \mathbf{1} & \mathbf{2} & \mathbf{1} & 0 & 1 & 0 \\ \mathbf{0} & \mathbf{1} & \mathbf{2} & 0 & 0 & 1 \end{bmatrix}.$$

37. Use Gauss–Jordan elimination on $[A \;\; I]$ to solve $AA^{-1} = I$:

$$\begin{bmatrix} 1 & a & b \\ 0 & 1 & c \\ 0 & 0 & 1 \end{bmatrix} \begin{bmatrix} \boldsymbol{x}_1 & \boldsymbol{x}_2 & \boldsymbol{x}_3 \end{bmatrix} = \begin{bmatrix} 1 & 0 & 0 \\ 0 & 1 & 0 \\ 0 & 0 & 1 \end{bmatrix}.$$

38. Invert these matrices A by the Gauss–Jordan method starting with $[A \;\; I]$:

$$A = \begin{bmatrix} 1 & 0 & 0 \\ 2 & 1 & 3 \\ 0 & 0 & 1 \end{bmatrix} \quad \text{and} \quad A = \begin{bmatrix} 1 & 1 & 1 \\ 1 & 2 & 2 \\ 1 & 2 & 3 \end{bmatrix}.$$

39. Exchange rows and continue with Gauss–Jordan to find A^{-1}:

$$\begin{bmatrix} A & I \end{bmatrix} = \begin{bmatrix} 0 & 2 & 1 & 0 \\ 2 & 2 & 0 & 1 \end{bmatrix}.$$

40. True or false (with a counterexample if false and a reason if true):

(a) A 4 by 4 matrix with a row of zeros is not invertible.
(b) A matrix with 1s down the main diagonal is invertible.
(c) If A is invertible then A^{-1} is invertible.
(d) If A^{T} is invertible then A is invertible.

41. For which three numbers c is this matrix not invertible, and why not?

$$A = \begin{bmatrix} 2 & c & c \\ c & c & c \\ 8 & 7 & c \end{bmatrix}.$$

42. Prove that A is invertible if $a \neq 0$ and $a \neq b$ (find the pivots and A^{-1}):

$$A = \begin{bmatrix} a & b & b \\ a & a & b \\ a & a & a \end{bmatrix}.$$

43. This matrix has a remarkable inverse. Find A^{-1} by elimination on $[A\ \ I]$. Extend to a 5 by 5 "alternating matrix" and guess its inverse:

$$A = \begin{bmatrix} 1 & -1 & 1 & -1 \\ 0 & 1 & -1 & 1 \\ 0 & 0 & 1 & -1 \\ 0 & 0 & 0 & 1 \end{bmatrix}.$$

44. If B has the columns of A in reverse order, solve $(A - B)x = 0$ to show that $A - B$ is not invertible. An example will lead you to x.

45. Find and check the inverses (assuming they exist) of these block matrices:

$$\begin{bmatrix} I & 0 \\ C & I \end{bmatrix} \quad \begin{bmatrix} A & 0 \\ C & D \end{bmatrix} \quad \begin{bmatrix} 0 & I \\ I & D \end{bmatrix}.$$

46. Use inv(S) to invert MATLAB's 4 by 4 symmetric matrix S = pascal(4). Create Pascal's lower triangular A = abs(pascal(4,1)) and test inv(S) = inv(A') * inv(A).

47. If A = ones(4,4) and b = rand(4,1), how does MATLAB tell you that $Ax = b$ has no solution? If b = ones(4,1), which solution to $Ax = b$ is found by $A\backslash b$?

48. M^{-1} shows the change in A^{-1} (useful to know) when a matrix is subtracted from A. Check part 3 by carefully multiplying MM^{-1} to get I:

1. $M = I - uv^{\mathrm{T}}$ and $M^{-1} = I + uv^{\mathrm{T}}/(1 - v^{\mathrm{T}}u)$.
2. $M = A - uv^{\mathrm{T}}$ and $M^{-1} = A^{-1} + A^{-1}uv^{\mathrm{T}}A^{-1}/(1 - v^{\mathrm{T}}A^{-1}u)$.
3. $M = I - UV$ and $M^{-1} = I_n + U(I_m - VU)^{-1}V$.
4. $M = A - UW^{-1}V$ and $M^{-1} = A^{-1} + A^{-1}U(W - VA^{-1}U)^{-1}VA^{-1}$.

The four identities come from the 1, 1 block when inverting these matrices:

$$\begin{bmatrix} I & u \\ v^{\mathrm{T}} & 1 \end{bmatrix} \qquad \begin{bmatrix} A & u \\ v^{\mathrm{T}} & 1 \end{bmatrix} \qquad \begin{bmatrix} I_n & U \\ V & I_m \end{bmatrix} \qquad \begin{bmatrix} A & U \\ V & W \end{bmatrix}.$$

Problems 49–55 are about the rules for transpose matrices.

49. Find A^{T} and A^{-1} and $(A^{-1})^{\mathrm{T}}$ and $(A^{\mathrm{T}})^{-1}$ for

$$A = \begin{bmatrix} 1 & 0 \\ 9 & 3 \end{bmatrix} \quad \text{and also} \quad A = \begin{bmatrix} 1 & c \\ c & 0 \end{bmatrix}.$$

50. Verify that $(AB)^{\mathrm{T}}$ equals $B^{\mathrm{T}}A^{\mathrm{T}}$ but those are different from $A^{\mathrm{T}}B^{\mathrm{T}}$:

$$A = \begin{bmatrix} 1 & 0 \\ 2 & 1 \end{bmatrix} \quad B = \begin{bmatrix} 1 & 3 \\ 0 & 1 \end{bmatrix} \quad AB = \begin{bmatrix} 1 & 3 \\ 2 & 7 \end{bmatrix}.$$

In case $AB = BA$ (not generally true!), how do you prove that $B^{\mathrm{T}}A^{\mathrm{T}} = A^{\mathrm{T}}B^{\mathrm{T}}$?

51. (a) The matrix $((AB)^{-1})^{\mathrm{T}}$ comes from $(A^{-1})^{\mathrm{T}}$ and $(B^{-1})^{\mathrm{T}}$. *In what order?*
(b) If U is upper triangular then $(U^{-1})^{\mathrm{T}}$ is ______ triangular.

52. Show that $A^2 = 0$ is possible but $A^{\mathrm{T}}A = 0$ is not possible (unless A = zero matrix).

53. (a) The row vector x^{T} times A times the column y produces what number?

$$x^{\mathrm{T}}Ay = \begin{bmatrix} 0 & 1 \end{bmatrix} \begin{bmatrix} 1 & 2 & 3 \\ 4 & 5 & 6 \end{bmatrix} \begin{bmatrix} 0 \\ 1 \\ 0 \end{bmatrix} = \_\_\_.$$

(b) This is the row $x^{\mathrm{T}}A =$ ______ times the column $y = (0, 1, 0)$.
(c) This is the row $x^{\mathrm{T}} = [0 \quad 1]$ times the column $Ay =$ ______.

54. When you transpose a block matrix $M = \begin{bmatrix} A & B \\ C & D \end{bmatrix}$ the result is $M^{\mathrm{T}} =$ ______. Test it. Under what conditions on A, B, C, D is the block matrix symmetric?

55. Explain why the inner product of x and y equals the inner product of Px and Py. Then $(Px)^{\mathrm{T}}(Py) = x^{\mathrm{T}}y$ says that $P^{\mathrm{T}}P = I$ for any permutation. With $x = (1, 2, 3)$ and $y = (1, 4, 2)$, choose P to show that $(Px)^{\mathrm{T}}y$ is not always equal to $x^{\mathrm{T}}(P^{\mathrm{T}}y)$.

Problems 56–60 are about symmetric matrices and their factorizations.

56. If $A = A^{\mathrm{T}}$ and $B = B^{\mathrm{T}}$, which of these matrices are certainly symmetric?
(a) $A^2 - B^2$ (b) $(A + B)(A - B)$ (c) ABA (d) $ABAB$.

57. If $A = A^{\mathrm{T}}$ needs a row exchange, then it also needs a column exchange to stay symmetric. In matrix language, PA loses the symmetry of A but ___ recovers the symmetry.

58. (a) How many entries of A can be chosen independently, if $A = A^{\mathrm{T}}$ is 5 by 5?
(b) How do L and D (5 by 5) give the same number of choices in LDL^{T}?

59. Suppose R is rectangular (m by n) and A is symmetric (m by m).
(a) Transpose $R^{\mathrm{T}}AR$ to show its symmetry. What shape is this matrix?
(b) Show why $R^{\mathrm{T}}R$ has no negative numbers on its diagonal.

60. Factor these symmetric matrices into $A = LDL^{\mathrm{T}}$. The matrix D is diagonal:

$$A = \begin{bmatrix} 1 & 3 \\ 3 & 2 \end{bmatrix} \quad \text{and} \quad A = \begin{bmatrix} 1 & b \\ b & c \end{bmatrix} \quad \text{and} \quad A = \begin{bmatrix} 2 & -1 & 0 \\ -1 & 2 & -1 \\ 0 & -1 & 2 \end{bmatrix}.$$

The next three problems are about applications of $(Ax)^{\mathrm{T}}y = x^{\mathrm{T}}(A^{\mathrm{T}}y)$.

61. Wires go between Boston, Chicago, and Seattle. Those cities are at voltages x_{B}, x_{C}, x_{S}. With unit resistances between cities, the three currents are in y:

$$y = Ax \quad \text{is} \quad \begin{bmatrix} y_{\mathrm{BC}} \\ y_{\mathrm{CS}} \\ y_{\mathrm{BS}} \end{bmatrix} = \begin{bmatrix} 1 & -1 & 0 \\ 0 & 1 & -1 \\ 1 & 0 & -1 \end{bmatrix} \begin{bmatrix} x_{\mathrm{B}} \\ x_{\mathrm{C}} \\ x_{\mathrm{S}} \end{bmatrix}.$$

(a) Find the total currents $A^{\mathrm{T}}y$ out of the three cities.
(b) Verify that $(Ax)^{\mathrm{T}}y$ agrees with $x^{\mathrm{T}}(A^{\mathrm{T}}y)$—six terms in both.

62. Producing x_1 trucks and x_2 planes requires $x_1 + 50x_2$ tons of steel, $40x_1 + 1000x_2$ pounds of rubber, and $2x_1 + 50x_2$ months of labor. If the unit costs y_1, y_2, y_3 are \$700 per ton, \$3 per pound, and \$3000 per month, what are the values of one truck and one plane? Those are the components of $A^{\mathrm{T}}y$.

63. Ax gives the amounts of steel, rubber, and labor to produce x in Problem 62. Find A. Then $(Ax)^{\mathrm{T}}y$ is the ______ of inputs while $x^{\mathrm{T}}(A^{\mathrm{T}}y)$ is the value of ______.

64. Here is a new factorization of A into *triangular times symmetric*:

$$\text{Start from } A = LDU. \text{ Then } A \text{ equals } L(U^{\mathrm{T}})^{-1} \text{ times } U^{\mathrm{T}}DU.$$

Why is $L(U^{\mathrm{T}})^{-1}$ triangular? Its diagonal is all 1s. Why is $U^{\mathrm{T}}DU$ symmetric?

65. A *group* of matrices includes AB and A^{-1} if it includes A and B. "Products and inverses stay in the group." Which of these sets are groups? Lower triangular matrices L with 1s on the diagonal, symmetric matrices S, positive matrices M, diagonal invertible matrices D, permutation matrices P. Invent two more matrix groups.

66. If every row of a 4 by 4 matrix contains the numbers 0, 1, 2, 3 in some order, can the matrix be symmetric? Can it be invertible?

67. Prove that no reordering of rows and reordering of columns can transpose a typical matrix.

68. A square ***northwest matrix*** B is zero in the southeast corner, below the antidiagonal that connects $(1, n)$ to $(n, 1)$. Will B^{T} and B^2 be northwest matrices? Will B^{-1} be northwest or southeast? What is the shape of BC = ***northwest times southeast***? You are allowed to combine permutations with the usual L and U (southwest and northeast).

69. Compare tic; inv(A); toc for A = rand(500) and A = rand(1000). The n^3 count says that computing time (measured by tic; toc) should multiply by 8 when n is doubled. Do you expect these random A to be invertible?

70. I = eye(1000); A = rand(1000); B = triu(A); produces a random *triangular* matrix B. Compare the times for inv(B) and $B\backslash I$. Backslash is engineered to use the zeros in B, while inv uses the zeros in I when reducing $[B \quad I]$ by Gauss–Jordan. (Compare also with inv(A) and $A\backslash I$ for the full matrix A.)

71. Show that L^{-1} has entries j/i for $i \le j$ (the $-1, 2, -1$ matrix has this L):

$$L = \begin{bmatrix} 1 & 0 & 0 & 0 \\ -\frac{1}{2} & 1 & 0 & 0 \\ 0 & -\frac{2}{3} & 1 & 0 \\ 0 & 0 & -\frac{3}{4} & 1 \end{bmatrix} \quad \text{and} \quad L^{-1} = \begin{bmatrix} 1 & 0 & 0 & 0 \\ \frac{1}{2} & 1 & 0 & 0 \\ \frac{1}{3} & \frac{2}{3} & 1 & 0 \\ \frac{1}{4} & \frac{2}{4} & \frac{3}{4} & 1 \end{bmatrix}.$$

Test this pattern for L = eye(5) − diag(1:5)\diag(1:4,−1) and inv(L).

1.7 SPECIAL MATRICES AND APPLICATIONS

This section has two goals. The first is to explain one way in which large linear systems $Ax = b$ can arise in practice. The truth is that a large and completely realistic problem in engineering or economics would lead us far afield. But there is one natural and important application that does not require a lot of preparation.

The other goal is to illustrate, by this same application, the special properties that coefficient matrices frequently have. Large matrices almost always have a clear pattern—frequently a pattern of symmetry, and *very many zero entries*. Since a sparse matrix contains far fewer than n^2 pieces of information, the computations ought to be fast. We look at *band matrices*, to see how concentration near the diagonal speeds up elimination. In fact we look at one special tridiagonal matrix.

The matrix itself can be seen in equation (6). It comes from changing a differential equation to a matrix equation. The continuous problem asks for $u(x)$ at every x, and a computer cannot solve it exactly. It has to be approximated by a discrete problem—the more unknowns we keep, the better will be the accuracy and the greater the expense. As a simple but still very typical continuous problem, our choice falls on the differential equation

$$-\frac{d^2u}{dx^2} = f(x), \quad 0 \le x \le 1. \tag{1}$$

This is a linear equation for the unknown function $u(x)$. Any combination $C + Dx$ could be added to any solution, since the second derivative of $C + Dx$ contributes nothing. The uncertainty left by these two arbitrary constants C and D is removed by a "*boundary condition*" at each end of the interval:

$$u(0) = 0, \qquad u(1) = 0. \tag{2}$$

The result is a *two-point boundary-value problem*, describing not a transient but a steady-state phenomenon—the temperature distribution in a rod, for example, with ends fixed at 0° and with a heat source $f(x)$.

Remember that our goal is to produce a discrete problem—in other words, a problem in linear algebra. For that reason we can only accept a finite amount of information about $f(x)$, say its values at n equally spaced points $x = h, x = 2h, \ldots, x = nh$. We compute approximate values $u_1, \ldots, u_n$ for the true solution u at these same points. At the ends $x = 0$ and $x = 1 = (n+1)h$, the boundary values are $u_0 = 0$ and $u_{n+1} = 0$.

The first question is: How do we replace the derivative d^2u/dx^2? The first derivative can be approximated by stopping $\Delta u/\Delta x$ at a finite stepsize, and not permitting h (or Δx) to approach zero. The difference Δu can be *forward*, *backward*, or *centered*:

$$\frac{\mathbf{\Delta u}}{\mathbf{\Delta x}} = \frac{u(x+h) - u(x)}{h} \quad \text{or} \quad \frac{u(x) - u(x-h)}{h} \quad \text{or} \quad \frac{u(x+h) - u(x-h)}{2h}. \tag{3}$$

The last is symmetric about x and it is the most accurate. For the second derivative there is just one combination that uses only the values at x and $x \pm h$:

$$\textbf{Second difference} \qquad \frac{d^2u}{dx^2} \approx \frac{\mathbf{\Delta^2 u}}{\mathbf{\Delta x^2}} = \frac{u(x+h) - 2u(x) + u(x-h)}{h^2}. \tag{4}$$

This also has the merit of being symmetric about x. To repeat, the right-hand side approaches the true value of d^2u/dx^2 as $h \to 0$, but we have to stop at a positive h.

At each meshpoint $x = jh$, the equation $-d^2u/dx^2 = f(x)$ is replaced by its discrete analogue (5). We multiplied through by h^2 to reach n equations $Au = b$:

$$\textbf{Difference equation} \qquad -u_{j+1} + 2u_j - u_{j-1} = h^2 f(jh) \quad \text{for } j = 1, \ldots, n. \tag{5}$$

The first and last equations ($j = 1$ and $j = n$) include $u_0 = 0$ and $u_{n+1} = 0$, which are known from the boundary conditions. These values would be shifted to the right-hand side of the equation if they were not zero. The structure of these n equations (5) can be better visualized in matrix form. We choose $h = \frac{1}{6}$, to get a 5 by 5 matrix A:

Matrix equation
$$\begin{bmatrix} 2 & -1 & & & \\ -1 & 2 & -1 & & \\ & -1 & 2 & -1 & \\ & & -1 & 2 & -1 \\ & & & -1 & 2 \end{bmatrix} \begin{bmatrix} u_1 \\ u_2 \\ u_3 \\ u_4 \\ u_5 \end{bmatrix} = h^2 \begin{bmatrix} f(h) \\ f(2h) \\ f(3h) \\ f(4h) \\ f(5h) \end{bmatrix}. \quad (6)$$

From now on, *we will work with equation* (6). It has a very regular coefficient matrix, whose order n can be very large. The matrix A possesses many special properties, and three of those properties are fundamental:

1. ***The matrix A is tridiagonal.*** All nonzero entries lie on the main diagonal and the two adjacent diagonals. Outside this band all entries are $a_{ij} = 0$. These zeros will bring a tremendous simplification to Gaussian elimination.
2. ***The matrix is symmetric.*** Each entry a_{ij} equals its mirror image a_{ji}, so that $A^{\mathrm{T}} = A$. The upper triangular U will be the transpose of the lower triangular L, and $A = LDL^{\mathrm{T}}$. This symmetry of A reflects the symmetry of d^2u/dx^2. An odd derivative like du/dx or d^3u/dx^3 would destroy the symmetry.
3. ***The matrix is positive definite.*** This extra property says that *the pivots are positive*. Row exchanges are unnecessary in theory and in practice. This is in contrast to the matrix B at the end of this section, which is not positive definite. Without a row exchange it is totally vulnerable to roundoff.

   Positive definiteness brings this whole course together (in Chapter 6)!

We return to the fact that A is tridiagonal. What effect does this have on elimination? The first stage of the elimination process produces zeros below the first pivot:

Elimination on A: Step 1
$$\begin{bmatrix} 2 & -1 & & & \\ -1 & 2 & -1 & & \\ & -1 & 2 & -1 & \\ & & -1 & 2 & -1 \\ & & & -1 & 2 \end{bmatrix} \rightarrow \begin{bmatrix} 2 & -1 & & & \\ 0 & \mathbf{\frac{3}{2}} & -1 & & \\ & -1 & 2 & -1 & \\ & & -1 & 2 & -1 \\ & & & -1 & 2 \end{bmatrix}.$$

Compared with a general 5 by 5 matrix, that step displays two major simplifications:

1. There was *only one nonzero entry* below the pivot.
2. The pivot row was *very short.*

The multiplier $\ell_{21} = -\frac{1}{2}$ came from one division. The new pivot $\frac{3}{2}$ came from *a single multiplication–subtraction*. Furthermore, *the tridiagonal pattern is preserved*: Every stage of elimination admits the simplifications (a) and (b).

The final result is the $LDU = LDL^{\mathrm{T}}$ factorization of A. Notice the pivots!

$$A = \begin{bmatrix} 1 & & & & \\ -\frac{1}{2} & 1 & & & \\ & -\frac{2}{3} & 1 & & \\ & & -\frac{3}{4} & 1 & \\ & & & -\frac{4}{5} & 1 \end{bmatrix} \begin{bmatrix} \mathbf{\frac{2}{1}} & & & & \\ & \mathbf{\frac{3}{2}} & & & \\ & & \mathbf{\frac{4}{3}} & & \\ & & & \mathbf{\frac{5}{4}} & \\ & & & & \mathbf{\frac{6}{5}} \end{bmatrix} \begin{bmatrix} 1 & -\frac{1}{2} & & & \\ & 1 & -\frac{2}{3} & & \\ & & 1 & -\frac{3}{4} & \\ & & & 1 & -\frac{4}{5} \\ & & & & 1 \end{bmatrix}.$$

The L and U factors of a tridiagonal matrix are bidiagonal. The three factors together have the same band structure of three essential diagonals ($3n-2$ parameters) as A. Note too that L and U are transposes of one another, as expected from the symmetry. The pivots $2/1$, $3/2$, $4/3$, $5/4$, $6/5$ are all positive. Their product is the ***determinant*** of A: $\det A = 6$. The pivots are obviously converging to 1, as n gets large. Such matrices make a computer very happy.

These sparse factors L and U completely change the usual operation count. Elimination on each column needs only two operations, as above, and there are n columns. *In place of $n^3/3$ operations we need only $2n$.* Tridiagonal systems $Ax = b$ can be solved almost instantly. *The cost of solving a tridiagonal system is proportional to n.*

A **band matrix** has $a_{ij} = 0$ except in the band $|i - j| < w$ (Figure 1.8). The "half bandwidth" is $w = 1$ for a diagonal matrix, $w = 2$ for a tridiagonal matrix, and $w = n$ for a full matrix. For each column, elimination requires $w(w-1)$ operations: a row of length w acts on $w - 1$ rows below. *Elimination on the n columns of a band matrix requires about w^2n operations.*

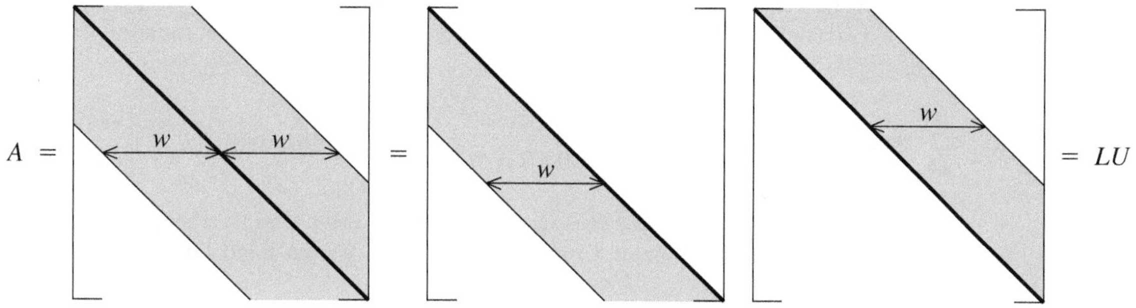

Figure 1.8 A band matrix A and its factors L and U.

As w approaches n, the matrix becomes full, and the count is roughly n^3. For an exact count, the lower right-hand corner has no room for bandwidth w. The precise number of divisions and multiplication–subtractions that produce L, D, and U (without assuming a symmetric A) is $P = \frac{1}{3}w(w-1)(3n-2w+1)$. For a full matrix with $w = n$, we recover $P = \frac{1}{3}n(n-1)(n+1)$. This is a whole number, since $n-1$, n, and $n+1$ are consecutive integers, and one of them is divisible by 3.

That is our last operation count, and we emphasize the main point. A finite-difference matrix like A has a full inverse. In solving $Ax = b$, *we are actually much worse off knowing A^{-1} than knowing L and U.* Multiplying A^{-1} by b takes n^2 steps, whereas $4n$ are sufficient for the forward elimination and back-substitution that produce $x = U^{-1}c = U^{-1}L^{-1}b = A^{-1}b$.

We hope this example reinforced the reader's understanding of elimination (which we now assume to be perfectly understood!). It is a genuine example of the large linear systems that are actually met in practice. The next chapter turns to the existence and the uniqueness of x, for m equations in n unknowns.

Roundoff Error

In theory the nonsingular case is completed. There is a full set of pivots (with row exchanges). In practice, *more row exchanges* may be equally necessary—or the computed solution can easily become worthless. We will devote two pages (entirely optional in class) to making elimination more stable—why it is needed and how it is done.

For a system of moderate size, say 100 by 100, elimination involves a third of a million operations ($\frac{1}{3}n^3$). With each operation we must expect a roundoff error. Normally, we keep a fixed number of significant digits (say three, for an extremely weak computer). Then adding two numbers of different sizes gives an error:

$$\textbf{Roundoff error} \qquad .456 + .00123 \rightarrow .457 \qquad \text{loses the digits 2 and 3.}$$

How do all these individual errors contribute to the final error in $Ax = b$?

This is not an easy problem. It was attacked by John von Neumann, who was the leading mathematician at the time when computers suddenly made a million operations possible. In fact the combination of Gauss and von Neumann gives the simple elimination algorithm a remarkably distinguished history, although even von Neumann overestimated the final roundoff error. It was Wilkinson who found the right way to answer the question, and his books are now classics.

Two simple examples will illustrate three important points about roundoff error. The examples are

$$\textbf{Ill-conditioned} \quad A = \begin{bmatrix} 1. & 1. \\ 1. & 1.0001 \end{bmatrix} \qquad \textbf{Well-conditioned} \quad B = \begin{bmatrix} .0001 & 1. \\ 1. & 1. \end{bmatrix}.$$

A is nearly singular whereas B is far from singular. If we slightly change the last entry of A to $a_{22} = 1$, it *is* singular. Consider two very close right-hand sides b:

$$\begin{aligned} u + \quad\quad v &= 2 \\ u + 1.0001v &= 2 \end{aligned} \qquad \text{and} \qquad \begin{aligned} u + \quad\quad v &= 2 \\ u + 1.0001v &= 2.0001 \end{aligned}$$

The solution to the first is $u = 2$, $v = 0$. The solution to the second is $u = v = 1$. *A change in the fifth digit of b was amplified to a change in the first digit of the solution. No numerical method can avoid this sensitivity to small perturbations.* The ill-conditioning can be shifted from one place to another, but it cannot be removed. The true solution is very sensitive, and the computed solution cannot be less so.

The second point is as follows.

10 Even a well-conditioned matrix like B can be ruined by a poor algorithm.

We regret to say that for the matrix B, direct Gaussian elimination is a poor algorithm. Suppose .0001 is accepted as the first pivot. Then 10,000 times the first row is subtracted from the second. The lower right entry becomes -9999, but roundoff to three places would give $-10{,}000$. Every trace of the entry 1 would disappear:

$$\begin{matrix}\textbf{Elimination on } \boldsymbol{B} \\ \textbf{with small pivot}\end{matrix} \qquad \begin{aligned} .0001u + v &= 1 \\ u + v &= 2 \end{aligned} \quad \longrightarrow \quad \begin{aligned} .0001u + v &= 1 \\ -9999v &= -9998. \end{aligned}$$

Roundoff will produce $-10{,}000v = -10{,}000$, or $v = 1$. This is correct to three decimal places. Back-substitution with the right $v = .9999$ would leave $u = 1$:

$$\textbf{Correct result} \qquad .0001u + .9999 = 1, \qquad \text{or} \qquad u = 1.$$

Instead, accepting $v = 1$, which is wrong only in the fourth place, we obtain $u = 0$:

$$\textbf{Wrong result} \qquad .0001u + 1 = 1, \qquad \text{or} \qquad u = 0.$$

The computed u is completely mistaken. B is well-conditioned but elimination is violently unstable. L, D, and U are completely out of scale with B:

$$B = \begin{bmatrix} 1 & 0 \\ 10{,}000 & 1 \end{bmatrix} \begin{bmatrix} .0001 & 0 \\ 0 & -9999 \end{bmatrix} \begin{bmatrix} 1 & 10{,}000 \\ 0 & 1 \end{bmatrix}.$$

The small pivot .0001 brought instability, and the remedy is clear—*exchange rows.*

1P A small pivot forces a practical change in elimination. Normally we compare each pivot with all possible pivots in the same column. Exchanging rows to obtain the largest possible pivot is called ***partial pivoting.***

For B, the pivot .0001 would be compared with the possible pivot 1 below it. A row exchange would take place immediately. In matrix terms, this is multiplication by a permutation matrix $P = \left[\begin{smallmatrix} 0 & 1 \\ 1 & 0 \end{smallmatrix}\right]$. The new matrix $C = PB$ has good factors:

$$C = \begin{bmatrix} 1 & 1 \\ .0001 & 1 \end{bmatrix} = \begin{bmatrix} 1 & 0 \\ .0001 & 1 \end{bmatrix} \begin{bmatrix} 1 & 0 \\ 0 & .9999 \end{bmatrix} \begin{bmatrix} 1 & 1 \\ 0 & 1 \end{bmatrix}$$

The pivots for C are 1 and .9999, much better than .0001 and -9999 for B.

The strategy of *complete pivoting* looks also in all later columns for the largest possible pivot. Not only a row but also a column exchange may be needed. (This is *post*multiplication by a permutation matrix.) The difficulty with being so conservative is the expense, and partial pivoting is quite adequate.

We have finally arrived at the fundamental algorithm of numerical linear algebra: ***elimination with partial pivoting.*** Some further refinements, such as watching to see whether a whole row or column needs to be rescaled, are still possible. But essentially the reader now knows what a computer does with a system of linear equations. Compared with the "theoretical" description—*find* A^{-1}, *and multiply* $A^{-1}b$—our description has consumed a lot of the reader's time (and patience). I wish there were an easier way to explain how x is actually found, but I do not think there is.

Problem Set 1.7

1. Write out the $LDU = LDL^{\mathrm{T}}$ factors of A in equation (6) when $n = 4$. Find the determinant as the product of the pivots in D.

2. Modify a_{11} in equation (6) from $a_{11} = 2$ to $a_{11} = 1$, and find the LDU factors of this new tridiagonal matrix.

3. Find the 5 by 5 matrix A_0 $\left(h = \frac{1}{6}\right)$ that approximates

$$-\frac{d^2u}{dx^2} = f(x), \qquad \frac{du}{dx}(0) = \frac{du}{dx}(1) = 0,$$

replacing these boundary conditions by $u_0 = u_1$ and $u_6 = u_5$. Check that your A_0 times the constant vector (C, C, C, C, C), yields zero; A_0 is *singular*. Analogously, if $u(x)$ is a solution of the continuous problem, then so is $u(x) + C$.

4. Write down the 3 by 3 finite-difference matrix equation $\left(h = \frac{1}{4}\right)$ for

$$-\frac{d^2u}{dx^2} + u = x, \qquad u(0) = u(1) = 0.$$

5. With $h = \frac{1}{4}$ and $f(x) = 4\pi^2 \sin 2\pi x$, the difference equation (5) is

$$\begin{bmatrix} 2 & -1 & 0 \\ -1 & 2 & -1 \\ 0 & -1 & 2 \end{bmatrix} \begin{bmatrix} u_1 \\ u_2 \\ u_3 \end{bmatrix} = \frac{\pi^2}{4} \begin{bmatrix} 1 \\ 0 \\ -1 \end{bmatrix}.$$

Solve for u_1, u_2, u_3 and find their error in comparison with the true solution $u = \sin 2\pi x$ at $x = \frac{1}{4}$, $x = \frac{1}{2}$, and $x = \frac{3}{4}$.

6. What 5 by 5 system replaces (6) if the boundary conditions are changed to $u(0) = 1$, $u(1) = 0$?

Problems 7–11 are about roundoff error and row exchanges.

7. Compute H^{-1} in two ways for the 3 by 3 Hilbert matrix

$$H = \begin{bmatrix} 1 & \frac{1}{2} & \frac{1}{3} \\ \frac{1}{2} & \frac{1}{3} & \frac{1}{4} \\ \frac{1}{3} & \frac{1}{4} & \frac{1}{5} \end{bmatrix},$$

first by exact computation and second by rounding off each number to three figures. This matrix H is ill-conditioned and row exchanges don't help.

8. For the same matrix H, compare the right-hand sides of $Hx = b$ when the solutions are $x = (1, 1, 1)$ and $x = (0, 6, -3.6)$.

9. Solve $Hx = b = (1, 0, \ldots, 0)$ for the 10 by 10 Hilbert matrix with $h_{ij} = 1/(i + j - 1)$, using any computer code for linear equations. Then change an entry of b by .0001 and compare the solutions.

10. Compare the pivots in direct elimination to those with partial pivoting for

$$A = \begin{bmatrix} .001 & 0 \\ 1 & 1000 \end{bmatrix}.$$

(This is actually an example that needs rescaling before elimination.)

11. Explain why partial pivoting produces multipliers ℓ_{ij} in L that satisfy $|\ell_{ij}| \le 1$. Can you construct a 3 by 3 example with all $|a_{ij}| \le 1$ whose last pivot is 4? This is the worst possible, since each entry is at most doubled when $|\ell_{ij}| \le 1$.

Chapter 1 Review Exercises

1.1 (a) Write down the 3 by 3 matrices with entries

$$a_{ij} = i - j \quad \text{and} \quad b_{ij} = \frac{i}{j}.$$

(b) Compute the products AB and BA and A^2.

1.2 For the matrices

$$A = \begin{bmatrix} 1 & 0 \\ 2 & 1 \end{bmatrix} \quad \text{and} \quad B = \begin{bmatrix} 1 & 2 \\ 0 & 1 \end{bmatrix},$$

compute AB and BA and A^{-1} and B^{-1} and $(AB)^{-1}$.

1.3 Find examples of 2 by 2 matrices with $a_{12} = \frac{1}{2}$ for which
(a) $A^2 = I$. (b) $A^{-1} = A^{\mathrm{T}}$. (c) $A^2 = A$.

1.4 Solve by elimination and back-substitution:

$$\begin{aligned} u \quad\;\; + w &= 4 \\ u + v \quad\;\; &= 3 \\ u + v + w &= 6 \end{aligned} \quad \text{and} \quad \begin{aligned} v + w &= 0 \\ u \quad\;\; + w &= 0 \\ u + v \quad\;\; &= 6. \end{aligned}$$

1.5 Factor the preceding matrices into $A = LU$ or $PA = LU$.

1.6 (a) There are sixteen 2 by 2 matrices whose entries are 1s and 0s. How many are invertible?
(b) (Much harder!) If you put 1s and 0s at random into the entries of a 10 by 10 matrix, is it more likely to be invertible or singular?

1.7 There are sixteen 2 by 2 matrices whose entries are 1s and -1s. How many are invertible?

1.8 How are the rows of EA related to the rows of A in the following cases?

$$E = \begin{bmatrix} 1 & 0 & 0 \\ 0 & 2 & 0 \\ 4 & 0 & 1 \end{bmatrix} \quad \text{or} \quad E = \begin{bmatrix} 1 & 1 & 1 \\ 0 & 0 & 0 \end{bmatrix} \quad \text{or} \quad E = \begin{bmatrix} 0 & 0 & 1 \\ 0 & 1 & 0 \\ 1 & 0 & 0 \end{bmatrix}.$$

1.9 Write down a 2 by 2 system with infinitely many solutions.

1.10 Find inverses if they exist, by inspection or by Gauss–Jordan:

$$A = \begin{bmatrix} 1 & 0 & 1 \\ 1 & 1 & 0 \\ 0 & 1 & 1 \end{bmatrix} \quad \text{and} \quad A = \begin{bmatrix} 2 & 1 & 0 \\ 1 & 2 & 1 \\ 0 & 1 & 2 \end{bmatrix} \quad \text{and} \quad A = \begin{bmatrix} 1 & 1 & -2 \\ 1 & -2 & 1 \\ -2 & 1 & 1 \end{bmatrix}.$$

1.11 If E is 2 by 2 and it adds the first equation to the second, what are E^2 and E^8 and $8E$?

1.12 True or false, with *reason* if true or *counterexample* if false:
(1) If A is invertible and its rows are in reverse order in B, then B is invertible.
(2) If A and B are symmetric then AB is symmetric.
(3) If A and B are invertible then BA is invertible.

(4) Every nonsingular matrix can be factored into the product $A = LU$ of a lower triangular L and an upper triangular U.

1.13 Solve $Ax = b$ by solving the triangular systems $Lc = b$ and $Ux = c$:

$$A = LU = \begin{bmatrix} 1 & 0 & 0 \\ 4 & 1 & 0 \\ 1 & 0 & 1 \end{bmatrix} \begin{bmatrix} 2 & 2 & 4 \\ 0 & 1 & 3 \\ 0 & 0 & 1 \end{bmatrix}, \qquad b = \begin{bmatrix} 0 \\ 0 \\ 1 \end{bmatrix}.$$

What part of A^{-1} have you found, with this particular b?

1.14 If possible, find 3 by 3 matrices B such that

(a) $BA = 2A$ for every A.
(b) $BA = 2B$ for every A.
(c) BA has the first and last rows of A reversed.
(d) BA has the first and last columns of A reversed.

1.15 Find the value for c in the following n by n inverse:

$$\text{if} \quad A = \begin{bmatrix} n & -1 & \cdot & -1 \\ -1 & n & \cdot & -1 \\ \cdot & \cdot & \cdot & -1 \\ -1 & -1 & -1 & n \end{bmatrix} \quad \text{then} \quad A^{-1} = \frac{1}{n+1} \begin{bmatrix} c & 1 & \cdot & 1 \\ 1 & c & \cdot & 1 \\ \cdot & \cdot & \cdot & 1 \\ 1 & 1 & 1 & c \end{bmatrix}.$$

1.16 For which values of k does

$$\begin{aligned} kx + \ y &= 1 \\ x + ky &= 1 \end{aligned}$$

have no solution, one solution, or infinitely many solutions?

1.17 Find the symmetric factorization $A = LDL^{\mathrm{T}}$ of

$$A = \begin{bmatrix} 1 & 2 & 0 \\ 2 & 6 & 4 \\ 0 & 4 & 11 \end{bmatrix} \quad \text{and} \quad A = \begin{bmatrix} a & b \\ b & c \end{bmatrix}.$$

1.18 Suppose A is the 4 by 4 identity matrix except for a vector v in column 2:

$$A = \begin{bmatrix} 1 & v_1 & 0 & 0 \\ 0 & v_2 & 0 & 0 \\ 0 & v_3 & 1 & 0 \\ 0 & v_4 & 0 & 1 \end{bmatrix}.$$

(a) Factor A into LU, assuming $v_2 \neq 0$.
(b) Find A^{-1}, which has the same form as A.

1.19 Solve by elimination, or show that there is no solution:

$$\begin{aligned} u + \ v + \ w &= 0 \\ u + 2v + 3w &= 0 \\ 3u + 5v + 7w &= 1 \end{aligned} \qquad \text{and} \qquad \begin{aligned} u + \ v + \ w &= 0 \\ u + \ v + 3w &= 0 \\ 3u + 5v + 7w &= 1. \end{aligned}$$

1.20 The n by n permutation matrices are an important example of a "group." If you multiply them you stay inside the group; they have inverses in the group; the identity is in the group; and the law $P_1(P_2P_3) = (P_1P_2)P_3$ is true—because it is true for all matrices.

(a) How many members belong to the groups of 4 by 4 and n by n permutation matrices?

(b) Find a power k so that all 3 by 3 permutation matrices satisfy $P^k = I$.

1.21 Describe the rows of DA and the columns of AD if $D = \begin{bmatrix} 2 & 0 \\ 0 & 5 \end{bmatrix}$.

1.22 (a) If A is invertible what is the inverse of A^{T}?

(b) If A is also symmetric what is the transpose of A^{-1}?

(c) Illustrate both formulas when $A = \begin{bmatrix} 2 & 1 \\ 1 & 1 \end{bmatrix}$.

1.23 By experiment with $n = 2$ and $n = 3$, find

$$\begin{bmatrix} 2 & 3 \\ 0 & 0 \end{bmatrix}^n, \quad \begin{bmatrix} 2 & 3 \\ 0 & 1 \end{bmatrix}^n, \quad \begin{bmatrix} 2 & 3 \\ 0 & 1 \end{bmatrix}^{-1}.$$

1.24 Starting with a first plane $u + 2v - w = 6$, find the equation for

(a) the parallel plane through the origin.

(b) a second plane that also contains the points $(6, 0, 0)$ and $(2, 2, 0)$.

(c) a third plane that meets the first and second in the point $(4, 1, 0)$.

1.25 What multiple of row 2 is subtracted from row 3 in forward elimination of A?

$$A = \begin{bmatrix} 1 & 0 & 0 \\ 2 & 1 & 0 \\ 0 & 5 & 1 \end{bmatrix} \begin{bmatrix} 1 & 2 & 0 \\ 0 & 1 & 5 \\ 0 & 0 & 1 \end{bmatrix}.$$

How do you know (without multiplying those factors) that A is *invertible*, *symmetric*, and *tridiagonal*? What are its pivots?

1.26 (a) What vector x will make Ax = column 1 of A + 2(column 3), for a 3 by 3 matrix A?

(b) Construct a matrix that has column 1 + 2(column 3) = 0. Check that A is singular (fewer than 3 pivots) and explain why that must be the case.

1.27 True or false, with reason if true and counterexample if false:

(1) If $L_1U_1 = L_2U_2$ (upper triangular U's with nonzero diagonal, lower triangular L's with unit diagonal), then $L_1 = L_2$ and $U_1 = U_2$. The LU factorization is unique.

(2) If $A^2 + A = I$ then $A^{-1} = A + I$.

(3) If all diagonal entries of A are zero, then A is singular.

1.28 By experiment or the Gauss–Jordan method compute

$$\begin{bmatrix} 1 & 0 & 0 \\ \ell & 1 & 0 \\ m & 0 & 1 \end{bmatrix}^n, \quad \begin{bmatrix} 1 & 0 & 0 \\ \ell & 1 & 0 \\ m & 0 & 1 \end{bmatrix}^{-1}, \quad \begin{bmatrix} 1 & 0 & 0 \\ \ell & 1 & 0 \\ 0 & m & 1 \end{bmatrix}^{-1}.$$

1.29 Write down the 2 by 2 matrices that

(a) reverse the direction of every vector.

(b) project every vector onto the x_2 axis.

(c) turn every vector counterclockwise through 90°.

(d) reflect every vector through the 45° line $x_1 = x_2$.

Chapter

2 Vector Spaces

2.1 VECTOR SPACES AND SUBSPACES

Elimination can simplify, one entry at a time, the linear system $Ax = b$. Fortunately it also simplifies the theory. The basic questions of *existence* and *uniqueness*—Is there one solution, or no solution, or an infinity of solutions?—are much easier to answer after elimination. We need to devote one more section to those questions, to find every solution for an m by n system. Then that circle of ideas will be complete.

But elimination produces only one kind of understanding of $Ax = b$. Our chief object is to achieve a different and deeper understanding. This chapter may be more difficult than the first one. It goes to the heart of linear algebra.

For the concept of a ***vector space***, we start immediately with the most important spaces. They are denoted by $\mathbf{R}^1, \mathbf{R}^2, \mathbf{R}^3, \ldots$; the space $\mathbf{R}^n$ consists of *all column vectors with n components*. (We write $\mathbf{R}$ because the components are real numbers.) $\mathbf{R}^2$ is represented by the usual x-y plane; the two components of the vector become the x and y coordinates of the corresponding point. The three components of a vector in $\mathbf{R}^3$ give a point in three-dimensional space. The one-dimensional space $\mathbf{R}^1$ is a line.

The valuable thing for linear algebra is that the extension to n dimensions is so straightforward. For a vector in $\mathbf{R}^7$ we just need the seven components, even if the geometry is hard to visualize. Within all vector spaces, two operations are possible:

> ***We can add any two vectors, and we can multiply all vectors by scalars.***
> **In other words, we can take linear combinations.**

Addition obeys the commutative law $x + y = y + x$; there is a "zero vector" satisfying $0 + x = x$; and there is a vector "$-x$" satisfying $-x + x = 0$. Eight properties (including those three) are fundamental; the full list is given in Problem 5 at the end of this section. ***A real vector space is a set of*** *vectors* ***together with rules for vector addition and multiplication by real numbers***. Addition and multiplication must produce vectors in the space, and they must satisfy the eight conditions.

Normally our vectors belong to one of the spaces $\mathbf{R}^n$; they are ordinary column vectors. If $x = (1, 0, 0, 3)$, then $2x$ (and also $x + x$) has components 2, 0, 0, 6. The formal definition allows other things to be "vectors"—provided that addition and scalar multiplication are all right. We give three examples:

1. *The infinite-dimensional space* $\mathbf{R}^\infty$. Its vectors have infinitely many components, as in $x = (1, 2, 1, 2, \ldots)$. The laws for $x + y$ and cx stay unchanged.

2. *The space of 3 by 2 matrices.* In this case the "vectors" are matrices! We can add two matrices, and $A + B = B + A$, and there is a zero matrix, and so on. This space is almost the same as $\mathbf{R}^6$. (The six components are arranged in a rectangle instead of a column.) Any choice of m and n would give, as a similar example, the vector space of all m by n matrices.
3. *The space of functions $f(x)$.* Here we admit all functions f that are defined on a fixed interval, say $0 \le x \le 1$. The space includes $f(x) = x^2$, $g(x) = \sin x$, their sum $(f + g)(x) = x^2 + \sin x$, and all multiples like $3x^2$ and $-\sin x$. The vectors are functions, and the dimension is somehow a larger infinity than for $\mathbf{R}^\infty$.

Other examples are given in the exercises, but the vector spaces we need most are somewhere else—***they are inside the standard spaces*** $\mathbf{R}^n$. We want to describe them and explain why they are important. Geometrically, think of the usual three-dimensional $\mathbf{R}^3$ and choose any plane through the origin. ***That plane is a vector space in its own right.*** If we multiply a vector in the plane by 3, or -3, or any other scalar, we get a vector in the same plane. If we add two vectors in the plane, their sum stays in the plane. This plane through $(0, 0, 0)$ illustrates one of the most fundamental ideas in linear algebra; it is a ***subspace*** of the original space $\mathbf{R}^3$.

DEFINITION A ***subspace*** of a vector space is a nonempty subset that satisfies the requirements for a vector space: ***Linear combinations stay in the subspace.***

(i) If we add any vectors x and y in the subspace, $x + y$ is *in the subspace.*

(ii) If we multiply any vector x in the subspace by any scalar c, cx is *in the subspace.*

Notice our emphasis on the word ***space***. A sub*space* is a subset that is "closed" under addition and scalar multiplication. Those operations follow the rules of the host space, keeping us ***inside the subspace***. The eight required properties are satisfied in the larger space and will automatically be satisfied in every subspace. Notice in particular that ***the zero vector will belong to every subspace***. That comes from rule (ii): Choose the scalar to be $c = 0$.

The smallest subspace $\mathbf{Z}$ contains only one vector, the zero vector. It is a "zero-dimensional space," containing only the point at the origin. Rules (i) and (ii) are satisfied, since the sum $0 + 0$ is in this one-point space, and so are all multiples $c0$. *This is the smallest possible vector space*: the empty set is not allowed. At the other extreme, the largest subspace is the whole of the original space. If the original space is $\mathbf{R}^3$, then the possible subspaces are easy to describe: $\mathbf{R}^3$ itself, any plane through the origin, any line through the origin, or the origin (the zero vector) alone.

The distinction between a subset and a subspace is made clear by examples. In each case, can you add vectors and multiply by scalars, without leaving the space?

Example 1 Consider all vectors in $\mathbf{R}^2$ whose components are positive or zero. This subset is the first quadrant of the x-y plane; the coordinates satisfy $x \ge 0$ and $y \ge 0$. It is *not a subspace*, even though it contains zero and addition does leave us within the subset. Rule (ii) is violated, since if the scalar is -1 and the vector is $[1 \quad 1]$, the multiple $cx = [-1 \quad -1]$ is in the third quadrant instead of the first.

If we include the third quadrant along with the first, scalar multiplication is all right. Every multiple cx will stay in this subset. However, rule (i) is now violated, since adding $[1 \ \ 2] + [-2 \ \ -1]$ gives $[-1 \ \ 1]$, which is not in either quadrant. The smallest subspace containing the first quadrant is the whole space $\mathbf{R}^2$.

Example 2 Start from the vector space of 3 by 3 matrices. One possible subspace is the set of *lower triangular matrices*. Another is the set of *symmetric matrices*. $A + B$ and cA are lower triangular if A and B are lower triangular, and they are symmetric if A and B are symmetric. Of course, the zero matrix is in both subspaces.

The Column Space of A

We now come to the key examples, the **column space** and the **nullspace** of a matrix A. ***The column space contains all linear combinations of the columns of A.*** It is a subspace of $\mathbf{R}^m$. We illustrate by a system of $m = 3$ equations in $n = 2$ unknowns:

$$\textbf{Combination of columns equals } b \qquad \begin{bmatrix} 1 & 0 \\ 5 & 4 \\ 2 & 4 \end{bmatrix} \begin{bmatrix} u \\ v \end{bmatrix} = \begin{bmatrix} b_1 \\ b_2 \\ b_3 \end{bmatrix}. \tag{1}$$

With $m > n$ we have more equations than unknowns—and *usually there will be no solution*. The system will be solvable only for a very "thin" subset of all possible b's. One way of describing this thin subset is so simple that it is easy to overlook.

2A The system $Ax = b$ is solvable if and only if the vector b can be expressed as a combination of the columns of A. Then b is in the column space.

This description involves nothing more than a restatement of $Ax = b$, *by columns*:

$$\textbf{Combination of columns} \qquad u \begin{bmatrix} 1 \\ 5 \\ 2 \end{bmatrix} + v \begin{bmatrix} 0 \\ 4 \\ 4 \end{bmatrix} = \begin{bmatrix} b_1 \\ b_2 \\ b_3 \end{bmatrix}. \tag{2}$$

These are the same three equations in two unknowns. Now the problem is: Find numbers u and v that multiply the first and second columns to produce b. The system is solvable exactly when such coefficients exist, and the vector (u, v) is the solution x.

We are saying that the attainable right-hand sides b are *all combinations of the columns of A*. One possible right-hand side is the first column itself; the weights are $u = 1$ and $v = 0$. Another possibility is the second column: $u = 0$ and $v = 1$. A third is the right-hand side $b = 0$. With $u = 0$ and $v = 0$, the vector $b = 0$ will always be attainable.

We can describe *all combinations* of the two columns geometrically: $Ax = b$ *can be solved if and only if b lies in the* ***plane*** *that is spanned by the two column vectors* (Figure 2.1). This is the thin set of attainable b. If b lies off the plane, then it is not a combination of the two columns. In that case $Ax = b$ has no solution.

What is important is that this plane is not just a subset of $\mathbf{R}^3$; it is a subspace. It is the ***column space*** of A, consisting of ***all combinations of the columns***. It is denoted by

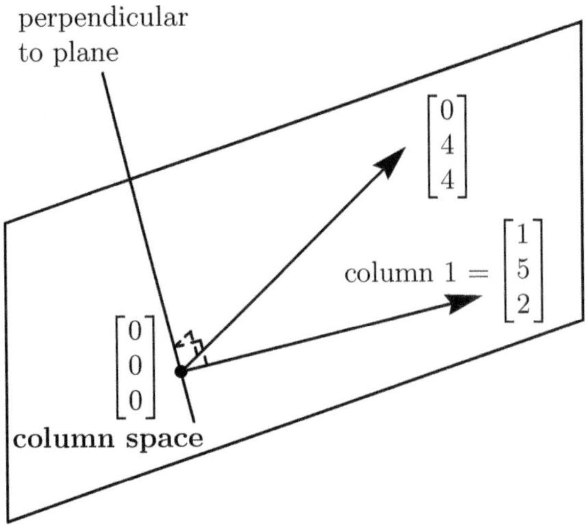

Figure 2.1 The column space $\boldsymbol{C}(A)$, a plane in three-dimensional space.

$\boldsymbol{C}(A)$. Requirements (i) and (ii) for a subspace of $\mathbf{R}^m$ are easy to check:

(i) Suppose b and b' lie in the column space, so that $Ax = b$ for some x and $Ax' = b'$ for some x'. Then $A(x + x') = b + b'$, so that $b + b'$ is also a combination of the columns. The column space of all attainable vectors b is closed under addition.

(ii) If b is in the column space $\boldsymbol{C}(A)$, so is any multiple cb. If some combination of columns produces b (say $Ax = b$), then multiplying that combination by c will produce cb. In other words, $A(cx) = cb$.

For another matrix A, the dimensions in Figure 2.1 may be very different. The smallest possible column space (one vector only) comes from the zero matrix $A = 0$. The only combination of the columns is $b = 0$. At the other extreme, suppose A is the 5 by 5 identity matrix. Then $\boldsymbol{C}(I)$ is the whole of $\mathbf{R}^5$; the five columns of I can combine to produce any five-dimensional vector b. This is not at all special to the identity matrix. *Any 5 by 5 matrix that is nonsingular will have the whole of* $\mathbf{R}^5$ *as its column space.* For such a matrix we can solve $Ax = b$ by Gaussian elimination; there are five pivots. Therefore every b is in $\boldsymbol{C}(A)$ for a nonsingular matrix.

You can see how Chapter 1 is contained in this chapter. There we studied n by n matrices whose column space is $\mathbf{R}^n$. Now we allow singular matrices, and rectangular matrices of any shape. Then $\boldsymbol{C}(A)$ can be somewhere between the zero space and the whole space $\mathbf{R}^m$. Together with its perpendicular space, it gives one of our two approaches to understanding $Ax = b$.

The Nullspace of *A*

The second approach to $Ax = b$ is "dual" to the first. We are concerned not only with attainable right-hand sides b, but also with the solutions x that attain them. The right-hand side $b = 0$ always allows the solution $x = 0$, but there may be infinitely many other solutions. (There always are, if there are more unknowns than equations, $n > m$.) ***The solutions to*** $\boldsymbol{Ax = 0}$ ***form a vector space—the nullspace of*** $\boldsymbol{A}$.

> The ***nullspace*** of a matrix consists of all vectors x such that $Ax = 0$. It is denoted by $N(A)$. It is a subspace of $\mathbf{R}^n$, just as the column space was a subspace of $\mathbf{R}^m$.

Requirement (i) holds: If $Ax = 0$ and $Ax' = 0$, then $A(x + x') = 0$. Requirement (ii) also holds: If $Ax = 0$ then $A(cx) = 0$. Both requirements fail if the right-hand side is not zero! Only the solutions to a *homogeneous* equation ($b = 0$) form a subspace. The nullspace is easy to find for the example given above; it is as small as possible:

$$\begin{bmatrix} 1 & 0 \\ 5 & 4 \\ 2 & 4 \end{bmatrix} \begin{bmatrix} u \\ v \end{bmatrix} = \begin{bmatrix} 0 \\ 0 \\ 0 \end{bmatrix}.$$

The first equation gives $u = 0$, and the second equation then forces $v = 0$. The nullspace contains only the vector $(0, 0)$. This matrix has "independent columns"—a key idea that comes soon.

The situation is changed when a third column is a combination of the first two:

$$\textbf{Larger nullspace} \qquad B = \begin{bmatrix} 1 & 0 & 1 \\ 5 & 4 & 9 \\ 2 & 4 & 6 \end{bmatrix}.$$

B has the same column space as A. The new column lies in the plane of Figure 2.1; it is the sum of the two column vectors we started with. But the nullspace of B contains the vector $(1, 1, -1)$ and automatically contains any multiple $(c, c, -c)$:

$$\textbf{Nullspace is a line} \qquad \begin{bmatrix} 1 & 0 & 1 \\ 5 & 4 & 9 \\ 2 & 4 & 6 \end{bmatrix} \begin{bmatrix} c \\ c \\ -c \end{bmatrix} = \begin{bmatrix} 0 \\ 0 \\ 0 \end{bmatrix}.$$

The nullspace of B is the line of all points $x = c$, $y = c$, $z = -c$. (The line goes through the origin, as any subspace must.) We want to be able, for any system $Ax = b$, to find $\boldsymbol{C}(A)$ and $\boldsymbol{N}(A)$: all attainable right-hand sides b and all solutions to $Ax = 0$.

The vectors b are in the column space and the vectors x are in the nullspace. We shall compute the dimensions of those subspaces and a convenient set of vectors to generate them. We hope to end up by understanding all *four* of the subspaces that are intimately related to each other and to A—the column space of A, the nullspace of A, and their two perpendicular spaces.

Problem Set 2.1

1. Construct a subset of the x-y plane $\mathbf{R}^2$ that is

(a) closed under vector addition and subtraction, but not scalar multiplication.
(b) closed under scalar multiplication but not under vector addition.

Hint: Starting with u and v, add and subtract for (a). Try cu and cv for (b).

2. Which of the following subsets of $\mathbf{R}^3$ are actually subspaces?

(a) The plane of vectors (b_1, b_2, b_3) with first component $b_1 = 0$.

(b) The plane of vectors b with $b_1 = 1$.
(c) The vectors b with $b_2 b_3 = 0$ (this is the union of two subspaces, the plane $b_2 = 0$ and the plane $b_3 = 0$).
(d) All combinations of two given vectors $(1, 1, 0)$ and $(2, 0, 1)$.
(e) The plane of vectors (b_1, b_2, b_3) that satisfy $b_3 - b_2 + 3b_1 = 0$.

3. Describe the column space and the nullspace of the matrices

$$A = \begin{bmatrix} 1 & -1 \\ 0 & 0 \end{bmatrix} \quad \text{and} \quad B = \begin{bmatrix} 0 & 0 & 3 \\ 1 & 2 & 3 \end{bmatrix} \quad \text{and} \quad C = \begin{bmatrix} 0 & 0 & 0 \\ 0 & 0 & 0 \end{bmatrix}.$$

4. What is the smallest subspace of 3 by 3 matrices that contains all symmetric matrices *and* all lower triangular matrices? What is the largest subspace that is contained in both of those subspaces?

5. Addition and scalar multiplication are required to satisfy these eight rules:

1. $x + y = y + x$.
2. $x + (y + z) = (x + y) + z$.
3. There is a unique "zero vector" such that $x + 0 = x$ for all x.
4. For each x there is a unique vector $-x$ such that $x + (-x) = 0$.
5. $1x = x$.
6. $(c_1 c_2)x = c_1(c_2 x)$.
7. $c(x + y) = cx + cy$.
8. $(c_1 + c_2)x = c_1 x + c_2 x$.

(a) Suppose addition in $\mathbf{R}^2$ adds an extra 1 to each component, so that $(3, 1) + (5, 0)$ equals $(9, 2)$ instead of $(8, 1)$. With scalar multiplication unchanged, which rules are broken?
(b) Show that the set of all positive real numbers, with $x + y$ and cx redefined to equal the usual xy and x^c, is a vector space. What is the "zero vector"?
(c) Suppose $(x_1, x_2) + (y_1, y_2)$ is defined to be $(x_1 + y_2, x_2 + y_1)$. With the usual $cx = (cx_1, cx_2)$, which of the eight conditions are not satisfied?

6. Let **P** be the plane in 3-space with equation $x + 2y + z = 6$. What is the equation of the plane $\mathbf{P}_0$ through the origin parallel to **P**? Are **P** and $\mathbf{P}_0$ subspaces of $\mathbf{R}^3$?

7. Which of the following are subspaces of $\mathbf{R}^\infty$?

(a) All sequences like $(1, 0, 1, 0, \ldots)$ that include infinitely many zeros.
(b) All sequences $(x_1, x_2, \ldots)$ with $x_j = 0$ from some point onward.
(c) All decreasing sequences: $x_{j+1} \le x_j$ for each j.
(d) All convergent sequences: the x_j have a limit as $j \to \infty$.
(e) All arithmetic progressions: $x_{j+1} - x_j$ is the same for all j.
(f) All geometric progressions $(x_1, kx_1, k^2 x_1, \ldots)$ allowing all k and x_1.

8. Which of the following descriptions are correct? The solutions x of

$$Ax = \begin{bmatrix} 1 & 1 & 1 \\ 1 & 0 & 2 \end{bmatrix} \begin{bmatrix} x_1 \\ x_2 \\ x_3 \end{bmatrix} = \begin{bmatrix} 0 \\ 0 \end{bmatrix}$$

form

(a) a plane.
(b) a line.
(c) a point.
(d) a subspace.
(e) the nullspace of A.
(f) the column space of A.

9. Show that the set of nonsingular 2 by 2 matrices is not a vector space. Show also that the set of *singular* 2 by 2 matrices is not a vector space.

10. The matrix $A = \begin{bmatrix} 2 & -2 \\ 2 & -2 \end{bmatrix}$ is a "vector" in the space $\mathbf{M}$ of all 2 by 2 matrices. Write the zero vector in this space, the vector $\frac{1}{2}A$, and the vector $-A$. What matrices are in the smallest subspace containing A?

11. (a) Describe a subspace of $\mathbf{M}$ that contains $A = \begin{bmatrix} 1 & 0 \\ 0 & 0 \end{bmatrix}$ but not $B = \begin{bmatrix} 0 & 0 \\ 0 & -1 \end{bmatrix}$.
(b) If a subspace of $\mathbf{M}$ contains A and B, must it contain I?
(c) Describe a subspace of $\mathbf{M}$ that contains no nonzero diagonal matrices.

12. The functions $f(x) = x^2$ and $g(x) = 5x$ are "vectors" in the vector space $\mathbf{F}$ of all real functions. The combination $3f(x) - 4g(x)$ is the function $h(x) =$ ______. Which rule is broken if multiplying $f(x)$ by c gives the function $f(cx)$?

13. If the sum of the "vectors" $f(x)$ and $g(x)$ in $\mathbf{F}$ is defined to be $f(g(x))$, then the "zero vector" is $g(x) = x$. Keep the usual scalar multiplication $cf(x)$, and find two rules that are broken.

14. Describe the smallest subspace of the 2 by 2 matrix space $\mathbf{M}$ that contains

(a) $\begin{bmatrix} 1 & 0 \\ 0 & 0 \end{bmatrix}$ and $\begin{bmatrix} 0 & 1 \\ 0 & 0 \end{bmatrix}$. (b) $\begin{bmatrix} 1 & 0 \\ 0 & 0 \end{bmatrix}$ and $\begin{bmatrix} 1 & 0 \\ 0 & 1 \end{bmatrix}$.

(c) $\begin{bmatrix} 1 & 1 \\ 0 & 0 \end{bmatrix}$. (d) $\begin{bmatrix} 1 & 1 \\ 0 & 0 \end{bmatrix}, \begin{bmatrix} 1 & 0 \\ 0 & 1 \end{bmatrix}, \begin{bmatrix} 0 & 1 \\ 0 & 1 \end{bmatrix}$.

15. Let $\mathbf{P}$ be the plane in $\mathbf{R}^3$ with equation $x + y - 2z = 4$. The origin $(0, 0, 0)$ is not in $\mathbf{P}$! Find two vectors in $\mathbf{P}$ and check that their sum is not in $\mathbf{P}$.

16. $\mathbf{P}_0$ is the plane through $(0, 0, 0)$ parallel to the plane $\mathbf{P}$ in Problem 15. What is the equation for $\mathbf{P}_0$? Find two vectors in $\mathbf{P}_0$ and check that their sum is in $\mathbf{P}_0$.

17. The four types of subspaces of $\mathbf{R}^3$ are planes, lines, $\mathbf{R}^3$ itself, or $\mathbf{Z}$ containing only $(0, 0, 0)$.

(a) Describe the three types of subspaces of $\mathbf{R}^2$.
(b) Describe the five types of subspaces of $\mathbf{R}^4$.

18. (a) The intersection of two planes through $(0, 0, 0)$ is probably a ______ but it could be a ______. It can't be the zero vector $\mathbf{Z}$!
(b) The intersection of a plane through $(0, 0, 0)$ with a line through $(0, 0, 0)$ is probably a ______ but it could be a ______.
(c) If $\mathbf{S}$ and $\mathbf{T}$ are subspaces of $\mathbf{R}^5$, their intersection $\mathbf{S} \cap \mathbf{T}$ (vectors in both subspaces) is a subspace of $\mathbf{R}^5$. *Check the requirements on $x + y$ and cx.*

19. Suppose **P** is a plane through (0, 0, 0) and **L** is a line through (0, 0, 0). The smallest vector space containing both **P** and **L** is either _______ or _______.

20. True or false for $\mathbf{M}$ = all 3 by 3 matrices (check addition using an example)?

(a) The skew-symmetric matrices in $\mathbf{M}$ (with $A^T = -A$) form a subspace.
(b) The unsymmetric matrices in $\mathbf{M}$ (with $A^T \neq A$) form a subspace.
(c) The matrices that have (1, 1, 1) in their nullspace form a subspace.

Problems 21–30 are about column spaces $C(A)$ and the equation $Ax = b$.

21. Describe the column spaces (lines or planes) of these particular matrices:

$$A = \begin{bmatrix} 1 & 2 \\ 0 & 0 \\ 0 & 0 \end{bmatrix} \quad \text{and} \quad B = \begin{bmatrix} 1 & 0 \\ 0 & 2 \\ 0 & 0 \end{bmatrix} \quad \text{and} \quad C = \begin{bmatrix} 1 & 0 \\ 2 & 0 \\ 0 & 0 \end{bmatrix}.$$

22. For which right-hand sides (find a condition on b_1, b_2, b_3) are these systems solvable?

$$\text{(a)} \quad \begin{bmatrix} 1 & 4 & 2 \\ 2 & 8 & 4 \\ -1 & -4 & -2 \end{bmatrix} \begin{bmatrix} x_1 \\ x_2 \\ x_3 \end{bmatrix} = \begin{bmatrix} b_1 \\ b_2 \\ b_3 \end{bmatrix}. \qquad \text{(b)} \quad \begin{bmatrix} 1 & 4 \\ 2 & 9 \\ -1 & -4 \end{bmatrix} \begin{bmatrix} x_1 \\ x_2 \end{bmatrix} = \begin{bmatrix} b_1 \\ b_2 \\ b_3 \end{bmatrix}.$$

23. Adding row 1 of A to row 2 produces B. Adding column 1 to column 2 produces C. A combination of the columns of _______ is also a combination of the columns of A. Which two matrices have the same column _______?

$$A = \begin{bmatrix} 1 & 2 \\ 2 & 4 \end{bmatrix} \quad \text{and} \quad B = \begin{bmatrix} 1 & 2 \\ 3 & 6 \end{bmatrix} \quad \text{and} \quad C = \begin{bmatrix} 1 & 3 \\ 2 & 6 \end{bmatrix}.$$

24. For which vectors (b_1, b_2, b_3) do these systems have a solution?

$$\begin{bmatrix} 1 & 1 & 1 \\ 0 & 1 & 1 \\ 0 & 0 & 1 \end{bmatrix} \begin{bmatrix} x_1 \\ x_2 \\ x_3 \end{bmatrix} = \begin{bmatrix} b_1 \\ b_2 \\ b_3 \end{bmatrix} \quad \text{and} \quad \begin{bmatrix} 1 & 1 & 1 \\ 0 & 1 & 1 \\ 0 & 0 & 0 \end{bmatrix} \begin{bmatrix} x_1 \\ x_2 \\ x_3 \end{bmatrix} = \begin{bmatrix} b_1 \\ b_2 \\ b_3 \end{bmatrix}.$$

25. (Recommended) If we add an extra column b to a matrix A, then the column space gets larger unless _______. Give an example in which the column space gets larger and an example in which it doesn't. Why is $Ax = b$ solvable exactly when the column space *doesn't* get larger by including b?

26. The columns of AB are combinations of the columns of A. This means: *The column space of AB is contained in* (possibly equal to) *the column space of* A. Give an example where the column spaces of A and AB are not equal.

27. If A is any 8 by 8 invertible matrix, then its column space is _______. Why?

28. True or false (with a counterexample if false)?

(a) The vectors b that are not in the column space $\boldsymbol{C}(A)$ form a subspace.
(b) If $\boldsymbol{C}(A)$ contains only the zero vector, then A is the zero matrix.
(c) The column space of $2A$ equals the column space of A.
(d) The column space of $A - I$ equals the column space of A.

29. Construct a 3 by 3 matrix whose column space contains $(1, 1, 0)$ and $(1, 0, 1)$ but not $(1, 1, 1)$. Construct a 3 by 3 matrix whose column space is only a line.

30. If the 9 by 12 system $Ax = b$ is solvable for every b, then $\boldsymbol{C}(A) =$ ______.

31. Why isn't $\mathbf{R}^2$ a subspace of $\mathbf{R}^3$?

2.2 SOLVING $Ax = 0$ AND $Ax = b$

Chapter 1 concentrated on square invertible matrices. There was one solution to $Ax = b$, and it was $x = A^{-1}b$. That solution was found by elimination (not by computing A^{-1}). A rectangular matrix brings new possibilities—U may not have a full set of pivots. This section goes onward from U to a reduced form R—**the simplest matrix that elimination can give**. R reveals all solutions immediately.

For an invertible matrix, the nullspace contains only $x = 0$ (multiply $Ax = 0$ by A^{-1}). The column space is the whole space ($Ax = b$ has a solution for every b). The new questions appear when the nullspace contains *more than the zero vector* and/or the column space contains *less than all vectors*:

1. Any vector x_n in the nullspace can be added to a particular solution x_p. The solutions to all linear equations have this form, $x = x_p + x_n$:

   Complete solution $\quad \boldsymbol{Ax_p = b}$ **and** $\boldsymbol{Ax_n = 0}$ **produce** $\boldsymbol{A(x_p + x_n) = b}$.

2. When the column space doesn't contain every b in $\mathbf{R}^m$, we need the conditions on b that make $Ax = b$ solvable.

A 3 by 4 example will be a good size. We will write down all solutions to $Ax = 0$. We will find the conditions for b to lie in the column space (so that $Ax = b$ is solvable). The 1 by 1 system $0x = b$, one equation and one unknown, shows two possibilities:

> $0x = b$ has *no solution* unless $b = 0$. The column space of the 1 by 1 zero matrix contains only $b = 0$.
>
> $0x = 0$ has *infinitely many solutions*. The nullspace contains *all* x. A particular solution is $x_p = 0$, and the complete solution is $x = x_p + x_n = 0 + (\text{any } x)$.

Simple, I admit. If you move up to 2 by 2, it's more interesting. The matrix $\begin{bmatrix} 1 & 1 \\ 2 & 2 \end{bmatrix}$ is not invertible: $y + z = b_1$ and $2y + 2z = b_2$ usually have no solution.

> There is ***no solution*** unless $b_2 = 2b_1$. The column space of A contains only those b's, the multiples of $(1, 2)$.
>
> When $b_2 = 2b_1$ there are ***infinitely many solutions***. A particular solution to $y + z = 2$ and $2y + 2z = 4$ is $x_p = (1, 1)$. The nullspace of A in Figure 2.2 contains $(-1, 1)$ and all its multiples $x_n = (-c, c)$:

Complete solution $\quad \begin{matrix} y + z = 2 \\ 2y + 2z = 4 \end{matrix}$ is solved by $x_p + x_n = \begin{bmatrix} 1 \\ 1 \end{bmatrix} + c\begin{bmatrix} -1 \\ 1 \end{bmatrix} = \begin{bmatrix} 1 - c \\ 1 + c \end{bmatrix}$.

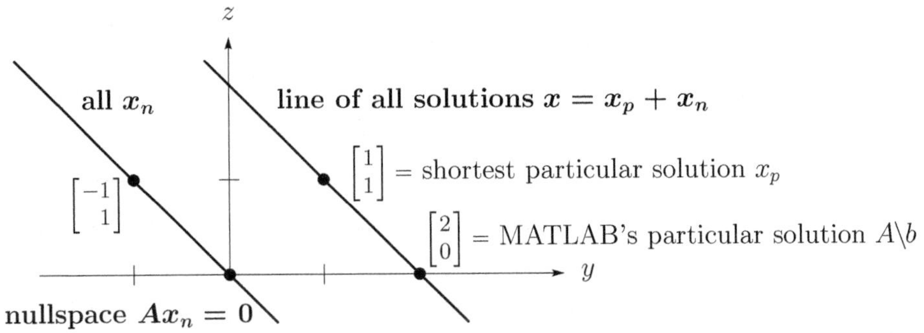

Figure 2.2 The parallel lines of solutions to $Ax_n = 0$ and $\begin{bmatrix}1 & 1\\2 & 2\end{bmatrix}\begin{bmatrix}y\\z\end{bmatrix} = \begin{bmatrix}2\\4\end{bmatrix}$.

Echelon Form *U* and Row Reduced Form *R*

We start by simplifying this 3 by 4 matrix, first to U and then further to R:

$$\textbf{Basic example} \qquad A = \begin{bmatrix}1 & 3 & 3 & 2\\2 & 6 & 9 & 7\\-1 & -3 & 3 & 4\end{bmatrix}.$$

The pivot $a_{11} = 1$ is nonzero. The usual elementary operations will produce zeros in the first column below this pivot. The bad news appears in column 2:

$$\textbf{No pivot in column 2} \qquad A \to \begin{bmatrix}1 & 3 & 3 & 2\\0 & \mathbf{0} & 3 & 3\\0 & \mathbf{0} & 6 & 6\end{bmatrix}.$$

The candidate for the second pivot has become zero: *unacceptable*. We look below that zero for a nonzero entry—intending to carry out a row exchange. In this case *the entry below it is also zero*. If A were square, this would signal that the matrix was singular. With a rectangular matrix, we must expect trouble anyway, and there is no reason to stop. All we can do is to *go on to the next column*, where the pivot entry is 3. Subtracting twice the second row from the third, we arrive at U:

$$\textbf{Echelon matrix } U \qquad U = \begin{bmatrix}\mathbf{1} & 3 & 3 & 2\\0 & 0 & \mathbf{3} & 3\\0 & 0 & 0 & 0\end{bmatrix}.$$

Strictly speaking, we proceed to the fourth column. A zero is in the third pivot position, and nothing can be done. U is upper triangular, but its pivots are not on the main diagonal. The nonzero entries of U have a "staircase pattern," or ***echelon form***. For the 5 by 8 case in Figure 2.3, the starred entries may or may not be zero.

We can always reach this echelon form U, with zeros below the pivots:

1. The pivots are the first nonzero entries in their rows.
2. Below each pivot is a column of zeros, obtained by elimination.
3. Each pivot lies to the right of the pivot in the row above. This produces the staircase pattern, and zero rows come last.

$$U = \begin{bmatrix} \bullet & * & * & * & * & * & * & * \\ 0 & \bullet & * & * & * & * & * & * \\ 0 & 0 & 0 & \bullet & * & * & * & * \\ 0 & 0 & 0 & 0 & 0 & 0 & 0 & \bullet \\ 0 & 0 & 0 & 0 & 0 & 0 & 0 & 0 \end{bmatrix} \qquad R = \begin{bmatrix} \mathbf{1} & \mathbf{0} & * & \mathbf{0} & * & * & * & \mathbf{0} \\ 0 & \mathbf{1} & * & \mathbf{0} & * & * & * & \mathbf{0} \\ 0 & 0 & 0 & \mathbf{1} & * & * & * & \mathbf{0} \\ 0 & 0 & 0 & 0 & 0 & 0 & 0 & \mathbf{1} \\ 0 & 0 & 0 & 0 & 0 & 0 & 0 & 0 \end{bmatrix}$$

Figure 2.3 The entries of a 5 by 8 echelon matrix U and its reduced form R.

Since we started with A and ended with U, the reader is certain to ask: Do we have $A = LU$ as before? There is no reason why not, since the elimination steps have not changed. Each step still subtracts a multiple of one row from a row beneath it. The inverse of each step adds back the multiple that was subtracted. These inverses come in the right order to put the multipliers directly into L:

$$\textbf{Lower triangular} \qquad L = \begin{bmatrix} 1 & 0 & 0 \\ 2 & 1 & 0 \\ -1 & 2 & 1 \end{bmatrix} \qquad \text{and} \quad A = LU.$$

Note that L is square. It has the same number of rows as A and U.

The only operation not required by our example, but needed in general, is row exchange by a permutation matrix P. Since we keep going to the next column when no pivots are available, there is no need to assume that A is nonsingular. Here is $PA = LU$ for all matrices:

2B For any m by n matrix A there is a permutation P, a lower triangular L with unit diagonal, and an m by n echelon matrix U, such that $PA = LU$.

Now comes R. We can go further than U, to make the matrix even simpler. Divide the second row by its pivot 3, so that ***all pivots are* 1**. Then use the pivot row to produce ***zero above the pivot***. This time we subtract a row from a *higher row*. The final result (the best form we can get) is the ***reduced row echelon form R***:

$$\begin{bmatrix} 1 & 3 & 3 & 2 \\ 0 & 0 & 3 & 3 \\ 0 & 0 & 0 & 0 \end{bmatrix} \longrightarrow \begin{bmatrix} 1 & 3 & 3 & 2 \\ 0 & 0 & \mathbf{1} & \mathbf{1} \\ 0 & 0 & 0 & 0 \end{bmatrix} \longrightarrow \begin{bmatrix} \mathbf{1} & \mathbf{3} & \mathbf{0} & \mathbf{-1} \\ \mathbf{0} & \mathbf{0} & \mathbf{1} & \mathbf{1} \\ \mathbf{0} & \mathbf{0} & \mathbf{0} & \mathbf{0} \end{bmatrix} = R.$$

This matrix R is the final result of elimination on A. MATLAB would use the command $R = \text{rref}(A)$. Of course rref(R) would give R again!

What is the row reduced form of a square invertible matrix? In that case R is the *identity matrix*. There is a full set of pivots, all equal to 1, with zeros above and below. So $\text{rref}(A) = I$, when A is invertible.

For a 5 by 8 matrix with four pivots, Figure 2.3 shows the reduced form R. **It still contains an identity matrix, in the four pivot rows and four pivot columns.** From R we will quickly find the nullspace of A. $Rx = 0$ has the same solutions as $Ux = 0$ and $Ax = 0$.

Pivot Variables and Free Variables

Our goal is to read off all the solutions to $Rx = 0$. The pivots are crucial:

Nullspace of R (pivot columns in boldface)
$$Rx = \begin{bmatrix} \mathbf{1} & 3 & \mathbf{0} & -1 \\ \mathbf{0} & 0 & \mathbf{1} & 1 \\ \mathbf{0} & 0 & \mathbf{0} & 0 \end{bmatrix} \begin{bmatrix} u \\ v \\ w \\ y \end{bmatrix} = \begin{bmatrix} 0 \\ 0 \\ 0 \end{bmatrix}.$$

The unknowns u, v, w, y go into two groups. One group contains the ***pivot variables***, those that correspond to ***columns with pivots***. The first and third columns contain the pivots, so $\boldsymbol{u}$ and $\boldsymbol{w}$ are the pivot variables. The other group is made up of the ***free variables***, corresponding to ***columns without pivots***. These are the second and fourth columns, so v and y are free variables.

To find the most general solution to $Rx = 0$ (or, equivalently, to $Ax = 0$) we may assign arbitrary values to the free variables. Suppose we call these values simply v and y. The pivot variables are completely determined in terms of v and y:

$$\boldsymbol{Rx = 0} \qquad \begin{aligned} \boldsymbol{u} + 3v - y &= 0 \quad \text{yields} \quad \boldsymbol{u} = -3v + y \\ \boldsymbol{w} + y &= 0 \quad \text{yields} \quad \boldsymbol{w} = - y \end{aligned} \tag{1}$$

There is a "double infinity" of solutions, with v and y free and independent. The complete solution is a combination of two **special solutions**:

Nullspace contains all combinations of special solutions
$$x = \begin{bmatrix} -3v + y \\ v \\ -y \\ y \end{bmatrix} = v \begin{bmatrix} \mathbf{-3} \\ \mathbf{1} \\ \mathbf{0} \\ \mathbf{0} \end{bmatrix} + y \begin{bmatrix} \mathbf{1} \\ \mathbf{0} \\ \mathbf{-1} \\ \mathbf{1} \end{bmatrix}. \tag{2}$$

Please look again at this complete solution to $Rx = 0$ and $Ax = 0$. The special solution $(-3, 1, 0, 0)$ has free variables $v = 1$, $y = 0$. The other special solution $(1, 0, -1, 1)$ has $v = 0$ and $y = 1$. *All solutions are linear combinations of these two.* The best way to find all solutions to $Ax = 0$ is from the special solutions:

1. After reaching $Rx = 0$, identify the pivot variables and free variables.
2. Give one free variable the value 1, set the other free variables to 0, and solve $Rx = 0$ for the pivot variables. This x is a special solution.
3. Every free variable produces its own "special solution" by step 2. The combinations of special solutions form the nullspace—all solutions to $Ax = 0$.

Within the four-dimensional space of all possible vectors x, the solutions to $Ax = 0$ form a ***two-dimensional subspace***—the nullspace of A. In the example, $N(A)$ is generated by the special vectors $(-3, 1, 0, 0)$ and $(1, 0, -1, 1)$. The combinations of these two vectors produce the whole nullspace.

Here is a little trick. The special solutions are especially easy from R. The numbers 3 and 0 and -1 and 1 lie in the "nonpivot columns" of R. **Reverse their signs to find the pivot variables** (not free) **in the special solutions**. I will put the two special solutions from equation (2) into a nullspace matrix N, so you see this neat pattern:

Nullspace matrix (columns are special solutions)

$$N = \begin{bmatrix} \mathbf{-3} & \mathbf{1} \\ 1 & 0 \\ \mathbf{0} & \mathbf{-1} \\ 0 & 1 \end{bmatrix} \begin{matrix} \text{not free} \\ \text{free} \\ \text{not free} \\ \text{free} \end{matrix}$$

The free variables have values 1 and 0. When the free columns moved to the right-hand side of equation (2), their coefficients 3 and 0 and -1 and 1 switched sign. That determined the pivot variables in the special solutions (the columns of N).

This is the place to recognize one extremely important theorem. Suppose a matrix has more columns than rows, $n > m$. Since m rows can hold at most m pivots, ***there must be at least n − m free variables***. There will be even *more* free variables if some rows of R reduce to zero; but no matter what, at least one variable must be free. This free variable can be assigned any value, leading to the following conclusion:

2C If $Ax = 0$ has more unknowns than equations ($n > m$), it has at least one special solution: There are more solutions than the trivial $x = 0$.

There must be infinitely many solutions, since any multiple cx will also satisfy $A(cx) = 0$. The nullspace contains the line through x. And if there are additional free variables, the nullspace becomes more than just a line in n-dimensional space. *The nullspace has the same "dimension" as the number of free variables and special solutions.*

This central idea—the ***dimension*** of a subspace—is made precise in the next section. We count the free variables for the nullspace. We count the pivot variables for the column space!

Solving $Ax = b$, $Ux = c$, and $Rx = d$

The case $b \neq 0$ is quite different from $b = 0$. The row operations on A must act also on the right-hand side (on b). We begin with letters (b_1, b_2, b_3) to find the solvability condition—for b to lie in the column space. Then we choose $b = (1, 5, 5)$ and find all solutions x.

For the original example $Ax = b = (b_1, b_2, b_3)$, apply to both sides the operations that led from A to U. The result is an upper triangular system $Ux = c$:

$$\mathbf{Ux = c} \qquad \begin{bmatrix} 1 & 3 & 3 & 2 \\ 0 & 0 & 3 & 3 \\ 0 & 0 & 0 & 0 \end{bmatrix} \begin{bmatrix} u \\ v \\ w \\ y \end{bmatrix} = \begin{bmatrix} b_1 \\ b_2 - 2b_1 \\ b_3 - 2b_2 + 5b_1 \end{bmatrix}. \qquad (3)$$

The vector c on the right-hand side, which appeared after the forward elimination steps, is just $L^{-1}b$ as in the previous chapter. Start now with $Ux = c$.

It is not clear that these equations have a solution. The third equation is very much in doubt, because its left-hand side is zero. ***The equations are inconsistent unless*** $\boldsymbol{b_3 - 2b_2 + 5b_1 = 0}$. Even though there are more unknowns than equations, there may be no solution. We know another way of answering the same question: $Ax = b$ can be solved if and only if b lies in the column space of A. This subspace comes from the four columns of A (not of U!):

$$\textbf{Columns of } A \text{ “span” the column space} \qquad \begin{bmatrix} 1 \\ 2 \\ -1 \end{bmatrix}, \quad \begin{bmatrix} 3 \\ 6 \\ -3 \end{bmatrix}, \quad \begin{bmatrix} 3 \\ 9 \\ 3 \end{bmatrix}, \quad \begin{bmatrix} 2 \\ 7 \\ 4 \end{bmatrix}.$$

Even though there are four vectors, their combinations only fill out a plane in three-dimensional space. Column 2 is three times column 1. The fourth column equals the third minus the first. *These dependent columns, the second and fourth, are exactly the ones without pivots.*

The column space $\boldsymbol{C}(A)$ can be described in two different ways. On the one hand, it is *the plane generated by columns 1 and 3*. The other columns lie in that plane, and contribute nothing new. Equivalently, it is the plane of all vectors b that satisfy $b_3 - 2b_2 + 5b_1 = 0$; this is the constraint if the system is to be solvable. ***Every column satisfies this constraint, so it is forced on b!*** Geometrically, we shall see that the vector $(5, -2, 1)$ is perpendicular to each column.

If b belongs to the column space, the solutions of $Ax = b$ are easy to find. The last equation in $Ux = c$ is $0 = 0$. To the free variables v and y, we may assign any values, as before. The pivot variables u and w are still determined by back-substitution. For a specific example with $b_3 - 2b_2 + 5b_1 = 0$, choose $b = (1, 5, 5)$:

$$\boldsymbol{Ax = b} \qquad \begin{bmatrix} 1 & 3 & 3 & 2 \\ 2 & 6 & 9 & 7 \\ -1 & -3 & 3 & 4 \end{bmatrix} \begin{bmatrix} u \\ v \\ w \\ y \end{bmatrix} = \begin{bmatrix} 1 \\ 5 \\ 5 \end{bmatrix}.$$

Forward elimination produces U on the left and c on the right:

$$\boldsymbol{Ux = c} \qquad \begin{bmatrix} 1 & 3 & 3 & 2 \\ 0 & 0 & 3 & 3 \\ 0 & 0 & 0 & 0 \end{bmatrix} \begin{bmatrix} u \\ v \\ w \\ y \end{bmatrix} = \begin{bmatrix} 1 \\ 3 \\ 0 \end{bmatrix}.$$

The last equation is $0 = 0$, as expected. Back-substitution gives

$$\begin{aligned} 3w + 3y &= 3 &\quad\text{or}\quad w &= 1 - y \\ u + 3v + 3w + 2y &= 1 &\quad\text{or}\quad u &= -2 - 3v + y. \end{aligned}$$

Again there is a double infinity of solutions: v and y are free, u and w are not:

$$\textbf{Complete solution } \boldsymbol{x = x_p + x_n} \qquad x = \begin{bmatrix} u \\ v \\ w \\ y \end{bmatrix} = \begin{bmatrix} -2 \\ 0 \\ 1 \\ 0 \end{bmatrix} + v \begin{bmatrix} -3 \\ 1 \\ 0 \\ 0 \end{bmatrix} + y \begin{bmatrix} 1 \\ 0 \\ -1 \\ 1 \end{bmatrix}. \tag{4}$$

This has all solutions to $Ax = 0$, plus the new $x_p = (-2, 0, 1, 0)$. That x_p is ***a particular solution*** to $Ax = b$. The last two terms with v and y yield more solutions (because they satisfy $Ax = 0$). ***Every solution to $\boldsymbol{Ax = b}$ is the sum of one particular solution and a solution to $\boldsymbol{Ax = 0}$:***

$$x_{\textbf{complete}} = x_{\textbf{particular}} + x_{\textbf{nullspace}}$$

The particular solution in equation (4) comes from solving the equation *with all free variables set to zero*. That is the only new part, since the nullspace is already computed. When you multiply the highlighted equation by A, you get $Ax_{\textbf{complete}} = b + 0$.

Geometrically, the solutions again fill a two-dimensional surface—but it is not a subspace. It does not contain $x = 0$. It is *parallel* to the nullspace we had before, shifted by the particular solution x_p as in Figure 2.2. Equation (4) is a good way to write the answer:

1. Reduce $Ax = b$ to $Ux = c$.
2. With free variables $= 0$, find a particular solution to $Ax_p = b$ and $Ux_p = c$.
3. Find the special solutions to $Ax = 0$ (or $Ux = 0$ or $Rx = 0$). Each free variable, in turn, is 1. Then $x = x_p +$ (any combination x_n of special solutions).

When the equation was $Ax = 0$, the particular solution was the zero vector! It fits the pattern, but $x_{\textbf{particular}} = 0$ was not written in equation (2). Now x_p is added to the nullspace solutions, as in equation (4).

Question: How does the reduced form R make this solution even clearer? You will see it in our example. Subtract equation 2 from equation 1, and then divide equation 2 by its pivot. On the left-hand side, this produces R, as before. On the right-hand side, these operations change $c = (1, 3, 0)$ to a new vector $d = (-2, 1, 0)$:

Reduced equation
$\boldsymbol{Rx = d}$

$$\begin{bmatrix} 1 & 3 & 0 & -1 \\ 0 & 0 & 1 & 1 \\ 0 & 0 & 0 & 0 \end{bmatrix} \begin{bmatrix} u \\ v \\ w \\ y \end{bmatrix} = \begin{bmatrix} -2 \\ 1 \\ 0 \end{bmatrix}. \tag{5}$$

Our particular solution x_p (one choice out of many) has free variables $v = y = 0$. Columns 2 and 4 can be ignored. Then we immediately have $u = -2$ and $w = 1$, exactly as in equation (4). **The entries of $\boldsymbol{d}$ go directly into $\boldsymbol{x_p}$.** This is because the identity matrix is sitting in the pivot columns of R!

Let me summarize this section, before working a new example. Elimination reveals the pivot variables and free variables. ***If there are r pivots, there are r pivot variables and n − r free variables***. That important number r will be given a name—it is the ***rank of the matrix***.

2D Suppose elimination reduces $Ax = b$ to $Ux = c$ and $Rx = d$, with r pivot rows and r pivot columns. **The rank of those matrices is $\boldsymbol{r}$.** The last $m - r$ rows of U and R are zero, so there is a solution only if the last $m - r$ entries of c and d are also zero.

The complete solution is $x = x_p + x_n$. One particular solution x_p has all free variables zero. Its pivot variables are the first r entries of d, so $Rx_p = d$.

The nullspace solutions x_n are combinations of $n - r$ special solutions, with one free variable equal to 1. The pivot variables in that special solution can be found in the corresponding column of R (with sign reversed).

You see how the rank r is crucial. It counts the pivot rows in the "row space" and the pivot columns in the column space. There are $n - r$ special solutions in the nullspace. There are $m - r$ solvability conditions on b or c or d.

Another Worked Example

The full picture uses elimination and pivot columns to find the column space, nullspace, and rank. The 3 by 4 matrix A has rank 2:

$$Ax = b \quad \text{is} \quad \begin{aligned} \mathbf{1}x_1 + \mathbf{2}x_2 + \mathbf{3}x_3 + \ \ \mathbf{5}x_4 &= b_1 \\ \mathbf{2}x_1 + \mathbf{4}x_2 + \mathbf{8}x_3 + \mathbf{12}x_4 &= b_2 \\ \mathbf{3}x_1 + \mathbf{6}x_2 + \mathbf{7}x_3 + \mathbf{13}x_4 &= b_3 \end{aligned} \tag{6}$$

1. Reduce $[A \ \ b]$ to $[U \ \ c]$, to reach a triangular system $Ux = c$.
2. Find the condition on b_1, b_2, b_3 to have a solution.
3. Describe the column space of A: Which plane in $\mathbf{R}^3$?
4. Describe the nullspace of A: Which special solutions in $\mathbf{R}^4$?
5. Find a particular solution to $Ax = (0, 6, -6)$ and the complete $x_p + x_n$.
6. Reduce $[U \ \ c]$ to $[R \ \ d]$: Special solutions from R and x_p from d.

Solution (Notice how the right-hand side is included as an extra column!)

1. The multipliers in elimination are 2 and 3 and -1, taking $[A \ \ b]$ to $[U \ \ c]$.

$$\left[\begin{array}{cccc|c} 1 & 2 & 3 & 5 & \mathbf{b_1} \\ 2 & 4 & 8 & 12 & \mathbf{b_2} \\ 3 & 6 & 7 & 13 & \mathbf{b_3} \end{array}\right] \rightarrow \left[\begin{array}{cccc|c} 1 & 2 & 3 & 5 & \mathbf{b_1} \\ 0 & 0 & 2 & 2 & \mathbf{b_2 - 2b_1} \\ 0 & 0 & -2 & -2 & \mathbf{b_3 - 3b_1} \end{array}\right] \rightarrow \left[\begin{array}{cccc|c} 1 & 2 & 3 & 5 & \mathbf{b_1} \\ 0 & 0 & 2 & 2 & \mathbf{b_2 - 2b_1} \\ 0 & 0 & 0 & 0 & \mathbf{b_3 + b_2 - 5b_1} \end{array}\right].$$

2. The last equation shows the solvability condition $b_3 + b_2 - 5b_1 = 0$. Then $0 = 0$.
3. The column space of A is the plane containing all combinations of the pivot columns $(1, 2, 3)$ and $(3, 8, 7)$. **Second description**: The column space contains all vectors with $b_3 + b_2 - 5b_1 = 0$. That makes $Ax = b$ solvable, so b is in the column space. *All columns of A pass this test $b_3 + b_2 - 5b_1 = 0$. This is the equation for the plane (in the first description of the column space).*
4. The special solutions in N have free variables $x_2 = 1, x_4 = 0$ and $x_2 = 0, x_4 = 1$:

Nullspace matrix
Special solutions to $Ax = 0$
Back-substitution in $Ux = 0$
Just switch signs in $Rx = 0$

$$N = \begin{bmatrix} -2 & -2 \\ 1 & 0 \\ 0 & -1 \\ 0 & 1 \end{bmatrix}.$$

5. Choose $b = (0, 6, -6)$, which has $b_3 + b_2 - 5b_1 = 0$. Elimination takes $Ax = b$ to $Ux = c = (0, 6, 0)$. Back-substitute with free variables $= 0$:

Particular solution to $Ax_p = (0, 6, -6)$

$$x_p = \begin{bmatrix} -9 \\ 0 \\ 3 \\ 0 \end{bmatrix} \begin{matrix} \\ \text{free} \\ \\ \text{free} \end{matrix}$$

The complete solution to $Ax = (0, 6, -6)$ is (this x_p) + (all x_n).

6. In the reduced R, the third column changes from $(3, 2, 0)$ to $(0, 1, 0)$. The right-hand side $c = (0, 6, 0)$ becomes $d = (-9, 3, 0)$. Then -9 and 3 go into x_p:

$$\begin{bmatrix} U & c \end{bmatrix} = \left[\begin{array}{cccc|c} 1 & 2 & 3 & 5 & 0 \\ 0 & 0 & 2 & 2 & 6 \\ 0 & 0 & 0 & 0 & 0 \end{array}\right] \longrightarrow \begin{bmatrix} R & d \end{bmatrix} = \left[\begin{array}{cccc|c} \mathbf{1} & 2 & 0 & 2 & \mathbf{-9} \\ 0 & 0 & \mathbf{1} & 1 & \mathbf{3} \\ 0 & 0 & 0 & 0 & 0 \end{array}\right].$$

That final matrix $[R \quad d]$ **is** $\text{rref}([A \quad b]) = \text{rref}([U \quad c])$. The numbers 2 and 0 and 2 and 1 in the free columns of R have opposite sign in the special solutions (the nullspace matrix N). Everything is revealed by $Rx = d$.

Problem Set 2.2

1. Construct a system with more unknowns than equations, but no solution. Change the right-hand side to zero and find all solutions x_n.

2. Reduce A and B to echelon form, to find their ranks. Which variables are free?

$$A = \begin{bmatrix} 1 & 2 & 0 & 1 \\ 0 & 1 & 1 & 0 \\ 1 & 2 & 0 & 1 \end{bmatrix} \qquad B = \begin{bmatrix} 1 & 2 & 3 \\ 4 & 5 & 6 \\ 7 & 8 & 9 \end{bmatrix}.$$

   Find the special solutions to $Ax = 0$ and $Bx = 0$. Find all solutions.

3. Find the echelon form U, the free variables, and the special solutions:

$$A = \begin{bmatrix} 0 & 1 & 0 & 3 \\ 0 & 2 & 0 & 6 \end{bmatrix}, \qquad b = \begin{bmatrix} b_1 \\ b_2 \end{bmatrix}.$$

   $Ax = b$ is consistent (has a solution) when b satisfies $b_2 =$ ______. Find the complete solution in the same form as equation (4).

4. Carry out the same steps as in the previous problem to find the complete solution of $Mx = b$:

$$M = \begin{bmatrix} 0 & 0 \\ 1 & 2 \\ 0 & 0 \\ 3 & 6 \end{bmatrix}, \qquad b = \begin{bmatrix} b_1 \\ b_2 \\ b_3 \\ b_4 \end{bmatrix}.$$

5. Write the complete solutions $x = x_p + x_n$ to these systems, as in equation (4):

$$\begin{bmatrix} 1 & 2 & 2 \\ 2 & 4 & 5 \end{bmatrix} \begin{bmatrix} u \\ v \\ w \end{bmatrix} = \begin{bmatrix} 1 \\ 4 \end{bmatrix} \qquad \begin{bmatrix} 1 & 2 & 2 \\ 2 & 4 & 4 \end{bmatrix} \begin{bmatrix} u \\ v \\ w \end{bmatrix} = \begin{bmatrix} 1 \\ 4 \end{bmatrix}.$$

6. Describe the set of attainable right-hand sides b (in the column space) for

$$\begin{bmatrix} 1 & 0 \\ 0 & 1 \\ 2 & 3 \end{bmatrix} \begin{bmatrix} u \\ v \end{bmatrix} = \begin{bmatrix} b_1 \\ b_2 \\ b_3 \end{bmatrix},$$

   by finding the constraints on b that turn the third equation into $0 = 0$ (after elimination). What is the rank, and a particular solution?

7. Find the value of c that makes it possible to solve $Ax = b$, and solve it:

$$\begin{aligned} u + v + 2w &= 2 \\ 2u + 3v - w &= 5 \\ 3u + 4v + w &= c. \end{aligned}$$

8. Under what conditions on b_1 and b_2 (if any) does $Ax = b$ have a solution?

$$A = \begin{bmatrix} 1 & 2 & 0 & 3 \\ 2 & 4 & 0 & 7 \end{bmatrix}, \qquad b = \begin{bmatrix} b_1 \\ b_2 \end{bmatrix}.$$

Find two vectors in the nullspace of A, and the complete solution to $Ax = b$.

9. (a) Find the special solutions to $Ux = 0$. Reduce U to R and repeat:

$$Ux = \begin{bmatrix} 1 & 2 & 3 & 4 \\ 0 & 0 & 1 & 2 \\ 0 & 0 & 0 & 0 \end{bmatrix} \begin{bmatrix} x_1 \\ x_2 \\ x_3 \\ x_4 \end{bmatrix} = \begin{bmatrix} 0 \\ 0 \\ 0 \end{bmatrix}.$$

(b) If the right-hand side is changed from $(0, 0, 0)$ to $(a, b, 0)$, what are all solutions?

10. Find a 2 by 3 system $Ax = b$ whose complete solution is

$$x = \begin{bmatrix} 1 \\ 2 \\ 0 \end{bmatrix} + w \begin{bmatrix} 1 \\ 3 \\ 1 \end{bmatrix}.$$

Find a 3 by 3 system with these solutions exactly when $b_1 + b_2 = b_3$.

11. Write a 2 by 2 system $Ax = b$ with many solutions x_n but no solution x_p. (Therefore the system has no solution.) Which b's allow an x_p?

12. Which of these rules give a correct definition of the *rank* of A?

(a) The number of nonzero rows in R.
(b) The number of columns minus the total number of rows.
(c) The number of columns minus the number of free columns.
(d) The number of 1s in R.

13. Find the reduced row echelon forms R and the rank of these matrices:

(a) The 3 by 4 matrix of all 1s.
(b) The 4 by 4 matrix with $a_{ij} = (-1)^{ij}$.
(c) The 3 by 4 matrix with $a_{ij} = (-1)^j$.

14. Find R for each of these (block) matrices, and the special solutions:

$$A = \begin{bmatrix} 0 & 0 & 0 \\ 0 & 0 & 3 \\ 2 & 4 & 6 \end{bmatrix} \qquad B = \begin{bmatrix} A & A \end{bmatrix} \qquad C = \begin{bmatrix} A & A \\ A & 0 \end{bmatrix}.$$

15. If the r pivot variables come first, the reduced R must look like

$$R = \begin{bmatrix} I & F \\ 0 & 0 \end{bmatrix} \qquad \begin{array}{l} I \text{ is } r \text{ by } r \\ F \text{ is } r \text{ by } n - r \end{array}$$

What is the nullspace matrix N containing the special solutions?

16. Suppose all r pivot variables come *last*. Describe the four blocks in the m by n reduced echelon form (the block B should be r by r):

$$R = \begin{bmatrix} A & B \\ C & D \end{bmatrix}.$$

What is the nullspace matrix N of special solutions? What is its shape?

17. (Silly problem) Describe all 2 by 3 matrices A_1 and A_2 with row echelon forms R_1 and R_2, such that $R_1 + R_2$ is the row echelon form of $A_1 + A_2$. Is it true that $R_1 = A_1$ and $R_2 = A_2$ in this case?

18. If A has r pivot columns, then A^{T} has r pivot columns. Give a 3 by 3 example for which the column numbers are different for A and A^{T}.

19. What are the special solutions to $Rx = 0$ and $R^{\mathrm{T}}y = 0$ for these R?

$$R = \begin{bmatrix} 1 & 0 & 2 & 3 \\ 0 & 1 & 4 & 5 \\ 0 & 0 & 0 & 0 \end{bmatrix} \qquad R = \begin{bmatrix} 0 & 1 & 2 \\ 0 & 0 & 0 \\ 0 & 0 & 0 \end{bmatrix}.$$

20. *If A has rank r, then it has an r by r submatrix S that is invertible.* Find that submatrix S from the pivot rows and pivot columns of each A:

$$A = \begin{bmatrix} 1 & 2 & 3 \\ 1 & 2 & 4 \end{bmatrix} \qquad A = \begin{bmatrix} 1 & 2 & 3 \\ 2 & 4 & 6 \end{bmatrix} \qquad A = \begin{bmatrix} 0 & 1 & 0 \\ 0 & 0 & 0 \\ 0 & 0 & 1 \end{bmatrix}.$$

21. Explain why the pivot rows and pivot columns of A (not R) always give an r by r invertible submatrix of A.

22. Find the ranks of AB and AM (rank 1 matrix times rank 1 matrix):

$$A = \begin{bmatrix} 1 & 2 \\ 2 & 4 \end{bmatrix} \quad \text{and} \quad B = \begin{bmatrix} 2 & 1 & 4 \\ 3 & 1.5 & 6 \end{bmatrix} \quad \text{and} \quad M = \begin{bmatrix} 1 & b \\ c & bc \end{bmatrix}.$$

23. Multiplying the rank 1 matrices $A = uv^{\mathrm{T}}$ and $B = wz^{\mathrm{T}}$ gives uz^{T} times the number ___. AB has rank 1 unless ___ $= 0$.

24. Every column of AB is a combination of the columns of A. Then the dimensions of the column spaces give **rank(AB) $\le$ rank(A)**. Problem: Prove also that **rank(AB) $\le$ rank(B)**.

25. (Important) Suppose A and B are n by n matrices, and $AB = I$. Prove from rank(AB) $\le$ rank(A) that the rank of A is n. So A is invertible and B must be its two-sided inverse. Therefore $BA = I$ (*which is not so obvious!*).

26. If A is 2 by 3 and C is 3 by 2, show from its rank that $CA \neq I$. Give an example in which $AC = I$. For $m < n$, a right inverse is not a left inverse.

27. Suppose A and B have the *same* reduced-row echelon form R. Explain how to change A to B by elementary row operations. So B equals an ______ matrix times A.

28. Every m by n matrix of rank r reduces to (m by r) times (r by n):

$$A = (\text{pivot columns of } A)(\text{first } r \text{ rows of } R) = (\textbf{COL})(\textbf{ROW}).$$

Write the 3 by 4 matrix A at the start of this section as the product of the 3 by 2 matrix from the pivot columns and the 2 by 4 matrix from R:

$$A = \begin{bmatrix} 1 & 3 & 3 & 2 \\ 2 & 6 & 9 & 7 \\ -1 & -3 & 3 & 4 \end{bmatrix}$$

29. Suppose A is an m by n matrix of rank r. Its reduced echelon form is R. Describe exactly the *reduced row echelon form of* R^{T} (not A^{T}).

30. (Recommended) Execute the six steps following equation (6) to find the column space and nullspace of A and the solution to $Ax = b$:

$$A = \begin{bmatrix} 2 & 4 & 6 & 4 \\ 2 & 5 & 7 & 6 \\ 2 & 3 & 5 & 2 \end{bmatrix} \qquad b = \begin{bmatrix} b_1 \\ b_2 \\ b_3 \end{bmatrix} = \begin{bmatrix} 4 \\ 3 \\ 5 \end{bmatrix}.$$

31. For every c, find R and the special solutions to $Ax = 0$:

$$A = \begin{bmatrix} 1 & 1 & 2 & 2 \\ 2 & 2 & 4 & 4 \\ 1 & c & 2 & 2 \end{bmatrix} \qquad \text{and} \qquad A = \begin{bmatrix} 1-c & 2 \\ 0 & 2-c \end{bmatrix}.$$

32. What is the nullspace matrix N (of special solutions) for A, B, C?

$$A = \begin{bmatrix} I & I \end{bmatrix} \quad \text{and} \quad B = \begin{bmatrix} I & I \\ 0 & 0 \end{bmatrix} \quad \text{and} \quad C = \begin{bmatrix} I & I & I \end{bmatrix}.$$

Problems 33–36 are about the solution of $Ax = b$. Follow the steps in the text to x_p and x_n. Reduce the augmented matrix $[A \;\; b]$.

33. Find the complete solutions of

$$\begin{aligned} x + 3y + 3z &= 1 \\ 2x + 6y + 9z &= 5 \\ -x - 3y + 3z &= 5 \end{aligned} \qquad \text{and} \qquad \begin{bmatrix} 1 & 3 & 1 & 2 \\ 2 & 6 & 4 & 8 \\ 0 & 0 & 2 & 4 \end{bmatrix} \begin{bmatrix} x \\ y \\ z \\ t \end{bmatrix} = \begin{bmatrix} 1 \\ 3 \\ 1 \end{bmatrix}.$$

34. Under what condition on b_1, b_2, b_3 is the following system solvable? Include b as a fourth column in $[A \;\; b]$. Find all solutions when that condition holds:

$$\begin{aligned} x + 2y - 2z &= b_1 \\ 2x + 5y - 4z &= b_2 \\ 4x + 9y - 8z &= b_3. \end{aligned}$$

35. What conditions on b_1, b_2, b_3, b_4 make each system solvable? *Solve for* x:

$$\begin{bmatrix} 1 & 2 \\ 2 & 4 \\ 2 & 5 \\ 3 & 9 \end{bmatrix} \begin{bmatrix} x_1 \\ x_2 \end{bmatrix} = \begin{bmatrix} b_1 \\ b_2 \\ b_3 \\ b_4 \end{bmatrix} \qquad \begin{bmatrix} 1 & 2 & 3 \\ 2 & 4 & 6 \\ 2 & 5 & 7 \\ 3 & 9 & 12 \end{bmatrix} \begin{bmatrix} x_1 \\ x_2 \\ x_3 \end{bmatrix} = \begin{bmatrix} b_1 \\ b_2 \\ b_3 \\ b_4 \end{bmatrix}.$$

36. Which vectors (b_1, b_2, b_3) are in the column space of A? Which combinations of the rows of A give zero?

$$\text{(a) } A = \begin{bmatrix} 1 & 2 & 1 \\ 2 & 6 & 3 \\ 0 & 2 & 5 \end{bmatrix} \qquad \text{(b) } A = \begin{bmatrix} 1 & 1 & 1 \\ 1 & 2 & 4 \\ 2 & 4 & 8 \end{bmatrix}.$$

37. Why can't a 1 by 3 system have $x_p = (2, 4, 0)$ and $x_n =$ any multiple of $(1, 1, 1)$?

38. (a) If $Ax = b$ has two solutions x_1 and x_2, find two solutions to $Ax = 0$.
(b) Then find another solution to $Ax = b$.

39. Explain why all these statements are false:

(a) The complete solution is any linear combination of x_p and x_n.
(b) A system $Ax = b$ has at most one particular solution.
(c) The solution x_p with all free variables zero is the shortest solution (minimum length $\|x\|$). (Find a 2 by 2 counterexample.)
(d) If A is invertible there is no solution x_n in the nullspace.

40. Suppose column 5 of U has no pivot. Then x_5 is a ______ variable. The zero vector (is) (is not) the only solution to $Ax = 0$. If $Ax = b$ has a solution, then it has ______ solutions.

41. If you know x_p (free variables = 0) and all special solutions for $Ax = b$, find x_p and all special solutions for these systems:

$$Ax = 2b \qquad \begin{bmatrix} A & A \end{bmatrix} \begin{bmatrix} x \\ X \end{bmatrix} = b \qquad \begin{bmatrix} A \\ A \end{bmatrix} \begin{bmatrix} x \end{bmatrix} = \begin{bmatrix} b \\ b \end{bmatrix}.$$

42. If $Ax = b$ has infinitely many solutions, why is it impossible for $Ax = B$ (new right-hand side) to have only one solution? Could $Ax = B$ have no solution?

43. Choose the number q so that (if possible) the ranks are (a) 1, (b) 2, (c) 3:

$$A = \begin{bmatrix} 6 & 4 & 2 \\ -3 & -2 & -1 \\ 9 & 6 & q \end{bmatrix} \quad \text{and} \quad B = \begin{bmatrix} 3 & 1 & 3 \\ q & 2 & q \end{bmatrix}.$$

44. Give examples of matrices A for which the number of solutions to $Ax = b$ is

(a) 0 or 1, depending on b.
(b) ∞, regardless of b.
(c) 0 or ∞, depending on b.
(d) 1, regardless of b.

45. Write all known relations between r and m and n if $Ax = b$ has

(a) no solution for some b.
(b) infinitely many solutions for every b.
(c) exactly one solution for some b, no solution for other b.
(d) exactly one solution for every b.

46. Apply Gauss–Jordan elimination (right-hand side becomes extra column) to $Ux = 0$ and $Ux = c$. Reach $Rx = 0$ and $Rx = d$:

$$\begin{bmatrix} U & 0 \end{bmatrix} = \begin{bmatrix} 1 & 2 & 3 & \mathbf{0} \\ 0 & 0 & 4 & \mathbf{0} \end{bmatrix} \quad \text{and} \quad \begin{bmatrix} U & c \end{bmatrix} = \begin{bmatrix} 1 & 2 & 3 & \mathbf{5} \\ 0 & 0 & 4 & \mathbf{8} \end{bmatrix}.$$

Solve $Rx = 0$ to find x_n (its free variable is $x_2 = 1$). Solve $Rx = d$ to find x_p (its free variable is $x_2 = 0$).

47. Apply elimination with the extra column to reach $Rx = 0$ and $Rx = d$:

$$\begin{bmatrix} U & 0 \end{bmatrix} = \begin{bmatrix} 3 & 0 & 6 & \mathbf{0} \\ 0 & 0 & 2 & \mathbf{0} \\ 0 & 0 & 0 & \mathbf{0} \end{bmatrix} \quad \text{and} \quad \begin{bmatrix} U & c \end{bmatrix} = \begin{bmatrix} 3 & 0 & 6 & \mathbf{9} \\ 0 & 0 & 2 & \mathbf{4} \\ 0 & 0 & 0 & \mathbf{5} \end{bmatrix}.$$

Solve $Rx = 0$ (free variable $= 1$). What are the solutions to $Rx = d$?

48. Reduce to $Ux = c$ (Gaussian elimination) and then $Rx = d$:

$$Ax = \begin{bmatrix} 1 & 0 & 2 & 3 \\ 1 & 3 & 2 & 0 \\ 2 & 0 & 4 & 9 \end{bmatrix} \begin{bmatrix} x_1 \\ x_2 \\ x_3 \\ x_4 \end{bmatrix} = \begin{bmatrix} 2 \\ 5 \\ 10 \end{bmatrix} = b.$$

Find a particular solution x_p and all nullspace solutions x_n.

49. Find A and B with the given property or explain why you can't.

(a) The only solution to $Ax = \begin{bmatrix} 1 \\ 2 \\ 3 \end{bmatrix}$ is $x = \begin{bmatrix} 0 \\ 1 \end{bmatrix}$.

(b) The only solution to $Bx = \begin{bmatrix} 0 \\ 1 \end{bmatrix}$ is $x = \begin{bmatrix} 1 \\ 2 \\ 3 \end{bmatrix}$.

50. The complete solution to $Ax = \begin{bmatrix} 1 \\ 3 \end{bmatrix}$ is $x = \begin{bmatrix} 1 \\ 0 \end{bmatrix} + c \begin{bmatrix} 0 \\ 1 \end{bmatrix}$. Find A.

51. The nullspace of a 3 by 4 matrix A is the line through $(2, 3, 1, 0)$.

(a) What is the *rank* of A and the complete solution to $Ax = 0$?
(b) What is the exact row reduced echelon form R of A?

52. Reduce these matrices A and B to their ordinary echelon forms U:

$$\text{(a)}\ A = \begin{bmatrix} 1 & 2 & 2 & 4 & 6 \\ 1 & 2 & 3 & 6 & 9 \\ 0 & 0 & 1 & 2 & 3 \end{bmatrix} \qquad \text{(b)}\ B = \begin{bmatrix} 2 & 4 & 2 \\ 0 & 4 & 4 \\ 0 & 8 & 8 \end{bmatrix}.$$

Find a special solution for each free variable and describe every solution to $Ax = 0$ and $Bx = 0$. Reduce the echelon forms U to R, and draw a box around the identity matrix in the pivot rows and pivot columns.

53. True or False? (Give reason if true, or counterexample to show it is false.)

(a) A square matrix has no free variables.
(b) An invertible matrix has no free variables.
(c) An m by n matrix has no more than n pivot variables.
(d) An m by n matrix has no more than m pivot variables.

54. Is there a 3 by 3 matrix with no zero entries for which $U = R = I$?

55. Put as many 1s as possible in a 4 by 7 echelon matrix U and in a *reduced* form R whose pivot columns are 2, 4, 5.

56. Suppose column 4 of a 3 by 5 matrix is all 0s. Then x_4 is certainly a ______ variable. The special solution for this variable is the vector $x =$ ______.

57. Suppose the first and last columns of a 3 by 5 matrix are the same (nonzero). Then ______ is a free variable. Find the special solution for this variable.

58. The equation $x - 3y - z = 0$ determines a plane in $\mathbf{R}^3$. What is the matrix A in this equation? Which are the free variables? The special solutions are $(3, 1, 0)$ and ______. The parallel plane $x - 3y - z = 12$ contains the particular point $(12, 0, 0)$. All points on this plane have the following form (fill in the first components):

$$\begin{bmatrix} x \\ y \\ z \end{bmatrix} = \begin{bmatrix} \ \\ 0 \\ 0 \end{bmatrix} + y \begin{bmatrix} \ \\ 1 \\ 0 \end{bmatrix} + z \begin{bmatrix} \ \\ 0 \\ 1 \end{bmatrix}.$$

59. Suppose column 1 + column 3 + column 5 = 0 in a 4 by 5 matrix with four pivots. Which column is sure to have no pivot (and which variable is free)? What is the special solution? What is the nullspace?

Problems 60–66 ask for matrices (if possible) with specific properties.

60. Construct a matrix whose nullspace consists of all combinations of $(2, 2, 1, 0)$ and $(3, 1, 0, 1)$.

61. Construct a matrix whose nullspace consists of all multiples of $(4, 3, 2, 1)$.

62. Construct a matrix whose column space contains $(1, 1, 5)$ and $(0, 3, 1)$ and whose nullspace contains $(1, 1, 2)$.

63. Construct a matrix whose column space contains $(1, 1, 0)$ and $(0, 1, 1)$ and whose nullspace contains $(1, 0, 1)$ and $(0, 0, 1)$.

64. Construct a matrix whose column space contains $(1, 1, 1)$ and whose nullspace is the line of multiples of $(1, 1, 1, 1)$.

65. Construct a 2 by 2 matrix whose nullspace equals its column space.

66. Why does no 3 by 3 matrix have a nullspace that equals its column space?

67. The reduced form R of a 3 by 3 matrix with randomly chosen entries is almost sure to be ______. What R is virtually certain if the random A is 4 by 3?

68. Show by example that these three statements are generally *false*:

(a) A and A^{T} have the same nullspace.
(b) A and A^{T} have the same free variables.
(c) If R is the reduced form $\mathrm{rref}(A)$ then R^{T} is $\mathrm{rref}(A^{\mathrm{T}})$.

69. If the special solutions to $Rx = 0$ are in the columns of these N, go backward to find the nonzero rows of the reduced matrices R:

$$N = \begin{bmatrix} 2 & 3 \\ 1 & 0 \\ 0 & 1 \end{bmatrix} \quad \text{and} \quad N = \begin{bmatrix} 0 \\ 0 \\ 1 \end{bmatrix} \quad \text{and} \quad N = \begin{bmatrix} \ \end{bmatrix} \quad \text{(empty 3 by 1).}$$

70. Explain why A and $-A$ always have the same reduced echelon form R.

2.3 LINEAR INDEPENDENCE, BASIS, AND DIMENSION

By themselves, the numbers m and n give an incomplete picture of the true size of a linear system. The matrix in our example had three rows and four columns, but the third row was only a combination of the first two. After elimination it became a zero row. It had no effect on the homogeneous problem $Ax = 0$. The four columns also failed to be independent, and the column space degenerated into a two-dimensional plane.

The important number that is beginning to emerge (the true size) is the ***rank r***. The rank was introduced as the *number of pivots* in the elimination process. Equivalently, the final matrix U has r nonzero rows. This definition could be given to a computer. But it would be wrong to leave it there because the rank has a simple and intuitive meaning: *The rank counts the number of genuinely independent rows in the matrix A*. We want definitions that are mathematical rather than computational.

The goal of this section is to explain and use four ideas:

1. Linear independence or dependence.
2. Spanning a subspace.
3. Basis for a subspace (a set of vectors).
4. Dimension of a subspace (a number).

The first step is to define ***linear independence***. Given a set of vectors $v_1, \ldots, v_k$, we look at their combinations $c_1v_1 + c_2v_2 + \cdots + c_kv_k$. The trivial combination, with all weights $c_i = 0$, obviously produces the zero vector: $0v_1 + \cdots + 0v_k = 0$. The question is whether this is the *only way* to produce zero. If so, the vectors are independent.

If any other combination of the vectors gives zero, they are *dependent*.

2E Suppose $c_1v_1 + \cdots + c_kv_k = 0$ only happens when $c_1 = \cdots = c_k = 0$. Then the vectors $v_1, \ldots, v_k$ are ***linearly independent***. If any c's are nonzero, the v's are ***linearly dependent***. One vector is a combination of the others.

Linear dependence is easy to visualize in three-dimensional space, when all vectors go out from the origin. Two vectors are dependent if they lie on the same line. *Three vectors are dependent if they lie in the same plane*. A random choice of three vectors, without any special accident, should produce linear independence (not in a plane). Four vectors are always linearly dependent in $\mathbf{R}^3$.

Example 1 If v_1 = zero vector, then the set is linearly dependent. We may choose $c_1 = 3$ and all other $c_i = 0$; this is a nontrivial combination that produces zero.

Example 2 The columns of the matrix

$$A = \begin{bmatrix} 1 & 3 & 3 & 2 \\ 2 & 6 & 9 & 5 \\ -1 & -3 & 3 & 0 \end{bmatrix}$$

are linearly dependent, since the second column is three times the first. The combination of columns with weights $-3, 1, 0, 0$ gives a column of zeros.

The rows are also linearly dependent; row 3 is two times row 2 minus five times row 1. (This is the same as the combination of b_1, b_2, b_3, that had to vanish on the right-hand side in order for $Ax = b$ to be consistent. Unless $b_3 - 2b_2 + 5b_1 = 0$, the third equation would not become $0 = 0$.)

Example 3 The columns of this triangular matrix are linearly *independent*:

$$\textbf{No zeros on the diagonal} \qquad A = \begin{bmatrix} 3 & 4 & 2 \\ 0 & 1 & 5 \\ 0 & 0 & 2 \end{bmatrix}.$$

Look for a combination of the columns that makes zero:

$$\textbf{Solve } Ac = \mathbf{0} \qquad c_1 \begin{bmatrix} 3 \\ 0 \\ 0 \end{bmatrix} + c_2 \begin{bmatrix} 4 \\ 1 \\ 0 \end{bmatrix} + c_3 \begin{bmatrix} 2 \\ 5 \\ 2 \end{bmatrix} = \begin{bmatrix} 0 \\ 0 \\ 0 \end{bmatrix}.$$

We have to show that c_1, c_2, c_3 are all forced to be zero. The last equation gives $c_3 = 0$. Then the next equation gives $c_2 = 0$, and substituting into the first equation forces $c_1 = 0$. The only combination to produce the zero vector is the trivial combination. ***The nullspace of A contains only the zero vector $c_1 = c_2 = c_3 = \mathbf{0}$.***

> ***The columns of A are independent exactly when $N(A) = \{$zero vector$\}$.***

A similar reasoning applies to the rows of A, which are also independent. Suppose

$$c_1(3, 4, 2) + c_2(0, 1, 5) + c_3(0, 0, 2) = (0, 0, 0).$$

From the first components we find $3c_1 = 0$ or $c_1 = 0$. Then the second components give $c_2 = 0$, and finally $c_3 = 0$.

The nonzero rows of any echelon matrix U must be independent. Furthermore, if we pick out *the columns that contain the pivots*, they also are linearly independent. In our earlier example, with

$$\begin{matrix}\textbf{Two independent rows} \\ \textbf{Two independent columns}\end{matrix} \qquad U = \begin{bmatrix} 1 & 3 & 3 & 2 \\ 0 & 0 & 3 & 1 \\ 0 & 0 & 0 & 0 \end{bmatrix},$$

the pivot columns 1 and 3 are independent. No set of three columns is independent, and certainly not all four. It is true that columns 1 and 4 are also independent, but if that last 1 were changed to 0 they would be dependent. *It is the columns with pivots that are guaranteed to be independent.* The general rule is this:

> **2F** The r nonzero rows of an echelon matrix U and a reduced matrix R are linearly independent. So are the r columns that contain pivots.

Example 4 The columns of the n by n identity matrix are independent:

$$I = \begin{bmatrix} 1 & 0 & \cdot & 0 \\ 0 & 1 & \cdot & 0 \\ \cdot & \cdot & \cdot & 0 \\ 0 & 0 & 0 & 1 \end{bmatrix}.$$

These columns $e_1, \ldots, e_n$ represent unit vectors in the coordinate directions; in $\mathbf{R}^4$,

$$e_1 = \begin{bmatrix} 1 \\ 0 \\ 0 \\ 0 \end{bmatrix}, \quad e_2 = \begin{bmatrix} 0 \\ 1 \\ 0 \\ 0 \end{bmatrix}, \quad e_3 = \begin{bmatrix} 0 \\ 0 \\ 1 \\ 0 \end{bmatrix}, \quad e_4 = \begin{bmatrix} 0 \\ 0 \\ 0 \\ 1 \end{bmatrix}.$$

Most sets of four vectors in $\mathbf{R}^4$ are independent. Those e's might be the safest.

To check any set of vectors $v_1, \ldots, v_n$ for independence, put them in the columns of A. Then solve the system $Ac = 0$; the vectors are dependent if there is a solution other than $c = 0$. With no free variables (*rank n*), there is no nullspace except $c = 0$; the vectors are independent. If the rank is less than n, at least one free variable can be nonzero and the columns are dependent.

One case has special importance. Let the n vectors have m components, so that A is an m by n matrix. Suppose now that $n > m$. There are too many columns to be independent! There cannot be n pivots, since there are not enough rows to hold them. The rank will be less than n. Every system $Ac = 0$ with more unknowns than equations has solutions $c \neq 0$.

2G A set of n vectors in $\mathbf{R}^m$ must be linearly dependent if $n > m$.

The reader will recognize this as a disguised form of 2C: Every m by n system $Ax = 0$ has nonzero solutions if $n > m$.

Example 5 These three columns in $\mathbf{R}^2$ cannot be independent:

$$A = \begin{bmatrix} 1 & 2 & 1 \\ 1 & 3 & 2 \end{bmatrix}.$$

To find the combination of the columns producing zero we solve $Ac = 0$:

$$A \to U = \begin{bmatrix} 1 & 2 & 1 \\ 0 & 1 & 1 \end{bmatrix}.$$

If we give the value 1 to the free variable c_3, then back-substitution in $Uc = 0$ gives $c_2 = -1$, $c_1 = 1$. With these three weights, the first column minus the second plus the third equals zero: Dependence.

Spanning a Subspace

Now we define what it means for a set of vectors to *span a space*. The column space of A is *spanned* by the columns. **Their combinations produce the whole space:**

2H If a vector space $\mathbf{V}$ consists of all linear combinations of $w_1, \ldots, w_\ell$, then these vectors ***span*** the space. Every vector v in $\mathbf{V}$ is some combination of the w's:

Every v comes from w's $\qquad v = c_1 w_1 + \cdots + c_\ell w_\ell \quad$ for some coefficients c_i.

It is permitted that a different combination of w's could give the same vector v. The c's need not be unique, because the spanning set might be excessively large—it could include the zero vector, or even all vectors.

Example 6 The vectors $w_1 = (1, 0, 0)$, $w_2 = (0, 1, 0)$, and $w_3 = (-2, 0, 0)$ span a plane (the x-y plane) in $\mathbf{R}^3$. The first two vectors also span this plane, whereas w_1 and w_3 span only a line.

Example 7 The column space of A is exactly ***the space that is spanned by its columns***. The row space is spanned by the rows. The definition is made to order. Multiplying A by any x gives a combination of the columns; it is a vector Ax in the column space.

The coordinate vectors $e_1, \dots, e_n$ coming from the identity matrix span $\mathbf{R}^n$. Every vector $b = (b_1, \dots, b_n)$ is a combination of those columns. In this example the weights are the components b_i themselves: $b = b_1 e_1 + \cdots + b_n e_n$. But the columns of other matrices also span $\mathbf{R}^n$!

Basis for a Vector Space

To decide if b is a combination of the columns, we try to solve $Ax = b$. To decide if the columns are independent, we solve $Ax = 0$. ***Spanning involves the column space, and independence involves the nullspace***. The coordinate vectors $e_1, \dots, e_n$ span $\mathbf{R}^n$ and they are linearly independent. Roughly speaking, ***no vectors in that set are wasted***. This leads to the crucial idea of a ***basis***.

2I A ***basis*** for $\mathbf{V}$ is a sequence of vectors having two properties at once:

1. The vectors are linearly independent (not too many vectors).

2. They span the space $\mathbf{V}$ (not too few vectors).

This combination of properties is absolutely fundamental to linear algebra. It means that every vector in the space is a combination of the basis vectors, because they span. It also means that the combination is unique: If $v = a_1 v_1 + \cdots + a_k v_k$ and also $v = b_1 v_1 + \cdots + b_k v_k$, then subtraction gives $0 = \sum (a_i - b_i) v_i$. Now independence plays its part; every coefficient $a_i - b_i$ must be zero. Therefore $a_i = b_i$. ***There is one and only one way to write v as a combination of the basis vectors***.

We had better say at once that the coordinate vectors $e_1, \dots, e_n$ are not the only basis for $\mathbf{R}^n$. Some things in linear algebra are unique, but not this. A vector space has ***infinitely many different bases***. Whenever a square matrix is invertible, its columns are independent—and they are a basis for $\mathbf{R}^n$. The two columns of this nonsingular matrix are a basis for $\mathbf{R}^2$:

$$A = \begin{bmatrix} 1 & 1 \\ 2 & 3 \end{bmatrix}$$

Every two-dimensional vector is a combination of those (independent!) columns.

Example 8 The x-y plane in Figure 2.4 is just $\mathbf{R}^2$. The vector v_1 by itself is linearly independent, but it fails to span $\mathbf{R}^2$. The three vectors v_1, v_2, v_3 certainly span $\mathbf{R}^2$, but are not independent. *Any two* of these vectors, say v_1 and v_2, have both properties—they span, and they are independent. So they form a basis. Notice again that *a vector space does not have a unique basis*.

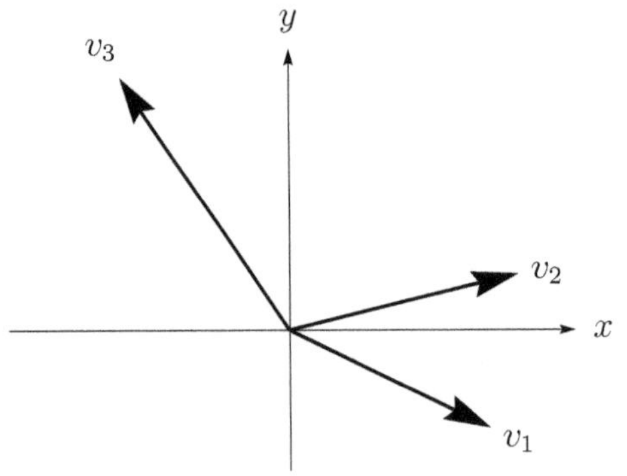

Figure 2.4 A spanning set v_1, v_2, v_3. Bases v_1, v_2 and v_1, v_3 and v_2, v_3.

Example 9 These four columns span the column space of U, but they are not independent:

$$\textbf{Echelon matrix} \qquad U = \begin{bmatrix} 1 & 3 & 3 & 2 \\ 0 & 0 & 3 & 1 \\ 0 & 0 & 0 & 0 \end{bmatrix}.$$

There are many possibilities for a basis, but we propose a specific choice: ***The columns that contain pivots*** (in this case the first and third, which correspond to the basic variables) ***are a basis for the column space***. These columns are independent, and it is easy to see that they span the space. In fact, the column space of U is just the x-y plane within $\mathbf{R}^3$. $\boldsymbol{C}(U)$ is *not the same* as the column space $\boldsymbol{C}(A)$ before elimination—but the *number* of independent columns didn't change.

To summarize: *The columns of any matrix span its column space*. If they are independent, they are a basis for the column space—whether the matrix is square or rectangular. If we are asking the columns to be a basis for the whole space $\mathbf{R}^n$, then the matrix must be square and invertible.

Dimension of a Vector Space

A space has infinitely many different bases, but there is something common to all of these choices. The ***number of basis vectors*** is a property of the space itself:

> **2J** Any two bases for a vector space $\mathbf{V}$ contain the same number of vectors. This number, which is shared by all bases and expresses the number of "degrees of freedom" of the space, is the ***dimension*** of $\mathbf{V}$.

We have to prove this fact: All possible bases contain the same number of vectors. The x-y plane in Figure 2.4 has two vectors in every basis; its dimension is 2.

In three dimensions we need three vectors, along the x-y-z axes or in three other (linearly independent!) directions. ***The dimension of the space*** $\mathbf{R}^n$ ***is*** n. The column space of U in Example 9 had dimension 2; it was a "two-dimensional subspace of $\mathbf{R}^3$." The zero matrix is rather exceptional, because its column space contains only the zero vector. By convention, the empty set is a basis for that space, and its dimension is zero.

Here is our first big theorem in linear algebra:

2K If $v_1, \ldots, v_m$ and $w_1, \ldots, w_n$ are both bases for the same vector space, then $m = n$. The number of vectors is the same.

Proof Suppose there are more w's than v's ($n > m$). We will arrive at a contradiction. Since the v's form a basis, they must span the space. *Every* w_j *can be written as a combination of the* v*'s*: If $w_1 = a_{11}v_1 + \cdots + a_{m1}v_m$, this is the first column of a matrix multiplication VA:

$$W = \begin{bmatrix} w_1 & w_2 & \ldots & w_n \end{bmatrix} = \begin{bmatrix} v_1 & \ldots & v_m \end{bmatrix} \begin{bmatrix} a_{11} & & \\ \vdots & & \\ a_{m1} & & \end{bmatrix} = VA.$$

We don't know each a_{ij}, but we know the shape of A (it is m by n). The second vector w_2 is also a combination of the v's. The coefficients in that combination fill the second column of A. The key is that A has a row for every v and a column for every w. A is a short, wide matrix, since $n > m$. ***There is a nonzero solution to*** $Ax = \mathbf{0}$. Then $VAx = 0$ which is $Wx = 0$. *A combination of the* w*'s gives zero!* The w's could not be a basis—so we cannot have $n > m$.

If $m > n$ we exchange the v's and w's and repeat the same steps. The only way to avoid a contradiction is to have $m = n$. This completes the proof that $m = n$. To repeat: The ***dimension of a space*** is the number of vectors in every basis. ■

This proof was used earlier to show that every set of $m + 1$ vectors in $\mathbf{R}^m$ must be dependent. The v's and w's need not be column vectors—the proof was all about the matrix A of coefficients. In fact we can see this general result: *In a subspace of dimension* k*, no set of more than* k *vectors can be independent, and no set of fewer than* k *vectors can span the space.*

There are other "dual" theorems, of which we mention only one. We can start with a set of vectors that is too small or too big, and end up with a basis:

2L Any linearly independent set in $\mathbf{V}$ can be extended to a basis, by adding more vectors if necessary.

Any spanning set in $\mathbf{V}$ can be reduced to a basis, by discarding vectors if necessary.

The point is that a basis is a ***maximal independent set***. It cannot be made larger without losing independence. A basis is also a ***minimal spanning set***. It cannot be made smaller and still span the space.

You must notice that the word "dimensional" is used in two different ways. We speak about a four-dimensional ***vector***, meaning a vector in $\mathbf{R}^4$. Now we have defined a four-dimensional ***subspace***; an example is the set of vectors in $\mathbf{R}^6$ whose first and last components are zero. The members of this four-dimensional subspace are six-dimensional vectors like $(0, 5, 1, 3, 4, 0)$.

One final note about the language of linear algebra. We never use the terms "basis of a matrix" or "rank of a space" or "dimension of a basis." These phrases have no meaning. It is *the dimension of the column space* that equals *the rank of the matrix*, as we prove in the coming section.

Problem Set 2.3

Problems 1–10 are about linear independence and linear dependence.

1. Show that v_1, v_2, v_3 are independent but v_1, v_2, v_3, v_4 are dependent:

$$v_1 = \begin{bmatrix}1\\0\\0\end{bmatrix} \quad v_2 = \begin{bmatrix}1\\1\\0\end{bmatrix} \quad v_3 = \begin{bmatrix}1\\1\\1\end{bmatrix} \quad v_4 = \begin{bmatrix}2\\3\\4\end{bmatrix}.$$

Solve $c_1v_1 + \cdots + c_4v_4 = 0$ or $Ac = 0$. The v's go in the columns of A.

2. Find the largest possible number of independent vectors among

$$v_1 = \begin{bmatrix}1\\-1\\0\\0\end{bmatrix} \quad v_2 = \begin{bmatrix}1\\0\\-1\\0\end{bmatrix} \quad v_3 = \begin{bmatrix}1\\0\\0\\-1\end{bmatrix} \quad v_4 = \begin{bmatrix}0\\1\\-1\\0\end{bmatrix} \quad v_5 = \begin{bmatrix}0\\1\\0\\-1\end{bmatrix} \quad v_6 = \begin{bmatrix}0\\0\\1\\-1\end{bmatrix}.$$

This number is the ______ of the space spanned by the v's.

3. Prove that if $a = 0$, $d = 0$, or $f = 0$ (3 cases), the columns of U are dependent:

$$U = \begin{bmatrix}a & b & c\\0 & d & e\\0 & 0 & f\end{bmatrix}.$$

4. If a, d, f in Problem 3 are all nonzero, show that the only solution to $Ux = 0$ is $x = 0$. Then U has independent columns.

5. Decide the dependence or independence of

(a) the vectors $(1, 3, 2)$, $(2, 1, 3)$, and $(3, 2, 1)$.
(b) the vectors $(1, -3, 2)$, $(2, 1, -3)$, and $(-3, 2, 1)$.

6. Choose three independent columns of U. Then make two other choices. Do the same for A. You have found bases for which spaces?

$$U = \begin{bmatrix}2 & 3 & 4 & 1\\0 & 6 & 7 & 0\\0 & 0 & 0 & 9\\0 & 0 & 0 & 0\end{bmatrix} \quad \text{and} \quad A = \begin{bmatrix}2 & 3 & 4 & 1\\0 & 6 & 7 & 0\\0 & 0 & 0 & 9\\4 & 6 & 8 & 2\end{bmatrix}.$$

7. If w_1, w_2, w_3 are independent vectors, show that the differences $v_1 = w_2 - w_3$, $v_2 = w_1 - w_3$, and $v_3 = w_1 - w_2$ are *dependent*. Find a combination of the v's that gives zero.

8. If w_1, w_2, w_3 are independent vectors, show that the sums $v_1 = w_2 + w_3$, $v_2 = w_1 + w_3$, and $v_3 = w_1 + w_2$ are *independent*. (Write $c_1v_1 + c_2v_2 + c_3v_3 = 0$ in terms of the w's. Find and solve equations for the c's.)

9. Suppose v_1, v_2, v_3, v_4 are vectors in $\mathbf{R}^3$.

(a) These four vectors are dependent because ______.
(b) The two vectors v_1 and v_2 will be dependent if ______.
(c) The vectors v_1 and $(0, 0, 0)$ are dependent because ______.

10. Find two independent vectors on the plane $x + 2y - 3z - t = 0$ in $\mathbf{R}^4$. Then find three independent vectors. Why not four? This plane is the nullspace of what matrix?

Problems 11–18 are about the space *spanned* by a set of vectors. Take all linear combinations of the vectors.

11. Describe the subspace of $\mathbf{R}^3$ (is it a line or a plane or $\mathbf{R}^3$?) spanned by

(a) the two vectors $(1, 1, -1)$ and $(-1, -1, 1)$.
(b) the three vectors $(0, 1, 1)$ and $(1, 1, 0)$ and $(0, 0, 0)$.
(c) the columns of a 3 by 5 echelon matrix with 2 pivots.
(d) all vectors with positive components.

12. The vector b is in the subspace spanned by the columns of A when there is a solution to ______. The vector c is in the row space of A when there is a solution to ______. *True or false*: If the zero vector is in the row space, the rows are dependent.

13. Find the dimensions of (a) the column space of A, (b) the column space of U, (c) the row space of A, (d) the row space of U. Which two of the spaces are the same?

$$A = \begin{bmatrix} 1 & 1 & 0 \\ 1 & 3 & 1 \\ 3 & 1 & -1 \end{bmatrix} \quad \text{and} \quad U = \begin{bmatrix} 1 & 1 & 0 \\ 0 & 2 & 1 \\ 0 & 0 & 0 \end{bmatrix}.$$

14. Choose $x = (x_1, x_2, x_3, x_4)$ in $\mathbf{R}^4$. It has 24 rearrangements like (x_2, x_1, x_3, x_4) and (x_4, x_3, x_1, x_2). Those 24 vectors, including x itself, span a subspace $\mathbf{S}$. Find specific vectors x so that the dimension of $\mathbf{S}$ is: (a) 0, (b) 1, (c) 3, (d) 4.

15. $v + w$ and $v - w$ are combinations of v and w. Write v and w as combinations of $v + w$ and $v - w$. The two pairs of vectors ______ the same space. When are they a basis for the same space?

16. Decide whether or not the following vectors are linearly independent, by solving $c_1v_1 + c_2v_2 + c_3v_3 + c_4v_4 = 0$:

$$v_1 = \begin{bmatrix} 1 \\ 1 \\ 0 \\ 0 \end{bmatrix}, \quad v_2 = \begin{bmatrix} 1 \\ 0 \\ 1 \\ 0 \end{bmatrix}, \quad v_3 = \begin{bmatrix} 0 \\ 0 \\ 1 \\ 1 \end{bmatrix}, \quad v_4 = \begin{bmatrix} 0 \\ 1 \\ 0 \\ 1 \end{bmatrix}.$$

Decide also if they span $\mathbf{R}^4$, by trying to solve $c_1v_1 + \cdots + c_4v_4 = (0, 0, 0, 1)$.

17. Suppose the vectors to be tested for independence are placed into the rows instead of the columns of A. How does the elimination process from A to U decide for or against independence?

18. To decide whether b is in the subspace spanned by $w_1, \ldots, w_n$, let the vectors w be the columns of A and try to solve $Ax = b$. What is the result for

(a) $w_1 = (1, 1, 0)$, $w_2 = (2, 2, 1)$, $w_3 = (0, 0, 2)$, $b = (3, 4, 5)$?
(b) $w_1 = (1, 2, 0)$, $w_2 = (2, 5, 0)$, $w_3 = (0, 0, 2)$, $w_4 = (0, 0, 0)$, and any b?

Problems 19–37 are about the requirements for a basis.

19. If $v_1, \ldots, v_n$ are linearly independent, the space they span has dimension ______. These vectors are a ______ for that space. If the vectors are the columns of an m by n matrix, then m is ______ than n.

20. Find a basis for each of these subspaces of $\mathbf{R}^4$:

(a) All vectors whose components are equal.
(b) All vectors whose components add to zero.
(c) All vectors that are perpendicular to $(1, 1, 0, 0)$ and $(1, 0, 1, 1)$.
(d) The column space (in $\mathbf{R}^2$) and nullspace (in $\mathbf{R}^5$) of $U = \begin{bmatrix} 1 & 0 & 1 & 0 & 1 \\ 0 & 1 & 0 & 1 & 0 \end{bmatrix}$.

21. Find three different bases for the column space of U above. Then find two different bases for the row space of U.

22. Suppose $v_1, v_2, \ldots, v_6$ are six vectors in $\mathbf{R}^4$.

(a) Those vectors (do)(do not)(might not) span $\mathbf{R}^4$.
(b) Those vectors (are)(are not)(might be) linearly independent.
(c) Any four of those vectors (are)(are not)(might be) a basis for $\mathbf{R}^4$.
(d) If those vectors are the columns of A, then $Ax = b$ (has) (does not have) (might not have) a solution.

23. The columns of A are n vectors from $\mathbf{R}^m$. If they are linearly independent, what is the rank of A? If they span $\mathbf{R}^m$, what is the rank? If they are a basis for $\mathbf{R}^m$, what then?

24. Find a basis for the plane $x - 2y + 3z = 0$ in $\mathbf{R}^3$. Then find a basis for the intersection of that plane with the xy-plane. Then find a basis for all vectors perpendicular to the plane.

25. Suppose the columns of a 5 by 5 matrix A are a basis for $\mathbf{R}^5$.

(a) The equation $Ax = 0$ has only the solution $x = 0$ because ______.
(b) If b is in $\mathbf{R}^5$ then $Ax = b$ is solvable because ______.

Conclusion: A is invertible. Its rank is 5.

26. Suppose $\mathbf{S}$ is a five-dimensional subspace of $\mathbf{R}^6$. True or false?

(a) Every basis for $\mathbf{S}$ can be extended to a basis for $\mathbf{R}^6$ by adding one more vector.
(b) Every basis for $\mathbf{R}^6$ can be reduced to a basis for $\mathbf{S}$ by removing one vector.

27. U comes from A by subtracting row 1 from row 3:

$$A = \begin{bmatrix} 1 & 3 & 2 \\ 0 & 1 & 1 \\ 1 & 3 & 2 \end{bmatrix} \quad \text{and} \quad U = \begin{bmatrix} 1 & 3 & 2 \\ 0 & 1 & 1 \\ 0 & 0 & 0 \end{bmatrix}.$$

Find bases for the two column spaces. Find bases for the two row spaces. Find bases for the two nullspaces.

28. True or false (give a good reason)?

(a) If the columns of a matrix are dependent, so are the rows.
(b) The column space of a 2 by 2 matrix is the same as its row space.
(c) The column space of a 2 by 2 matrix has the same dimension as its row space.
(d) The columns of a matrix are a basis for the column space.

29. For which numbers c and d do these matrices have rank 2?

$$A = \begin{bmatrix} 1 & 2 & 5 & 0 & 5 \\ 0 & 0 & c & 2 & 2 \\ 0 & 0 & 0 & d & 2 \end{bmatrix} \quad \text{and} \quad B = \begin{bmatrix} c & d \\ d & c \end{bmatrix}.$$

30. By locating the pivots, find a basis for the column space of

$$U = \begin{bmatrix} 0 & 5 & 4 & 3 \\ 0 & 0 & 2 & 1 \\ 0 & 0 & 0 & 0 \\ 0 & 0 & 0 & 0 \end{bmatrix}.$$

Express each column that is not in the basis as a combination of the basic columns. Find also a matrix A with this echelon form U, but a different column space.

31. Find a counterexample to the following statement: If v_1, v_2, v_3, v_4 is a basis for the vector space $\mathbf{R}^4$, and if $\mathbf{W}$ is a subspace, then some subset of the v's is a basis for $\mathbf{W}$.

32. Find the dimensions of these vector spaces:

(a) The space of all vectors in $\mathbf{R}^4$ whose components add to zero.
(b) The nullspace of the 4 by 4 identity matrix.
(c) The space of all 4 by 4 matrices.

33. Suppose $\mathbf{V}$ is known to have dimension k. Prove that

(a) any k independent vectors in $\mathbf{V}$ form a basis;
(b) any k vectors that span $\mathbf{V}$ form a basis.

In other words, if the number of vectors is known to be correct, either of the two properties of a basis implies the other.

34. Prove that if $\mathbf{V}$ and $\mathbf{W}$ are three-dimensional subspaces of $\mathbf{R}^5$, then $\mathbf{V}$ and $\mathbf{W}$ must have a nonzero vector in common. *Hint*: Start with bases for the two subspaces, making six vectors in all.

35. *True or false*?

(a) If the columns of A are linearly independent, then $Ax = b$ has exactly one solution for every b.
(b) A 5 by 7 matrix never has linearly independent columns.

36. If A is a 64 by 17 matrix of rank 11, how many independent vectors satisfy $Ax = 0$? How many independent vectors satisfy $A^{\mathrm{T}}y = 0$?

37. Find a basis for each of these subspaces of 3 by 3 matrices:

(a) All diagonal matrices.
(b) All symmetric matrices ($A^{\mathrm{T}} = A$).
(c) All skew-symmetric matrices ($A^{\mathrm{T}} = -A$).

Problems 38–42 are about spaces in which the "vectors" are functions.

38. (a) Find all functions that satisfy $\frac{dy}{dx} = 0$.
(b) Choose a particular function that satisfies $\frac{dy}{dx} = 3$.
(c) Find all functions that satisfy $\frac{dy}{dx} = 3$.

39. The cosine space $\mathbf{F}_3$ contains all combinations $y(x) = A\cos x + B\cos 2x + C\cos 3x$. Find a basis for the subspace that has $y(0) = 0$.

40. Find a basis for the space of functions that satisfy

(a) $\dfrac{dy}{dx} - 2y = 0$.

(b) $\dfrac{dy}{dx} - \dfrac{y}{x} = 0$.

41. Suppose $y_1(x)$, $y_2(x)$, $y_3(x)$ are three different functions of x. The vector space they span could have dimension 1, 2, or 3. Give an example of y_1, y_2, y_3 to show each possibility.

42. Find a basis for the space of polynomials $p(x)$ of degree ≤ 3. Find a basis for the subspace with $p(1) = 0$.

43. Write the 3 by 3 identity matrix as a combination of the other five permutation matrices! Then show that those five matrices are linearly independent. (Assume a combination gives zero, and check entries to prove each term is zero.) The five permutations are a basis for the subspace of 3 by 3 matrices with row and column sums all equal.

44. *Review*: Which of the following are bases for $\mathbf{R}^3$?

(a) $(1, 2, 0)$ and $(0, 1, -1)$.
(b) $(1, 1, -1), (2, 3, 4), (4, 1, -1), (0, 1, -1)$.
(c) $(1, 2, 2), (-1, 2, 1), (0, 8, 0)$.
(d) $(1, 2, 2), (-1, 2, 1), (0, 8, 6)$.

45. *Review*: Suppose A is 5 by 4 with rank 4. Show that $Ax = b$ has no solution when the 5 by 5 matrix $[A \;\; b]$ is invertible. Show that $Ax = b$ is solvable when $[A \;\; b]$ is singular.

2.4 THE FOUR FUNDAMENTAL SUBSPACES

The previous section dealt with definitions rather than constructions. We know what a basis is, but not how to find one. Now, starting from an explicit description of a subspace, we would like to compute an explicit basis.

Subspaces can be described in two ways. First, we may be given a set of vectors that span the space. (*Example*: The columns span the column space.) Second, we may be told which conditions the vectors in the space must satisfy. (*Example*: The nullspace consists of all vectors that satisfy $Ax = 0$.)

The first description may include useless vectors (dependent columns). The second description may include repeated conditions (dependent rows). We can't write a basis by inspection, and a systematic procedure is necessary.

The reader can guess what that procedure will be. When elimination on A produces an echelon matrix U or a reduced R, we will find a basis for each of the subspaces associated with A. Then we have to look at the extreme case of **full rank**:

> *When the rank is as large as possible, $r = n$ or $r = m$ or $r = m = n$, the matrix has a* **left-inverse** *B or a* **right-inverse** *C or a* **two-sided** *A^{-1}.*

To organize the whole discussion, we take each of the four subspaces in turn. Two of them are familiar and two are new.

1. The ***column space*** of A is denoted by $C(A)$. Its dimension is the rank r.
2. The ***nullspace*** of A is denoted by $N(A)$. Its dimension is $n - r$.
3. The ***row space*** of A is the *column space* of A^T. It is $C(A^T)$, and it is spanned by the rows of A. Its dimension is also r.
4. The ***left nullspace*** of A is the *nullspace of* A^T. It contains all vectors y such that $A^Ty = 0$, and it is written $N(A^T)$. Its dimension is ______.

The point about the last two subspaces is that *they come from* A^T. If A is an m by n matrix, you can see which "host" spaces contain the four subspaces by looking at the number of components:

> The nullspace $N(A)$ and row space $C(A^T)$ are subspaces of $\mathbf{R}^n$.
> The left nullspace $N(A^T)$ and column space $C(A)$ are subspaces of $\mathbf{R}^m$.

The rows have n components and the columns have m. For a simple matrix like

$$A = U = R = \begin{bmatrix} 1 & 0 & 0 \\ 0 & 0 & 0 \end{bmatrix},$$

the column space is the line through $\begin{bmatrix} 1 \\ 0 \end{bmatrix}$. The row space is the line through $\begin{bmatrix} 1 & 0 & 0 \end{bmatrix}^T$. It is in $\mathbf{R}^3$. The nullspace is a plane in $\mathbf{R}^3$ and the left nullspace is a line in $\mathbf{R}^2$:

$$N(A) \text{ contains } \begin{bmatrix} 0 \\ 1 \\ 0 \end{bmatrix} \text{ and } \begin{bmatrix} 0 \\ 0 \\ 1 \end{bmatrix}, \qquad N(A^T) \text{ contains } \begin{bmatrix} 0 \\ 1 \end{bmatrix}.$$

Note that all vectors are column vectors. Even the rows are transposed, and the row space of A is the *column* space of A^T. Our problem will be to connect the four spaces for U (after elimination) to the four spaces for A:

Basic example

$$U = \begin{bmatrix} 1 & 3 & 3 & 2 \\ 0 & 0 & 3 & 3 \\ 0 & 0 & 0 & 0 \end{bmatrix} \quad \text{came from} \quad A = \begin{bmatrix} 1 & 3 & 3 & 2 \\ 2 & 6 & 9 & 7 \\ -1 & -3 & 3 & 4 \end{bmatrix}.$$

For novelty, we take the four subspaces in a more interesting order.

3. The row space of A For an echelon matrix like U, the row space is clear. It contains all combinations of the rows, as every row space does—but here the third row contributes nothing. The first two rows are a basis for the row space. A similar rule applies to every echelon matrix U or R, with r pivots and r nonzero rows: ***The nonzero rows are a basis, and the row space has dimension r***. That makes it easy to deal with the original matrix A.

2M The row space of A has the same dimension r as the row space of U, and it has the same bases, because ***the row spaces of A and U (and R) are the same***.

The reason is that each elementary operation leaves the row space unchanged. The rows in U are combinations of the original rows in A. Therefore the row space of U contains nothing new. At the same time, because every step can be reversed, nothing is lost; the rows of A can be recovered from U. It is true that A and U have different rows, but the *combinations* of the rows are identical: *same space*!

Note that we did not start with the m rows of A, which span the row space, and discard $m - r$ of them to end up with a basis. According to 2L, we could have done so. But it might be hard to decide which rows to keep and which to discard, so it was easier just to take the nonzero rows of U.

2. **The nullspace of A** Elimination simplifies a system of linear equations without changing the solutions. The system $Ax = 0$ is reduced to $Ux = 0$, and this process is reversible. ***The nullspace of A is the same as the nullspace of U and R***. Only r of the equations $Ax = 0$ are independent. Choosing the $n - r$ "special solutions" to $Ax = 0$ provides a definite basis for the nullspace:

2N The nullspace $N(A)$ has dimension $n - r$. The "special solutions" are a basis—each free variable is given the value 1, while the other free variables are 0. Then $Ax = 0$ or $Ux = 0$ or $Rx = 0$ gives the pivot variables by back-substitution.

This is exactly the way we have been solving $Ux = 0$. The basic example above has pivots in columns 1 and 3. Therefore its free variables are the second and fourth v and y. The basis for the nullspace is

$$\textbf{Special solutions}\qquad \begin{matrix} v = 1 \\ y = 0 \end{matrix} \quad x_1 = \begin{bmatrix} -3 \\ 1 \\ 0 \\ 0 \end{bmatrix}; \qquad \begin{matrix} v = 0 \\ y = 1 \end{matrix} \quad x_2 = \begin{bmatrix} 1 \\ 0 \\ -1 \\ 1 \end{bmatrix}.$$

Any combination $c_1x_1 + c_2x_2$ has c_1 as its v component, and c_2 as its y component. The only way to have $c_1x_1 + c_2x_2 = 0$ is to have $c_1 = c_2 = 0$, so these vectors are independent. They also span the nullspace; the complete solution is $vx_1 + yx_2$. Thus the $n - r = 4 - 2$ vectors are a basis.

The nullspace is also called the *kernel* of A, and its dimension $n - r$ is the *nullity*.

1. **The column space of A** The column space is sometimes called the **range**. This is consistent with the usual idea of the range, as the set of all possible values $f(x)$; x is in the domain and $f(x)$ is in the range. In our case the function is $f(x) = Ax$. Its domain consists of all x in $\mathbf{R}^n$; its range is all possible vectors Ax, which is the column space. (In an earlier edition of this book we called it $R(A)$.)

Our problem is to find bases for the column spaces of U and A. ***Those spaces are different*** (just look at the matrices!) but their dimensions are the same.

The first and third columns of U are a basis for its column space. They are the ***columns with pivots***. Every other column is a combination of those two. Furthermore, the same is true of the original A—even though its columns are different. ***The pivot columns of A are a basis for its column space.*** The second column is three times the first, just as in U. The fourth column equals (column 3) − (column 1). The same nullspace is telling us those dependencies.

The reason is this: $Ax = 0$ *exactly when* $Ux = 0$. The two systems are equivalent and have the same solutions. The fourth column of U was also (column 3) − (column 1). Every linear dependence $Ax = 0$ among the columns of A is matched by a dependence $Ux = 0$ among the columns of U, with exactly the same coefficients. *If a set of columns of A is independent, then so are the corresponding columns of U, and vice versa.*

To find a basis for the column space $\boldsymbol{C}(A)$, we use what is already done for U. The r columns containing pivots are a basis for the column space of U. We will pick those same r columns in A:

20 The dimension of the column space $\boldsymbol{C}(A)$ equals the rank r, which also equals the dimension of the row space: ***The number of independent columns equals the number of independent rows.*** A basis for $\boldsymbol{C}(A)$ is formed by the r columns of A that correspond, in U, to the columns containing pivots.

The row space and the column space have the same dimension r! This is one of the most important theorems in linear algebra. It is often abbreviated as "***row rank = column rank.***" It expresses a result that, for a random 10 by 12 matrix, is not at all obvious. It also says something about square matrices: *If the rows of a square matrix are linearly independent, then so are the columns* (and vice versa). Again, that does not seem self-evident (at least, not to the author).

To see once more that both the row and column spaces of U have dimension r, consider a typical situation with rank $r = 3$. The echelon matrix U certainly has three independent rows:

$$U = \begin{bmatrix} d_1 & * & * & * & * & * \\ 0 & 0 & 0 & d_2 & * & * \\ 0 & 0 & 0 & 0 & 0 & d_3 \\ 0 & 0 & 0 & 0 & 0 & 0 \end{bmatrix}.$$

We claim that U also has three independent columns, and no more. The columns have only three nonzero components. If we can show that the pivot columns—the first, fourth, and sixth—are linearly independent, they must be a basis (for the column space of U, not A!). Suppose a combination of these pivot columns produced zero:

$$c_1 \begin{bmatrix} d_1 \\ 0 \\ 0 \\ 0 \end{bmatrix} + c_2 \begin{bmatrix} * \\ d_2 \\ 0 \\ 0 \end{bmatrix} + c_3 \begin{bmatrix} * \\ * \\ d_3 \\ 0 \end{bmatrix} = \begin{bmatrix} 0 \\ 0 \\ 0 \\ 0 \end{bmatrix}.$$

Working upward in the usual way, c_3 must be zero because the pivot $d_3 \neq 0$, then c_2 must be zero because $d_2 \neq 0$, and finally $c_1 = 0$. This establishes independence and completes the proof. Since $Ax = 0$ if and only if $Ux = 0$, the first, fourth, and sixth columns of A—whatever the original matrix A was, which we do not even know in this example—are a basis for $\boldsymbol{C}(A)$.

The row space and column space both became clear after elimination on A. Now comes the fourth fundamental subspace, which has been keeping quietly out of sight. Since the first three spaces were $\boldsymbol{C}(A)$, $\boldsymbol{N}(A)$, and $\boldsymbol{C}(A^{\mathrm{T}})$, the fourth space must be $\boldsymbol{N}(A^{\mathrm{T}})$. It is the nullspace of the transpose, or the ***left nullspace*** of A. $A^{\mathrm{T}}y = 0$ means $y^{\mathrm{T}}A = 0$, and the vector appears on the left-hand side of A.

4. The left nullspace of A (= the nullspace of A^{T}) If A is an m by n matrix, then A^{T} is n by m. Its nullspace is a subspace of $\mathbf{R}^m$; the vector y has m components. Written as $y^{\mathrm{T}}A = 0$, those components multiply the *rows* of A to produce the zero row:

$$y^{\mathrm{T}}A = \begin{bmatrix} y_1 & \cdots & y_m \end{bmatrix} \begin{bmatrix} & & \\ & A & \\ & & \end{bmatrix} = \begin{bmatrix} 0 & \cdots & 0 \end{bmatrix}.$$

The dimension of this nullspace $\boldsymbol{N}(A^{\mathrm{T}})$ is easy to find. For *any* matrix, ***the number of pivot variables plus the number of free variables must match the total number of columns***. For A, that was $r + (n - r) = n$. In other words, rank plus nullity equals n:

dimension of $\boldsymbol{C}(A)$ + dimension of $\boldsymbol{N}(A)$ = number of columns.

This law applies equally to A^{T}, which has m columns. A^{T} is just as good a matrix as A. But the dimension of its column space is also r, so

$$r + \text{dimension } (\boldsymbol{N}(A^{\mathrm{T}})) = m. \tag{1}$$

2P The left nullspace $\boldsymbol{N}(A^{\mathrm{T}})$ has dimension $m - r$.

The $m - r$ solutions to $y^{\mathrm{T}}A = 0$ are hiding somewhere in elimination. The rows of A combine to produce the $m - r$ *zero rows* of U. Start from $PA = LU$, or $L^{-1}PA = U$. The last $m - r$ rows of the invertible matrix $L^{-1}P$ must be a basis of y's in the left nullspace—because they multiply A to give the zero rows in U.

In our 3 by 4 example, the zero row was row 3 − 2(row 2) + 5(row 1). Therefore the components of y are $5, -2, 1$. This is the same combination as in $b_3 - 2b_2 + 5b_1$ on the right-hand side, leading to $0 = 0$ as the final equation. That vector y is a basis for the left nullspace, which has dimension $m - r = 3 - 2 = 1$. It is the last row of $L^{-1}P$, and produces the zero row in U—and we can often see it without computing L^{-1}. When desperate, it is always possible just to solve $A^{\mathrm{T}}y = 0$.

I realize that so far in this book we have given no reason to care about $\boldsymbol{N}(A^{\mathrm{T}})$. It is correct but not convincing if I write in italics that *the left nullspace is also important*. The next section does better by finding a physical meaning for y from Kirchhoff's Current Law.

Now we know the dimensions of the four spaces. We can summarize them in a table, and it even seems fair to advertise them as the

Fundamental Theorem of Linear Algebra, Part I

1. $\boldsymbol{C}(A)$ = column space of A; dimension r.
2. $\boldsymbol{N}(A)$ = nullspace of A; dimension $n - r$.
3. $\boldsymbol{C}(A^{\mathrm{T}})$ = row space of A; dimension r.
4. $\boldsymbol{N}(A^{\mathrm{T}})$ = left nullspace of A; dimension $m - r$.

Example 1 $A = \begin{bmatrix} 1 & 2 \\ 3 & 6 \end{bmatrix}$ has $m = n = 2$, and rank $r = 1$.

1. The ***column space*** contains all multiples of $\left[\begin{smallmatrix} 1 \\ 3 \end{smallmatrix}\right]$. The second column is in the same direction and contributes nothing new.
2. The ***nullspace*** contains all multiples of $\left[\begin{smallmatrix} -2 \\ 1 \end{smallmatrix}\right]$. This vector satisfies $Ax = 0$.
3. The ***row space*** contains all multiples of $\left[\begin{smallmatrix} 1 \\ 2 \end{smallmatrix}\right]$. I write it as a column vector, since strictly speaking it is in the column space of A^{T}.
4. The ***left nullspace*** contains all multiples of $y = \left[\begin{smallmatrix} -3 \\ 1 \end{smallmatrix}\right]$. The rows of A with coefficients -3 and 1 add to zero, so $A^{\mathrm{T}}y = 0$.

In this example *all four subspaces are lines*. That is an accident, coming from $r = 1$ and $n - r = 1$ and $m - r = 1$. Figure 2.5 shows that two pairs of lines are perpendicular. That is no accident!

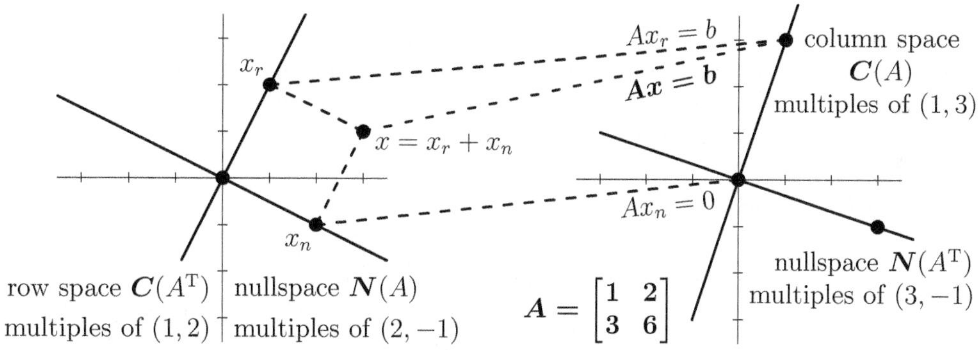

Figure 2.5 The four fundamental subspaces (lines) for the singular matrix A.

If you change the last entry of A from 6 to 7, all the dimensions are different. The column space and row space have dimension $r = 2$. The nullspace and left nullspace contain only the vectors $x = 0$ and $y = 0$. *The matrix is invertible.*

Existence of Inverses

We know that if A has a left-inverse ($BA = I$) and a right-inverse ($AC = I$), then the two inverses are equal: $B = B(AC) = (BA)C = C$. Now, from the rank of a matrix, it is easy to decide which matrices actually have these inverses. Roughly speaking, ***an inverse exists only when the rank is as large as possible***.

The rank always satisfies $r \leq m$ and also $r \leq n$. An m by n matrix cannot have more than m independent rows or n independent columns. There is not space for more than m pivots, or more than n. We want to prove that when $r = m$ there is a right-inverse, and $Ax = b$ always has a solution. When $r = n$ there is a left-inverse, and the solution (*if it exists*) is unique.

Only a square matrix can have both $r = m$ and $r = n$, and therefore only a square matrix can achieve both existence and uniqueness. Only a square matrix has a two-sided inverse.

2Q EXISTENCE: Full row rank $r = m$. $Ax = b$ has ***at least*** one solution x for every b if and only if the columns span $\mathbf{R}^m$. Then A has a **right-inverse** C such that $AC = I_m$ (m by m). This is possible only if $m \leq n$.

UNIQUENESS: Full column rank $r = n$. $Ax = b$ has ***at most*** one solution x for every b if and only if the columns are linearly independent. Then A has an n by m **left-inverse** B such that $BA = I_n$. This is possible only if $m \geq n$.

In the existence case, one possible solution is $x = Cb$, since then $Ax = ACb = b$. But there will be other solutions if there are other right-inverses. The number of solutions when the columns span $\mathbf{R}^m$ is 1 or ∞.

In the uniqueness case, if there is a solution to $Ax = b$, it has to be $x = BAx = Bb$. But there may be no solution. The number of solutions is 0 or 1.

There are simple formulas for the best left and right inverses, if they exist:

$$\textbf{One-sided inverses} \qquad B = (A^{\mathrm{T}}A)^{-1}A^{\mathrm{T}} \qquad \text{and} \qquad C = A^{\mathrm{T}}(AA^{\mathrm{T}})^{-1}.$$

Certainly $BA = I$ and $AC = I$. What is not so certain is that $A^{\mathrm{T}}A$ and AA^{T} are actually invertible. We show in Chapter 3 that $A^{\mathrm{T}}A$ does have an inverse if the rank is n, and AA^{T} has an inverse when the rank is m. Thus the formulas make sense exactly when the rank is as large as possible, and the one-sided inverses are found.

Example 2 Consider a simple 2 by 3 matrix of rank 2:

$$A = \begin{bmatrix} 4 & 0 & 0 \\ 0 & 5 & 0 \end{bmatrix}.$$

Since $r = m = 2$, the theorem guarantees a right-inverse C:

$$AC = \begin{bmatrix} 4 & 0 & 0 \\ 0 & 5 & 0 \end{bmatrix} \begin{bmatrix} \frac{1}{4} & 0 \\ 0 & \frac{1}{5} \\ c_{31} & c_{32} \end{bmatrix} = \begin{bmatrix} 1 & 0 \\ 0 & 1 \end{bmatrix}.$$

There are many right-inverses because the last row of C is completely arbitrary. This is a case of existence but not uniqueness. The matrix A has no left-inverse because the last column of BA is certain to be zero. The specific right-inverse $C = A^{\mathrm{T}}(AA^{\mathrm{T}})^{-1}$ chooses c_{31} and c_{32} to be zero:

$$\textbf{Best right-inverse} \qquad A^{\mathrm{T}}(AA^{\mathrm{T}})^{-1} = \begin{bmatrix} 4 & 0 \\ 0 & 5 \\ 0 & 0 \end{bmatrix} \begin{bmatrix} \frac{1}{16} & 0 \\ 0 & \frac{1}{25} \end{bmatrix} = \begin{bmatrix} \frac{1}{4} & 0 \\ 0 & \frac{1}{5} \\ 0 & 0 \end{bmatrix} = C.$$

This is the *pseudoinverse*—a way of choosing the best C in Section 6.3. The transpose of A yields an example with infinitely many *left*-inverses:

$$BA^{\mathrm{T}} = \begin{bmatrix} \frac{1}{4} & 0 & b_{13} \\ 0 & \frac{1}{5} & b_{23} \end{bmatrix} \begin{bmatrix} 4 & 0 \\ 0 & 5 \\ 0 & 0 \end{bmatrix} = \begin{bmatrix} 1 & 0 \\ 0 & 1 \end{bmatrix}.$$

Now it is the last column of B that is completely arbitrary. The best left-inverse (also the pseudoinverse) has $b_{13} = b_{23} = 0$. This is a "uniqueness case," when the rank is $r = n$.

There are no free variables, since $n - r = 0$. If there is a solution it will be the only one. You can see when this example has one solution or no solution:

$$\begin{bmatrix} 4 & 0 \\ 0 & 5 \\ 0 & 0 \end{bmatrix} \begin{bmatrix} x_1 \\ x_2 \end{bmatrix} = \begin{bmatrix} b_1 \\ b_2 \\ b_3 \end{bmatrix} \quad \text{is solvable exactly when} \quad b_3 = 0.$$

A rectangular matrix cannot have both existence and uniqueness. If m is different from n, we cannot have $r = m$ and $r = n$.

A square matrix is the opposite. If $m = n$, we cannot have one property *without* the other. A square matrix has a left-inverse if and only if it has a right-inverse. There is only one inverse, namely $B = C = A^{-1}$. *Existence implies uniqueness and uniqueness implies existence, when the matrix is square.* The condition for invertibility is **full rank**: $r = m = n$. Each of these conditions is a necessary and sufficient test:

1. The columns span $\mathbf{R}^n$, so $Ax = b$ has at least one solution for every b.
2. The columns are independent, so $Ax = 0$ has only the solution $x = 0$.

This list can be made much longer, especially if we look ahead to later chapters. Every condition is equivalent to every other, and ensures that A is invertible.

3. The rows of A span $\mathbf{R}^n$.
4. The rows are linearly independent.
5. Elimination can be completed: $PA = LDU$, with all n pivots.
6. The determinant of A is not zero.
7. Zero is not an eigenvalue of A.
8. $A^{\mathrm{T}}A$ is positive definite.

Here is a typical application to polynomials $P(t)$ of degree $n - 1$. The only such polynomial that vanishes at $t_1, \ldots, t_n$ is $P(t) \equiv 0$. No other polynomial of degree $n - 1$ can have n roots. This is uniqueness, and it implies existence: Given any values $b_1, \ldots, b_n$, there *exists* a polynomial of degree $n - 1$ interpolating these values: $P(t_i) = b_i$. The point is that we are dealing with a square matrix; the number n of coefficients in $P(t) = x_1 + x_2 t + \cdots + x_n t^{n-1}$ matches the number of equations:

Interpolation
$P(t_i) = b_i$

$$\begin{bmatrix} 1 & t_1 & t_1^2 & \cdots & t_1^{n-1} \\ 1 & t_2 & t_2^2 & \cdots & t_2^{n-1} \\ \vdots & \vdots & \vdots & \vdots & \vdots \\ 1 & t_n & t_n^2 & \cdots & t_n^{n-1} \end{bmatrix} \begin{bmatrix} x_1 \\ x_2 \\ \vdots \\ x_n \end{bmatrix} = \begin{bmatrix} b_1 \\ b_2 \\ \vdots \\ b_n \end{bmatrix}.$$

That *Vandermonde matrix* is n by n and full rank. $Ax = b$ always has a solution—a polynomial can be passed through any b_i at distinct points t_i. Later we shall actually find the determinant of A; it is not zero.

Matrices of Rank 1

Finally comes the easiest case, when the rank is as *small* as possible (except for the zero matrix with rank 0). One basic theme of mathematics is, given something complicated, to show how it can be broken into simple pieces. For linear algebra, the simple pieces are matrices of ***rank* 1**:

$$\textbf{Rank 1} \qquad A = \begin{bmatrix} 2 & 1 & 1 \\ 4 & 2 & 2 \\ 8 & 4 & 4 \\ -2 & -1 & -1 \end{bmatrix} \quad \text{has } r = 1.$$

Every row is a multiple of the first row, so the row space is one-dimensional. In fact, we can write the whole matrix as *the product of a column vector and a row vector*:

$$\boldsymbol{A = (\textbf{column})(\textbf{row})} \qquad \begin{bmatrix} 2 & 1 & 1 \\ 4 & 2 & 2 \\ 8 & 4 & 4 \\ -2 & -1 & -1 \end{bmatrix} = \begin{bmatrix} 1 \\ 2 \\ 4 \\ -1 \end{bmatrix} \begin{bmatrix} 2 & 1 & 1 \end{bmatrix}.$$

The product of a 4 by 1 matrix and a 1 by 3 matrix is a 4 by 3 matrix. *This product has rank* 1. At the same time, the columns are all multiples of the same column vector; the column space shares the dimension $r = 1$ and reduces to a line.

***Every matrix of rank* 1 *has the simple form* $A = uv^{\mathrm{T}}$ *= column times row*.**

The rows are all multiples of the same vector v^{T}, and the columns are all multiples of u. The row space and column space are lines—the easiest case.

Problem Set 2.4

1. True or false: If $m = n$, then the row space of A equals the column space. If $m < n$, then the nullspace has a larger dimension than _______.

2. Find the dimension and construct a basis for the four subspaces associated with each of the matrices

$$A = \begin{bmatrix} 0 & 1 & 4 & 0 \\ 0 & 2 & 8 & 0 \end{bmatrix} \quad \text{and} \quad U = \begin{bmatrix} 0 & 1 & 4 & 0 \\ 0 & 0 & 0 & 0 \end{bmatrix}.$$

3. Find the dimension and a basis for the four fundamental subspaces for

$$A = \begin{bmatrix} 1 & 2 & 0 & 1 \\ 0 & 1 & 1 & 0 \\ 1 & 2 & 0 & 1 \end{bmatrix} \quad \text{and} \quad U = \begin{bmatrix} 1 & 2 & 0 & 1 \\ 0 & 1 & 1 & 0 \\ 0 & 0 & 0 & 0 \end{bmatrix}.$$

4. Describe the four subspaces in three-dimensional space associated with

$$A = \begin{bmatrix} 0 & 1 & 0 \\ 0 & 0 & 1 \\ 0 & 0 & 0 \end{bmatrix}.$$

5. If the product AB is the zero matrix, $AB = 0$, show that the column space of B is contained in the nullspace of A. (Also the row space of A is in the left nullspace of B, since each row of A multiplies B to give a zero row.)

6. Suppose A is an m by n matrix of rank r. Under what conditions on those numbers does

(a) A have a two-sided inverse: $AA^{-1} = A^{-1}A = I$?
(b) $Ax = b$ have *infinitely many* solutions for *every* b?

7. Why is there no matrix whose row space and nullspace both contain $(1, 1, 1)$?

8. Suppose the only solution to $Ax = 0$ (m equations in n unknowns) is $x = 0$. What is the rank and why? The columns of A are linearly ______.

9. Find a 1 by 3 matrix whose nullspace consists of all vectors in $\mathbf{R}^3$ such that $x_1 + 2x_2 + 4x_3 = 0$. Find a 3 by 3 matrix with that same nullspace.

10. If $Ax = b$ always has at least one solution, show that the only solution to $A^{\mathrm{T}}y = 0$ is $y = 0$. *Hint*: What is the rank?

11. If $Ax = 0$ has a nonzero solution, show that $A^{\mathrm{T}}y = f$ fails to be solvable for some right-hand sides f. Construct an example of A and f.

12. Find the rank of A and write the matrix as $A = uv^{\mathrm{T}}$:

$$A = \begin{bmatrix} 1 & 0 & 0 & 3 \\ 0 & 0 & 0 & 0 \\ 2 & 0 & 0 & 6 \end{bmatrix} \quad \text{and} \quad A = \begin{bmatrix} 2 & -2 \\ 6 & -6 \end{bmatrix}.$$

13. If a, b, c are given with $a \neq 0$, choose d so that

$$A = \begin{bmatrix} a & b \\ c & d \end{bmatrix} = uv^{\mathrm{T}}$$

has rank 1. What are the pivots?

14. Find a left-inverse and/or a right-inverse (when they exist) for

$$A = \begin{bmatrix} 1 & 1 & 0 \\ 0 & 1 & 1 \end{bmatrix} \quad \text{and} \quad M = \begin{bmatrix} 1 & 0 \\ 1 & 1 \\ 0 & 1 \end{bmatrix} \quad \text{and} \quad T = \begin{bmatrix} a & b \\ 0 & a \end{bmatrix}.$$

15. If the columns of A are linearly independent (A is m by n), then the rank is ______, the nullspace is ______, the row space is ______, and there exists a ______-inverse.

16. (*A paradox*) Suppose A has a right-inverse B. Then $AB = I$ leads to $A^{\mathrm{T}}AB = A^{\mathrm{T}}$ or $B = (A^{\mathrm{T}}A)^{-1}A^{\mathrm{T}}$. But that satisfies $BA = I$; it is a *left*-inverse. Which step is not justified?

17. Find a matrix A that has $\mathbf{V}$ as its row space, and a matrix B that has $\mathbf{V}$ as its nullspace, if $\mathbf{V}$ is the subspace spanned by

$$\begin{bmatrix} 1 \\ 1 \\ 0 \end{bmatrix}, \quad \begin{bmatrix} 1 \\ 2 \\ 0 \end{bmatrix}, \quad \begin{bmatrix} 1 \\ 5 \\ 0 \end{bmatrix}.$$

18. Find a basis for each of the four subspaces of

$$A = \begin{bmatrix} 0 & 1 & 2 & 3 & 4 \\ 0 & 1 & 2 & 4 & 6 \\ 0 & 0 & 0 & 1 & 2 \end{bmatrix} = \begin{bmatrix} 1 & 0 & 0 \\ 1 & 1 & 0 \\ 0 & 1 & 1 \end{bmatrix} \begin{bmatrix} 0 & 1 & 2 & 3 & 4 \\ 0 & 0 & 0 & 1 & 2 \\ 0 & 0 & 0 & 0 & 0 \end{bmatrix}.$$

19. If A has the same four fundamental subspaces as B, does $A = cB$?

20. (a) If a 7 by 9 matrix has rank 5, what are the dimensions of the four subspaces? What is the sum of all four dimensions?
(b) If a 3 by 4 matrix has rank 3, what are its column space and left nullspace?

21. Construct a matrix with the required property, or explain why you can't.
(a) Column space contains $\begin{bmatrix}1\\1\\0\end{bmatrix}, \begin{bmatrix}0\\0\\1\end{bmatrix}$, row space contains $\begin{bmatrix}1\\2\end{bmatrix}, \begin{bmatrix}2\\5\end{bmatrix}$.
(b) Column space has basis $\begin{bmatrix}1\\2\\3\end{bmatrix}$, nullspace has basis $\begin{bmatrix}3\\2\\1\end{bmatrix}$.
(c) Dimension of nullspace $= 1 +$ dimension of left nullspace.
(d) Left nullspace contains $\begin{bmatrix}1\\3\end{bmatrix}$, row space contains $\begin{bmatrix}3\\1\end{bmatrix}$.
(e) Row space = column space, nullspace $\neq$ left nullspace.

22. Without elimination, find dimensions and bases for the four subspaces for

$$A = \begin{bmatrix}0 & 3 & 3 & 3\\0 & 0 & 0 & 0\\0 & 1 & 0 & 1\end{bmatrix} \quad \text{and} \quad B = \begin{bmatrix}1 & 1\\4 & 4\\5 & 5\end{bmatrix}.$$

23. Suppose the 3 by 3 matrix A is invertible. Write bases for the four subspaces for A, and also for the 3 by 6 matrix $B = [A \quad A]$.

24. What are the dimensions of the four subspaces for A, B, and C, if I is the 3 by 3 identity matrix and 0 is the 3 by 2 zero matrix?

$$A = \begin{bmatrix}I & 0\end{bmatrix} \quad \text{and} \quad B = \begin{bmatrix}I & I\\0^{\mathrm{T}} & 0^{\mathrm{T}}\end{bmatrix} \quad \text{and} \quad C = \begin{bmatrix}0\end{bmatrix}.$$

25. Which subspaces are the same for these matrices of different sizes?
(a) $[A]$ and $\begin{bmatrix}A\\A\end{bmatrix}$. (b) $\begin{bmatrix}A\\A\end{bmatrix}$ and $\begin{bmatrix}A & A\\A & A\end{bmatrix}$.
Prove that all three matrices have the same rank r.

26. If the entries of a 3 by 3 matrix are chosen randomly between 0 and 1, what are the most likely dimensions of the four subspaces? What if the matrix is 3 by 5?

27. (Important) A is an m by n matrix of rank r. Suppose there are right-hand sides b for which $Ax = b$ has *no solution*.
(a) What inequalities ($<$ or $\leq$) must be true between m, n, and r?
(b) How do you know that $A^{\mathrm{T}}y = 0$ has a nonzero solution?

28. Construct a matrix with $(1, 0, 1)$ and $(1, 2, 0)$ as a basis for its row space and its column space. Why can't this be a basis for the row space and nullspace?

29. Without computing A, find bases for the four fundamental subspaces:

$$A = \begin{bmatrix}1 & 0 & 0\\6 & 1 & 0\\9 & 8 & 1\end{bmatrix} \begin{bmatrix}1 & 2 & 3 & 4\\0 & 1 & 2 & 3\\0 & 0 & 1 & 2\end{bmatrix}.$$

30. If you exchange the first two rows of a matrix A, which of the four subspaces stay the same? If $y = (1, 2, 3, 4)$ is in the left nullspace of A, write down a vector in the left nullspace of the new matrix.

31. Explain why $v = (1, 0, -1)$ cannot be a row of A and also be in the nullspace.

32. Describe the four subspaces of $\mathbf{R}^3$ associated with

$$A = \begin{bmatrix} 0 & 1 & 0 \\ 0 & 0 & 1 \\ 0 & 0 & 0 \end{bmatrix} \quad \text{and} \quad I + A = \begin{bmatrix} 1 & 1 & 0 \\ 0 & 1 & 1 \\ 0 & 0 & 1 \end{bmatrix}.$$

33. (Left nullspace) Add the extra column b and reduce A to echelon form:

$$\begin{bmatrix} A & b \end{bmatrix} = \begin{bmatrix} 1 & 2 & 3 & b_1 \\ 4 & 5 & 6 & b_2 \\ 7 & 8 & 9 & b_3 \end{bmatrix} \to \begin{bmatrix} 1 & 2 & 3 & b_1 \\ 0 & -3 & -6 & b_2 - 4b_1 \\ 0 & 0 & 0 & b_3 - 2b_2 + b_1 \end{bmatrix}.$$

A combination of the rows of A has produced the zero row. What combination is it? (Look at $b_3 - 2b_2 + b_1$ on the right-hand side.) Which vectors are in the nullspace of A^{T} and which are in the nullspace of A?

34. Following the method of Problem 33, reduce A to echelon form and look at zero rows. The b column tells which combinations you have taken of the rows:

(a) $\begin{bmatrix} 1 & 2 & b_1 \\ 3 & 4 & b_2 \\ 4 & 6 & b_3 \end{bmatrix}$. (b) $\begin{bmatrix} 1 & 2 & b_1 \\ 2 & 3 & b_2 \\ 2 & 4 & b_3 \\ 2 & 5 & b_4 \end{bmatrix}$.

From the b column after elimination, read off $m - r$ basis vectors in the left nullspace of A (combinations of rows that give zero).

35. Suppose A is the sum of two matrices of rank one: $A = uv^{\mathrm{T}} + wz^{\mathrm{T}}$.

(a) Which vectors span the column space of A?
(b) Which vectors span the row space of A?
(c) The rank is less than 2 if ______ or if ______.
(d) Compute A and its rank if $u = z = (1, 0, 0)$ and $v = w = (0, 0, 1)$.

36. Without multiplying matrices, find bases for the row and column spaces of A:

$$A = \begin{bmatrix} 1 & 2 \\ 4 & 5 \\ 2 & 7 \end{bmatrix} \begin{bmatrix} 3 & 0 & 3 \\ 1 & 1 & 2 \end{bmatrix}.$$

How do you know from these shapes that A is not invertible?

37. True or false (with a reason or a counterexample)?

(a) A and A^{T} have the same number of pivots.
(b) A and A^{T} have the same left nullspace.
(c) If the row space equals the column space then $A^{\mathrm{T}} = A$.
(d) If $A^{\mathrm{T}} = -A$ then the row space of A equals the column space.

38. If $AB = 0$, the columns of B are in the nullspace of A. If those vectors are in $\mathbf{R}^n$, prove that $\text{rank}(A) + \text{rank}(B) \le n$.

39. Can tic-tac-toe be completed (5 ones and 4 zeros in A) so that $\text{rank}(A) = 2$ but neither side passed up a winning move?

40. Construct any 2 by 3 matrix of rank 1. Copy Figure 2.5 and put one vector in each subspace (two in the nullspace). Which vectors are orthogonal?

41. Redraw Figure 2.5 for a 3 by 2 matrix of rank $r = 2$. Which subspace is $\mathbf{Z}$ (zero vector only)? The nullspace part of any vector x in $\mathbf{R}^2$ is $x_n =$ ______.

2.5 GRAPHS AND NETWORKS

I am not entirely happy with the 3 by 4 matrix in the previous section. From a theoretical point of view it was very satisfactory; the four subspaces were computable and their dimensions r, $n - r$, r, $m - r$ were nonzero. But the example was not produced by a genuine application. It did not show how fundamental those subspaces really are.

This section introduces a class of rectangular matrices with two advantages. They are simple, and they are important. They are ***incidence matrices of graphs***, and every entry is 1, -1, or 0. What is remarkable is that the same is true of L and U and basis vectors for all four subspaces. Those subspaces play a central role in network theory. We emphasize that the word "graph" does not refer to the graph of a function (like a parabola for $y = x^2$). There is a second meaning, completely different, which is closer to computer science than to calculus—and it is easy to explain. *This section is optional*, but it gives a chance to see rectangular matrices in action—and how the square symmetric matrix $A^{\mathrm{T}}A$ turns up in the end.

A ***graph*** consists of a set of vertices or *nodes*, and a set of *edges* that connect them. The graph in Figure 2.6 has 4 nodes and 5 edges. It does not have an edge between nodes 1 and 4 (and edges from a node to itself are forbidden). This graph is *directed*, because of the arrow in each edge.

The ***edge-node incidence matrix*** is 5 by 4, with a row for every edge. ***If the edge goes from node j to node k, then that row has -1 in column j and $+1$ in column k.*** The incidence matrix A is shown next to the graph (and you could recover the graph if you only had A). Row 1 shows the edge from node 1 to node 2. Row 5 comes from the fifth edge, from node 3 to node 4.

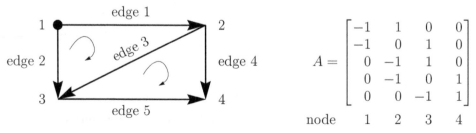

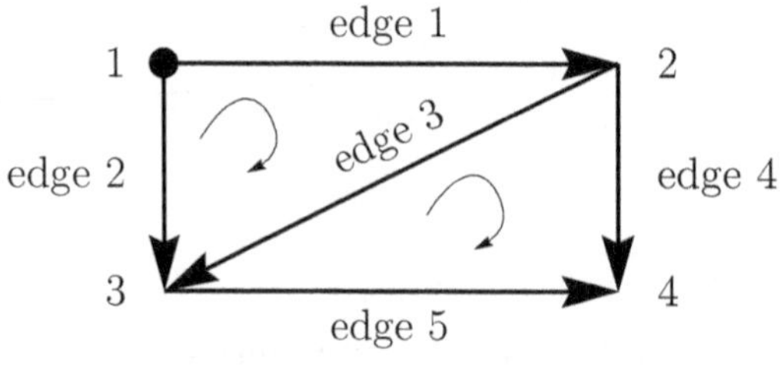

$$A = \begin{bmatrix} -1 & 1 & 0 & 0 \\ -1 & 0 & 1 & 0 \\ 0 & -1 & 1 & 0 \\ 0 & -1 & 0 & 1 \\ 0 & 0 & -1 & 1 \end{bmatrix}$$

node 1 2 3 4

Figure 2.6 A directed graph (5 edges, 4 nodes, 2 loops) and its incidence matrix A.

Notice the columns of A. Column 3 gives information about node 3—it tells which edges enter and leave. Edges 2 and 3 go in, edge 5 goes out (with the minus sign). A is sometimes called the *connectivity* matrix, or the *topology* matrix. When the graph has m edges and n nodes, A is m by n (and normally $m > n$). Its transpose is the "node-edge" incidence matrix.

Each of the four fundamental subspaces has a meaning in terms of the graph. We can do linear algebra, or write about voltages and currents. We do both!

Nullspace of *A*: Is there a combination of the columns that gives $Ax = 0$? Normally the answer comes from elimination, but here it comes at a glance. *The columns add up to the zero column*. The nullspace contains $x = (1, 1, 1, 1)$, since $Ax = 0$. The equation $Ax = b$ does not have a unique solution (if it has a solution at all). Any "constant vector" $x = (c, c, c, c)$ can be added to any particular solution of $Ax = b$. The complete solution has this arbitrary constant c (like the $+C$ when we integrate in calculus).

This has a meaning if we think of x_1, x_2, x_3, x_4 as the ***potentials*** (the voltages) ***at the nodes***. The five components of Ax give the ***differences*** in potential across the five edges. The difference across edge 1 is $x_2 - x_1$, from the ± 1 in the first row.

The equation $Ax = b$ asks: Given the differences $b_1, \ldots, b_5$, find the actual potentials $x_1, \ldots, x_4$. But that is impossible to do! We can raise or lower all the potentials by the same constant c, and the differences will not change—confirming that $x = (c, c, c, c)$ is in the nullspace of A. Those are the only vectors in the nullspace, since $Ax = 0$ means equal potentials across every edge. The nullspace of this incidence matrix is one-dimensional. ***The rank is* $\mathbf{4 - 1 = 3}$.**

Column Space: For which differences $b_1, \ldots, b_5$ can we solve $Ax = b$? To find a direct test, look back at the matrix. Row 1 plus row 3 equals row 2. On the right-hand side we need $b_1 + b_3 = b_2$, or no solution is possible. Similarly, row 3 plus row 5 is row 4. The right-hand side must satisfy $b_3 + b_5 = b_4$, for elimination to arrive at $0 = 0$. To repeat, if b is in the column space, then

$$b_1 - b_2 + b_3 = 0 \quad \text{and} \quad b_3 - b_4 + b_5 = 0. \tag{1}$$

Continuing the search, we also find that rows $1 + 4$ equal rows $2 + 5$. But this is nothing new; subtracting the equations in (1) already produces $b_1 + b_4 = b_2 + b_5$. There are *two conditions* on the five components, because the column space has dimension $5 - 2$. Those conditions would come from elimination, but here they have a meaning on the graph.

Loops: Kirchhoff's Voltage Law says that *potential differences around a loop must add to zero*. Around the upper loop in Figure 2.6, the differences satisfy $(x_2 - x_1) + (x_3 - x_2) = (x_3 - x_1)$. Those differences are $b_1 + b_3 = b_2$. To circle the lower loop and arrive back at the same potential, we need $b_3 + b_5 = b_4$.

2R The test for b to be in the column space is ***Kirchhoff's Voltage Law***:

The sum of potential differences around a loop must be zero.

Left Nullspace: To solve $A^{\mathrm{T}}y = 0$, we find its meaning on the graph. The vector y has five components, one for each edge. These numbers represent **currents** flowing along the five edges. Since A^{T} is 4 by 5, the equations $A^{\mathrm{T}}y = 0$ give four conditions on those five currents. They are conditions of "conservation" at each node: **Flow in equals flow out at every node**:

$$A^{\mathrm{T}}y = \mathbf{0} \qquad \begin{aligned} -y_1 - y_2 \phantom{{}- y_4} &= 0 &\quad& \text{Total current to node 1 is zero} \\ y_1 - y_3 - y_4 &= 0 && \text{to node 2} \\ y_2 + y_3 - y_5 &= 0 && \text{to node 3} \\ y_4 + y_5 &= 0 && \text{to node 4} \end{aligned}$$

The beauty of network theory is that both A and A^{T} have important roles.

Solving $A^{\mathrm{T}}y = 0$ means finding a set of currents that do not "pile up" at any node. The traffic keeps circulating, and the simplest solutions are **currents around small loops**. Our graph has two loops, and we send 1 amp of current around each loop:

$$\textbf{Loop vectors} \qquad y_1^{\mathrm{T}} = \begin{bmatrix} 1 & -1 & 1 & 0 & 0 \end{bmatrix} \quad \text{and} \quad y_2^{\mathrm{T}} = \begin{bmatrix} 0 & 0 & 1 & -1 & 1 \end{bmatrix}.$$

Each loop produces a vector y in the left nullspace. The component $+1$ or -1 indicates whether the current goes with or against the arrow. The combinations of y_1 and y_2 fill the left nullspace, so y_1 and y_2 are a basis (the dimension had to be $m - r = 5 - 3 = 2$). In fact $y_1 - y_2 = (1, -1, 0, 1, -1)$ gives the big loop around the outside of the graph.

The column space and left nullspace are closely related. The left nullspace contains $y_1 = (1, -1, 1, 0, 0)$, and the vectors in the column space satisfy $b_1 - b_2 + b_3 = 0$. Then $y^{\mathrm{T}}b = 0$: Vectors in the column space and left nullspace are perpendicular! That is soon to become Part Two of the "Fundamental Theorem of Linear Algebra."

Row Space: The row space of A contains vectors in $\mathbf{R}^4$, but not all vectors. Its dimension is the rank $r = 3$. Elimination will find three independent rows, and we can also look to the graph. The first three rows are *dependent* (row 1 + row 3 = row 2, and those edges form a loop). *Rows* 1, 2, 4 *are independent because edges* 1, 2, 4 *contain no loops.*

Rows 1, 2, 4 are a basis for the row space. *In each row the entries add to zero.* Every combination (f_1, f_2, f_3, f_4) in the row space will have that same property:

$$\boldsymbol{f} \textbf{ in row space} \quad f_1 + f_2 + f_3 + f_4 = 0 \qquad \boldsymbol{x} \textbf{ in nullspace} \quad x = c(1, 1, 1, 1) \qquad (2)$$

Again this illustrates the Fundamental Theorem: The row space is perpendicular to the nullspace. *If f is in the row space and x is in the nullspace then $f^{\mathrm{T}}x = 0$.*

For A^{T}, the basic law of network theory is ***Kirchhoff's Current Law***. *The total flow into every node is zero.* The numbers f_1, f_2, f_3, f_4 are current sources into the nodes. The source f_1 must balance $-y_1 - y_2$, which is the flow leaving node 1 (along edges 1 and 2). That is the first equation in $A^{\mathrm{T}}y = f$. Similarly at the other three nodes—conservation of charge requires *flow in* = *flow out*. The beautiful thing is that $\boldsymbol{A}^{\mathrm{T}}$ ***is exactly the right matrix for the Current Law.***

2S The equations $A^{\mathrm{T}}y = f$ at the nodes express ***Kirchhoff's Current Law***:

The net current into every node is zero. Flow in = Flow out.

This law can only be satisfied if the total current from outside is $f_1 + f_2 + f_3 + f_4 = 0$. With $f = 0$, the law $A^{\mathrm{T}}y = 0$ is satisfied by ***a current that goes around a loop.***

Spanning Trees and Independent Rows

Every component of y_1 and y_2 in the left nullspace is 1 or -1 or 0 (from loop flows). The same is true of $x = (1, 1, 1, 1)$ in the nullspace, and all the entries in $PA = LDU$! The key point is that every elimination step has a meaning for the graph.

You can see it in the first step for our matrix A: *subtract row* 1 *from row* 2. This replaces edge 2 by a new edge "1 minus 2":

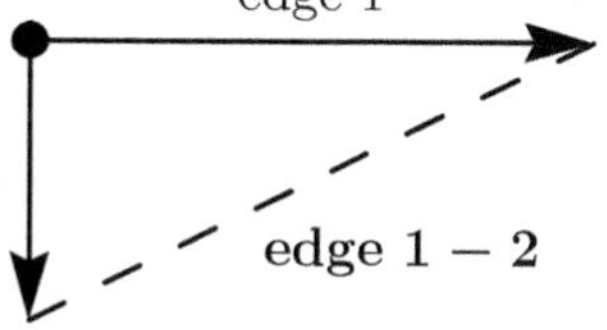

row 1	-1	1	0	0
row 2	-1	0	1	0
row 1 − 2	**0**	**1**	$\mathbf{-1}$	**0**

That elimination step destroys an edge and creates a new edge. Here the new edge "1 − 2" is just the old edge 3 in the opposite direction. The next elimination step will produce zeros in row 3 of the matrix. This shows that rows 1, 2, 3 are dependent. *Rows are dependent if the corresponding edges contain a loop.*

At the end of elimination we have a full set of r independent rows. **Those r edges form a tree—a graph with no loops**. Our graph has $r = 3$, and edges 1, 2, 4 form one possible tree. The full name is *spanning tree* because the tree "spans" all nodes of the graph. A spanning tree has $n - 1$ edges if the graph is connected, and including one more edge will produce a loop.

In the language of linear algebra, $n - 1$ is the rank of the incidence matrix A. The row space has dimension $n - 1$. The spanning tree from elimination gives a basis for that row space—each edge in the tree corresponds to a row in the basis.

The fundamental theorem of linear algebra connects the dimensions of the subspaces:

Nullspace: dimension 1, contains $x = (1, \ldots, 1)$.
Column space: dimension $r = n - 1$, any $n - 1$ columns are independent.
Row space: dimension $r = n - 1$, independent rows from any spanning tree.
Left nullspace: dimension $m - r = m - n + 1$, contains y's from the loops.

Those four lines give ***Euler's formula***, which in some way is the first theorem in topology. It counts zero-dimensional nodes minus one-dimensional edges plus two-dimensional loops. Now it has a linear algebra proof for any connected graph:

$$(\textbf{\# of nodes}) - (\textbf{\# of edges}) + (\textbf{\# of loops}) = (n) - (m) + (m - n + 1) = \mathbf{1}. \qquad (3)$$

For a single loop of 10 nodes and 10 edges, the Euler number is $10 - 10 + 1$. If those 10 nodes are each connected to an eleventh node in the center, then $11 - 20 + 10$ is still 1.

Every vector f in the row space has $x^{\mathrm{T}} f = f_1 + \cdots + f_n = 0$—the currents from outside add to zero. Every vector b in the column space has $y^{\mathrm{T}} b = 0$—the potential differences add to zero around all loops. In a moment we link x to y by a third law (***Ohm's law for each resistor***). First we stay with the matrix A for an application that seems frivolous but is not.

The Ranking of Football Teams

At the end of the season, the polls rank college football teams. The ranking is mostly an average of opinions, and it sometimes becomes vague after the top dozen colleges. We want to rank all teams on a more mathematical basis.

The first step is to recognize the graph. If team j played team k, there is an edge between them. The *teams* are the *nodes*, and the *games* are the *edges*. There are a few hundred nodes and a few thousand edges—which will be given a direction by an arrow from the visiting team to the home team. Figure 2.7 shows part of the Ivy League, and some serious teams, and also a college that is not famous for big time football. Fortunately for that college (from which I am writing these words) the graph is not connected. Mathematically speaking, we cannot prove that MIT is not number 1 (unless it happens to play a game against somebody).

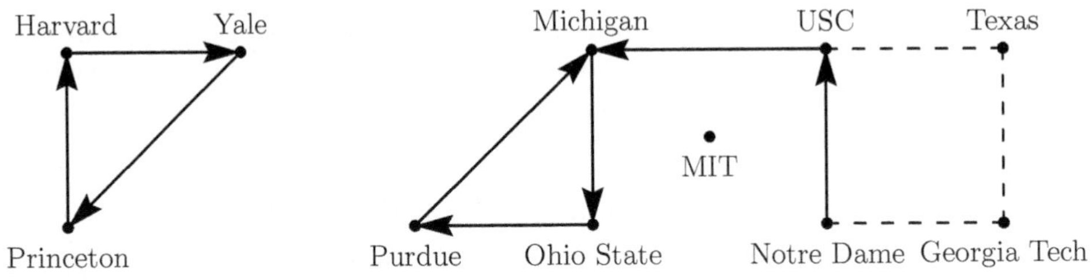

Figure 2.7 Part of the graph for college football.

If football were perfectly consistent, we could assign a "potential" x_j to every team. Then if visiting team v played home team h, the one with higher potential would win. In the ideal case, the difference b in the score would exactly equal the difference $x_h - x_v$ in their potentials. They wouldn't even have to play the game! There would be complete agreement that the team with highest potential is the best.

This method has two difficulties (at least). We are trying to find a number x for every team, and we want $x_h - x_v = b_i$ for every game. That means a few thousand equations and only a few hundred unknowns. The equations $x_h - x_v = b_i$ go into a linear system $Ax = b$, in which A is an ***incidence matrix***. Every game has a row, with $+1$ in column h and -1 in column v—to indicate which teams are in that game.

First difficulty: If b is not in the column space there is no solution. The scores must fit perfectly or exact potentials cannot be found. Second difficulty: If A has nonzero vectors in its nullspace, the potentials x are not well determined. In the first case x does not exist; in the second case x is not unique. Probably both difficulties are present.

The nullspace always contains the vector of 1s, since A looks only at the *differences* $x_h - x_v$. To determine the potentials we can arbitrarily assign zero potential to Harvard. (I am speaking mathematically, not meanly.) But if the graph is not connected, every separate piece of the graph contributes a vector to the nullspace. There is even the vector with $x_{\mathrm{MIT}} = 1$ and all other $x_j = 0$. We have to ground not only Harvard but one team in each piece. (There is nothing unfair in assigning zero potential; if all other potentials are below zero then the grounded team ranks first.) The dimension of the nullspace is the *number of pieces* of the graph—and there will be no way to rank one piece against another, since they play no games.

The column space looks harder to describe. Which scores fit perfectly with a set of potentials? Certainly $Ax = b$ is unsolvable if Harvard beats Yale, Yale beats Princeton, and Princeton beats Harvard. More than that, the score differences in that loop of games ***have to add to zero***:

$$\textbf{Kirchhoff's law for score differences} \qquad b_{\mathrm{HY}} + b_{\mathrm{YP}} + b_{\mathrm{PH}} = 0.$$

This is also a law of linear algebra. $Ax = b$ can be solved when b satisfies the same linear dependencies as the rows of A. Then elimination leads to $0 = 0$.

In reality, b is almost certainly not in the column space. Football scores are not that consistent. To obtain a ranking we can use ***least squares***: Make Ax as close as possible to b. That is in Chapter 3, and we mention only one adjustment. The winner gets a bonus of 50 or even 100 points on top of the score difference. Otherwise winning by 1 is too close to losing by 1. This brings the computed rankings very close to the polls, and Dr. Leake (Notre Dame) gave a full analysis in *Management Science in Sports* (1976).

After writing that subsection, I found the following in the *New York Times*:

> In its final rankings for 1985, the computer placed Miami (10-2) in the seventh spot above Tennessee (9-1-2). A few days after publication, packages containing oranges and angry letters from disgruntled Tennessee fans began arriving at the *Times* sports department. The irritation stems from the fact that Tennessee thumped Miami 35-7 in the Sugar Bowl. Final AP and UPI polls ranked Tennessee fourth, with Miami significantly lower.
>
> Yesterday morning nine cartons of oranges arrived at the loading dock. They were sent to Bellevue Hospital with a warning that the quality and contents of the oranges were uncertain.

So much for that application of linear algebra.

Networks and Discrete Applied Mathematics

A graph becomes a ***network*** when numbers $c_1, \ldots, c_m$ are assigned to the edges. The number c_i can be the *length* of edge i, or its *capacity*, or its *stiffness* (if it contains a spring), or its *conductance* (if it contains a resistor). Those numbers go into a diagonal matrix C, which is m by m. C reflects "material properties," in contrast to the incidence matrix A—which gives information about the connections.

Our description will be in electrical terms. On edge i, the conductance is c_i and the resistance is $1/c_i$. Ohm's Law says that the current y_i through the resistor is proportional to the voltage drop e_i:

Ohm's Law $\quad y_i = c_i e_i \qquad$ (current) = (conductance)(voltage drop).

This is also written $E = IR$, voltage drop equals current times resistance. As a vector equation on all edges at once, ***Ohm's Law is*** $\boldsymbol{y = Ce}$.

We need Kirchhoff's Voltage Law and Current Law to complete the framework:

KVL: The voltage drops around each loop add to zero.
KCL: The currents y_i (and f_i) into each node add to zero.

The voltage law allows us to assign potentials $x_1, \dots, x_n$ to the nodes. Then the differences around a loop give a sum like $(x_2 - x_1) + (x_3 - x_2) + (x_1 - x_3) = 0$, in which everything cancels. The current law asks us to add the currents into each node by the multiplication $A^{\mathrm{T}}y$. If there are no external sources of current, *Kirchhoff's Current Law is* $A^{\mathrm{T}}y = 0$.

The other equation is Ohm's Law, but we need to find the voltage drop e across the resistor. The multiplication Ax gave the potential difference between the nodes. Reversing the signs, $-Ax$ gives the *drop* in potential. Part of that drop may be due to a ***battery*** in the edge of strength b_i. The rest of the drop is $e = b - Ax$ across the resistor:

$$\textbf{Ohm's Law} \qquad y = C(b - Ax) \quad \text{or} \quad C^{-1}y + Ax = b. \tag{4}$$

The ***fundamental equations of equilibrium*** combine Ohm and Kirchhoff into a central problem of applied mathematics. These equations appear everywhere:

$$\textbf{Equilibrium equations} \qquad \begin{aligned} C^{-1}y + Ax &= b \\ A^{\mathrm{T}}y \qquad &= f. \end{aligned} \tag{5}$$

That is a linear symmetric system, from which e has disappeared. The unknowns are the currents y and the potentials x. You see the symmetric block matrix:

$$\textbf{Block form} \qquad \begin{bmatrix} C^{-1} & A \\ A^{\mathrm{T}} & 0 \end{bmatrix} \begin{bmatrix} y \\ x \end{bmatrix} = \begin{bmatrix} b \\ f \end{bmatrix}. \tag{6}$$

For block elimination the pivot is C^{-1}, the multiplier is $A^{\mathrm{T}}C$, and subtraction knocks out A^{T} below the pivot. The result is

$$\begin{bmatrix} C^{-1} & A \\ 0 & -A^{\mathrm{T}}CA \end{bmatrix} \begin{bmatrix} y \\ x \end{bmatrix} = \begin{bmatrix} b \\ f - A^{\mathrm{T}}Cb \end{bmatrix}$$

The equation for x alone is in the bottom row, with the symmetric matrix $A^{\mathrm{T}}CA$:

$$\textbf{Fundamental equation} \qquad A^{\mathrm{T}}CAx = A^{\mathrm{T}}Cb - f. \tag{7}$$

Then back-substitution in the first equation produces y. Nothing mysterious—substitute $y = C(b - Ax)$ into $A^{\mathrm{T}}y = f$ to reach (7).

Important remark One potential must be fixed in advance: $x_n = 0$. The nth node is ***grounded***, and the nth column of the original incidence matrix is removed. The resulting matrix is what we now mean by A; its $n - 1$ columns are independent. The square matrix

$A^{\mathrm{T}}CA$, which is the key to solving equation (7) for x, is an invertible matrix of order $n-1$:

$$\underset{n-1 \text{ by } m}{\begin{bmatrix} & A^{\mathrm{T}} & \end{bmatrix}} \underset{m \text{ by } m}{\begin{bmatrix} & & \\ & C & \\ & & \end{bmatrix}} \underset{m \text{ by } n-1}{\begin{bmatrix} \\ A \\ \\ \end{bmatrix}} = \underset{n-1 \text{ by } n-1}{\begin{bmatrix} A^{\mathrm{T}}CA \end{bmatrix}}$$

Example 1 Suppose a battery b_3 and a current source f_2 (and five resistors) connect four nodes. Node 4 is grounded and the potential $x_4 = 0$ is fixed.

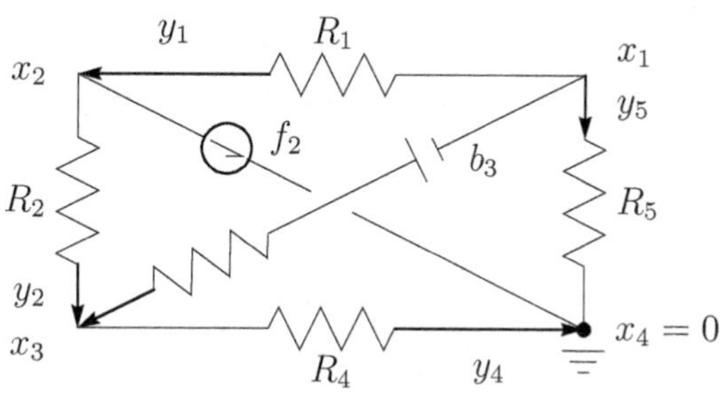

The first thing is the current law $A^{\mathrm{T}}y = f$ at nodes 1, 2, 3:

$$\begin{aligned} -y_1 - y_3 - y_5 &= 0 \\ y_1 - y_2 &= f_2 \\ y_2 + y_3 - y_4 &= 0 \end{aligned} \quad \text{has} \quad A^{\mathrm{T}} = \begin{bmatrix} -1 & 0 & -1 & 0 & -1 \\ 1 & -1 & 0 & 0 & 0 \\ 0 & 1 & 1 & -1 & 0 \end{bmatrix}.$$

No equation is written for node 4, where the current law is $y_4 + y_5 + f_2 = 0$. This follows from adding the other three equations.

The other equation is $C^{-1}y + Ax = b$. The potentials x are connected to the currents y by Ohm's Law. The diagonal matrix C contains the five conductances $c_i = 1/R_i$. The right-hand side accounts for the battery of strength b_3 in edge 3. The block form has $C^{-1}y + Ax = b$ above $A^{\mathrm{T}}y = f$:

$$\begin{bmatrix} C^{-1} & A \\ A^{\mathrm{T}} & 0 \end{bmatrix} \begin{bmatrix} y \\ x \end{bmatrix} = \begin{bmatrix} R_1 & & & & & -1 & 1 & 0 \\ & R_2 & & & & 0 & -1 & 1 \\ & & R_3 & & & -1 & 0 & 1 \\ & & & R_4 & & 0 & 0 & -1 \\ & & & & R_5 & -1 & 0 & 0 \\ -1 & 0 & -1 & 0 & -1 & & & \\ 1 & -1 & 0 & 0 & 0 & & & \\ 0 & 1 & 1 & -1 & 0 & & & \end{bmatrix} \begin{bmatrix} y_1 \\ y_2 \\ y_3 \\ y_4 \\ y_5 \\ x_1 \\ x_2 \\ x_3 \end{bmatrix} = \begin{bmatrix} 0 \\ 0 \\ b_3 \\ 0 \\ 0 \\ 0 \\ f_2 \\ 0 \end{bmatrix}$$

The system is 8 by 8, with five currents and three potentials. Elimination of y's reduces to the 3 by 3 system $A^{\mathrm{T}}CAx = A^{\mathrm{T}}Cb - f$. The matrix $A^{\mathrm{T}}CA$ contains the reciprocals $c_i = 1/R_i$ (because in elimination you divide by the pivots). We also show the fourth row and column, from the grounded node, outside the 3 by 3 matrix:

$$A^{\mathrm{T}}CA = \begin{bmatrix} c_1 + c_3 + c_5 & -c_1 & -c_3 \\ -c_1 & c_1 + c_2 & -c_2 \\ -c_3 & -c_2 & c_2 + c_3 + c_4 \end{bmatrix} \begin{matrix} -c_5 & \text{(node 1)} \\ 0 & \text{(node 2)} \\ -c_4 & \text{(node 3)} \end{matrix}$$
$$\begin{matrix} -c_5 & 0 & -c_4 & c_4 + c_5 & \text{(node 4)} \end{matrix}$$

The first entry is $1+1+1$, or $c_1+c_3+c_5$ when C is included, because edges 1, 3, 5 touch node 1. The next diagonal entry is $1+1$ or c_1+c_2, from the edges touching node 2. Off the diagonal the c's appear with minus signs. *The edges to the grounded node* 4 belong in the *fourth* row and column, which are deleted when column 4 is removed from A (making $A^{\mathrm{T}}CA$ invertible). The 4 by 4 matrix would have all rows and columns adding to zero, and $(1, 1, 1, 1)$ would be in its nullspace.

Notice that $A^{\mathrm{T}}CA$ is symmetric. It has positive pivots and it comes from the **basic framework of applied mathematics** illustrated in Figure 2.8.

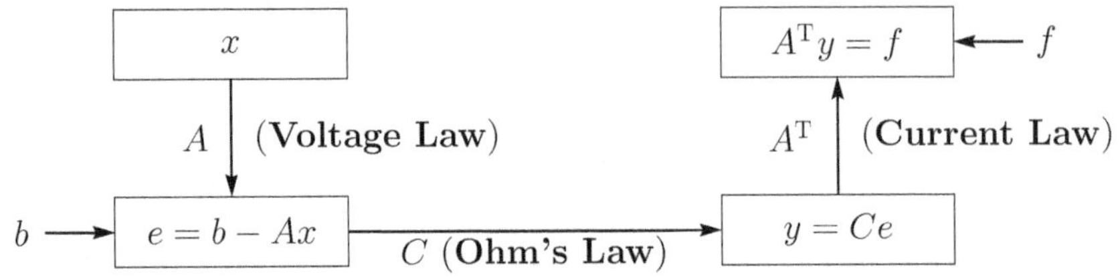

Figure 2.8 The framework for equilibrium: sources b and f, three steps to $A^{\mathrm{T}}CA$.

In mechanics, x and y become displacements and stresses. In fluids, the unknowns are pressure and flow rate. In statistics, e is the error and x is the best least-squares fit to the data. These matrix equations and the corresponding differential equations are in our textbook *Introduction to Applied Mathematics*, and the new *Applied Mathematics and Scientific Computing*. (See `www.wellesleycambridge.com`.)

We end this chapter at that high point—the ***formulation*** of a fundamental problem in applied mathematics. Often that requires more insight than the ***solution*** of the problem. We solved linear equations in Chapter 1, as the first step in linear algebra. To set up the equations has required the deeper insight of Chapter 2. The contribution of mathematics, and of people, is not computation but intelligence.

Problem Set 2.5

1. For the 3-node triangular graph in the figure following, write the 3 by 3 incidence matrix A. Find a solution to $Ax = 0$ and describe all other vectors in the nullspace of A. Find a solution to $A^{\mathrm{T}}y = 0$ and describe all other vectors in the left nullspace of A.

2. For the same 3 by 3 matrix, show directly from the columns that every vector b in the column space will satisfy $b_1 + b_2 - b_3 = 0$. Derive the same thing from the three

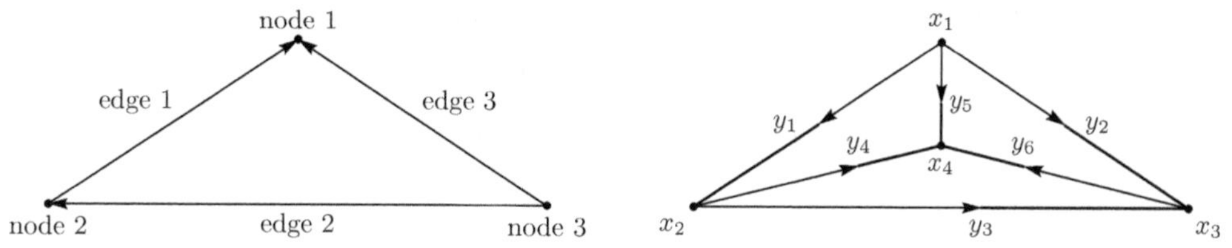

rows—the equations in the system $Ax = b$. What does that mean about potential differences around a loop?

3. Show directly from the rows that every vector f in the row space will satisfy $f_1 + f_2 + f_3 = 0$. Derive the same thing from the three equations $A^{\mathrm{T}}y = f$. What does that mean when the f's are currents into the nodes?

4. Compute the 3 by 3 matrix $A^{\mathrm{T}}A$, and show that it is symmetric but singular—what vectors are in its nullspace? Removing the last column of A (and last row of A^{T}) leaves the 2 by 2 matrix in the upper left corner; show that it is *not* singular.

5. Put the diagonal matrix C with entries c_1, c_2, c_3 in the middle and compute $A^{\mathrm{T}}CA$. Show again that the 2 by 2 matrix in the upper left corner is invertible.

6. Write the 6 by 4 incidence matrix A for the second graph in the figure. The vector $(1, 1, 1, 1)$ is in the nullspace of A, but now there will be $m - n + 1 = 3$ independent vectors that satisfy $A^{\mathrm{T}}y = 0$. Find three vectors y and *connect them to the loops in the graph.*

7. If that second graph represents six games between four teams, and the score differences are $b_1, \ldots, b_6$, when is it possible to assign potentials $x_1, \ldots, x_4$ so that the potential differences agree with the b's? You are finding (from Kirchhoff or from elimination) the conditions that make $Ax = b$ solvable.

8. Write down the dimensions of the four fundamental subspaces for this 6 by 4 incidence matrix, and a basis for each subspace.

9. Compute $A^{\mathrm{T}}A$ and $A^{\mathrm{T}}CA$, where the 6 by 6 diagonal matrix C has entries $c_1, \ldots, c_6$. How can you tell from the graph where the c's will appear on the main diagonal of $A^{\mathrm{T}}CA$?

10. Draw a graph with numbered and directed edges (and numbered nodes) whose incidence matrix is

$$A = \begin{bmatrix} -1 & 1 & 0 & 0 \\ -1 & 0 & 1 & 0 \\ 0 & 1 & 0 & -1 \\ 0 & 0 & -1 & 1 \end{bmatrix}.$$

Is this graph a tree? (Are the rows of A independent?) Show that removing the last edge produces a spanning tree. Then the remaining rows are a basis for ______?

11. With the last column removed from the preceding A, and with the numbers 1, 2, 2, 1 on the diagonal of C, write out the 7 by 7 system

$$\begin{aligned} C^{-1}y + Ax &= 0 \\ A^{\mathrm{T}}y \qquad &= f. \end{aligned}$$

Eliminating y_1, y_2, y_3, y_4 leaves three equations $A^{\mathrm{T}}CAx = -f$ for x_1, x_2, x_3. Solve the equations when $f = (1, 1, 6)$. With those currents entering nodes 1, 2, 3 of the network, what are the potentials at the nodes and currents on the edges?

12. If A is a 12 by 7 incidence matrix from a connected graph, what is its rank? How many free variables are there in the solution to $Ax = b$? How many free variables are there in the solution to $A^{\mathrm{T}}y = f$? How many edges must be removed to leave a spanning tree?

13. In the graph above with 4 nodes and 6 edges, find all 16 spanning trees.

14. If MIT beats Harvard 35-0, Yale ties Harvard, and Princeton beats Yale 7-6, what score differences in the other 3 games (H-P, MIT-P, MIT-Y) will allow potential differences that agree with the score differences? If the score differences are known for the games in a spanning tree, they are known for all games.

15. In our method for football rankings, should the strength of the opposition be considered—or is that already built in?

16. If there is an edge between every pair of nodes (a complete graph), how many edges are there? The graph has n nodes, and edges from a node to itself are not allowed.

17. For both graphs drawn below, verify *Euler's formula*:
(**# of nodes**) − (**# of edges**) + (**# of loops**) = 1.

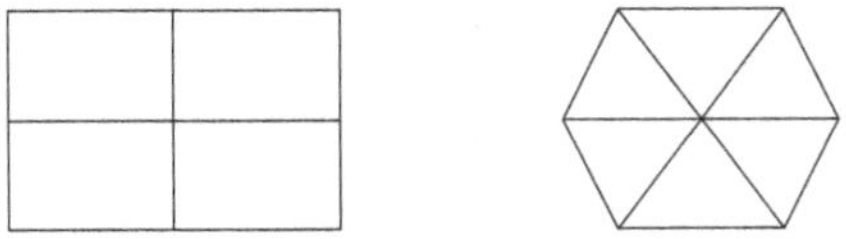

18. Multiply matrices to find $A^{\mathrm{T}}A$, and guess how its entries come from the graph:

(a) The diagonal of $A^{\mathrm{T}}A$ tells how many _______ into each node.
(b) The off-diagonals -1 or 0 tell which pairs of nodes are _______.

19. Why does the nullspace of $A^{\mathrm{T}}A$ contain $(1, 1, 1, 1)$? What is its rank?

20. Why does a complete graph with $n = 6$ nodes have $m = 15$ edges? A spanning tree connecting all six nodes has _______ edges. There are $n^{n-2} = 6^4$ spanning trees!

21. The *adjacency matrix* of a graph has $M_{ij} = 1$ if nodes i and j are connected by an edge (otherwise $M_{ij} = 0$). For the graph in Problem 6 with 6 nodes and 4 edges, write down M and also M^2. Why does $(M^2)_{ij}$ count the number of 2-*step paths* from node i to node j?

2.6 LINEAR TRANSFORMATIONS

We know how a matrix moves subspaces around when we multiply by A. The nullspace goes into the zero vector. All vectors go into the column space, since Ax is always a combination of the columns. You will soon see something beautiful—that A takes its row space into its column space, and on those spaces of dimension r it is 100 percent invertible. That is the real action of A. It is partly hidden by nullspaces and left nullspaces, which lie at right angles and go their own way (toward zero).

What matters now is what happens *inside* the space—which means inside n-dimensional space, if A is n by n. That demands a closer look.

Suppose x is an n-dimensional vector. When A multiplies x, it ***transforms*** that vector into a new vector Ax. This happens at every point x of the n-dimensional space $\mathbf{R}^n$. The whole space is transformed, or "mapped into itself," by the matrix A. Figure 2.9 illustrates four transformations that come from matrices:

$$A = \begin{bmatrix} c & 0 \\ 0 & c \end{bmatrix}$$

1. A multiple of the identity matrix, $A = cI$, ***stretches*** every vector by the same factor c. The whole space expands or contracts (or somehow goes through the origin and out the opposite side, when c is negative).

$$A = \begin{bmatrix} 0 & -1 \\ 1 & 0 \end{bmatrix}$$

2. A ***rotation*** matrix turns the whole space around the origin. This example turns all vectors through 90°, transforming every point (x, y) to $(-y, x)$.

$$A = \begin{bmatrix} 0 & 1 \\ 1 & 0 \end{bmatrix}$$

3. A ***reflection*** matrix transforms every vector into its image on the opposite side of a mirror. In this example the mirror is the 45° line $y = x$, and a point like $(2, 2)$ is unchanged. A point like $(2, -2)$ is reversed to $(-2, 2)$. On a combination like $v = (2, 2) + (2, -2) = (4, 0)$, the matrix leaves one part and reverses the other part. The output is $Av = (2, 2) + (-2, 2) = (0, 4)$.

   That reflection matrix is also a permutation matrix! It is algebraically so simple, sending (x, y) to (y, x), that the geometric picture was concealed.

$$A = \begin{bmatrix} 1 & 0 \\ 0 & 0 \end{bmatrix}$$

4. A ***projection*** matrix takes the whole space onto a lower-dimensional subspace (not invertible). The example transforms each vector (x, y) in the plane to the nearest point $(x, 0)$ on the horizontal axis. That axis is the column space of A. The y-axis that projects to $(0, 0)$ is the nullspace.

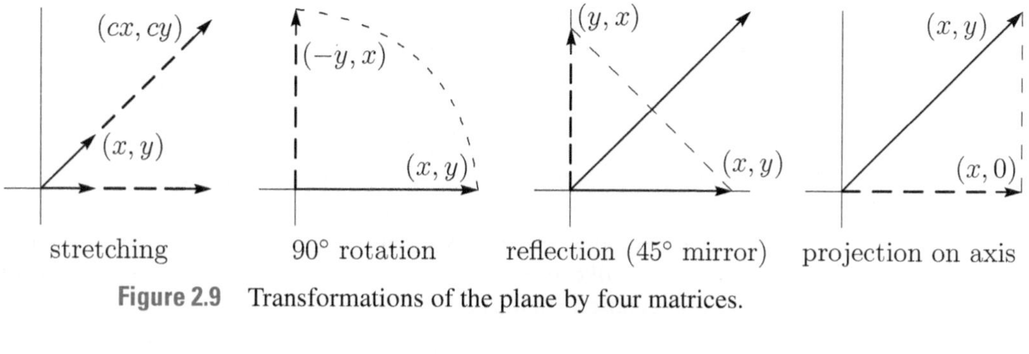

Figure 2.9 Transformations of the plane by four matrices.

Those examples could be lifted into three dimensions. There are matrices to stretch the earth or spin it or reflect it across the plane of the equator (north pole transforming to south pole). There is a matrix that projects everything onto that plane (both poles to the center). It is also important to recognize that matrices cannot do everything, and some transformations $T(x)$ are *not possible* with Ax:

(i) It is impossible to move the origin, since $A0 = 0$ for every matrix.
(ii) If the vector x goes to x', then $2x$ must go to $2x'$. In general cx must go to cx', since $A(cx) = c(Ax)$.
(iii) If the vectors x and y go to x' and y', then their sum $x + y$ must go to $x' + y'$—since $A(x + y) = Ax + Ay$.

Matrix multiplication imposes those rules on the transformation. The second rule contains the first (take $c = 0$ to get $A0 = 0$). We saw rule (iii) in action when $(4, 0)$ was reflected across the 45° line. It was split into $(2, 2) + (2, -2)$ and the two parts were reflected separately. The same could be done for projections: split, project separately, and add the projections. These rules apply to ***any transformation that comes from a matrix***.

Their importance has earned them a name: Transformations that obey rules (i)–(iii) are called ***linear transformations***. The rules can be combined into one requirement:

2T For all numbers c and d and all vectors x and y, matrix multiplication satisfies the rule of linearity:

$$A(cx + dy) = c(Ax) + d(Ay). \tag{1}$$

Every transformation $T(x)$ that meets this requirement is a ***linear transformation***.

Any matrix leads immediately to a linear transformation. The more interesting question is in the opposite direction: *Does every linear transformation lead to a matrix*? The object of this section is to find the answer, *yes*. This is the foundation of an approach to linear algebra—starting with property (1) and developing its consequences—that is much more abstract than the main approach in this book. We preferred to begin directly with matrices, and now we see how they represent linear transformations.

A transformation need not go from $\mathbf{R}^n$ to the same space $\mathbf{R}^n$. It is absolutely permitted to transform vectors in $\mathbf{R}^n$ to vectors in a different space $\mathbf{R}^m$. That is exactly what is done by an m by n matrix! The original vector x has n components, and the transformed vector Ax has m components. The rule of linearity is equally satisfied by rectangular matrices, so they also produce linear transformations.

Having gone that far, there is no reason to stop. The operations in the linearity condition (1) are addition and scalar multiplication, but x and y need not be column vectors in $\mathbf{R}^n$. Those are not the only spaces. By definition, *any vector space allows the combinations* $cx + dy$—the "vectors" are x and y, but they may actually be polynomials or matrices or functions $x(t)$ and $y(t)$. As long as the transformation satisfies equation (1), it is linear.

We take as examples the spaces $\mathbf{P}_n$, in which the vectors are polynomials $p(t)$ of degree n. They look like $p = a_0 + a_1t + \cdots + a_nt^n$, and the dimension of the vector space is $n + 1$ (because with the constant term, there are $n + 1$ coefficients).

Example 1 The operation of ***differentiation***, $A = d/dt$, is linear:

$$Ap(t) = \frac{d}{dt}(a_0 + a_1 t + \cdots + a_n t^n) = a_1 + \cdots + n a_n t^{n-1}. \tag{2}$$

The nullspace of this A is the one-dimensional space of constants: $da_0/dt = 0$. The column space is the n-dimensional space $\mathbf{P}_{n-1}$; the right-hand side of equation (2) is always in that space. The sum of nullity ($= 1$) and rank ($= n$) is the dimension of the original space $\mathbf{P}_n$.

Example 2 ***Integration*** from 0 to t is also linear (*it takes* $\mathbf{P}_n$ *to* $\mathbf{P}_{n+1}$):

$$Ap(t) = \int_0^t (a_0 + \cdots + a_n t^n)\, dt = a_0 t + \cdots + \frac{a_n}{n+1} t^{n+1}. \tag{3}$$

This time there is no nullspace (except for the zero vector, as always!) but integration does not produce all polynomials in $\mathbf{P}_{n+1}$. The right side of equation (3) has no constant term. Probably the constant polynomials will be the left nullspace.

Example 3 ***Multiplication*** by a fixed polynomial like $2 + 3t$ is linear:

$$Ap(t) = (2 + 3t)(a_0 + \cdots + a_n t^n) = 2a_0 + \cdots + 3a_n t^{n+1}.$$

Again this transforms $\mathbf{P}_n$ to $\mathbf{P}_{n+1}$, with no nullspace except $p = 0$.

In these examples (and in almost all examples), linearity is not difficult to verify. It hardly even seems interesting. If it is there, it is practically impossible to miss. Nevertheless, it is the most important property a transformation can have.* Of course most transformations are not linear—for example, to square the polynomial ($Ap = p^2$), or to add 1 ($Ap = p + 1$), or to keep the positive coefficients ($A(t - t^2) = t$). It will be linear transformations, and *only those*, that lead us back to matrices.

Transformations Represented by Matrices

Linearity has a crucial consequence: ***If we know Ax for each vector in a basis, then we know Ax for each vector in the entire space***. Suppose the basis consists of the n vectors $x_1, \ldots, x_n$. Every other vector x is a combination of those particular vectors (they span the space). Then linearity determines Ax:

Linearity If $x = c_1 x_1 + \cdots + c_n x_n$ then $Ax = c_1(Ax_1) + \cdots + c_n(Ax_n)$. (4)

The transformation $T(x) = Ax$ has no freedom left, after it has decided what to do with the basis vectors. The rest is determined by linearity. The requirement (1) for two vectors x and y leads to condition (4) for n vectors $x_1, \ldots, x_n$. The transformation does have a free hand with the vectors in the basis (they are independent). When those are settled, the transformation of every vector is settled.

* Invertibility is perhaps in second place as an important property.

Example 4 What linear transformation takes x_1 and x_2 to Ax_1 and Ax_2?

$$x_1 = \begin{bmatrix}1\\0\end{bmatrix} \quad \text{goes to} \quad Ax_1 = \begin{bmatrix}2\\3\\4\end{bmatrix}; \qquad x_2 = \begin{bmatrix}0\\1\end{bmatrix} \quad \text{goes to} \quad Ax_2 = \begin{bmatrix}4\\6\\8\end{bmatrix}.$$

It must be multiplication $T(x) = Ax$ by the matrix

$$A = \begin{bmatrix}2 & 4\\3 & 6\\4 & 8\end{bmatrix}.$$

Starting with a different basis $(1, 1)$ and $(2, -1)$, this same A is also the only linear transformation with

$$A\begin{bmatrix}1\\1\end{bmatrix} = \begin{bmatrix}6\\9\\12\end{bmatrix} \quad \text{and} \quad A\begin{bmatrix}2\\-1\end{bmatrix} = \begin{bmatrix}0\\0\\0\end{bmatrix}.$$

Next we find matrices that represent differentiation and integration. ***First we must decide on a basis***. For the polynomials of degree 3 there is a natural choice for the four basis vectors:

$$\textbf{Basis for } \mathbf{P}_3 \qquad p_1 = 1, \quad p_2 = t, \quad p_3 = t^2, \quad p_4 = t^3.$$

That basis is not unique (it never is), but some choice is necessary and this is the most convenient. The derivatives of those four basis vectors are $0, 1, 2t, 3t^2$:

$$\textbf{Action of } d/dt \qquad Ap_1 = 0, \quad Ap_2 = p_1, \quad Ap_3 = 2p_2, \quad Ap_4 = 3p_3. \tag{5}$$

"d/dt" is acting exactly like a matrix, but which matrix? Suppose we were in the usual four-dimensional space with the usual basis—the coordinate vectors $p_1 = (1, 0, 0, 0)$, $p_2 = (0, 1, 0, 0)$, $p_3 = (0, 0, 1, 0)$, $p_4 = (0, 0, 0, 1)$. The matrix is decided by equation (5):

$$\textbf{Differentiation matrix} \qquad A_{\text{diff}} = \begin{bmatrix}0 & 1 & 0 & 0\\0 & 0 & 2 & 0\\0 & 0 & 0 & 3\\0 & 0 & 0 & 0\end{bmatrix}.$$

Ap_1 is its first column, which is zero. Ap_2 is the second column, which is p_1. Ap_3 is $2p_2$, and Ap_4 is $3p_3$. The nullspace contains p_1 (the derivative of a constant is zero). The column space contains p_1, p_2, p_3 (the derivative of a cubic is a quadratic). The derivative of a combination like $p = 2 + t - t^2 - t^3$ is decided by linearity, and there is nothing new about that—it is the way we all differentiate. It would be crazy to memorize the derivative of every polynomial.

The matrix can differentiate that $p(t)$, because matrices build in linearity!

$$\frac{dp}{dt} = Ap \rightarrow \begin{bmatrix}0 & 1 & 0 & 0\\0 & 0 & 2 & 0\\0 & 0 & 0 & 3\\0 & 0 & 0 & 0\end{bmatrix}\begin{bmatrix}2\\1\\-1\\-1\end{bmatrix} = \begin{bmatrix}1\\-2\\-3\\0\end{bmatrix} \rightarrow 1 - 2t - 3t^2.$$

In short, *the matrix carries all the essential information.* If the basis is known, and the matrix is known, then the transformation of every vector is known.

The coding of the information is simple. To transform a space to itself, one basis is enough. A transformation from one space to another requires a basis for each.

2U Suppose the vectors $x_1, \dots, x_n$ are a basis for the space $\mathbf{V}$, and vectors $y_1, \dots, y_m$ are a basis for $\mathbf{W}$. Each linear transformation T from $\mathbf{V}$ to $\mathbf{W}$ is represented by a matrix A. The jth column is found by applying T to the jth basis vector x_j, and writing $T(x_j)$ as a combination of the y's:

$$\textbf{Column } j \textbf{ of } A \qquad T(x_j) = Ax_j = a_{1j}y_1 + a_{2j}y_2 + \cdots + a_{mj}y_m. \tag{6}$$

For the differentiation matrix, column 1 came from the first basis vector $p_1 = 1$. Its derivative is zero, so column 1 is zero. The last column came from $(d/dt)t^3 = 3t^2$. Since $3t^2 = 0p_1 + 0p_2 + 3p_3 + 0p_4$, the last column contained 0, 0, 3, 0. The rule (6) constructs the matrix, a column at a time.

We do the same for integration. That goes from cubics to quartics, transforming $\mathbf{V} = \mathbf{P}_3$ into $\mathbf{W} = \mathbf{P}_4$, so we need a basis for $\mathbf{W}$. The natural choice is $y_1 = 1$, $y_2 = t$, $y_3 = t^2$, $y_4 = t^3$, $y_5 = t^4$, spanning the polynomials of degree 4. The matrix A will be m by n, or 5 by 4. It comes from applying integration to each basis vector of $\mathbf{V}$:

$$\int_0^t 1\,dt = t \quad \text{or} \quad Ax_1 = y_2, \quad \dots, \quad \int_0^t t^3\,dt = \frac{1}{4}t^4 \quad \text{or} \quad Ax_4 = \frac{1}{4}y_5.$$

$$\textbf{Integration matrix} \qquad A_{\text{int}} = \begin{bmatrix} 0 & 0 & 0 & 0 \\ 1 & 0 & 0 & 0 \\ 0 & \frac{1}{2} & 0 & 0 \\ 0 & 0 & \frac{1}{3} & 0 \\ 0 & 0 & 0 & \frac{1}{4} \end{bmatrix}.$$

Differentiation and integration are *inverse operations*. Or at least integration *followed* by differentiation brings back the original function. To make that happen for matrices, we need the differentiation matrix from quartics down to cubics, which is 4 by 5:

$$A_{\text{diff}} = \begin{bmatrix} 0 & 1 & 0 & 0 & 0 \\ 0 & 0 & 2 & 0 & 0 \\ 0 & 0 & 0 & 3 & 0 \\ 0 & 0 & 0 & 0 & 4 \end{bmatrix} \quad \text{and} \quad A_{\text{diff}}A_{\text{int}} = \begin{bmatrix} 1 & & & \\ & 1 & & \\ & & 1 & \\ & & & 1 \end{bmatrix}.$$

Differentiation is a ***left-inverse*** of integration. Rectangular matrices cannot have two-sided inverses! In the opposite order, $A_{\text{int}}A_{\text{diff}} = I$ cannot be true. The 5 by 5 product has zeros in column 1. The derivative of a constant is zero. In the other columns $A_{\text{int}}A_{\text{diff}}$ is the identity and the integral of the derivative of t^n is t^n.

Rotations Q, Projections P, and Reflections H

This section began with 90° rotations, projections onto the x-axis, and reflections through the 45° line. Their matrices were especially simple:

$$Q = \begin{bmatrix} 0 & -1 \\ 1 & 0 \end{bmatrix} \qquad P = \begin{bmatrix} 1 & 0 \\ 0 & 0 \end{bmatrix} \qquad H = \begin{bmatrix} 0 & 1 \\ 1 & 0 \end{bmatrix}.$$

(rotation) (projection) (reflection)

The underlying linear transformations of the x-y plane are also simple. But rotations through other angles, projections onto other lines, and reflections in other mirrors are almost as easy to visualize. They are still linear transformations, provided that the origin is fixed: $A0 = 0$. They *must* be represented by matrices. Using the natural basis $\begin{bmatrix} 1 \\ 0 \end{bmatrix}$ and $\begin{bmatrix} 0 \\ 1 \end{bmatrix}$, we want to discover those matrices.

1. Rotation Figure 2.10 shows rotation through an angle θ. It also shows the effect on the two basis vectors. The first one goes to $(\cos\theta, \sin\theta)$, whose length is still 1; it lies on the "θ-line." The second basis vector $(0, 1)$ rotates into $(-\sin\theta, \cos\theta)$. By rule (6), those numbers go into the columns of the matrix (we use c and s for $\cos\theta$ and $\sin\theta$). This family of rotations Q_θ is a perfect chance to test the correspondence between transformations and matrices:

*Does the **inverse** of Q_θ equal $Q_{-\theta}$* (rotation backward through θ)? *Yes.*

$$Q_\theta Q_{-\theta} = \begin{bmatrix} c & -s \\ s & c \end{bmatrix} \begin{bmatrix} c & s \\ -s & c \end{bmatrix} = \begin{bmatrix} 1 & 0 \\ 0 & 1 \end{bmatrix}.$$

*Does the **square** of Q_θ equal $Q_{2\theta}$* (rotation through a double angle)? *Yes.*

$$Q_\theta^2 = \begin{bmatrix} c & -s \\ s & c \end{bmatrix} \begin{bmatrix} c & -s \\ s & c \end{bmatrix} = \begin{bmatrix} c^2 - s^2 & -2cs \\ 2cs & c^2 - s^2 \end{bmatrix} = \begin{bmatrix} \cos 2\theta & -\sin 2\theta \\ \sin 2\theta & \cos 2\theta \end{bmatrix}.$$

*Does the **product** of Q_θ and Q_φ equal $Q_{\theta+\varphi}$* (rotation through θ then φ)? *Yes.*

$$Q_\theta Q_\varphi = \begin{bmatrix} \cos\theta\cos\varphi - \sin\theta\sin\varphi & \cdots \\ \sin\theta\cos\varphi + \cos\theta\sin\varphi & \cdots \end{bmatrix} = \begin{bmatrix} \cos(\theta+\varphi) & \cdots \\ \sin(\theta+\varphi) & \cdots \end{bmatrix}.$$

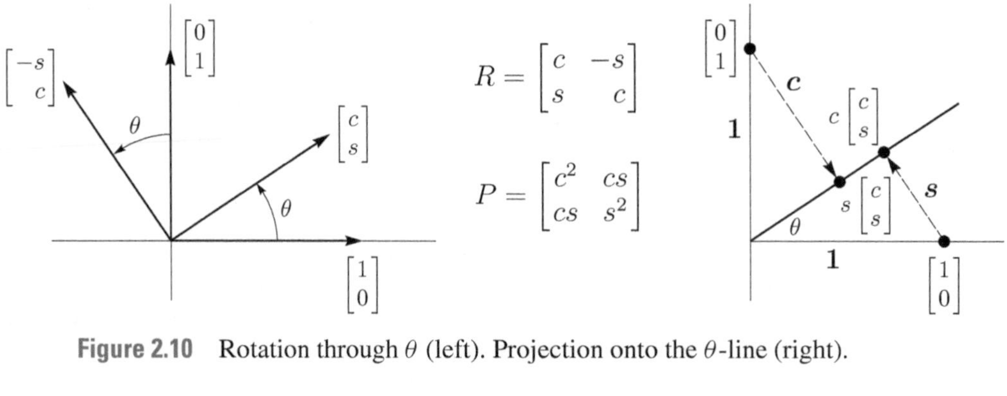

Figure 2.10 Rotation through θ (left). Projection onto the θ-line (right).

The last case contains the first two. The inverse appears when φ is $-\theta$, and the square appears when φ is $+\theta$. All three questions were decided by trigonometric identities (and they give a new way to remember those identities). It was no accident that all the answers were yes. *Matrix multiplication is defined exactly so that* ***the product of the matrices corresponds to the product of the transformations***.

2V Suppose A and B are linear transformations from **V** to **W** and from **U** to **V**. Their product AB starts with a vector u in **U**, goes to Bu in **V**, and finishes with ABu in **W**. This "composition" AB is again a linear transformation (from **U** to **W**). Its matrix is the product of the individual matrices representing A and B.

For $A_{\text{diff}}A_{\text{int}}$, the composite transformation was the identity (and $A_{\text{int}}A_{\text{diff}}$ annihilated all constants). For rotations, the order of multiplication does not matter. Then $\mathbf{U} = \mathbf{V} = \mathbf{W}$ is the x-y plane, and $Q_\theta Q_\varphi$ is the same as $Q_\varphi Q_\theta$. For a rotation and a reflection, the order makes a difference.

Technical note: To construct the matrices, we need bases for **V** and **W**, and then for **U** and **V**. By keeping the same basis for **V**, the product matrix goes correctly from the basis in **U** to the basis in **W**. If we distinguish the transformation A from its matrix (call that $[A]$), then the product rule 2V becomes extremely concise: $[AB] = [A][B]$. The rule for multiplying matrices in Chapter 1 was totally determined by this requirement—it must match the product of linear transformations.

2. Projection Figure 2.10 also shows the projection of $(1, 0)$ onto the θ-line. The length of the projection is $c = \cos\theta$. Notice that the *point* of projection is not (c, s), as I mistakenly thought; that vector has length 1 (it is the rotation), so we must multiply by c. Similarly the projection of $(0, 1)$ has length s, and falls at $s(c, s) = (cs, s^2)$. That gives the second column of the projection matrix P:

$$\textbf{Projection onto } \boldsymbol{\theta}\textbf{-line} \qquad P = \begin{bmatrix} c^2 & cs \\ cs & s^2 \end{bmatrix}.$$

This matrix has no inverse, because the transformation has no inverse. Points on the perpendicular line are projected onto the origin; that line is the nullspace of P. Points on the θ-line are projected to themselves! Projecting twice is the same as projecting once, and $P^2 = P$:

$$P^2 = \begin{bmatrix} c^2 & cs \\ cs & s^2 \end{bmatrix}^2 = \begin{bmatrix} c^2(c^2+s^2) & cs(c^2+s^2) \\ cs(c^2+s^2) & s^2(c^2+s^2) \end{bmatrix} = P.$$

Of course $c^2 + s^2 = \cos^2\theta + \sin^2\theta = 1$. ***A projection matrix equals its own square***.

3. Reflection Figure 2.11 shows the reflection of $(1, 0)$ in the θ-line. The length of the reflection equals the length of the original, as it did after rotation—but here the θ-line stays where it is. The perpendicular line reverses direction; all points go straight through the mirror. Linearity decides the rest.

$$\textbf{Reflection matrix} \qquad H = \begin{bmatrix} 2c^2-1 & 2cs \\ 2cs & 2s^2-1 \end{bmatrix}.$$

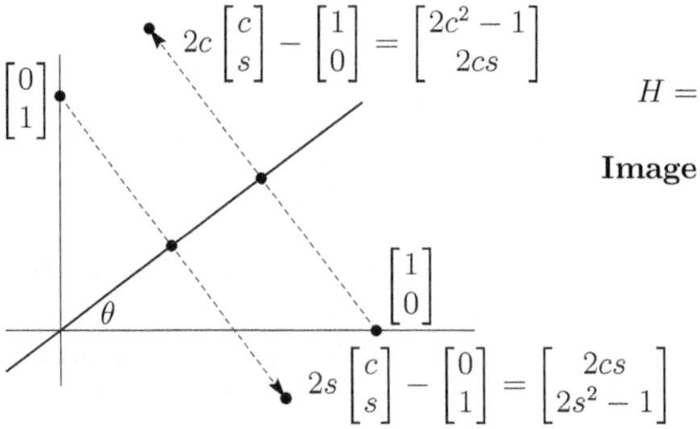

$$H = 2P - I = \begin{bmatrix} 2c^2-1 & 2cs \\ 2cs & 2s^2-1 \end{bmatrix}$$

Image + original = 2 × projection

$$Hx + x = 2Px$$

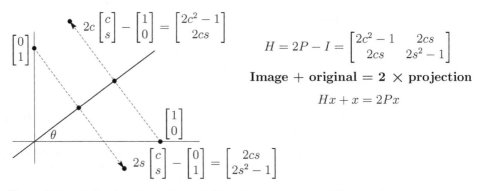

Figure 2.11 Reflection through the θ-line: the geometry and the matrix.

This matrix H has the remarkable property $H^2 = I$. ***Two reflections bring back the original.*** A reflection is its own inverse, $H = H^{-1}$, which is clear from the geometry but less clear from the matrix. One approach is through the relationship of reflections to projections: $H = 2P - I$. This means that $Hx + x = 2Px$—the image plus the original equals twice the projection. It also confirms that $H^2 = I$:

$$H^2 = (2P - I)^2 = 4P^2 - 4P + I = I, \qquad \text{since } P^2 = P.$$

Other transformations Ax can increase the length of x; stretching and shearing are in the exercises. Each example has a matrix to represent it—which is the main point of this section. But there is also the question of choosing a basis, and we emphasize that *the matrix depends on the choice of basis*. Suppose the first basis vector is ***on the θ-line*** and the second basis vector is ***perpendicular***:

(i) The projection matrix is back to $P = \begin{bmatrix} 1 & 0 \\ 0 & 0 \end{bmatrix}$. This matrix is constructed as always: its first column comes from the first basis vector (projected to itself). The second column comes from the basis vector that is projected to zero.

(ii) For reflections, that same basis gives $H = \begin{bmatrix} 1 & 0 \\ 0 & -1 \end{bmatrix}$. The second basis vector is reflected onto its negative, to produce this second column. The matrix H is still $2P - I$ when the same basis is used for H and P.

(iii) For rotations, the matrix is not changed. Those lines are still rotated through θ, and $Q = \begin{bmatrix} c & -s \\ s & c \end{bmatrix}$ as before.

The whole question of choosing the best basis is absolutely central, and we come back to it in Chapter 5. The goal is to make the matrix diagonal, as achieved for P and H. To make Q diagonal requires complex vectors, since all real vectors are rotated.

We mention here the effect on the matrix of a *change of basis*, while the linear transformation stays the same. ***The matrix A*** (or Q or P or H) ***is altered to $S^{-1}AS$.*** Thus a single transformation is represented by different matrices (via different bases, accounted for by S). The theory of eigenvectors will lead to this formula $S^{-1}AS$, and to the best basis.

Problem Set 2.6

1. What matrix has the effect of rotating every vector through 90° and then projecting the result onto the x-axis? What matrix represents projection onto the x-axis followed by projection onto the y-axis?

2. Does the product of 5 reflections and 8 rotations of the x-y plane produce a rotation or a reflection?

3. The matrix $A = \begin{bmatrix} 2 & 0 \\ 0 & 1 \end{bmatrix}$ produces a ***stretching*** in the x-direction. Draw the circle $x^2 + y^2 = 1$ and sketch around it the points $(2x, y)$ that result from multiplication by A. What shape is that curve?

4. Every straight line remains straight after a linear transformation. If z is halfway between x and y, show that Az is halfway between Ax and Ay.

5. The matrix $A = \begin{bmatrix} 1 & 0 \\ 3 & 1 \end{bmatrix}$ yields a ***shearing*** transformation, which leaves the y-axis unchanged. Sketch its effect on the x-axis, by indicating what happens to $(1, 0)$ and $(2, 0)$ and $(-1, 0)$—and how the whole axis is transformed.

6. What 3 by 3 matrices represent the transformations that
   (a) project every vector onto the x-y plane?
   (b) reflect every vector through the x-y plane?
   (c) rotate the x-y plane through 90°, leaving the z-axis alone?
   (d) rotate the x-y plane, then x-z, then y-z, through 90°?
   (e) carry out the same three rotations, but each one through 180°?

7. On the space $\mathbf{P}_3$ of cubic polynomials, what matrix represents d^2/dt^2? Construct the 4 by 4 matrix from the standard basis $1, t, t^2, t^3$. Find its nullspace and column space. What do they mean in terms of polynomials?

8. From the cubics $\mathbf{P}_3$ to the fourth-degree polynomials $\mathbf{P}_4$, what matrix represents multiplication by $2 + 3t$? The columns of the 5 by 4 matrix A come from applying the transformation to $1, t, t^2, t^3$.

9. The solutions to the linear differential equation $d^2u/dt^2 = u$ form a vector space (since combinations of solutions are still solutions). Find two independent solutions, to give a basis for that solution space.

10. With initial values $u = x$ and $du/dt = y$ at $t = 0$, what combination of basis vectors in Problem 9 solves $u'' = u$? This transformation from initial values to solution is linear. What is its 2 by 2 matrix (using $x = 1$, $y = 0$ and $x = 0$, $y = 1$ as basis for $\mathbf{V}$, and your basis for $\mathbf{W}$)?

11. Verify directly from $c^2 + s^2 = 1$ that reflection matrices satisfy $H^2 = I$.

12. Suppose A is a linear transformation from the x-y plane to itself. Why does $A^{-1}(x + y) = A^{-1}x + A^{-1}y$? If A is represented by the matrix M, explain why A^{-1} is represented by M^{-1}.

13. The product $(AB)C$ of linear transformations starts with a vector x and produces $u = Cx$. Then rule 2V applies AB to u and reaches $(AB)Cx$.

(a) Is this result the same as separately applying C then B then A?
(b) Is the result the same as applying BC followed by A? Parentheses are unnecessary and the associative law $(AB)C = A(BC)$ holds for linear transformations. This is the best proof of the same law for matrices.

14. Prove that T^2 is a linear transformation if T is linear (from $\mathbf{R}^3$ to $\mathbf{R}^3$).

15. The space of all 2 by 2 matrices has the four basis "vectors"

$$\begin{bmatrix} 1 & 0 \\ 0 & 0 \end{bmatrix}, \quad \begin{bmatrix} 0 & 1 \\ 0 & 0 \end{bmatrix}, \quad \begin{bmatrix} 0 & 0 \\ 1 & 0 \end{bmatrix}, \quad \begin{bmatrix} 0 & 0 \\ 0 & 1 \end{bmatrix}.$$

For the linear transformation of *transposing*, find its matrix A with respect to this basis. Why is $A^2 = I$?

16. Find the 4 by 4 cyclic permutation matrix: (x_1, x_2, x_3, x_4) is transformed to $Ax = (x_2, x_3, x_4, x_1)$. What is the effect of A^2? Show that $A^3 = A^{-1}$.

17. Find the 4 by 3 matrix A that represents a *right shift*: (x_1, x_2, x_3) is transformed to $(0, x_1, x_2, x_3)$. Find also the *left shift* matrix B from $\mathbf{R}^4$ back to $\mathbf{R}^3$, transforming (x_1, x_2, x_3, x_4) to (x_2, x_3, x_4). What are the products AB and BA?

18. In the vector space P_3 of all $p(x) = a_0 + a_1x + a_2x^2 + a_3x^3$, let $\mathbf{S}$ be the subset of polynomials with $\int_0^1 p(x)\,dx = 0$. Verify that $\mathbf{S}$ is a subspace and find a basis.

19. A *nonlinear* transformation is invertible if $T(x) = b$ has exactly one solution for every b. The example $T(x) = x^2$ is not invertible because $x^2 = b$ has two solutions for positive b and no solution for negative b. Which of the following transformations (from the real numbers $\mathbf{R}^1$ to the real numbers $\mathbf{R}^1$) are invertible? None are linear, not even (c).

(a) $T(x) = x^3$.
(b) $T(x) = e^x$.
(c) $T(x) = x + 11$.
(d) $T(x) = \cos x$.

20. What is the axis and the rotation angle for the transformation that takes (x_1, x_2, x_3) into (x_2, x_3, x_1)?

21. A linear transformation must leave the zero vector fixed: $T(0) = 0$. Prove this from $T(v + w) = T(v) + T(w)$ by choosing $w =$ ______. Prove it also from the requirement $T(cv) = cT(v)$ by choosing $c =$ ______.

22. Which of these transformations is not linear? The input is $v = (v_1, v_2)$.

(a) $T(v) = (v_2, v_1)$.
(b) $T(v) = (v_1, v_1)$.
(c) $T(v) = (0, v_1)$.
(d) $T(v) = (0, 1)$.

23. If S and T are linear with $S(v) = T(v) = v$, then $S(T(v)) = v$ or v^2?

24. Suppose $T(v) = v$, except that $T(0, v_2) = (0, 0)$. Show that this transformation satisfies $T(cv) = cT(v)$ but not $T(v + w) = T(v) + T(w)$.

25. Which of these transformations satisfy $T(v+w) = T(v)+T(w)$, and which satisfy $T(cv) = cT(v)$?

(a) $T(v) = v/\|v\|$.
(b) $T(v) = v_1 + v_2 + v_3$.
(c) $T(v) = (v_1, 2v_2, 3v_3)$.
(d) $T(v) =$ largest component of v.

26. For these transformations of $\mathbf{V} = \mathbf{R}^2$ to $\mathbf{W} = \mathbf{R}^2$, find $T(T(v))$.

(a) $T(v) = -v$.
(b) $T(v) = v + (1, 1)$.
(c) $T(v) = 90°$ rotation $= (-v_2, v_1)$.
(d) $T(v) =$ projection $= \left(\dfrac{v_1 + v_2}{2}, \dfrac{v_1 + v_2}{2}\right)$.

27. The "cyclic" transformation T is defined by $T(v_1, v_2, v_3) = (v_2, v_3, v_1)$. What is $T(T(T(v)))$? What is $T^{100}(v)$?

28. Find the *range* and *kernel* (those are new words for the column space and nullspace) of T.

(a) $T(v_1, v_2) = (v_2, v_1)$. (b) $T(v_1, v_2, v_3) = (v_1, v_2)$.
(c) $T(v_1, v_2) = (0, 0)$. (d) $T(v_1, v_2) = (v_1, v_1)$.

29. A linear transformation from $\mathbf{V}$ to $\mathbf{W}$ has an *inverse* from $\mathbf{W}$ to $\mathbf{V}$ when the range is all of $\mathbf{W}$ and the kernel contains only $v = 0$. Why are these transformations not invertible?

(a) $T(v_1, v_2) = (v_2, v_2)$ $\quad \mathbf{W} = \mathbf{R}^2$.
(b) $T(v_1, v_2) = (v_1, v_2, v_1 + v_2)$ $\quad \mathbf{W} = \mathbf{R}^3$.
(c) $T(v_1, v_2) = v_1$ $\quad \mathbf{W} = \mathbf{R}^1$.

30. Suppose a linear T transforms $(1, 1)$ to $(2, 2)$ and $(2, 0)$ to $(0, 0)$. Find $T(v)$ when

(a) $v = (2, 2)$. (b) $v = (3, 1)$. (c) $v = (-1, 1)$. (d) $v = (a, b)$.

Problems 31–35 may be harder. The input space V contains all 2 by 2 matrices M.

31. M is any 2 by 2 matrix and $A = \begin{bmatrix} 1 & 2 \\ 3 & 4 \end{bmatrix}$. The linear transformation T is defined by $T(M) = AM$. What rules of matrix multiplication show that T is linear?

32. Suppose $A = \begin{bmatrix} 1 & 2 \\ 3 & 6 \end{bmatrix}$. Show that the identity matrix I is not in the range of T. Find a nonzero matrix M such that $T(M) = AM$ is zero.

33. Suppose T transposes every matrix M. Try to find a matrix A that gives $AM = M^{\mathrm{T}}$ for every M. Show that no matrix A will do it. *To professors:* Is this a linear transformation that doesn't come from a matrix?

34. The transformation T that transposes every matrix is definitely linear. Which of these extra properties are true?

(a) $T^2 =$ identity transformation.
(b) The kernel of T is the zero matrix.
(c) Every matrix is in the range of T.
(d) $T(M) = -M$ is impossible.

35. Suppose $T(M) = \begin{bmatrix} 1 & 0 \\ 0 & 0 \end{bmatrix} \begin{bmatrix} M \end{bmatrix} \begin{bmatrix} 0 & 0 \\ 0 & 1 \end{bmatrix}$. Find a matrix with $T(M) \neq 0$. Describe all matrices with $T(M) = 0$ (the kernel of T) and all output matrices $T(M)$ (the range of T).

Problems 36–40 are about changing the basis.

36. (a) What matrix transforms $(1, 0)$ into $(2, 5)$ and transforms $(0, 1)$ to $(1, 3)$?

(b) What matrix transforms $(2, 5)$ to $(1, 0)$ and $(1, 3)$ to $(0, 1)$?
(c) Why does no matrix transform $(2, 6)$ to $(1, 0)$ and $(1, 3)$ to $(0, 1)$?

37. (a) What matrix M transforms $(1, 0)$ and $(0, 1)$ to (r, t) and (s, u)?
(b) What matrix N transforms (a, c) and (b, d) to $(1, 0)$ and $(0, 1)$?
(c) What condition on a, b, c, d will make part (b) impossible?

38. (a) How do M and N in Problem 37 yield the matrix that transforms (a, c) to (r, t) and (b, d) to (s, u)?
(b) What matrix transforms $(2, 5)$ to $(1, 1)$ and $(1, 3)$ to $(0, 2)$?

39. If you keep the same basis vectors but put them in a different order, the change-of-basis matrix M is a ______ matrix. If you keep the basis vectors in order but change their lengths, M is a ______ matrix.

40. The matrix that transforms $(1, 0)$ and $(0, 1)$ to $(1, 4)$ and $(1, 5)$ is $M =$ ______. The combination $a(1, 4) + b(1, 5)$ that equals $(1, 0)$ has $(a, b) = (\;\; , \;\;)$. How are those new coordinates of $(1, 0)$ related to M or M^{-1}?

41. What are the three equations for A, B, C if the parabola $Y = A + Bx + Cx^2$ equals 4 at $x = a$, 5 at $x = b$, and 6 at $x = c$? Find the determinant of the 3 by 3 matrix. For which numbers a, b, c will it be impossible to find this parabola Y?

42. Suppose v_1, v_2, v_3 are eigenvectors for T. This means $T(v_i) = \lambda_i v_i$ for $i = 1, 2, 3$. What is the matrix for T when the input and output bases are the v's?

43. Every invertible linear transformation can have I as its matrix. For the output basis just choose $w_i = T(v_i)$. Why must T be invertible?

44. Suppose T is reflection across the x-axis and S is reflection across the y-axis. The domain $\mathbf{V}$ is the x-y plane. If $v = (x, y)$ what is $S(T(v))$? Find a simpler description of the product ST.

45. Suppose T is reflection across the 45° line, and S is reflection across the y-axis. If $v = (2, 1)$ then $T(v) = (1, 2)$. Find $S(T(v))$ and $T(S(v))$. This shows that generally $ST \neq TS$.

46. Show that the product ST of two reflections is a rotation. Multiply these reflection matrices to find the rotation angle:

$$\begin{bmatrix} \cos 2\theta & \sin 2\theta \\ \sin 2\theta & -\cos 2\theta \end{bmatrix} \quad \begin{bmatrix} \cos 2\alpha & \sin 2\alpha \\ \sin 2\alpha & -\cos 2\alpha \end{bmatrix}.$$

47. The 4 by 4 *Hadamard matrix* is entirely $+1$ and -1:

$$H = \begin{bmatrix} 1 & 1 & 1 & 1 \\ 1 & -1 & 1 & -1 \\ 1 & 1 & -1 & -1 \\ 1 & -1 & -1 & 1 \end{bmatrix}.$$

Find H^{-1} and write $v = (7, 5, 3, 1)$ as a combination of the columns of H.

48. Suppose we have two bases $v_1, \ldots, v_n$ and $w_1, \ldots, w_n$ for $\mathbf{R}^n$. If a vector has coefficients b_i in one basis and c_i in the other basis, what is the change-of-basis matrix in $b = Mc$? Start from

$$b_1v_1 + \cdots + b_nv_n = Vb = c_1w_1 + \cdots + c_nw_n = Wc.$$

Your answer represents $T(v) = v$ with input basis of v's and output basis of w's. Because of different bases, the matrix is not I.

49. True or false: If we know $T(v)$ for n different nonzero vectors in $\mathbf{R}^n$, then we know $T(v)$ for every vector in $\mathbf{R}^n$.

50. (Recommended) Suppose all vectors x in the unit square $0 \le x_1 \le 1, 0 \le x_2 \le 1$ are transformed to Ax (A is 2 by 2).

(a) What is the shape of the transformed region (all Ax)?
(b) For which matrices A is that region a square?
(c) For which A is it a line?
(d) For which A is the new area still 1?

Chapter 2 Review Exercises

2.1 Find a basis for the following subspaces of $\mathbf{R}^4$:

(a) The vectors for which $x_1 = 2x_4$.
(b) The vectors for which $x_1 + x_2 + x_3 = 0$ and $x_3 + x_4 = 0$.
(c) The subspace spanned by $(1, 1, 1, 1)$, $(1, 2, 3, 4)$, and $(2, 3, 4, 5)$.

2.2 By giving a basis, describe a two-dimensional subspace of $\mathbf{R}^3$ that contains none of the coordinate vectors $(1, 0, 0)$, $(0, 1, 0)$, $(0, 0, 1)$.

2.3 True or false, with counterexample if false:

(a) If the vectors $x_1, \ldots, x_m$ span a subspace S, then $\dim S = m$.
(b) The intersection of two subspaces of a vector space cannot be empty.
(c) If $Ax = Ay$, then $x = y$.
(d) The row space of A has a unique basis that can be computed by reducing A to echelon form.
(e) If a square matrix A has independent columns, so does A^2.

2.4 What is the echelon form U of A?

$$A = \begin{bmatrix} 1 & 2 & 0 & 2 & 1 \\ -1 & -2 & 1 & 1 & 0 \\ 1 & 2 & -3 & -7 & -2 \end{bmatrix}.$$

What are the dimensions of its four fundamental subspaces?

2.5 Find the rank and the nullspace of

$$A = \begin{bmatrix} 0 & 0 & 1 \\ 0 & 0 & 1 \\ 1 & 1 & 1 \end{bmatrix} \quad \text{and} \quad B = \begin{bmatrix} 0 & 0 & 1 & 2 \\ 0 & 0 & 1 & 2 \\ 1 & 1 & 1 & 0 \end{bmatrix}.$$

2.6 Find bases for the four fundamental subspaces associated with

$$A = \begin{bmatrix} 1 & 2 \\ 3 & 6 \end{bmatrix}, \qquad B = \begin{bmatrix} 0 & 0 \\ 1 & 2 \end{bmatrix}, \qquad C = \begin{bmatrix} 1 & 1 & 0 & 0 \\ 0 & 1 & 0 & 1 \end{bmatrix}.$$

2.7 What is the most general solution to $u + v + w = 1$, $u - w = 2$?

2.8 (a) Construct a matrix whose nullspace contains the vector $x = (1, 1, 2)$.
(b) Construct a matrix whose left nullspace contains $y = (1, 5)$.
(c) Construct a matrix whose column space is spanned by $(1, 1, 2)$ and whose row space is spanned by $(1, 5)$.
(d) If you are given any three vectors in $\mathbf{R}^6$ and any three vectors in $\mathbf{R}^5$, is there a 6 by 5 matrix whose column space is spanned by the first three and whose row space is spanned by the second three?

2.9 In the vector space of 2 by 2 matrices,
(a) is the set of rank 1 matrices a subspace?
(b) what subspace is spanned by the permutation matrices?
(c) what subspace is spanned by the positive matrices (all $a_{ij} > 0$)?
(d) what subspace is spanned by the invertible matrices?

2.10 Invent a vector space that contains all linear transformations from $\mathbf{R}^n$ to $\mathbf{R}^n$. You have to decide on a rule for addition. What is its dimension?

2.11 (a) Find the rank of A, and give a basis for its nullspace.

$$A = LU = \begin{bmatrix} 1 & & & \\ 2 & 1 & & \\ 2 & 1 & 1 & \\ 3 & 2 & 4 & 1 \end{bmatrix} \begin{bmatrix} 1 & 2 & 0 & 1 & 2 & 1 \\ 0 & 0 & 2 & 2 & 0 & 0 \\ 0 & 0 & 0 & 0 & 0 & 1 \\ 0 & 0 & 0 & 0 & 0 & 0 \end{bmatrix}.$$

(b) The first 3 rows of U are a basis for the row space of A—true or false? Columns 1, 3, 6 of U are a basis for the column space of A—true or false? The four rows of A are a basis for the row space of A—true or false?
(c) Find as many linearly independent vectors b as possible for which $Ax = b$ has a solution.
(d) In elimination on A, what multiple of the third row is subtracted to knock out the fourth row?

2.12 If A is an n by $n - 1$ matrix, and its rank is $n - 2$, what is the dimension of its nullspace?

2.13 Use elimination to find the triangular factors in $A = LU$, if

$$A = \begin{bmatrix} a & a & a & a \\ a & b & b & b \\ a & b & c & c \\ a & b & c & d \end{bmatrix}.$$

Under what conditions on the numbers a, b, c, d are the columns linearly independent?

2.14 Do the vectors $(1, 1, 3)$, $(2, 3, 6)$, and $(1, 4, 3)$ form a basis for $\mathbf{R}^3$?

2.15 What do you know about $C(A)$ when the number of solutions to $Ax = b$ is

(a) 0 or 1, depending on b.
(b) ∞, independent of b.
(c) 0 or ∞, depending on b.
(d) 1, regardless of b.

2.16 In the previous exercise, how is r related to m and n in each example?

2.17 If x is a vector in $\mathbf{R}^n$, and $x^{\mathrm{T}}y = 0$ for every y, prove that $x = 0$.

2.18 If A is an n by n matrix such that $A^2 = A$ and rank $A = n$, prove that $A = I$.

2.19 What subspace of 3 by 3 matrices is spanned by the elementary matrices E_{ij}, with 1s on the diagonal and at most one nonzero entry below?

2.20 How many 5 by 5 permutation matrices are there? Are they linearly independent? Do they span the space of all 5 by 5 matrices? No need to write them all down.

2.21 What is the rank of the n by n matrix with every entry equal to 1? How about the "checkerboard matrix," with $a_{ij} = 0$ when $i + j$ is even, $a_{ij} = 1$ when $i + j$ is odd?

2.22 (a) $Ax = b$ has a solution under what conditions on b, for the following A and b?

$$A = \begin{bmatrix} 1 & 2 & 0 & 3 \\ 0 & 0 & 0 & 0 \\ 2 & 4 & 0 & 1 \end{bmatrix} \quad \text{and} \quad b = \begin{bmatrix} b_1 \\ b_2 \\ b_3 \end{bmatrix}.$$

(b) Find a basis for the nullspace of A.
(c) Find the general solution to $Ax = b$, when a solution exists.
(d) Find a basis for the column space of A.
(e) What is the rank of A^{T}?

2.23 How can you construct a matrix that transforms the coordinate vectors e_1, e_2, e_3 into three given vectors v_1, v_2, v_3? When will that matrix be invertible?

2.24 If e_1, e_2, e_3 are in the column space of a 3 by 5 matrix, does it have a left-inverse? Does it have a right-inverse?

2.25 Suppose T is the linear transformation on $\mathbf{R}^3$ that takes each point (u, v, w) to $(u + v + w, u + v, u)$. Describe what T^{-1} does to the point (x, y, z).

2.26 *True or false*?

(a) Every subspace of $\mathbf{R}^4$ is the nullspace of some matrix.
(b) If A has the same nullspace as A^{T}, the matrix must be square.
(c) The transformation that takes x to $mx + b$ is linear (from $\mathbf{R}^1$ to $\mathbf{R}^1$).

2.27 Find bases for the four fundamental subspaces of

$$A_1 = \begin{bmatrix} 1 & 2 & 0 & 3 \\ 0 & 2 & 2 & 2 \\ 0 & 0 & 0 & 0 \\ 0 & 0 & 0 & 4 \end{bmatrix} \quad \text{and} \quad A_2 = \begin{bmatrix} 1 \\ 1 \\ 1 \end{bmatrix} \begin{bmatrix} 1 & 4 \end{bmatrix}.$$

2.28 (a) If the rows of A are linearly independent (A is m by n) then the rank is _______, the column space is _______, and the left nullspace is _______.
(b) If A is 8 by 10 with a two-dimensional nullspace, show that $Ax = b$ can be solved for every b.

2.29 Describe the linear transformations of the x-y plane that are represented with standard basis (1, 0) and (0, 1) by the matrices

$$A_1 = \begin{bmatrix} 1 & 0 \\ 0 & -1 \end{bmatrix}, \quad A_2 = \begin{bmatrix} 1 & 0 \\ 2 & 1 \end{bmatrix}, \quad A_3 = \begin{bmatrix} 0 & 1 \\ -1 & 0 \end{bmatrix}.$$

2.30 (a) If A is square, show that the nullspace of A^2 contains the nullspace of A.
(b) Show also that the column space of A^2 is contained in the column space of A.

2.31 When does the rank-1 matrix $A = uv^{\mathrm{T}}$ have $A^2 = 0$?

2.32 (a) Find a basis for the space of all vectors in $\mathbf{R}^6$ with $x_1 + x_2 = x_3 + x_4 = x_5 + x_6$.
(b) Find a matrix with that subspace as its nullspace.
(c) Find a matrix with that subspace as its column space.

2.33 Suppose the matrices in $PA = LU$ are

$$\begin{bmatrix} 0 & 1 & 0 & 0 \\ 1 & 0 & 0 & 0 \\ 0 & 0 & 0 & 1 \\ 0 & 0 & 1 & 0 \end{bmatrix} \begin{bmatrix} 0 & 0 & 1 & -3 & 2 \\ 2 & -1 & 4 & 2 & 1 \\ 4 & -2 & 9 & 1 & 4 \\ 2 & -1 & 5 & -1 & 5 \end{bmatrix}$$

$$= \begin{bmatrix} 1 & 0 & 0 & 0 \\ 0 & 1 & 0 & 0 \\ 1 & 1 & 1 & 0 \\ 2 & 1 & 0 & 1 \end{bmatrix} \begin{bmatrix} 2 & -1 & 4 & 2 & 1 \\ 0 & 0 & 1 & -3 & 2 \\ 0 & 0 & 0 & 0 & 2 \\ 0 & 0 & 0 & 0 & 0 \end{bmatrix}.$$

(a) What is the rank of A?
(b) What is a basis for the row space of A?
(c) *True or false*: Rows 1, 2, 3 of A are linearly independent.
(d) What is a basis for the column space of A?
(e) What is the dimension of the left nullspace of A?
(f) What is the general solution to $Ax = 0$?

Chapter

3 Orthogonality

3.1 ORTHOGONAL VECTORS AND SUBSPACES

A basis is a set of independent vectors that span a space. Geometrically, it is a set of coordinate axes. A vector space is defined without those axes, but every time I think of the x-y plane or three-dimensional space or $\mathbf{R}^n$, the axes are there. They are usually perpendicular! *The coordinate axes that the imagination constructs are practically always orthogonal.* In choosing a basis, we tend to choose an orthogonal basis.

The idea of an orthogonal basis is one of the foundations of linear algebra. We need a basis to convert geometric constructions into algebraic calculations, and we need an orthogonal basis to make those calculations simple. A further specialization makes the basis just about optimal: The vectors should have *length* 1. For an ***orthonormal basis*** (orthogonal unit vectors), we will find

1. the length $\|x\|$ of a vector;
2. the test $x^{\mathrm{T}}y = 0$ for perpendicular vectors; and
3. how to create perpendicular vectors from linearly independent vectors.

More than just vectors, *subspaces* can also be perpendicular. We will discover, so beautifully and simply that it will be a delight to see, that ***the fundamental subspaces meet at right angles***. Those four subspaces are perpendicular in pairs, two in $\mathbf{R}^m$ and two in $\mathbf{R}^n$. That will complete the fundamental theorem of linear algebra.

The first step is to find the ***length of a vector***. It is denoted by $\|x\|$, and in two dimensions it comes from the hypotenuse of a right triangle (Figure 3.1a). The square of the length was given a long time ago by Pythagoras: $\|x\|^2 = x_1^2 + x_2^2$.

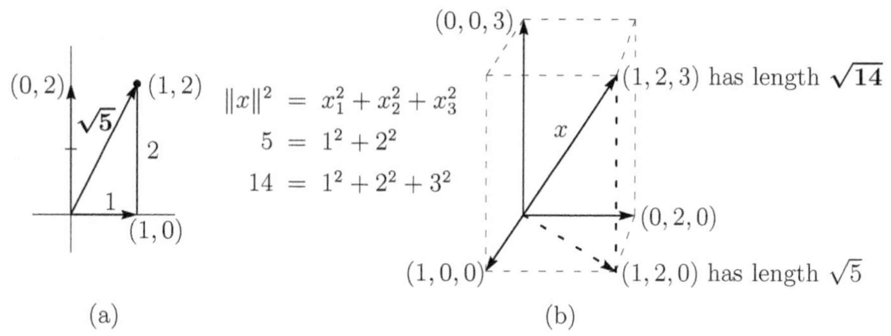

Figure 3.1 The length of vectors (x_1, x_2) and (x_1, x_2, x_3).

In three-dimensional space, $x = (x_1, x_2, x_3)$ is the diagonal of a box (Figure 3.1b). Its length comes from *two* applications of the Pythagorean formula. The two-dimensional case takes care of $(x_1, x_2, 0) = (1, 2, 0)$ across the base. This forms a right angle with the vertical side $(0, 0, x_3) = (0, 0, 3)$. The hypotenuse of the bold triangle (Pythagoras again) is the length $\|x\|$ we want:

$$\textbf{Length in 3D} \qquad \|x\|^2 = 1^2 + 2^2 + 3^2 \quad \text{and} \quad \|x\| = \sqrt{x_1^2 + x_2^2 + x_3^2}.$$

The extension to $x = (x_1, \ldots, x_n)$ in n dimensions is immediate. By Pythagoras $n - 1$ times, ***the length*** $\|\boldsymbol{x}\|$ ***in*** $\mathbf{R}^n$ ***is the positive square root of*** $\boldsymbol{x}^{\mathrm{T}}\boldsymbol{x}$:

$$\textbf{Length squared} \qquad \|x\|^2 = x_1^2 + x_2^2 + \cdots + x_n^2 = x^{\mathrm{T}}x. \tag{1}$$

The sum of squares matches $x^{\mathrm{T}}x$—and the length of $x = (1, 2, -3)$ is $\sqrt{14}$:

$$x^{\mathrm{T}}x = \begin{bmatrix} 1 & 2 & -3 \end{bmatrix} \begin{bmatrix} 1 \\ 2 \\ -3 \end{bmatrix} = 1^2 + 2^2 + (-3)^2 = 14.$$

Orthogonal Vectors

How can we decide whether two vectors x and y are perpendicular? What is the test for orthogonality in Figure 3.2? In the plane spanned by x and y, those vectors are orthogonal provided they form a *right triangle*. We go back to $a^2 + b^2 = c^2$:

$$\textbf{Sides of a right triangle} \qquad \|x\|^2 + \|y\|^2 = \|x - y\|^2. \tag{2}$$

Applying the length formula (1), this test for orthogonality in $\mathbf{R}^n$ becomes

$$\left(x_1^2 + \cdots + x_n^2\right) + \left(y_1^2 + \cdots + y_n^2\right) = (x_1 - y_1)^2 + \cdots + (x_n - y_n)^2.$$

The right-hand side has an extra $-2x_i y_i$ from each $(x_i - y_i)^2$:

$$\text{right-hand side} = \left(x_1^2 + \cdots + x_n^2\right) - 2(x_1 y_1 + \cdots + x_n y_n) + \left(y_1^2 + \cdots + y_n^2\right).$$

We have a right triangle when that sum of cross-product terms $x_i y_i$ *is zero*:

$$\textbf{Orthogonal vectors} \qquad x^{\mathrm{T}}y = x_1 y_1 + \cdots + x_n y_n = 0. \tag{3}$$

This sum is $x^{\mathrm{T}}y = \sum x_i y_i = y^{\mathrm{T}}x$, the row vector x^{T} times the column vector y:

$$\textbf{Inner product} \qquad x^{\mathrm{T}}y = \begin{bmatrix} x_1 & \ldots & x_n \end{bmatrix} \begin{bmatrix} y_1 \\ \vdots \\ y_n \end{bmatrix} = x_1 y_1 + \cdots + x_n y_n. \tag{4}$$

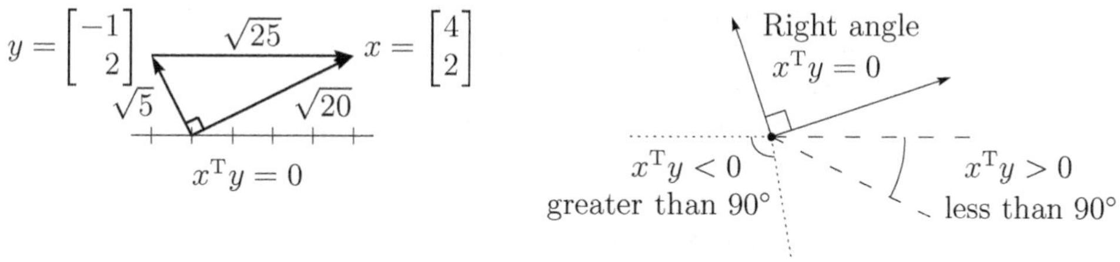

Figure 3.2 A right triangle with $5 + 20 = 25$. Dotted angle 100°, dashed angle 30°.

This number is sometimes called the scalar product or dot product, and denoted by (x, y) or $x \cdot y$. We will use the name ***inner product*** and keep the notation x^Ty.

3A The inner product x^Ty is zero if and only if x and y are orthogonal vectors. If $x^Ty > 0$, their angle is less than 90°. If $x^Ty < 0$, their angle is greater than 90°.

The length squared is the inner product of x with itself: $x^Tx = x_1^2 + \cdots + x_n^2 = \|x\|^2$. The only vector with length zero—the only vector orthogonal to itself—is the zero vector. This vector $x = 0$ is orthogonal to every vector in $\mathbf{R}^n$.

Example 1 $(2, 2, -1)$ is orthogonal to $(-1, 2, 2)$. Both have length $\sqrt{4+4+1} = 3$.

Useful fact: **If nonzero vectors $v_1, \ldots, v_k$ are mutually orthogonal** (every vector is perpendicular to every other), **then those vectors are linearly independent**.

Proof Suppose $c_1v_1 + \cdots + c_kv_k = 0$. To show that c_1 must be zero, take the inner product of both sides with v_1. Orthogonality of the v's leaves only one term:

$$v_1^T(c_1v_1 + \cdots + c_kv_k) = c_1v_1^Tv_1 = 0. \tag{5}$$

The vectors are nonzero, so $v_1^Tv_1 \neq 0$ and therefore $c_1 = 0$. The same is true of every c_i. The only combination of the v's producing zero has all $c_i = 0$: *independence*! ■

The coordinate vectors $e_1, \ldots, e_n$ in $\mathbf{R}^n$ are the most important orthogonal vectors. Those are the columns of the identity matrix. They form the simplest basis for $\mathbf{R}^n$, and they are *unit vectors*—each has length $\|e_i\| = 1$. They point along the coordinate axes. If these axes are rotated, the result is a new **orthonormal basis**: a new system of *mutually orthogonal unit vectors*. In $\mathbf{R}^2$ we have $\cos^2\theta + \sin^2\theta = 1$:

Orthonormal vectors in $\mathbf{R}^2$ $\quad v_1 = (\cos\theta, \sin\theta)$ and $v_2 = (-\sin\theta, \cos\theta)$.

Orthogonal Subspaces

We come to the orthogonality of two subspaces. **Every vector** *in one subspace must be orthogonal to* **every vector** *in the other subspace*. Subspaces of $\mathbf{R}^3$ can have dimension 0, 1, 2, or 3. The subspaces are represented by lines or planes through the origin—and in the extreme cases, by the origin alone or the whole space. The subspace $\{0\}$ is orthogonal to all subspaces. A line can be orthogonal to another line, or it can be orthogonal to a plane, but *a plane cannot be orthogonal to a plane*.

I have to admit that the front wall and side wall of a room look like perpendicular planes in $\mathbf{R}^3$. But by our definition, that is not so! There are lines v and w in the front and side walls that do not meet at a right angle. The line along the corner is in *both* walls, and it is certainly not orthogonal to itself.

3B Two subspaces $\mathbf{V}$ and $\mathbf{W}$ of the same space $\mathbf{R}^n$ are *orthogonal* if every vector v in $\mathbf{V}$ is orthogonal to every vector w in $\mathbf{W}$: $v^{\mathrm{T}}w = 0$ for all v and w.

Example 2 Suppose $\mathbf{V}$ is the plane spanned by $v_1 = (1, 0, 0, 0)$ and $v_2 = (1, 1, 0, 0)$. If $\mathbf{W}$ is the line spanned by $w = (0, 0, 4, 5)$, then w is orthogonal to both v's. The line $\mathbf{W}$ will be orthogonal to the whole plane $\mathbf{V}$.

In this case, with subspaces of dimension 2 and 1 in $\mathbf{R}^4$, there is room for a third subspace. The line $\mathbf{L}$ through $z = (0, 0, 5, -4)$ is perpendicular to $\mathbf{V}$ and $\mathbf{W}$. Then the dimensions add to $2 + 1 + 1 = 4$. What space is perpendicular to all of $\mathbf{V}$, $\mathbf{W}$, and $\mathbf{L}$?

The important orthogonal subspaces don't come by accident, and they come two at a time. In fact orthogonal subspaces are unavoidable: ***They are the fundamental subspaces!*** The first pair is the *nullspace* and *row space*. Those are subspaces of $\mathbf{R}^n$—the rows have n components and so does the vector x in $Ax = 0$. We have to show, using $Ax = 0$, that ***the rows of A are orthogonal to the nullspace vector x***.

3C **Fundamental theorem of orthogonality** The row space is orthogonal to the nullspace (in $\mathbf{R}^n$). The column space is orthogonal to the left nullspace (in $\mathbf{R}^m$).

First proof Suppose x is a vector in the nullspace. Then $Ax = 0$, and this system of m equations can be written out as rows of A multiplying x:

Every row is orthogonal to x

$$Ax = \begin{bmatrix} \cdots & \textbf{row 1} & \cdots \\ \cdots & \text{row 2} & \cdots \\ & \vdots & \\ \cdots & \text{row } m & \cdots \end{bmatrix} \begin{bmatrix} x_1 \\ x_2 \\ \vdots \\ x_n \end{bmatrix} = \begin{bmatrix} \mathbf{0} \\ 0 \\ \vdots \\ 0 \end{bmatrix}. \tag{6}$$

The main point is already in the first equation: *row* 1 *is orthogonal to x*. Their inner product is zero; that is equation 1. Every right-hand side is zero, so x is orthogonal to every row. Therefore x is orthogonal to every *combination* of the rows. Each x in the nullspace is orthogonal to each vector in the row space, so $\boldsymbol{N}(A) \perp \boldsymbol{C}(A^{\mathrm{T}})$.

The other pair of orthogonal subspaces comes from $A^{\mathrm{T}}y = 0$, or $y^{\mathrm{T}}A = 0$:

$$y^{\mathrm{T}}A = \begin{bmatrix} y_1 & \cdots & y_m \end{bmatrix} \begin{bmatrix} \mathbf{c} & & \text{c} \\ \mathbf{o} & & \text{o} \\ \mathbf{l} & & \text{l} \\ \mathbf{u} & \cdots & \text{u} \\ \mathbf{m} & & \text{m} \\ \mathbf{n} & & \text{n} \\ & & \\ \mathbf{1} & & n \end{bmatrix} = \begin{bmatrix} \mathbf{0} & \cdots & 0 \end{bmatrix}. \tag{7}$$

The vector y is orthogonal to every column. The equation says so, from the zeros on the right-hand side. Therefore y is orthogonal to every combination of the columns.

It is orthogonal to the column space, and it is a typical vector in the left nullspace: $N(A^T) \perp C(A)$. This is the same as the first half of the theorem, with A replaced by A^T. ■

Second proof The contrast with this "coordinate-free proof" should be useful to the reader. It shows a more "abstract" method of reasoning. I wish I knew which proof is clearer, and more permanently understood.

If x is in the nullspace then $Ax = 0$. If v is in the row space, it is a combination of the rows: $v = A^T z$ for some vector z. Now, in one line:

$$\textbf{Nullspace} \perp \textbf{Row space} \qquad v^T x = (A^T z)^T x = z^T A x = z^T 0 = 0. \tag{8}$$

■

Example 3 Suppose A has rank 1, so its row space and column space are lines:

$$\textbf{Rank-1 matrix} \qquad A = \begin{bmatrix} 1 & 3 \\ 2 & 6 \\ 3 & 9 \end{bmatrix}.$$

The rows are multiples of $(1, 3)$. The nullspace contains $x = (-3, 1)$, which is orthogonal to all the rows. The nullspace and row space are perpendicular lines in $\mathbf{R}^2$:

$$\begin{bmatrix} 1 & 3 \end{bmatrix} \begin{bmatrix} 3 \\ -1 \end{bmatrix} = 0 \quad \text{and} \quad \begin{bmatrix} 2 & 6 \end{bmatrix} \begin{bmatrix} 3 \\ -1 \end{bmatrix} = 0 \quad \text{and} \quad \begin{bmatrix} 3 & 9 \end{bmatrix} \begin{bmatrix} 3 \\ -1 \end{bmatrix} = 0.$$

In contrast, the other two subspaces are in $\mathbf{R}^3$. The column space is the line through $(1, 2, 3)$. The left nullspace must be the *perpendicular plane* $y_1 + 2y_2 + 3y_3 = 0$. That equation is exactly the content of $y^T A = 0$.

The first two subspaces (the two lines) had dimensions $1 + 1 = 2$ in the space $\mathbf{R}^2$. The second pair (line and plane) had dimensions $1 + 2 = 3$ in the space $\mathbf{R}^3$. In general, *the row space and nullspace have dimensions that add to* $r + (n - r) = n$. The other pair adds to $r + (m - r) = m$. Something more than orthogonality is occurring, and I have to ask your patience about that one further point: **the dimensions**.

It is certainly true that the nullspace is perpendicular to the row space—but it is not the whole truth. $N(A)$ *contains every vector orthogonal to the row space*. The nullspace was formed from *all* solutions to $Ax = 0$.

DEFINITION Given a subspace $\mathbf{V}$ of $\mathbf{R}^n$, the space of *all* vectors orthogonal to $\mathbf{V}$ is called the **orthogonal complement** of $\mathbf{V}$. It is denoted by $\mathbf{V}^\perp$ = "$\mathbf{V}$ perp."

Using this terminology, the nullspace is the orthogonal complement of the row space: $N(A) = (C(A^T))^\perp$. At the same time, the row space contains all vectors that are orthogonal to the nullspace. A vector z can't be orthogonal to the nullspace but outside the row space. Adding z as an extra row of A would enlarge the row space, but we know that there is a fixed formula $r + (n - r) = n$:

$$\textbf{Dimension formula} \qquad \text{dim(row space)} + \text{dim(nullspace)} = \text{number of columns}.$$

Every vector orthogonal to the nullspace is in the row space: $C(A^T) = (N(A))^\perp$.

The same reasoning applied to A^{T} produces the dual result: *The left nullspace* $\boldsymbol{N}(A^{\mathrm{T}})$ *and the column space* $\boldsymbol{C}(A)$ *are orthogonal complements*. Their dimensions add up to $(m-r)+r=m$. This completes the second half of the fundamental theorem of linear algebra. The first half gave the dimensions of the four subspaces, including the fact that row rank = column rank. Now we know that those subspaces are perpendicular. More than that, the subspaces are orthogonal complements.

3D Fundamental Theorem of Linear Algebra, Part II

The nullspace is the *orthogonal complement* of the row space in $\mathbf{R}^n$.
The left nullspace is the *orthogonal complement* of the column space in $\mathbf{R}^m$.

To repeat, the row space contains everything orthogonal to the nullspace. The column space contains everything orthogonal to the left nullspace. That is just a sentence, hidden in the middle of the book, but *it decides exactly which equations can be solved*! Looked at directly, $Ax=b$ requires b to be in the column space. Looked at indirectly, $Ax=b$ **requires b to be perpendicular to the left nullspace**.

3E $Ax=b$ is solvable if and only if $y^{\mathrm{T}}b=0$ whenever $y^{\mathrm{T}}A=0$.

The direct approach was "b must be a combination of the columns." The indirect approach is "b must be orthogonal to every vector that is orthogonal to the columns." That doesn't sound like an improvement (to put it mildly). But if only one or two vectors are orthogonal to the columns, it is much easier to check those one or two conditions $y^{\mathrm{T}}b=0$. A good example is Kirchhoff's Voltage Law in Section 2.5. Testing for zero around loops is much easier than recognizing combinations of the columns.

***When the left-hand sides of $Ax=b$ add to zero, the right-hand sides must, too*:**

$$\begin{aligned} x_1-x_2&=b_1\\ x_2-x_3&=b_2\\ x_3-x_1&=b_3 \end{aligned} \quad \text{is solvable if and only if } b_1+b_2+b_3=0. \text{ Here } A=\begin{bmatrix} 1 & -1 & 0\\ 0 & 1 & -1\\ -1 & 0 & 1 \end{bmatrix}.$$

This test $b_1+b_2+b_3=0$ makes b orthogonal to $y=(1,1,1)$ in the left nullspace. By the Fundamental Theorem, b is a combination of the columns!

The Matrix and the Subspaces

We emphasize that $\mathbf{V}$ and $\mathbf{W}$ can be orthogonal without being complements. Their dimensions can be too small. The line $\mathbf{V}$ spanned by $(0,1,0)$ is orthogonal to the line $\mathbf{W}$ spanned by $(0,0,1)$, but $\mathbf{V}$ is not $\mathbf{W}^{\perp}$. The orthogonal complement of $\mathbf{W}$ is a two-dimensional plane, and the line is only part of $\mathbf{W}^{\perp}$. When the dimensions are right, orthogonal subspaces *are* necessarily orthogonal complements:

$$\text{If} \quad \mathbf{W}=\mathbf{V}^{\perp} \quad \text{then} \quad \mathbf{V}=\mathbf{W}^{\perp} \quad \text{and} \quad \dim\mathbf{V}+\dim\mathbf{W}=n.$$

In other words $\mathbf{V}^{\perp\perp}=\mathbf{V}$. The dimensions of $\mathbf{V}$ and $\mathbf{W}$ are right, and the whole space $\mathbf{R}^n$ is being decomposed into two perpendicular parts (Figure 3.3).

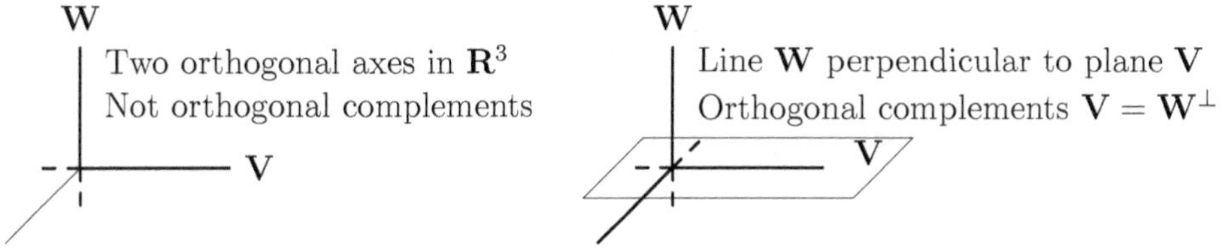

Figure 3.3 Orthogonal complements in $\mathbf{R}^3$: a plane and a line (not two lines).

Splitting $\mathbf{R}^n$ into orthogonal parts will split every vector into $x = v + w$. The vector v is the projection onto the subspace $\mathbf{V}$. The orthogonal component w is the projection of x onto $\mathbf{W}$. The next sections show how to find those projections of x. They lead to what is probably the most important figure in the book (Figure 3.4).

Figure 3.4 summarizes the fundamental theorem of linear algebra. It illustrates the true effect of a matrix—what is happening inside the multiplication Ax. The nullspace is carried to the zero vector. Every Ax is in the column space. Nothing is carried to the left nullspace. *The real action is between the row space and column space*, and you see it by looking at a typical vector x. It has a "row space component" and a "nullspace component," with $x = x_r + x_n$. When multiplied by A, this is $Ax = Ax_r + Ax_n$:

The nullspace component goes to zero: $Ax_n = 0$.
The row space component goes to the column space: $Ax_r = Ax$.

Of course everything goes to the column space—the matrix cannot do anything else. I tried to make the row and column spaces the same size, with equal dimension r.

3F From the row space to the column space, A is actually invertible. Every vector b in the column space comes from exactly one vector x_r in the row space.

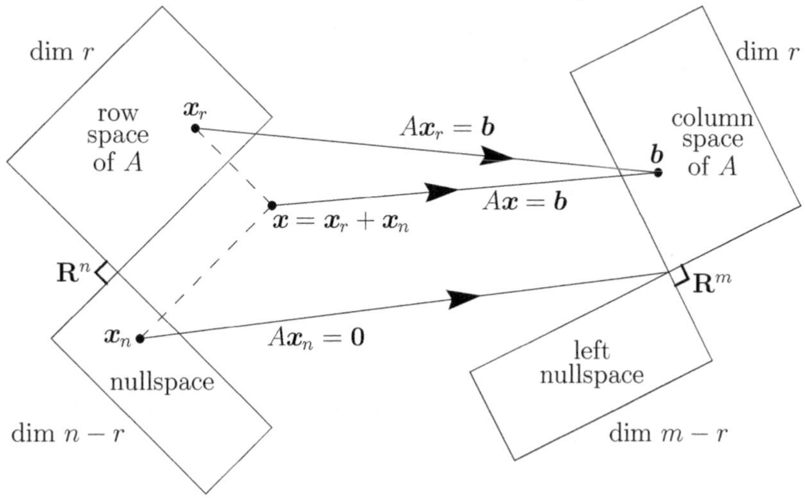

Figure 3.4 The true action $Ax = A(x_{\mathbf{row}} + x_{\mathbf{null}})$ of any m by n matrix.

Proof Every b in the column space is a combination Ax of the columns. In fact, b is Ax_r, with x_r in the row space, since the nullspace component gives $Ax_n = 0$. If another vector x_r' in the row space gives $Ax_r' = b$, then $A(x_r - x_r') = b - b = 0$. This puts $x_r - x_r'$ in the nullspace and the row space, which makes it orthogonal to itself. Therefore it is zero, and $x_r = x_r'$. Exactly one vector in the row space is carried to b. ■

Every matrix transforms its row space onto its column space.

On those r-dimensional spaces A is invertible. On its nullspace A is zero. When A is diagonal, you see the invertible submatrix holding the r nonzeros.

A^{T} goes in the opposite direction, from $\mathbf{R}^m$ to $\mathbf{R}^n$ and from $\boldsymbol{C}(A)$ back to $\boldsymbol{C}(A^{\mathrm{T}})$. Of course the transpose is not the inverse! A^{T} moves the spaces correctly, but not the individual vectors. That honor belongs to A^{-1} if it exists—and it only exists if $r = m = n$. We cannot ask A^{-1} to bring back a whole nullspace out of the zero vector.

When A^{-1} fails to exist, the best substitute is the ***pseudoinverse*** A^+. This inverts A where that is possible: $A^+Ax = x$ for x in the row space. On the left nullspace, nothing can be done: $A^+y = 0$. Thus A^+ inverts A where it is invertible, and has the same rank r. One formula for A^+ depends on the ***singular value decomposition***—for which we first need to know about eigenvalues.

Problem Set 3.1

1. Find the lengths and the inner product of $x = (1, 4, 0, 2)$ and $y = (2, -2, 1, 3)$.

2. Give an example in $\mathbf{R}^2$ of linearly independent vectors that are not orthogonal. Also, give an example of orthogonal vectors that are not independent.

3. Two lines in the plane are perpendicular when the product of their slopes is -1. Apply this to the vectors $x = (x_1, x_2)$ and $y = (y_1, y_2)$, whose slopes are x_2/x_1 and y_2/y_1, to derive again the orthogonality condition $x^{\mathrm{T}}y = 0$.

4. How do we know that the ith row of an invertible matrix B is orthogonal to the jth column of B^{-1}, if $i \neq j$?

5. Which pairs are orthogonal among the vectors v_1, v_2, v_3, v_4?

$$v_1 = \begin{bmatrix} 1 \\ 2 \\ -2 \\ 1 \end{bmatrix}, \quad v_2 = \begin{bmatrix} 4 \\ 0 \\ 4 \\ 0 \end{bmatrix}, \quad v_3 = \begin{bmatrix} 1 \\ -1 \\ -1 \\ -1 \end{bmatrix}, \quad v_4 = \begin{bmatrix} 1 \\ 1 \\ 1 \\ 1 \end{bmatrix}.$$

6. Find all vectors in $\mathbf{R}^3$ that are orthogonal to $(1, 1, 1)$ and $(1, -1, 0)$. Produce an orthonormal basis from these vectors (mutually orthogonal unit vectors).

7. Find a vector x orthogonal to the row space of A, and a vector y orthogonal to the column space, and a vector z orthogonal to the nullspace:

$$A = \begin{bmatrix} 1 & 2 & 1 \\ 2 & 4 & 3 \\ 3 & 6 & 4 \end{bmatrix}.$$

8. If **V** and **W** are orthogonal subspaces, show that the only vector they have in common is the zero vector: $\mathbf{V} \cap \mathbf{W} = \{0\}$.

9. Find the orthogonal complement of the plane spanned by the vectors $(1, 1, 2)$ and $(1, 2, 3)$, by taking these to be the rows of A and solving $Ax = 0$. Remember that the complement is a whole line.

10. Construct a homogeneous equation in three unknowns whose solutions are the linear combinations of the vectors $(1, 1, 2)$ and $(1, 2, 3)$. This is the reverse of the previous exercise, but the two problems are really the same.

11. The fundamental theorem is often stated in the form of *Fredholm's alternative*: For any A and b, one and only one of the following systems has a solution:

(i) $Ax = b$.

(ii) $A^{\mathrm{T}}y = 0, \; y^{\mathrm{T}}b \neq 0$.

Either b is in the column space $\boldsymbol{C}(A)$ or there is a y in $\boldsymbol{N}(A^{\mathrm{T}})$ such that $y^{\mathrm{T}}b \neq 0$. Show that it is contradictory for (i) and (ii) both to have solutions.

12. Find a basis for the orthogonal complement of the row space of A:

$$A = \begin{bmatrix} 1 & 0 & 2 \\ 1 & 1 & 4 \end{bmatrix}.$$

Split $x = (3, 3, 3)$ into a row space component x_r and a nullspace component x_n.

13. Illustrate the action of A^{T} by a picture corresponding to Figure 3.4, sending $\boldsymbol{C}(A)$ back to the row space and the left nullspace to zero.

14. Show that $x - y$ is orthogonal to $x + y$ if and only if $\|x\| = \|y\|$.

15. Find a matrix whose row space contains $(1, 2, 1)$ and whose nullspace contains $(1, -2, 1)$, or prove that there is no such matrix.

16. Find all vectors that are perpendicular to $(1, 4, 4, 1)$ and $(2, 9, 8, 2)$.

17. If **V** is the orthogonal complement of **W** in $\mathbf{R}^n$, is there a matrix with row space **V** and nullspace **W**? Starting with a basis for **V**, construct such a matrix.

18. If $\mathbf{S} = \{0\}$ is the subspace of $\mathbf{R}^4$ containing only the zero vector, what is $\mathbf{S}^{\perp}$? If **S** is spanned by $(0, 0, 0, 1)$, what is $\mathbf{S}^{\perp}$? What is $(\mathbf{S}^{\perp})^{\perp}$?

19. *Why are these statements false*?

(a) If **V** is orthogonal to **W**, then $\mathbf{V}^{\perp}$ is orthogonal to $\mathbf{W}^{\perp}$.

(b) **V** orthogonal to **W** and **W** orthogonal to **Z** makes **V** orthogonal to **Z**.

20. Let **S** be a subspace of $\mathbf{R}^n$. Explain what $(\mathbf{S}^{\perp})^{\perp} = \mathbf{S}$ means and why it is true.

21. Let **P** be the plane in $\mathbf{R}^2$ with equation $x + 2y - z = 0$. Find a vector perpendicular to **P**. What matrix has the plane **P** as its nullspace, and what matrix has **P** as its row space?

22. Let **S** be the subspace of $\mathbf{R}^4$ containing all vectors with $x_1 + x_2 + x_3 + x_4 = 0$. Find a basis for the space $\mathbf{S}^{\perp}$, containing all vectors orthogonal to **S**.

23. Construct an unsymmetric 2 by 2 matrix of rank 1. Copy Figure 3.4 and put one vector in each subspace. Which vectors are orthogonal?

24. Redraw Figure 3.4 for a 3 by 2 matrix of rank $r = 2$. Which subspace is $\mathbf{Z}$ (zero vector only)? The nullspace part of any vector x in $\mathbf{R}^2$ is $x_n =$ _______.

25. Construct a matrix with the required property or say why that is impossible.

(a) Column space contains $\begin{bmatrix} 1 \\ 2 \\ -3 \end{bmatrix}$ and $\begin{bmatrix} 2 \\ -3 \\ 5 \end{bmatrix}$, nullspace contains $\begin{bmatrix} 1 \\ 1 \\ 1 \end{bmatrix}$.

(b) Row space contains $\begin{bmatrix} 1 \\ 2 \\ -3 \end{bmatrix}$ and $\begin{bmatrix} 2 \\ -3 \\ 5 \end{bmatrix}$, nullspace contains $\begin{bmatrix} 1 \\ 1 \\ 1 \end{bmatrix}$.

(c) $Ax = \begin{bmatrix} 1 \\ 1 \\ 1 \end{bmatrix}$ has a solution and $A^{\mathrm{T}} \begin{bmatrix} 1 \\ 0 \\ 0 \end{bmatrix} = \begin{bmatrix} 0 \\ 0 \\ 0 \end{bmatrix}$.

(d) Every row is orthogonal to every column (A is not the zero matrix).

(e) The columns add up to a column of 0s, the rows add to a row of 1s.

26. If $AB = 0$ then the columns of B are in the _______ of A. The rows of A are in the _______ of B. Why can't A and B be 3 by 3 matrices of rank 2?

27. (a) If $Ax = b$ has a solution and $A^{\mathrm{T}}y = 0$, then y is perpendicular to _______.
(b) If $A^{\mathrm{T}}y = c$ has a solution and $Ax = 0$, then x is perpendicular to _______.

28. This is a system of equations $Ax = b$ with *no solution*:

$$\begin{aligned} x + 2y + 2z &= 5 \\ 2x + 2y + 3z &= 5 \\ 3x + 4y + 5z &= 9. \end{aligned}$$

Find numbers y_1, y_2, y_3 to multiply the equations so they add to $0 = 1$. You have found a vector y in which subspace? The inner product $y^{\mathrm{T}}b$ is 1.

29. In Figure 3.4, how do we know that Ax_r is equal to Ax? How do we know that this vector is in the column space? If $A = \begin{bmatrix} 1 & 1 \\ 1 & 1 \end{bmatrix}$ and $x = \begin{bmatrix} 1 \\ 0 \end{bmatrix}$, what is x_r?

30. If Ax is in the nullspace of A^{T} then $Ax = 0$. Reason: Ax is also in the _______ of A and the spaces are _______. *Conclusion*: $A^{\mathrm{T}}A$ *has the same nullspace as* A.

31. Suppose A is a symmetric matrix ($A^{\mathrm{T}} = A$).

(a) Why is its column space perpendicular to its nullspace?

(b) If $Ax = 0$ and $Az = 5z$, which subspaces contain these "eigenvectors" x and z? **Symmetric matrices have perpendicular eigenvectors** (see Section 5.5).

32. (Recommended) Draw Figure 3.4 to show each subspace for

$$A = \begin{bmatrix} 1 & 2 \\ 3 & 6 \end{bmatrix} \quad \text{and} \quad B = \begin{bmatrix} 1 & 0 \\ 3 & 0 \end{bmatrix}.$$

33. Find the pieces x_r and x_n, and draw Figure 3.4 properly, if

$$A = \begin{bmatrix} 1 & -1 \\ 0 & 0 \\ 0 & 0 \end{bmatrix} \quad \text{and} \quad x = \begin{bmatrix} 2 \\ 0 \end{bmatrix}.$$

Problems 34–44 are about orthogonal subspaces.

34. Put bases for the orthogonal subspaces $\mathbf{V}$ and $\mathbf{W}$ into the columns of matrices V and W. *Why does* $V^{\mathrm{T}}W =$ *zero matrix*? This matches $v^{\mathrm{T}}w = 0$ for vectors.

35. The floor and the wall are not orthogonal subspaces because they share a nonzero vector (along the line where they meet). Two planes in $\mathbf{R}^3$ cannot be orthogonal! Find a vector in both column spaces $\boldsymbol{C}(A)$ and $\boldsymbol{C}(B)$:

$$A = \begin{bmatrix} 1 & 2 \\ 1 & 3 \\ 1 & 2 \end{bmatrix} \quad \text{and} \quad B = \begin{bmatrix} 5 & 4 \\ 6 & 3 \\ 5 & 1 \end{bmatrix}.$$

This will be a vector Ax and also $B\widehat{x}$. Think 3 by 4 with the matrix $[A \;\; B]$.

36. Extend Problem 35 to a p-dimensional subspace $\mathbf{V}$ and a q-dimensional subspace $\mathbf{W}$ of $\mathbf{R}^n$. What inequality on $p + q$ guarantees that $\mathbf{V}$ intersects $\mathbf{W}$ in a nonzero vector? These subspaces cannot be orthogonal.

37. Prove that every y in $\boldsymbol{N}(A^{\mathrm{T}})$ is perpendicular to every Ax in the column space, using the matrix shorthand of equation (8). Start from $A^{\mathrm{T}}y = 0$.

38. If $\mathbf{S}$ is the subspace of $\mathbf{R}^3$ containing only the zero vector, what is $\mathbf{S}^{\perp}$? If $\mathbf{S}$ is spanned by $(1, 1, 1)$, what is $\mathbf{S}^{\perp}$? If $\mathbf{S}$ is spanned by $(2, 0, 0)$ and $(0, 0, 3)$, what is $\mathbf{S}^{\perp}$?

39. Suppose $\mathbf{S}$ only contains $(1, 5, 1)$ and $(2, 2, 2)$ (not a subspace). Then $\mathbf{S}^{\perp}$ is the nullspace of the matrix $A =$ ______. $\mathbf{S}^{\perp}$ is a subspace even if $\mathbf{S}$ is not.

40. Suppose $\mathbf{L}$ is a one-dimensional subspace (a line) in $\mathbf{R}^3$. Its orthogonal complement $\mathbf{L}^{\perp}$ is the ______ perpendicular to $\mathbf{L}$. Then $(\mathbf{L}^{\perp})^{\perp}$ is a ______ perpendicular to $\mathbf{L}^{\perp}$. In fact $(\mathbf{L}^{\perp})^{\perp}$ is the same as ______.

41. Suppose $\mathbf{V}$ is the whole space $\mathbf{R}^4$. Then $\mathbf{V}^{\perp}$ contains only the vector ______. Then $(\mathbf{V}^{\perp})^{\perp}$ is ______. So $(\mathbf{V}^{\perp})^{\perp}$ is the same as ______.

42. Suppose $\mathbf{S}$ is spanned by the vectors $(1, 2, 2, 3)$ and $(1, 3, 3, 2)$. Find two vectors that span $\mathbf{S}^{\perp}$. This is the same as solving $Ax = 0$ for which A?

43. If $\mathbf{P}$ is the plane of vectors in $\mathbf{R}^4$ satisfying $x_1 + x_2 + x_3 + x_4 = 0$, write a basis for $\mathbf{P}^{\perp}$. Construct a matrix that has $\mathbf{P}$ as its nullspace.

44. If a subspace $\mathbf{S}$ is contained in a subspace $\mathbf{V}$, prove that $\mathbf{S}^{\perp}$ contains $\mathbf{V}^{\perp}$.

Problems 45–50 are about perpendicular columns and rows.

45. Suppose an n by n matrix is invertible: $AA^{-1} = I$. Then the first column of A^{-1} is orthogonal to the space spanned by which rows of A?

46. Find $A^{\mathrm{T}}A$ if the columns of A are unit vectors, all mutually perpendicular.

47. Construct a 3 by 3 matrix A with no zero entries whose columns are mutually perpendicular. Compute $A^{\mathrm{T}}A$. Why is it a diagonal matrix?

48. The lines $3x + y = b_1$ and $6x + 2y = b_2$ are ______. They are the same line if______. In that case (b_1, b_2) is perpendicular to the vector ______. The nullspace of the matrix is the line $3x + y =$ ______. One particular vector in that nullspace is ______.

49. Why is each of these statements false?

(a) $(1, 1, 1)$ is perpendicular to $(1, 1, -2)$, so the planes $x + y + z = 0$ and $x + y - 2z = 0$ are orthogonal subspaces.

(b) The subspace spanned by $(1, 1, 0, 0, 0)$ and $(0, 0, 0, 1, 1)$ is the orthogonal complement of the subspace spanned by $(1, -1, 0, 0, 0)$ and $(2, -2, 3, 4, -4)$.

(c) Two subspaces that meet only in the zero vector are orthogonal.

50. Find a matrix with $v = (1, 2, 3)$ in the row space and column space. Find another matrix with v in the nullspace and column space. Which pairs of subspaces can v *not* be in?

51. Suppose A is 3 by 4, B is 4 by 5, and $AB = 0$. Prove $\text{rank}(A) + \text{rank}(B) \leq 4$.

52. The command $N = \text{null}(A)$ will produce a basis for the nullspace of A. Then the command $B = \text{null}(N')$ will produce a basis for the ______ of A.

3.2 COSINES AND PROJECTIONS ONTO LINES

Vectors with $x^{\mathrm{T}}y = 0$ are orthogonal. Now we allow inner products that are ***not zero***, and angles that are ***not right angles***. We want to connect inner products to angles, and also to transposes. In Chapter 1 the transpose was constructed by flipping over a matrix as if it were some kind of pancake. We have to do better than that.

One fact is unavoidable: *The orthogonal case is the most important.* Suppose we want to find the distance from a point b to the line in the direction of the vector a. We are looking along that line for the point p closest to b. The key is in the geometry: ***The line connecting b to p*** (the dotted line in Figure 3.5) ***is perpendicular to a***. *This fact will allow us to find the projection p.* Even though a and b are not orthogonal, the distance problem automatically brings in orthogonality.

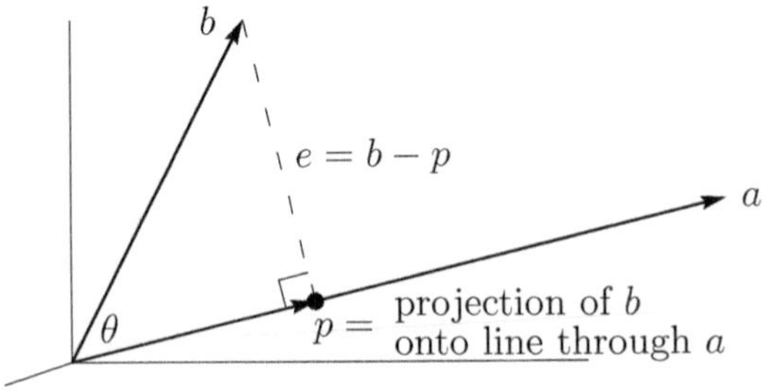

Figure 3.5 The projection p is the point (on the line through a) closest to b.

The situation is the same when we are given a plane (or any subspace **S**) instead of a line. Again the problem is to find the point p on that subspace that is closest to b. ***This point p is the projection of b onto the subspace.*** A perpendicular line from b to **S** meets the subspace at p. Geometrically, that gives the distance between points b and subspaces **S**. But there are two questions that need to be asked:

1. Does this projection actually arise in practical applications?
2. If we have a basis for the subspace **S**, is there a formula for the projection p?

The answers are certainly yes. This is exactly the problem of the ***least-squares solution to an overdetermined system***. The vector b represents the data from experiments or questionnaires, and it contains too many errors to be found in the subspace **S**. When we try to write b as a combination of the basis vectors for **S**, it cannot be done—the equations are inconsistent, and $Ax = b$ has no solution.

The least-squares method selects p as the best choice to replace b. There can be no doubt of the importance of this application. In economics and statistics, least squares enters *regression analysis*. In geodesy, the U.S. mapping survey tackled 2.5 million equations in 400,000 unknowns.

A formula for p is easy when the subspace is a line. We will project b onto a in several different ways, and relate the projection p to inner products and angles. Projection onto a higher dimensional subspace is by far the most important case; it corresponds to a least-squares problem with several parameters, and it is solved in Section 3.3. The formulas are even simpler when we produce an orthogonal basis for **S**.

Inner Products and Cosines

We pick up the discussion of inner products and angles. You will soon see that it is not the angle, but ***the cosine of the angle***, that is directly related to inner products. We look back to trigonometry in the two-dimensional case to find that relationship. Suppose the vectors a and b make angles α and β with the x-axis (Figure 3.6).

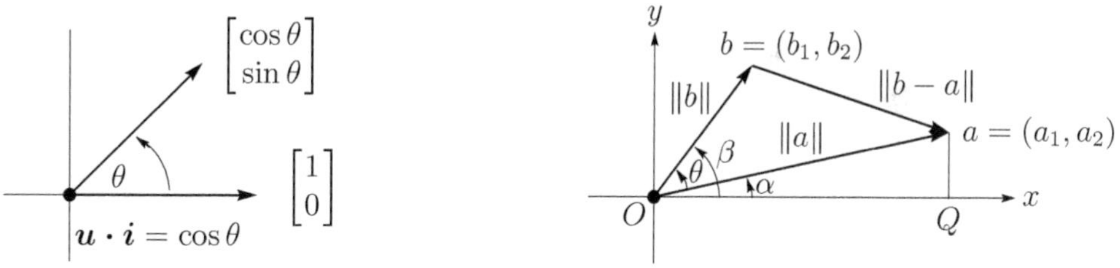

Figure 3.6 The cosine of the angle $\theta = \beta - \alpha$ using inner products.

The length $\|a\|$ is the hypotenuse in the triangle OaQ. So the sine and cosine of α are

$$\sin\alpha = \frac{a_2}{\|a\|}, \qquad \cos\alpha = \frac{a_1}{\|a\|}.$$

For the angle β, the sine is $b_2/\|b\|$ and the cosine is $b_1/\|b\|$. The cosine of $\theta = \beta - \alpha$ comes from an identity that no one could forget:

Cosine formula $$\cos\theta = \cos\beta\cos\alpha + \sin\beta\sin\alpha = \frac{a_1b_1 + a_2b_2}{\|a\|\,\|b\|}. \tag{1}$$

The numerator in this formula is exactly the inner product of a and b. It gives the relationship between $a^{\mathrm{T}}b$ and $\cos\theta$:

3G The cosine of the angle between any nonzero vectors a and b is

$$\textbf{Cosine of } \boldsymbol{\theta} \qquad \cos\theta = \frac{a^{\mathrm{T}}b}{\|a\|\,\|b\|}. \tag{2}$$

This formula is dimensionally correct; if we double the length of b, then both numerator and denominator are doubled, and the cosine is unchanged. Reversing the sign of b, on the other hand, reverses the sign of $\cos\theta$—and changes the angle by 180°.

There is another law of trigonometry that leads directly to the same result. It is not so unforgettable as the formula in equation (1), but it relates the lengths of the sides of any triangle:

$$\textbf{Law of Cosines} \qquad \|b-a\|^2 = \|b\|^2 + \|a\|^2 - 2\|b\|\,\|a\|\cos\theta. \tag{3}$$

When θ is a right angle, we are back to Pythagoras: $\|b-a\|^2 = \|b\|^2 + \|a\|^2$. For any angle θ, the expression $\|b-a\|^2$ is $(b-a)^{\mathrm{T}}(b-a)$, and equation (3) becomes

$$b^{\mathrm{T}}b - 2a^{\mathrm{T}}b + a^{\mathrm{T}}a = b^{\mathrm{T}}b + a^{\mathrm{T}}a - 2\|b\|\,\|a\|\cos\theta.$$

Canceling $b^{\mathrm{T}}b$ and $a^{\mathrm{T}}a$ on both sides of this equation, you recognize formula (2) for the cosine: $a^{\mathrm{T}}b = \|a\|\,\|b\|\cos\theta$. In fact, this proves the cosine formula in n dimensions, since we only have to worry about the plane triangle Oab.

Projection onto a Line

Now we want to find the projection point p. This point must be some multiple $p = \widehat{x}a$ of the given vector a—every point on the line is a multiple of a. The problem is to compute the coefficient $\widehat{x}$. All we need is the geometrical fact that ***the line from b to the closest point $p = \widehat{x}a$ is perpendicular to the vector a***:

$$(b - \widehat{x}a) \perp a, \quad \text{or} \quad a^{\mathrm{T}}(b - \widehat{x}a) = 0, \quad \text{or} \quad \widehat{x} = \frac{a^{\mathrm{T}}b}{a^{\mathrm{T}}a}. \tag{4}$$

That gives the formula for the number $\widehat{x}$ and the projection p:

3H The projection of the vector b onto the line in the direction of a is $p = \widehat{x}a$:

$$\textbf{Projection onto a line} \qquad p = \widehat{x}a = \frac{a^{\mathrm{T}}b}{a^{\mathrm{T}}a}a. \tag{5}$$

This allows us to redraw Figure 3.5 with a correct formula for p (Figure 3.7).

This leads to the Schwarz inequality in equation (6), which is the most important inequality in mathematics. A special case is the fact that arithmetic means $\frac{1}{2}(x+y)$ are larger than geometric means $\sqrt{xy}$. (It is also equivalent—see Problem 1 at the end of this section—to the triangle inequality for vectors.) The Schwarz inequality seems to come almost accidentally from the statement that $\|e\|^2 = \|b-p\|^2$ in Figure 3.7 cannot

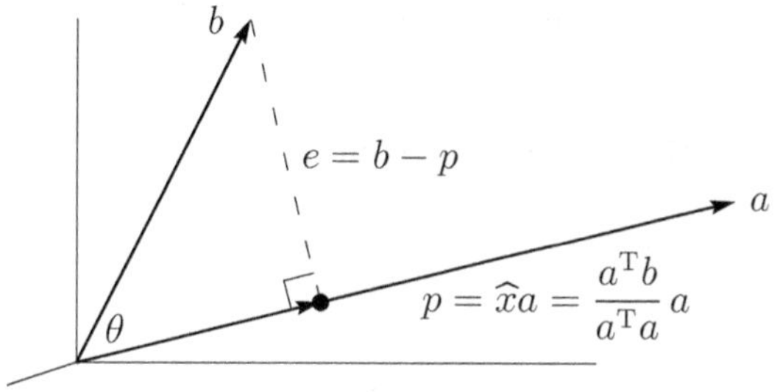

Figure 3.7 The projection p of b onto a, with $\cos\theta = \dfrac{Op}{Ob} = \dfrac{a^{\mathrm{T}}b}{\|a\|\,\|b\|}$.

be negative:

$$\left\| b - \frac{a^{\mathrm{T}}b}{a^{\mathrm{T}}a}a \right\|^2 = b^{\mathrm{T}}b - 2\frac{(a^{\mathrm{T}}b)^2}{a^{\mathrm{T}}a} + \left(\frac{a^{\mathrm{T}}b}{a^{\mathrm{T}}a}\right)^2 a^{\mathrm{T}}a = \frac{(b^{\mathrm{T}}b)(a^{\mathrm{T}}a) - (a^{\mathrm{T}}b)^2}{(a^{\mathrm{T}}a)} \geq 0.$$

This tells us that $(b^{\mathrm{T}}b)(a^{\mathrm{T}}a) \geq (a^{\mathrm{T}}b)^2$—and then we take square roots:

3I All vectors a and b satisfy the ***Schwarz inequality***, which is $|\cos\theta| \leq 1$ in $\mathbf{R}^n$:

Schwarz inequality $\quad |a^{\mathrm{T}}b| \leq \|a\|\,\|b\|.$ (6)

According to formula (2), the ratio between $a^{\mathrm{T}}b$ and $\|a\|\,\|b\|$ is exactly $|\cos\theta|$. Since all cosines lie in the interval $-1 \leq \cos\theta \leq 1$, this gives another proof of equation (6): *the Schwarz inequality is the same as* $|\cos\theta| \leq 1$. In some ways that is a more easily understood proof, because cosines are so familiar. Either proof is all right in $\mathbf{R}^n$, but notice that ours came directly from the calculation of $\|b - p\|^2$. This stays nonnegative when we introduce new possibilities for the lengths and inner products. The name of Cauchy is also attached to this inequality $|a^{\mathrm{T}}b| \leq \|a\|\,\|b\|$, and the Russians refer to it as the Cauchy-Schwarz-Buniakowsky inequality! Mathematical historians seem to agree that Buniakowsky's claim is genuine.

One final observation about $|a^{\mathrm{T}}b| \leq \|a\|\,\|b\|$. *Equality holds if and only if b is a multiple of a.* The angle is $\theta = 0°$ or $\theta = 180°$ and the cosine is 1 or -1. In this case b is identical with its projection p, and the distance between b and the line is zero.

Example 1 Project $b = (1, 2, 3)$ onto the line through $a = (1, 1, 1)$ to get $\widehat{x}$ and p:

$$\widehat{x} = \frac{a^{\mathrm{T}}b}{a^{\mathrm{T}}a} = \frac{6}{3} = 2.$$

The projection is $p = \widehat{x}a = (2, 2, 2)$. The angle between a and b has

$$\cos\theta = \frac{\|p\|}{\|b\|} = \frac{\sqrt{12}}{\sqrt{14}} \quad \text{and also} \quad \cos\theta = \frac{a^{\mathrm{T}}b}{\|a\|\,\|b\|} = \frac{6}{\sqrt{3}\sqrt{14}}.$$

The Schwarz inequality $|a^{\mathrm{T}}b| \leq \|a\|\,\|b\|$ is $6 \leq \sqrt{3}\sqrt{14}$. If we write 6 as $\sqrt{36}$, that is the same as $\sqrt{36} \leq \sqrt{42}$. The cosine is less than 1, because b is not parallel to a.

Projection Matrix of Rank 1

The projection of b onto the line through a lies at $p = a(a^{\mathrm{T}}b/a^{\mathrm{T}}a)$. That is our formula $p = \widehat{x}a$, but it is written with a slight twist: The vector a is put before the number $\widehat{x} = a^{\mathrm{T}}b/a^{\mathrm{T}}a$. There is a reason behind that apparently trivial change. Projection onto a line is carried out by a ***projection matrix*** P, and written in this new order we can see what it is. *P is the matrix that multiplies b and produces p*:

$$P = a\frac{a^{\mathrm{T}}b}{a^{\mathrm{T}}a} \quad \text{so the projection matrix is} \quad P = \frac{aa^{\mathrm{T}}}{a^{\mathrm{T}}a}. \tag{7}$$

That is a column times a row—a square matrix—divided by the number $a^{\mathrm{T}}a$.

Example 2 The matrix that projects onto the line through $a = (1, 1, 1)$ is

$$P = \frac{aa^{\mathrm{T}}}{a^{\mathrm{T}}a} = \frac{1}{3}\begin{bmatrix}1\\1\\1\end{bmatrix}\begin{bmatrix}1 & 1 & 1\end{bmatrix} = \begin{bmatrix}\frac{1}{3} & \frac{1}{3} & \frac{1}{3}\\ \frac{1}{3} & \frac{1}{3} & \frac{1}{3}\\ \frac{1}{3} & \frac{1}{3} & \frac{1}{3}\end{bmatrix}.$$

This matrix has two properties that we will see as typical of projections:

1. **P is a symmetric matrix.**
2. **Its square is itself: $P^2 = P$.**

P^2b is the projection of Pb—and Pb is already on the line! So $P^2b = Pb$. This matrix P also gives a great example of the four fundamental subspaces:

The column space consists of the line through $a = (1, 1, 1)$.
The nullspace consists of the plane perpendicular to a.
The rank is $r = 1$.

Every column is a multiple of a, and so is $Pb = \widehat{x}a$. The vectors that project to $p = 0$ are especially important. They satisfy $a^{\mathrm{T}}b = 0$—they are perpendicular to a and their component along the line is zero. They lie in the nullspace = perpendicular plane.

Actually that example is too perfect. It has the nullspace orthogonal to the column space, which is haywire. The nullspace should be orthogonal to the *row space*. But because P is symmetric, its row and column spaces are the same.

Remark on scaling The projection matrix $aa^{\mathrm{T}}/a^{\mathrm{T}}a$ is the same if a is doubled:

$$a = \begin{bmatrix}2\\2\\2\end{bmatrix} \quad \text{gives} \quad P = \frac{1}{12}\begin{bmatrix}2\\2\\2\end{bmatrix}\begin{bmatrix}2 & 2 & 2\end{bmatrix} = \begin{bmatrix}\frac{1}{3} & \frac{1}{3} & \frac{1}{3}\\ \frac{1}{3} & \frac{1}{3} & \frac{1}{3}\\ \frac{1}{3} & \frac{1}{3} & \frac{1}{3}\end{bmatrix} \quad \text{as before.}$$

The line through a is the same, and that's all the projection matrix cares about. If a has unit length, the denominator is $a^{\mathrm{T}}a = 1$ and the matrix is just $P = aa^{\mathrm{T}}$.

Example 3 Project onto the "θ-direction" in the x-y plane. The line goes through $a = (\cos\theta, \sin\theta)$ and the matrix is symmetric with $P^2 = P$:

$$P = \frac{aa^{\mathrm{T}}}{a^{\mathrm{T}}a} = \frac{\begin{bmatrix} c \\ s \end{bmatrix} \begin{bmatrix} c & s \end{bmatrix}}{\begin{bmatrix} c & s \end{bmatrix} \begin{bmatrix} c \\ s \end{bmatrix}} = \begin{bmatrix} c^2 & cs \\ cs & s^2 \end{bmatrix}.$$

Here c is $\cos\theta$, s is $\sin\theta$, and $c^2 + s^2 = 1$ in the denominator. This matrix P was discovered in Section 2.6 on linear transformations. Now we know P in any number of dimensions. We emphasize that it produces the projection p:

To project b onto a, multiply by the projection matrix P: $p = Pb$.

Transposes from Inner Products

Finally we connect inner products to A^{T}. Up to now, A^{T} is simply the reflection of A across its main diagonal; the rows of A become the columns of A^{T}, and vice versa. The entry in row i, column j of A^{T} is the (j, i) entry of A:

$$\textbf{Transpose by reflection} \qquad (A^{\mathrm{T}})_{ij} = (A)_{ji}.$$

There is a deeper significance to A^{T}. Its close connection to inner products gives a new and much more "abstract" definition of the transpose:

3J The transpose A^{T} can be defined by the following property: The inner product of Ax with y equals the inner product of x with $A^{\mathrm{T}}y$. Formally, this simply means that

$$(Ax)^{\mathrm{T}}y = x^{\mathrm{T}}A^{\mathrm{T}}y = x^{\mathrm{T}}(A^{\mathrm{T}}y). \tag{8}$$

This definition gives us another (better) way to verify the formula $(AB)^{\mathrm{T}} = B^{\mathrm{T}}A^{\mathrm{T}}$. Use equation (8) twice:

$$\textbf{Move } \boldsymbol{A} \textbf{ then move } \boldsymbol{B} \qquad (ABx)^{\mathrm{T}}y = (Bx)^{\mathrm{T}}(A^{\mathrm{T}}y) = x^{\mathrm{T}}(B^{\mathrm{T}}A^{\mathrm{T}}y).$$

The transposes turn up in reverse order on the right side, just as the inverses do in the formula $(AB)^{-1} = B^{-1}A^{-1}$. We mention again that these two formulas meet to give the remarkable combination $(A^{-1})^{\mathrm{T}} = (A^{\mathrm{T}})^{-1}$.

Problem Set 3.2

1. (a) Given any two positive numbers x and y, choose the vector b equal to $(\sqrt{x}, \sqrt{y})$, and choose $a = (\sqrt{y}, \sqrt{x})$. Apply the Schwarz inequality to compare the arithmetic mean $\frac{1}{2}(x + y)$ with the geometric mean $\sqrt{xy}$.

(b) Suppose we start with a vector from the origin to the point x, and then add a vector of length $\|y\|$ connecting x to $x + y$. The third side of the triangle goes from the origin to $x + y$. *The triangle inequality asserts that this distance cannot be greater than the sum of the first two*:

$$\|x + y\| \le \|x\| + \|y\|.$$

After squaring both sides, and expanding $(x + y)^T(x + y)$, reduce this to the Schwarz inequality.

2. Verify that the length of the projection in Figure 3.7 is $\|p\| = \|b\| \cos\theta$, using formula (5).

3. What multiple of $a = (1, 1, 1)$ is closest to the point $b = (2, 4, 4)$? Find also the point closest to a on the line through b.

4. Explain why the Schwarz inequality becomes an equality in the case that a and b lie on the same line through the origin, and only in that case. What if they lie on opposite sides of the origin?

5. In n dimensions, what angle does the vector $(1, 1, \dots, 1)$ make with the coordinate axes? What is the projection matrix P onto that vector?

6. The Schwarz inequality has a one-line proof if a and b are normalized ahead of time to be unit vectors:

$$|a^T b| = \left|\sum a_j b_j\right| \le \sum |a_j||b_j| \le \sum \frac{|a_j|^2 + |b_j|^2}{2} = \frac{1}{2} + \frac{1}{2} = \|a\|\,\|b\|.$$

Which previous problem justifies the middle step?

7. By choosing the correct vector b in the Schwarz inequality, prove that

$$(a_1 + \cdots + a_n)^2 \le n\left(a_1^2 + \cdots + a_n^2\right).$$

When does equality hold?

8. The methane molecule CH_4 is arranged as if the carbon atom were at the center of a regular tetrahedron with four hydrogen atoms at the vertices. If vertices are placed at $(0, 0, 0)$, $(1, 1, 0)$, $(1, 0, 1)$, and $(0, 1, 1)$—note that all six edges have length $\sqrt{2}$, so the tetrahedron is regular—what is the cosine of the angle between the rays going from the center $\left(\frac{1}{2}, \frac{1}{2}, \frac{1}{2}\right)$ to the vertices? (The bond angle itself is about 109.5°, an old friend of chemists.)

9. Square the matrix $P = aa^T/a^Ta$, which projects onto a line, and show that $P^2 = P$. (Note the number a^Ta in the middle of the matrix aa^Taa^T!)

10. Is the projection matrix P invertible? Why or why not?

11. (a) Find the projection matrix P_1 onto the line through $a = \begin{bmatrix} 1 \\ 3 \end{bmatrix}$ and also the matrix P_2 that projects onto the line perpendicular to a.
(b) Compute $P_1 + P_2$ and P_1P_2 and explain.

12. Find the matrix that projects every point in the plane onto the line $x + 2y = 0$.

13. Prove that the *trace* of $P = aa^T/a^Ta$—which is the sum of its diagonal entries—always equals 1.

14. What matrix P projects every point in $\mathbf{R}^3$ onto the line of intersection of the planes $x + y + t = 0$ and $x - t = 0$?

15. Show that the length of Ax equals the length of $A^{\mathrm{T}}x$ if $AA^{\mathrm{T}} = A^{\mathrm{T}}A$.

16. Suppose P is the projection matrix onto the line through a.

(a) Why is the inner product of x with Py equal to the inner product of Px with y?

(b) Are the two angles the same? Find their cosines if $a = (1, 1, -1)$, $x = (2, 0, 1)$, $y = (2, 1, 2)$.

(c) Why is the inner product of Px with Py again the same? What is the angle between those two?

Problems 17–26 ask for projections onto lines. Also errors $e = b - p$ and matrices P.

17. Project the vector b onto the line through a. Check that e is perpendicular to a:

$$\text{(a)}\ \ b = \begin{bmatrix}1\\2\\2\end{bmatrix} \ \text{ and } \ a = \begin{bmatrix}1\\1\\1\end{bmatrix}. \qquad \text{(b)}\ \ b = \begin{bmatrix}1\\3\\1\end{bmatrix} \ \text{ and } \ a = \begin{bmatrix}-1\\-3\\-1\end{bmatrix}.$$

18. *Draw* the projection of b onto a and also compute it from $p = \widehat{x}a$:

$$\text{(a)}\ \ b = \begin{bmatrix}\cos\theta\\\sin\theta\end{bmatrix} \ \text{ and } \ a = \begin{bmatrix}1\\0\end{bmatrix}. \qquad \text{(b)}\ \ b = \begin{bmatrix}1\\1\end{bmatrix} \ \text{ and } \ a = \begin{bmatrix}1\\-1\end{bmatrix}.$$

19. In Problem 17, find the projection matrix $P = aa^{\mathrm{T}}/a^{\mathrm{T}}a$ onto the line through each vector a. Verify in both cases that $P^2 = P$. Multiply Pb in each case to compute the projection p.

20. Construct the projection matrices P_1 and P_2 onto the lines through the a's in Problem 18. Is it true that $(P_1 + P_2)^2 = P_1 + P_2$? This *would* be true if $P_1P_2 = 0$.

For Problems 21–26, consult the accompanying figures.

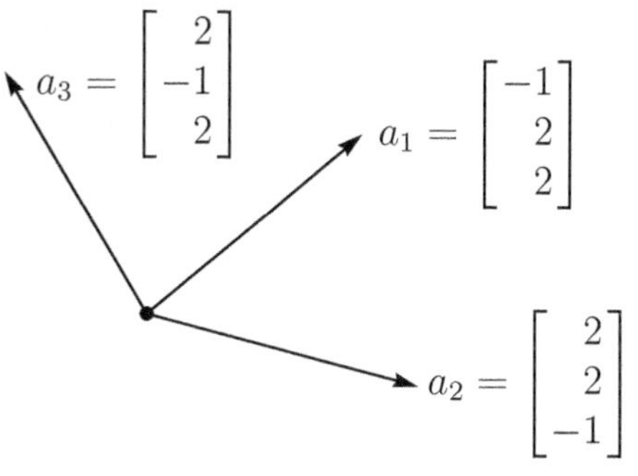

Problems 21–23

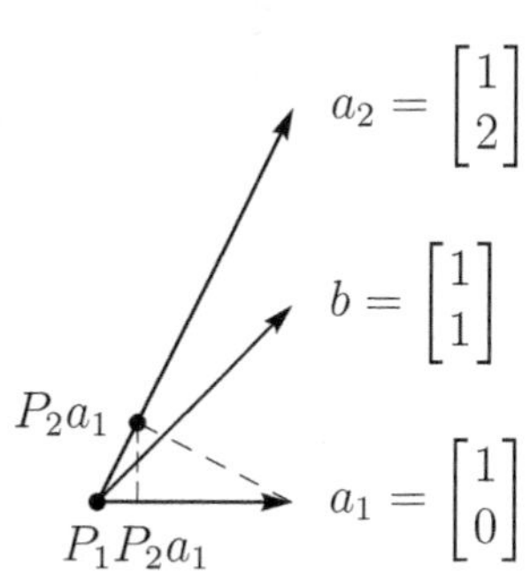

Problems 24–26

21. Compute the projection matrices $aa^{\mathrm{T}}/a^{\mathrm{T}}a$ onto the lines through $a_1 = (-1, 2, 2)$ and $a_2 = (2, 2, -1)$. Multiply those projection matrices and explain why their product P_1P_2 is what it is.

22. Project $b = (1, 0, 0)$ onto the lines through a_1 and a_2 in Problem 21 and also onto $a_3 = (2, -1, 2)$. Add the three projections $p_1 + p_2 + p_3$.

23. Continuing Problems 21–22, find the projection matrix P_3 onto $a_3 = (2, -1, 2)$. Verify that $P_1 + P_2 + P_3 = I$. The basis a_1, a_2, a_3 is orthogonal!

24. Project the vector $b = (1, 1)$ onto the lines through $a_1 = (1, 0)$ and $a_2 = (1, 2)$. Draw the projections p_1 and p_2 and add $p_1 + p_2$. The projections do not add to b because the a's are not orthogonal.

25. In Problem 24, the projection of b onto the *plane* of a_1 and a_2 will equal b. Find $P = A(A^{\mathrm{T}}A)^{-1}A^{\mathrm{T}}$ for $A = \begin{bmatrix} a_1 & a_2 \end{bmatrix} = \begin{bmatrix} 1 & 1 \\ 0 & 2 \end{bmatrix}$.

26. Project $a_1 = (1, 0)$ onto $a_2 = (1, 2)$. Then project the result back onto a_1. Draw these projections and multiply the projection matrices $P_1 P_2$: Is this a projection?

3.3 PROJECTIONS AND LEAST SQUARES

Up to this point, $Ax = b$ either has a solution or not. If b is not in the column space $\boldsymbol{C}(A)$, the system is inconsistent and Gaussian elimination fails. This failure is almost certain when there are several equations and only one unknown:

$$\textbf{More equations than unknowns—no solution?} \qquad \begin{aligned} 2x &= b_1 \\ 3x &= b_2 \\ 4x &= b_3. \end{aligned}$$

This is solvable when b_1, b_2, b_3 are in the ratio 2:3:4. The solution x will exist only if b is on the same line as the column $a = (2, 3, 4)$.

In spite of their unsolvability, inconsistent equations arise all the time in practice. They have to be solved! One possibility is to determine x from part of the system, and ignore the rest; this is hard to justify if all m equations come from the same source. Rather than expecting no error in some equations and large errors in the others, it is much better *to choose the x that minimizes an average error E in the m equations.*

The most convenient "average" comes from the *sum of squares*:

$$\textbf{Squared error} \qquad E^2 = (2x - b_1)^2 + (3x - b_2)^2 + (4x - b_3)^2.$$

If there is an exact solution, the minimum error is $E = 0$. In the more likely case that b is not proportional to a, the graph of E^2 will be a parabola. The minimum error is at the lowest point, where the derivative is zero:

$$\frac{dE^2}{dx} = 2[(2x - b_1)2 + (3x - b_2)3 + (4x - b_3)4] = 0.$$

Solving for x, the least-squares solution of this model system $ax = b$ is denoted by $\widehat{x}$:

$$\textbf{Least-squares solution} \qquad \widehat{x} = \frac{2b_1 + 3b_2 + 4b_3}{2^2 + 3^2 + 4^2} = \frac{a^{\mathrm{T}}b}{a^{\mathrm{T}}a}.$$

You recognize $a^{\mathrm{T}}b$ in the numerator and $a^{\mathrm{T}}a$ in the denominator.

The general case is the same. We "solve" $ax = b$ by minimizing

$$E^2 = \|ax - b\|^2 = (a_1x - b_1)^2 + \cdots + (a_mx - b_m)^2.$$

The derivative of E^2 is zero at the point $\widehat{x}$, if

$$(a_1\widehat{x} - b_1)a_1 + \cdots + (a_m\widehat{x} - b_m)a_m = 0.$$

We are minimizing the distance from b to the line through a, and calculus gives the same answer, $\widehat{x} = (a_1b_1 + \cdots + a_mb_m)/(a_1^2 + \cdots + a_m^2)$, that geometry did earlier:

3K The least-squares solution to a problem $ax = b$ in one unknown is $\widehat{x} = \dfrac{a^{\mathrm{T}}b}{a^{\mathrm{T}}a}$.

You see that we keep coming back to the geometrical interpretation of a least-squares problem—to minimize a distance. By setting the derivative of E^2 to zero, calculus confirms the geometry of the previous section. *The error vector e connecting b to p must be perpendicular to a*:

$$\textbf{Orthogonality of } \boldsymbol{a} \textbf{ and } \boldsymbol{e} \qquad a^{\mathrm{T}}(b - \widehat{x}a) = a^{\mathrm{T}}b - \frac{a^{\mathrm{T}}b}{a^{\mathrm{T}}a}a^{\mathrm{T}}a = 0.$$

As a side remark, notice the degenerate case $a = 0$. All multiples of a are zero, and the line is only a point. Therefore $p = 0$ is the only candidate for the projection. But the formula for $\widehat{x}$ becomes a meaningless $0/0$, and correctly reflects the fact that $\widehat{x}$ is completely undetermined. All values of x give the same error $E = \|0x - b\|$, so E^2 is a horizontal line instead of a parabola. The "pseudoinverse" assigns the definite value $\widehat{x} = 0$, which is a more "symmetric" choice than any other number.

Least-Squares Problems with Several Variables

Now we are ready for the serious step, ***to project b onto a subspace***—rather than just onto a line. This problem arises from $Ax = b$ when A is an m by n matrix. Instead of one column and one unknown x, the matrix now has n columns. The number m of observations is still larger than the number n of unknowns, so it must be expected that $Ax = b$ will be inconsistent. *Probably, there will not exist a choice of x that perfectly fits the data b*. In other words, the vector b probably will not be a combination of the columns of A; it will be outside the column space.

Again the problem is to choose $\widehat{x}$ so as to minimize the error, and again this minimization will be done in the least-squares sense. The error is $E = \|Ax - b\|$, and ***this is exactly the distance from b to the point Ax in the column space***. Searching for the least-squares solution $\widehat{x}$, which minimizes E, is the same as locating the point $p = A\widehat{x}$ that is closer to b than any other point in the column space.

We may use geometry or calculus to determine $\widehat{x}$. In n dimensions, we prefer the appeal of geometry; p must be the "projection of b onto the column space." ***The error vector e = b − A$\widehat{x}$ must be perpendicular to that space*** (Figure 3.8). Finding $\widehat{x}$ and the projection $p = A\widehat{x}$ is so fundamental that we do it in two ways:

1. All vectors perpendicular to the column space lie in the *left nullspace*. Thus the error vector $e = b - A\widehat{x}$ must be in the nullspace of A^{T}:

$$A^{\mathrm{T}}(b - A\widehat{x}) = 0 \qquad \text{or} \qquad \boldsymbol{A^{\mathrm{T}}A\widehat{x} = A^{\mathrm{T}}b}.$$

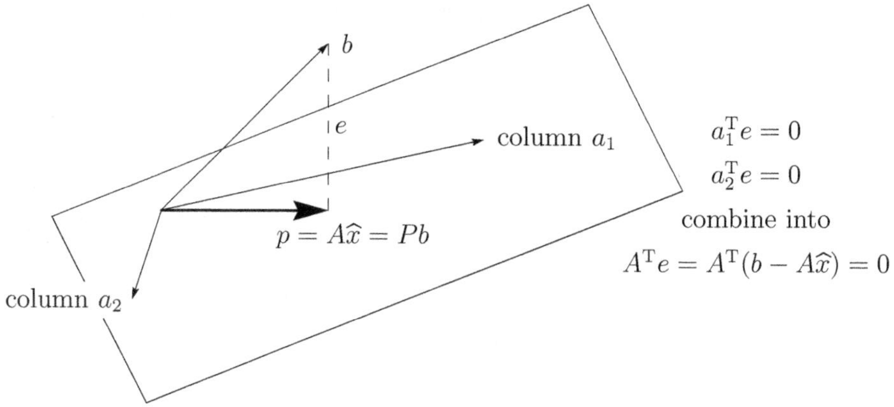

Figure 3.8 Projection onto the column space of a 3 by 2 matrix.

2. The error vector must be perpendicular to *each column* $a_1, \dots, a_n$ of A:

$$\begin{matrix} a_1^{\mathrm{T}}(b - A\widehat{x}) = 0 \\ \vdots \\ a_n^{\mathrm{T}}(b - A\widehat{x}) = 0 \end{matrix} \quad \text{or} \quad \begin{bmatrix} a_1^{\mathrm{T}} \\ \vdots \\ a_n^{\mathrm{T}} \end{bmatrix} \begin{bmatrix} \\ b - A\widehat{x} \\ \\ \end{bmatrix} = 0.$$

This is again $A^{\mathrm{T}}(b - A\widehat{x}) = 0$ and $A^{\mathrm{T}}A\widehat{x} = A^{\mathrm{T}}b$. The calculus way is to take partial derivatives of $E^2 = (Ax - b)^{\mathrm{T}}(Ax - b)$. That gives the same $2A^{\mathrm{T}}Ax - 2A^{\mathrm{T}}b = 0$. The fastest way is just ***to multiply the unsolvable equation $Ax = b$ by A^{T}***. All these equivalent methods produce a square coefficient matrix $A^{\mathrm{T}}A$. It is symmetric (its transpose is not AA^{T}!) and it is the fundamental matrix of this chapter.

The equations $A^{\mathrm{T}}A\widehat{x} = A^{\mathrm{T}}b$ are known in statistics as the ***normal equations***.

3L When $Ax = b$ is inconsistent, its least-squares solution minimizes $\|Ax - b\|^2$:

$$\textbf{Normal equations} \qquad A^{\mathrm{T}}A\widehat{x} = A^{\mathrm{T}}b. \tag{1}$$

$A^{\mathrm{T}}A$ is invertible exactly when the columns of A are linearly independent! Then,

$$\textbf{Best estimate } \widehat{x} \qquad \widehat{x} = (A^{\mathrm{T}}A)^{-1}A^{\mathrm{T}}b. \tag{2}$$

The projection of b onto the column space is the nearest point $A\widehat{x}$:

$$\textbf{Projection} \qquad p = A\widehat{x} = A(A^{\mathrm{T}}A)^{-1}A^{\mathrm{T}}b. \tag{3}$$

We choose an example in which our intuition is as good as the formulas:

$$A = \begin{bmatrix} 1 & 2 \\ 1 & 3 \\ 0 & 0 \end{bmatrix}, \qquad b = \begin{bmatrix} 4 \\ 5 \\ 6 \end{bmatrix}, \qquad \begin{matrix} Ax = b \quad \text{has no solution} \\ A^{\mathrm{T}}A\widehat{x} = A^{\mathrm{T}}b \quad \text{gives the best } x. \end{matrix}$$

Both columns end with a zero, so $\boldsymbol{C}(A)$ is the x-y plane within three-dimensional space. The projection of $b = (4, 5, 6)$ is $p = (4, 5, 0)$—the x and y components stay the same but $z = 6$ will disappear. That is confirmed by solving the normal equations:

$$A^{\mathrm{T}}A = \begin{bmatrix} 1 & 1 & 0 \\ 2 & 3 & 0 \end{bmatrix} \begin{bmatrix} 1 & 2 \\ 1 & 3 \\ 0 & 0 \end{bmatrix} = \begin{bmatrix} 2 & 5 \\ 5 & 13 \end{bmatrix}.$$

$$\widehat{x} = (A^{\mathrm{T}}A)^{-1}A^{\mathrm{T}}b = \begin{bmatrix} 13 & -5 \\ -5 & 2 \end{bmatrix} \begin{bmatrix} 1 & 1 & 0 \\ 2 & 3 & 0 \end{bmatrix} \begin{bmatrix} 4 \\ 5 \\ 6 \end{bmatrix} = \begin{bmatrix} 2 \\ 1 \end{bmatrix}.$$

$$\textbf{Projection} \qquad p = A\widehat{x} = \begin{bmatrix} 1 & 2 \\ 1 & 3 \\ 0 & 0 \end{bmatrix} \begin{bmatrix} 2 \\ 1 \end{bmatrix} = \begin{bmatrix} 4 \\ 5 \\ 0 \end{bmatrix}.$$

In this special case, the best we can do is to solve the first two equations of $Ax = b$. Then $\widehat{x}_1 = 2$ and $\widehat{x}_2 = 1$. The error in the equation $0x_1 + 0x_2 = 6$ is sure to be 6.

Remark 1 Suppose b is actually *in* the column space of A—it is a combination $b = Ax$ of the columns. Then the projection of b is still b:

$$\textbf{b in column space} \qquad p = A(A^{\mathrm{T}}A)^{-1}A^{\mathrm{T}}Ax = Ax = b.$$

The closest point p is just b itself—which is obvious.

Remark 2 At the other extreme, suppose b is *perpendicular* to every column, so $A^{\mathrm{T}}b = 0$. In this case b projects to the zero vector:

$$\textbf{b in left nullspace} \qquad p = A(A^{\mathrm{T}}A)^{-1}A^{\mathrm{T}}b = A(A^{\mathrm{T}}A)^{-1}0 = 0.$$

Remark 3 When A is square and invertible, the column space is the whole space. Every vector projects to itself, p equals b, and $\widehat{x} = x$:

$$\textbf{If A is invertible} \qquad p = A(A^{\mathrm{T}}A)^{-1}A^{\mathrm{T}}b = AA^{-1}(A^{\mathrm{T}})^{-1}A^{\mathrm{T}}b = b.$$

This is the only case when we can take apart $(A^{\mathrm{T}}A)^{-1}$, *and write it as* $A^{-1}(A^{\mathrm{T}})^{-1}$. When A is rectangular that is not possible.

Remark 4 Suppose A has only one column, containing a. Then the matrix $A^{\mathrm{T}}A$ is the number $a^{\mathrm{T}}a$ and $\widehat{x}$ is $a^{\mathrm{T}}b/a^{\mathrm{T}}a$. We return to the earlier formula.

The Cross-Product Matrix $A^{\mathrm{T}}A$

The matrix $A^{\mathrm{T}}A$ is certainly symmetric. Its transpose is $(A^{\mathrm{T}}A)^{\mathrm{T}} = A^{\mathrm{T}}A^{\mathrm{TT}}$, which is $A^{\mathrm{T}}A$ again. Its i, j entry (and j, i entry) is the inner product of column i of A with column j of A. The key question is the invertibility of $A^{\mathrm{T}}A$, and fortunately

> ***$A^{\mathrm{T}}A$ has the same nullspace as A.***

Certainly if $Ax = 0$ then $A^{\mathrm{T}}Ax = 0$. Vectors x in the nullspace of A are also in the nullspace of $A^{\mathrm{T}}A$. To go in the other direction, start by supposing that $A^{\mathrm{T}}Ax = 0$, and take the inner product with x to show that $Ax = 0$:

$$x^{\mathrm{T}}A^{\mathrm{T}}Ax = 0, \quad \text{or} \quad \|Ax\|^2 = 0, \quad \text{or} \quad Ax = 0.$$

The two nullspaces are identical. In particular, if A has independent columns (and only $x = 0$ is in its nullspace), then the same is true for $A^{\mathrm{T}}A$:

3M If A has independent columns, then $A^{\mathrm{T}}A$ is *square, symmetric*, and *invertible*.

We show later that $A^{\mathrm{T}}A$ is also positive definite (all pivots and eigenvalues are positive).

This case is by far the most common and most important. Independence is not so hard in m-dimensional space if $m > n$. We assume it in what follows.

Projection Matrices

We have shown that the closest point to b is $p = A(A^{\mathrm{T}}A)^{-1}A^{\mathrm{T}}b$. *This formula expresses in matrix terms the construction of a perpendicular line from b to the column space of* A. The matrix that gives p is a projection matrix, denoted by P:

$$\textbf{Projection matrix} \qquad P = A(A^{\mathrm{T}}A)^{-1}A^{\mathrm{T}}. \tag{4}$$

This matrix projects any vector b onto the column space of A.* In other words, $p = Pb$ is the component of b in the column space, and the error $e = b - Pb$ is the component in the orthogonal complement. ($I - P$ is also a projection matrix! It projects b onto the orthogonal complement, and the projection is $b - Pb$.)

In short, we have a matrix formula for splitting any b into two perpendicular components. Pb is in the column space $\boldsymbol{C}(A)$, and the other component $(I - P)b$ is in the left nullspace $\boldsymbol{N}(A^{\mathrm{T}})$—which is orthogonal to the column space.

These projection matrices can be understood geometrically and algebraically.

3N The projection matrix $P = A(A^{\mathrm{T}}A)^{-1}A^{\mathrm{T}}$ has two basic properties:

(i) It equals its square: $P^2 = P$.

(ii) It equals its transpose: $P^{\mathrm{T}} = P$.

Conversely, any symmetric matrix with $P^2 = P$ represents a projection.

Proof It is easy to see why $P^2 = P$. If we start with any b, then Pb lies in the subspace we are projecting onto. ***When we project again nothing is changed***. The vector Pb is already in the subspace, and $P(Pb)$ is still Pb. In other words $P^2 = P$. Two or three or fifty projections give the same point p as the first projection:

$$P^2 = A(A^{\mathrm{T}}A)^{-1}A^{\mathrm{T}}A(A^{\mathrm{T}}A)^{-1}A^{\mathrm{T}} = A(A^{\mathrm{T}}A)^{-1}A^{\mathrm{T}} = P.$$

---

* There may be a risk of confusion with permutation matrices, also denoted by P, but the risk should be small, and we try never to let both appear on the same page.

To prove that P is also symmetric, take its transpose. Multiply the transposes in reverse order, and use symmetry of $(A^{\mathrm{T}}A)^{-1}$, to come back to P:

$$P^{\mathrm{T}} = (A^{\mathrm{T}})^{\mathrm{T}}((A^{\mathrm{T}}A)^{-1})^{\mathrm{T}}A^{\mathrm{T}} = A((A^{\mathrm{T}}A)^{\mathrm{T}})^{-1}A^{\mathrm{T}} = A(A^{\mathrm{T}}A)^{-1}A^{\mathrm{T}} = P.$$

For the converse, we have to deduce from $P^2 = P$ and $P^{\mathrm{T}} = P$ that Pb **is the projection of b onto the column space of P**. The error vector $b - Pb$ is *orthogonal to the space*. For any vector Pc in the space, the inner product is zero:

$$(b - Pb)^{\mathrm{T}}Pc = b^{\mathrm{T}}(I - P)^{\mathrm{T}}Pc = b^{\mathrm{T}}(P - P^2)c = 0.$$

Thus $b - Pb$ is orthogonal to the space, and Pb is the projection onto the column space. ■

Example 1 Suppose A is actually invertible. If it is 4 by 4, then its four columns are independent and its column space is all of $\mathbf{R}^4$. What is the projection *onto the whole space*? It is the identity matrix.

$$P = A(A^{\mathrm{T}}A)^{-1}A^{\mathrm{T}} = AA^{-1}(A^{\mathrm{T}})^{-1}A^{\mathrm{T}} = I. \qquad (5)$$

The identity matrix is symmetric, $I^2 = I$, and the error $b - Ib$ is zero.

The point of all other examples is that what happened in equation (5) is *not allowed*. To repeat: We cannot invert the separate parts A^{T} and A when those matrices are rectangular. It is the square matrix $A^{\mathrm{T}}A$ that is invertible.

Least-Squares Fitting of Data

Suppose we do a series of experiments, and expect the output b to be a linear function of the input t. We look for a ***straight line*** $b = C + Dt$. For example:

1. At different times we measure the distance to a satellite on its way to Mars. In this case t is the time and b is the distance. Unless the motor was left on or gravity is strong, the satellite should move with nearly constant velocity v: $b = b_0 + vt$.
2. We vary the load on a structure, and measure the movement it produces. In this experiment t is the load and b is the reading from the strain gauge. Unless the load is so great that the material becomes plastic, a linear relation $b = C + Dt$ is normal in the theory of elasticity.
3. The cost of producing t books like this one is nearly linear, $b = C + Dt$, with editing and typesetting in C and then printing and binding in D. C is the set-up cost and D is the cost for each additional book.

How to compute C and D? If there is no experimental error, then two measurements of b will determine the line $b = C + Dt$. But if there is error, we must be prepared to "average" the experiments and find an optimal line. That line is not to be confused with the line through a on which b was projected in the previous section! In fact, since there are two unknowns C and D to be determined, we now project onto a *two-dimensional* subspace. A perfect experiment would give a perfect C and D:

$$\begin{aligned} C + Dt_1 &= b_1 \\ C + Dt_2 &= b_2 \\ &\vdots \\ C + Dt_m &= b_m. \end{aligned} \tag{6}$$

This is an *overdetermined* system, with m equations and only two unknowns. If errors are present, it will have no solution. A has two columns, and $x = (C, D)$:

$$\begin{bmatrix} 1 & t_1 \\ 1 & t_2 \\ \vdots & \vdots \\ 1 & t_m \end{bmatrix} \begin{bmatrix} C \\ D \end{bmatrix} = \begin{bmatrix} b_1 \\ b_2 \\ \vdots \\ b_m \end{bmatrix}, \quad \text{or} \quad Ax = b. \tag{7}$$

The best solution $(\widehat{C}, \widehat{D})$ is the $\widehat{x}$ that minimizes the squared error E^2:

$$\textbf{Minimize} \qquad E^2 = \|b - Ax\|^2 = (b_1 - C - Dt_1)^2 + \cdots + (b_m - C - Dt_m)^2.$$

The vector $p = A\widehat{x}$ is as close as possible to b. Of all straight lines $b = C + Dt$, we are choosing the one that best fits the data (Figure 3.9). On the graph, the errors are the ***vertical distances*** $b - C - Dt$ to the straight line (not perpendicular distances!). It is the vertical distances that are squared, summed, and minimized.

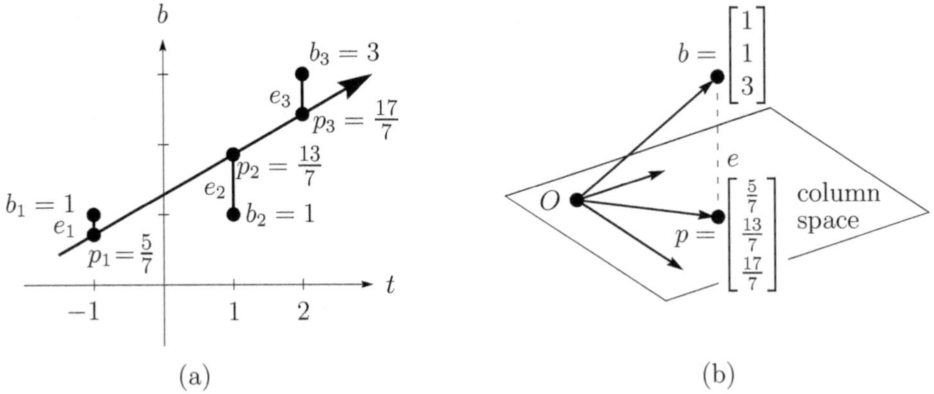

Figure 3.9 Straight-line approximation matches the projection p of b.

Example 2 Three measurements b_1, b_2, b_3 are marked on Figure 3.9a:

$$b = 1 \quad \text{at} \quad t = -1, \qquad b = 1 \quad \text{at} \quad t = 1, \qquad b = 3 \quad \text{at} \quad t = 2.$$

Note that the values $t = -1, 1, 2$ are not required to be equally spaced. The first step is *to write the equations that* ***would*** *hold if a line could go through all three points.*

Then every $C + Dt$ would agree exactly with b:

$$Ax = b \quad \text{is} \quad \begin{aligned} C - D &= 1 \\ C + D &= 1 \\ C + 2D &= 3 \end{aligned} \quad \text{or} \quad \begin{bmatrix} 1 & -1 \\ 1 & 1 \\ 1 & 2 \end{bmatrix} \begin{bmatrix} C \\ D \end{bmatrix} = \begin{bmatrix} 1 \\ 1 \\ 3 \end{bmatrix}.$$

If those equations $Ax = b$ could be solved, there would be no errors. They can't be solved because the points are not on a line. Therefore they are solved by least squares:

$$A^{\mathrm{T}}A\widehat{x} = A^{\mathrm{T}}b \quad \text{is} \quad \begin{bmatrix} 3 & 2 \\ 2 & 6 \end{bmatrix} \begin{bmatrix} \widehat{C} \\ \widehat{D} \end{bmatrix} = \begin{bmatrix} 5 \\ 6 \end{bmatrix}.$$

The best solution is $\widehat{C} = \frac{9}{7}$, $\widehat{D} = \frac{4}{7}$ and the best line is $\frac{9}{7} + \frac{4}{7}t$.

Note the beautiful connections between the two figures. The problem is the same but the art shows it differently. In Figure 3.9b, b is not a combination of the columns $(1, 1, 1)$ and $(-1, 1, 2)$. In Figure 3.9, the three points are not on a line. Least squares replaces points b that are not on a line by points p that are! Unable to solve $Ax = b$, we solve $A\widehat{x} = p$.

The line $\frac{9}{7} + \frac{4}{7}t$ has heights $\frac{5}{7}, \frac{13}{7}, \frac{17}{7}$ at the measurement times $-1, 1, 2$. ***Those points do lie on a line.*** Therefore the vector $p = \left(\frac{5}{7}, \frac{13}{7}, \frac{17}{7}\right)$ is in the column space. *This vector is the projection.* Figure 3.9b is in three dimensions (or m dimensions if there are m points) and Figure 3.9a is in two dimensions (or n dimensions if there are n parameters).

Subtracting p from b, the errors are $e = \left(\frac{2}{7}, -\frac{6}{7}, \frac{4}{7}\right)$. Those are the vertical errors in Figure 3.9a, and they are the components of the dashed vector in Figure 3.9b. This error vector is orthogonal to the first column $(1, 1, 1)$, since $\frac{2}{7} - \frac{6}{7} + \frac{4}{7} = 0$. It is orthogonal to the second column $(-1, 1, 2)$, because $-\frac{2}{7} - \frac{6}{7} + \frac{8}{7} = 0$. It is orthogonal to the column space, and it is in the left nullspace.

Question: If the measurements $b = \left(\frac{2}{7}, -\frac{6}{7}, \frac{4}{7}\right)$ were those errors, what would be the best line and the best $\widehat{x}$? Answer: The zero line—which is the horizontal axis—and $\widehat{x} = 0$. Projection to zero.

We can quickly summarize the equations for fitting by a straight line. The first column of A contains 1s, and the second column contains the times t_i. Therefore $A^{\mathrm{T}}A$ contains the sum of the 1s and the t_i and the t_i^2:

30 The measurements $b_1, \ldots, b_m$ are given at distinct points $t_1, \ldots, t_m$. Then the straight line $\widehat{C} + \widehat{D}t$ which minimizes E^2 comes from least squares:

$$A^{\mathrm{T}}A \begin{bmatrix} \widehat{C} \\ \widehat{D} \end{bmatrix} = A^{\mathrm{T}}b \quad \text{or} \quad \begin{bmatrix} m & \sum t_i \\ \sum t_i & \sum t_i^2 \end{bmatrix} \begin{bmatrix} \widehat{C} \\ \widehat{D} \end{bmatrix} = \begin{bmatrix} \sum b_i \\ \sum t_i b_i \end{bmatrix}.$$

Remark The mathematics of least squares is not limited to fitting the data by straight lines. In many experiments there is no reason to expect a linear relationship, and it would be crazy to look for one. Suppose we are handed some radioactive material. The output b will be the reading on a Geiger counter at various times t. We may know that we are holding a mixture of two chemicals, and we may know their half-lives (or rates of decay), but we do not know how much of each is in our hands. If these two unknown amounts are C and D, then the Geiger counter readings would behave like the sum of two exponentials (and not like a straight line):

$$b = Ce^{-\lambda t} + De^{-\mu t}. \tag{8}$$

In practice, the Geiger counter is not exact. Instead, we make readings $b_1, \ldots, b_m$ at times $t_1, \ldots, t_m$, and equation (8) is approximately satisfied:

$$Ax = b \quad \text{is} \quad \begin{aligned} Ce^{-\lambda t_1} &+ De^{-\mu t_1} \approx b_1 \\ &\vdots \\ Ce^{-\lambda t_m} &+ De^{-\mu t_m} \approx b_m. \end{aligned}$$

If there are more than two readings, $m > 2$, then in all likelihood we cannot solve for C and D. But the least-squares principle will give optimal values $\widehat{C}$ and $\widehat{D}$.

The situation would be completely different if we knew the amounts C and D, and were trying to discover the decay rates λ and μ. This is a problem in *nonlinear least squares*, and it is harder. We would still form E^2, the sum of the squares of the errors, and minimize it. But setting its derivatives to zero will not give linear equations for the optimal λ and μ. In the exercises, we stay with linear least squares.

Weighted Least Squares

A simple least-squares problem is the estimate $\widehat{x}$ of a patient's weight from two observations $x = b_1$ and $x = b_2$. Unless $b_1 = b_2$, we are faced with an inconsistent system of two equations in one unknown:

$$\begin{bmatrix} 1 \\ 1 \end{bmatrix} [x] = \begin{bmatrix} b_1 \\ b_2 \end{bmatrix}.$$

Up to now, we accepted b_1 and b_2 as equally reliable. We looked for the value $\widehat{x}$ that minimized $E^2 = (x - b_1)^2 + (x - b_2)^2$:

$$\frac{dE^2}{dx} = 0 \quad \text{at} \quad \widehat{x} = \frac{b_1 + b_2}{2}.$$

The optimal $\widehat{x}$ is the average. The same conclusion comes from $A^{\mathrm{T}}A\widehat{x} = A^{\mathrm{T}}b$. In fact $A^{\mathrm{T}}A$ is a 1 by 1 matrix, and the normal equation is $2\widehat{x} = b_1 + b_2$.

Now suppose the two observations are not trusted to the same degree. The value $x = b_1$ may be obtained from a more accurate scale—or, in a statistical problem, from a larger sample—than $x = b_2$. Nevertheless, if b_2 contains some information, we are not willing to rely totally on b_1. The simplest compromise is to attach different weights w_1^2 and w_2^2, and choose the $\widehat{x}_W$ that minimizes the *weighted sum of squares*:

$$\textbf{Weighted error} \qquad E^2 = w_1^2(x - b_1)^2 + w_2^2(x - b_2)^2.$$

If $w_1 > w_2$, more importance is attached to b_1. The minimizing process (derivative $= 0$) tries harder to make $(x - b_1)^2$ small:

$$\frac{dE^2}{dx} = 2\left[w_1^2(x - b_1) + w_2^2(x - b_2)\right] = 0 \quad \text{at} \quad \widehat{x}_W = \frac{w_1^2 b_1 + w_2^2 b_2}{w_1^2 + w_2^2}. \tag{9}$$

Instead of the average of b_1 and b_2 (for $w_1 = w_2 = 1$), $\widehat{x}_W$ is a ***weighted average*** of the data. This average is closer to b_1 than to b_2.

The ordinary least-squares problem leading to $\widehat{x}_W$ comes from changing $Ax = b$ to the new system $WAx = Wb$. ***This changes the solution from $\widehat{x}$ to $\widehat{x}_W$.*** The matrix $W^{\mathrm{T}}W$ turns up on both sides of the weighted normal equations:

The least squares solution to $WAx = Wb$ is $\widehat{x}_W$:

Weighted normal equations $\quad (A^{\mathrm{T}}W^{\mathrm{T}}WA)\widehat{x}_W = A^{\mathrm{T}}W^{\mathrm{T}}Wb.$

What happens to the picture of b projected to $A\widehat{x}$? The projection $A\widehat{x}_W$ is still the point in the column space that is closest to b. But the word "closest" has a new meaning when the length involves W. The *weighted length* of x equals the ordinary length of Wx. Perpendicularity no longer means $y^{\mathrm{T}}x = 0$; in the new system the test is $(Wy)^{\mathrm{T}}(Wx) = 0$. The matrix $W^{\mathrm{T}}W$ appears in the middle. In this new sense, the projection $A\widehat{x}_W$ and the error $b - A\widehat{x}_W$ are again perpendicular.

That last paragraph describes ***all inner products***: They come from invertible matrices W. They involve only the symmetric combination $C = W^{\mathrm{T}}W$. ***The inner product of x and y is $y^{\mathrm{T}}Cx$.*** For an orthogonal matrix $W = Q$, when this combination is $C = Q^{\mathrm{T}}Q = I$, the inner product is not new or different. Rotating the space leaves the inner product unchanged. Every other W changes the length and inner product.

For any invertible matrix W, these rules define a new inner product and length:

$$\textbf{Weighted by } W \qquad (x, y)_W = (Wy)^{\mathrm{T}}(Wx) \qquad \textit{and} \qquad \|x\|_W = \|Wx\|. \tag{10}$$

Since W is invertible, no vector is assigned length zero (except the zero vector). All possible inner products—which depend linearly on x and y and are positive when $x = y \neq 0$—are found in this way, from some matrix $C = W^{\mathrm{T}}W$.

In practice, the important question is the choice of C. The best answer comes from statisticians, and originally from Gauss. We may know that the average error is zero. That is the "expected value" of the error in b—although the error is not really expected to be zero! We may also know the ***average of the square*** of the error; that is the ***variance***. If the errors in the b_i are independent of each other, and their variances are σ_i^2, then ***the right weights are $w_i = 1/\sigma_i$***. A more accurate measurement, which means a smaller variance, gets a heavier weight.

In addition to unequal reliability, *the observations may not be independent.* If the errors are coupled—the polls for President are not independent of those for Senator, and certainly not of those for Vice-President—then W has off-diagonal terms. The best unbiased matrix $C = W^{\mathrm{T}}W$ is the ***inverse of the covariance matrix***—whose i, j entry is the expected value of (error in b_i) times (error in b_j). Then the main diagonal of C^{-1} contains the variances σ_i^2, which are the average of (error in $b_i)^2$.

Example 3 Suppose two bridge partners both guess (after the bidding) the total number of spades they hold. For each guess, the errors -1, 0, 1 might have equal probability $\frac{1}{3}$. Then the expected error is zero and the variance is $\frac{2}{3}$:

$$E(e) = \tfrac{1}{3}(-1) + \tfrac{1}{3}(0) + \tfrac{1}{3}(1) = 0$$
$$E(e^2) = \tfrac{1}{3}(-1)^2 + \tfrac{1}{3}(0)^2 + \tfrac{1}{3}(1)^2 = \tfrac{2}{3}.$$

The two guesses are dependent, because they are based on the same bidding—but not identical, because they are looking at different hands. Say the chance that they are both too high or both too low is zero, but the chance of opposite errors is $\frac{1}{3}$. Then $E(e_1e_2) = \frac{1}{3}(-1)$, and the inverse of the covariance matrix is $W^{\mathrm{T}}W$:

$$\begin{bmatrix} E(e_1^2) & E(e_1e_2) \\ E(e_1e_2) & E(e_2^2) \end{bmatrix}^{-1} = \begin{bmatrix} \frac{2}{3} & -\frac{1}{3} \\ -\frac{1}{3} & \frac{2}{3} \end{bmatrix}^{-1} = \begin{bmatrix} 2 & 1 \\ 1 & 2 \end{bmatrix} = C = W^{\mathrm{T}}W.$$

This matrix goes into the middle of the weighted normal equations.

Problem Set 3.3

1. Find the best least-squares solution $\widehat{x}$ to $3x = 10$, $4x = 5$. What error E^2 is minimized? Check that the error vector $(10 - 3\widehat{x}, 5 - 4\widehat{x})$ is perpendicular to the column $(3, 4)$.

2. Suppose the values $b_1 = 1$ and $b_2 = 7$ at times $t_1 = 1$ and $t_2 = 2$ are fitted by a line $b = Dt$ *through the origin*. Solve $D = 1$ and $2D = 7$ by least squares, and sketch the best line.

3. Solve $Ax = b$ by least squares, and find $p = A\widehat{x}$ if

$$A = \begin{bmatrix} 1 & 0 \\ 0 & 1 \\ 1 & 1 \end{bmatrix}, \qquad b = \begin{bmatrix} 1 \\ 1 \\ 0 \end{bmatrix}.$$

Verify that the error $b - p$ is perpendicular to the columns of A.

4. Write out $E^2 = \|Ax - b\|^2$ and set to zero its derivatives with respect to u and v, if

$$A = \begin{bmatrix} 1 & 0 \\ 0 & 1 \\ 1 & 1 \end{bmatrix}, \qquad x = \begin{bmatrix} u \\ v \end{bmatrix}, \qquad b = \begin{bmatrix} 1 \\ 3 \\ 4 \end{bmatrix}.$$

Compare the resulting equations with $A^{\mathrm{T}}A\widehat{x} = A^{\mathrm{T}}b$, confirming that calculus as well as geometry gives the normal equations. Find the solution $\widehat{x}$ and the projection $p = A\widehat{x}$. Why is $p = b$?

5. The following system has no solution:

$$Ax = \begin{bmatrix} 1 & -1 \\ 1 & 0 \\ 1 & 1 \end{bmatrix} \begin{bmatrix} C \\ D \end{bmatrix} = \begin{bmatrix} 4 \\ 5 \\ 9 \end{bmatrix} = b.$$

Sketch and solve a straight-line fit that leads to the minimization of the quadratic $(C - D - 4)^2 + (C - 5)^2 + (C + D - 9)^2$. What is the projection of b onto the column space of A?

6. Find the projection of b onto the column space of A:

$$A = \begin{bmatrix} 1 & 1 \\ 1 & -1 \\ -2 & 4 \end{bmatrix}, \qquad b = \begin{bmatrix} 1 \\ 2 \\ 7 \end{bmatrix}.$$

Split b into $p+q$, with p in the column space and q perpendicular to that space. Which of the four subspaces contains q?

7. Find the projection matrix P onto the space spanned by $a_1 = (1, 0, 1)$ and $a_2 = (1, 1, -1)$.

8. If P is the projection matrix onto a k-dimensional subspace $\mathbf{S}$ of the whole space $\mathbf{R}^n$, what is the column space of P and what is its rank?

9. (a) If $P = P^{\mathrm{T}}P$, show that P is a projection matrix.
(b) What subspace does the matrix $P = 0$ project onto?

10. If the vectors a_1, a_2, and b are orthogonal, what are $A^{\mathrm{T}}A$ and $A^{\mathrm{T}}b$? What is the projection of b onto the plane of a_1 and a_2?

11. Suppose P is the projection matrix onto the subspace $\mathbf{S}$ and Q is the projection onto the orthogonal complement $\mathbf{S}^{\perp}$. What are $P+Q$ and PQ? Show that $P-Q$ is its own inverse.

12. If $\mathbf{V}$ is the subspace spanned by $(1, 1, 0, 1)$ and $(0, 0, 1, 0)$, find

(a) a basis for the orthogonal complement $\mathbf{V}^{\perp}$.
(b) the projection matrix P onto $\mathbf{V}$.
(c) the vector in $\mathbf{V}$ closest to the vector $b = (0, 1, 0, -1)$ in $\mathbf{V}^{\perp}$.

13. Find the best straight-line fit (least squares) to the measurements

$$\begin{array}{llllll} b=4 & \text{at} & t=-2, & b=3 & \text{at} & t=-1, \\ b=1 & \text{at} & t=0, & b=0 & \text{at} & t=2. \end{array}$$

Then find the projection of $b = (4, 3, 1, 0)$ onto the column space of

$$A = \begin{bmatrix} 1 & -2 \\ 1 & -1 \\ 1 & 0 \\ 1 & 2 \end{bmatrix}.$$

14. The vectors $a_1 = (1, 1, 0)$ and $a_2 = (1, 1, 1)$ span a plane in $\mathbf{R}^3$. Find the projection matrix P onto the plane, and find a nonzero vector b that is projected to zero.

15. If P is the projection matrix onto a line in the x-y plane, draw a figure to describe the effect of the "reflection matrix" $H = I - 2P$. Explain both geometrically and algebraically why $H^2 = I$.

16. Show that if u has unit length, then the rank-1 matrix $P = uu^{\mathrm{T}}$ is a projection matrix: It has properties (i) and (ii) in 3N. By choosing $u = a/\|a\|$, P becomes the projection onto the line through a, and Pb is the point $p = \widehat{x}a$. Rank-1 projections correspond exactly to least-squares problems in one unknown.

17. What 2 by 2 matrix projects the x-y plane onto the -45° line $x + y = 0$?

18. We want to fit a plane $y = C + Dt + Ez$ to the four points

$$\begin{array}{llll} y=3 & \text{at} \quad t=1,\ z=1 & y=6 & \text{at} \quad t=0,\ z=3 \\ y=5 & \text{at} \quad t=2,\ z=1 & y=0 & \text{at} \quad t=0,\ z=0. \end{array}$$

(a) Find 4 equations in 3 unknowns to pass a plane through the points (if there is such a plane).
(b) Find 3 equations in 3 unknowns for the best least-squares solution.

19. If $P_C = A(A^{\mathrm{T}}A)^{-1}A^{\mathrm{T}}$ is the projection onto the column space of A, what is the projection P_R onto the row space? (It is not P_C^{T}!)

20. If P is the projection onto the column space of A, what is the projection onto the left nullspace?

21. Suppose L_1 is the line through the origin in the direction of a_1 and L_2 is the line through b in the direction of a_2. To find the closest points x_1a_1 and $b + x_2a_2$ on the two lines, write the two equations for the x_1 and x_2 that minimize $\|x_1a_1 - x_2a_2 - b\|$. Solve for x if $a_1 = (1, 1, 0)$, $a_2 = (0, 1, 0)$, $b = (2, 1, 4)$.

22. Find the best line $C + Dt$ to fit $b = 4, 2, -1, 0, 0$ at times $t = -2, -1, 0, 1, 2$.

23. Show that the best least-squares fit to a set of measurements $y_1, \dots, y_m$ by a *horizontal line* (a constant function $y = C$) is their average

$$C = \frac{y_1 + \cdots + y_m}{m}.$$

24. Find the best straight-line fit to the following measurements, and sketch your solution:

$$\begin{array}{llllll} y = 2 & \text{at} & t = -1, & y = 0 & \text{at} & t = 0, \\ y = -3 & \text{at} & t = 1, & y = -5 & \text{at} & t = 2. \end{array}$$

25. Suppose that instead of a straight line, we fit the data in Problem 24 by a parabola: $y = C + Dt + Et^2$. In the inconsistent system $Ax = b$ that comes from the four measurements, what are the coefficient matrix A, the unknown vector x, and the data vector b? You need not compute $\widehat{x}$.

26. A Middle-Aged man was stretched on a rack to lengths $L = 5$, 6, and 7 feet under applied forces of $F = 1$, 2, and 4 tons. Assuming Hooke's law $L = a + bF$, find his normal length a by least squares.

Problems 27–31 introduce basic ideas of statistics—the foundation for least squares.

27. (Recommended) This problem projects $b = (b_1, \dots, b_m)$ onto the line through $a = (1, \dots, 1)$. We solve m equations $ax = b$ in 1 unknown (by least squares).

(a) Solve $a^{\mathrm{T}}a\widehat{x} = a^{\mathrm{T}}b$ to show that $\widehat{x}$ is the *mean* (the average) of the b's.
(b) Find $e = b - a\widehat{x}$, the *variance* $\|e\|^2$, and the *standard deviation* $\|e\|$.
(c) The horizontal line $\widehat{b} = 3$ is closest to $b = (1, 2, 6)$. Check that $p = (3, 3, 3)$ is perpendicular to e and find the projection matrix P.

28. First assumption behind least squares: Each measurement error has ***mean zero***. Multiply the 8 error vectors $b - Ax = (\pm 1, \pm 1, \pm 1)$ by $(A^{\mathrm{T}}A)^{-1}A^{\mathrm{T}}$ to show that the 8 vectors $\widehat{x} - x$ also average to zero. The estimate $\widehat{x}$ is *unbiased*.

29. Second assumption behind least squares: The m errors e_i are independent with variance σ^2, so the average of $(b - Ax)(b - Ax)^{\mathrm{T}}$ is $\sigma^2 I$. Multiply on the left by $(A^{\mathrm{T}}A)^{-1}A^{\mathrm{T}}$ and on the right by $A(A^{\mathrm{T}}A)^{-1}$ to show that the average of $(\widehat{x}-x)(\widehat{x}-x)^{\mathrm{T}}$ is $\sigma^2(A^{\mathrm{T}}A)^{-1}$. This is the all-important ***covariance matrix*** for the error in $\widehat{x}$.

30. A doctor takes four readings of your heart rate. The best solution to $x = b_1, \ldots, x = b_4$ is the average $\widehat{x}$ of $b_1, \ldots, b_4$. The matrix A is a column of 1s. Problem 29 gives the expected error $(\widehat{x} - x)^2$ as $\sigma^2(A^{\mathrm{T}}A)^{-1} =$ ______. By averaging, the variance drops from σ^2 to $\sigma^2/4$.

31. If you know the average $\widehat{x}_9$ of 9 numbers $b_1, \ldots, b_9$, how can you quickly find the average $\widehat{x}_{10}$ with one more number b_{10}? The idea of *recursive* least squares is to avoid adding 10 numbers. What coefficient of $\widehat{x}_9$ correctly gives $\widehat{x}_{10}$?

$$\widehat{x}_{10} = \tfrac{1}{10}b_{10} + \_\_\_\, \widehat{x}_9 = \tfrac{1}{10}(b_1 + \cdots + b_{10}).$$

Problems 32–37 use four points $b = (0, 8, 8, 20)$ to bring out more ideas.

32. With $b = 0, 8, 8, 20$ at $t = 0, 1, 3, 4$, set up and solve the normal equations $A^{\mathrm{T}}A\widehat{x} = A^{\mathrm{T}}b$. For the best straight line as in Figure 3.9a, find its four heights p_i and four errors e_i. What is the minimum value $E^2 = e_1^2 + e_2^2 + e_3^2 + e_4^2$?

33. (Line $C + Dt$ does go through p's) With $b = 0, 8, 8, 20$ at times $t = 0, 1, 3, 4$, write the four equations $Ax = b$ (unsolvable). Change the measurements to $p = 1, 5, 13, 17$ and find an exact solution to $A\widehat{x} = p$.

34. Check that $e = b - p = (-1, 3, -5, 3)$ is perpendicular to both columns of A. What is the shortest distance $\|e\|$ from b to the column space of A?

35. For the closest parabola $b = C + Dt + Et^2$ to the same four points, write the unsolvable equations $Ax = b$ in three unknowns $x = (C, D, E)$. Set up the three normal equations $A^{\mathrm{T}}A\widehat{x} = A^{\mathrm{T}}b$ (solution not required). You are now fitting a parabola to four points—what is happening in Figure 3.9b?

36. For the closest cubic $b = C + Dt + Et^2 + Ft^3$ to the same four points, write the four equations $Ax = b$. Solve them by elimination. This cubic now goes exactly through the points. What are p and e?

37. The average of the four times is $\widehat{t} = \frac{1}{4}(0 + 1 + 3 + 4) = 2$. The average of the four b's is $\widehat{b} = \frac{1}{4}(0 + 8 + 8 + 20) = 9$.

(a) Verify that the best line goes *through the center point* $(\widehat{t}, \widehat{b}) = (2, 9)$.

(b) Explain why $C + D\widehat{t} = \widehat{b}$ comes from the first equation in $A^{\mathrm{T}}A\widehat{x} = A^{\mathrm{T}}b$.

38. What happens to the weighted average $\widehat{x}_W = (w_1^2b_1 + w_2^2b_2)/(w_1^2 + w_2^2)$ if the first weight w_1 approaches zero? The measurement b_1 is totally unreliable.

39. From m independent measurements $b_1, \ldots, b_m$ of your pulse rate, weighted by $w_1, \ldots, w_m$, what is the weighted average that replaces equation (9)? It is the best estimate when the statistical variances are $\sigma_i^2 = 1/w_i^2$.

40. If $W = \begin{bmatrix} 2 & 0 \\ 0 & 1 \end{bmatrix}$, find the W-inner product of $x = (2, 3)$ and $y = (1, 1)$, and the W-length of x. What line of vectors is W-perpendicular to y?

41. Find the weighted least-squares solution $\widehat{x}_W$ to $Ax = b$:

$$A = \begin{bmatrix} 1 & 0 \\ 1 & 1 \\ 1 & 2 \end{bmatrix} \qquad b = \begin{bmatrix} 0 \\ 1 \\ 1 \end{bmatrix} \qquad W = \begin{bmatrix} 2 & 0 & 0 \\ 0 & 1 & 0 \\ 0 & 0 & 1 \end{bmatrix}.$$

Check that the projection $A\widehat{x}_W$ is still perpendicular (in the W-inner product!) to the error $b - A\widehat{x}_W$.

42. (a) Suppose you guess your professor's age, making errors $e = -2, -1, 5$ with probabilities $\frac{1}{2}, \frac{1}{4}, \frac{1}{4}$. Check that the expected error $E(e)$ is zero and find the variance $E(e^2)$.

(b) If the professor guesses too (or tries to remember), making errors $-1, 0, 1$ with probabilities $\frac{1}{8}, \frac{6}{8}, \frac{1}{8}$, what weights w_1 and w_2 give the reliability of your guess and the professor's guess?

3.4 ORTHOGONAL BASES AND GRAM-SCHMIDT

In an orthogonal basis, every vector is perpendicular to every other vector. The coordinate axes are mutually orthogonal. That is just about optimal, and the one possible improvement is easy: Divide each vector by its length, to make it a *unit vector*. That changes an ***orthogonal*** basis into an ***orthonormal*** basis of q's:

3P The vectors $q_1, \ldots, q_n$ are ***orthonormal*** if

$$q_i^{\mathrm{T}} q_j = \begin{cases} 0 & \text{whenever } i \neq j, \quad \text{giving the orthogonality;} \\ 1 & \text{whenever } i = j, \quad \text{giving the normalization.} \end{cases}$$

A matrix with orthonormal columns will be called Q.

The most important example is the *standard basis*. For the x-y plane, the best-known axes $e_1 = (1, 0)$ and $e_2 = (0, 1)$ are not only perpendicular but horizontal and vertical. Q is the 2 by 2 identity matrix. In n dimensions the standard basis $e_1, \ldots, e_n$ again consists of *the columns of* $Q = I$:

Standard basis $$e_1 = \begin{bmatrix} 1 \\ 0 \\ 0 \\ \vdots \\ 0 \end{bmatrix}, \quad e_2 = \begin{bmatrix} 0 \\ 1 \\ 0 \\ \vdots \\ 0 \end{bmatrix}, \quad \ldots, \quad e_n = \begin{bmatrix} 0 \\ 0 \\ 0 \\ \vdots \\ 1 \end{bmatrix}.$$

That is not the only orthonormal basis! We can rotate the axes without changing the right angles at which they meet. These rotation matrices will be examples of Q.

If we have a subspace of $\mathbf{R}^n$, the standard vectors e_i might not lie in that subspace. But the subspace always has an orthonormal basis, and it can be constructed in a simple way out of any basis whatsoever. This construction, which converts a skewed set of axes into a perpendicular set, is known as ***Gram-Schmidt orthogonalization***.

To summarize, the three topics basic to this section are:

1. The definition and properties of orthogonal matrices Q.
2. The solution of $Qx = b$, either n by n or rectangular (least squares).
3. The Gram-Schmidt process and its interpretation as a new factorization $A = QR$.

Orthogonal Matrices

3Q If Q (square or rectangular) has orthonormal columns, then $Q^{\mathrm{T}}Q = I$:

$$\textbf{Orthonormal columns} \quad \begin{bmatrix} \text{---} & q_1^{\mathrm{T}} & \text{---} \\ \text{---} & q_2^{\mathrm{T}} & \text{---} \\ & & \\ \text{---} & q_n^{\mathrm{T}} & \text{---} \end{bmatrix} \begin{bmatrix} | & | & & | \\ q_1 & q_2 & & q_n \\ | & | & & | \end{bmatrix} = \begin{bmatrix} 1 & 0 & \cdot & 0 \\ 0 & 1 & \cdot & 0 \\ \cdot & \cdot & \cdot & \cdot \\ 0 & 0 & \cdot & 1 \end{bmatrix} = I. \quad (1)$$

An orthogonal matrix is a square matrix with orthonormal columns.* Then Q^{T} is Q^{-1}. For square orthogonal matrices, ***the transpose is the inverse***.

When row i of Q^{T} multiplies column j of Q, the result is $q_i^{\mathrm{T}}q_j = 0$. On the diagonal where $i = j$, we have $q_i^{\mathrm{T}}q_i = 1$. That is the normalization to unit vectors of length 1.

Note that $Q^{\mathrm{T}}Q = I$ even if Q is rectangular. But then Q^{T} is only a left-inverse.

Example 1

$$Q = \begin{bmatrix} \cos\theta & -\sin\theta \\ \sin\theta & \cos\theta \end{bmatrix}, \qquad Q^{\mathrm{T}} = Q^{-1} = \begin{bmatrix} \cos\theta & \sin\theta \\ -\sin\theta & \cos\theta \end{bmatrix}.$$

Q rotates every vector through the angle θ, and Q^{T} rotates it back through $-\theta$. The columns are clearly orthogonal, and they are orthonormal because $\sin^2\theta + \cos^2\theta = 1$. The matrix Q^{T} is just as much an orthogonal matrix as Q.

Example 2 Any permutation matrix P is an orthogonal matrix. The columns are certainly unit vectors and certainly orthogonal—because the 1 appears in a different place in each column: The transpose is the inverse.

$$\text{If } P = \begin{bmatrix} 0 & 1 & 0 \\ 0 & 0 & 1 \\ 1 & 0 & 0 \end{bmatrix} \quad \text{then } P^{-1} = P^{\mathrm{T}} = \begin{bmatrix} 0 & 0 & 1 \\ 1 & 0 & 0 \\ 0 & 1 & 0 \end{bmatrix}.$$

An anti-diagonal P, with $P_{13} = P_{22} = P_{31} = 1$, takes the x-y-z axes into the z-y-x axes—a "right-handed" system into a "left-handed" system. So we were wrong if we suggested that every orthogonal Q represents a rotation. *A reflection is also allowed.* $P = \begin{bmatrix} 0 & 1 \\ 1 & 0 \end{bmatrix}$ reflects every point (x, y) into (y, x), its mirror image across the 45° line. Geometrically, an orthogonal Q is the product of a rotation and a reflection.

There does remain one property that is shared by rotations and reflections, and in fact by every orthogonal matrix. It is not shared by projections, which are not orthogonal or even invertible. Projections reduce the length of a vector, whereas orthogonal matrices

---

* Orthonormal matrix would have been a better name, but it is too late to change. Also, there is no accepted word for a rectangular matrix with orthonormal columns. We still write Q, but we won't call it an "orthogonal matrix" unless it is square.

have a property that is the most important and most characteristic of all:

3R Multiplication by any Q preserves lengths:

Lengths unchanged $\|Qx\| = \|x\|$ for every vector x. (2)

It also preserves inner products and angles, since $(Qx)^{\mathrm{T}}(Qy) = x^{\mathrm{T}}Q^{\mathrm{T}}Qy = x^{\mathrm{T}}y$.

The preservation of lengths comes directly from $Q^{\mathrm{T}}Q = I$:

$$\|Qx\|^2 = \|x\|^2 \quad \text{because} \quad (Qx)^{\mathrm{T}}(Qx) = x^{\mathrm{T}}Q^{\mathrm{T}}Qx = x^{\mathrm{T}}x. \tag{3}$$

All inner products and lengths are preserved, when the space is rotated or reflected.

We come now to the calculation that uses the special property $Q^{\mathrm{T}} = Q^{-1}$. If we have a basis, then any vector is a combination of the basis vectors. This is exceptionally simple for an orthonormal basis, which will be a key idea behind Fourier series. The problem is *to find the coefficients of the basis vectors*:

Write b as a combination $\boldsymbol{b = x_1q_1 + x_2q_2 + \cdots + x_nq_n}$.

To compute x_1 there is a neat trick. *Multiply both sides of the equation by* q_1^{T}. On the left-hand side is $q_1^{\mathrm{T}}b$. On the right-hand side all terms disappear (because $q_1^{\mathrm{T}}q_j = 0$) except the first term. We are left with

$$q_1^{\mathrm{T}}b = x_1q_1^{\mathrm{T}}q_1.$$

Since $q_1^{\mathrm{T}}q_1 = 1$, we have found $x_1 = q_1^{\mathrm{T}}b$. Similarly the second coefficient is $x_2 = q_2^{\mathrm{T}}b$; that term survives when we multiply by q_2^{T}. The other terms die of orthogonality. Each piece of b has a simple formula, and recombining the pieces gives back b:

$$\textbf{\textit{Every vector b is equal to }} (q_1^{\mathrm{T}}b)q_1 + (q_2^{\mathrm{T}}b)q_2 + \cdots + (q_n^{\mathrm{T}}b)q_n. \tag{4}$$

I can't resist putting this orthonormal basis into a square matrix Q. The vector equation $x_1q_1 + \cdots + x_nq_n = b$ is identical to $Qx = b$. (The columns of Q multiply the components of x.) Its solution is $x = Q^{-1}b$. But since $Q^{-1} = Q^{\mathrm{T}}$—this is where orthonormality enters—the solution is also $x = Q^{\mathrm{T}}b$:

$$x = Q^{\mathrm{T}}b = \begin{bmatrix} \text{——} & q_1^{\mathrm{T}} & \text{——} \\ & & \\ \text{——} & q_n^{\mathrm{T}} & \text{——} \end{bmatrix} \begin{bmatrix} \\ b \\ \\ \end{bmatrix} = \begin{bmatrix} q_1^{\mathrm{T}}b \\ \\ q_n^{\mathrm{T}}b \end{bmatrix} \tag{5}$$

The components of x are the inner products $q_i^{\mathrm{T}}b$, as in equation (4).

The matrix form also shows what happens when the columns are *not* orthonormal. Expressing b as a combination $x_1a_1 + \cdots + x_na_n$ is the same as solving $Ax = b$. The basis vectors go into the columns of A. In that case we need A^{-1}, which takes work. In the orthonormal case we only need Q^{T}.

Remark 1 The ratio $a^{\mathrm{T}}b/a^{\mathrm{T}}a$ appeared earlier, when we projected b onto a line. Here a is q_1, the denominator is 1, and the projection is $(q_1^{\mathrm{T}}b)q_1$. Thus we have a new interpretation for formula (4): *Every vector b is the sum of its one-dimensional projections onto the lines through the q's.*

Since those projections are orthogonal, Pythagoras should still be correct. The square of the hypotenuse should still be the sum of squares of the components:

$$\|b\|^2 = (q_1^{\mathrm{T}}b)^2 + (q_2^{\mathrm{T}}b)^2 + \cdots + (q_n^{\mathrm{T}}b)^2 \quad \text{which is} \quad \|Q^{\mathrm{T}}b\|^2. \tag{6}$$

Remark 2 Since $Q^{\mathrm{T}} = Q^{-1}$, we also have $QQ^{\mathrm{T}} = I$. When Q comes before Q^{T}, multiplication takes the inner products of the *rows* of Q. (For $Q^{\mathrm{T}}Q$ it was the columns.) Since the result is again the identity matrix, we come to a surprising conclusion: ***The rows of a square matrix are orthonormal whenever the columns are***. The rows point in completely different directions from the columns, and I don't see geometrically why they are forced to be orthonormal—but they are.

Orthonormal columns
Orthonormal rows

$$Q = \begin{bmatrix} 1/\sqrt{3} & 1/\sqrt{2} & 1/\sqrt{6} \\ 1/\sqrt{3} & 0 & -2/\sqrt{6} \\ 1/\sqrt{3} & -1/\sqrt{2} & 1/\sqrt{6} \end{bmatrix}.$$

Rectangular Matrices with Orthonormal Columns

This chapter is about $Ax = b$, when A is not necessarily square. For $Qx = b$ we now admit the same possibility—there may be more rows than columns. The n orthonormal vectors q_i in the columns of Q have $m > n$ components. Then Q is an m by n matrix and we cannot expect to solve $Qx = b$ exactly. *We solve it by least squares.*

If there is any justice, orthonormal columns should make the problem simple. It worked for square matrices, and now it will work for rectangular matrices. The key is to notice that *we still have* $Q^{\mathrm{T}}Q = I$. So Q^{T} is still the ***left-inverse*** of Q.

For least squares that is all we need. The normal equations came from multiplying $Ax = b$ by the transpose matrix, to give $A^{\mathrm{T}}A\widehat{x} = A^{\mathrm{T}}b$. Now the normal equations are $Q^{\mathrm{T}}Q\widehat{x} = Q^{\mathrm{T}}b$. But $Q^{\mathrm{T}}Q$ is the identity matrix! Therefore $\widehat{x} = Q^{\mathrm{T}}b$, whether Q is square and $\widehat{x}$ is an exact solution, or Q is rectangular and we need least squares.

3S If Q has orthonormal columns, the least-squares problem becomes easy:

$Qx = b$	rectangular system with no solution for most b.
$Q^{\mathrm{T}}Q\widehat{x} = Q^{\mathrm{T}}b$	normal equation for the best $\widehat{x}$—in which $Q^{\mathrm{T}}Q = I$.
$\widehat{x} = Q^{\mathrm{T}}b$	$\widehat{x}_i$ is $q_i^{\mathrm{T}}b$.
$p = Q\widehat{x}$	the projection of b is $(q_1^{\mathrm{T}}b)q_1 + \cdots + (q_n^{\mathrm{T}}b)q_n$.
$p = QQ^{\mathrm{T}}b$	the projection matrix is $P = QQ^{\mathrm{T}}$.

The last formulas are like $p = A\widehat{x}$ and $P = A(A^{\mathrm{T}}A)^{-1}A^{\mathrm{T}}$. When the columns are orthonormal, the "cross-product matrix" $A^{\mathrm{T}}A$ becomes $Q^{\mathrm{T}}Q = I$. The hard part of least squares disappears when vectors are orthonormal. The projections onto the axes are uncoupled, and p is the sum $p = (q_1^{\mathrm{T}}b)q_1 + \cdots + (q_n^{\mathrm{T}}b)q_n$.

We emphasize that those projections do not reconstruct b. In the square case $m = n$, they did. In the rectangular case $m > n$, they don't. They give the projection p and not the original vector b—which is all we can expect when there are more equations than unknowns, and the q's are no longer a basis. The projection matrix is usually

$A(A^{\mathrm{T}}A)^{-1}A^{\mathrm{T}}$, and here it simplifies to

$$P = Q(Q^{\mathrm{T}}Q)^{-1}Q^{\mathrm{T}} \quad \text{or} \quad P = QQ^{\mathrm{T}}. \tag{7}$$

Notice that $Q^{\mathrm{T}}Q$ is the n by n identity matrix, whereas QQ^{T} is an m by m projection P. It is the identity matrix on the columns of Q (P leaves them alone). But QQ^{T} is the zero matrix on the orthogonal complement (the nullspace of Q^{T}).

Example 3 The following case is simple but typical. Suppose we project a point $b = (x, y, z)$ onto the x-y plane. Its projection is $p = (x, y, 0)$, and this is the sum of the separate projections onto the x- and y-axes:

$$q_1 = \begin{bmatrix} 1 \\ 0 \\ 0 \end{bmatrix} \quad \text{and} \quad (q_1^{\mathrm{T}}b)q_1 = \begin{bmatrix} x \\ 0 \\ 0 \end{bmatrix}; \qquad q_2 = \begin{bmatrix} 0 \\ 1 \\ 0 \end{bmatrix} \quad \text{and} \quad (q_2^{\mathrm{T}}b)q_2 = \begin{bmatrix} 0 \\ y \\ 0 \end{bmatrix}.$$

The overall projection matrix is

$$P = q_1q_1^{\mathrm{T}} + q_2q_2^{\mathrm{T}} = \begin{bmatrix} 1 & 0 & 0 \\ 0 & 1 & 0 \\ 0 & 0 & 0 \end{bmatrix}, \quad \text{and} \quad P\begin{bmatrix} x \\ y \\ z \end{bmatrix} = \begin{bmatrix} x \\ y \\ 0 \end{bmatrix}.$$

Projection onto a plane = sum of projections onto orthonormal q_1 and q_2.

Example 4 When the measurement times average to zero, fitting a straight line leads to orthogonal columns. Take $t_1 = -3$, $t_2 = 0$, and $t_3 = 3$. Then the attempt to fit $y = C + Dt$ leads to three equations in two unknowns:

$$\begin{aligned} C + Dt_1 &= y_1 \\ C + Dt_2 &= y_2, \\ C + Dt_3 &= y_3 \end{aligned} \quad \text{or} \quad \begin{bmatrix} 1 & -3 \\ 1 & 0 \\ 1 & 3 \end{bmatrix} \begin{bmatrix} C \\ D \end{bmatrix} = \begin{bmatrix} y_1 \\ y_2 \\ y_3 \end{bmatrix}.$$

The columns $(1, 1, 1)$ *and* $(-3, 0, 3)$ *are orthogonal.* We can project y separately onto each column, and the best coefficients $\widehat{C}$ and $\widehat{D}$ can be found separately:

$$\widehat{C} = \frac{\begin{bmatrix} 1 & 1 & 1 \end{bmatrix}\begin{bmatrix} y_1 & y_2 & y_3 \end{bmatrix}^{\mathrm{T}}}{1^2 + 1^2 + 1^2}, \qquad \widehat{D} = \frac{\begin{bmatrix} -3 & 0 & 3 \end{bmatrix}\begin{bmatrix} y_1 & y_2 & y_3 \end{bmatrix}^{\mathrm{T}}}{(-3)^2 + 0^2 + 3^2}.$$

Notice that $\widehat{C} = (y_1 + y_2 + y_3)/3$ is the *mean* of the data. $\widehat{C}$ gives the best fit by a horizontal line, whereas $\widehat{D}t$ is the best fit by a straight line through the origin. *The columns are orthogonal, so the sum of these two separate pieces is the best fit by any straight line whatsoever.* The columns are not unit vectors, so $\widehat{C}$ and $\widehat{D}$ have the length squared in the denominator.

Orthogonal columns are so much better that it is worth changing to that case. If the average of the observation times is not zero—it is $\bar{t} = (t_1 + \cdots + t_m)/m$—then the time origin can be shifted by $\bar{t}$. Instead of $y = C + Dt$ we work with $y = c + d(t - \bar{t})$. The best line is the same! As in the example, we find

$$\widehat{c} = \frac{\begin{bmatrix}1 & \cdots & 1\end{bmatrix}\begin{bmatrix}y_1 & \cdots & y_m\end{bmatrix}^{\mathrm{T}}}{1^2 + 1^2 + \cdots + 1^2} = \frac{y_1 + \cdots + y_m}{m}$$

$$\widehat{d} = \frac{\begin{bmatrix}(t_1 - \bar{t}) & \cdots & (t_m - \bar{t})\end{bmatrix}\begin{bmatrix}y_1 & \cdots & y_m\end{bmatrix}^{\mathrm{T}}}{(t_1 - \bar{t})^2 + \cdots + (t_m - \bar{t})^2} = \frac{\sum(t_i - \bar{t})y_i}{\sum(t_i - \bar{t})^2}. \tag{8}$$

The best $\widehat{c}$ is the mean, and we also get a convenient formula for $\widehat{d}$. The earlier $A^{\mathrm{T}}A$ had the off-diagonal entries $\sum t_i$, and shifting the time by $\bar{t}$ made these entries zero. This shift is an example of the Gram-Schmidt process, ***which orthogonalizes the situation in advance***.

Orthogonal matrices are crucial to numerical linear algebra, because they introduce no instability. While lengths stay the same, roundoff is under control. Orthogonalizing vectors has become an essential technique. Probably it comes second only to elimination. And it leads to a factorization $A = QR$ that is nearly as famous as $A = LU$.

The Gram-Schmidt Process

Suppose you are given three independent vectors a, b, c. If they are orthonormal, life is easy. To project a vector v onto the first one, you compute $(a^{\mathrm{T}}v)a$. To project the same vector v onto the plane of the first two, you just add $(a^{\mathrm{T}}v)a + (b^{\mathrm{T}}v)b$. To project onto the span of a, b, c, you add three projections. All calculations require only the inner products $a^{\mathrm{T}}v$, $b^{\mathrm{T}}v$, and $c^{\mathrm{T}}v$. But to make this true, we are forced to say, "***If*** they are orthonormal." Now we propose to find a way to ***make*** them orthonormal.

The method is simple. We are given a, b, c and we want q_1, q_2, q_3. There is no problem with q_1: it can go in the direction of a. We divide by the length, so that $q_1 = a/\|a\|$ is a unit vector. The real problem begins with q_2—which has to be orthogonal to q_1. If the second vector b has any component in the direction of q_1 (which is the direction of a), ***that component has to be subtracted***:

$$\textbf{Second vector} \qquad B = b - (q_1^{\mathrm{T}}b)q_1 \quad \text{and} \quad q_2 = B/\|B\|. \tag{9}$$

B is orthogonal to q_1. It is the part of b that goes in a new direction, and not in the direction of a. In Figure 3.10, B is perpendicular to q_1. It sets the direction for q_2.

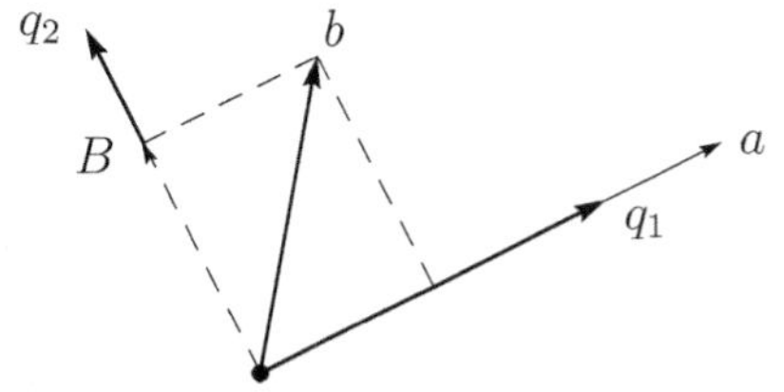

Figure 3.10 The q_1 component of b is removed; a and B normalized to q_1 and q_2.

At this point q_1 and q_2 are set. The third orthogonal direction starts with c. It will not be in the plane of q_1 and q_2, which is the plane of a and b. However, it may have a component in that plane, and that has to be subtracted. (If the result is $C = 0$, this signals that a, b, c were not independent in the first place.) What is left is the component C we want, the part that is in a new direction perpendicular to the plane:

$$\textbf{Third vector} \qquad C = c - (q_1^{\mathrm{T}}c)q_1 - (q_2^{\mathrm{T}}c)q_2 \quad \text{and} \quad q_3 = C/\|C\|. \tag{10}$$

This is the one idea of the whole Gram-Schmidt process, ***to subtract from every new vector its components in the directions that are already settled***. That idea is used over and over again.* When there is a fourth vector, we subtract away its components in the directions of q_1, q_2, q_3.

Example 5 **Gram-Schmidt** Suppose the independent vectors are a, b, c:

$$a = \begin{bmatrix} 1 \\ 0 \\ 1 \end{bmatrix}, \qquad b = \begin{bmatrix} 1 \\ 0 \\ 0 \end{bmatrix}, \qquad c = \begin{bmatrix} 2 \\ 1 \\ 0 \end{bmatrix}.$$

To find q_1, make the first vector into a unit vector: $q_1 = a/\sqrt{2}$. To find q_2, subtract from the second vector its component in the first direction:

$$B = b - (q_1^{\mathrm{T}}b)q_1 = \begin{bmatrix} 1 \\ 0 \\ 0 \end{bmatrix} - \frac{1}{\sqrt{2}} \begin{bmatrix} 1/\sqrt{2} \\ 0 \\ 1/\sqrt{2} \end{bmatrix} = \frac{1}{2} \begin{bmatrix} 1 \\ 0 \\ -1 \end{bmatrix}.$$

The normalized q_2 is B divided by its length, to produce a unit vector:

$$q_2 = \begin{bmatrix} 1/\sqrt{2} \\ 0 \\ -1/\sqrt{2} \end{bmatrix}.$$

To find q_3, subtract from c its components along q_1 and q_2:

$$\begin{aligned} C &= c - (q_1^{\mathrm{T}}c)q_1 - (q_2^{\mathrm{T}}c)q_2 \\ &= \begin{bmatrix} 2 \\ 1 \\ 0 \end{bmatrix} - \sqrt{2} \begin{bmatrix} 1/\sqrt{2} \\ 0 \\ 1/\sqrt{2} \end{bmatrix} - \sqrt{2} \begin{bmatrix} 1/\sqrt{2} \\ 0 \\ -1/\sqrt{2} \end{bmatrix} = \begin{bmatrix} 0 \\ 1 \\ 0 \end{bmatrix}. \end{aligned}$$

This is already a unit vector, so it is q_3. I went to desperate lengths to cut down the number of square roots (the painful part of Gram-Schmidt). The result is a set of orthonormal vectors q_1, q_2, q_3, which go into the columns of an orthogonal matrix Q:

$$\textbf{Orthonormal basis} \qquad Q = \begin{bmatrix} \\ q_1 & q_2 & q_3 \\ \\ \end{bmatrix} = \begin{bmatrix} 1/\sqrt{2} & 1/\sqrt{2} & 0 \\ 0 & 0 & 1 \\ 1/\sqrt{2} & -1/\sqrt{2} & 0 \end{bmatrix}.$$

---

* If Gram thought of it first, what was left for Schmidt?

3T The Gram-Schmidt process starts with independent vectors $a_1, \dots, a_n$ and ends with orthonormal vectors $q_1, \dots, q_n$. At step j it subtracts from a_j its components in the directions $q_1, \dots, q_{j-1}$ that are already settled:

$$A_j = a_j - (q_1^{\mathrm{T}} a_j) q_1 - \cdots - (q_{j-1}^{\mathrm{T}} a_j) q_{j-1}. \tag{11}$$

Then q_j is the unit vector $A_j / \|A_j\|$.

Remark on the calculations I think it is easier to compute the orthogonal a, B, C, without forcing their lengths to equal one. Then square roots enter only at the end, when dividing by those lengths. The example above would have the same B and C, without using square roots. Notice the $\frac{1}{2}$ from $a^{\mathrm{T}} b / a^{\mathrm{T}} a$ instead of $\frac{1}{\sqrt{2}}$ from $q^{\mathrm{T}} b$:

$$B = \begin{bmatrix} 1 \\ 0 \\ 0 \end{bmatrix} - \frac{1}{2} \begin{bmatrix} 1 \\ 0 \\ 1 \end{bmatrix} \quad \text{and then} \quad C = \begin{bmatrix} 2 \\ 1 \\ 0 \end{bmatrix} - \begin{bmatrix} 1 \\ 0 \\ 1 \end{bmatrix} - 2 \begin{bmatrix} \frac{1}{2} \\ 0 \\ -\frac{1}{2} \end{bmatrix}.$$

The Factorization $A = QR$

We started with a matrix A, whose columns were a, b, c. We ended with a matrix Q, whose columns are q_1, q_2, q_3. What is the relation between those matrices? The matrices A and Q are m by n when the n vectors are in m-dimensional space, and there has to be a third matrix that connects them.

The idea is to write the a's as combinations of the q's. The vector b in Figure 3.10 is a combination of the orthonormal q_1 and q_2, and we know what combination it is:

$$b = (q_1^{\mathrm{T}} b) q_1 + (q_2^{\mathrm{T}} b) q_2.$$

Every vector in the plane is the sum of its q_1 and q_2 components. Similarly c is the sum of its q_1, q_2, q_3 components: $c = (q_1^{\mathrm{T}} c) q_1 + (q_2^{\mathrm{T}} c) q_2 + (q_3^{\mathrm{T}} c) q_3$. If we express that in matrix form we have ***the new factorization A* = *QR***:

$$\textbf{\textit{QR} factors} \qquad A = \begin{bmatrix} & & \\ a & b & c \\ & & \end{bmatrix} = \begin{bmatrix} & & \\ q_1 & q_2 & q_3 \\ & & \end{bmatrix} \begin{bmatrix} q_1^{\mathrm{T}} a & q_1^{\mathrm{T}} b & q_1^{\mathrm{T}} c \\ & q_2^{\mathrm{T}} b & q_2^{\mathrm{T}} c \\ & & q_3^{\mathrm{T}} c \end{bmatrix} = QR \tag{12}$$

Notice the zeros in the last matrix! R is *upper triangular* because of the way Gram-Schmidt was done. The first vectors a and q_1 fell on the same line. Then q_1, q_2 were in the same plane as a, b. The third vectors c and q_3 were not involved until step 3.

The QR factorization is like $A = LU$, except that the first factor Q has orthonormal columns. The second factor is called R, because the nonzeros are to the *right* of the diagonal (and the letter U is already taken). The off-diagonal entries of R are the numbers $q_1^{\mathrm{T}} b = 1/\sqrt{2}$ and $q_1^{\mathrm{T}} c = q_2^{\mathrm{T}} c = \sqrt{2}$, found above. The whole factorization is

$$A = \begin{bmatrix} 1 & 1 & 2 \\ 0 & 0 & 1 \\ 1 & 0 & 0 \end{bmatrix} = \begin{bmatrix} 1/\sqrt{2} & 1/\sqrt{2} & 0 \\ 0 & 0 & 1 \\ 1/\sqrt{2} & -1/\sqrt{2} & 0 \end{bmatrix} \begin{bmatrix} \sqrt{2} & 1/\sqrt{2} & \sqrt{2} \\ & 1/\sqrt{2} & \sqrt{2} \\ & & 1 \end{bmatrix} = QR.$$

You see the lengths of a, B, C on the diagonal of R. The orthonormal vectors q_1, q_2, q_3, which are the whole object of orthogonalization, are in the first factor Q.

Maybe QR is not as beautiful as LU (because of the square roots). Both factorizations are vitally important to the theory of linear algebra, and absolutely central to the calculations. If LU is Hertz, then QR is Avis.

The entries $r_{ij} = q_i^{\mathrm{T}} a_j$ appear in formula (11), when $\|A_j\| q_j$ is substituted for A_j:

$$a_j = (q_1^{\mathrm{T}} a_j) q_1 + \cdots + (q_{j-1}^{\mathrm{T}} a_j) q_{j-1} + \|A_j\| q_j = Q \text{ times column } j \text{ of } R. \qquad (13)$$

3U Every m by n matrix with independent columns can be factored into $A = QR$. The columns of Q are orthonormal, and R is upper triangular and invertible. When $m = n$ and all matrices are square, Q becomes an orthogonal matrix.

I must not forget the main point of orthogonalization. It simplifies the least-squares problem $Ax = b$. The normal equations are still correct, but $A^{\mathrm{T}} A$ becomes easier:

$$A^{\mathrm{T}} A = R^{\mathrm{T}} Q^{\mathrm{T}} Q R = R^{\mathrm{T}} R. \qquad (14)$$

The fundamental equation $A^{\mathrm{T}} A \widehat{x} = A^{\mathrm{T}} b$ simplifies to a triangular system:

$$R^{\mathrm{T}} R \widehat{x} = R^{\mathrm{T}} Q^{\mathrm{T}} b \qquad \text{or} \qquad R \widehat{x} = Q^{\mathrm{T}} b. \qquad (15)$$

Instead of solving $QRx = b$, which can't be done, we solve $R\widehat{x} = Q^{\mathrm{T}} b$, which is just back-substitution because R is triangular. The real cost is the mn^2 operations of Gram-Schmidt, which are needed to find Q and R in the first place.

The same idea of orthogonality applies to functions. The sines and cosines are orthogonal; the powers $1, x, x^2$ are not. When $f(x)$ is written as a combination of sines and cosines, that is a ***Fourier series***. Each term is a projection onto a line—the line in function space containing multiples of $\cos nx$ or $\sin nx$. It is completely parallel to the vector case, and very important. And finally we have a job for Schmidt: To orthogonalize the powers of x and produce the Legendre polynomials.

Function Spaces and Fourier Series

This is a brief and optional section, but it has a number of good intentions:

1. to introduce the most famous infinite-dimensional vector space (*Hilbert space*);
2. to extend the ideas of length and inner product from vectors v to functions $f(x)$;
3. to recognize the Fourier series as a sum of one-dimensional projections (the orthogonal "columns" are the sines and cosines);
4. to apply Gram-Schmidt orthogonalization to the polynomials $1, x, x^2, \ldots$; and
5. to find the best approximation to $f(x)$ by a straight line.

We will try to follow this outline, which opens up a range of new applications for linear algebra, in a systematic way.

1. Hilbert Space. After studying $\mathbf{R}^n$, it is natural to think of the space $\mathbf{R}^\infty$. It contains all vectors $v = (v_1, v_2, v_3, \ldots)$ with an infinite sequence of components. This space is actually too big when there is no control on the size of components v_j. A much better idea is to keep the familiar definition of length, using a sum of squares, and *to include* *only those vectors that have a **finite length***:

$$\textbf{Length squared} \qquad \|v\|^2 = v_1^2 + v_2^2 + v_3^2 + \cdots \tag{16}$$

The infinite series must converge to a finite sum. This leaves $\left(1, \frac{1}{2}, \frac{1}{3}, \dots\right)$ but not $(1, 1, 1, \dots)$. Vectors with finite length can be added ($\|v + w\| \le \|v\| + \|w\|$) and multiplied by scalars, so they form a vector space. It is the celebrated ***Hilbert space***.

Hilbert space is the natural way to let the number of dimensions become infinite, and at the same time to keep the geometry of ordinary Euclidean space. Ellipses become infinite-dimensional ellipsoids, and perpendicular lines are recognized exactly as before. The vectors v and w are orthogonal when their inner product is zero:

$$\textbf{Orthogonality} \qquad v^{\mathrm{T}} w = v_1 w_1 + v_2 w_2 + v_3 w_3 + \cdots = 0.$$

This sum is guaranteed to converge, and for any two vectors it still obeys the Schwarz inequality $|v^{\mathrm{T}} w| \le \|v\|\,\|w\|$. The cosine, even in Hilbert space, is never larger than 1.

There is another remarkable thing about this space: It is found under a great many different disguises. Its "vectors" can turn into functions, which is the second point.

2. Lengths and Inner Products. Suppose $f(x) = \sin x$ on the interval $0 \le x \le 2\pi$. This f is like a vector with a whole continuum of components, the values of $\sin x$ along the whole interval. To find the length of such a vector, the usual rule of adding the squares of the components becomes impossible. This summation is replaced, in a natural and inevitable way, by *integration*:

$$\textbf{Length } \|f\| \textbf{ of function} \qquad \|f\|^2 = \int_0^{2\pi} (f(x))^2\,dx = \int_0^{2\pi} (\sin x)^2\,dx = \pi. \tag{17}$$

Our Hilbert space has become a ***function space***. The vectors are functions, we have a way to measure their length, and the space contains all those functions that have a finite length—just as in equation (16). It does not contain the function $F(x) = 1/x$, because the integral of $1/x^2$ is infinite.

The same idea of replacing summation by integration produces the ***inner product of two functions***: If $f(x) = \sin x$ and $g(x) = \cos x$, then their inner product is

$$(f, g) = \int_0^{2\pi} f(x) g(x)\,dx = \int_0^{2\pi} \sin x \cos x\,dx = 0. \tag{18}$$

This is exactly like the vector inner product $f^{\mathrm{T}} g$. It is still related to the length by $(f, f) = \|f\|^2$. The Schwarz inequality is still satisfied: $|(f, g)| \le \|f\|\,\|g\|$. Of course, two functions like $\sin x$ and $\cos x$—whose inner product is zero—will be called orthogonal. They are even orthonormal after division by their length $\sqrt{\pi}$.

3. The ***Fourier series*** of a function is an expansion into sines and cosines:

$$f(x) = a_0 + a_1 \cos x + b_1 \sin x + a_2 \cos 2x + b_2 \sin 2x + \cdots.$$

To compute a coefficient like b_1, *multiply* both sides by the corresponding function $\sin x$ and *integrate* from 0 to 2π. (The function $f(x)$ is given on that interval.) In other words, take the inner product of both sides with $\sin x$:

$$\int_0^{2\pi} f(x)\sin x\,dx = a_0\int_0^{2\pi}\sin x\,dx + a_1\int_0^{2\pi}\cos x\sin x\,dx + b_1\int_0^{2\pi}(\sin x)^2\,dx + \cdots.$$

On the right-hand side, every integral is zero except one—the one in which $\sin x$ multiplies itself. *The sines and cosines are mutually orthogonal* as in equation (18). Therefore b_1 is the left-hand side divided by that one nonzero integral:

$$b_1 = \frac{\int_0^{2\pi} f(x)\sin x\,dx}{\int_0^{2\pi}(\sin x)^2\,dx} = \frac{(f, \sin x)}{(\sin x, \sin x)}.$$

The Fourier coefficient a_1 would have $\cos x$ in place of $\sin x$, and a_2 would use $\cos 2x$.

The whole point is to see the analogy with projections. The component of the vector b along the line spanned by a is $b^{\mathrm{T}}a/a^{\mathrm{T}}a$. A ***Fourier series is projecting $f(x)$ onto $\sin x$***. Its component p in this direction is exactly $b_1 \sin x$.

The coefficient b_1 is the least squares solution of the inconsistent equation $b_1 \sin x = f(x)$. This brings $b_1 \sin x$ as close as possible to $f(x)$. All the terms in the series are projections onto a sine or cosine. Since the sines and cosines are orthogonal, *the Fourier series gives the coordinates of the "vector" $f(x)$ with respect to a set of* (infinitely many) *perpendicular axes.*

4. Gram-Schmidt for Functions. There are plenty of useful functions other than sines and cosines, and they are not always orthogonal. The simplest are the powers of x, and unfortunately there is no interval on which even 1 and x^2 are perpendicular. (Their inner product is always positive, because it is the integral of x^2.) Therefore the closest parabola to $f(x)$ is *not* the sum of its projections onto 1, x, and x^2. There will be a matrix like $(A^{\mathrm{T}}A)^{-1}$, and this coupling is given by the ill-conditioned **Hilbert matrix**. On the interval $0 \le x \le 1$,

$$A^{\mathrm{T}}A = \begin{bmatrix} (1,1) & (1,x) & (1,x^2) \\ (x,1) & (x,x) & (x,x^2) \\ (x^2,1) & (x^2,x) & (x^2,x^2) \end{bmatrix} = \begin{bmatrix} \int 1 & \int x & \int x^2 \\ \int x & \int x^2 & \int x^3 \\ \int x^2 & \int x^3 & \int x^4 \end{bmatrix} = \begin{bmatrix} 1 & \frac{1}{2} & \frac{1}{3} \\ \frac{1}{2} & \frac{1}{3} & \frac{1}{4} \\ \frac{1}{3} & \frac{1}{4} & \frac{1}{5} \end{bmatrix}.$$

This matrix has a large inverse, because the axes $1, x, x^2$ are far from perpendicular. The situation becomes impossible if we add a few more axes. *It is virtually hopeless to solve $A^{\mathrm{T}}A\widehat{x} = A^{\mathrm{T}}b$ for the closest polynomial of degree ten.*

More precisely, it is hopeless to solve this by Gaussian elimination; every roundoff error would be amplified by more than 10^{13}. On the other hand, we cannot just give up; approximation by polynomials has to be possible. The right idea is to switch to orthogonal axes (by Gram-Schmidt). We look for combinations of 1, x, and x^2 that *are* orthogonal.

It is convenient to work with a symmetrically placed interval like $-1 \le x \le 1$, because this makes all the odd powers of x orthogonal to all the even powers:

$$(1, x) = \int_{-1}^{1} x\,dx = 0, \qquad (x, x^2) = \int_{-1}^{1} x^3\,dx = 0.$$

Therefore the Gram-Schmidt process can begin by accepting $v_1 = 1$ and $v_2 = x$ as the first two perpendicular axes. Since $(x, x^2) = 0$, it only has to correct the angle between

1 and x^2. By formula (10), the third orthogonal polynomial is

Orthogonalize $$v_3 = x^2 - \frac{(1,x^2)}{(1,1)}1 - \frac{(x,x^2)}{(x,x)}x = x^2 - \frac{\int_{-1}^{1} x^2\,dx}{\int_{-1}^{1} 1\,dx} = x^2 - \frac{1}{3}.$$

The polynomials constructed in this way are called the ***Legendre polynomials*** and they are orthogonal to each other over the interval $-1 \le x \le 1$.

Check $$\left(1, x^2 - \frac{1}{3}\right) = \int_{-1}^{1}\left(x^2 - \frac{1}{3}\right)dx = \left[\frac{x^3}{3} - \frac{x}{3}\right]_{-1}^{1} = 0.$$

The closest polynomial of degree ten is now computable, without disaster, by projecting onto each of the first 10 (or 11) Legendre polynomials.

5. **Best Straight Line.** Suppose we want to approximate $y = x^5$ by a straight line $C + Dx$ between $x = 0$ and $x = 1$. There are at least three ways of finding that line, and if you compare them the whole chapter might become clear!

1. Solve $\begin{bmatrix}1 & x\end{bmatrix}\begin{bmatrix}C\\D\end{bmatrix} = x^5$ by least squares. The equation $A^{\mathrm{T}}A\widehat{x} = A^{\mathrm{T}}b$ is

$$\begin{bmatrix}(1,1) & (1,x)\\(x,1) & (x,x)\end{bmatrix}\begin{bmatrix}C\\D\end{bmatrix} = \begin{bmatrix}(1,x^5)\\(x,x^5)\end{bmatrix} \quad \text{or} \quad \begin{bmatrix}1 & \frac{1}{2}\\ \frac{1}{2} & \frac{1}{3}\end{bmatrix}\begin{bmatrix}C\\D\end{bmatrix} = \begin{bmatrix}\frac{1}{6}\\ \frac{1}{7}\end{bmatrix}.$$

2. Minimize $E^2 = \int_0^1 (x^5 - C - Dx)^2\,dx = \frac{1}{11} - \frac{2}{6}C - \frac{2}{7}D + C^2 + CD + \frac{1}{3}D^2$. The derivatives with respect to C and D, after dividing by 2, bring back the normal equations of method 1 (and the solution is $\widehat{C} = \frac{1}{6} - \frac{5}{14}$, $\widehat{D} = \frac{5}{7}$):

$$-\frac{1}{6} + C + \frac{1}{2}D = 0 \quad \text{and} \quad -\frac{1}{7} + \frac{1}{2}C + \frac{1}{3}D = 0.$$

3. Apply Gram-Schmidt to replace x by $x - (1,x)/(1,1)$. That is $x - \frac{1}{2}$, which is orthogonal to 1. Now the one-dimensional projections add to the best line:

$$C + Dx = \frac{(x^5,1)}{(1,1)}1 + \frac{(x^5, x - \frac{1}{2})}{(x - \frac{1}{2}, x - \frac{1}{2})}\left(x - \tfrac{1}{2}\right) = \frac{1}{6} + \frac{5}{7}\left(x - \frac{1}{2}\right).$$

Problem Set 3.4

1. (a) Write the four equations for fitting $y = C + Dt$ to the data

$$\begin{array}{llll} y = -4 \text{ at } t = -2, & y = -3 \text{ at } t = -1 \\ y = -1 \text{ at } t = 1, & y = 0 \text{ at } t = 2. \end{array}$$

Show that the columns are orthogonal.

(b) Find the optimal straight line, draw its graph, and write E^2.

(c) Interpret the zero error in terms of the original system of four equations in two unknowns: The right-hand side $(-4, -3, -1, 0)$ is in the ______ space.

2. Project $b = (0, 3, 0)$ onto each of the orthonormal vectors $a_1 = \left(\frac{2}{3}, \frac{2}{3}, -\frac{1}{3}\right)$ and $a_2 = \left(-\frac{1}{3}, \frac{2}{3}, \frac{2}{3}\right)$, and then find its projection p onto the plane of a_1 and a_2.

3. Find also the projection of $b = (0, 3, 0)$ onto $a_3 = \left(\frac{2}{3}, -\frac{1}{3}, \frac{2}{3}\right)$, and add the three projections. Why is $P = a_1a_1^{\mathrm{T}} + a_2a_2^{\mathrm{T}} + a_3a_3^{\mathrm{T}}$ equal to I?

4. If Q_1 and Q_2 are orthogonal matrices, so that $Q^{\mathrm{T}}Q = I$, show that Q_1Q_2 is also orthogonal. If Q_1 is rotation through θ, and Q_2 is rotation through ϕ, what is Q_1Q_2? Can you find the trigonometric identities for $\sin(\theta+\phi)$ and $\cos(\theta+\phi)$ in the matrix multiplication Q_1Q_2?

5. If u is a unit vector, show that $Q = I - 2uu^{\mathrm{T}}$ is a symmetric orthogonal matrix. (It is a reflection, also known as a Householder transformation.) Compute Q when $u^{\mathrm{T}} = \begin{bmatrix} \frac{1}{2} & \frac{1}{2} & -\frac{1}{2} & -\frac{1}{2} \end{bmatrix}$.

6. Find a third column so that the matrix

$$Q = \begin{bmatrix} 1/\sqrt{3} & 1/\sqrt{14} & \\ 1/\sqrt{3} & 2/\sqrt{14} & \\ 1/\sqrt{3} & -3/\sqrt{14} & \end{bmatrix}$$

is orthogonal. It must be a unit vector that is orthogonal to the other columns; how much freedom does this leave? Verify that the rows automatically become orthonormal at the same time.

7. Show, by forming $b^{\mathrm{T}}b$ directly, that Pythagoras's law holds for any combination $b = x_1q_1 + \cdots + x_nq_n$ of orthonormal vectors: $\|b\|^2 = x_1^2 + \cdots + x_n^2$. In matrix terms, $b = Qx$, so this again proves that lengths are preserved: $\|Qx\|^2 = \|x\|^2$.

8. Project the vector $b = (1, 2)$ onto two vectors that are not orthogonal, $a_1 = (1, 0)$ and $a_2 = (1, 1)$. Show that, unlike the orthogonal case, the sum of the two one-dimensional projections does not equal b.

9. If the vectors q_1, q_2, q_3 are orthonormal, what combination of q_1 and q_2 is closest to q_3?

10. If q_1 and q_2 are the outputs from Gram-Schmidt, what were the possible input vectors a and b?

11. Show that an orthogonal matrix that is upper triangular must be diagonal.

12. What multiple of $a_1 = \begin{bmatrix} 1 \\ 1 \end{bmatrix}$ should be subtracted from $a_2 = \begin{bmatrix} 4 \\ 0 \end{bmatrix}$ to make the result orthogonal to a_1? Factor $\begin{bmatrix} 1 & 4 \\ 1 & 0 \end{bmatrix}$ into QR with orthonormal vectors in Q.

13. Apply the Gram-Schmidt process to

$$a = \begin{bmatrix} 0 \\ 0 \\ 1 \end{bmatrix}, \quad b = \begin{bmatrix} 0 \\ 1 \\ 1 \end{bmatrix}, \quad c = \begin{bmatrix} 1 \\ 1 \\ 1 \end{bmatrix}$$

and write the result in the form $A = QR$.

14. From the nonorthogonal a, b, c, find orthonormal vectors q_1, q_2, q_3:

$$a = \begin{bmatrix} 1 \\ 1 \\ 0 \end{bmatrix}, \quad b = \begin{bmatrix} 1 \\ 0 \\ 1 \end{bmatrix}, \quad c = \begin{bmatrix} 0 \\ 1 \\ 1 \end{bmatrix}.$$

15. Find an orthonormal set q_1, q_2, q_3 for which q_1, q_2 span the column space of

$$A = \begin{bmatrix} 1 & 1 \\ 2 & -1 \\ -2 & 4 \end{bmatrix}.$$

Which fundamental subspace contains q_3? What is the least-squares solution of $Ax = b$ if $b = \begin{bmatrix} 1 & 2 & 7 \end{bmatrix}^T$?

16. Express the Gram-Schmidt orthogonalization of a_1, a_2 as $A = QR$:

$$a_1 = \begin{bmatrix} 1 \\ 2 \\ 2 \end{bmatrix}, \qquad a_2 = \begin{bmatrix} 1 \\ 3 \\ 1 \end{bmatrix}.$$

Given n vectors a_i with m components, what are the shapes of A, Q, and R?

17. With the same matrix A as in Problem 16, and with $b = \begin{bmatrix} 1 & 1 & 1 \end{bmatrix}^T$, use $A = QR$ to solve the least-squares problem $Ax = b$.

18. If $A = QR$, find a simple formula for the projection matrix P onto the column space of A.

19. Show that these *modified Gram-Schmidt* steps produce the same C as in equation (10):

$$C^* = c - (q_1^T c)q_1 \qquad \text{and} \qquad C = C^* - (q_2^T C^*)\, q_2.$$

This is much more stable, to subtract the projections one at a time.

20. In Hilbert space, find the length of the vector $v = (1/\sqrt{2}, 1/\sqrt{4}, 1/\sqrt{8}, \ldots)$ and the length of the function $f(x) = e^x$ (over the interval $0 \le x \le 1$). What is the inner product over this interval of e^x and e^{-x}?

21. What is the closest function $a \cos x + b \sin x$ to the function $f(x) = \sin 2x$ on the interval from $-\pi$ to π? What is the closest straight line $c + dx$?

22. By setting the derivative to zero, find the value of b_1 that minimizes

$$\|b_1 \sin x - \cos x\|^2 = \int_0^{2\pi} (b_1 \sin x - \cos x)^2 \, dx.$$

Compare with the Fourier coefficient b_1.

23. Find the Fourier coefficients a_0, a_1, b_1 of the step function $y(x)$, which equals 1 on the interval $0 \le x \le \pi$ and 0 on the remaining interval $\pi < x < 2\pi$:

$$a_0 = \frac{(y, 1)}{(1, 1)} \qquad a_1 = \frac{(y, \cos x)}{(\cos x, \cos x)} \qquad b_1 = \frac{(y, \sin x)}{(\sin x, \sin x)}.$$

24. Find the fourth Legendre polynomial. It is a cubic $x^3 + ax^2 + bx + c$ that is orthogonal to 1, x, and $x^2 - \frac{1}{3}$ over the interval $-1 \le x \le 1$.

25. What is the closest straight line to the parabola $y = x^2$ over $-1 \le x \le 1$?

26. In the Gram-Schmidt formula (10), verify that C is orthogonal to q_1 and q_2.

27. Find an orthonormal basis for the subspace spanned by $a_1 = (1, -1, 0, 0)$, $a_2 = (0, 1, -1, 0)$, $a_3 = (0, 0, 1, -1)$.

28. Apply Gram-Schmidt to $(1, -1, 0)$, $(0, 1, -1)$, and $(1, 0, -1)$, to find an orthonormal basis on the plane $x_1 + x_2 + x_3 = 0$. What is the dimension of this subspace, and how many nonzero vectors come out of Gram-Schmidt?

29. (Recommended) Find orthogonal vectors A, B, C by Gram-Schmidt from a, b, c:

$$a = (1, -1, 0, 0) \qquad b = (0, 1, -1, 0) \qquad c = (0, 0, 1, -1).$$

A, B, C and a, b, c are bases for the vectors perpendicular to $d = (1, 1, 1, 1)$.

30. If $A = QR$ then $A^{\mathrm{T}}A = R^{\mathrm{T}}R =$ ______ triangular times ______ triangular. *Gram-Schmidt on A corresponds to elimination on $A^{\mathrm{T}}A$.* Compare

$$A = \begin{bmatrix} 1 & 0 & 0 \\ -1 & 1 & 0 \\ 0 & -1 & 1 \\ 0 & 0 & -1 \end{bmatrix} \qquad \text{with} \qquad A^{\mathrm{T}}A = \begin{bmatrix} 2 & -1 & 0 \\ -1 & 2 & -1 \\ 0 & -1 & 2 \end{bmatrix}.$$

For $A^{\mathrm{T}}A$, the pivots are $2, \frac{3}{2}, \frac{4}{3}$ and the multipliers are $-\frac{1}{2}$ and $-\frac{2}{3}$.

(a) Using those multipliers in A, show that column 1 of A and $B =$ column 2 $-\frac{1}{2}$(column 1) and $C =$ column 3 $-\frac{2}{3}$ (column 2) are orthogonal.

(b) Check that $\|\text{column } 1\|^2 = 2$, $\|B\|^2 = \frac{3}{2}$, and $\|C\|^2 = \frac{4}{3}$, using the pivots.

31. True or false (give an example in either case):

(a) Q^{-1} is an orthogonal matrix when Q is an orthogonal matrix.

(b) If Q (3 by 2) has orthonormal columns then $\|Qx\|$ always equals $\|x\|$.

32. (a) Find a basis for the subspace $\mathbf{S}$ in $\mathbf{R}^4$ spanned by all solutions of

$$x_1 + x_2 + x_3 - x_4 = 0.$$

(b) Find a basis for the orthogonal complement $\mathbf{S}^{\perp}$.

(c) Find b_1 in $\mathbf{S}$ and b_2 in $\mathbf{S}^{\perp}$ so that $b_1 + b_2 = b = (1, 1, 1, 1)$.

3.5 THE FAST FOURIER TRANSFORM

The Fourier series is linear algebra in infinite dimensions. The "vectors" are functions $f(x)$; they are projected onto the sines and cosines; that produces the Fourier coefficients a_k and b_k. From this infinite sequence of sines and cosines, multiplied by a_k and b_k, we can reconstruct $f(x)$. That is the classical case, which Fourier dreamt about, but in actual calculations it is the ***discrete Fourier transform*** that we compute. Fourier still lives, but in finite dimensions.

This is pure linear algebra, based on orthogonality. The input is a sequence of numbers $y_0, \ldots, y_{n-1}$, instead of a function $f(x)$. The output $c_0, \ldots, c_{n-1}$ has the same length n. The relation between y and c is linear, so it must be given by a matrix. This is the ***Fourier matrix F***, and the whole technology of digital signal processing depends on it. The Fourier matrix has remarkable properties.

Signals are digitized, whether they come from speech or images or sonar or TV (or even oil exploration). The signals are transformed by the matrix F, and later they can be transformed back—to reconstruct. What is crucially important is that F and F^{-1} can be quick:

> ***F^{-1} must be simple. The multiplications by F and F^{-1} must be fast.***

Those are both true. F^{-1} has been known for years, and it looks just like F. In fact, F is symmetric and orthogonal (apart from a factor $\sqrt{n}$), and it has only one drawback: Its entries are ***complex numbers***. That is a small price to pay, and we pay it below. The difficulties are minimized by the fact that *all entries of F and F^{-1} are powers of a single number w*. That number has $w^n = 1$.

The 4 by 4 discrete Fourier transform uses $w = i$ (and notice $i^4 = 1$). The success of the whole DFT depends on F times its complex conjugate $\overline{F}$:

$$F\overline{F} = \begin{bmatrix} 1 & 1 & 1 & 1 \\ 1 & i & i^2 & i^3 \\ 1 & i^2 & i^4 & i^6 \\ 1 & i^3 & i^6 & i^9 \end{bmatrix} \begin{bmatrix} 1 & 1 & 1 & 1 \\ 1 & (-i) & (-i)^2 & (-i)^3 \\ 1 & (-i)^2 & (-i)^4 & (-i)^6 \\ 1 & (-i)^3 & (-i)^6 & (-i)^9 \end{bmatrix} = 4I. \tag{1}$$

Immediately $F\overline{F} = 4I$ tells us that $F^{-1} = \overline{F}/4$. The columns of F are orthogonal (to give the zero entries in $4I$). The n by n matrices will have $F\overline{F} = nI$. Then the inverse of F is just $\overline{F}/n$. In a moment we will look at the complex number $w = e^{2\pi i/n}$ (which equals i for $n = 4$).

It is remarkable that F is so easy to invert. If that were all (and up to 1965 it *was* all), the discrete transform would have an important place. Now there is more. The multiplications by F and F^{-1} can be done in an extremely fast and ingenious way. Instead of n^2 separate multiplications, coming from the n^2 entries in the matrix, the matrix–vector products Fc and $F^{-1}y$ require only $\frac{1}{2}n \log n$ steps. This rearrangement of the multiplication is called the ***Fast Fourier Transform***.

The section begins with w and its properties, moves on to F^{-1}, and ends with the **FFT**—the fast transform. The great application in signal processing is *filtering*, and the key to its success is the *convolution rule*. In matrix language, all "circulant matrices" are diagonalized by F. So they reduce to two FFTs and a diagonal matrix.

Complex Roots of Unity

Real equations can have complex solutions. The equation $x^2 + 1 = 0$ led to the invention of i (and also to $-i$!). That was declared to be a solution, and the case was closed. If someone asked about $x^2 - i = 0$, there was an answer: The square roots of a complex number are again complex numbers. You must allow combinations $x + iy$, with a real part x and an imaginary part y, but no further inventions are necessary. Every real or complex polynomial of degree n has a full set of n roots (possibly complex and possibly repeated). That is the fundamental theorem of algebra.

We are interested in equations like $x^4 = 1$. That has four solutions—the ***fourth roots of unity***. The two square roots of unity are 1 and -1. The fourth roots are the square roots of the square roots, 1 and -1, i and $-i$. The number i will satisfy $i^4 = 1$

because it satisfies $i^2 = -1$. For the eighth roots of unity we need the square roots of i, and that brings us to $w = (1+i)/\sqrt{2}$. Squaring w produces $(1 + 2i + i^2)/2$, which is i—because $1 + i^2$ is zero. Then $w^8 = i^4 = 1$. There has to be a system here.

The complex numbers $\cos\theta + i\sin\theta$ in the Fourier matrix are extremely special. The real part is plotted on the x-axis and the imaginary part on the y-axis (Figure 3.11). Then the number w lies on the ***unit circle***; its distance from the origin is $\cos^2\theta + \sin^2\theta = 1$. It makes an angle θ with the horizontal. The whole plane enters in Chapter 5, where complex numbers will appear as eigenvalues (even of real matrices). Here we need only special points w, all of them on the unit circle, in order to solve $w^n = 1$.

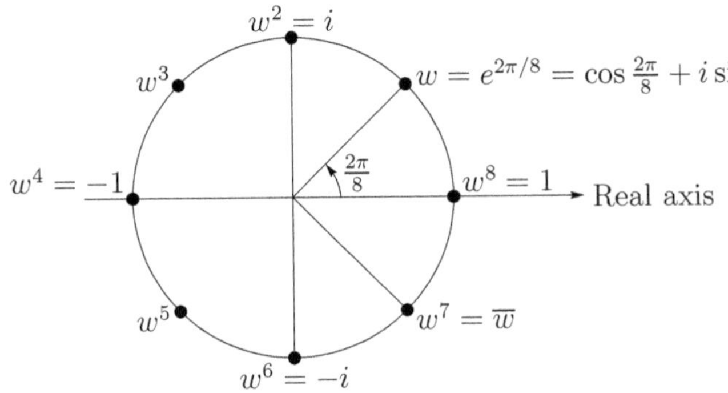

Figure 3.11 The eight solutions to $z^8 = 1$ are $1, w, w^2, \ldots, w^7$ with $w = (1+i)/\sqrt{2}$.

The square of w can be found directly (it just doubles the angle):

$$w^2 = (\cos\theta + i\sin\theta)^2 = \cos^2\theta - \sin^2\theta + 2i\sin\theta\cos\theta.$$

The real part $\cos^2\theta - \sin^2\theta$ is $\cos 2\theta$, and the imaginary part $2\sin\theta\cos\theta$ is $\sin 2\theta$. (Note that i is not included; the imaginary part is a real number.) Thus $w^2 = \cos 2\theta + i\sin 2\theta$. The square of w is still on the unit circle, but ***at the double angle*** 2θ. That makes us suspect that w^n lies at the angle $n\theta$, and we are right.

There is a better way to take powers of w. The combination of cosine and sine is a complex exponential, with amplitude one and phase angle θ:

$$\cos\theta + i\sin\theta = e^{i\theta}. \tag{2}$$

The rules for multiplying, like $(e^2)(e^3) = e^5$, continue to hold when the exponents $i\theta$ are imaginary. ***The powers of*** $\boldsymbol{w = e^{i\theta}}$ ***stay on the unit circle***:

$$\textbf{Powers of } \boldsymbol{w} \qquad w^2 = e^{i2\theta}, \quad w^n = e^{in\theta}, \quad \frac{1}{w} = e^{-i\theta}. \tag{3}$$

The nth power is at the angle $n\theta$. When $n = -1$, ***the reciprocal*** $\mathbf{1/w}$ ***has angle*** $\boldsymbol{-\theta}$. If we multiply $\cos\theta + i\sin\theta$ by $\cos(-\theta) + i\sin(-\theta)$, we get the answer 1:

$$e^{i\theta}e^{-i\theta} = (\cos\theta + i\sin\theta)(\cos\theta - i\sin\theta) = \cos^2\theta + \sin^2\theta = 1.$$

Note I remember the day when a letter came to MIT from a prisoner in New York, asking if Euler's formula (2) was true. It is really astonishing that three of the key functions of mathematics should come together in such a graceful way. Our best answer was to look at the power series for the exponential:

$$e^{i\theta} = 1 + i\theta + \frac{(i\theta)^2}{2!} + \frac{(i\theta)^3}{3!} + \cdots.$$

The real part $1 - \theta^2/2 + \cdots$ is $\cos\theta$. The imaginary part $\theta - \theta^3/6 + \cdots$ is the sine. The formula is correct, and I wish we had sent a more beautiful proof.

With this formula, we can solve $w^n = 1$. It becomes $e^{in\theta} = 1$, so that $n\theta$ must carry us around the unit circle and back to the start. The solution is to choose $\theta = 2\pi/n$: *The "primitive" nth root of unity is*

$$w_n = e^{2\pi i/n} = \cos\frac{2\pi}{n} + i\sin\frac{2\pi}{n}. \tag{4}$$

Its nth power is $e^{2\pi i}$, which equals 1. For $n = 8$, this root is $(1+i)/\sqrt{2}$:

$$w_4 = \cos\frac{\pi}{2} + i\sin\frac{\pi}{2} = i \qquad \text{and} \qquad w_8 = \cos\frac{\pi}{4} + i\sin\frac{\pi}{4} = \frac{1+i}{\sqrt{2}}$$

The fourth root is at $\theta = 90°$, which is $\frac{1}{4}(360°)$. The other fourth roots are the powers $i^2 = -1$, $i^3 = -i$, and $i^4 = 1$. The other eighth roots are the powers $w_8^2, w_8^3, \ldots, w_8^8$. The roots are equally spaced around the unit circle, at intervals of $2\pi/n$. Note again that the square of w_8 is w_4, which will be essential in the Fast Fourier Transform. ***The roots add up to zero.*** First $1 + i - 1 - i = 0$, and then

$$\textbf{Sum of eighth roots} \qquad 1 + w_8 + w_8^2 + \cdots + w_8^7 = 0. \tag{5}$$

One proof is to multiply the left side by w_8, which leaves it unchanged. (It yields $w_8 + w_8^2 + \cdots + w_8^8$, and w_8^8 equals 1.) The eight points each move through 45°, but they remain the same eight points. Since zero is the only number that is unchanged when multiplied by w_8, the sum must be zero. When n is even the roots cancel in pairs (like $1 + i^2 = 0$ and $i + i^3 = 0$). But the three cube roots of 1 also add to zero.

The Fourier Matrix and Its Inverse

In the continuous case, the Fourier series can reproduce $f(x)$ over a whole interval. It uses infinitely many sines and cosines (or exponentials). In the discrete case, with only n coefficients $c_0, \ldots, c_{n-1}$ to choose, we only ask for *equality at n points*. That gives n equations. We reproduce the four values $y = 2, 4, 6, 8$ when $Fc = y$:

$$\boldsymbol{Fc = y} \qquad \begin{aligned} c_0 + c_1 + c_2 + c_3 &= 2 \\ c_0 + ic_1 + i^2c_2 + i^3c_3 &= 4 \\ c_0 + i^2c_1 + i^4c_2 + i^6c_3 &= 6 \\ c_0 + i^3c_1 + i^6c_2 + i^9c_3 &= 8. \end{aligned} \tag{6}$$

The input sequence is $y = 2, 4, 6, 8$. The output sequence is c_0, c_1, c_2, c_3. The four equations (6) look for a four-term Fourier series that matches the inputs at four equally spaced points x on the interval from 0 to 2π:

$$\textbf{Discrete Fourier Series} \qquad c_0 + c_1e^{ix} + c_2e^{2ix} + c_3e^{3ix} = \begin{matrix} 2 & \text{at} & x = 0 \\ 4 & \text{at} & x = \pi/2 \\ 6 & \text{at} & x = \pi \\ 8 & \text{at} & x = 3\pi/2. \end{matrix}$$

Those are the four equations in system (6). At $x = 2\pi$ the series returns $y_0 = 2$ and continues periodically. The Discrete Fourier Series is best written in this *complex* form, as a combination of exponentials e^{ikx} rather than $\sin kx$ and $\cos kx$.

For every n, the matrix connecting y to c can be inverted. It represents n equations, requiring the finite series $c_0 + c_1e^{ix} + \cdots$ (***n* terms**) to agree with y (***at n points***). The first agreement is at $x = 0$, where $c_0 + \cdots + c_{n-1} = y_0$. The remaining points bring powers of w, and the full problem is $Fc = y$:

$$\boldsymbol{Fc = y} \qquad \begin{bmatrix} 1 & 1 & 1 & \cdot & 1 \\ 1 & w & w^2 & \cdot & w^{n-1} \\ 1 & w^2 & w^4 & \cdot & w^{2(n-1)} \\ \cdot & \cdot & \cdot & \cdot & \cdot \\ 1 & w^{n-1} & w^{2(n-1)} & \cdot & w^{(n-1)^2} \end{bmatrix} \begin{bmatrix} c_0 \\ c_1 \\ c_2 \\ \cdot \\ c_{n-1} \end{bmatrix} = \begin{bmatrix} y_0 \\ y_1 \\ y_2 \\ \cdot \\ y_{n-1} \end{bmatrix}. \qquad (7)$$

There stands the Fourier matrix F with entries $F_{jk} = w^{jk}$. It is natural to number the rows and columns from 0 to $n - 1$, instead of 1 to n. The first row has $j = 0$, the first column has $k = 0$, and all their entries are $w^0 = 1$.

To find the c's we have to invert F. In the 4 by 4 case, F^{-1} was built from $1/i = -i$. That is the general rule, that F^{-1} comes from the complex number $w^{-1} = \overline{w}$. It lies at the angle $-2\pi/n$, where w was at the angle $+2\pi/n$:

3V The inverse matrix is built from the powers of $w^{-1} = 1/w = \overline{w}$:

$$F^{-1} = \frac{1}{n} \begin{bmatrix} 1 & 1 & 1 & \cdot & 1 \\ 1 & w^{-1} & w^{-2} & \cdot & w^{-(n-1)} \\ 1 & w^{-2} & w^{-4} & \cdot & \cdot \\ \cdot & \cdot & \cdot & \cdot & \cdot \\ 1 & w^{-(n-1)} & w^{-2(n-1)} & \cdot & w^{-(n-1)^2} \end{bmatrix} = \frac{\overline{F}}{n}. \qquad (8)$$

$$\text{Thus} \quad F = \begin{bmatrix} 1 & 1 & 1 \\ 1 & e^{2\pi i/3} & e^{4\pi i/3} \\ 1 & e^{4\pi i/3} & e^{8\pi i/3} \end{bmatrix} \quad \text{has} \quad F^{-1} = \frac{1}{3} \begin{bmatrix} 1 & 1 & 1 \\ 1 & e^{-2\pi i/3} & e^{-4\pi i/3} \\ 1 & e^{-4\pi i/3} & e^{-8\pi i/3} \end{bmatrix}.$$

Row j of F times column j of F^{-1} is always $(1 + 1 + \cdots + 1)/n = 1$. The harder part is off the diagonal, to show that row j of F times column k of F^{-1} gives zero:

$$1 \cdot 1 + w^j w^{-k} + w^{2j} w^{-2k} + \cdots + w^{(n-1)j} w^{-(n-1)k} = 0 \quad \text{if} \quad j \neq k. \qquad (9)$$

The key is to notice that those terms are the powers of $W = w^j w^{-k}$:

$$1 + W + W^2 + \cdots + W^{n-1} = 0. \qquad (10)$$

This number W is still a root of unity: $W^n = w^{nj} w^{-nk}$ is equal to $1^j 1^{-k} = 1$. Since j is different from k, W is different from 1. It is one of the *other* roots on the unit circle.

Those roots all satisfy $1 + W + \cdots + W^{n-1} = 0$. Another proof comes from

$$1 - W^n = (1 - W)(1 + W + W^2 + \cdots + W^{n-1}). \tag{11}$$

Since $W^n = 1$, the left side is zero. But W is not 1, so the last factor must be zero. ***The columns of F are orthogonal.***

The Fast Fourier Transform

Fourier analysis is a beautiful theory, and it is also very practical. To analyze a waveform into its frequencies is the best way to take a signal apart. The reverse process brings it back. For physical and mathematical reasons the exponentials are special, and we can pinpoint one central cause: ***If you differentiate*** e^{ikx}***, or integrate it, or translate*** x ***to*** $x + h$***, the result is still a multiple of*** e^{ikx}. Exponentials are exactly suited to differential equations, integral equations, and difference equations. Each frequency component goes its own way, as an eigenvector, and then they recombine into the solution. The analysis and synthesis of signals—computing c from y and y from c—is a central part of scientific computing.

We want to show that Fc and $F^{-1}y$ can be done quickly. The key is in the relation of F_4 to F_2—or rather to *two copies* of F_2, which go into a matrix F_2^*:

$$F_4 = \begin{bmatrix} 1 & 1 & 1 & 1 \\ 1 & i & i^2 & i^3 \\ 1 & i^2 & i^4 & i^6 \\ 1 & i^3 & i^6 & i^9 \end{bmatrix} \quad \text{is close to} \quad F_2^* = \begin{bmatrix} 1 & 1 & & \\ 1 & -1 & & \\ & & 1 & 1 \\ & & 1 & -1 \end{bmatrix}.$$

F_4 contains the powers of $w_4 = i$, the *fourth root* of 1. F_2^* contains the powers of $w_2 = -1$, the *square root* of 1. Note especially that half the entries in F_2^* are zero. The 2 by 2 transform, done twice, requires only half as much work as a direct 4 by 4 transform. If 64 by 64 transform could be replaced by two 32 by 32 transforms, the work would be cut in half (plus the cost of reassembling the results). What makes this true, and possible in practice, is the simple connection between w_{64} and w_{32}:

$$(w_{64})^2 = w_{32}, \quad \text{or} \quad (e^{2\pi i/64})^2 = e^{2\pi i/32}.$$

The 32nd root is twice as far around the circle as the 64th root. If $w^{64} = 1$, then $(w^2)^{32} = 1$. The mth root is the square of the nth root, if m is half of n:

$$w_n^2 = w_m \quad \text{if} \quad m = \tfrac{1}{2}n. \tag{12}$$

The speed of the FFT, in the standard form presented here, depends on working with highly composite numbers like $2^{10} = 1024$. Without the fast transform, it takes $(1024)^2$ multiplications to produce F times c (which we want to do often). By contrast, a fast transform can do each multiplication in only $5 \cdot 1024$ steps. ***It is 200 times faster***, because it replaces one factor of 1024 by 5. In general it replaces n^2 multiplications by $\frac{1}{2}n\ell$, when n is 2^ℓ. By connecting F_n to two copies of $F_{n/2}$, and then to four copies of $F_{n/4}$, and eventually to a very small F, the usual n^2 steps are reduced to $\frac{1}{2}n\log_2 n$.

We need to see how $y = F_n c$ (a vector with n components) can be recovered from two vectors that are only half as long. The first step is to divide c itself, by separating its even-numbered components from its odd-numbered components:

$$c' = (c_0, c_2, \ldots, c_{n-2}) \quad \text{and} \quad c'' = (c_1, c_3, \ldots, c_{n-1}).$$

The coefficients just go alternately into c' and c''. From those vectors, the half-size transform gives $y' = F_m c'$ and $y'' = F_m c''$. *Those are the two multiplications by the smaller matrix* F_m. The central problem is to recover y from the half-size vectors y' and y'', and Cooley and Tukey noticed how it could be done:

3W The first m and the last m components of the vector $y = F_n c$ are

$$\begin{aligned} y_j &= y'_j + w_n^j y''_j, \quad j = 0, \ldots, m-1 \\ y_{j+m} &= y'_j - w_n^j y''_j, \quad j = 0, \ldots, m-1. \end{aligned} \tag{13}$$

Thus the three steps are: split c into c' and c'', transform them by F_m into y' and y'', and reconstruct y from equation (13).

We verify in a moment that this gives the correct y. (You may prefer the flow graph to the algebra.) ***This idea can be repeated. We go from F_{1024} to F_{512} to F_{256}.*** The final count is $\frac{1}{2}n\ell$, when starting with the power $n = 2^\ell$ and going all the way to $n = 1$—where no multiplication is needed. This number $\frac{1}{2}n\ell$ satisfies the rule given above: *twice the count for m, plus m extra multiplications, produces the count for n*:

$$2\left(\frac{1}{2}m(\ell - 1)\right) + m = \frac{1}{2}n\ell.$$

Another way to count: There are ℓ steps from $n = 2^\ell$ to $n = 1$. Each step needs $n/2$ multiplications by $D_{n/2}$ in equation (13), which is really a factorization of F_n:

One FFT step
$$F_{1024} = \begin{bmatrix} I_{512} & D_{512} \\ I_{512} & -D_{512} \end{bmatrix} \begin{bmatrix} F_{512} & \\ & F_{512} \end{bmatrix} \begin{bmatrix} \textbf{even–odd} \\ \textbf{permutation} \end{bmatrix}. \tag{14}$$

The cost is only slightly more than linear. Fourier analysis has been completely transformed by the FFT. To verify equation (13), split y_j into *even* and *odd*:

$$y_j = \sum_{k=0}^{n-1} w_n^{jk} c_k \quad \text{is identical to} \quad \sum_{k=0}^{m-1} w_n^{2kj} c_{2k} + \sum_{k=0}^{m-1} w_n^{(2k+1)j} c_{2k+1}.$$

Each sum on the right has $m = \frac{1}{2}n$ terms. Since w_n^2 is w_m, the two sums are

$$y_j = \sum_{k=0}^{m-1} w_m^{kj} c'_k + w_n^j \sum_{k=0}^{m-1} w_m^{kj} c''_k = y'_j + w_n^j y''_j. \tag{15}$$

For the second part of equation (13), $j + m$ in place of j produces a sign change:

Inside the sums, $w_m^{k(j+m)}$ remains w_m^{kj} since $w_m^{km} = 1^k = 1$.

Outside, $w_n^{j+m} = -w_n^j$ because $w_n^m = e^{2\pi i m/n} = e^{\pi i} = -1$.

The FFT idea is easily modified to allow other prime factors of n (not only powers of 2). If n itself is a prime, a completely different algorithm is used.

Example 1 The steps from $n = 4$ to $m = 2$ are

$$\begin{bmatrix} c_0 \\ c_1 \\ c_2 \\ c_3 \end{bmatrix} \to \begin{bmatrix} c_0 \\ c_2 \\ c_1 \\ c_3 \end{bmatrix} \to \begin{bmatrix} F_2 c' \\ \\ F_2 c'' \end{bmatrix} \to \begin{bmatrix} \\ y \\ \\ \end{bmatrix}.$$

Combined, the three steps multiply c by F_4 to give y. Since each step is linear, it must come from a matrix, and the product of those matrices must be F_4:

$$\begin{bmatrix} 1 & 1 & 1 & 1 \\ 1 & i & i^2 & i^3 \\ 1 & i^2 & i^4 & i^6 \\ 1 & i^3 & i^6 & i^9 \end{bmatrix} = \begin{bmatrix} 1 & & 1 & \\ & 1 & & i \\ 1 & & -1 & \\ & 1 & & -i \end{bmatrix} \begin{bmatrix} 1 & 1 & & \\ 1 & -1 & & \\ & & 1 & 1 \\ & & 1 & -1 \end{bmatrix} \begin{bmatrix} 1 & & & \\ & & 1 & \\ & 1 & & \\ & & & 1 \end{bmatrix}. \tag{16}$$

You recognize the two copies of F_2 in the center. At the right is the permutation matrix that separates c into c' and c''. At the left is the matrix that multiplies by w_n^j. If we started with F_8, the middle matrix would contain two copies of F_4. ***Each of those would be split as above.*** Thus the FFT amounts to a giant factorization of the Fourier matrix! The single matrix F with n^2 nonzeros is a product of approximately $\ell = \log_2 n$ matrices (and a permutation) with a total of only $n\ell$ nonzeros.

The Complete FFT and the Butterfly

The first step of the FFT changes multiplication by F_n to two multiplications by F_m. The even-numbered components (c_0, c_2) are transformed separately from (c_1, c_3). Figure 3.12 gives a flow graph for $n = 4$.

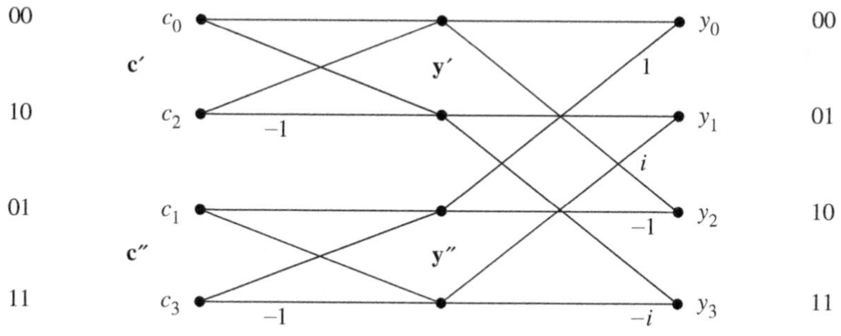

Figure 3.12 Flow graph for the Fast Fourier Transform with $n = 4$.

For $n = 8$, the key idea is ***to replace each F_4 box by F_2 boxes***. The new factor $w_4 = i$ is the square of the old factor $w = w_8 = e^{2\pi i/8}$. The flow graph shows the order that the c's enter the FFT and the $\log_2 n$ stages that take them through it—and it also shows the simplicity of the logic.

Every stage needs $\frac{1}{2}n$ multiplications so the final count is $\frac{1}{2}n\log n$. There is an amazing rule for the overall permutation of c's before entering the FFT: Write the subscripts $0, \ldots, 7$ in binary and *reverse the order of their bits*. The subscripts appear in "bit-reversed order" on the left side of the graph. Even numbers come before odd (numbers ending in 0 come before numbers ending in 1).

Problem Set 3.5

1. What are F^2 and F^4 for the 4 by 4 Fourier matrix F?

2. Find a permutation P of the columns of F that produces $FP = \overline{F}$ (n by n). Combine with $F\overline{F} = nI$ to find F^2 and F^4 for the n by n Fourier matrix.

3. If you form a 3 by 3 submatrix of the 6 by 6 matrix F_6, keeping only the entries in its first, third, and fifth rows and columns, what is that submatrix?

4. Mark all the sixth roots of 1 in the complex plane. What is the primitive root w_6? (Find its real and imaginary part.) Which power of w_6 is equal to $1/w_6$? What is $1 + w + w^2 + w^3 + w^4 + w^5$?

5. Find all solutions to the equation $e^{ix} = -1$, and all solutions to $e^{i\theta} = i$.

6. What are the square and the square root of w_{128}, the primitive 128th root of 1?

7. Solve the 4 by 4 system (6) if the right-hand sides are $y_0 = 2$, $y_1 = 0$, $y_2 = 2$, $y_3 = 0$. In other words, solve $F_4c = y$.

8. Solve the same system with $y = (2, 0, -2, 0)$ by knowing F_4^{-1} and computing $c = F_4^{-1}y$. Verify that $c_0 + c_1e^{ix} + c_2e^{2ix} + c_3e^{3ix}$ takes the values $2, 0, -2, 0$ at the points $x = 0, \pi/2, \pi, 3\pi/2$.

9. (a) If $y = (1, 1, 1, 1)$, show that $c = (1, 0, 0, 0)$ satisfies $F_4c = y$.
   (b) Now suppose $y = (1, 0, 0, 0)$, and find c.

10. For $n = 2$, write y_0 from the first line of equation (13) and y_1 from the second line. For $n = 4$, use the first line to find y_0 and y_1, and the second to find y_2 and y_3, all in terms of y' and y''.

11. Compute $y = F_4c$ by the three steps of the Fast Fourier Transform if $c = (1, 0, 1, 0)$.

12. Compute $y = F_8c$ by the three steps of the Fast Fourier Transform if $c = (1, 0, 1, 0, 1, 0, 1, 0)$. Repeat the computation with $c = (0, 1, 0, 1, 0, 1, 0, 1)$.

13. For the 4 by 4 matrix, write out the formulas for c_0, c_1, c_2, c_3 and verify that *if f is odd then c is odd*. The vector f is odd if $f_{n-j} = -f_j$; for $n = 4$ that means $f_0 = 0$, $f_3 = -f_1$, $f_2 = 0$ as in $\sin 0, \sin\pi/2, \sin\pi, \sin 3\pi/2$. This is copied by c and it leads to a fast sine transform.

14. Multiply the three matrices in equation (16) and compare with F. In which six entries do you need to know that $i^2 = -1$?

15. Invert the three factors in equation (14) to find a fast factorization of F^{-1}.

16. F is symmetric. So transpose equation (14) to find a new Fast Fourier Transform!

17. All entries in the factorization of F_6 involve powers of w = sixth root of 1:

$$F_6 = \begin{bmatrix} I & D \\ I & -D \end{bmatrix} \begin{bmatrix} F_3 & \\ & F_3 \end{bmatrix} \begin{bmatrix} P \end{bmatrix}.$$

Write these factors with $1, w, w^2$ in D and $1, w^2, w^4$ in F_3. Multiply!

Problems 18–20 introduce the idea of an eigenvector and eigenvalue, when a matrix times a vector is a multiple of that vector. This is the theme of Chapter 5.

18. The columns of the Fourier matrix F are the *eigenvectors* of the cyclic permutation P. Multiply PF to find the eigenvalues λ_0 to λ_3:

$$\begin{bmatrix} 0 & 1 & 0 & 0 \\ 0 & 0 & 1 & 0 \\ 0 & 0 & 0 & 1 \\ 1 & 0 & 0 & 0 \end{bmatrix} \begin{bmatrix} 1 & 1 & 1 & 1 \\ 1 & i & i^2 & i^3 \\ 1 & i^2 & i^4 & i^6 \\ 1 & i^3 & i^6 & i^9 \end{bmatrix} = \begin{bmatrix} 1 & 1 & 1 & 1 \\ 1 & i & i^2 & i^3 \\ 1 & i^2 & i^4 & i^6 \\ 1 & i^3 & i^6 & i^9 \end{bmatrix} \begin{bmatrix} \lambda_0 & & & \\ & \lambda_1 & & \\ & & \lambda_2 & \\ & & & \lambda_3 \end{bmatrix}.$$

This is $PF = F\Lambda$ or $P = F\Lambda F^{-1}$.

19. Two eigenvectors of this circulant matrix C are $(1, 1, 1, 1)$ and $(1, i, i^2, i^3)$. What are the eigenvalues e_0 and e_1?

$$\begin{bmatrix} c_0 & c_1 & c_2 & c_3 \\ c_3 & c_0 & c_1 & c_2 \\ c_2 & c_3 & c_0 & c_1 \\ c_1 & c_2 & c_3 & c_0 \end{bmatrix} \begin{bmatrix} 1 \\ 1 \\ 1 \\ 1 \end{bmatrix} = e_0 \begin{bmatrix} 1 \\ 1 \\ 1 \\ 1 \end{bmatrix} \quad \text{and} \quad C \begin{bmatrix} 1 \\ i \\ i^2 \\ i^3 \end{bmatrix} = e_1 \begin{bmatrix} 1 \\ i \\ i^2 \\ i^3 \end{bmatrix}.$$

20. Find the eigenvalues of the "periodic" $-1, 2, -1$ matrix C. The -1s in the corners of C make it periodic (**a circulant matrix**):

$$C = \begin{bmatrix} 2 & -1 & 0 & -1 \\ -1 & 2 & -1 & 0 \\ 0 & -1 & 2 & -1 \\ -1 & 0 & -1 & 2 \end{bmatrix} \quad \text{has } c_0 = 2,\ c_1 = -1,\ c_2 = 0,\ c_3 = -1.$$

21. To multiply C times x, when $C = FEF^{-1}$, we can multiply $F(E(F^{-1}x))$ instead. The direct Cx uses n^2 separate multiplications. Knowing E and F, the second way uses only $n \log_2 n + n$ multiplications. How many of those come from E, how many from F, and how many from F^{-1}?

22. How could you quickly compute these four components of Fc starting from $c_0 + c_2$, $c_0 - c_2$, $c_1 + c_3$, $c_1 - c_3$? You are finding the Fast Fourier Transform!

$$Fc = \begin{bmatrix} c_0 + c_1 + c_2 + c_3 \\ c_0 + ic_1 + i^2c_2 + i^3c_3 \\ c_0 + i^2c_1 + i^4c_2 + i^6c_3 \\ c_0 + i^3c_1 + i^6c_2 + i^9c_3 \end{bmatrix}.$$

Chapter 3 Review Exercises

3.1 Find the length of $a = (2, -2, 1)$, and write two independent vectors that are perpendicular to a.

3.2 Find all vectors that are perpendicular to $(1, 3, 1)$ and $(2, 7, 2)$, by making those the rows of A and solving $Ax = 0$.

3.3 What is the angle between $a = (2, -2, 1)$ and $b = (1, 2, 2)$?

3.4 What is the projection p of $b = (1, 2, 2)$ onto $a = (2, -2, 1)$?

3.5 Find the cosine of the angle between the vectors $(3, 4)$ and $(4, 3)$.

3.6 Where is the projection of $b = (1, 1, 1)$ onto the plane spanned by $(1, 0, 0)$ and $(1, 1, 0)$?

3.7 The system $Ax = b$ has a solution if and only if b is orthogonal to which of the four fundamental subspaces?

3.8 Which straight line gives the best fit to the following data: $b = 0$ at $t = 0$, $b = 0$ at $t = 1$, $b = 12$ at $t = 3$?

3.9 Construct the projection matrix P onto the space spanned by $(1, 1, 1)$ and $(0, 1, 3)$.

3.10 Which constant function is closest to $y = x^4$ (in the least-squares sense) over the interval $0 \leq x \leq 1$?

3.11 If Q is orthogonal, is the same true of Q^3?

3.12 Find all 3 by 3 orthogonal matrices whose entries are zeros and ones.

3.13 What multiple of a_1 should be subtracted from a_2, to make the result orthogonal to a_1? Sketch a figure.

3.14 Factor

$$\begin{bmatrix} \cos\theta & \sin\theta \\ \sin\theta & 0 \end{bmatrix}$$

into QR, recognizing that the first column is already a unit vector.

3.15 If every entry in an orthogonal matrix is either $\frac{1}{4}$ or $-\frac{1}{4}$, how big is the matrix?

3.16 Suppose the vectors $q_1, \ldots, q_n$ are orthonormal. If $b = c_1 q_1 + \cdots + c_n q_n$, give a formula for the first coefficient c_1 in terms of b and the q's.

3.17 What words describe the equation $A^{\mathrm{T}}A\widehat{x} = A^{\mathrm{T}}b$, the vector $p = A\widehat{x} = Pb$, and the matrix $P = A(A^{\mathrm{T}}A)^{-1}A^{\mathrm{T}}$?

3.18 If the orthonormal vectors $q_1 = \left(\frac{2}{3}, \frac{2}{3}, -\frac{1}{3}\right)$ and $q_2 = \left(-\frac{1}{3}, \frac{2}{3}, \frac{2}{3}\right)$ are the columns of Q, what are the matrices $Q^{\mathrm{T}}Q$ and QQ^{T}? Show that QQ^{T} is a projection matrix (onto the plane of q_1 and q_2).

3.19 If $v_1, \ldots, v_n$ is an orthonormal basis for $\mathbf{R}^n$, show that $v_1 v_1^T + \cdots + v_n v_n^T = I$.

3.20 *True or false*: If the vectors x and y are orthogonal, and P is a projection, then Px and Py are orthogonal.

3.21 Try to fit a line $b = C + Dt$ through the points $b = 0$, $t = 2$, and $b = 6$, $t = 2$, and show that the normal equations break down. Sketch all the optimal lines, minimizing the sum of squares of the two errors.

3.22 What point on the plane $x + y - z = 0$ is closest to $b = (2, 1, 0)$?

3.23 Find an orthonormal basis for $\mathbf{R}^3$ starting with the vector $(1, 1, -1)$.

3.24 CT scanners examine the patient from different directions and produce a matrix giving the densities of bone and tissue at each point. Mathematically, the problem is to recover a matrix from its projections. In the 2 by 2 case, can you recover the matrix A if you know the sum along each row and down each column?

3.25 Can you recover a 3 by 3 matrix if you know its row sums and column sums, and also the sums down the main diagonal and the four other parallel diagonals?

3.26 Find an orthonormal basis for the plane $x - y + z = 0$, and find the matrix P that projects onto the plane. What is the nullspace of P?

3.27 Let $A = \begin{bmatrix} 3 & 1 & -1 \end{bmatrix}$, and let $\mathbf{V}$ be the nullspace of A.

(a) Find a basis for $\mathbf{V}$ and a basis for $\mathbf{V}^\perp$.

(b) Write an orthonormal basis for $\mathbf{V}^\perp$, and find the projection matrix P_1 that projects vectors in $\mathbf{R}^3$ onto $\mathbf{V}^\perp$.

(c) Find the projection matrix P_2 that projects vectors in $\mathbf{R}^3$ onto $\mathbf{V}$.

3.28 Use Gram-Schmidt to construct an orthonormal pair q_1, q_2 from $a_1 = (4, 5, 2, 2)$ and $a_2 = (1, 2, 0, 0)$. Express a_1 and a_2 as combinations of q_1 and q_2, and find the triangular R in $A = QR$.

3.29 For any A, b, x, and y, show that

(a) if $Ax = b$ and $y^T A = 0$, then $y^T b = 0$.

(b) if $Ax = 0$ and $A^T y = b$, then $x^T b = 0$.

What theorem does this prove about the fundamental subspaces?

3.30 Is there a matrix whose row space contains $(1, 1, 0)$ and whose nullspace contains $(0, 1, 1)$?

3.31 The distance from a plane $a^T x = c$ (in m-dimensional space) to the origin is $|c|/\|a\|$. How far is the plane $x_1 + x_2 - x_3 - x_4 = 8$ from the origin, and what point on it is nearest?

3.32 In the parallelogram with corners at 0, v, w, and $v + w$, show that the sum of the squared lengths of the four sides equals the sum of the squared lengths of the two diagonals.

3.33 (a) Find an orthonormal basis for the column space of A.

$$A = \begin{bmatrix} 1 & -6 \\ 3 & 6 \\ 4 & 8 \\ 5 & 0 \\ 7 & 8 \end{bmatrix}.$$

(b) Write A as QR, where Q has orthonormal columns and R is upper triangular.
(c) Find the least-squares solution to $Ax = b$, if $b = (-3, 7, 1, 0, 4)$.

3.34 With weighting matrix $W = \begin{bmatrix} 2 & 1 \\ 1 & 0 \end{bmatrix}$, what is the W-inner product of $(1, 0)$ with $(0, 1)$?

3.35 To solve a rectangular system $Ax = b$, we replace A^{-1} (which doesn't exist) by $(A^{\mathrm{T}}A)^{-1}A^{\mathrm{T}}$ (which exists if A has independent columns). Show that this is a left-inverse of A but not a right-inverse. On the left of A it gives the identity; on the right it gives the projection P.

3.36 Find the straight line $C + Dt$ that best fits the measurements $b = 0, 1, 2, 5$ at times $t = 0, 1, 3, 4$.

3.37 Find the curve $y = C + D2^t$ which gives the best least-squares fit to the measurements $y = 6$ at $t = 0$, $y = 4$ at $t = 1$, $y = 0$ at $t = 2$. Write the three equations that are solved if the curve goes through the three points, and find the best C and D.

3.38 If the columns of A are orthogonal to each other, what can you say about the form of $A^{\mathrm{T}}A$? If the columns are orthonormal, what can you say then?

3.39 Under what condition on the columns of A (which may be rectangular) is $A^{\mathrm{T}}A$ invertible?

Chapter

4 Determinants

4.1 INTRODUCTION

Determinants are much further from the center of linear algebra than they were a hundred years ago. Mathematics keeps changing direction! After all, a single number can tell only so much about a matrix. Still, it is amazing how much this number can do.

One viewpoint is this: The determinant provides an explicit "formula" for each entry of A^{-1} and $A^{-1}b$. This formula will not change the way we compute; even the determinant itself is found by elimination. In fact, elimination can be regarded as the most efficient way to substitute the entries of an n by n matrix into the formula. What the formula does is to show how A^{-1} depends on the n^2 entries of A, and how it varies when those entries vary.

We can list four of the main uses of determinants:

1. They test for invertibility. ***If the determinant of A is zero, then A is singular. If* det $A \neq 0$*, then A is invertible*** (and A^{-1} involves $1/\det A$).

The most important application, and the reason this chapter is essential to the book, is to the family of matrices $A - \lambda I$. The parameter λ is subtracted all along the main diagonal, and the problem is to find the *eigenvalues* for which $A - \lambda I$ is singular. The test is $\det(A - \lambda I) = 0$. This polynomial of degree n in λ has exactly n roots. The matrix has n eigenvalues. This is a fact that follows from the determinant formula, and not from a computer.

2. The determinant of A equals the ***volume*** of a box in n-dimensional space. The edges of the box come from the rows of A (Figure 4.1). The columns of A would give an entirely different box with the same volume.

The simplest box is a little cube $dV = dx\,dy\,dz$, as in $\iiint f(x,y,z)\,dV$. Suppose we change to cylindrical coordinates by $x = r\cos\theta$, $y = r\sin\theta$, $z = z$. Just as a small interval dx is stretched to $(dx/du)\,du$—when u replaces x in a single integral—so the volume element becomes $J\,dr\,d\theta\,dz$. The *Jacobian determinant* is the three-dimensional analogue of the stretching factor dx/du:

$$\textbf{Jacobian} \qquad J = \begin{vmatrix} \partial x/\partial r & \partial x/\partial\theta & \partial x/\partial z \\ \partial y/\partial r & \partial y/\partial\theta & \partial y/\partial z \\ \partial z/\partial r & \partial z/\partial\theta & \partial z/\partial z \end{vmatrix} = \begin{vmatrix} \cos\theta & -r\sin\theta & 0 \\ \sin\theta & r\cos\theta & 0 \\ 0 & 0 & 1 \end{vmatrix}.$$

The value of this determinant is $J = r$. It is the r in the cylindrical volume element

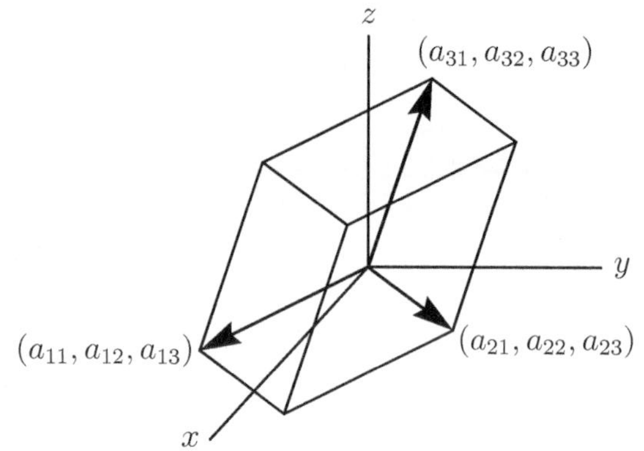

Figure 4.1 The box formed from the rows of A: volume $= |\text{determinant}|$.

$r\,dr\,d\theta\,dz$; this element is our little box. (It looks curved if we try to draw it, but probably it gets straighter as the edges become infinitesimal.)

3. The determinant gives a formula for each pivot. Theoretically, we could predict when a pivot entry will be zero, requiring a row exchange. From the formula ***determinant*** $= \pm$ ***(product of the pivots)***, it follows that *regardless of the order of elimination, the product of the pivots remains the same apart from sign.*

Years ago, this led to the belief that it was useless to escape a very small pivot by exchanging rows, since eventually the small pivot would catch up with us. But what usually happens in practice, if an abnormally small pivot is not avoided, is that it is very soon followed by an abnormally large one. This brings the product back to normal but it leaves the numerical solution in ruins.

4. The determinant measures the dependence of $A^{-1}b$ on each element of b. If one parameter is changed in an experiment, or one observation is corrected, the "influence coefficient" in A^{-1} is a ratio of determinants.

There is one more problem about the determinant. It is difficult not only to decide on its importance, and its proper place in the theory of linear algebra, but also to choose the best definition. Obviously, $\det A$ will not be some extremely simple function of n^2 variables; otherwise A^{-1} would be much easier to find than it actually is.

The simple things about the determinant are not the explicit formulas, but the properties it possesses. This suggests the natural place to begin. The determinant can be (and will be) defined by its three most basic properties: $\det I = 1$, **the sign is reversed by a row exchange, the determinant is linear in each row separately**. The problem is then to show, by systematically using these properties, how the determinant can be computed. This will bring us back to the product of the pivots.

Section 4.2 explains these three defining properties of the determinant, and their most important consequences. Section 4.3 gives two more formulas for the determinant—the "big formula" with $n!$ terms, and a formula "by induction." In Section 4.4 the determinant is applied to find A^{-1}. Then we compute $x = A^{-1}b$ by ***Cramer's rule***. And finally, in an optional remark on permutations, we show that whatever the order in which the properties are used, the result is always the same—the defining properties are self-consistent.

Here is a light-hearted question about permutations. ***How many exchanges does it take to change VISA into AVIS?*** Is this permutation odd or even?

4.2 PROPERTIES OF THE DETERMINANT

This will be a pretty long list. Fortunately each rule is easy to understand, and even easier to illustrate, for a 2 by 2 example. Therefore we shall verify that the familiar definition in the 2 by 2 case,

$$\det \begin{bmatrix} a & b \\ c & d \end{bmatrix} = \begin{vmatrix} a & b \\ c & d \end{vmatrix} = ad - bc,$$

possesses every property in the list. (Notice the two accepted notations for the determinant, $\det A$ and $|A|$.) Properties 4–10 will be deduced from the previous ones. **Every property is a consequence of the first three**. We emphasize that the rules apply to square matrices *of any size*.

1. *The determinant of the identity matrix is* 1.

$$\textbf{det}\, \boldsymbol{I} = \mathbf{1} \qquad \begin{vmatrix} 1 & 0 \\ 0 & 1 \end{vmatrix} = 1 \quad \text{and} \quad \begin{vmatrix} 1 & 0 & 0 \\ 0 & 1 & 0 \\ 0 & 0 & 1 \end{vmatrix} = 1 \quad \text{and} \ldots$$

2. *The determinant changes sign when two rows are exchanged.*

$$\textbf{Row exchange} \qquad \begin{vmatrix} c & d \\ a & b \end{vmatrix} = cb - ad = -\begin{vmatrix} a & b \\ c & d \end{vmatrix}.$$

The determinant of every *permutation matrix* is $\det P = \pm 1$. By row exchanges, we can turn P into the identity matrix. Each row exchange switches the sign of the determinant, until we reach $\det I = 1$. Now come all other matrices!

3. *The determinant depends linearly on the first row*. Suppose A, B, C are the same from the second row down—and row 1 of A is a linear combination of the first rows of B and C. Then the rule says: $\det A$ *is the same combination of* $\det B$ *and* $\det C$.

Linear combinations involve two operations—adding vectors and multiplying by scalars. Therefore this rule can be split into two parts:

$$\textbf{Add vectors in row 1} \qquad \begin{vmatrix} a + a' & b + b' \\ c & d \end{vmatrix} = \begin{vmatrix} a & b \\ c & d \end{vmatrix} + \begin{vmatrix} a' & b' \\ c & d \end{vmatrix}.$$

$$\textbf{Multiply by } \boldsymbol{t} \textbf{ in row 1} \qquad \begin{vmatrix} ta & tb \\ c & d \end{vmatrix} = t\begin{vmatrix} a & b \\ c & d \end{vmatrix}.$$

Notice that the first part is *not* the false statement $\det(B + C) = \det B + \det C$. You cannot add all the rows: only one row is allowed to change. Both sides give the answer $ad + a'd - bc - b'c$.

The second part is not the false statement $\det(tA) = t \det A$. The matrix tA has a factor t in *every* row (and the determinant is multiplied by t^n). It is like the volume of a box, when all sides are stretched by 4. In n dimensions the volume and determinant go up by 4^n. If only one side is stretched, the volume and determinant go up by 4; that is rule 3. By rule 2, there is nothing special about the first row.

The determinant is now settled, but that fact is not at all obvious. Therefore we gradually use these rules to find the determinant of any matrix.

4. *If two rows of A are equal, then* $\det A = 0$.

$$\textbf{Equal rows} \qquad \begin{vmatrix} a & b \\ a & b \end{vmatrix} = ab - ba = 0.$$

This follows from rule 2, since if the equal rows are exchanged, the determinant is supposed to change sign. But it also has to stay the same, because the matrix stays the same. The only number which can do that is zero, so $\det A = 0$. (The reasoning fails if $1 = -1$, which is the case in Boolean algebra. Then rule 4 should replace rule 2 as one of the defining properties.)

5. *Subtracting a multiple of one row from another row leaves the same determinant.*

$$\textbf{Row operation} \qquad \begin{vmatrix} a - \ell c & b - \ell d \\ c & d \end{vmatrix} = \begin{vmatrix} a & b \\ c & d \end{vmatrix}.$$

Rule 3 would say that there is a further term $-\ell \begin{vmatrix} c & d \\ c & d \end{vmatrix}$, but that term is zero by rule 4. The usual elimination steps do not affect the determinant!

6. *If A has a row of zeros, then* $\det A = 0$.

$$\textbf{Zero row} \qquad \begin{vmatrix} 0 & 0 \\ c & d \end{vmatrix} = 0.$$

One proof is to add some other row to the zero row. The determinant is unchanged, by rule 5. Because the matrix will now have two identical rows, $\det A = 0$ by rule 4.

7. *If A is triangular, then* $\det A$ *is the product* $a_{11}a_{22}\cdots a_{nn}$ *of the diagonal entries. If the triangular A has 1s along the diagonal, then* $\det A = 1$.

$$\textbf{Triangular matrix} \qquad \begin{vmatrix} a & b \\ 0 & d \end{vmatrix} = ad \qquad \begin{vmatrix} a & 0 \\ c & d \end{vmatrix} = ad.$$

Proof Suppose the diagonal entries are nonzero. Then elimination can remove all the off-diagonal entries, without changing the determinant (by rule 5). If A is lower triangular, the steps are downward as usual. If A is upper triangular, the *last* column is cleared out first—using multiples of a_{nn}. Either way we reach the diagonal matrix D:

$$D = \begin{bmatrix} a_{11} & & \\ & \ddots & \\ & & a_{nn} \end{bmatrix} \quad \text{has} \quad \det D = a_{11}a_{22}\cdots a_{nn} \det I = a_{11}a_{22}\cdots a_{nn}.$$

To find $\det D$ we patiently apply rule 3. Factoring out a_{11} and then a_{22} and finally a_{nn} leaves the identity matrix. At last we have a use for rule 1: $\det I = 1$. ■

If a diagonal entry is zero then elimination will produce a zero row. By rule 5 these elimination steps do not change the determinant. By rule 6 the zero row means a zero determinant. This means: When a triangular matrix is *singular* (because of a zero on the main diagonal) its determinant is *zero*.

This is a key property. **All singular matrices have a zero determinant.**

8. *If A is singular, then* $\det A = 0$. *If A is invertible, then* $\det A \neq 0$.

$$\textbf{Singular matrix} \qquad \begin{bmatrix} a & b \\ c & d \end{bmatrix} \quad \text{is not invertible if and only if} \quad ad - bc = 0.$$

If A is singular, elimination leads to a zero row in U. Then $\det A = \det U = 0$. If A is nonsingular, elimination puts the pivots $d_1, \dots, d_n$ on the main diagonal. We have a "product of pivots" formula for $\det A$! The sign depends on whether the number of row exchanges is even or odd:

$$\textbf{Product of pivots} \qquad \det A = \pm \det U = \pm\, d_1 d_2 \cdots d_n. \tag{1}$$

The ninth property is the product rule. I would say it is the most surprising.

9. *The determinant of AB is the product of* $\det A$ *times* $\det B$.

$$\textbf{Product rule } |A||B| = |AB| \qquad \begin{vmatrix} a & b \\ c & d \end{vmatrix} \begin{vmatrix} e & f \\ g & h \end{vmatrix} = \begin{vmatrix} ae + bg & af + bh \\ ce + dg & cf + dh \end{vmatrix}.$$

A particular case of this rule gives the determinant of A^{-1}. It must be $1/\det A$:

$$\det \boldsymbol{A}^{-1} = \frac{1}{\det \boldsymbol{A}} \quad \text{because} \quad (\det A)(\det A^{-1}) = \det AA^{-1} = \det I = 1. \tag{2}$$

In the 2 by 2 case, the product rule could be patiently checked:

$$(ad - bc)(eh - fg) = (ae + bg)(cf + dh) - (af + bh)(ce + dg).$$

In the n by n case we suggest two possible proofs—since this is the least obvious rule. Both proofs assume that A and B are nonsingular; otherwise AB is singular, and the equation $\det AB = (\det A)(\det B)$ is easily verified. By rule 8, it becomes $0 = 0$.

(i) We prove that the ratio $d(A) = \det AB/\det B$ has properties 1–3. Then $d(A)$ must equal $\det A$. For example, $d(I) = \det B/\det B = 1$; rule 1 is satisfied. If two rows of A are exchanged, so are the same two rows of AB, and the sign of d changes as required by rule 2. A linear combination in the first row of A gives the same linear combination in the first row of AB. Then rule 3 for the determinant of AB, divided by the fixed quantity $\det B$, leads to rule 3 for the ratio $d(A)$. Thus $d(A) = \det AB/\det B$ *coincides with* $\det A$, which is our product formula.

(ii) This second proof is less elegant. For a diagonal matrix, $\det DB = (\det D)(\det B)$ follows by factoring each d_i from its row. Reduce a general matrix A to D by elimination—from A to U as usual, and from U to D by upward elimination. The determinant does not change, except for a sign reversal when rows are exchanged. The same steps reduce AB to DB, with precisely the same effect on the determinant. But for DB it is already confirmed that rule 9 is correct.

10. *The transpose of A has the same determinant as A itself:* $\det A^{\mathrm{T}} = \det A$.

$$\textbf{Transpose rule} \qquad |A| = \begin{vmatrix} a & b \\ c & d \end{vmatrix} = \begin{vmatrix} a & c \\ b & d \end{vmatrix} = |A^{\mathrm{T}}|.$$

Again the singular case is separate; A is singular if and only if A^{T} is singular, and we have $0 = 0$. If A is nonsingular, then it allows the factorization $PA = LDU$, and we apply rule 9 for the determinant of a product:

$$\det P \det A = \det L \det D \det U. \tag{3}$$

Transposing $PA = LDU$ gives $A^{\mathrm{T}}P^{\mathrm{T}} = U^{\mathrm{T}}D^{\mathrm{T}}L^{\mathrm{T}}$, and again by rule 9,

$$\det A^{\mathrm{T}} \det P^{\mathrm{T}} = \det U^{\mathrm{T}} \det D^{\mathrm{T}} \det L^{\mathrm{T}}. \tag{4}$$

This is simpler than it looks, because L, U, L^{T}, and U^{T} are triangular with unit diagonal. By rule 7, their determinants all equal 1. Also, any diagonal matrix is the same as its transpose: $D = D^{\mathrm{T}}$. We only have to show that $\det P = \det P^{\mathrm{T}}$.

Certainly $\det P$ is 1 or -1, because P comes from I by row exchanges. Observe also that $PP^{\mathrm{T}} = I$. (The 1 in the first row of P matches the 1 in the first column of P^{T}, and misses the 1s in the other columns.) Therefore $\det P \det P^{\mathrm{T}} = \det I = 1$, and P and P^{T} must have the same determinant: both 1 or both -1.

We conclude that the products (3) and (4) are the same, and $\det A = \det A^{\mathrm{T}}$. This fact practically doubles our list of properties, because every rule that applied to the rows can now be applied to the columns: *The determinant changes sign when two columns are exchanged, two equal columns (or a column of zeros) produce a zero determinant, and the determinant depends linearly on each individual column.* The proof is just to transpose the matrix and work with the rows.

I think it is time to stop and call the list complete. It only remains to find a definite formula for the determinant, and to put that formula to use.

Problem Set 4.2

1. If a 4 by 4 matrix has $\det A = \frac{1}{2}$, find $\det(2A)$, $\det(-A)$, $\det(A^2)$, and $\det(A^{-1})$.

2. If a 3 by 3 matrix has $\det A = -1$, find $\det\left(\frac{1}{2}A\right)$, $\det(-A)$, $\det(A^2)$, and $\det(A^{-1})$.

3. *Row exchange*: Add row 1 of A to row 2, then subtract row 2 from row 1. Then add row 1 to row 2 and multiply row 1 by -1 to reach B. Which rules show the following?

$$\det B = \begin{vmatrix} c & d \\ a & b \end{vmatrix} \quad \text{equals} \quad -\det A = -\begin{vmatrix} a & b \\ c & d \end{vmatrix}.$$

Those rules could replace Rule 2 in the definition of the determinant.

4. By applying row operations to produce an upper triangular U, compute

$$\det \begin{bmatrix} 1 & 2 & -2 & 0 \\ 2 & 3 & -4 & 1 \\ -1 & -2 & 0 & 2 \\ 0 & 2 & 5 & 3 \end{bmatrix} \quad \text{and} \quad \det \begin{bmatrix} 2 & -1 & 0 & 0 \\ -1 & 2 & -1 & 0 \\ 0 & -1 & 2 & -1 \\ 0 & 0 & -1 & -2 \end{bmatrix}.$$

Exchange rows 3 and 4 of the second matrix and recompute the pivots and determinant.

Note Some readers will already know a formula for 3 by 3 determinants. It has six terms (equation (2) of the next section), three going parallel to the main diagonal and three others going the opposite way with minus signs. There is a similar formula for 4 by 4 determinants, ***but it contains*** $\mathbf{4! = 24}$ ***terms*** (*not just eight*). You cannot even be sure that a minus sign goes with the reverse diagonal, as the next exercises show.

5. Count row exchanges to find these determinants:

$$\det \begin{bmatrix} 0 & 0 & 0 & 1 \\ 0 & 0 & 1 & 0 \\ 0 & 1 & 0 & 0 \\ 1 & 0 & 0 & 0 \end{bmatrix} = +1 \quad \text{and} \quad \det \begin{bmatrix} 0 & 1 & 0 & 0 \\ 0 & 0 & 1 & 0 \\ 0 & 0 & 0 & 1 \\ 1 & 0 & 0 & 0 \end{bmatrix} = -1.$$

6. For each n, how many exchanges will put (row n, row $n-1$, ..., row 1) into the normal order (row 1, ..., row $n-1$, row n)? Find $\det P$ for the n by n permutation with 1s on the reverse diagonal. Problem 5 had $n = 4$.

7. Find the determinants of:

(a) a rank one matrix

$$A = \begin{bmatrix} 1 \\ 4 \\ 2 \end{bmatrix} \begin{bmatrix} 2 & -1 & 2 \end{bmatrix}.$$

(b) the upper triangular matrix

$$U = \begin{bmatrix} 4 & 4 & 8 & 8 \\ 0 & 1 & 2 & 2 \\ 0 & 0 & 2 & 6 \\ 0 & 0 & 0 & 2 \end{bmatrix}.$$

(c) the lower triangular matrix U^{T}.

(d) the inverse matrix U^{-1}.

(e) the "reverse-triangular" matrix that results from row exchanges,

$$M = \begin{bmatrix} 0 & 0 & 0 & 2 \\ 0 & 0 & 2 & 6 \\ 0 & 1 & 2 & 2 \\ 4 & 4 & 8 & 8 \end{bmatrix}.$$

8. Show how rule 6 (det = 0 if a row is zero) comes directly from rules 2 and 3.

9. Suppose you do two row operations *at once*, going from

$$\begin{bmatrix} a & b \\ c & d \end{bmatrix} \quad \text{to} \quad \begin{bmatrix} a - mc & b - md \\ c - \ell a & d - \ell b \end{bmatrix}.$$

Find the determinant of the new matrix, by rule 3 or by direct calculation.

10. If Q is an orthogonal matrix, so that $Q^{\mathrm{T}}Q = I$, prove that $\det Q$ equals $+1$ or -1. What kind of box is formed from the rows (or columns) of Q?

11. Prove again that $\det Q = 1$ or -1 using only the product rule. If $|\det Q| > 1$ then $\det Q^n$ blows up. How do you know this can't happen to Q^n?

12. Use row operations to verify that the 3 by 3 "Vandermonde determinant" is

$$\det\begin{bmatrix}1 & a & a^2\\ 1 & b & b^2\\ 1 & c & c^2\end{bmatrix} = (b-a)(c-a)(c-b).$$

13. (a) A skew-symmetric matrix satisfies $K^{\mathrm{T}} = -K$, as in

$$K = \begin{bmatrix}0 & a & b\\ -a & 0 & c\\ -b & -c & 0\end{bmatrix}.$$

In the 3 by 3 case, why is $\det(-K) = (-1)^3 \det K$? On the other hand $\det K^{\mathrm{T}} = \det K$ (always). Deduce that the determinant must be zero.

(b) Write down a 4 by 4 skew-symmetric matrix with $\det K$ *not* zero.

14. True or false, with reason if true and counterexample if false:

(a) If A and B are identical except that $b_{11} = 2a_{11}$, then $\det B = 2\det A$.
(b) The determinant is the product of the pivots.
(c) If A is invertible and B is singular, then $A + B$ is invertible.
(d) If A is invertible and B is singular, then AB is singular.
(e) The determinant of $AB - BA$ is zero.

15. If every row of A adds to zero, prove that $\det A = 0$. If every row adds to 1, prove that $\det(A - I) = 0$. Show by example that this does not imply $\det A = 1$.

16. Find these 4 by 4 determinants by Gaussian elimination:

$$\det\begin{bmatrix}11 & 12 & 13 & 14\\ 21 & 22 & 23 & 24\\ 31 & 32 & 33 & 34\\ 41 & 42 & 43 & 44\end{bmatrix} \quad\text{and}\quad \det\begin{bmatrix}1 & t & t^2 & t^3\\ t & 1 & t & t^2\\ t^2 & t & 1 & t\\ t^3 & t^2 & t & 1\end{bmatrix}.$$

17. Find the determinants of

$$A = \begin{bmatrix}4 & 2\\ 1 & 3\end{bmatrix}, \qquad A^{-1} = \frac{1}{10}\begin{bmatrix}3 & -2\\ -1 & 4\end{bmatrix}, \qquad A - \lambda I = \begin{bmatrix}4-\lambda & 2\\ 1 & 3-\lambda\end{bmatrix}.$$

For which values of λ is $A - \lambda I$ a singular matrix?

18. Evaluate $\det A$ by reducing the matrix to triangular form (rules 5 and 7).

$$A = \begin{bmatrix}1 & 1 & 3\\ 0 & 4 & 6\\ 1 & 5 & 8\end{bmatrix}, \qquad B = \begin{bmatrix}1 & 1 & 3\\ 0 & 4 & 6\\ 0 & 0 & 1\end{bmatrix}, \qquad C = \begin{bmatrix}1 & 1 & 3\\ 0 & 4 & 6\\ 1 & 5 & 9\end{bmatrix}.$$

What are the determinants of B, C, AB, $A^{\mathrm{T}}A$, and C^{T}?

19. Suppose that $CD = -DC$, and find the flaw in the following argument: Taking determinants gives $(\det C)(\det D) = -(\det D)(\det C)$, so either $\det C = 0$ or $\det D = 0$. Thus $CD = -DC$ is only possible if C or D is singular.

20. Do these matrices have determinant 0, 1, 2, or 3?

$$A = \begin{bmatrix} 0 & 0 & 1 \\ 1 & 0 & 0 \\ 0 & 1 & 0 \end{bmatrix} \quad B = \begin{bmatrix} 0 & 1 & 1 \\ 1 & 0 & 1 \\ 1 & 1 & 0 \end{bmatrix} \quad C = \begin{bmatrix} 1 & 1 & 1 \\ 1 & 1 & 1 \\ 1 & 1 & 1 \end{bmatrix}.$$

21. The inverse of a 2 by 2 matrix seems to have determinant = 1:

$$\det A^{-1} = \det \frac{1}{ad - bc} \begin{bmatrix} d & -b \\ -c & a \end{bmatrix} = \frac{ad - bc}{ad - bc} = 1.$$

What is wrong with this calculation? What is the correct $\det A^{-1}$?

Problems 22–28 use the rules to compute specific determinants.

22. Reduce A to U and find $\det A$ = product of the pivots:

$$A = \begin{bmatrix} 1 & 1 & 1 \\ 1 & 2 & 2 \\ 1 & 2 & 3 \end{bmatrix} \quad \text{and} \quad A = \begin{bmatrix} 1 & 2 & 3 \\ 2 & 2 & 3 \\ 3 & 3 & 3 \end{bmatrix}.$$

23. By applying row operations to produce an upper triangular U, compute

$$\det \begin{bmatrix} 1 & 2 & 3 & 0 \\ 2 & 6 & 6 & 1 \\ -1 & 0 & 0 & 3 \\ 0 & 2 & 0 & 7 \end{bmatrix} \quad \text{and} \quad \det \begin{bmatrix} 2 & 1 & 1 & 1 \\ 1 & 2 & 1 & 1 \\ 1 & 1 & 2 & 1 \\ 1 & 1 & 1 & 2 \end{bmatrix}.$$

24. Use row operations to simplify and compute these determinants:

$$\det \begin{bmatrix} 101 & 201 & 301 \\ 102 & 202 & 302 \\ 103 & 203 & 303 \end{bmatrix} \quad \text{and} \quad \det \begin{bmatrix} 1 & t & t^2 \\ t & 1 & t \\ t^2 & t & 1 \end{bmatrix}.$$

25. Elimination reduces A to U. Then $A = LU$:

$$A = \begin{bmatrix} 3 & 3 & 4 \\ 6 & 8 & 7 \\ -3 & 5 & -9 \end{bmatrix} = \begin{bmatrix} 1 & 0 & 0 \\ 2 & 1 & 0 \\ -1 & 4 & 1 \end{bmatrix} \begin{bmatrix} 3 & 3 & 4 \\ 0 & 2 & -1 \\ 0 & 0 & -1 \end{bmatrix} = LU.$$

Find the determinants of L, U, A, $U^{-1}L^{-1}$, and $U^{-1}L^{-1}A$.

26. If a_{ij} is i times j, show that $\det A = 0$. (Exception when $A = [1]$.)

27. If a_{ij} is $i + j$, show that $\det A = 0$. (Exception when $n = 1$ or 2.)

28. Compute the determinants of these matrices by row operations:

$$A = \begin{bmatrix} 0 & a & 0 \\ 0 & 0 & b \\ c & 0 & 0 \end{bmatrix}, \quad B = \begin{bmatrix} 0 & a & 0 & 0 \\ 0 & 0 & b & 0 \\ 0 & 0 & 0 & c \\ d & 0 & 0 & 0 \end{bmatrix}, \quad \text{and} \quad C = \begin{bmatrix} a & a & a \\ a & b & b \\ a & b & c \end{bmatrix}.$$

29. What is wrong with this proof that projection matrices have $\det P = 1$?

$$P = A(A^{\mathrm{T}}A)^{-1}A^{\mathrm{T}} \quad \text{so} \quad |P| = |A| \frac{1}{|A^{\mathrm{T}}||A|} |A^{\mathrm{T}}| = 1.$$

30. (Calculus question) Show that the partial derivatives of $\ln(\det A)$ give A^{-1}:

$$f(a,b,c,d) = \ln(ad - bc) \qquad \text{leads to} \qquad \begin{bmatrix} \partial f/\partial a & \partial f/\partial c \\ \partial f/\partial b & \partial f/\partial d \end{bmatrix} = A^{-1}.$$

31. (MATLAB) The Hilbert matrix **hilb**(n) has i, j entry equal to $1/(i+j-1)$. Print the determinants of **hilb**(1), **hilb**(2), $\ldots$, **hilb**(10). Hilbert matrices are hard to work with! What are the pivots?

32. (MATLAB) What is a typical determinant (experimentally) of **rand**(n) and **randn**(n) for $n = 50, 100, 200, 400$? (And what does "Inf" mean in MATLAB?)

33. Using MATLAB, find the largest determinant of a 4 by 4 matrix of 0s and 1s.

34. If you know that $\det A = 6$, what is the determinant of B?

$$\det A = \begin{vmatrix} \text{row 1} \\ \text{row 2} \\ \text{row 3} \end{vmatrix} = 6 \qquad \det B = \begin{vmatrix} \text{row 1} + \text{row 2} \\ \text{row 2} + \text{row 3} \\ \text{row 3} + \text{row 1} \end{vmatrix} = \underline{\quad}$$

35. Suppose the 4 by 4 matrix M has four equal rows all containing a, b, c, d. We know that $\det(M) = 0$. The problem is to find $\det(I + M)$ by any method:

$$\det(I + M) = \begin{vmatrix} 1+a & b & c & d \\ a & 1+b & c & d \\ a & b & 1+c & d \\ a & b & c & 1+d \end{vmatrix}.$$

Partial credit if you find this determinant when $a = b = c = d = 1$. Sudden death if you say that $\det(I + M) = \det I + \det M$.

4.3 FORMULAS FOR THE DETERMINANT

The first formula has already appeared. Row operations produce the pivots in D:

4A If A is invertible, then $PA = LDU$ and $\det P = \pm 1$. The product rule gives

$$\det A = \pm \det L \det D \det U = \pm(\textbf{product of the pivots}). \qquad (1)$$

The sign ± 1 depends on whether the number of row exchanges is even or odd. The triangular factors have $\det L = \det U = 1$ and $\det D = d_1 \cdots d_n$.

In the 2 by 2 case, the standard LDU factorization is

$$\begin{bmatrix} a & b \\ c & d \end{bmatrix} = \begin{bmatrix} 1 & 0 \\ c/a & 1 \end{bmatrix} \begin{bmatrix} \boldsymbol{a} & 0 \\ 0 & \boldsymbol{(ad - bc)/a} \end{bmatrix} \begin{bmatrix} 1 & b/a \\ 0 & 1 \end{bmatrix}.$$

The product of the pivots is $ad - bc$. That is the determinant of the diagonal matrix D. If the first step is a row exchange, the pivots are c and $(-\det A)/c$.

Example 1 The $-1, 2, -1$ second difference matrix has pivots $2/1, 3/2, \ldots$ in D:

$$\begin{bmatrix} 2 & -1 & & & \\ -1 & 2 & -1 & & \\ & -1 & 2 & \cdot & \\ & & \cdot & \cdot & -1 \\ & & & -1 & 2 \end{bmatrix} = LDU = L \begin{bmatrix} 2 & & & & \\ & 3/2 & & & \\ & & 4/3 & & \\ & & & \cdot & \\ & & & & (n+1)/n \end{bmatrix} U.$$

Its determinant is the product of its pivots. The numbers $2, \ldots, n$ all cancel:

$$\det A = 2\left(\frac{3}{2}\right)\left(\frac{4}{3}\right)\cdots\left(\frac{n+1}{n}\right) = n+1.$$

MATLAB computes the determinant from the pivots. But concentrating all information into the pivots makes it impossible to figure out how a change in one entry would affect the determinant. We want to find an explicit expression for the determinant in terms of the n^2 entries.

For $n = 2$, we will be proving that $ad - bc$ is correct. For $n = 3$, the determinant formula is again pretty well known (it has six terms):

$$\begin{vmatrix} a_{11} & \boldsymbol{a_{12}} & a_{13} \\ a_{21} & a_{22} & \boldsymbol{a_{23}} \\ \boldsymbol{a_{31}} & a_{32} & a_{33} \end{vmatrix} = \begin{matrix} +a_{11}a_{22}a_{33} + \boldsymbol{a_{12}a_{23}a_{31}} + a_{13}a_{21}a_{32} \\ -a_{11}a_{23}a_{32} - a_{12}a_{21}a_{33} - a_{13}a_{22}a_{31}. \end{matrix} \tag{2}$$

Our goal is to derive these formulas directly from the defining properties 1–3 of $\det A$. If we can handle $n = 2$ and $n = 3$ in an organized way, you will see the pattern.

To start, each row can be broken down into vectors in the coordinate directions:

$$\begin{bmatrix} a & b \end{bmatrix} = \begin{bmatrix} a & 0 \end{bmatrix} + \begin{bmatrix} 0 & b \end{bmatrix} \quad \text{and} \quad \begin{bmatrix} c & d \end{bmatrix} = \begin{bmatrix} c & 0 \end{bmatrix} + \begin{bmatrix} 0 & d \end{bmatrix}.$$

Then we apply the property of linearity, first in row 1 and then in row 2:

Separate into $n^n = 2^2$ easy determinants

$$\begin{aligned} \begin{vmatrix} a & b \\ c & d \end{vmatrix} &= \begin{vmatrix} a & 0 \\ c & d \end{vmatrix} + \begin{vmatrix} 0 & b \\ c & d \end{vmatrix} \\ &= \begin{vmatrix} a & 0 \\ c & 0 \end{vmatrix} + \begin{vmatrix} a & 0 \\ 0 & d \end{vmatrix} + \begin{vmatrix} 0 & b \\ c & 0 \end{vmatrix} + \begin{vmatrix} 0 & b \\ 0 & d \end{vmatrix}. \end{aligned} \tag{3}$$

Every row splits into n coordinate directions, so this expansion has n^n terms. Most of those terms (all but $n! = n$ factorial) will be automatically zero. When two rows are in the same coordinate direction, one will be a multiple of the other, and

$$\begin{vmatrix} a & 0 \\ c & 0 \end{vmatrix} = 0, \quad \begin{vmatrix} 0 & b \\ 0 & d \end{vmatrix} = 0.$$

We pay attention *only when the rows point in different directions*. ***The nonzero terms have to come in different columns***. Suppose the first row has a nonzero term in column α, the second row is nonzero in column β, and finally the nth row in column ν. The column numbers $\alpha, \beta, \ldots, \nu$ are all different. They are a reordering, or ***permutation***, of the numbers $1, 2, \ldots, n$. The 3 by 3 case produces $3! = 6$ determinants:

$$\begin{vmatrix} a_{11} & \mathbf{a_{12}} & a_{13} \\ a_{21} & a_{22} & \mathbf{a_{23}} \\ \mathbf{a_{31}} & a_{32} & a_{33} \end{vmatrix} = \begin{vmatrix} a_{11} & & \\ & a_{22} & \\ & & a_{33} \end{vmatrix} + \begin{vmatrix} & \mathbf{a_{12}} & \\ & & \mathbf{a_{23}} \\ \mathbf{a_{31}} & & \end{vmatrix} + \begin{vmatrix} & & a_{13} \\ a_{21} & & \\ & a_{32} & \end{vmatrix}$$

$$+ \begin{vmatrix} a_{11} & & \\ & & a_{23} \\ & a_{32} & \end{vmatrix} + \begin{vmatrix} & a_{12} & \\ a_{21} & & \\ & & a_{33} \end{vmatrix} + \begin{vmatrix} & & a_{13} \\ & a_{22} & \\ a_{31} & & \end{vmatrix}. \tag{4}$$

All but these $n!$ determinants are zero, because a column is repeated. (There are n choices for the first column α, $n-1$ remaining choices for β, and finally only one choice for the last column ν. All but one column will be used by that time, when we "snake" down the rows of the matrix). In other words, ***there are $n!$ ways to permute the numbers $1, 2, \ldots, n$***. The column numbers give the permutations:

Column numbers $(\alpha, \beta, \nu) = (1, 2, 3)$, $\mathbf{(2, 3, 1)}$, $(3, 1, 2)$, $(1, 3, 2)$, $(2, 1, 3)$, $(3, 2, 1)$.

Those are the $3! = 6$ permutations of $(1, 2, 3)$; the first one is the identity.

The determinant of A is now reduced to six separate and much simpler determinants. Factoring out the a_{ij}, there is a term for every one of the six permutations:

$$\det A = a_{11}a_{22}a_{33} \begin{vmatrix} 1 & & \\ & 1 & \\ & & 1 \end{vmatrix} + \mathbf{a_{12}a_{23}a_{31}} \begin{vmatrix} & \mathbf{1} & \\ & & \mathbf{1} \\ \mathbf{1} & & \end{vmatrix} + a_{13}a_{21}a_{32} \begin{vmatrix} & & 1 \\ 1 & & \\ & 1 & \end{vmatrix}$$

$$+ a_{11}a_{23}a_{32} \begin{vmatrix} 1 & & \\ & & 1 \\ & 1 & \end{vmatrix} + a_{12}a_{21}a_{33} \begin{vmatrix} & 1 & \\ 1 & & \\ & & 1 \end{vmatrix} + a_{13}a_{22}a_{31} \begin{vmatrix} & & 1 \\ & 1 & \\ 1 & & \end{vmatrix}. \tag{5}$$

Every term is a product of $n = 3$ entries a_{ij}, with *each row and column represented once*. If the columns come in the order $(\alpha, \ldots, \nu)$, that term is the product $a_{1\alpha} \cdots a_{n\nu}$ times the determinant of a permutation matrix P. The determinant of the whole matrix is the sum of these $n!$ terms, and ***that sum is the explicit formula we are after***:

Big Formula $$\det A = \sum_{\text{all } P\text{'s}} (a_{1\alpha}a_{2\beta} \cdots a_{n\nu}) \det P. \tag{6}$$

For an n by n matrix, this sum is taken over all $n!$ permutations $(\alpha, \ldots, \nu)$ of the numbers $(1, \ldots, n)$. The permutation gives the column numbers as we go down the matrix. The 1s appear in P at the same places where the a's appeared in A.

It remains to find the determinant of P. Row exchanges transform it to the identity matrix, and each exchange reverses the sign of the determinant:

$$\det P = +1 \text{ or } -1 \textit{ for an even } \text{or} \textit{ odd number of row exchanges}.$$

$$(1, 3, 2) \text{ is odd so } \begin{vmatrix} 1 & & \\ & & 1 \\ & 1 & \end{vmatrix} = -1 \qquad (3, 1, 2) \text{ is even so } \begin{vmatrix} & & 1 \\ 1 & & \\ & 1 & \end{vmatrix} = 1$$

(1, 3, 2) requires one exchange and (3, 1, 2) requires two exchanges to recover (1, 2, 3). These are two of the six $\pm$ signs. For $n = 2$, we only have (1, 2) and (2, 1):

$$\det A = a_{11}a_{22} \det \begin{bmatrix} 1 & 0 \\ 0 & 1 \end{bmatrix} + a_{12}a_{21} \det \begin{bmatrix} 0 & 1 \\ 1 & 0 \end{bmatrix} = a_{11}a_{22} - a_{12}a_{21} \text{ (or } ad - bc).$$

No one can claim that the big formula (6) is particularly simple. Nevertheless, it is possible to see why it has properties 1–3. For $A = I$, every product of the a_{ij} will be zero, except for the column sequence $(1, 2, \dots, n)$. This term gives $\det I = 1$. Property 2 will be checked in the next section, because here we are most interested in property 3: The determinant should depend linearly on the first row $a_{11}, a_{12}, \dots, a_{1n}$.

Look at all the terms $a_{1\alpha}a_{2\beta}\cdots a_{n\nu}$ involving a_{11}. The first column is $\alpha = 1$. This leaves some permutation $(\beta, \dots, \nu)$ of the remaining columns $(2, \dots, n)$. We collect all these terms together as $a_{11}C_{11}$, where the coefficient of a_{11} is a smaller determinant—*with row* 1 *and column* 1 *removed*:

$$\textbf{Cofactor of } a_{11} \qquad C_{11} = \sum (a_{2\beta}\cdots a_{n\nu}) \det P = \det(\text{submatrix of } A). \qquad (7)$$

Similarly, the entry a_{12} is multiplied by some smaller determinant C_{12}. Grouping all the terms that start with the same a_{1j}, formula (6) becomes

$$\textbf{Cofactors along row 1} \qquad \det A = a_{11}C_{11} + a_{12}C_{12} + \cdots + a_{1n}C_{1n}. \qquad (8)$$

This shows that $\det A$ depends linearly on the entries $a_{11}, \dots, a_{1n}$ of the first row.

Example 2 For a 3 by 3 matrix, this way of collecting terms gives

$$\det A = a_{11}(\boldsymbol{a_{22}a_{33} - a_{23}a_{32}}) + a_{12}(\boldsymbol{a_{23}a_{31} - a_{21}a_{33}}) + a_{13}(\boldsymbol{a_{21}a_{32} - a_{22}a_{31}}). \quad (9)$$

The ***cofactors*** C_{11}, C_{12}, C_{13} are the 2 by 2 determinants in parentheses.

Expansion of det *A* in Cofactors

We want one more formula for the determinant. If this meant starting again from scratch, it would be too much. But *the formula is already discovered—it is* (8), *and the only point is to identify the cofactors* C_{1j} *that multiply* a_{1j}.

We know that C_{1j} depends on rows $2, \dots, n$. Row 1 is already accounted for by a_{1j}. Furthermore, a_{1j} also accounts for the jth column, so its cofactor C_{1j} must depend entirely on *the other columns*. No row or column can be used twice in the same term. What we are really doing is splitting the determinant into the following sum:

$$\textbf{Cofactor splitting} \quad \begin{vmatrix} a_{11} & a_{12} & a_{13} \\ a_{21} & a_{22} & a_{23} \\ a_{31} & a_{32} & a_{33} \end{vmatrix} = \begin{vmatrix} a_{11} & & \\ & a_{22} & a_{23} \\ & a_{32} & a_{33} \end{vmatrix} + \begin{vmatrix} & a_{12} & \\ a_{21} & & a_{23} \\ a_{31} & & a_{33} \end{vmatrix} + \begin{vmatrix} & & a_{13} \\ a_{21} & a_{22} & \\ a_{31} & a_{32} & \end{vmatrix}.$$

For a determinant of order n, this splitting gives n smaller determinants (***minors***) of order $n - 1$; you see the three 2 by 2 submatrices. The submatrix M_{1j} is formed by *throwing away row* 1 *and column* j. Its determinant is multiplied by a_{1j}—and by a plus or minus sign. These signs alternate as in $\det M_{11}$, $-\det M_{12}$, $\det M_{13}$:

$$\textbf{Cofactors of row 1} \qquad C_{1j} = (-1)^{1+j} \det M_{1j}.$$

The second cofactor C_{12} is $a_{23}a_{31} - a_{21}a_{33}$, which is $\det M_{12}$ times -1. This same technique works on every n by n matrix. The splitting above confirms that C_{11} is the determinant of the lower right corner M_{11}.

There is a similar expansion on any other row, say row i. It could be proved by exchanging row i with row 1. *Remember to delete row i and column j of A for M_{ij}*:

4B The determinant of A is a combination of any row i times its cofactors:

det *A* by cofactors $$\det A = a_{i1}C_{i1} + a_{i2}C_{i2} + \cdots + a_{in}C_{in}. \quad (10)$$

The cofactor C_{ij} is the determinant of M_{ij} with the correct sign:

delete row *i* and column *j* $$C_{ij} = (-1)^{i+j} \det M_{ij}. \quad (11)$$

These formulas express $\det A$ as a combination of determinants of order $n-1$. *We could have defined the determinant by induction on n.* A 1 by 1 matrix has $\det A = a_{11}$, and then equation (10) defines the determinants of 2 by 2 matrices, 3 by 3 matrices, and n by n matrices. We preferred to define the determinant by its properties, which are much simpler to explain. The explicit formula (6) and the cofactor formula (10) followed directly from these properties.

There is one more consequence of $\det A = \det A^{\mathrm{T}}$. We can expand in cofactors of a *column* of A, which is a row of A^{T}. Down column j of A,

$$\det A = a_{1j}C_{1j} + a_{2j}C_{2j} + \cdots + a_{nj}C_{nj}. \quad (12)$$

Example 3 The 4 by 4 second difference matrix A_4 has only two nonzeros in row 1:

Use cofactors $$A_4 = \begin{bmatrix} 2 & -1 & 0 & 0 \\ -1 & 2 & -1 & 0 \\ 0 & -1 & 2 & -1 \\ 0 & 0 & -1 & 2 \end{bmatrix}.$$

C_{11} comes from erasing row 1 and column 1, which leaves the $-1, 2, -1$ pattern:

$$C_{11} = \det A_3 = \det \begin{bmatrix} 2 & -1 & 0 \\ -1 & 2 & -1 \\ 0 & -1 & 2 \end{bmatrix}.$$

For $a_{12} = -1$ it is column 2 that gets removed, and we need its cofactor C_{12}:

$$C_{12} = (-1)^{1+2} \det \begin{bmatrix} -1 & -1 & 0 \\ 0 & 2 & -1 \\ 0 & -1 & 2 \end{bmatrix} = +\det \begin{bmatrix} 2 & -1 \\ -1 & 2 \end{bmatrix} = \det A_2.$$

This left us with the 2 by 2 determinant. Altogether row 1 has produced $2C_{11} - C_{12}$:

$$\det A_4 = 2(\det A_3) - \det A_2 = 2(4) - 3 = 5$$

The same idea applies to A_5 and A_6, and every A_n:

Recursion by cofactors $$\det A_n = 2(\det A_{n-1}) - \det A_{n-2}. \quad (13)$$

This gives the determinant of increasingly bigger matrices. At every step the determinant of A_n is $n+1$, from the previous determinants n and $n-1$:

$$\textbf{-1, 2, -1 matrix} \qquad \det A_n = 2(n) - (n-1) = n+1\,.$$

The answer $n+1$ agrees with the product of pivots at the start of this section.

Problem Set 4.3

1. For these matrices, find the only nonzero term in the big formula (6):

$$A = \begin{bmatrix} 0 & 1 & 0 & 0 \\ 1 & 0 & 1 & 0 \\ 0 & 1 & 0 & 1 \\ 0 & 0 & 1 & 0 \end{bmatrix} \quad \text{and} \quad B = \begin{bmatrix} 0 & 0 & 1 & 2 \\ 0 & 3 & 4 & 5 \\ 6 & 7 & 8 & 9 \\ 0 & 0 & 0 & 1 \end{bmatrix}.$$

There is only one way of choosing four nonzero entries from different rows and different columns. By deciding even or odd, compute $\det A$ and $\det B$.

2. Expand those determinants in cofactors of the first row. Find the cofactors (they include the signs $(-1)^{i+j}$) and the determinants of A and B.

3. *True or false*?

(a) The determinant of $S^{-1}AS$ equals the determinant of A.
(b) If $\det A = 0$ then at least one of the cofactors must be zero.
(c) A matrix whose entries are 0s and 1s has determinant 1, 0, or -1.

4. (a) Find the LU factorization, the pivots, and the determinant of the 4 by 4 matrix whose entries are a_{ij} = smaller of i and j. (Write out the matrix.)
(b) Find the determinant if a_{ij} = smaller of n_i and n_j, where $n_1 = 2$, $n_2 = 6$, $n_3 = 8$, $n_4 = 10$. Can you give a general rule for any $n_1 \le n_2 \le n_3 \le n_4$?

5. Let F_n be the determinant of the 1, 1, -1 tridiagonal matrix (n by n):

$$F_n = \det \begin{bmatrix} 1 & -1 & & & \\ 1 & 1 & -1 & & \\ & 1 & 1 & -1 & \\ & & \cdot & \cdot & \cdot \\ & & & 1 & 1 \end{bmatrix}.$$

By expanding in cofactors along row 1, show that $F_n = F_{n-1} + F_{n-2}$. This yields the *Fibonacci sequence* 1, 2, 3, 5, 8, 13, ... for the determinants.

6. Suppose A_n is the n by n tridiagonal matrix with 1s on the three diagonals:

$$A_1 = [1], \qquad A_2 = \begin{bmatrix} 1 & 1 \\ 1 & 1 \end{bmatrix}, \qquad A_3 = \begin{bmatrix} 1 & 1 & 0 \\ 1 & 1 & 1 \\ 0 & 1 & 1 \end{bmatrix}, \quad \ldots$$

Let D_n be the determinant of A_n; we want to find it.

(a) Expand in cofactors along the first row to show that $D_n = D_{n-1} - D_{n-2}$.
(b) Starting from $D_1 = 1$ and $D_2 = 0$, find $D_3, D_4, \ldots, D_8$. By noticing how these numbers cycle around (with what period?) find D_{1000}.

7. (a) Evaluate this determinant by cofactors of row 1:

$$\begin{vmatrix} 4 & 4 & 4 & 4 \\ 1 & 2 & 0 & 1 \\ 2 & 0 & 1 & 2 \\ 1 & 1 & 0 & 2 \end{vmatrix}.$$

(b) Check by subtracting column 1 from the other columns and recomputing.

8. Compute the determinants of A_2, A_3, A_4. Can you predict A_n?

$$A_2 = \begin{bmatrix} 0 & 1 \\ 1 & 0 \end{bmatrix} \quad A_3 = \begin{bmatrix} 0 & 1 & 1 \\ 1 & 0 & 1 \\ 1 & 1 & 0 \end{bmatrix} \quad A_4 = \begin{bmatrix} 0 & 1 & 1 & 1 \\ 1 & 0 & 1 & 1 \\ 1 & 1 & 0 & 1 \\ 1 & 1 & 1 & 0 \end{bmatrix}.$$

Use row operations to produce zeros, or use cofactors of row 1.

9. How many multiplications to find an n by n determinant from

(a) the big formula (6)?
(b) the cofactor formula (10), building from the count for $n-1$?
(c) the product of pivots formula (including the elimination steps)?

10. In a 5 by 5 matrix, does a $+$ sign or $-$ sign go with $a_{15}a_{24}a_{33}a_{42}a_{51}$ down the reverse diagonal? In other words, is $P = (5, 4, 3, 2, 1)$ even or odd? The checkerboard pattern of $\pm$ signs for cofactors does *not* give $\det P$.

11. If A is m by n and B is n by m, explain why

$$\det \begin{bmatrix} 0 & A \\ -B & I \end{bmatrix} = \det AB. \quad \left(\textit{Hint}: \text{Postmultiply by } \begin{bmatrix} I & 0 \\ B & I \end{bmatrix}.\right)$$

Do an example with $m < n$ and an example with $m > n$. Why does your second example automatically have $\det AB = 0$?

12. Suppose the matrix A is fixed, except that a_{11} varies from $-\infty$ to $+\infty$. Give examples in which $\det A$ is always zero or never zero. Then show from the cofactor expansion (8) that otherwise $\det A = 0$ for exactly *one value* of a_{11}.

Problems 13–23 use the big formula with $n!$ terms: $|A| = \sum \pm a_{1\alpha}a_{2\beta}\cdots a_{n\nu}$.

13. Compute the determinants of A, B, C from six terms. Independent rows?

$$A = \begin{bmatrix} 1 & 2 & 3 \\ 3 & 1 & 2 \\ 3 & 2 & 1 \end{bmatrix} \quad B = \begin{bmatrix} 1 & 2 & 3 \\ 4 & 4 & 4 \\ 5 & 6 & 7 \end{bmatrix} \quad C = \begin{bmatrix} 1 & 1 & 1 \\ 1 & 1 & 0 \\ 1 & 0 & 0 \end{bmatrix}.$$

14. Compute the determinants of A, B, C. Are their columns independent?

$$A = \begin{bmatrix} 1 & 1 & 0 \\ 1 & 0 & 1 \\ 0 & 1 & 1 \end{bmatrix} \quad B = \begin{bmatrix} 1 & 2 & 3 \\ 4 & 5 & 6 \\ 7 & 8 & 9 \end{bmatrix} \quad C = \begin{bmatrix} A & 0 \\ 0 & B \end{bmatrix}.$$

15. Show that det $A = 0$, regardless of the five nonzeros marked by x's:

$$A = \begin{bmatrix} x & x & x \\ 0 & 0 & x \\ 0 & 0 & x \end{bmatrix}. \qquad \text{(What is the rank of } A\text{?)}$$

16. This problem shows in two ways that det $A = 0$ (the x's are any numbers):

$$A = \begin{bmatrix} x & x & x & x & x \\ x & x & x & x & x \\ 0 & 0 & 0 & x & x \\ 0 & 0 & 0 & x & x \\ 0 & 0 & 0 & x & x \end{bmatrix}. \qquad \begin{matrix} \text{5 by 5 matrix} \\ \text{3 by 3 zero matrix} \\ \text{Always singular} \end{matrix}$$

(a) How do you know that the rows are linearly dependent?
(b) Explain why all 120 terms are zero in the big formula for det A.

17. Find two ways to choose nonzeros from four different rows and columns:

$$A = \begin{bmatrix} 1 & 0 & 0 & 1 \\ 0 & 1 & 1 & 1 \\ 1 & 1 & 0 & 1 \\ 1 & 0 & 0 & 1 \end{bmatrix} \qquad B = \begin{bmatrix} 1 & 0 & 0 & 2 \\ 0 & 3 & 4 & 5 \\ 5 & 4 & 0 & 3 \\ 2 & 0 & 0 & 1 \end{bmatrix}. \quad (B \text{ has the same zeros as } A.)$$

Is det A equal to $1 + 1$ or $1 - 1$ or $-1 - 1$? What is det B?

18. Place the smallest number of zeros in a 4 by 4 matrix that will guarantee det $A = 0$. Place as many zeros as possible while still allowing det $A \neq 0$.

19. (a) If $a_{11} = a_{22} = a_{33} = 0$, how many of the six terms in det A will be zero?
(b) If $a_{11} = a_{22} = a_{33} = a_{44} = 0$, how many of the 24 products $a_{1j}a_{2k}a_{3\ell}a_{4m}$ are sure to be zero?

20. How many 5 by 5 permutation matrices have det $P = +1$? Those are even permutations. Find one that needs four exchanges to reach the identity matrix.

21. If det $A \neq 0$, at least one of the $n!$ terms in the big formula (6) is not zero. Deduce that some ordering of the rows of A leaves no zeros on the diagonal. (Don't use P from elimination; that PA can have zeros on the diagonal.)

22. Prove that 4 is the largest determinant for a 3 by 3 matrix of 1s and -1s.

23. How many permutations of $(1, 2, 3, 4)$ are even and what are they? Extra credit: What are all the possible 4 by 4 determinants of $I + P_{\text{even}}$?

Problems 24–33 use cofactors $C_{ij} = (-1)^{i+j}$ det M_{ij}. Delete row i, column j.

24. Find cofactors and then transpose. Multiply C_A^{T} and C_B^{T} by A and B!

$$A = \begin{bmatrix} 2 & 1 \\ 3 & 6 \end{bmatrix} \qquad B = \begin{bmatrix} 1 & 2 & 3 \\ 4 & 5 & 6 \\ 7 & 0 & 0 \end{bmatrix}.$$

25. Find the cofactor matrix C and compare AC^{T} with A^{-1}:

$$A = \begin{bmatrix} 2 & -1 & 0 \\ -1 & 2 & -1 \\ 0 & -1 & 2 \end{bmatrix} \qquad A^{-1} = \frac{1}{4}\begin{bmatrix} 3 & 2 & 1 \\ 2 & 4 & 2 \\ 1 & 2 & 3 \end{bmatrix}.$$

26. The matrix B_n is the $-1, 2, -1$ matrix A_n except that $b_{11} = 1$ instead of $a_{11} = 2$. Using cofactors of the *last* row of B_4, show that $|B_4| = 2|B_3| - |B_2| = 1$:

$$B_4 = \begin{bmatrix} 1 & -1 & & \\ -1 & 2 & -1 & \\ & -1 & 2 & -1 \\ & & -1 & 2 \end{bmatrix} \qquad B_3 = \begin{bmatrix} 1 & -1 & \\ -1 & 2 & -1 \\ & -1 & 2 \end{bmatrix}.$$

The recursion $|B_n| = 2|B_{n-1}| - |B_{n-2}|$ is the same as for the A's. The difference is in the starting values 1, 1, 1 for $n = 1, 2, 3$. *What are the pivots?*

27. B_n is still the same as A_n except for $b_{11} = 1$. So use linearity in the first row, where $[1\ \ -1\ \ 0]$ equals $[2\ \ -1\ \ 0]$ minus $[1\ \ 0\ \ 0]$:

$$|B_n| = \begin{vmatrix} 1 & -1 & & 0 \\ -1 & & & \\ & & A_{n-1} & \\ 0 & & & \end{vmatrix} = \begin{vmatrix} 2 & -1 & & 0 \\ -1 & & & \\ & & A_{n-1} & \\ 0 & & & \end{vmatrix} - \begin{vmatrix} 1 & 0 & & 0 \\ -1 & & & \\ & & A_{n-1} & \\ 0 & & & \end{vmatrix}.$$

Linearity in row 1 gives $|B_n| = |A_n| - |A_{n-1}| =$ ___.

28. The n by n determinant C_n has 1s above and below the main diagonal:

$$C_1 = |0| \quad C_2 = \begin{vmatrix} 0 & 1 \\ 1 & 0 \end{vmatrix} \quad C_3 = \begin{vmatrix} 0 & 1 & 0 \\ 1 & 0 & 1 \\ 0 & 1 & 0 \end{vmatrix} \quad C_4 = \begin{vmatrix} 0 & 1 & 0 & 0 \\ 1 & 0 & 1 & 0 \\ 0 & 1 & 0 & 1 \\ 0 & 0 & 1 & 0 \end{vmatrix}.$$

(a) What are the determinants of C_1, C_2, C_3, C_4?
(b) By cofactors find the relation between C_n and C_{n-1} and C_{n-2}. Find C_{10}.

29. Problem 28 has 1s just above and below the main diagonal. Going down the matrix, which order of columns (if any) gives all 1s? Explain why that permutation is *even* for $n = 4, 8, 12, \ldots$ and *odd* for $n = 2, 6, 10, \ldots$

$$C_n = 0 \text{ (odd } n) \qquad C_n = 1\ (n = 4, 8, \ldots) \qquad C_n = -1\ (n = 2, 6, \ldots).$$

30. Explain why this Vandermonde determinant contains x^3 but not x^4 or x^5:

$$V_4 = \det \begin{bmatrix} 1 & a & a^2 & a^3 \\ 1 & b & b^2 & b^3 \\ 1 & c & c^2 & c^3 \\ 1 & x & x^2 & x^3 \end{bmatrix}.$$

The determinant is zero at $x =$ ___, ___, and ___. The cofactor of x^3 is $V_3 = (b-a)(c-a)(c-b)$. Then $V_4 = (x-a)(x-b)(x-c)V_3$.

31. Compute the determinants S_1, S_2, S_3 of these 1, 3, 1 tridiagonal matrices:

$$S_1 = \begin{vmatrix} 3 \end{vmatrix} \qquad S_2 = \begin{vmatrix} 3 & 1 \\ 1 & 3 \end{vmatrix} \qquad S_3 = \begin{vmatrix} 3 & 1 & 0 \\ 1 & 3 & 1 \\ 0 & 1 & 3 \end{vmatrix}.$$

Make a Fibonacci guess for S_4 and verify that you are right.

32. Cofactors of those 1, 3, 1 matrices give $S_n = 3S_{n-1} - S_{n-2}$. Challenge: *Show that S_n is the Fibonacci number F_{2n+2} by proving $F_{2n+2} = 3F_{2n} - F_{2n-2}$.* Keep using Fibonacci's rule $F_k = F_{k-1} + F_{k-2}$.

33. Change 3 to 2 in the upper left corner of the matrices in Problem 32. Why does that subtract S_{n-1} from the determinant S_n? Show that the determinants become the Fibonacci numbers 2, 5, 13 (always F_{2n+1}).

Problems 34–36 are about block matrices and block determinants.

34. With 2 by 2 blocks, you cannot always use block determinants!

$$\begin{vmatrix} A & B \\ 0 & D \end{vmatrix} = |A|\,|D| \qquad \text{but} \qquad \begin{vmatrix} A & B \\ C & D \end{vmatrix} \neq |A|\,|D| - |C|\,|B|.$$

(a) Why is the first statement true? Somehow B doesn't enter.
(b) Show by example that equality fails (as shown) when C enters.
(c) Show by example that the answer $\det(AD - CB)$ is also wrong.

35. With block multiplication, $A = LU$ has $A_k = L_kU_k$ in the upper left corner:

$$A = \begin{bmatrix} A_k & * \\ * & * \end{bmatrix} = \begin{bmatrix} L_k & 0 \\ * & * \end{bmatrix} \begin{bmatrix} U_k & * \\ 0 & * \end{bmatrix}.$$

(a) Suppose the first three pivots of A are 2, 3, -1. What are the determinants of L_1, L_2, L_3 (with diagonal 1s), U_1, U_2, U_3, and A_1, A_2, A_3?
(b) If A_1, A_2, A_3 have determinants 5, 6, 7, find the three pivots.

36. Block elimination subtracts CA^{-1} times the first row $[A \;\; B]$ from the second row $[C \;\; D]$. This leaves the *Schur complement* $D - CA^{-1}B$ in the corner:

$$\begin{bmatrix} I & 0 \\ -CA^{-1} & I \end{bmatrix} \begin{bmatrix} A & B \\ C & D \end{bmatrix} = \begin{bmatrix} A & B \\ 0 & D - CA^{-1}B \end{bmatrix}.$$

Take determinants of these matrices to prove correct rules for square blocks:

$$\begin{vmatrix} A & B \\ C & D \end{vmatrix} = \underset{\text{if } A^{-1} \text{ exists}}{|A|\,|D - CA^{-1}B|} = \underset{\text{if } AC = CA}{|AD - CB|}.$$

37. A 3 by 3 determinant has three products "down to the right" and three "down to the left" with minus signs. Compute the six terms in the figure to find D. Then explain without determinants why this matrix is or is not invertible:

$$D = \begin{vmatrix} 1 & 2 & 3 & 1 & 2 \\ 4 & 5 & 6 & 4 & 5 \\ 7 & 8 & 9 & 7 & 8 \end{vmatrix} \cdot$$

$$- \quad - \quad - \quad + \quad + \quad +$$

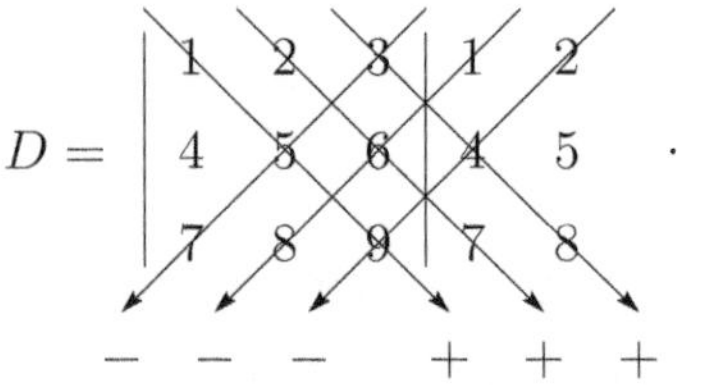

38. For A_4 in Problem 6, five of the $4! = 24$ terms in the big formula (6) are nonzero. Find those five terms to show that $D_4 = -1$.

39. For the 4 by 4 tridiagonal matrix (entries $-1, 2, -1$), find the five terms in the big formula that give $\det A = 16 - 4 - 4 - 4 + 1$.

40. Find the determinant of this cyclic P by cofactors of row 1. How many exchanges reorder 4, 1, 2, 3 into 1, 2, 3, 4? Is $|P^2| = +1$ or -1?

$$P = \begin{bmatrix} 0 & 0 & 0 & 1 \\ 1 & 0 & 0 & 0 \\ 0 & 1 & 0 & 0 \\ 0 & 0 & 1 & 0 \end{bmatrix} \qquad P^2 = \begin{bmatrix} 0 & 0 & 1 & 0 \\ 0 & 0 & 0 & 1 \\ 1 & 0 & 0 & 0 \\ 0 & 1 & 0 & 0 \end{bmatrix} = \begin{bmatrix} 0 & I \\ I & 0 \end{bmatrix}.$$

41. $A = 2 * \text{eye}(n) - \text{diag}(\text{ones}(n-1, 1), 1) - \text{diag}(\text{ones}(n-1, 1), -1)$ is the $-1, 2, -1$ matrix. Change $A(1, 1)$ to 1 so $\det A = 1$. Predict the entries of A^{-1} based on $n = 3$ and test the prediction for $n = 4$.

42. (MATLAB) The $-1, 2, -1$ matrices have determinant $n + 1$. Compute $(n + 1)A^{-1}$ for $n = 3$ and 4, and verify your guess for $n = 5$. (Inverses of tridiagonal matrices have the rank-1 form $\boldsymbol{uv}^{\mathrm{T}}$ above the diagonal.)

43. All **Pascal matrices** have determinant 1. If I subtract 1 from the n, n entry, why does the determinant become zero? (Use rule 3 or a cofactor.)

$$\det \begin{bmatrix} 1 & 1 & 1 & 1 \\ 1 & 2 & 3 & 4 \\ 1 & 3 & 6 & 10 \\ 1 & 4 & 10 & 20 \end{bmatrix} = 1 \text{ (known)} \qquad \det \begin{bmatrix} 1 & 1 & 1 & 1 \\ 1 & 2 & 3 & 4 \\ 1 & 3 & 6 & 10 \\ 1 & 4 & 10 & 19 \end{bmatrix} = \mathbf{0} \text{ (explain).}$$

4.4 APPLICATIONS OF DETERMINANTS

This section follows through on four major applications: *inverse of A, solving Ax = b, volumes of boxes*, and *pivots*. They are among the key computations in linear algebra (done by elimination). Determinants give formulas for the answers.

1. **Computation of A^{-1}.** The 2 by 2 case shows how cofactors go into A^{-1}:

$$\begin{bmatrix} a & b \\ c & d \end{bmatrix}^{-1} = \frac{1}{ad - bc} \begin{bmatrix} d & -b \\ -c & a \end{bmatrix} = \frac{1}{\det A} \begin{bmatrix} C_{11} & C_{21} \\ C_{12} & C_{22} \end{bmatrix}.$$

We are dividing by the determinant, and A is invertible exactly when $\det A$ is nonzero. The number $C_{11} = d$ is the cofactor of a. The number $C_{12} = -c$ is the cofactor of b (note the minus sign). That number C_{12} goes in row 2, column 1!

The row a, b times the column C_{11}, C_{12} produces $ad - bc$. This is the cofactor expansion of $\det A$. That is the clue we need: $\boldsymbol{A^{-1}}$ **divides the cofactors by det** $\boldsymbol{A}$.

Cofactor matrix **C is transposed** $\quad A^{-1} = \dfrac{C^{\mathrm{T}}}{\det A} \quad$ means $\quad (A^{-1})_{ij} = \dfrac{C_{ji}}{\det A}. \quad$ (1)

Our goal is to verify this formula for A^{-1}. We have to see why $AC^{\mathrm{T}} = (\det A)I$:

$$\begin{bmatrix} a_{11} & \cdots & a_{1n} \\ \vdots & & \vdots \\ a_{n1} & \cdots & a_{nn} \end{bmatrix} \begin{bmatrix} C_{11} & \cdots & C_{n1} \\ \vdots & & \vdots \\ C_{1n} & \cdots & C_{nn} \end{bmatrix} = \begin{bmatrix} \det A & \cdots & 0 \\ \vdots & & \vdots \\ 0 & \cdots & \det A \end{bmatrix}. \qquad (2)$$

With cofactors $C_{11}, \ldots, C_{1n}$ in the first *column* and not the first row, they multiply $a_{11}, \ldots, a_{1n}$ and give the diagonal entry $\det A$. Every row of A multiplies its cofactors (*the cofactor expansion*) to give the same answer $\det A$ on the diagonal.

The critical question is: *Why do we get zeros off the diagonal*? If we combine the entries a_{1j} from row 1 with the cofactors C_{2j} for row 2, why is the result zero?

$$\textbf{row 1 of A, row 2 of C} \qquad a_{11}C_{21} + a_{12}C_{22} + \cdots + a_{1n}C_{2n} = 0. \qquad (3)$$

The answer is: We are computing the determinant of a new matrix B, with a new row 2. The first row of A is copied into the second row of B. Then B has two equal rows, and $\det B = 0$. Equation (3) is the expansion of $\det B$ along its row 2, where B has exactly the same cofactors as A (because the second row is thrown away to find those cofactors). The remarkable matrix multiplication (2) is correct.

That multiplication $AC^{\mathrm{T}} = (\det A)I$ immediately gives A^{-1}. Remember that the cofactor from deleting row i and column j of A goes into *row j and column i* of C^{T}. Dividing by the number $\det A$ (if it is not zero!) gives $A^{-1} = C^{\mathrm{T}}/\det A$.

Example 1 The inverse of a sum matrix is a difference matrix:

$$A = \begin{bmatrix} 1 & 1 & 1 \\ 0 & 1 & 1 \\ 0 & 0 & 1 \end{bmatrix} \quad \text{has} \quad A^{-1} = \frac{C^{\mathrm{T}}}{\det A} = \begin{bmatrix} 1 & -1 & 0 \\ 0 & 1 & -1 \\ 0 & 0 & 1 \end{bmatrix}.$$

The minus signs enter because cofactors always include $(-1)^{i+j}$.

2. The Solution of $Ax = b$. The multiplication $x = A^{-1}b$ is just $C^{\mathrm{T}}b$ divided by $\det A$. There is a famous way in which to write the answer $(x_1, \ldots, x_n)$:

4C ***Cramer's rule***: The jth component of $x = A^{-1}b$ is the ratio

$$x_j = \frac{\det B_j}{\det A}, \quad \text{where} \quad B_j = \begin{bmatrix} a_{11} & a_{12} & \boldsymbol{b_1} & a_{1n} \\ \vdots & \vdots & \vdots & \vdots \\ a_{n1} & a_{n2} & \boldsymbol{b_n} & a_{nn} \end{bmatrix} \text{ has } b \text{ in column } j. \qquad (4)$$

Proof Expand det B_j in cofactors of its jth column (which is b). Since the cofactors ignore that column, det B_j is exactly the jth component in the product $C^{\mathrm{T}}b$:

$$\det B_j = b_1C_{1j} + b_2C_{2j} + \cdots + b_nC_{nj}.$$

Dividing this by det A gives x_j. Each component of x is a *ratio of two determinants*. That fact might have been recognized from Gaussian elimination, but it never was. ■

Example 2 The solution of

$$\begin{aligned} x_1 + 3x_2 &= 0 \\ 2x_1 + 4x_2 &= 6 \end{aligned}$$

has 0 and 6 in the first column for x_1 and in the second column for x_2:

$$x_1 = \frac{\begin{vmatrix} 0 & 3 \\ 6 & 4 \end{vmatrix}}{\begin{vmatrix} 1 & 3 \\ 2 & 4 \end{vmatrix}} = \frac{-18}{-2} = 9, \qquad x_2 = \frac{\begin{vmatrix} 1 & 0 \\ 2 & 6 \end{vmatrix}}{\begin{vmatrix} 1 & 3 \\ 2 & 4 \end{vmatrix}} = \frac{6}{-2} = -3.$$

The denominators are always det A. For 1000 equations Cramer's Rule would need 1001 determinants. To my dismay I found in a book called *Mathematics for the Millions* that Cramer's Rule was actually recommended (and elimination was thrown aside):

> To deal with a set involving the four variables u, v, w, z, we first have to eliminate one of them in each of three pairs to derive three equations in three variables and then proceed as for the three-fold left-hand set to derive values for two of them. The reader who does so as an exercise will begin to realize how formidably laborious the method of elimination becomes, when we have to deal with more than three variables. This consideration invites us to explore the possibility of a *speedier method* ...

The "speedier method" is Cramer's Rule! If the author planned to compute 1001 determinants, I would call it *Mathematics for the Millionaire*.

3. The Volume of a Box. The connection between the determinant and the volume is clearest when all angles are *right angles*—the edges are perpendicular, and the box is rectangular. Then the volume is the product of the edge lengths: *volume* $= \ell_1\ell_2\cdots\ell_n$.

We want to obtain the same $\ell_1\ell_2\cdots\ell_n$ from det A, *when the edges of that box are the rows of* A. With right angles, these rows are orthogonal and AA^{T} is diagonal:

Right-angled box
Orthogonal rows

$$AA^{\mathrm{T}} = \begin{bmatrix} \text{row } 1 \\ \vdots \\ \text{row } n \end{bmatrix} \begin{bmatrix} \mathrm{r} \\ \mathrm{o} \\ \mathrm{w} \\ 1 \end{bmatrix} \cdots \begin{bmatrix} \mathrm{r} \\ \mathrm{o} \\ \mathrm{w} \\ n \end{bmatrix} = \begin{bmatrix} \ell_1^2 & & 0 \\ & \ddots & \\ 0 & & \ell_n^2 \end{bmatrix}.$$

The ℓ_i are the lengths of the rows (the edges), and the zeros off the diagonal come because the rows are orthogonal. Using the product and transposing rules,

$$\textbf{Right-angle case} \qquad \ell_1^2 \ell_2^2 \cdots l_n^2 = \det(AA^{\mathrm{T}}) = (\det A)(\det A^{\mathrm{T}}) = (\det A)^2.$$

The square root of this equation says that ***the determinant equals the volume***. The *sign* of $\det A$ will indicate whether the edges form a "right-handed" set of coordinates, as in the usual x-y-z system, or a left-handed system like y-x-z.

If the angles are not 90°, the volume is not the product of the lengths. In the plane (Figure 4.2), the "volume" of a parallelogram equals the base ℓ times the height h. The vector $b - p$ of length h is the second row $b = (a_{21}, a_{22})$, minus its projection p onto the first row. The key point is this: By rule 5, $\det A$ is unchanged when a multiple of row 1 is subtracted from row 2. *We can change the parallelogram to a rectangle*, where it is already proved that volume = determinant.

In n dimensions, it takes longer to make each box rectangular, but the idea is the same. The volume and determinant are unchanged if we subtract from each row its projection onto the space spanned by the preceding rows—leaving a perpendicular "height vector" like pb. This Gram-Schmidt process produces orthogonal rows, with volume = determinant. So the same equality must have held for the original rows.

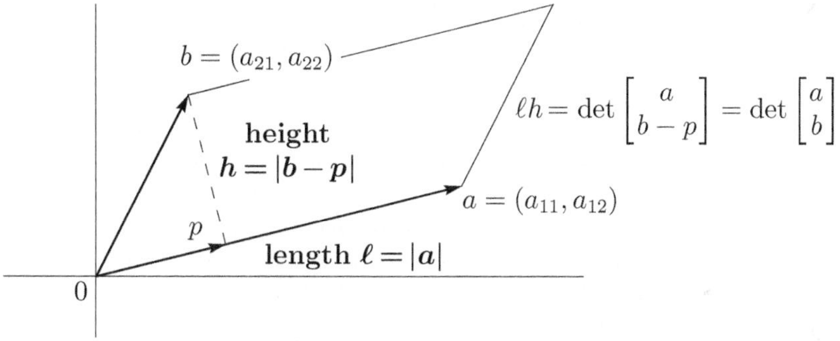

Figure 4.2 Volume (area) of the parallelogram $= \ell$ times $h = |\det A|$.

This completes the link between volumes and determinants, but it is worth coming back one more time to the simplest case. We know that

$$\det \begin{bmatrix} 1 & 0 \\ 0 & 1 \end{bmatrix} = 1, \qquad \det \begin{bmatrix} 1 & 0 \\ c & 1 \end{bmatrix} = 1.$$

These determinants give the volumes—or areas, since we are in two dimensions—drawn in Figure 4.3. The parallelogram has unit base and unit height; its area is also 1.

4. A Formula for the Pivots. We can finally discover when elimination is possible without row exchanges. The key observation is that the first k pivots are completely determined by the submatrix A_k in the upper left corner of A. *The remaining rows and*

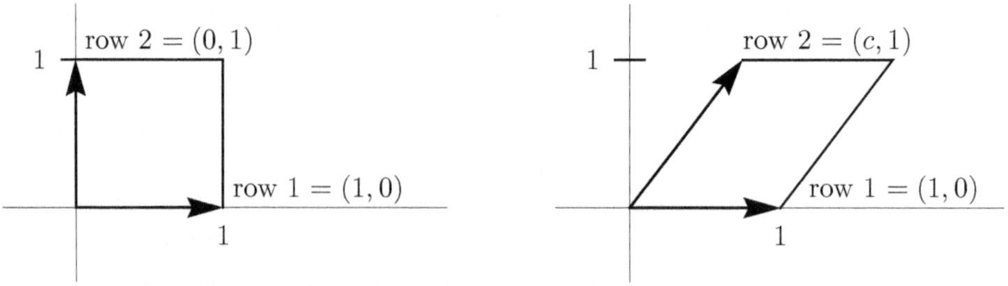

Figure 4.3 The areas of a unit square and a unit parallelogram are both 1.

columns of A have no effect on this corner of the problem:

Elimination on A includes elimination on A_2
$$A = \begin{bmatrix} \boldsymbol{a} & \boldsymbol{b} & e \\ \boldsymbol{c} & \boldsymbol{d} & f \\ g & h & i \end{bmatrix} \to \begin{bmatrix} \boldsymbol{a} & \boldsymbol{b} & e \\ \boldsymbol{0} & \boldsymbol{(ad-bc)/a} & (af-ec)/a \\ g & h & i \end{bmatrix}.$$

Certainly the first pivot depended only on the first row and column. The second pivot $(ad-bc)/a$ depends only on the 2 by 2 corner submatrix A_2. The rest of A does not enter until the third pivot. Actually it is not just the pivots, but the entire upper-left corners of L, D, and U, that are determined by the upper-left corner of A:

$$A = LDU = \begin{bmatrix} 1 & & \\ c/a & 1 & \\ * & * & 1 \end{bmatrix} \begin{bmatrix} a & & \\ & (ad-bc)/a & \\ & & * \end{bmatrix} \begin{bmatrix} 1 & b/a & * \\ & 1 & * \\ & & 1 \end{bmatrix}.$$

What we see in the first two rows and columns is exactly the factorization of the corner submatrix A_2. This is a general rule if there are no row exchanges:

4D If A is factored into LDU, the upper left corners satisfy $A_k = L_k D_k U_k$. For every k, the submatrix A_k is going through a Gaussian elimination of its own.

The proof is to see that this corner can be settled first, before even looking at other eliminations. Or use the laws for ***block multiplication***:

$$LDU = \begin{bmatrix} \boldsymbol{L_k} & 0 \\ B & C \end{bmatrix} \begin{bmatrix} \boldsymbol{D_k} & 0 \\ 0 & E \end{bmatrix} \begin{bmatrix} \boldsymbol{U_k} & F \\ 0 & G \end{bmatrix} = \begin{bmatrix} \boldsymbol{L_k D_k U_k} & L_k D_k F \\ B D_k U_k & B D_k F + CEG \end{bmatrix}.$$

Comparing the last matrix with A, the corner $L_k D_k U_k$ coincides with A_k. Then:

$$\det A_k = \det L_k \det D_k \det U_k = \det D_k = d_1 d_2 \cdots d_k.$$

The product of the first k pivots is the determinant of A_k. This is the same rule that we know already for the whole matrix. Since the determinant of A_{k-1} will be given by $d_1 d_2 \cdots d_{k-1}$, we can isolate each pivot d_k as a ***ratio of determinants***:

Formula for pivots
$$\frac{\det A_k}{\det A_{k-1}} = \frac{d_1 d_2 \cdots d_k}{d_1 d_2 \cdots d_{k-1}} = d_k. \tag{5}$$

In our example above, the second pivot was exactly this ratio $(ad-bc)/a$. It is the determinant of A_2 divided by the determinant of A_1. (By convention $\det A_0 = 1$, so that the first pivot is $a/1 = a$.) Multiplying together all the individual pivots, we recover

$$d_1 d_2 \cdots d_n = \frac{\det A_1}{\det A_0} \frac{\det A_2}{\det A_1} \cdots \frac{\det A_n}{\det A_{n-1}} = \frac{\det A_n}{\det A_0} = \det A.$$

From equation (5) we can finally read off the answer to our original question: ***The pivot entries are all nonzero whenever the numbers*** **$\det A_k$** ***are all nonzero:***

4E Elimination can be completed without row exchanges (so $P = I$ and $A = LU$), if and only if the leading submatrices $A_1, A_2, \ldots, A_n$ are all nonsingular.

That does it for determinants, except for an optional remark on property 2—the sign reversal on row exchanges. The ***determinant of a permutation matrix P*** was the only questionable point in the big formula. Independent of the particular row exchanges linking P to I, is the number of exchanges always even or always odd? If so, its determinant is well defined by rule 2 as either $+1$ or -1.

Starting from $(3, 2, 1)$, a single exchange of 3 and 1 would achieve the natural order $(1, 2, 3)$. So would an exchange of 3 and 2, then 3 and 1, and then 2 and 1. In both sequences, the number of exchanges is odd. The assertion is that *an even number of exchanges can never produce the natural order, beginning with* $(3, 2, 1)$.

Here is a proof. Look at each pair of numbers in the permutation, and let N count the pairs in which the larger number comes first. Certainly $N = 0$ for the natural order $(1, 2, 3)$. The order $(3, 2, 1)$ has $N = 3$ since all pairs $(3, 2)$, $(3, 1)$, and $(2, 1)$ are wrong. We will show that *every exchange alters N by an odd number*. Then to arrive at $N = 0$ (the natural order) takes a number of exchanges having the same evenness or oddness as N.

When neighbors are exchanged, N changes by $+1$ or -1. *Any exchange can be achieved by an odd number of exchanges of neighbors*. This will complete the proof; an odd number of odd numbers is odd. To exchange the first and fourth entries below, which happen to be 2 and 3, we use five exchanges (an odd number) of neighbors:

$$(\mathbf{2}, 1, 4, \mathbf{3}) \to (1, \mathbf{2}, 4, \mathbf{3}) \to (1, 4, \mathbf{2}, \mathbf{3}) \to (1, 4, \mathbf{3}, \mathbf{2}) \to (1, \mathbf{3}, 4, \mathbf{2}) \to (\mathbf{3}, 1, 4, \mathbf{2}).$$

We need $\ell - k$ exchanges of neighbors to move the entry in place k to place ℓ. Then $\ell - k - 1$ exchanges move the one originally in place ℓ (and now found in place $\ell - 1$) back down to place k. Since $(\ell - k) + (\ell - k - 1)$ is odd, the proof is complete. The determinant not only has all the properties found earlier, it even exists.

Problem Set 4.4

1. Find the determinant and all nine cofactors C_{ij} of this triangular matrix:

$$A = \begin{bmatrix} 1 & 2 & 3 \\ 0 & 4 & 0 \\ 0 & 0 & 5 \end{bmatrix}.$$

Form C^{T} and verify that $AC^{\mathrm{T}} = (\det A)I$. What is A^{-1}?

2. Use the cofactor matrix C to invert these symmetric matrices:

$$A = \begin{bmatrix} 2 & -1 & 0 \\ -1 & 2 & -1 \\ 0 & -1 & 2 \end{bmatrix} \quad \text{and} \quad B = \begin{bmatrix} 1 & 1 & 1 \\ 1 & 2 & 2 \\ 1 & 2 & 3 \end{bmatrix}.$$

3. Find x, y, and z by Cramer's Rule in equation (4):

$$\begin{aligned} ax + by &= 1 \\ cx + dy &= 0 \end{aligned} \quad \text{and} \quad \begin{aligned} x + 4y - z &= 1 \\ x + y + z &= 0 \\ 2x \qquad + 3z &= 0. \end{aligned}$$

4. (a) Find the determinant when a vector x replaces column j of the identity (consider $x_j = 0$ as a separate case):

$$\text{if} \quad M = \begin{bmatrix} 1 & & x_1 & & \\ & 1 & \cdot & & \\ & & x_j & & \\ & & \cdot & 1 & \\ & & x_n & & 1 \end{bmatrix} \quad \text{then } \det M = \underline{\quad}.$$

(b) If $Ax = b$, show that AM is the matrix B_j in equation (4), with b in column j.

(c) Derive *Cramer's rule* by taking determinants in $AM = B_j$.

5. (a) Draw the triangle with vertices $A = (2, 2)$, $B = (-1, 3)$, and $C = (0, 0)$. By regarding it as half of a parallelogram, explain why its area equals

$$\text{area}\,(ABC) = \frac{1}{2} \det \begin{bmatrix} 2 & 2 \\ -1 & 3 \end{bmatrix}.$$

(b) Move the third vertex to $C = (1, -4)$ and justify the formula

$$\text{area}\,(ABC) = \frac{1}{2} \det \begin{bmatrix} x_1 & y_1 & 1 \\ x_2 & y_2 & 1 \\ x_3 & y_3 & 1 \end{bmatrix} = \frac{1}{2} \det \begin{bmatrix} 2 & 2 & 1 \\ -1 & 3 & 1 \\ 1 & -4 & 1 \end{bmatrix}.$$

Hint: Subtracting the last row from each of the others leaves

$$\det \begin{bmatrix} 2 & 2 & 1 \\ -1 & 3 & 1 \\ 1 & -4 & 1 \end{bmatrix} = \det \begin{bmatrix} 1 & 6 & 0 \\ -2 & 7 & 0 \\ 1 & -4 & 1 \end{bmatrix} = \det \begin{bmatrix} 1 & 6 \\ -2 & 7 \end{bmatrix}.$$

Sketch $A' = (1, 6)$, $B' = (-2, 7)$, $C' = (0, 0)$ and their relation to A, B, C.

6. Explain in terms of volumes why $\det 3A = 3^n \det A$ for an n by n matrix A.

7. Predict in advance, and confirm by elimination, the pivot entries of

$$A = \begin{bmatrix} 2 & 1 & 2 \\ 4 & 5 & 0 \\ 2 & 7 & 0 \end{bmatrix} \quad \text{and} \quad B = \begin{bmatrix} 2 & 1 & 2 \\ 4 & 5 & 3 \\ 2 & 7 & 0 \end{bmatrix}.$$

8. Find all the odd permutations of the numbers $\{1, 2, 3, 4\}$. They come from an odd number of exchanges and lead to $\det P = -1$.

9. Suppose the permutation P takes $(1, 2, 3, 4, 5)$ to $(5, 4, 1, 2, 3)$.

(a) What does P^2 do to $(1, 2, 3, 4, 5)$?

(b) What does P^{-1} do to $(1, 2, 3, 4, 5)$?

10. If P is an odd permutation, explain why P^2 is even but P^{-1} is odd.

11. Prove that if you keep multiplying A by the same permutation matrix P, the first row eventually comes back to its original place.

12. If A is a 5 by 5 matrix with all $|a_{ij}| \le 1$, then $\det A \le$ __. Volumes or the big formula or pivots should give some upper bound on the determinant.

Problems 13–17 are about Cramer's Rule for $x = A^{-1}b$.

13. Solve these linear equations by Cramer's Rule $x_j = \det B_j / \det A$:

$$\text{(a)}\quad \begin{aligned} 2x_1 + 5x_2 &= 1 \\ x_1 + 4x_2 &= 2. \end{aligned} \qquad \text{(b)}\quad \begin{aligned} 2x_1 + x_2 &= 1 \\ x_1 + 2x_2 + x_3 &= 0 \\ x_2 + 2x_3 &= 0. \end{aligned}$$

14. Use Cramer's Rule to solve for y (only). Call the 3 by 3 determinant D:

$$\text{(a)}\quad \begin{aligned} ax + by &= 1 \\ cx + dy &= 0. \end{aligned} \qquad \text{(b)}\quad \begin{aligned} ax + by + cz &= 1 \\ dx + ey + fz &= 0 \\ gx + hy + iz &= 0. \end{aligned}$$

15. Cramer's Rule breaks down when $\det A = 0$. Example (a) has no solution, whereas (b) has infinitely many. What are the ratios $x_j = \det B_j / \det A$?

$$\text{(a)}\quad \begin{aligned} 2x_1 + 3x_2 &= 1 \\ 4x_1 + 6x_2 &= 1. \end{aligned} \quad \text{(parallel lines)} \qquad \text{(b)}\quad \begin{aligned} 2x_1 + 3x_2 &= 1 \\ 4x_1 + 6x_2 &= 2. \end{aligned} \quad \text{(same line)}$$

16. *Quick proof of Cramer's rule.* The determinant is a linear function of column 1. It is zero if two columns are equal. When $\boldsymbol{b} = A\boldsymbol{x} = x_1\boldsymbol{a}_1 + x_2\boldsymbol{a}_2 + x_3\boldsymbol{a}_3$ goes into column 1 to produce B_1, the determinant is

$$\begin{vmatrix} \boldsymbol{b} & \boldsymbol{a}_2 & \boldsymbol{a}_3 \end{vmatrix} = \begin{vmatrix} x_1\boldsymbol{a}_1 + x_2\boldsymbol{a}_2 + x_3\boldsymbol{a}_3 & \boldsymbol{a}_2 & \boldsymbol{a}_3 \end{vmatrix} = x_1 \begin{vmatrix} \boldsymbol{a}_1 & \boldsymbol{a}_2 & \boldsymbol{a}_3 \end{vmatrix} = x_1 \det A.$$

(a) What formula for x_1 comes from left side = right side?
(b) What steps lead to the middle equation?

17. If the right side b is the *last column* of A, solve the 3 by 3 system $Ax = b$. Explain how each determinant in Cramer's Rule leads to your solution x.

Problems 18–26 are about $A^{-1} = C^{\mathrm{T}} / \det A$. Remember to transpose C.

18. Find A^{-1} from the cofactor formula $C^{\mathrm{T}} / \det A$. Use symmetry in part (b):

$$\text{(a)}\ A = \begin{bmatrix} 1 & 2 & 0 \\ 0 & 3 & 0 \\ 0 & 4 & 1 \end{bmatrix}. \qquad \text{(b)}\ A = \begin{bmatrix} 2 & -1 & 0 \\ -1 & 2 & -1 \\ 0 & -1 & 2 \end{bmatrix}.$$

19. If all the cofactors are zero, how do you know that A has no inverse? If none of the cofactors are zero, is A sure to be invertible?

20. Find the cofactors of A and multiply AC^{T} to find $\det A$:

$$A = \begin{bmatrix} 1 & 1 & 4 \\ 1 & 2 & 2 \\ 1 & 2 & 5 \end{bmatrix}, \qquad C = \begin{bmatrix} 6 & -3 & 0 \\ \cdot & \cdot & \cdot \\ \cdot & \cdot & \cdot \end{bmatrix}, \quad \text{and} \quad AC^{\mathrm{T}} = \underline{\qquad}.$$

If you change that corner entry from 4 to 100, why is $\det A$ unchanged?

21. Suppose $\det A = 1$ and you know all the cofactors. How can you find A?

22. From the formula $AC^{\mathrm{T}} = (\det A)I$ show that $\det C = (\det A)^{n-1}$.

23. (For professors only) If you know all 16 cofactors of a 4 by 4 invertible matrix A, how would you find A?

24. If all entries of A are integers, and $\det A = 1$ or -1, prove that all entries of A^{-1} are integers. Give a 2 by 2 example.

25. L is lower triangular and S is symmetric. Assume they are invertible:

$$L = \begin{bmatrix} a & 0 & 0 \\ b & c & 0 \\ d & e & f \end{bmatrix} \qquad S = \begin{bmatrix} a & b & d \\ b & c & e \\ d & e & f \end{bmatrix}.$$

(a) Which three cofactors of L are zero? Then L^{-1} is lower triangular.
(b) Which three pairs of cofactors of S are equal? Then S^{-1} is symmetric.

26. For $n = 5$ the matrix C contains ___ cofactors and each 4 by 4 cofactor contains ___ terms and each term needs ___ multiplications. Compare with $5^3 = 125$ for the Gauss–Jordan computation of A^{-1}.

Problems 27–36 are about area and volume by determinants.

27. (a) Find the area of the parallelogram with edges $v = (3, 2)$ and $w = (1, 4)$.
(b) Find the area of the triangle with sides v, w, and $v + w$. Draw it.
(c) Find the area of the triangle with sides v, w, and $w - v$. Draw it.

28. A box has edges from $(0, 0, 0)$ to $(3, 1, 1)$, $(1, 3, 1)$, and $(1, 1, 3)$. Find its volume and also find the area of each parallelogram face.

29. (a) The corners of a triangle are $(2, 1)$, $(3, 4)$, and $(0, 5)$. What is the area?
(b) A new corner at $(-1, 0)$ makes it lopsided (four sides). Find the area.

30. The parallelogram with sides $(2, 1)$ and $(2, 3)$ has the same area as the parallelogram with sides $(2, 2)$ and $(1, 3)$. Find those areas from 2 by 2 determinants and say why they must be equal. (I can't see why from a picture. Please write to me if you do.)

31. The Hadamard matrix H has orthogonal rows. The box is a hypercube!

$$\text{What is } \det H = \begin{vmatrix} 1 & 1 & 1 & 1 \\ 1 & 1 & -1 & -1 \\ 1 & -1 & -1 & 1 \\ 1 & -1 & 1 & -1 \end{vmatrix} = \text{volume of a hypercube in } \mathbf{R}^4?$$

32. If the columns of a 4 by 4 matrix have lengths L_1, L_2, L_3, L_4, what is the largest possible value for the determinant (based on volume)? If all entries are 1 or -1, what are those lengths and the maximum determinant?

33. Show by a picture how a rectangle with area x_1y_2 minus a rectangle with area x_2y_1 produces the area $x_1y_2 - x_2y_1$ of a parallelogram.

34. When the edge vectors $\boldsymbol{a}, \boldsymbol{b}, \boldsymbol{c}$ are perpendicular, the volume of the box is $\|\boldsymbol{a}\|$ times $\|\boldsymbol{b}\|$ times $\|\boldsymbol{c}\|$. The matrix $A^{\mathrm{T}}A$ is _______. Find $\det A^{\mathrm{T}}A$ and $\det A$.

35. An n-dimensional cube has how many corners? How many edges? How many $(n-1)$-dimensional faces? The n-cube whose edges are the rows of $2I$ has volume ______. A hypercube computer has parallel processors at the corners with connections along the edges.

36. The triangle with corners $(0,0)$, $(1,0)$, $(0,1)$ has area $\frac{1}{2}$. The pyramid with four corners $(0,0,0)$, $(1,0,0)$, $(0,1,0)$, $(0,0,1)$ has volume ______. The pyramid in $\mathbf{R}^4$ with five corners at $(0,0,0,0)$ and the rows of I has what volume?

Problems 37–40 are about areas dA and volumes dV in calculus.

37. Polar coordinates satisfy $x = r\cos\theta$ and $y = r\sin\theta$. Polar area $J\,dr\,d\theta$ includes J:

$$J = \begin{vmatrix} \partial x/\partial r & \partial x/\partial\theta \\ \partial y/\partial r & \partial y/\partial\theta \end{vmatrix} = \begin{vmatrix} \cos\theta & -r\sin\theta \\ \sin\theta & r\cos\theta \end{vmatrix}.$$

The two columns are orthogonal. Their lengths are ______. Thus $J =$ ______.

38. Spherical coordinates ρ, ϕ, θ give $x = \rho\sin\phi\cos\theta$, $y = \rho\sin\phi\sin\theta$, $z = \rho\cos\phi$. Find the Jacobian matrix of 9 partial derivatives: $\partial x/\partial\rho$, $\partial x/\partial\phi$, $\partial x/\partial\theta$ are in row 1. Simplify its determinant to $J = \rho^2\sin\phi$. Then $dV = \rho^2\sin\phi\,d\rho\,d\phi\,d\theta$.

39. The matrix that connects r, θ to x, y is in Problem 37. Invert that matrix:

$$J^{-1} = \begin{vmatrix} \partial r/\partial x & \partial r/\partial y \\ \partial\theta/\partial x & \partial\theta/\partial y \end{vmatrix} = \begin{vmatrix} \cos\theta & ? \\ ? & ? \end{vmatrix} = ?$$

It is surprising that $\partial r/\partial x = \partial x/\partial r$. The product $JJ^{-1} = I$ gives the chain rule

$$\frac{\partial x}{\partial x} = \frac{\partial x}{\partial r}\frac{\partial r}{\partial x} + \frac{\partial x}{\partial\theta}\frac{\partial\theta}{\partial x} = 1.$$

40. The triangle with corners $(0,0)$, $(6,0)$, and $(1,4)$ has area ______. When you rotate it by $\theta = 60°$ the area is ______. The rotation matrix has

$$\text{determinant} = \begin{vmatrix} \cos\theta & -\sin\theta \\ \sin\theta & \cos\theta \end{vmatrix} = \begin{vmatrix} \frac{1}{2} & ? \\ ? & ? \end{vmatrix} = ?$$

41. Let $P = (1,0,-1)$, $Q = (1,1,1)$, and $R = (2,2,1)$. Choose S so that $PQRS$ is a parallelogram, and compute its area. Choose T, U, V so that $OPQRSTUV$ is a tilted box, and compute its volume.

42. Suppose (x,y,z), $(1,1,0)$, and $(1,2,1)$ lie on a plane through the origin. What determinant is zero? What equation does this give for the plane?

43. Suppose (x,y,z) is a linear combination of $(2,3,1)$ and $(1,2,3)$. What determinant is zero? What equation does this give for the plane of all combinations?

44. If $Ax = (1,0,\ldots,0)$ show how Cramer's Rule gives $x =$ *first column of* A^{-1}.

45. (VISA to AVIS) This takes an odd number of exchanges (IVSA, AVSI, AVIS). Count the pairs of letters in VISA and AVIS that are reversed from alphabetical order. The difference should be odd.

Chapter 4 Review Exercises

4.1 Find the determinants of

$$\begin{bmatrix} 1 & 1 & 1 & 1 \\ 1 & 1 & 1 & 2 \\ 1 & 1 & 3 & 1 \\ 1 & 4 & 1 & 1 \end{bmatrix} \quad \text{and} \quad \begin{bmatrix} 2 & -1 & 0 & -1 \\ -1 & 2 & -1 & 0 \\ 0 & -1 & 2 & -1 \\ -1 & 0 & -1 & 2 \end{bmatrix}.$$

4.2 If $B = M^{-1}AM$, why is $\det B = \det A$? Show also that $\det A^{-1}B = 1$.

4.3 Starting with A, multiply its first row by 3 to produce B, and subtract the first row of B from the second to produce C. How is $\det C$ related to $\det A$?

4.4 Solve $3u + 2v = 7$, $4u + 3v = 11$ by Cramer's rule.

4.5 If the entries of A and A^{-1} are all integers, how do you know that both determinants are 1 or -1? *Hint*: What is $\det A$ times $\det A^{-1}$?

4.6 Find all the cofactors, and the inverse or the nullspace, of

$$\begin{bmatrix} 3 & 5 \\ 6 & 9 \end{bmatrix}, \quad \begin{bmatrix} \cos\theta & -\sin\theta \\ \sin\theta & \cos\theta \end{bmatrix}, \quad \text{and} \quad \begin{bmatrix} a & b \\ a & b \end{bmatrix}.$$

4.7 What is the volume of the parallelepiped with four of its vertices at $(0, 0, 0)$, $(-1, 2, 2)$, $(2, -1, 2)$, and $(2, 2, -1)$? Where are the other four vertices?

4.8 How many terms are in the expansion of a 5 by 5 determinant, and how many are sure to be zero if $a_{21} = 0$?

4.9 If P_1 is an even permutation matrix and P_2 is odd, deduce from $P_1 + P_2 = P_1(P_1{}^{\mathrm{T}} + P_2{}^{\mathrm{T}})P_2$ that $\det(P_1 + P_2) = 0$.

4.10 If $\det A > 0$, show that A can be connected to I by a continuous chain of matrices $A(t)$ all with positive determinants. (The straight path $A(t) = A + t(I - A)$ does go from $A(0) = A$ to $A(1) = I$, but in between $A(t)$ might be singular. The problem is not so easy, and solutions are welcomed by the author.)

4.11 Explain why the point (x, y) is on the line through $(2, 8)$ and $(4, 7)$ if

$$\det \begin{bmatrix} x & y & 1 \\ 2 & 8 & 1 \\ 4 & 7 & 1 \end{bmatrix} = 0, \qquad \text{or} \qquad x + 2y - 18 = 0.$$

4.12 In analogy with the previous exercise, what is the equation for (x, y, z) to be on the plane through $(2, 0, 0)$, $(0, 2, 0)$, and $(0, 0, 4)$? It involves a 4 by 4 determinant.

4.13 If the points (x, y, z), $(2, 1, 0)$, and $(1, 1, 1)$ lie on a plane through the origin, what determinant is zero? Are the vectors $(1, 0, -1)$, $(2, 1, 0)$, $(1, 1, 1)$ independent?

4.14 If every row of A has either a single $+1$, or a single -1, or one of each (and is otherwise zero), show that $\det A = 1$ or -1 or 0.

4.15 If $C = \begin{bmatrix} a & b \\ c & d \end{bmatrix}$ and $D = \begin{bmatrix} u & v \\ w & z \end{bmatrix}$, then $CD = -DC$ yields 4 equations $Ax = 0$:

$$CD + DC = 0 \qquad \text{is} \qquad \begin{bmatrix} 2a & c & b & 0 \\ b & a+d & 0 & b \\ c & 0 & a+d & c \\ 0 & c & b & 2d \end{bmatrix} \begin{bmatrix} u \\ v \\ w \\ z \end{bmatrix} = \begin{bmatrix} 0 \\ 0 \\ 0 \\ 0 \end{bmatrix}.$$

(a) Show that $\det A = 0$ if $a + d = 0$. Solve for u, v, w, z, the entries of D.
(b) Show that $\det A = 0$ if $ad = bc$ (so C is singular).

In all other cases, $CD = -DC$ is only possible with $D =$ zero matrix.

4.16 The circular shift permutes $(1, 2, \ldots, n)$ into $(2, 3, \ldots, 1)$. What is the corresponding permutation matrix P, and (depending on n) what is its determinant?

4.17 Find the determinant of $A =$ eye(5) + ones(5) and if possible eye(n) + ones(n).

Chapter

5 Eigenvalues and Eigenvectors

5.1 INTRODUCTION

This chapter begins the "second half" of linear algebra. The first half was about $Ax = b$. The new problem $Ax = \lambda x$ will still be solved by simplifying a matrix—making it diagonal if possible. *The basic step is no longer to subtract a multiple of one row from another.* Elimination changes the eigenvalues, which we don't want.

Determinants give a transition from $Ax = b$ to $Ax = \lambda x$. In both cases the determinant leads to a "formal solution": to Cramer's rule for $x = A^{-1}b$, and to the polynomial $\det(A - \lambda I)$, whose roots will be the eigenvalues. (All matrices are now square; the eigenvalues of a rectangular matrix make no more sense than its determinant.) The determinant can actually be used if $n = 2$ or 3. For large n, computing λ is more difficult than solving $Ax = b$.

The first step is to understand how eigenvalues can be useful. One of their applications is to ordinary differential equations. We shall not assume that the reader is an expert on differential equations! If you can differentiate x^n, $\sin x$, and e^x, you know enough. As a specific example, consider the coupled pair of equations

$$\begin{aligned} \frac{dv}{dt} &= 4v - 5w, \quad v = 8 \quad \text{at} \quad t = 0, \\ \frac{dw}{dt} &= 2v - 3w, \quad w = 5 \quad \text{at} \quad t = 0. \end{aligned} \tag{1}$$

This is an ***initial-value problem***. The unknown is specified at time $t = 0$ by the given initial values 8 and 5. The problem is to find $v(t)$ and $w(t)$ for later times $t > 0$.

It is easy to write the system in matrix form. Let the unknown vector be $u(t)$, with initial value $u(0)$. The coefficient matrix is A:

Vector unknown $$u(t) = \begin{bmatrix} v(t) \\ w(t) \end{bmatrix}, \quad u(0) = \begin{bmatrix} 8 \\ 5 \end{bmatrix}, \quad A = \begin{bmatrix} 4 & -5 \\ 2 & -3 \end{bmatrix}.$$

The two coupled equations become the vector equation we want:

Matrix form $$\frac{du}{dt} = Au \quad \text{with} \quad u = u(0) \text{ at } t = 0. \tag{2}$$

This is the basic statement of the problem. Note that it is a first-order equation—no higher derivatives appear—and it is *linear* in the unknowns. It also has *constant coefficients*; the matrix A is independent of time.

How do we find $u(t)$? If there were only one unknown instead of two, that question would be easy to answer. We would have a scalar instead of a vector equation:

$$\textbf{Single equation} \qquad \frac{du}{dt} = au \quad \text{with} \quad u = u(0) \text{ at } t = 0. \tag{3}$$

The solution to this equation is the one thing you need to know:

$$\textbf{Pure exponential} \qquad u(t) = e^{at}u(0). \tag{4}$$

At the initial time $t = 0$, u equals $u(0)$ because $e^0 = 1$. The derivative of e^{at} has the required factor a, so that $du/dt = au$. Thus the initial condition and the equation are both satisfied.

Notice the behavior of u for large times. The equation is unstable if $a > 0$, neutrally stable if $a = 0$, or stable if $a < 0$; the factor e^{at} approaches infinity, remains bounded, or goes to zero. If a were a complex number, $a = \alpha + i\beta$, then the same tests would be applied to the real part α. The complex part produces oscillations $e^{i\beta t} = \cos\beta t + i\sin\beta t$. Decay or growth is governed by the factor $e^{\alpha t}$.

So much for a single equation. We shall take a direct approach to systems, and look for solutions with the *same exponential dependence on t* just found in the scalar case:

$$\begin{aligned} v(t) &= e^{\lambda t}y \\ w(t) &= e^{\lambda t}z \end{aligned} \tag{5}$$

or in vector notation

$$u(t) = e^{\lambda t}x. \tag{6}$$

This is the whole key to differential equations $du/dt = Au$: ***Look for pure exponential solutions***. Substituting $v = e^{\lambda t}y$ and $w = e^{\lambda t}z$ into the equation, we find

$$\begin{aligned} \lambda e^{\lambda t}y &= 4e^{\lambda t}y - 5e^{\lambda t}z \\ \lambda e^{\lambda t}z &= 2e^{\lambda t}y - 3e^{\lambda t}z. \end{aligned}$$

The factor $e^{\lambda t}$ is common to every term, and can be removed. This cancellation is the reason for assuming the same exponent λ for both unknowns; it leaves

$$\textbf{Eigenvalue problem} \qquad \begin{aligned} 4y - 5z &= \lambda y \\ 2y - 3z &= \lambda z. \end{aligned} \tag{7}$$

That is the eigenvalue equation. In matrix form it is $Ax = \lambda x$. You can see it again if we use $u = e^{\lambda t}x$—a number $e^{\lambda t}$ that grows or decays times a fixed vector x. ***Substituting into $du/dt = Au$ gives $\lambda e^{\lambda t}x = Ae^{\lambda t}x$. The cancellation of $e^{\lambda t}$ produces***

$$\textbf{Eigenvalue equation} \qquad Ax = \lambda x. \tag{8}$$

Now we have the fundamental equation of this chapter. It involves two unknowns λ and x. It is an algebra problem, and differential equations can be forgotten! The number λ (lambda) is an ***eigenvalue*** of the matrix A, and the vector x is the associated ***eigenvector***. Our goal is to find the eigenvalues and eigenvectors, λ's and x's, and to use them.

The Solutions of $Ax = \lambda x$

Notice that $Ax = \lambda x$ is a nonlinear equation; λ multiplies x. If we could discover λ, then the equation for x would be linear. In fact we could write $\lambda I x$ in place of λx, and bring this term over to the left side:

$$(A - \lambda I)x = 0. \tag{9}$$

The identity matrix keeps matrices and vectors straight; the equation $(A - \lambda)x = 0$ is shorter, but mixed up. This is the key to the problem:

The vector x is in the nullspace of $A - \lambda I$.
The number λ is chosen so that $A - \lambda I$ has a nullspace.

Of course every matrix has a nullspace. It was ridiculous to suggest otherwise, but you see the point. We want a *nonzero* eigenvector x. The vector $x = 0$ always satisfies $Ax = \lambda x$, but it is useless in solving differential equations. The goal is to build $u(t)$ out of exponentials $e^{\lambda t}x$, and *we are interested only in those particular values λ for which there is a nonzero eigenvector x*. To be of any use, the nullspace of $A - \lambda I$ must contain vectors other than zero. In short, $A - \lambda I$ ***must be singular***.

For this, the determinant gives a conclusive test.

5A The number λ is an eigenvalue of A if and only if $A - \lambda I$ is singular:

$$\det(A - \lambda I) = 0. \tag{10}$$

This is the characteristic equation. Each λ is associated with eigenvectors x:

$$(A - \lambda I)x = 0 \quad \text{or} \quad Ax = \lambda x. \tag{11}$$

In our example, we shift A by λI to make it singular:

$$\textbf{Subtract } \boldsymbol{\lambda I} \qquad A - \lambda I = \begin{bmatrix} 4-\lambda & -5 \\ 2 & -3-\lambda \end{bmatrix}.$$

Note that λ is subtracted only from the main diagonal (because it multiplies I).

$$\textbf{Determinant} \qquad |A - \lambda I| = (4-\lambda)(-3-\lambda) + 10 \quad \text{or} \quad \lambda^2 - \lambda - 2.$$

This is the *characteristic polynomial.* Its roots, where the determinant is zero, are the eigenvalues. They come from the general formula for the roots of a quadratic, or from factoring into $\lambda^2 - \lambda - 2 = (\lambda + 1)(\lambda - 2)$. That is zero if $\lambda = -1$ or $\lambda = 2$, as the general formula confirms:

$$\textbf{Eigenvalues} \qquad \lambda = \frac{-b \pm \sqrt{b^2-4ac}}{2a} = \frac{1 \pm \sqrt{9}}{2} = -1 \text{ and } 2.$$

There are two eigenvalues, because a quadratic has two roots. Every 2 by 2 matrix $A - \lambda I$ has λ^2 (and no higher power of λ) in its determinant.

The values $\lambda = -1$ and $\lambda = 2$ lead to a solution of $Ax = \lambda x$ or $(A - \lambda I)x = 0$. A matrix with zero determinant is singular, so there must be nonzero vectors x in its nullspace. In fact the nullspace contains a whole *line* of eigenvectors; it is a subspace!

$$\lambda_1 = -1: \qquad (A - \lambda_1 I)x = \begin{bmatrix} 5 & -5 \\ 2 & -2 \end{bmatrix} \begin{bmatrix} y \\ z \end{bmatrix} = \begin{bmatrix} 0 \\ 0 \end{bmatrix}.$$

The solution (the first eigenvector) is any nonzero multiple of x_1:

$$\textbf{Eigenvector for } \boldsymbol{\lambda_1} \qquad x_1 = \begin{bmatrix} 1 \\ 1 \end{bmatrix}.$$

The computation for λ_2 is done separately:

$$\lambda_2 = 2: \qquad (A - \lambda_2 I)x = \begin{bmatrix} 2 & -5 \\ 2 & -5 \end{bmatrix} \begin{bmatrix} y \\ z \end{bmatrix} = \begin{bmatrix} 0 \\ 0 \end{bmatrix}.$$

The second eigenvector is any nonzero multiple of x_2:

$$\textbf{Eigenvector for } \boldsymbol{\lambda_2} \qquad x_2 = \begin{bmatrix} 5 \\ 2 \end{bmatrix}.$$

You might notice that the columns of $A - \lambda_1 I$ give x_2, and the columns of $A - \lambda_2 I$ are multiples of x_1. This is special (and useful) for 2 by 2 matrices.

In the 3 by 3 case, I often set a component of x equal to 1 and solve $(A - \lambda I)x = 0$ for the other components. Of course if x is an eigenvector then so is $7x$ and so is $-x$. All vectors in the nullspace of $A - \lambda I$ (which we call the *eigenspace*) will satisfy $Ax = \lambda x$. In our example the eigenspaces are the lines through $x_1 = (1, 1)$ and $x_2 = (5, 2)$.

Before going back to the application (the differential equation), we emphasize the steps in solving $Ax = \lambda x$:

1. ***Compute the determinant of $A - \lambda I$.*** With λ subtracted along the diagonal, this determinant is a polynomial of degree n. It starts with $(-\lambda)^n$.
2. ***Find the roots of this polynomial.*** The n roots are the eigenvalues of A.
3. ***For each eigenvalue solve the equation $(A - \lambda I)x = 0$.*** Since the determinant is zero, there are solutions other than $x = 0$. Those are the eigenvectors.

In the differential equation, this produces the special solutions $u = e^{\lambda t}x$. They are the *pure exponential solutions* to $du/dt = Au$. Notice e^{-t} and e^{2t}:

$$u(t) = e^{\lambda_1 t}x_1 = e^{-t}\begin{bmatrix} 1 \\ 1 \end{bmatrix} \qquad \text{and} \qquad u(t) = e^{\lambda_2 t}x_2 = e^{2t}\begin{bmatrix} 5 \\ 2 \end{bmatrix}.$$

These two special solutions give the complete solution. They can be multiplied by any numbers c_1 and c_2, and they can be added together. When u_1 and u_2 satisfy the linear equation $du/dt = Au$, so does their sum $u_1 + u_2$:

$$\textbf{Complete solution} \qquad u(t) = c_1 e^{\lambda_1 t} x_1 + c_2 e^{\lambda_2 t} x_2 \tag{12}$$

This is ***superposition***, and it applies to differential equations (homogeneous and linear) just as it applied to matrix equations $Ax = 0$. The nullspace is always a subspace, and combinations of solutions are still solutions.

Now we have two free parameters c_1 and c_2, and it is reasonable to hope that they can be chosen to satisfy the initial condition $u = u(0)$ at $t = 0$:

$$\textbf{Initial condition} \qquad c_1 x_1 + c_2 x_2 = u(0) \quad \text{or} \quad \begin{bmatrix} 1 & 5 \\ 1 & 2 \end{bmatrix} \begin{bmatrix} c_1 \\ c_2 \end{bmatrix} = \begin{bmatrix} 8 \\ 5 \end{bmatrix}. \tag{13}$$

The constants are $c_1 = 3$ and $c_2 = 1$, and ***the solution to the original equation is***

$$u(t) = 3e^{-t} \begin{bmatrix} 1 \\ 1 \end{bmatrix} + e^{2t} \begin{bmatrix} 5 \\ 2 \end{bmatrix}. \tag{14}$$

Writing the two components separately, we have $v(0) = 8$ and $w(0) = 5$:

$$\textbf{Solution} \qquad v(t) = 3e^{-t} + 5e^{2t}, \qquad w(t) = 3e^{-t} + 2e^{2t}.$$

The key was in the eigenvalues λ and eigenvectors x. Eigenvalues are important in themselves, and not just part of a trick for finding u. Probably the homeliest example is that of soldiers going over a bridge.* Traditionally, they stop marching and just walk across. If they happen to march at a frequency equal to one of the eigenvalues of the bridge, it would begin to oscillate. (Just as a child's swing does; you soon notice the natural frequency of a swing, and by matching it you make the swing go higher.) An engineer tries to keep the natural frequencies of his bridge or rocket away from those of the wind or the sloshing of fuel. And at the other extreme, a stockbroker spends his life trying to get in line with the natural frequencies of the market. The eigenvalues are the most important feature of practically any dynamical system.

Summary and Examples

To summarize, this introduction has shown how λ and x appear naturally and automatically when solving $du/dt = Au$. Such an equation has *pure exponential solutions* $u = e^{\lambda t}x$; the eigenvalue gives the rate of growth or decay, and the eigenvector x develops at this rate. The other solutions will be *mixtures* of these pure solutions, and the mixture is adjusted to fit the initial conditions.

The key equation was $Ax = \lambda x$. Most vectors x will not satisfy such an equation. They change direction when multiplied by A, so that Ax is not a multiple of x. This means that ***only certain special numbers λ are eigenvalues, and only certain special vectors x are eigenvectors***. We can watch the behavior of each eigenvector, and then

* One which I never really believed—but a bridge did crash this way in 1831.

combine these "normal modes" to find the solution. To say the same thing in another way, *the underlying matrix can be diagonalized.*

The diagonalization in Section 5.2 will be applied to difference equations, Fibonacci numbers, and Markov processes, and also to differential equations. In every example, we start by computing the eigenvalues and eigenvectors; there is no shortcut to avoid that. Symmetric matrices are especially easy. "Defective matrices" lack a full set of eigenvectors, so they are not diagonalizable. Certainly they have to be discussed, but we will not allow them to take over the book.

We start with examples of particularly good matrices.

Example 1 Everything is clear when A is a ***diagonal matrix***:

$$A = \begin{bmatrix} 3 & 0 \\ 0 & 2 \end{bmatrix} \quad \text{has} \quad \lambda_1 = 3 \quad \text{with} \quad x_1 = \begin{bmatrix} 1 \\ 0 \end{bmatrix}, \quad \lambda_2 = 2 \quad \text{with} \quad x_2 = \begin{bmatrix} 0 \\ 1 \end{bmatrix}.$$

On each eigenvector A acts like a multiple of the identity: $Ax_1 = 3x_1$ and $Ax_2 = 2x_2$. Other vectors like $x = (1, 5)$ are mixtures $x_1 + 5x_2$ of the two eigenvectors, and when A multiplies x_1 and x_2 it produces the eigenvalues $\lambda_1 = 3$ and $\lambda_2 = 2$:

$$A \quad \text{times} \quad x_1 + 5x_2 \quad \text{is} \quad 3x_1 + 10x_2 = \begin{bmatrix} 3 \\ 10 \end{bmatrix}.$$

This is Ax for a typical vector x—not an eigenvector. But the action of A is determined by its eigenvectors and eigenvalues.

Example 2 The eigenvalues of a ***projection matrix*** are 1 or 0!

$$P = \begin{bmatrix} \frac{1}{2} & \frac{1}{2} \\ \frac{1}{2} & \frac{1}{2} \end{bmatrix} \quad \text{has} \quad \lambda_1 = 1 \quad \text{with} \quad x_1 = \begin{bmatrix} 1 \\ 1 \end{bmatrix}, \quad \lambda_2 = 0 \quad \text{with} \quad x_2 = \begin{bmatrix} 1 \\ -1 \end{bmatrix}.$$

We have $\lambda = 1$ when x projects to itself, and $\lambda = 0$ when x projects to the zero vector. The column space of P is filled with eigenvectors, and so is the nullspace. If those spaces have dimension r and $n - r$, then $\lambda = 1$ is repeated r times and $\lambda = 0$ is repeated $n - r$ times (*always* n *λ's*):

Four eigenvalues allowing repeats
$$P = \begin{bmatrix} 1 & 0 & 0 & 0 \\ 0 & 0 & 0 & 0 \\ 0 & 0 & 0 & 0 \\ 0 & 0 & 0 & 1 \end{bmatrix} \quad \text{has} \quad \lambda = 1, 1, 0, 0.$$

There is nothing exceptional about $\boldsymbol{\lambda = 0}$. Like every other number, zero might be an eigenvalue and it might not. If it is, then its eigenvectors satisfy $Ax = 0x$. Thus x is in the nullspace of A. A zero eigenvalue signals that A is singular (not invertible); its determinant is zero. Invertible matrices have all $\lambda \neq 0$.

Example 3 The eigenvalues are on the main diagonal when A is ***triangular***:

$$\det(A - \lambda I) = \begin{vmatrix} 1-\lambda & 4 & 5 \\ 0 & \frac{3}{4}-\lambda & 6 \\ 0 & 0 & \frac{1}{2}-\lambda \end{vmatrix} = (1-\lambda)\left(\tfrac{3}{4}-\lambda\right)\left(\tfrac{1}{2}-\lambda\right).$$

The determinant is just the product of the diagonal entries. It is zero if $\lambda = 1$, $\lambda = \frac{3}{4}$, or $\lambda = \frac{1}{2}$; the eigenvalues were already sitting along the main diagonal.

This example, in which the eigenvalues can be found by inspection, points to one main theme of the chapter: To transform A into a diagonal or triangular matrix *without changing its eigenvalues*. We emphasize once more that the Gaussian factorization $A = LU$ is not suited to this purpose. The eigenvalues of U may be visible on the diagonal, but they are ***not*** the eigenvalues of A.

For most matrices, there is no doubt that the eigenvalue problem is computationally more difficult than $Ax = b$. With linear systems, a finite number of elimination steps produced the exact answer in a finite time. (Or equivalently, Cramer's rule gave an exact formula for the solution.) No such formula can give the eigenvalues, or Galois would turn in his grave. For a 5 by 5 matrix, $\det(A - \lambda I)$ involves λ^5. Galois and Abel proved that there can be no algebraic formula for the roots of a fifth-degree polynomial.

All they will allow is a few simple checks on the eigenvalues, *after* they have been computed, and we mention two good ones: ***sum and product***.

5B The ***sum*** of the n eigenvalues equals the sum of the n diagonal entries:

$$\textbf{Trace of } \boldsymbol{A} = \boldsymbol{\lambda_1 + \cdots + \lambda_n = a_{11} + \cdots + a_{nn}}. \tag{15}$$

Furthermore, the ***product*** of the n eigenvalues equals the ***determinant*** of A.

The projection matrix P had diagonal entries $\frac{1}{2}, \frac{1}{2}$ and eigenvalues $1, 0$. Then $\frac{1}{2} + \frac{1}{2}$ agrees with $1 + 0$ as it should. So does the determinant, which is $0 \cdot 1 = 0$. A singular matrix, with zero determinant, has one or more of its eigenvalues equal to zero.

There should be no confusion between the diagonal entries and the eigenvalues. For a triangular matrix they are the same—but that is exceptional. Normally the pivots, diagonal entries, and eigenvalues are completely different. And for a 2 by 2 matrix, the trace and determinant tell us everything:

$$\begin{bmatrix} a & b \\ c & d \end{bmatrix} \quad \text{has trace } a + d, \text{ and determinant } ad - bc$$

$$\det(A - \lambda I) = \det \begin{vmatrix} a - \lambda & b \\ c & d - \lambda \end{vmatrix} = \lambda^2 - (\text{trace})\lambda + \text{determinant}$$

$$\text{The eigenvalues are } \lambda = \frac{\text{trace} \pm [(\text{trace})^2 - 4\det]^{1/2}}{2}.$$

Those two λ's add up to the trace; Exercise 9 gives $\sum \lambda_i = $ trace for all matrices.

Eigshow

There is a MATLAB demo (just type eigshow), displaying the eigenvalue problem for a 2 by 2 matrix. It starts with the unit vector $x = (1, 0)$. *The mouse makes this vector move around the unit circle.* At the same time the screen shows Ax, in color and also moving. Possibly Ax is ahead of x. Possibly Ax is behind x. *Sometimes Ax is parallel to x.* At that parallel moment, $Ax = \lambda x$ (twice in the second figure).

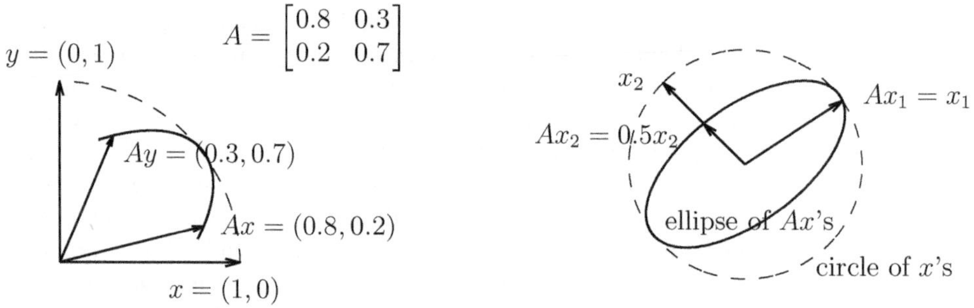

The eigenvalue λ is the length of Ax, when the unit eigenvector x is parallel. The built-in choices for A illustrate three possibilities: 0, 1, or 2 real eigenvectors.

1. There are *no real eigenvectors. Ax stays behind or ahead of x.* This means the eigenvalues and eigenvectors are complex, as they are for the rotation Q.
2. There is only *one* line of eigenvectors (unusual). The moving directions Ax and x meet but don't cross. This happens for the last 2 by 2 matrix below.
3. There are eigenvectors in *two* independent directions. This is typical! Ax crosses x at the first eigenvector x_1, and it crosses back at the second eigenvector x_2.

Suppose A is singular (rank 1). Its column space is a line. The vector Ax has to stay on that line while x circles around. One eigenvector x is along the line. Another eigenvector appears when $Ax_2 = 0$. Zero is an eigenvalue of a singular matrix.

You can mentally follow x and Ax for these six matrices. How many eigenvectors and where? When does Ax go clockwise, instead of counterclockwise with x?

$$A = \begin{bmatrix} 2 & 0 \\ 0 & 1 \end{bmatrix} \quad \begin{bmatrix} 2 & 0 \\ 0 & -1 \end{bmatrix} \quad \begin{bmatrix} 0 & 1 \\ 1 & 0 \end{bmatrix} \quad \begin{bmatrix} 0 & 1 \\ -1 & 0 \end{bmatrix} \quad \begin{bmatrix} 1 & 1 \\ 1 & 1 \end{bmatrix} \quad \begin{bmatrix} 1 & 1 \\ 0 & 1 \end{bmatrix}$$

Problem Set 5.1

1. Find the eigenvalues and eigenvectors of the matrix $A = \begin{bmatrix} 1 & -1 \\ 2 & 4 \end{bmatrix}$. Verify that the trace equals the sum of the eigenvalues, and the determinant equals their product.

2. With the same matrix A, solve the differential equation $du/dt = Au$, $u(0) = \begin{bmatrix} 0 \\ 6 \end{bmatrix}$. What are the two pure exponential solutions?

3. If we shift to $A - 7I$, what are the eigenvalues and eigenvectors and how are they related to those of A?

$$B = A - 7I = \begin{bmatrix} -6 & -1 \\ 2 & -3 \end{bmatrix}.$$

4. Solve $du/dt = Pu$, when P is a projection:

$$\frac{du}{dt} = \begin{bmatrix} \frac{1}{2} & \frac{1}{2} \\ \frac{1}{2} & \frac{1}{2} \end{bmatrix} u \quad \text{with} \quad u(0) = \begin{bmatrix} 5 \\ 3 \end{bmatrix}.$$

Part of $u(0)$ increases exponentially while the nullspace part stays fixed.

5. Find the eigenvalues and eigenvectors of

$$A = \begin{bmatrix} 3 & 4 & 2 \\ 0 & 1 & 2 \\ 0 & 0 & 0 \end{bmatrix} \quad \text{and} \quad B = \begin{bmatrix} 0 & 0 & 2 \\ 0 & 2 & 0 \\ 2 & 0 & 0 \end{bmatrix}.$$

Check that $\lambda_1 + \lambda_2 + \lambda_3$ equals the trace and $\lambda_1\lambda_2\lambda_3$ equals the determinant.

6. Give an example to show that the eigenvalues can be changed when a multiple of one row is subtracted from another. Why is a zero eigenvalue *not* changed by the steps of elimination?

7. Suppose that λ is an eigenvalue of A, and x is its eigenvector: $Ax = \lambda x$.

(a) Show that this same x is an eigenvector of $B = A - 7I$, and find the eigenvalue. This should confirm Exercise 3.

(b) Assuming $\lambda \neq 0$, show that x is also an eigenvector of A^{-1}—and find the eigenvalue.

8. Show that the determinant equals the product of the eigenvalues by imagining that the characteristic polynomial is factored into

$$\det(A - \lambda I) = (\lambda_1 - \lambda)(\lambda_2 - \lambda)\cdots(\lambda_n - \lambda), \tag{16}$$

and making a clever choice of λ.

9. Show that the trace equals the sum of the eigenvalues, in two steps. First, find the coefficient of $(-\lambda)^{n-1}$ on the right side of equation (16). Next, find all the terms in

$$\det(A - \lambda I) = \det \begin{bmatrix} a_{11} - \lambda & a_{12} & \cdots & a_{1n} \\ a_{21} & a_{22} - \lambda & \cdots & a_{2n} \\ \vdots & \vdots & & \vdots \\ a_{n1} & a_{n2} & \cdots & a_{nn} - \lambda \end{bmatrix}$$

that involve $(-\lambda)^{n-1}$. They all come from the main diagonal! Find that coefficient of $(-\lambda)^{n-1}$ and compare.

10. (a) Construct 2 by 2 matrices such that the eigenvalues of AB are not the products of the eigenvalues of A and B, and the eigenvalues of $A + B$ are not the sums of the individual eigenvalues.

(b) Verify, however, that the sum of the eigenvalues of $A + B$ equals the sum of all the individual eigenvalues of A and B, and similarly for products. Why is this true?

11. ***The eigenvalues of A equal the eigenvalues of*** A^{T}. This is because $\det(A - \lambda I)$ equals $\det(A^{\mathrm{T}} - \lambda I)$. That is true because _______. Show by an example that the eigenvectors of A and A^{T} are *not* the same.

12. Find the eigenvalues and eigenvectors of

$$A = \begin{bmatrix} 3 & 4 \\ 4 & -3 \end{bmatrix} \quad \text{and} \quad A = \begin{bmatrix} a & b \\ b & a \end{bmatrix}.$$

13. If B has eigenvalues 1, 2, 3, C has eigenvalues 4, 5, 6, and D has eigenvalues 7, 8, 9, what are the eigenvalues of the 6 by 6 matrix $A = \begin{bmatrix} B & C \\ 0 & D \end{bmatrix}$?

14. Find the rank and all four eigenvalues for both the matrix of ones and the checkerboard matrix:

$$A = \begin{bmatrix} 1 & 1 & 1 & 1 \\ 1 & 1 & 1 & 1 \\ 1 & 1 & 1 & 1 \\ 1 & 1 & 1 & 1 \end{bmatrix} \quad \text{and} \quad C = \begin{bmatrix} 0 & 1 & 0 & 1 \\ 1 & 0 & 1 & 0 \\ 0 & 1 & 0 & 1 \\ 1 & 0 & 1 & 0 \end{bmatrix}.$$

Which eigenvectors correspond to nonzero eigenvalues?

15. What are the rank and eigenvalues when A and C in the previous exercise are n by n? Remember that the eigenvalue $\lambda = 0$ is repeated $n - r$ times.

16. If A is the 4 by 4 matrix of ones, find the eigenvalues and the determinant of $A - I$.

17. Choose the third row of the "companion matrix"

$$A = \begin{bmatrix} 0 & 1 & 0 \\ 0 & 0 & 1 \\ \cdot & \cdot & \cdot \end{bmatrix}$$

so that its characteristic polynomial $|A - \lambda I|$ is $-\lambda^3 + 4\lambda^2 + 5\lambda + 6$.

18. Suppose A has eigenvalues 0, 3, 5 with independent eigenvectors u, v, w.

(a) Give a basis for the nullspace and a basis for the column space.
(b) Find a particular solution to $Ax = v + w$. Find all solutions.
(c) Show that $Ax = u$ has no solution. (If it had a solution, then ______ would be in the column space.)

19. The powers A^k of this matrix A approaches a limit as $k \to \infty$:

$$A = \begin{bmatrix} .8 & .3 \\ .2 & .7 \end{bmatrix}, \quad A^2 = \begin{bmatrix} .70 & .45 \\ .30 & .55 \end{bmatrix}, \quad \text{and} \quad A^\infty = \begin{bmatrix} .6 & .6 \\ .4 & .4 \end{bmatrix}.$$

The matrix A^2 is halfway between A and A^∞. Explain why $A^2 = \frac{1}{2}(A + A^\infty)$ from the eigenvalues and eigenvectors of these three matrices.

20. Find the eigenvalues and the eigenvectors of these two matrices:

$$A = \begin{bmatrix} 1 & 4 \\ 2 & 3 \end{bmatrix} \quad \text{and} \quad A + I = \begin{bmatrix} 2 & 4 \\ 2 & 4 \end{bmatrix}.$$

$A + I$ has the ______ eigenvectors as A. Its eigenvalues are ______ by 1.

21. Compute the eigenvalues and eigenvectors of A and A^{-1}:

$$A = \begin{bmatrix} 0 & 2 \\ 2 & 3 \end{bmatrix} \quad \text{and} \quad A^{-1} = \begin{bmatrix} -3/4 & 1/2 \\ 1/2 & 0 \end{bmatrix}.$$

A^{-1} has the ______ eigenvectors as A. When A has eigenvalues λ_1 and λ_2, its inverse has eigenvalues ______.

22. Compute the eigenvalues and eigenvectors of A and A^2:

$$A = \begin{bmatrix} -1 & 3 \\ 2 & 0 \end{bmatrix} \quad \text{and} \quad A^2 = \begin{bmatrix} 7 & -3 \\ -2 & 6 \end{bmatrix}.$$

A^2 has the same ______ as A. When A has eigenvalues λ_1 and λ_2, A^2 has eigenvalues ______.

23. (a) If you know x is an eigenvector, the way to find λ is to ______.
(b) If you know λ is an eigenvalue, the way to find x is to ______.

24. What do you do to $Ax = \lambda x$, in order to prove (a), (b), and (c)?

(a) λ^2 is an eigenvalue of A^2, as in Problem 22.
(b) λ^{-1} is an eigenvalue of A^{-1}, as in Problem 21.
(c) $\lambda + 1$ is an eigenvalue of $A + I$, as in Problem 20.

25. From the unit vector $u = \left(\frac{1}{6}, \frac{1}{6}, \frac{3}{6}, \frac{5}{6}\right)$, construct the rank-1 projection matrix $P = uu^{\mathrm{T}}$.

(a) Show that $Pu = u$. Then u is an eigenvector with $\lambda = 1$.
(b) If v is perpendicular to u show that $Pv =$ zero vector. Then $\lambda = 0$.
(c) Find three independent eigenvectors of P all with eigenvalue $\lambda = 0$.

26. Solve $\det(Q - \lambda I) = 0$ by the quadratic formula, to reach $\lambda = \cos\theta \pm i \sin\theta$:

$$Q = \begin{bmatrix} \cos\theta & -\sin\theta \\ \sin\theta & \cos\theta \end{bmatrix} \quad \text{rotates the } xy\text{-plane by the angle } \theta.$$

Find the eigenvectors of Q by solving $(Q - \lambda I)x = 0$. Use $i^2 = -1$.

27. Every permutation matrix leaves $x = (1, 1, \ldots, 1)$ unchanged. Then $\lambda = 1$. Find two more λ's for these permutations:

$$P = \begin{bmatrix} 0 & 1 & 0 \\ 0 & 0 & 1 \\ 1 & 0 & 0 \end{bmatrix} \quad \text{and} \quad P = \begin{bmatrix} 0 & 0 & 1 \\ 0 & 1 & 0 \\ 1 & 0 & 0 \end{bmatrix}.$$

28. If A has $\lambda_1 = 4$ and $\lambda_2 = 5$, then $\det(A - \lambda I) = (\lambda - 4)(\lambda - 5) = \lambda^2 - 9\lambda + 20$. Find three matrices that have trace $a + d = 9$, determinant 20, and $\lambda = 4, 5$.

29. A 3 by 3 matrix B is known to have eigenvalues 0, 1, 2. This information is enough to find three of these:

(a) the rank of B,
(b) the determinant of $B^{\mathrm{T}}B$,

(c) the eigenvalues of $B^{\mathrm{T}}B$, and
(d) the eigenvalues of $(B+I)^{-1}$.

30. Choose the second row of $A = \begin{bmatrix} 0 & 1 \\ * & * \end{bmatrix}$ so that A has eigenvalues 4 and 7.

31. Choose a, b, c, so that $\det(A - \lambda I) = 9\lambda - \lambda^3$. Then the eigenvalues are $-3, 0, 3$:

$$A = \begin{bmatrix} 0 & 1 & 0 \\ 0 & 0 & 1 \\ a & b & c \end{bmatrix}.$$

32. Construct any 3 by 3 Markov matrix M: positive entries down each column add to 1. If $e = (1, 1, 1)$, verify that $M^{\mathrm{T}}e = e$. By Problem 11, $\lambda = 1$ is also an eigenvalue of M. Challenge: A 3 by 3 singular Markov matrix with trace $\frac{1}{2}$ has eigenvalues $\lambda =$ ______.

33. Find three 2 by 2 matrices that have $\lambda_1 = \lambda_2 = 0$. The trace is zero and the determinant is zero. The matrix A might not be 0 but check that $A^2 = 0$.

34. This matrix is singular with rank 1. Find three λ's and three eigenvectors:

$$A = \begin{bmatrix} 1 \\ 2 \\ 1 \end{bmatrix} \begin{bmatrix} 2 & 1 & 2 \end{bmatrix} = \begin{bmatrix} 2 & 1 & 2 \\ 4 & 2 & 4 \\ 2 & 1 & 2 \end{bmatrix}.$$

35. Suppose A and B have the same eigenvalues $\lambda_1, \ldots, \lambda_n$ with the same independent eigenvectors $x_1, \ldots, x_n$. Then $A = B$. *Reason*: Any vector x is a combination $c_1x_1 + \cdots + c_nx_n$. What is Ax? What is Bx?

36. (Review) Find the eigenvalues of A, B, and C:

$$A = \begin{bmatrix} 1 & 2 & 3 \\ 0 & 4 & 5 \\ 0 & 0 & 6 \end{bmatrix}, \quad B = \begin{bmatrix} 0 & 0 & 1 \\ 0 & 2 & 0 \\ 3 & 0 & 0 \end{bmatrix}, \quad \text{and} \quad C = \begin{bmatrix} 2 & 2 & 2 \\ 2 & 2 & 2 \\ 2 & 2 & 2 \end{bmatrix}.$$

37. When $a + b = c + d$, show that $(1, 1)$ is an eigenvector and find both eigenvalues:

$$A = \begin{bmatrix} a & b \\ c & d \end{bmatrix}.$$

38. When P exchanges rows 1 and 2 *and* columns 1 and 2, the eigenvalues don't change. Find eigenvectors of A and PAP for $\lambda = 11$:

$$A = \begin{bmatrix} 1 & 2 & 1 \\ 3 & 6 & 3 \\ 4 & 8 & 4 \end{bmatrix} \quad \text{and} \quad PAP = \begin{bmatrix} 6 & 3 & 3 \\ 2 & 1 & 1 \\ 8 & 4 & 4 \end{bmatrix}.$$

39. Challenge problem: *Is there a real* 2 *by* 2 *matrix* (other than I) *with* $A^3 = I$? Its eigenvalues must satisfy $\lambda^3 = I$. They can be $e^{2\pi i/3}$ and $e^{-2\pi i/3}$. What trace and determinant would this give? Construct A.

40. There are six 3 by 3 permutation matrices P. What numbers can be the *determinants* of P? What numbers can be *pivots*? What numbers can be the *trace* of P? What *four numbers* can be eigenvalues of P?

5.2 DIAGONALIZATION OF A MATRIX

We start right off with the one essential computation. It is perfectly simple and will be used in every section of this chapter. ***The eigenvectors diagonalize a matrix***:

5C Suppose the n by n matrix A has n linearly independent eigenvectors. If these eigenvectors are the columns of a matrix S, then $S^{-1}AS$ is a diagonal matrix Λ. The eigenvalues of A are on the diagonal of Λ:

Diagonalization $$S^{-1}AS = \Lambda = \begin{bmatrix} \lambda_1 & & & \\ & \lambda_2 & & \\ & & \ddots & \\ & & & \lambda_n \end{bmatrix}. \tag{1}$$

We call S the "eigenvector matrix" and Λ the "eigenvalue matrix"—using a capital lambda because of the small lambdas for the eigenvalues on its diagonal.

Proof Put the eigenvectors x_i in the columns of S, and compute AS by columns:

$$AS = A\begin{bmatrix} | & | & & | \\ x_1 & x_2 & \cdots & x_n \\ | & | & & | \end{bmatrix} = \begin{bmatrix} | & | & & | \\ \lambda_1 x_1 & \lambda_2 x_2 & \cdots & \lambda_n x_n \\ | & | & & | \end{bmatrix}.$$

Then the trick is to split this last matrix into a quite different product $S\Lambda$:

$$\begin{bmatrix} \lambda_1 x_1 & \lambda_2 x_2 & \cdots & \lambda_n x_n \end{bmatrix} = \begin{bmatrix} x_1 & x_2 & \cdots & x_n \end{bmatrix} \begin{bmatrix} \lambda_1 & & & \\ & \lambda_2 & & \\ & & \ddots & \\ & & & \lambda_n \end{bmatrix}.$$

It is crucial to keep these matrices in the right order. If Λ came before S (instead of after), then λ_1 would multiply the entries in the first row. We want λ_1 to appear in the first column. As it is, $S\Lambda$ is correct. Therefore,

$$AS = S\Lambda, \quad \text{or } S^{-1}AS = \Lambda, \quad \text{or } A = S\Lambda S^{-1}. \tag{2}$$

S is invertible, because its columns (the eigenvectors) were assumed to be independent.

We add four remarks before giving any examples or applications. ■

Remark 1 If the matrix A has no repeated eigenvalues—the numbers $\lambda_1, \ldots, \lambda_n$ are distinct—then its n eigenvectors are automatically independent (see 5D below). Therefore ***any matrix with distinct eigenvalues can be diagonalized***.

Remark 2 The diagonalizing matrix S is *not unique*. An eigenvector x can be multiplied by a constant, and remains an eigenvector. We can multiply the columns of S by any nonzero constants, and produce a new diagonalizing S. Repeated eigenvalues leave even more freedom in S. For the trivial example $A = I$, any invertible S will do: $S^{-1}IS$ is always diagonal (Λ is just I). All vectors are eigenvectors of the identity.

Remark 3 *Other matrices S will not produce a diagonal* Λ. Suppose the first column of S is y. Then the first column of $S\Lambda$ is $\lambda_1 y$. If this is to agree with the first column of AS, which by matrix multiplication is Ay, then y must be an eigenvector: $Ay = \lambda_1 y$. The *order* of the eigenvectors in S and the eigenvalues in Λ is automatically the same.

Remark 4 Not all matrices possess n linearly independent eigenvectors, so ***not all matrices are diagonalizable***. The standard example of a "defective matrix" is

$$A = \begin{bmatrix} 0 & 1 \\ 0 & 0 \end{bmatrix}.$$

Its eigenvalues are $\lambda_1 = \lambda_2 = 0$, since it is triangular with zeros on the diagonal:

$$\det(A - \lambda I) = \det \begin{bmatrix} -\lambda & 1 \\ 0 & -\lambda \end{bmatrix} = \lambda^2.$$

All eigenvectors of this A are multiples of the vector $(1, 0)$:

$$\begin{bmatrix} 0 & 1 \\ 0 & 0 \end{bmatrix} x = \begin{bmatrix} 0 \\ 0 \end{bmatrix}, \qquad \text{or} \qquad x = \begin{bmatrix} c \\ 0 \end{bmatrix}.$$

$\lambda = 0$ is a double eigenvalue—its *algebraic multiplicity* is 2. But the *geometric multiplicity* is 1—there is only one independent eigenvector. We can't construct S.

Here is a more direct proof that this A is not diagonalizable. Since $\lambda_1 = \lambda_2 = 0$, Λ would have to be the zero matrix. But if $\Lambda = S^{-1}AS = 0$, then we premultiply by S and postmultiply by S^{-1}, to deduce falsely that $A = 0$. There is no invertible S.

That failure of diagonalization was ***not*** a result of $\lambda = 0$. It came from $\lambda_1 = \lambda_2$:

$$\textbf{Repeated eigenvalues} \qquad A = \begin{bmatrix} 3 & 1 \\ 0 & 3 \end{bmatrix} \qquad \text{and} \qquad A = \begin{bmatrix} 2 & -1 \\ 1 & 0 \end{bmatrix}.$$

Their eigenvalues are 3, 3 and 1, 1. They are not singular! The problem is the shortage of eigenvectors—which are needed for S. That needs to be emphasized:

> ***Diagonalizability of A depends on enough eigenvectors.***
> ***Invertibility of A depends on nonzero eigenvalues.***

There is no connection between diagonalizability (n independent eigenvectors) and invertibility (no zero eigenvalues). The only indication given by the eigenvalues is this: *Diagonalization can fail only if there are repeated eigenvalues*. Even then, it does not always fail. $A = I$ has repeated eigenvalues $1, 1, \ldots, 1$ but it is already diagonal! There is no shortage of eigenvectors in that case.

The test is to check, for an eigenvalue that is repeated p times, whether there are p independent eigenvectors—in other words, whether $A - \lambda I$ has rank $n - p$. To complete that circle of ideas, we have to show that *distinct* eigenvalues present no problem.

5D If eigenvectors $x_1, \ldots, x_k$ correspond to *different eigenvalues* $\lambda_1, \ldots, \lambda_k$, then those eigenvectors are linearly independent.

Suppose first that $k = 2$, and that some combination of x_1 and x_2 produces zero: $c_1x_1 + c_2x_2 = 0$. Multiplying by A, we find $c_1\lambda_1x_1 + c_2\lambda_2x_2 = 0$. Subtracting λ_2 times the previous equation, the vector x_2 disappears:

$$c_1(\lambda_1 - \lambda_2)x_1 = 0.$$

Since $\lambda_1 \neq \lambda_2$ and $x_1 \neq 0$, we are forced into $c_1 = 0$. Similarly $c_2 = 0$, and the two vectors are independent; only the trivial combination gives zero.

This same argument extends to any number of eigenvectors: If some combination produces zero, multiply by A, subtract λ_k times the original combination, and x_k disappears—leaving a combination of $x_1, \ldots, x_{k-1}$, which produces zero. By repeating the same steps (this is really *mathematical induction*) we end up with a multiple of x_1 that produces zero. This forces $c_1 = 0$, and ultimately every $c_i = 0$. Therefore eigenvectors that come from distinct eigenvalues are automatically independent.

A matrix with n distinct eigenvalues can be diagonalized. This is the typical case.

Examples of Diagonalization

The main point of this section is $S^{-1}AS = \Lambda$. The eigenvector matrix S converts A into its eigenvalue matrix Λ (diagonal). We see this for projections and rotations.

Example 1 The projection $A = \begin{bmatrix} \frac{1}{2} & \frac{1}{2} \\ \frac{1}{2} & \frac{1}{2} \end{bmatrix}$ has eigenvalue matrix $\Lambda = \begin{bmatrix} 1 & 0 \\ 0 & 0 \end{bmatrix}$. The eigenvectors go into the columns of S:

$$S = \begin{bmatrix} 1 & 1 \\ 1 & -1 \end{bmatrix} \quad \text{and} \quad AS = S\Lambda = \begin{bmatrix} 1 & 0 \\ 1 & 0 \end{bmatrix}.$$

That last equation can be verified at a glance. Therefore $S^{-1}AS = \Lambda$.

Example 2 The eigenvalues themselves are not so clear for a ***rotation***:

$$\textbf{90° rotation} \qquad K = \begin{bmatrix} 0 & -1 \\ 1 & 0 \end{bmatrix} \qquad \text{has} \qquad \det(K - \lambda I) = \lambda^2 + 1.$$

How can a vector be rotated and still have its direction unchanged? Apparently it can't—except for the zero vector, which is useless. But there must be eigenvalues, and we must be able to solve $du/dt = Ku$. The characteristic polynomial $\lambda^2 + 1$ should still have two roots—but those roots are *not real*.

You see the way out. The eigenvalues of K are *imaginary numbers*, $\lambda_1 = i$ and $\lambda_2 = -i$. The eigenvectors are also not real. Somehow, in turning through 90°, they are multiplied by i or $-i$:

$$(K-\lambda_1 I)x_1 = \begin{bmatrix} -i & -1 \\ 1 & -i \end{bmatrix}\begin{bmatrix} y \\ z \end{bmatrix} = \begin{bmatrix} 0 \\ 0 \end{bmatrix} \quad \text{and} \quad x_1 = \begin{bmatrix} 1 \\ -i \end{bmatrix}$$

$$(K-\lambda_2 I)x_2 = \begin{bmatrix} i & -1 \\ 1 & i \end{bmatrix}\begin{bmatrix} y \\ z \end{bmatrix} = \begin{bmatrix} 0 \\ 0 \end{bmatrix} \quad \text{and} \quad x_2 = \begin{bmatrix} 1 \\ i \end{bmatrix}.$$

The eigenvalues are distinct, even if imaginary, and the eigenvectors are independent. They go into the columns of S:

$$S = \begin{bmatrix} 1 & 1 \\ -i & i \end{bmatrix} \quad \text{and} \quad S^{-1}KS = \begin{bmatrix} i & 0 \\ 0 & -i \end{bmatrix}.$$

We are faced with an inescapable fact, that ***complex numbers are needed even for real matrices***. If there are too few real eigenvalues, there are always n complex eigenvalues. (Complex includes real, when the imaginary part is zero.) If there are too few eigenvectors in the real world $\mathbf{R}^3$, or in $\mathbf{R}^n$, we look in $\mathbf{C}^3$ or $\mathbf{C}^n$. The space $\mathbf{C}^n$ contains all column vectors with complex components, and it has new definitions of length and inner product and orthogonality. But it is not more difficult than $\mathbf{R}^n$, and in Section 5.5 we make an easy conversion to the complex case.

Powers and Products: A^k and AB

There is one more situation in which the calculations are easy. ***The eigenvalues of A^2 are exactly $\lambda_1^2, \dots, \lambda_n^2$, and every eigenvector of A is also an eigenvector of A^2.*** We start from $Ax = \lambda x$, and multiply again by A:

$$A^2x = A\lambda x = \lambda Ax = \lambda^2 x. \tag{3}$$

Thus λ^2 is an eigenvalue of A^2, with the same eigenvector x. If the first multiplication by A leaves the direction of x unchanged, then so does the second.

The same result comes from diagonalization, by squaring $S^{-1}AS = \Lambda$:

Eigenvalues of A^2 $\quad (S^{-1}AS)(S^{-1}AS) = \Lambda^2 \quad$ or $\quad S^{-1}A^2S = \Lambda^2.$

The matrix A^2 is diagonalized by the same S, so the eigenvectors are unchanged. The eigenvalues are squared. This continues to hold for any power of A:

5E The eigenvalues of A^k are $\lambda_1^k, \dots, \lambda_n^k$, and each eigenvector of A is still an eigenvector of A^k. When S diagonalizes A, it also diagonalizes A^k:

$$\Lambda^k = (S^{-1}AS)(S^{-1}AS)\cdots(S^{-1}AS) = S^{-1}A^kS. \tag{4}$$

Each S^{-1} cancels an S, except for the first S^{-1} and the last S.

If A is invertible this rule also applies to its inverse (the power $k=-1$). ***The eigenvalues of A^{-1} are $1/\lambda_i$.*** That can be seen even without diagonalizing:

$$\textit{if} \quad Ax = \lambda x \quad \textit{then} \quad x = \lambda A^{-1}x \quad \textit{and} \quad \frac{1}{\lambda}x = A^{-1}x.$$

Example 3 If K is rotation through 90°, then K^2 is rotation through 180° (which means $-I$) and K^{-1} is rotation through −90°:

$$K = \begin{bmatrix} 0 & -1 \\ 1 & 0 \end{bmatrix}, \qquad K^2 = \begin{bmatrix} -1 & 0 \\ 0 & -1 \end{bmatrix}, \qquad \text{and} \qquad K^{-1} = \begin{bmatrix} 0 & 1 \\ -1 & 0 \end{bmatrix}.$$

The eigenvalues of K are i and $-i$; their squares are -1 and -1; their reciprocals are $1/i = -i$ and $1/(-i) = i$. Then K^4 is a complete rotation through 360°:

$$K^4 = \begin{bmatrix} 1 & 0 \\ 0 & 1 \end{bmatrix} \qquad \text{and also} \qquad \Lambda^4 = \begin{bmatrix} i^4 & 0 \\ 0 & (-i)^4 \end{bmatrix} = \begin{bmatrix} 1 & 0 \\ 0 & 1 \end{bmatrix}.$$

For a ***product of two matrices***, we can ask about the eigenvalues of AB—but we won't get a good answer. It is very tempting to try the same reasoning, hoping to prove what is *not in general true*. If λ is an eigenvalue of A and μ is an eigenvalue of B, here is the false proof that AB has the eigenvalue $\mu\lambda$:

$$\textbf{False proof} \qquad ABx = A\mu x = \mu Ax = \mu\lambda x.$$

The mistake lies in assuming that A and B share the *same* eigenvector x. In general, they do not. We could have two matrices with zero eigenvalues, while AB has $\lambda = 1$:

$$AB = \begin{bmatrix} 0 & 1 \\ 0 & 0 \end{bmatrix} \begin{bmatrix} 0 & 0 \\ 1 & 0 \end{bmatrix} = \begin{bmatrix} 1 & 0 \\ 0 & 0 \end{bmatrix}.$$

The eigenvectors of this A and B are completely different, which is typical. For the same reason, the eigenvalues of $A + B$ generally have nothing to do with $\lambda + \mu$.

This false proof does suggest what *is* true. If the eigenvector is the same for A and B, then the eigenvalues multiply and AB has the eigenvalue $\mu\lambda$. But there is something more important. There is an easy way to recognize when A and B share a full set of eigenvectors, and that is a key question in quantum mechanics:

5F Diagonalizable matrices share the same eigenvector matrix S if and only if $AB = BA$.

Proof If the same S diagonalizes both $A = S\Lambda_1 S^{-1}$ and $B = S\Lambda_2 S^{-1}$, we can multiply in either order:

$$AB = S\Lambda_1 S^{-1} S\Lambda_2 S^{-1} = S\Lambda_1\Lambda_2 S^{-1} \quad \text{and} \quad BA = S\Lambda_2 S^{-1} S\Lambda_1 S^{-1} = S\Lambda_2\Lambda_1 S^{-1}.$$

Since $\Lambda_1\Lambda_2 = \Lambda_2\Lambda_1$ (diagonal matrices always commute) we have $AB = BA$.

In the opposite direction, suppose $AB = BA$. Starting from $Ax = \lambda x$, we have

$$ABx = BAx = B\lambda x = \lambda Bx.$$

Thus x and Bx are both eigenvectors of A, sharing the same λ (or else $Bx = 0$). If we assume for convenience that the eigenvalues of A are distinct—the eigenspaces are all one-dimensional—then Bx *must be a multiple of* x. In other words x is an eigenvector of B as well as A. The proof with repeated eigenvalues is a little longer. ■

Heisenberg's uncertainty principle comes from noncommuting matrices, like position P and momentum Q. Position is symmetric, momentum is skew-symmetric, and together they satisfy $QP - PQ = I$. The uncertainty principle follows directly from the Schwarz inequality $(Qx)^{\mathrm{T}}(Px) \le \|Qx\|\|Px\|$ of Section 3.2:

$$\|x\|^2 = x^{\mathrm{T}}x = x^{\mathrm{T}}(QP - PQ)x \le 2\|Qx\|\|Px\|.$$

The product of $\|Qx\|/\|x\|$ and $\|Px\|/\|x\|$— momentum and position errors, when the wave function is x—is at least $\frac{1}{2}$. It is impossible to get both errors small, because when you try to measure the position of a particle you change its momentum.

At the end we come back to $A = S\Lambda S^{-1}$. That factorization is particularly suited to take powers of A, and the simplest case A^2 makes the point. The LU factorization is hopeless when squared, but $S\Lambda S^{-1}$ is perfect. The square is $S\Lambda^2 S^{-1}$, and the eigenvectors are unchanged. By following those eigenvectors we will solve difference equations and differential equations.

Problem Set 5.2

1. Factor the following matrices into $S\Lambda S^{-1}$:

$$A = \begin{bmatrix} 1 & 1 \\ 1 & 1 \end{bmatrix} \quad \text{and} \quad A = \begin{bmatrix} 2 & 1 \\ 0 & 0 \end{bmatrix}.$$

2. Find the matrix A whose eigenvalues are 1 and 4, and whose eigenvectors are $\begin{bmatrix} 3 \\ 1 \end{bmatrix}$ and $\begin{bmatrix} 2 \\ 1 \end{bmatrix}$, respectively. (*Hint*: $A = S\Lambda S^{-1}$.)

3. Find *all* the eigenvalues and eigenvectors of

$$A = \begin{bmatrix} 1 & 1 & 1 \\ 1 & 1 & 1 \\ 1 & 1 & 1 \end{bmatrix}$$

and write two different diagonalizing matrices S.

4. If a 3 by 3 upper triangular matrix has diagonal entries 1, 2, 7, how do you know it can be diagonalized? What is Λ?

5. Which of these matrices cannot be diagonalized?

$$A_1 = \begin{bmatrix} 2 & -2 \\ 2 & -2 \end{bmatrix} \quad A_2 = \begin{bmatrix} 2 & 0 \\ 2 & -2 \end{bmatrix} \quad A_3 = \begin{bmatrix} 2 & 0 \\ 2 & 2 \end{bmatrix}.$$

6. (a) If $A^2 = I$, what are the possible eigenvalues of A?
(b) If this A is 2 by 2, and not I or $-I$, find its trace and determinant.
(c) If the first row is $(3, -1)$, what is the second row?

7. If $A = \begin{bmatrix} 4 & 3 \\ 1 & 2 \end{bmatrix}$, find A^{100} by diagonalizing A.

8. Suppose $A = uv^{\mathrm{T}}$ is a column times a row (a rank-1 matrix).
(a) By multiplying A times u, show that u is an eigenvector. What is λ?
(b) What are the other eigenvalues of A (and why)?
(c) Compute trace (A) from the sum on the diagonal and the sum of λ's.

9. Show by direct calculation that AB and BA have the same trace when

$$A = \begin{bmatrix} a & b \\ c & d \end{bmatrix} \quad \text{and} \quad B = \begin{bmatrix} q & r \\ s & t \end{bmatrix}.$$

Deduce that $AB - BA = I$ is impossible (except in infinite dimensions).

10. Suppose A has eigenvalues 1, 2, 4. What is the trace of A^2? What is the determinant of $(A^{-1})^{\mathrm{T}}$?

11. If the eigenvalues of A are 1, 1, 2, which of the following are certain to be true? Give a reason if true or a counterexample if false:

(a) A is invertible.
(b) A is diagonalizable.
(c) A is not diagonalizable.

12. Suppose the only eigenvectors of A are multiples of $x = (1, 0, 0)$. True or false:

(a) A is not invertible.
(b) A has a repeated eigenvalue.
(c) A is not diagonalizable.

13. Diagonalize the matrix $A = \begin{bmatrix} 5 & 4 \\ 4 & 5 \end{bmatrix}$ and find one of its square roots—a matrix such that $R^2 = A$. How many square roots will there be?

14. Suppose the eigenvector matrix S has $S^{\mathrm{T}} = S^{-1}$. Show that $A = S\Lambda S^{-1}$ is symmetric and has orthogonal eigenvectors.

Problems 15–24 are about the eigenvalue and eigenvector matrices.

15. Factor these two matrices into $A = S\Lambda S^{-1}$:

$$A = \begin{bmatrix} 1 & 2 \\ 0 & 3 \end{bmatrix} \quad \text{and} \quad A = \begin{bmatrix} 1 & 1 \\ 2 & 2 \end{bmatrix}.$$

16. If $A = S\Lambda S^{-1}$ then $A^3 = (\quad)(\quad)(\quad)$ and $A^{-1} = (\quad)(\quad)(\quad)$.

17. If A has $\lambda_1 = 2$ with eigenvector $x_1 = \begin{bmatrix} 1 \\ 0 \end{bmatrix}$ and $\lambda_2 = 5$ with $x_2 = \begin{bmatrix} 1 \\ 1 \end{bmatrix}$, use $S\Lambda S^{-1}$ to find A. No other matrix has the same λ's and x's.

18. Suppose $A = S\Lambda S^{-1}$. What is the eigenvalue matrix for $A + 2I$? What is the eigenvector matrix? Check that $A + 2I = (\quad)(\quad)(\quad)^{-1}$.

19. True or false: If the n columns of S (eigenvectors of A) are independent, then

(a) A is invertible.
(b) A is diagonalizable.
(c) S is invertible.
(d) S is diagonalizable.

20. If the eigenvectors of A are the columns of I, then A is a ______ matrix. If the eigenvector matrix S is triangular, then S^{-1} is triangular and A is triangular.

21. Describe all matrices S that diagonalize this matrix A:

$$A = \begin{bmatrix} 4 & 0 \\ 1 & 2 \end{bmatrix}.$$

Then describe all matrices that diagonalize A^{-1}.

22. Write the most general matrix that has eigenvectors $\begin{bmatrix} 1 \\ 1 \end{bmatrix}$ and $\begin{bmatrix} 1 \\ -1 \end{bmatrix}$.

23. Find the eigenvalues of A and B and $A + B$:

$$A = \begin{bmatrix} 1 & 0 \\ 1 & 1 \end{bmatrix}, \quad B = \begin{bmatrix} 1 & 1 \\ 0 & 1 \end{bmatrix}, \quad A + B = \begin{bmatrix} 2 & 1 \\ 1 & 2 \end{bmatrix}.$$

Eigenvalues of $A + B$ (are equal to)(are not equal to) eigenvalues of A plus eigenvalues of B.

24. Find the eigenvalues of A, B, AB, and BA:

$$A = \begin{bmatrix} 1 & 0 \\ 1 & 1 \end{bmatrix}, \quad B = \begin{bmatrix} 1 & 1 \\ 0 & 1 \end{bmatrix}, \quad AB = \begin{bmatrix} 1 & 1 \\ 1 & 2 \end{bmatrix}, \quad \text{and} \quad BA = \begin{bmatrix} 2 & 1 \\ 1 & 1 \end{bmatrix}.$$

Eigenvalues of AB (are equal to)(are not equal to) eigenvalues of A times eigenvalues of B. Eigenvalues of AB (are)(are not) equal to eigenvalues of BA.

Problems 25–28 are about the diagonalizability of A.

25. True or false: If the eigenvalues of A are 2, 2, 5, then the matrix is certainly

(a) invertible.
(b) diagonalizable.
(b) not diagonalizable.

26. If the eigenvalues of A are 1 and 0, write everything you know about the matrices A and A^2.

27. Complete these matrices so that $\det A = 25$. Then trace $= 10$, and $\lambda = 5$ is repeated! Find an eigenvector with $Ax = 5x$. These matrices will not be diagonalizable because there is no second line of eigenvectors.

$$A = \begin{bmatrix} 8 & \\ & 2 \end{bmatrix}, \quad A = \begin{bmatrix} 9 & 4 \\ & 1 \end{bmatrix}, \quad \text{and} \quad A = \begin{bmatrix} 10 & 5 \\ -5 & \end{bmatrix}.$$

28. The matrix $A = \begin{bmatrix} 3 & 1 \\ 0 & 3 \end{bmatrix}$ is not diagonalizable because the rank of $A - 3I$ is ___. Change one entry to make A diagonalizable. Which entries could you change?

Problems 29–33 are about powers of matrices.

29. $A^k = S\Lambda^k S^{-1}$ approaches the zero matrix as $k \to \infty$ if and only if every λ has absolute value less than ___. Does $A^k \to 0$ or $B^k \to 0$?

$$A = \begin{bmatrix} .6 & .4 \\ .4 & .6 \end{bmatrix} \quad \text{and} \quad B = \begin{bmatrix} .6 & .9 \\ .1 & .6 \end{bmatrix}.$$

30. (Recommended) Find Λ and S to diagonalize A in Problem 29. What is the limit of Λ^k as $k \to \infty$? What is the limit of $S\Lambda^k S^{-1}$? In the columns of this limiting matrix you see the ______.

31. Find Λ and S to diagonalize B in Problem 29. What is $B^{10}u_0$ for these u_0?

$$u_0 = \begin{bmatrix} 3 \\ 1 \end{bmatrix}, \qquad u_0 = \begin{bmatrix} 3 \\ -1 \end{bmatrix}, \quad \text{and} \quad u_0 = \begin{bmatrix} 6 \\ 0 \end{bmatrix}.$$

32. Diagonalize A and compute $S\Lambda^k S^{-1}$ to prove this formula for A^k:

$$A = \begin{bmatrix} 2 & 1 \\ 1 & 2 \end{bmatrix} \qquad \text{has} \qquad A^k = \frac{1}{2}\begin{bmatrix} 3^k+1 & 3^k-1 \\ 3^k-1 & 3^k+1 \end{bmatrix}.$$

33. Diagonalize B and compute $S\Lambda^k S^{-1}$ to prove this formula for B^k:

$$B = \begin{bmatrix} 3 & 1 \\ 0 & 2 \end{bmatrix} \qquad \text{has} \qquad B^k = \begin{bmatrix} 3^k & 3^k-2^k \\ 0 & 2^k \end{bmatrix}.$$

Problems 34–44 are new applications of $A = S\Lambda S^{-1}$.

34. Suppose that $A = S\Lambda S^{-1}$. Take determinants to prove that $\det A = \lambda_1\lambda_2\cdots\lambda_n =$ product of λ's. This quick proof only works when A is ______.

35. The trace of S times ΛS^{-1} equals the trace of ΛS^{-1} times S. So the trace of a diagonalizable A equals the trace of Λ, which is ______.

36. If $A = S\Lambda S^{-1}$, diagonalize the block matrix $B = \begin{bmatrix} A & 0 \\ 0 & 2A \end{bmatrix}$. Find its eigenvalue and eigenvector matrices.

37. Consider all 4 by 4 matrices A that are diagonalized by the same fixed eigenvector matrix S. Show that the A's form a subspace (cA and $A_1 + A_2$ have this same S). What is this subspace when $S = I$? What is its dimension?

38. Suppose $A^2 = A$. On the left side A multiplies each column of A. Which of our four subspaces contains eigenvectors with $\lambda = 1$? Which subspace contains eigenvectors with $\lambda = 0$? From the dimensions of those subspaces, A has a full set of independent eigenvectors and can be diagonalized.

39. Suppose $Ax = \lambda x$. If $\lambda = 0$, then x is in the nullspace. If $\lambda \neq 0$, then x is in the column space. Those spaces have dimensions $(n-r) + r = n$. So why doesn't every square matrix have n linearly independent eigenvectors?

40. Substitute $A = S\Lambda S^{-1}$ into the product $(A - \lambda_1 I)(A - \lambda_2 I)\cdots(A - \lambda_n I)$ and explain why this produces the *zero matrix*. We are substituting the matrix A for the number λ in the polynomial $p(\lambda) = \det(A - \lambda I)$. The ***Cayley–Hamilton Theorem*** says that this product is always $p(A) =$ *zero matrix*, even if A is not diagonalizable.

41. Test the Cayley–Hamilton Theorem on Fibonacci's matrix $A = \begin{bmatrix} 1 & 1 \\ 1 & 0 \end{bmatrix}$. The theorem predicts that $A^2 - A - I = 0$, since $\det(A - \lambda I)$ is $\lambda^2 - \lambda - 1$.

42. If $A = \begin{bmatrix} a & b \\ 0 & d \end{bmatrix}$, then $\det(A - \lambda I)$ is $(\lambda - a)(\lambda - d)$. Check the Cayley–Hamilton statement that $(A - aI)(A - dI) =$ *zero matrix*.

43. If $A = \begin{bmatrix} 1 & 0 \\ 0 & 2 \end{bmatrix}$ and $AB = BA$, show that $B = \begin{bmatrix} a & b \\ c & d \end{bmatrix}$ is also diagonal. B has the same eigen______ as A, but different eigen______. These diagonal matrices B form a two-dimensional subspace of matrix space. $AB - BA = 0$ gives four equations for the unknowns **a**, **b**, **c**, **d**—find the rank of the 4 by 4 matrix.

44. If A is 5 by 5, then $AB - BA =$ zero matrix gives 25 equations for the 25 entries in B. Show that the 25 by 25 matrix is singular by noticing a simple nonzero solution B.

45. Find the eigenvalues and eigenvectors for both of these Markov matrices A and A^∞. Explain why A^{100} is close to A^∞:

$$A = \begin{bmatrix} .6 & .2 \\ .4 & .8 \end{bmatrix} \quad \text{and} \quad A^\infty = \begin{bmatrix} 1/3 & 1/3 \\ 2/3 & 2/3 \end{bmatrix}.$$

5.3 DIFFERENCE EQUATIONS AND POWERS A^k

Difference equations $u_{k+1} = Au_k$ move forward in a finite number of finite steps. A differential equation takes an infinite number of infinitesimal steps, but the two theories stay absolutely in parallel. It is the same analogy between the discrete and the continuous that appears over and over in mathematics. A good illustration is compound interest, when the time step gets shorter.

Suppose you invest \$1000 at 6% interest. Compounded once a year, the principal P is multiplied by 1.06. *This is a difference equation* $P_{k+1} = AP_k = 1.06\,P_k$ *with a time step of one year.* After 5 years, the original $P_0 = 1000$ has been multiplied 5 times:

$$\textbf{Yearly} \qquad P_5 = (1.06)^5\,P_0 \quad \text{which is} \quad (1.06)^5\,1000 = \$1338.$$

Now suppose the time step is reduced to a month. The new difference equation is $p_{k+1} = (1 + .06/12)p_k$. After 5 years, or 60 months, you have \$11 more:

$$\textbf{Monthly} \qquad p_{60} = \left(1 + \frac{.06}{12}\right)^{60} p_0 \quad \text{which is} \quad (1.005)^{60}\,1000 = \$1349.$$

The next step is to compound every day, on 5(365) days. This only helps a little:

$$\textbf{Daily compounding} \qquad \left(1 + \frac{.06}{365}\right)^{5\cdot 365} 1000 = \$1349.83.$$

Finally, to keep their employees really moving, banks offer *continuous compounding*. The interest is added on at every instant, and the difference equation breaks down. You can hope that the treasurer does not know calculus (which is all about limits as $\Delta t \to 0$). The bank could compound the interest N times a year, so $\Delta t = 1/N$:

$$\textbf{Continuously} \qquad \left(1 + \frac{.06}{N}\right)^{5N} 1000 \quad \to \quad e^{.30}\,1000 = \$1349.87.$$

Or the bank can switch to a differential equation—the limit of the difference equation $p_{k+1} = (1 + .06\Delta t)p_k$. Moving p_k to the left side and dividing by Δt,

$$\textbf{Discrete to continuous} \qquad \frac{p_{k+1} - p_k}{\Delta t} = .06p_k \quad \text{approaches} \quad \frac{dp}{dt} = .06p. \qquad (1)$$

The solution is $p(t) = e^{.06t}p_0$. After $t = 5$ years, this again amounts to \$1349.87. The principal stays finite, even when it is compounded every instant—and the improvement over compounding every day is only four cents.

Fibonacci Numbers

The main object of this section is to solve $u_{k+1} = Au_k$. That leads us to A^k and **powers of matrices**. Our second example is the famous ***Fibonacci sequence***:

Fibonacci numbers $\quad 0, 1, 1, 2, 3, 5, 8, 13, \ldots.$

You see the pattern: Every Fibonacci number is the sum of the two previous F's:

$$\textbf{Fibonacci equation} \qquad F_{k+2} = F_{k+1} + F_k. \tag{2}$$

That is the difference equation. It turns up in a most fantastic variety of applications, and deserves a book of its own. Leaves grow in a spiral pattern, and on the apple or oak you find five growths for every two turns around the stem. The pear tree has eight for every three turns, and the willow is 13:5. The champion seems to be a sunflower whose seeds chose an almost unbelievable ratio of $F_{12}/F_{13} = 144/233$.*

How could we find the 1000th Fibonacci number, without starting at $F_0 = 0$ and $F_1 = 1$, and working all the way out to F_{1000}? The goal is to solve the difference equation $F_{k+2} = F_{k+1} + F_k$. **This can be reduced to a one-step equation $u_{k+1} = Au_k$. Every step multiplies $u_k = (F_{k+1}, F_k)$ by a matrix A:**

$$\begin{aligned} F_{k+2} &= F_{k+1} + F_k \\ F_{k+1} &= F_{k+1} \end{aligned} \qquad \text{becomes} \qquad u_{k+1} = \begin{bmatrix} \mathbf{1} & \mathbf{1} \\ \mathbf{1} & \mathbf{0} \end{bmatrix} \begin{bmatrix} F_{k+1} \\ F_k \end{bmatrix} = Au_k. \tag{3}$$

The one-step system $u_{k+1} = Au_k$ is easy to solve. It starts from u_0. After one step it produces $u_1 = Au_0$. Then u_2 is Au_1, which is A^2u_0. *Every step brings a multiplication by A*, and after k steps there are k multiplications:

> ***The solution to a difference equation $u_{k+1} = Au_k$ is $u_k = A^k u_0$.***

The real problem is to find some quick way to compute the powers A^k, and thereby find the 1000th Fibonacci number. The key lies in the eigenvalues and eigenvectors:

5G If A can be diagonalized, $A = S\Lambda S^{-1}$, then A^k comes from Λ^k:

$$u_k = A^k u_0 = (S\Lambda S^{-1})(S\Lambda S^{-1})\cdots(S\Lambda S^{-1})u_0 = S\Lambda^k S^{-1}u_0. \tag{4}$$

The columns of S are the eigenvectors of A. Writing $S^{-1}u_0 = c$, the solution becomes

$$u_k = S\Lambda^k c = \begin{bmatrix} x_1 & \cdots & x_n \end{bmatrix} \begin{bmatrix} \lambda_1^k & & \\ & \ddots & \\ & & \lambda_n^k \end{bmatrix} \begin{bmatrix} c_1 \\ \vdots \\ c_n \end{bmatrix} = c_1\lambda_1^k x_1 + \cdots + c_n\lambda_n^k x_n. \tag{5}$$

After k steps, u_k is a combination of the n "pure solutions" $\lambda^k x$.

---

* For these botanical applications, see D'Arcy Thompson's book *On Growth and Form* (Cambridge University Press, 1942) or Peter Stevens's beautiful *Patterns in Nature* (Little, Brown, 1974). Hundreds of other properties of the F_n have been published in the *Fibonacci Quarterly*. Apparently Fibonacci brought Arabic numerals into Europe, about 1200 A.D.

These formulas give two different approaches to the same solution $u_k = S\Lambda^k S^{-1}u_0$. The first formula recognized that A^k is identical with $S\Lambda^k S^{-1}$, and we could stop there. But the second approach brings out the analogy with a differential equation: ***The pure exponential solutions*** $e^{\lambda_i t}x_i$ ***are now the pure powers*** $\lambda_i^k x_i$. The eigenvectors x_i are amplified by the eigenvalues λ_i. By combining these special solutions to match u_0—that is where c came from—we recover the correct solution $u_k = S\Lambda^k S^{-1}u_0$.

In any specific example like Fibonacci's, the first step is to find the eigenvalues:

$$A - \lambda I = \begin{bmatrix} 1-\lambda & 1 \\ 1 & -\lambda \end{bmatrix} \quad \text{has} \quad \det(A - \lambda I) = \lambda^2 - \lambda - 1$$

$$\textbf{Two eigenvalues} \qquad \lambda_1 = \frac{1+\sqrt{5}}{2} \quad \text{and} \quad \lambda_2 = \frac{1-\sqrt{5}}{2}.$$

The second row of $A - \lambda I$ is $(1, -\lambda)$. To get $(A - \lambda I)x = 0$, the eigenvector is $x = (\lambda, 1)$. The first Fibonacci numbers $F_0 = 0$ and $F_1 = 1$ go into u_0, and $S^{-1}u_0 = c$:

$$S^{-1}u_0 = \begin{bmatrix} \lambda_1 & \lambda_2 \\ 1 & 1 \end{bmatrix}^{-1} \begin{bmatrix} 1 \\ 0 \end{bmatrix} \quad \text{gives} \quad c = \begin{bmatrix} 1/(\lambda_1 - \lambda_2) \\ -1/(\lambda_1 - \lambda_2) \end{bmatrix} = \frac{1}{\sqrt{5}} \begin{bmatrix} 1 \\ -1 \end{bmatrix}.$$

Those are the constants in $u_k = c_1\lambda_1^k x_1 + c_2\lambda_2^k x_2$. Both eigenvectors x_1 and x_2 have second component 1. That leaves $F_k = c_1\lambda_1^k + c_2\lambda_2^k$ in the second component of u_k:

$$\textbf{Fibonacci numbers} \qquad F_k = \frac{1}{\sqrt{5}} \left[\left(\frac{1+\sqrt{5}}{2} \right)^k - \left(\frac{1-\sqrt{5}}{2} \right)^k \right].$$

This is the answer we wanted. The fractions and square roots look surprising because Fibonacci's rule $F_{k+2} = F_{k+1} + F_k$ must produce whole numbers. Somehow that formula for F_k must give an integer. In fact, since the second term $[(1-\sqrt{5})/2]^k/\sqrt{5}$ is always less than $\frac{1}{2}$, it must just move the first term to the nearest integer:

$$F_{1000} = \text{nearest integer to } \frac{1}{\sqrt{5}} \left(\frac{1+\sqrt{5}}{2} \right)^{1000}.$$

This is an enormous number, and F_{1001} will be even bigger. The fractions are becoming insignificant, and the ratio F_{1001}/F_{1000} must be very close to $(1+\sqrt{5})/2 \approx 1.618$. Since λ_2^k is insignificant compared to λ_1^k, the ratio F_{k+1}/F_k approaches λ_1.

That is a typical difference equation, leading to the powers of $A = \begin{bmatrix} 1 & 1 \\ 1 & 0 \end{bmatrix}$. It involved $\sqrt{5}$ because the eigenvalues did. If we choose a matrix with $\lambda_1 = 1$ and $\lambda_2 = 6$, we can focus on the simplicity of the computation—*after A has been diagonalized*:

$$A = \begin{bmatrix} -4 & -5 \\ 10 & 11 \end{bmatrix} \quad \text{has } \lambda = 1 \text{ and } 6, \text{ with } x_1 = \begin{bmatrix} 1 \\ -1 \end{bmatrix} \text{ and } x_2 = \begin{bmatrix} -1 \\ 2 \end{bmatrix}$$

$$A^k = S\Lambda^k S^{-1} \quad \text{is} \quad \begin{bmatrix} 1 & -1 \\ -1 & 2 \end{bmatrix} \begin{bmatrix} \mathbf{1^k} & 0 \\ 0 & \mathbf{6^k} \end{bmatrix} \begin{bmatrix} 2 & 1 \\ 1 & 1 \end{bmatrix} = \begin{bmatrix} 2 - 6^k & 1 - 6^k \\ -2 + 2\cdot 6^k & -1 + 2\cdot 6^k \end{bmatrix}.$$

The powers 6^k and 1^k appear in that last matrix A^k, mixed in by the eigenvectors.

For the difference equation $u_{k+1} = Au_k$, we emphasize the main point. Every eigenvector x produces a "pure solution" with powers of λ:

One solution is $\boldsymbol{u_0 = x, \quad u_1 = \lambda x, \quad u_2 = \lambda^2 x, \ldots}$

When the initial u_0 is an eigenvector x, this is *the* solution: $u_k = \lambda^k x$. In general u_0 is not an eigenvector. But if u_0 is a *combination* of eigenvectors, the solution u_k is the same combination of these special solutions.

5H If $u_0 = c_1x_1 + \cdots + c_nx_n$, then after k steps $u_k = c_1\lambda_1^k x_1 + \cdots + c_n\lambda_n^k x_n$. Choose the c's to match the starting vector u_0:

$$u_0 = \begin{bmatrix} & & \\ x_1 & \cdots & x_n \\ & & \end{bmatrix} \begin{bmatrix} c_1 \\ \vdots \\ c_n \end{bmatrix} = Sc \quad \text{and} \quad c = S^{-1}u_0. \tag{6}$$

Markov Matrices

There was an exercise in Chapter 1, about moving in and out of California, that is worth another look. These were the rules:

Each year $\frac{1}{10}$ of the people outside California move in, and $\frac{2}{10}$ of the people inside California move out. We start with y_0 people outside and z_0 inside.

At the end of the first year the numbers outside and inside are y_1 and z_1:

$$\textbf{Difference equation} \quad \begin{aligned} y_1 &= .9y_0 + .2z_0 \\ z_1 &= .1y_0 + .8z_0 \end{aligned} \quad \text{or} \quad \begin{bmatrix} y_1 \\ z_1 \end{bmatrix} = \begin{bmatrix} .9 & .2 \\ .1 & .8 \end{bmatrix} \begin{bmatrix} y_0 \\ z_0 \end{bmatrix}.$$

This problem and its matrix have the two essential properties of a ***Markov process:***

1. The total number of people stays fixed: ***Each column of the Markov matrix adds up to*** **1**. Nobody is gained or lost.
2. The numbers outside and inside can never become negative: ***The matrix has no negative entries***. The powers A^k are all nonnegative.*

We solve this Markov difference equation using $u_k = S\Lambda^k S^{-1}u_0$. Then we show that the population approaches a "steady state." First A has to be diagonalized:

$$A - \lambda I = \begin{bmatrix} .9 - \lambda & .2 \\ .1 & .8 - \lambda \end{bmatrix} \quad \text{has} \quad \det(A - \lambda I) = \lambda^2 - 1.7\lambda + .7$$

$$\boldsymbol{\lambda_1 = 1 \text{ and } \lambda_2 = .7}: \quad A = S\Lambda S^{-1} = \begin{bmatrix} \frac{2}{3} & \frac{1}{3} \\ \frac{1}{3} & -\frac{1}{3} \end{bmatrix} \begin{bmatrix} 1 & \\ & .7 \end{bmatrix} \begin{bmatrix} 1 & 1 \\ 1 & -2 \end{bmatrix}.$$

* Furthermore, history is completely disregarded; each new u_{k+1} depends only on the current u_k. Perhaps even our lives are examples of Markov processes, but I hope not.

To find A^k, and the distribution after k years, change $S\Lambda S^{-1}$ to $S\Lambda^k S^{-1}$:

$$\begin{bmatrix} y_k \\ z_k \end{bmatrix} = A^k \begin{bmatrix} y_0 \\ z_0 \end{bmatrix} = \begin{bmatrix} \frac{2}{3} & \frac{1}{3} \\ \frac{1}{3} & -\frac{1}{3} \end{bmatrix} \begin{bmatrix} 1^k & \\ & .7^k \end{bmatrix} \begin{bmatrix} 1 & 1 \\ 1 & -2 \end{bmatrix} \begin{bmatrix} y_0 \\ z_0 \end{bmatrix}$$

$$= (y_0 + z_0) \begin{bmatrix} \frac{2}{3} \\ \frac{1}{3} \end{bmatrix} + (y_0 - 2z_0)(.7)^k \begin{bmatrix} \frac{1}{3} \\ -\frac{1}{3} \end{bmatrix}.$$

Those two terms are $c_1\lambda_1^k x_1 + c_2\lambda_2^k x_2$. The factor $\lambda_1^k = 1$ is hidden in the first term. In the long run, the other factor $(.7)^k$ becomes extremely small. ***The solution approaches a limiting state $u_\infty = (y_\infty, z_\infty)$*:**

$$\textbf{Steady state} \qquad \begin{bmatrix} y_\infty \\ z_\infty \end{bmatrix} = (y_0 + z_0) \begin{bmatrix} \frac{2}{3} \\ \frac{1}{3} \end{bmatrix}.$$

The total population is still $y_0 + z_0$, but in the limit $\frac{2}{3}$ of this population is outside California and $\frac{1}{3}$ is inside. This is true no matter what the initial distribution may have been! If the year starts with $\frac{2}{3}$ outside and $\frac{1}{3}$ inside, then it ends the same way:

$$\begin{bmatrix} .9 & .2 \\ .1 & .8 \end{bmatrix} \begin{bmatrix} \frac{2}{3} \\ \frac{1}{3} \end{bmatrix} = \begin{bmatrix} \frac{2}{3} \\ \frac{1}{3} \end{bmatrix}, \qquad \text{or} \qquad Au_\infty = u_\infty.$$

***The steady state is the eigenvector of A corresponding to $\lambda = 1$*.** Multiplication by A, from one time step to the next, leaves u_∞ unchanged.

The theory of Markov processes is illustrated by that California example:

5I A Markov matrix A has all $a_{ij} \geq 0$, with each column adding to 1.

(a) $\lambda_1 = 1$ is an eigenvalue of A.
(b) Its eigenvector x_1 is nonnegative—and it is a steady state, since $Ax_1 = x_1$.
(c) The other eigenvalues satisfy $|\lambda_i| \leq 1$.
(d) If A or any power of A has all *positive* entries, these other $|\lambda_i|$ are below 1. The solution $A^k u_0$ approaches a multiple of x_1—which is the steady state u_∞.

To find the right multiple of x_1, use the fact that the total population stays the same. If California started with all 90 million people out, it ended with 60 million out and 30 million in. It ends the same way if all 90 million were originally inside.

We note that many authors transpose the matrix so its *rows* add to 1.

Remark Our description of a Markov process was deterministic; populations moved in fixed proportions. But if we look at a single individual, the fractions that move become *probabilities*. With probability $\frac{1}{10}$, an individual outside California moves in. If inside, the probability of moving out is $\frac{2}{10}$. The movement becomes a *random process*, and A is called a ***transition matrix***.

The components of $u_k = A^k u_0$ specify the probability that the individual is outside or inside the state. These probabilities are never negative, and add to 1—everybody has to be somewhere. That brings us back to the two fundamental properties of a Markov matrix: Each column adds to 1, and no entry is negative.

Why is $\lambda = 1$ always an eigenvalue? Each column of $A - I$ adds up to $1 - 1 = 0$. Therefore the rows of $A - I$ add up to the zero row, they are linearly dependent, and $\det(A - I) = 0$.

Except for very special cases, u_k will approach the corresponding eigenvector.* In the formula $u_k = c_1\lambda_1^k x_1 + \cdots + c_n\lambda_n^k x_n$, no eigenvalue can be larger than 1. (Otherwise the probabilities u_k would blow up.) If all other eigenvalues are strictly smaller than $\lambda_1 = 1$, then the first term in the formula will be dominant. The other λ_i^k go to zero, and $u_k \to c_1x_1 = u_\infty =$ steady state.

This is an example of one of the central themes of this chapter: Given information about A, find information about its eigenvalues. Here we found $\lambda_{\max} = 1$.

Stability of $u_{k+1} = Au_k$

There is an obvious difference between Fibonacci numbers and Markov processes. The numbers F_k become larger and larger, while by definition any "probability" is between 0 and 1. The Fibonacci equation is *unstable*. So is the compound interest equation $P_{k+1} = 1.06P_k$; the principal keeps growing forever. If the Markov probabilities decreased to zero, that equation would be stable; but they do not, since at every stage they must add to 1. Therefore a Markov process is *neutrally stable*.

We want to study the behavior of $u_{k+1} = Au_k$ as $k \to \infty$. Assuming that A can be diagonalized, u_k will be a combination of pure solutions:

$$\textbf{Solution at time } \boldsymbol{k} \qquad u_k = S\Lambda^k S^{-1}u_0 = c_1\lambda_1^k x_1 + \cdots + c_n\lambda_n^k x_n.$$

The growth of u_k is governed by the λ_i^k. ***Stability depends on the eigenvalues***:

5J The difference equation $u_{k+1} = Au_k$ is

stable if all eigenvalues satisfy $|\lambda_i| < 1$;
neutrally stable if some $|\lambda_i| = 1$ and all the other $|\lambda_i| < 1$; and
unstable if at least one eigenvalue has $|\lambda_i| > 1$.

In the stable case, the powers A^k approach zero and so does $u_k = A^k u_0$.

Example 1 This matrix A is certainly stable:

$$A = \begin{bmatrix} 0 & 4 \\ 0 & \frac{1}{2} \end{bmatrix} \quad \text{has eigenvalues 0 and } \tfrac{1}{2}.$$

The λ's are on the main diagonal because A is triangular. Starting from any u_0, and following the rule $u_{k+1} = Au_k$, the solution must eventually approach zero:

$$u_0 = \begin{bmatrix} 0 \\ 1 \end{bmatrix}, \quad u_1 = \begin{bmatrix} 4 \\ \frac{1}{2} \end{bmatrix}, \quad u_2 = \begin{bmatrix} 2 \\ \frac{1}{4} \end{bmatrix}, \quad u_3 = \begin{bmatrix} 1 \\ \frac{1}{8} \end{bmatrix}, \quad u_4 = \begin{bmatrix} \frac{1}{2} \\ \frac{1}{16} \end{bmatrix}, \quad \cdots$$

---

* If everybody outside moves in and everybody inside moves out, then the populations are reversed every year and there is no steady state. The transition matrix is $A = \begin{bmatrix} 0 & 1 \\ 1 & 0 \end{bmatrix}$ and -1 is an eigenvalue as well as $+1$—which cannot happen if all $a_{ij} > 0$.

The larger eigenvalue $\lambda = \frac{1}{2}$ governs the decay; after the first step every u_k is $\frac{1}{2}u_{k-1}$. The real effect of the first step is to split u_0 into the two eigenvectors of A:

$$u_0 = \begin{bmatrix} 8 \\ 1 \end{bmatrix} + \begin{bmatrix} -8 \\ 0 \end{bmatrix} \quad \text{and then} \quad u_k = \left(\frac{1}{2}\right)^k \begin{bmatrix} 8 \\ 1 \end{bmatrix} + (0)^k \begin{bmatrix} -8 \\ 0 \end{bmatrix}.$$

Positive Matrices and Applications in Economics

By developing the Markov ideas we can find a small gold mine (*entirely optional*) of matrix applications in economics.

Example 2 ***Leontief's input-output matrix***

This is one of the first great successes of mathematical economics. To illustrate it, we construct a *consumption matrix*—in which a_{ij} gives the amount of product j that is needed to create one unit of product i:

$$A = \begin{bmatrix} .4 & 0 & .1 \\ 0 & .1 & .8 \\ .5 & .7 & .1 \end{bmatrix}. \qquad \begin{matrix} \text{(steel)} \\ \text{(food)} \\ \text{(labor)} \end{matrix}$$

The first question is: Can we produce y_1 units of steel, y_2 units of food, and y_3 units of labor? We must start with larger amounts p_1, p_2, p_3, because some part is consumed by the production itself. The amount consumed is Ap, and it leaves a net production of $p - Ap$.

Problem *To find a vector p such that $p - Ap = y$, or $p = (I - A)^{-1}y$.*

On the surface, we are only asking if $I - A$ is invertible. But there is a nonnegative twist to the problem. Demand and production, y and p, are nonnegative. Since p is $(I-A)^{-1}y$, the real question is about the matrix that multiplies y:

When is $(I - A)^{-1}$ a nonnegative matrix?

Roughly speaking, A cannot be too large. If production consumes too much, nothing is left as output. The key is in the largest eigenvalue λ_1 of A, which must be below 1:

If $\lambda_1 > 1$, $(I - A)^{-1}$ fails to be nonnegative.
If $\lambda_1 = 1$, $(I - A)^{-1}$ fails to exist.
If $\lambda_1 < 1$, $(I - A)^{-1}$ is a converging sum of nonnegative matrices:

$$\textbf{Geometric series} \qquad (I - A)^{-1} = I + A + A^2 + A^3 + \cdots. \tag{7}$$

The 3 by 3 example has $\lambda_1 = .9$, and output exceeds input. Production can go on.

Those are easy to prove, once we know the main fact about a nonnegative matrix like A: ***Not only is the largest eigenvalue λ_1 positive, but so is the eigenvector x_1***. Then $(I - A)^{-1}$ has the same eigenvector, with eigenvalue $1/(1 - \lambda_1)$.

If λ_1 exceeds 1, that last number is negative. The matrix $(I - A)^{-1}$ will take the positive vector x_1 to a negative vector $x_1/(1 - \lambda_1)$. In that case $(I - A)^{-1}$ is definitely not nonnegative. If $\lambda_1 = 1$, then $I - A$ is singular. The productive case is $\lambda_1 < 1$, when the powers of A go to zero (stability) and the infinite series $I + A + A^2 + \cdots$ converges.

Multiplying this series by $I - A$ leaves the identity matrix—all higher powers cancel—so $(I - A)^{-1}$ is a sum of nonnegative matrices. We give two examples:

$$A = \begin{bmatrix} 0 & 2 \\ 2 & 0 \end{bmatrix} \text{ has } \lambda_1 = 2 \text{ and the economy is lost}$$

$$A = \begin{bmatrix} .5 & 2 \\ 0 & .5 \end{bmatrix} \text{ has } \lambda_1 = \frac{1}{2} \text{ and we can produce anything.}$$

The matrices $(I - A)^{-1}$ in those two cases are $-\frac{1}{3}\begin{bmatrix} 1 & 2 \\ 2 & 1 \end{bmatrix}$ and $\begin{bmatrix} 2 & 8 \\ 0 & 2 \end{bmatrix}$.

Leontief's inspiration was to find a model that uses genuine data from the real economy. The table for 1958 contained 83 industries in the United States, with a "transactions table" of consumption and production for each one. The theory also reaches beyond $(I - A)^{-1}$, to decide natural prices and questions of optimization. Normally labor is in limited supply and ought to be minimized. And, of course, the economy is not always linear.

Example 3 ***The prices in a*** *closed* ***input-output model***

The model is called "closed" when everything produced is also consumed. Nothing goes outside the system. In that case A goes back to a *Markov matrix*. ***The columns add up to* 1**. We might be talking about the *value* of steel and food and labor, instead of the number of units. The vector p represents prices instead of production levels.

Suppose p_0 is a vector of prices. Then Ap_0 multiplies prices by amounts to give the value of each product. That is a new set of prices which the system uses for the next set of values A^2p_0. The question is whether the prices approach equilibrium. Are there prices such that $p = Ap$, and does the system take us there?

You recognize p as the (nonnegative) eigenvector of the Markov matrix A, with $\lambda = 1$. It is the steady state p_∞, and it is approached from any starting point p_0. By repeating a transaction over and over, the price tends to equilibrium.

The "Perron–Frobenius theorem" gives the key properties of a ***positive matrix***—not to be confused with a *positive definite* matrix, which is symmetric and has all its eigenvalues positive. Here all the entries a_{ij} are positive.

5K If A is a positive matrix, so is its largest eigenvalue: $\lambda_1 >$ all other $|\lambda_i|$. Every component of the corresponding eigenvector x_1 is also positive.

Proof Suppose $A > 0$. The key idea is to look at all numbers t such that $Ax \geq tx$ for some nonnegative vector x (other than $x = 0$). We are allowing inequality in $Ax \geq tx$ in order to have many positive candidates t. For the largest value $t_{\max}$ (which is attained), we will show that ***equality holds***: $Ax = t_{\max}x$.

Otherwise, if $Ax \geq t_{\max}x$ is not an equality, multiply by A. Because A is positive, that produces a strict inequality $A^2x > t_{\max}Ax$. Therefore the positive vector $y = Ax$ satisfies $Ay > t_{\max}y$, and $t_{\max}$ could have been larger. This contradiction forces the equality $Ax = t_{\max}x$, and we have an eigenvalue. Its eigenvector x is positive (not just nonnegative) because on the left-hand side of that equality Ax is sure to be positive.

To see that no eigenvalue can be larger than t_{max}, suppose $Az = \lambda z$. Since λ and z may involve negative or complex numbers, we take absolute values: $|\lambda|\,|z| = |Az| \le A|z|$ by the "triangle inequality." This $|z|$ is a nonnegative vector, so $|\lambda|$ is one of the possible candidates t. Therefore $|\lambda|$ cannot exceed λ_1, which was t_{max}. ■

Example 4 ***Von Neumann's model of an expanding economy***
We go back to the 3 by 3 matrix A that gave the consumption of steel, food, and labor. If the outputs are s_1, f_1, ℓ_1, then the required inputs are

$$u_0 = \begin{bmatrix} .4 & 0 & .1 \\ 0 & .1 & .8 \\ .5 & .7 & .1 \end{bmatrix} \begin{bmatrix} s_1 \\ f_1 \\ \ell_1 \end{bmatrix} = Au_1.$$

In economics the difference equation is backward! Instead of $u_1 = Au_0$ we have $u_0 = Au_1$. If A is small (as it is), then production does not consume everything—and the economy can grow. The eigenvalues of A^{-1} will govern this growth. But again there is a nonnegative twist, since steel, food, and labor cannot come in negative amounts. Von Neumann asked for the maximum rate t at which the economy can expand and *still stay nonnegative*, meaning that $u_1 \ge tu_0 \ge 0$.

Thus the problem requires $u_1 \ge tAu_1$. It is like the Perron–Frobenius theorem, with A on the other side. As before, equality holds when t reaches t_{max}—which is the eigenvalue associated with the positive eigenvector of A^{-1}. In this example the expansion factor is $\frac{10}{9}$:

$$x = \begin{bmatrix} 1 \\ 5 \\ 5 \end{bmatrix} \quad \text{and} \quad Ax = \begin{bmatrix} .4 & 0 & .1 \\ 0 & .1 & .8 \\ .5 & .7 & .1 \end{bmatrix} \begin{bmatrix} 1 \\ 5 \\ 5 \end{bmatrix} = \begin{bmatrix} 0.9 \\ 4.5 \\ 4.5 \end{bmatrix} = \frac{9}{10}x.$$

With steel–food–labor in the ratio 1–5–5, the economy grows as quickly as possible: ***The maximum growth rate is*** $\mathbf{1/\lambda_1}$.

Problem Set 5.3

1. Prove that every third Fibonacci number in 0, 1, 1, 2, 3, ... is even.

2. Bernadelli studied a beetle "which lives three years only, and propagates in its third year." They survive the first year with probability $\frac{1}{2}$, and the second with probability $\frac{1}{3}$, and then produce six females on the way out:

$$\textbf{Beetle matrix} \qquad A = \begin{bmatrix} 0 & 0 & 6 \\ \frac{1}{2} & 0 & 0 \\ 0 & \frac{1}{3} & 0 \end{bmatrix}.$$

   Show that $A^3 = I$, and follow the distribution of 3000 beetles for six years.

3. For the Fibonacci matrix $A = \begin{bmatrix} 1 & 1 \\ 1 & 0 \end{bmatrix}$, compute A^2, A^3, and A^4. Then use the text and a calculator to find F_{20}.

4. Suppose each "Gibonacci" number G_{k+2} is the *average* of the two previous numbers G_{k+1} and G_k. Then $G_{k+2} = \frac{1}{2}(G_{k+1} + G_k)$:

$$\begin{aligned} G_{k+2} &= \tfrac{1}{2}G_{k+1} + \tfrac{1}{2}G_k \\ G_{k+1} &= G_{k+1} \end{aligned} \quad \text{is} \quad \begin{bmatrix} G_{k+2} \\ G_{k+1} \end{bmatrix} = \begin{bmatrix} & A & \end{bmatrix} \begin{bmatrix} G_{k+1} \\ G_k \end{bmatrix}.$$

(a) Find the eigenvalues and eigenvectors of A.
(b) Find the limit as $n \to \infty$ of the matrices $A^n = S\Lambda^n S^{-1}$.
(c) If $G_0 = 0$ and $G_1 = 1$, show that the Gibonacci numbers approach $\frac{2}{3}$.

5. Diagonalize the Fibonacci matrix by completing S^{-1}:

$$\begin{bmatrix} 1 & 1 \\ 1 & 0 \end{bmatrix} = \begin{bmatrix} \lambda_1 & \lambda_2 \\ 1 & 1 \end{bmatrix} \begin{bmatrix} \lambda_1 & 0 \\ 0 & \lambda_2 \end{bmatrix} \begin{bmatrix} & \\ & \end{bmatrix}.$$

Do the multiplication $S\Lambda^k S^{-1} \begin{bmatrix} 1 \\ 0 \end{bmatrix}$ to find its second component. This is the kth Fibonacci number $F_k = (\lambda_1^k - \lambda_2^k)/(\lambda_1 - \lambda_2)$.

6. The numbers λ_1^k and λ_2^k satisfy the Fibonacci rule $F_{k+2} = F_{k+1} + F_k$:

$$\lambda_1^{k+2} = \lambda_1^{k+1} + \lambda_1^k \quad \text{and} \quad \lambda_2^{k+2} = \lambda_2^{k+1} + \lambda_2^k.$$

Prove this by using the original equation for the λ's (multiply it by λ^k). Then any combination of λ_1^k and λ_2^k satisfies the rule. The combination $F_k = (\lambda_1^k - \lambda_2^k)/(\lambda_1 - \lambda_2)$ gives the right start of $F_0 = 0$ and $F_1 = 1$.

7. Lucas started with $L_0 = 2$ and $L_1 = 1$. The rule $L_{k+2} = L_{k+1} + L_k$ is the same, so A is still Fibonacci's matrix. Add its eigenvectors $x_1 + x_2$:

$$\begin{bmatrix} \lambda_1 \\ 1 \end{bmatrix} + \begin{bmatrix} \lambda_2 \\ 1 \end{bmatrix} = \begin{bmatrix} \frac{1}{2}(1+\sqrt{5}) \\ 1 \end{bmatrix} + \begin{bmatrix} \frac{1}{2}(1-\sqrt{5}) \\ 1 \end{bmatrix} = \begin{bmatrix} 1 \\ 2 \end{bmatrix} = \begin{bmatrix} L_1 \\ L_0 \end{bmatrix}.$$

Multiplying by A^k, the second component is $L_k = \lambda_1^k + \lambda_2^k$. Compute the Lucas number L_{10} slowly by $L_{k+2} = L_{k+1} + L_k$, and compute approximately by λ_1^{10}.

8. Suppose there is an epidemic in which every month half of those who are well become sick, and a quarter of those who are sick become dead. Find the steady state for the corresponding Markov process

$$\begin{bmatrix} d_{k+1} \\ s_{k+1} \\ w_{k+1} \end{bmatrix} = \begin{bmatrix} 1 & \frac{1}{4} & 0 \\ 0 & \frac{3}{4} & \frac{1}{2} \\ 0 & 0 & \frac{1}{2} \end{bmatrix} \begin{bmatrix} d_k \\ s_k \\ w_k \end{bmatrix}.$$

9. Write the 3 by 3 transition matrix for a chemistry course that is taught in two sections, if every week $\frac{1}{4}$ of those in Section A and $\frac{1}{3}$ of those in Section B drop the course, and $\frac{1}{6}$ of each section transfer to the other section.

10. Find the limiting values of y_k and z_k ($k \to \infty$) if

$$\begin{aligned} y_{k+1} &= .8y_k + .3z_k \qquad & y_0 &= 0 \\ z_{k+1} &= .2y_k + .7z_k \qquad & z_0 &= 5. \end{aligned}$$

Also find formulas for y_k and z_k from $A^k = S\Lambda^k S^{-1}$.

11. (a) From the fact that column 1 + column 2 = 2(column 3), so the columns are linearly dependent, find one eigenvalue and one eigenvector of A:

$$A = \begin{bmatrix} .2 & .4 & .3 \\ .4 & .2 & .3 \\ .4 & .4 & .4 \end{bmatrix}.$$

(b) Find the other eigenvalues of A (it is Markov).

(c) If $u_0 = (0, 10, 0)$, find the limit of $A^k u_0$ as $k \to \infty$.

12. Suppose there are three major centers for Move-It-Yourself trucks. Every month half of those in Boston and in Los Angeles go to Chicago, the other half stay where they are, and the trucks in Chicago are split equally between Boston and Los Angeles. Set up the 3 by 3 transition matrix A, and find the steady state u_∞ corresponding to the eigenvalue $\lambda = 1$.

13. (a) In what range of a and b is the following equation a Markov process?

$$u_{k+1} = Au_k = \begin{bmatrix} a & b \\ 1-a & 1-b \end{bmatrix} u_k, \qquad u_0 = \begin{bmatrix} 1 \\ 1 \end{bmatrix}.$$

(b) Compute $u_k = S\Lambda^k S^{-1} u_0$ for any a and b.

(c) Under what condition on a and b does u_k approach a finite limit as $k \to \infty$, and what is the limit? Does A have to be a Markov matrix?

14. Multinational companies in the Americas, Asia, and Europe have assets of \$4 trillion. At the start, \$2 trillion are in the Americas and \$2 trillion in Europe. Each year $\frac{1}{2}$ the American money stays home, and $\frac{1}{4}$ goes to each of Asia and Europe. For Asia and Europe, $\frac{1}{2}$ stays home and $\frac{1}{2}$ is sent to the Americas.

(a) Find the matrix that gives

$$\begin{bmatrix} \text{Americas} \\ \text{Asia} \\ \text{Europe} \end{bmatrix}_{\text{year } k+1} = A \begin{bmatrix} \text{Americas} \\ \text{Asia} \\ \text{Europe} \end{bmatrix}_{\text{year } k}.$$

(b) Find the eigenvalues and eigenvectors of A.

(c) Find the limiting distribution of the \$4 trillion as the world ends.

(d) Find the distribution of the \$4 trillion at year k.

15. If A is a Markov matrix, show that the sum of the components of Ax equals the sum of the components of x. Deduce that if $Ax = \lambda x$ with $\lambda \neq 1$, the components of the eigenvector add to zero.

16. The solution to $du/dt = Au = \begin{bmatrix} 0 & -1 \\ 1 & 0 \end{bmatrix} u$ (eigenvalues i and $-i$) goes around in a circle: $u = (\cos t, \sin t)$. Suppose we approximate du/dt by forward, backward, and centered differences **F**, **B**, **C**:

(**F**) $u_{n+1} - u_n = Au_n$ or $u_{n+1} = (I + A)u_n$ (this is Euler's method).

(**B**) $u_{n+1} - u_n = Au_{n+1}$ or $u_{n+1} = (I - A)^{-1}u_n$ (backward Euler).

(**C**) $u_{n+1} - u_n = \frac{1}{2}A(u_{n+1} + u_n)$ or $u_{n+1} = \left(I - \frac{1}{2}A\right)^{-1}\left(I + \frac{1}{2}A\right)u_n$.

Find the eigenvalues of $I + A$, $(I - A)^{-1}$, and $\left(I - \frac{1}{2}A\right)^{-1}\left(I + \frac{1}{2}A\right)$. For which difference equation does the solution u_n stay on a circle?

17. What values of α produce instability in $v_{n+1} = \alpha(v_n + w_n)$, $w_{n+1} = \alpha(v_n + w_n)$?

18. Find the largest a, b, c for which these matrices are stable or neutrally stable:

$$\begin{bmatrix} a & -.8 \\ .8 & .2 \end{bmatrix}, \quad \begin{bmatrix} b & .8 \\ 0 & .2 \end{bmatrix}, \quad \begin{bmatrix} c & .8 \\ .2 & c \end{bmatrix}.$$

19. Multiplying term by term, check that $(I - A)(I + A + A^2 + \cdots) = I$. This series represents $(I - A)^{-1}$. It is nonnegative when A is nonnegative, provided it has a finite sum; the condition for that is $\lambda_{\max} < 1$. Add up the infinite series, and confirm that it equals $(I - A)^{-1}$, for the consumption matrix

$$A = \begin{bmatrix} 0 & 1 & 1 \\ 0 & 0 & 1 \\ 0 & 0 & 0 \end{bmatrix} \quad \text{which has } \lambda_{\max} = 0.$$

20. For $A = \begin{bmatrix} 0 & .2 \\ 0 & .5 \end{bmatrix}$, find the powers A^k (including A^0) and show explicitly that their sum agrees with $(I - A)^{-1}$.

21. Explain by mathematics or economics why increasing the "consumption matrix" A must increase $t_{\max} = \lambda_1$ (and slow down the expansion).

22. What are the limits as $k \to \infty$ (the steady states) of the following?

$$\begin{bmatrix} .4 & .2 \\ .6 & .8 \end{bmatrix}^k \begin{bmatrix} 1 \\ 0 \end{bmatrix}, \quad \begin{bmatrix} .4 & .2 \\ .6 & .8 \end{bmatrix}^k \begin{bmatrix} 0 \\ 1 \end{bmatrix}, \quad \begin{bmatrix} .4 & .2 \\ .6 & .8 \end{bmatrix}^k.$$

Problems 23–29 are about $A = S\Lambda S^{-1}$ and $A^k = S\Lambda^k S^{-1}$

23. Diagonalize A and compute $S\Lambda^k S^{-1}$ to prove this formula for A^k:

$$A = \begin{bmatrix} 3 & 2 \\ 2 & 3 \end{bmatrix} \quad \text{has} \quad A^k = \frac{1}{2}\begin{bmatrix} 5^k + 1 & 5^k - 1 \\ 5^k - 1 & 5^k + 1 \end{bmatrix}.$$

24. Diagonalize B and compute $S\Lambda^k S^{-1}$ to prove this formula for B^k:

$$B = \begin{bmatrix} 3 & 1 \\ 0 & 2 \end{bmatrix} \quad \text{has} \quad B^k = \begin{bmatrix} 3^k & 3^k - 2^k \\ 0 & 2^k \end{bmatrix}.$$

25. The eigenvalues of A are 1 and 9, the eigenvalues of B are -1 and 9:

$$A = \begin{bmatrix} 5 & 4 \\ 4 & 5 \end{bmatrix} \quad \text{and} \quad B = \begin{bmatrix} 4 & 5 \\ 5 & 4 \end{bmatrix}.$$

Find a matrix square root of A from $R = S\sqrt{\Lambda}\,S^{-1}$. Why is there no real matrix square root of B?

26. If A and B have the same λ's with the same full set of independent eigenvectors, their factorizations into ______ are the same. So $A = B$.

27. Suppose A and B have the same full set of eigenvectors, so that $A = S\Lambda_1 S^{-1}$ and $B = S\Lambda_2 S^{-1}$. Prove that $AB = BA$.

28. (a) When do the eigenvectors for $\lambda = 0$ span the nullspace $N(A)$?
(b) When do all the eigenvectors for $\lambda \neq 0$ span the column space $C(A)$?

29. The powers A^k approach zero if all $|\lambda_i| < 1$, and they blow up if any $|\lambda_i| > 1$. Peter Lax gives four striking examples in his book *Linear Algebra*.

$$A = \begin{bmatrix} 3 & 2 \\ 1 & 4 \end{bmatrix} \qquad B = \begin{bmatrix} 3 & 2 \\ -5 & -3 \end{bmatrix} \qquad C = \begin{bmatrix} 5 & 7 \\ -3 & -4 \end{bmatrix} \qquad D = \begin{bmatrix} 5 & 6.9 \\ -3 & -4 \end{bmatrix}$$

$$\|A^{1024}\| > 10^{700} \qquad B^{1024} = I \qquad C^{1024} = -C \qquad \|D^{1024}\| < 10^{-78}$$

Find the eigenvalues $\lambda = e^{i\theta}$ of B and C to show that $B^4 = I$ and $C^3 = -I$.

5.4 DIFFERENTIAL EQUATIONS AND e^{At}

Wherever you find a system of equations, rather than a single equation, matrix theory has a part to play. For difference equations, the solution $u_k = A^k u_0$ depended on the powers of A. For differential equations, the solution $u(t) = e^{At}u(0)$ depends on the ***exponential*** of A. To define this exponential, and to understand it, we turn right away to an example:

$$\textbf{Differential equation} \qquad \frac{du}{dt} = Au = \begin{bmatrix} -2 & 1 \\ 1 & -2 \end{bmatrix} u. \tag{1}$$

The first step is always to find the eigenvalues (-1 and -3) and the eigenvectors:

$$A\begin{bmatrix} 1 \\ 1 \end{bmatrix} = (-1)\begin{bmatrix} 1 \\ 1 \end{bmatrix} \quad \text{and} \quad A\begin{bmatrix} 1 \\ -1 \end{bmatrix} = (-3)\begin{bmatrix} 1 \\ -1 \end{bmatrix}.$$

Then several approaches lead to $u(t)$. Probably the best is to match the general solution to the initial vector $u(0)$ at $t = 0$.

The general solution is a combination of pure exponential solutions. These are solutions of the special form $ce^{\lambda t}x$, where λ is an eigenvalue of A and x is its eigenvector. These pure solutions satisfy the differential equation, since $d/dt(ce^{\lambda t}x) = A(ce^{\lambda t}x)$. (They were our introduction to eigenvalues at the start of the chapter.) In this 2 by 2 example, there are two pure exponentials to be combined:

$$\textbf{Solution} \qquad u(t) = c_1 e^{\lambda_1 t}x_1 + c_2 e^{\lambda_2 t}x_2 \quad \text{or} \quad u = \begin{bmatrix} 1 & 1 \\ 1 & -1 \end{bmatrix}\begin{bmatrix} e^{-t} & \\ & e^{-3t} \end{bmatrix}\begin{bmatrix} c_1 \\ c_2 \end{bmatrix}. \tag{2}$$

At time zero, when the exponentials are $e^0 = 1$, $u(0)$ determines c_1 and c_2:

$$\textbf{Initial condition} \qquad u(0) = c_1x_1 + c_2x_2 = \begin{bmatrix} 1 & 1 \\ 1 & -1 \end{bmatrix}\begin{bmatrix} c_1 \\ c_2 \end{bmatrix} = Sc.$$

You recognize S, the matrix of eigenvectors. The constants $c = S^{-1}u(0)$ are the same as they were for difference equations. Substituting them back into equation (2), the solution is

$$u(t) = \begin{bmatrix} 1 & 1 \\ 1 & -1 \end{bmatrix}\begin{bmatrix} e^{-t} & \\ & e^{-3t} \end{bmatrix}\begin{bmatrix} c_1 \\ c_2 \end{bmatrix} = S\begin{bmatrix} e^{-t} & \\ & e^{-3t} \end{bmatrix}S^{-1}u(0). \tag{3}$$

Here is the fundamental formula of this section: $Se^{\Lambda t}S^{-1}u(0)$ solves the differential equation, just as $S\Lambda^k S^{-1}u_0$ solved the difference equation:

$$u(t) = Se^{\Lambda t}S^{-1}u(0) \quad \text{with} \quad \Lambda = \begin{bmatrix} -1 & \\ & -3 \end{bmatrix} \quad \text{and} \quad e^{\Lambda t} = \begin{bmatrix} e^{-t} & \\ & e^{-3t} \end{bmatrix}. \tag{4}$$

There are two more things to be done with this example. One is to complete the mathematics, by giving a direct definition of the ***exponential of a matrix***. The other is to give a physical interpretation of the equation and its solution. It is the kind of differential equation that has useful applications.

The exponential of a diagonal matrix Λ is easy; $e^{\Lambda t}$ just has the n numbers $e^{\lambda t}$ on the diagonal. For a general matrix A, the natural idea is to imitate the power series $e^x = 1 + x + x^2/2! + x^3/3! + \cdots$. If we replace x by At and 1 by I, this sum is an n by n matrix:

Matrix exponential $$e^{At} = I + At + \frac{(At)^2}{2!} + \frac{(At)^3}{3!} + \cdots. \tag{5}$$

The series always converges, and its sum e^{At} has the right properties:

$$(e^{As})(e^{At}) = e^{A(s+t)}, \qquad (e^{At})(e^{-At}) = I, \quad \text{and} \quad \frac{d}{dt}(e^{At}) = Ae^{At}. \tag{6}$$

From the last one, $u(t) = e^{At}u(0)$ solves the differential equation. This solution must be the same as the form $Se^{\Lambda t}S^{-1}u(0)$ used for computation. To prove directly that those solutions agree, remember that each power $(S\Lambda S^{-1})^k$ telescopes into $A^k = S\Lambda^k S^{-1}$ (because S^{-1} cancels S). The whole exponential is diagonalized by S:

$$\begin{aligned} e^{At} &= I + S\Lambda S^{-1}t + \frac{S\Lambda^2 S^{-1}t^2}{2!} + \frac{S\Lambda^3 S^{-1}t^3}{3!} + \cdots \\ &= S\left(I + \Lambda t + \frac{(\Lambda t)^2}{2!} + \frac{(\Lambda t)^3}{3!} + \cdots\right)S^{-1} = Se^{\Lambda t}S^{-1}. \end{aligned}$$

Example 1 In equation (1), the exponential of $A = \begin{bmatrix} -2 & 1 \\ 1 & -2 \end{bmatrix}$ has $\Lambda = \begin{bmatrix} -1 & \\ & -3 \end{bmatrix}$:

$$e^{At} = Se^{\Lambda t}S^{-1} = \begin{bmatrix} 1 & 1 \\ 1 & -1 \end{bmatrix} \begin{bmatrix} e^{-t} & \\ & e^{-3t} \end{bmatrix} \begin{bmatrix} 1 & 1 \\ 1 & -1 \end{bmatrix}^{-1} = \frac{1}{2}\begin{bmatrix} e^{-t} + e^{-3t} & e^{-t} - e^{-3t} \\ e^{-t} - e^{-3t} & e^{-t} + e^{-3t} \end{bmatrix}.$$

At $t = 0$ we get $e^0 = I$. The infinite series e^{At} gives the answer for all t, but a series can be hard to compute. The form $Se^{\Lambda t}S^{-1}$ gives the same answer when A can be diagonalized; it requires n independent eigenvectors in S. This simpler form leads to a *combination of n exponentials $e^{\lambda t}x$*—which is the best solution of all:

5L If A can be diagonalized, $A = S\Lambda S^{-1}$, then $du/dt = Au$ has the solution

$$u(t) = e^{At}u(0) = Se^{\Lambda t}S^{-1}u(0). \tag{7}$$

The columns of S are the eigenvectors $x_1, \ldots, x_n$ of A. Multiplying gives

$$\begin{aligned} u(t) &= \begin{bmatrix} & & \\ x_1 & \cdots & x_n \\ & & \end{bmatrix} \begin{bmatrix} e^{\lambda_1 t} & & \\ & \ddots & \\ & & e^{\lambda_n t} \end{bmatrix} S^{-1}u(0) \\ &= c_1 e^{\lambda_1 t}x_1 + \cdots + c_n e^{\lambda_n t}x_n = \text{combination of } e^{\lambda t}x. \end{aligned} \tag{8}$$

The constants c_i that match the initial conditions $u(0)$ are $c = S^{-1}u(0)$.

This gives a complete analogy with difference equations and $S\Lambda S^{-1}u_0$. In both cases we assumed that A could be diagonalized, since otherwise it has fewer than n eigenvectors and we have not found enough special solutions. The missing solutions do exist, but they are more complicated than pure exponentials $e^{\lambda t}x$. They involve "generalized eigenvectors" and factors like $te^{\lambda t}$. (To compute this defective case we can use the Jordan form in Appendix B, and find e^{Jt}.) **The formula $u(t) = e^{At}u(0)$ remains completely correct.**

The matrix e^{At} is ***never singular***. One proof is to look at its eigenvalues; if λ is an eigenvalue of A, then $e^{\lambda t}$ is the corresponding eigenvalue of e^{At}—and $e^{\lambda t}$ can never be zero. Another approach is to compute the determinant of the exponential:

$$\det e^{At} = e^{\lambda_1 t}e^{\lambda_2 t}\cdots e^{\lambda_n t} = e^{\text{trace}\,(At)}. \tag{9}$$

Quick proof that e^{At} is invertible: *Just recognize e^{-At} as its inverse.*

This invertibility is fundamental for differential equations. If n solutions are linearly independent at $t = 0$, *they remain linearly independent forever*. If the initial vectors are $v_1, \ldots, v_n$, we can put the solutions $e^{At}v$ into a matrix:

$$\begin{bmatrix} e^{At}v_1 & \cdots & e^{At}v_n \end{bmatrix} = e^{At}\begin{bmatrix} v_1 & \cdots & v_n \end{bmatrix}.$$

The determinant of the left-hand side is the *Wronskian*. It never becomes zero, because it is the product of two nonzero determinants. Both matrices on the right-hand side are invertible.

Remark Not all differential equations come to us as a first-order system $du/dt = Au$. We may start from a single equation of higher order, like $y''' - 3y'' + 2y' = 0$. To convert to a 3 by 3 system, introduce $v = y'$ and $w = v'$ as additional unknowns along with y itself. Then these two equations combine with the original one to give $u' = Au$:

$$\begin{aligned} y' &= v \\ v' &= w \\ w' &= 3w - 2v \end{aligned} \qquad \text{or} \qquad u' = \begin{bmatrix} 0 & 1 & 0 \\ 0 & 0 & 1 \\ 0 & -2 & 3 \end{bmatrix}\begin{bmatrix} y \\ v \\ w \end{bmatrix} = Au.$$

We are back to a first-order system. The problem can be solved two ways. In a course on differential equations, you would substitute $y = e^{\lambda t}$ into $y''' - 3y'' + 2y' = 0$:

$$(\lambda^3 - 3\lambda^2 + 2\lambda)e^{\lambda t} = 0 \qquad \text{or} \qquad \lambda(\lambda - 1)(\lambda - 2)e^{\lambda t} = 0. \tag{10}$$

The three pure exponential solutions are $y = e^{0t}$, $y = e^t$, and $y = e^{2t}$. No eigenvectors are involved. In a linear algebra course, we find the eigenvalues of A:

$$\det(A - \lambda I) = \begin{bmatrix} -\lambda & 1 & 0 \\ 0 & -\lambda & 1 \\ 0 & -2 & 3 - \lambda \end{bmatrix} = -\lambda^3 + 3\lambda^2 - 2\lambda = 0. \tag{11}$$

Equations (10) and (11) are the same! The same three exponents appear: $\lambda = 0$, $\lambda = 1$, and $\lambda = 2$. This is a general rule which makes the two methods consistent; the growth rates of the solutions stay fixed when the equations change form. It seems to us that solving the third-order equation is quicker.

The physical significance of $du/dt = \begin{bmatrix} -2 & 1 \\ 1 & -2 \end{bmatrix}u$ is easy to explain and at the same time genuinely important. This differential equation describes a process of *diffusion*.

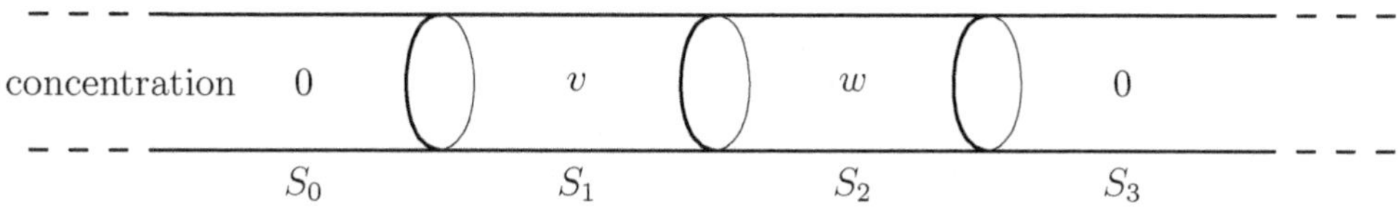

Figure 5.1 A model of diffusion between four segments.

Divide an infinite pipe into four segments (Figure 5.1). At time $t = 0$, the middle segments contain concentrations $v(0)$ and $w(0)$ of a chemical. ***At each time t, the diffusion rate between two adjacent segments is the difference in concentrations.*** Within each segment, the concentration remains uniform (zero in the infinite segments). The process is continuous in time but discrete in space; the unknowns are $v(t)$ and $w(t)$ in the two inner segments S_1 and S_2.

The concentration $v(t)$ in S_1 is changing in two ways. There is diffusion into S_0, and into or out of S_2. The net rate of change is dv/dt, and dw/dt is similar:

$$\textbf{Flow rate into } \mathbf{S_1} \quad \frac{dv}{dt} = (w - v) + (0 - v)$$

$$\textbf{Flow rate into } \mathbf{S_2} \quad \frac{dw}{dt} = (0 - w) + (v - w).$$

This law of diffusion exactly matches our example $du/dt = Au$:

$$u = \begin{bmatrix} v \\ w \end{bmatrix} \qquad \text{and} \qquad \frac{du}{dt} = \begin{bmatrix} -2v + w \\ v - 2w \end{bmatrix} = \begin{bmatrix} -2 & 1 \\ 1 & -2 \end{bmatrix} u.$$

The eigenvalues -1 and -3 will govern the solution. They give the rate at which the concentrations decay, and λ_1 is the more important because only an exceptional set of starting conditions can lead to "superdecay" at the rate e^{-3t}. In fact, those conditions must come from the eigenvector $(1, -1)$. If the experiment admits only nonnegative concentrations, superdecay is impossible and the limiting rate must be e^{-t}. The solution that decays at this slower rate corresponds to the eigenvector $(1, 1)$. Therefore the two concentrations will become nearly equal (typical for diffusion) as $t \to \infty$.

One more comment on this example: It is a discrete approximation, with only two unknowns, to the continuous diffusion described by this partial differential equation:

$$\textbf{Heat equation} \qquad \frac{\partial u}{\partial t} = \frac{\partial^2 u}{\partial x^2}.$$

That heat equation is approached by dividing the pipe into smaller and smaller segments, of length $1/N$. The discrete system with N unknowns is governed by

$$\frac{d}{dt}\begin{bmatrix} u_1 \\ \cdot \\ \cdot \\ u_N \end{bmatrix} = \begin{bmatrix} -2 & 1 & & \\ 1 & -2 & \cdot & \\ & \cdot & \cdot & 1 \\ & & 1 & -2 \end{bmatrix} \begin{bmatrix} u_1 \\ \cdot \\ \cdot \\ u_N \end{bmatrix} = Au. \tag{12}$$

This is the finite difference matrix with the $1, -2, 1$ pattern. The right side Au approaches the second derivative d^2u/dx^2, after a scaling factor N^2 comes from the flow problem. In the limit as $N \to \infty$, we reach the ***heat equation*** $\partial u/\partial t = \partial^2 u/\partial x^2$. Its solutions are still combinations of pure exponentials, but now there are infinitely many. Instead of eigenvectors from $Ax = \lambda x$, we have *eigenfunctions* from $d^2u/dx^2 = \lambda u$. Those are $u(x) = \sin n\pi x$ with $\lambda = -n^2\pi^2$. Then the solution to the heat equation is

$$u(t) = \sum_{n=1}^{\infty} c_n e^{-n^2\pi^2 t} \sin n\pi x.$$

The constants c_n are determined by the initial condition. The novelty is that the eigenvectors are functions $u(x)$, because the problem is continuous and not discrete.

Stability of Differential Equations

Just as for difference equations, the eigenvalues decide how $u(t)$ behaves as $t \to \infty$. As long as A can be diagonalized, there will be n pure exponential solutions to the differential equation, and any specific solution $u(t)$ is some combination

$$u(t) = Se^{\Lambda t}S^{-1}u_0 = c_1 e^{\lambda_1 t}x_1 + \cdots + c_n e^{\lambda_n t}x_n.$$

Stability is governed by those factors $e^{\lambda_i t}$. If they all approach zero, then $u(t)$ approaches zero; if they all stay bounded, then $u(t)$ stays bounded; if one of them blows up, then except for very special starting conditions the solution will blow up. Furthermore, the size of $e^{\lambda t}$ depends only on the real part of λ. ***It is only the real parts of the eigenvalues that govern stability***: If $\lambda = a + ib$, then

$$e^{\lambda t} = e^{at}e^{ibt} = e^{at}(\cos bt + i \sin bt) \quad \text{and the magnitude is} \quad |e^{\lambda t}| = e^{at}.$$

This decays for $a < 0$, it is constant for $a = 0$, and it explodes for $a > 0$. The imaginary part is producing oscillations, but the amplitude comes from the real part.

5M The differential equation $du/dt = Au$ is

stable and $e^{At} \to 0$ whenever all $\operatorname{Re} \lambda_i < 0$,

neutrally stable when all $\operatorname{Re} \lambda_i \le 0$ and $\operatorname{Re} \lambda_1 = 0$, and

unstable and e^{At} is unbounded if any eigenvalue has $\operatorname{Re} \lambda_i > 0$.

In some texts the condition $\operatorname{Re} \lambda < 0$ is called *asymptotic* stability, because it guarantees decay for large times t. Our argument depended on having n pure exponential solutions, but even if A is not diagonalizable (and there are terms like $te^{\lambda t}$) the result is still true: ***All solutions approach zero if and only if all eigenvalues have*** $\mathbf{Re}\,\boldsymbol{\lambda} < \mathbf{0}$.

Stability is especially easy to decide for a 2 by 2 system (which is very common in applications). The equation is

$$\frac{du}{dt} = \begin{bmatrix} a & b \\ c & d \end{bmatrix} u,$$

and we need to know when both eigenvalues of that matrix have negative real parts. (Note again that the eigenvalues can be complex numbers.) The stability tests are

Re $\lambda_1 < 0$	***The trace $a + d$ must be negative.***
Re $\lambda_2 < 0$	***The determinant $ad - bc$ must be positive.***

When the eigenvalues are real, those tests guarantee them to be negative. Their product is the determinant; it is positive when the eigenvalues have the same sign. Their sum is the trace; it is negative when both eigenvalues are negative.

When the eigenvalues are a complex pair $x \pm iy$, the tests still succeed. The trace is their sum $2x$ (which is < 0) and the determinant is $(x+iy)(x-iy) = x^2 + y^2 > 0$. Figure 5.2 shows the one stable quadrant, trace < 0 and determinant > 0. It also shows the parabolic boundary line between real and complex eigenvalues. The reason for the parabola is in the quadratic equation for the eigenvalues:

$$\det \begin{bmatrix} a-\lambda & b \\ c & d-\lambda \end{bmatrix} = \lambda^2 - (\text{trace})\lambda + (\det) = 0. \tag{13}$$

The quadratic formula for λ leads to the parabola $(\text{trace})^2 = 4(\det)$:

$$\lambda_1 \text{ and } \lambda_2 = \frac{1}{2}\left[\text{trace} \pm \sqrt{(\text{trace})^2 - 4(\det)}\,\right]. \tag{14}$$

Above the parabola, the number under the square root is negative—so λ is not real. On the parabola, the square root is zero and λ is repeated. Below the parabola the square roots are real. *Every symmetric matrix has real eigenvalues*, since if $b = c$, then

$$(\text{trace})^2 - 4(\det) = (a+d)^2 - 4(ad - b^2) = (a-d)^2 + 4b^2 \geq 0.$$

For complex eigenvalues, b and c have opposite signs and are sufficiently large.

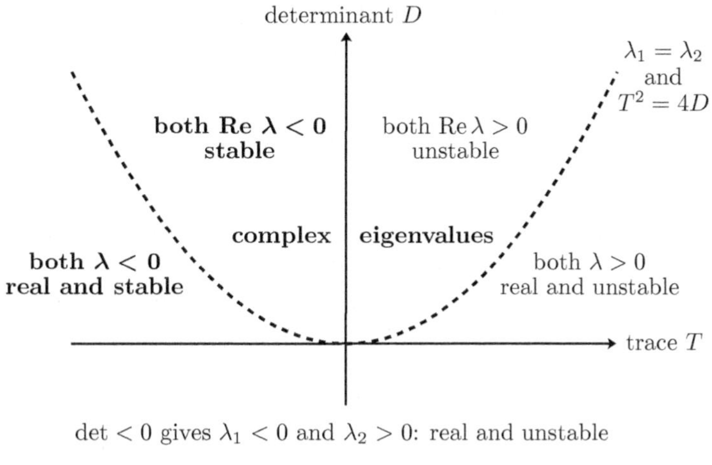

Figure 5.2 Stability and instability regions for a 2 by 2 matrix.

Example 2 One from each quadrant: only #2 is stable:

$$\begin{bmatrix}1 & 0\\0 & 2\end{bmatrix} \quad \begin{bmatrix}-1 & 0\\0 & -2\end{bmatrix} \quad \begin{bmatrix}1 & 0\\0 & -2\end{bmatrix} \quad \begin{bmatrix}-1 & 0\\0 & 2\end{bmatrix}$$

On the boundaries of the second quadrant, the equation is neutrally stable. On the horizontal axis, one eigenvalue is zero (because the determinant is $\lambda_1\lambda_2 = 0$). On the vertical axis above the origin, both eigenvalues are purely imaginary (because the trace is zero). Crossing those axes are the two ways that stability is lost.

The n by n case is more difficult. A test for Re $\lambda_i < 0$ came from Routh and Hurwitz, who found a series of inequalities on the entries a_{ij}. I do not think this approach is much good for a large matrix; the computer can probably find the eigenvalues with more certainty than it can test these inequalities. Lyapunov's idea was to find a *weighting matrix W so that the weighted length $\|Wu(t)\|$ is always decreasing*. If there exists such a W, then $\|Wu\|$ will decrease steadily to zero, and after a few ups and downs u must get there too (stability). The real value of Lyapunov's method is for a nonlinear equation—then stability can be proved without knowing a formula for $u(t)$.

Example 3 $du/dt = \begin{bmatrix}0 & -1\\1 & 0\end{bmatrix} u$ sends $u(t)$ around a circle, starting from $u(0) = (1, 0)$.

Since trace $= 0$ and det $= 1$, we have purely imaginary eigenvalues:

$$\begin{bmatrix}-\lambda & -1\\1 & -\lambda\end{bmatrix} = \lambda^2 + 1 = 0 \qquad \text{so} \qquad \lambda = +i \text{ and } -i.$$

The eigenvectors are $(1, -i)$ and $(1, i)$, and the solution is

$$u(t) = \frac{1}{2}e^{it}\begin{bmatrix}1\\-i\end{bmatrix} + \frac{1}{2}e^{-it}\begin{bmatrix}1\\i\end{bmatrix}.$$

That is correct but not beautiful. By substituting $\cos t \pm i \sin t$ for e^{it} and e^{-it}, *real numbers will reappear*: The circling solution is $u(t) = (\cos t, \sin t)$.

Starting from a different $u(0) = (a, b)$, the solution $u(t)$ ends up as

$$u(t) = \begin{bmatrix}a\cos t - b\sin t\\b\cos t + a\sin t\end{bmatrix} = \begin{bmatrix}\cos t & -\sin t\\\sin t & \cos t\end{bmatrix}\begin{bmatrix}a\\b\end{bmatrix}. \tag{15}$$

There we have something important! The last matrix is multiplying $u(0)$, so it must be the exponential e^{At}. (Remember that $u(t) = e^{At}u(0)$.) That matrix of cosines and sines is our leading example of an *orthogonal matrix*. The columns have length 1, their inner product is zero, and we have a confirmation of a wonderful fact:

If A is skew-symmetric ($A^{\mathrm{T}} = -A$) then e^{At} is an orthogonal matrix.

$A^{\mathrm{T}} = -A$ gives a conservative system. No energy is lost in damping or diffusion:

$$A^{\mathrm{T}} = -A, \qquad (e^{At})^{\mathrm{T}} = e^{-At}, \qquad \text{and} \qquad \|e^{At}u(0)\| = \|u(0)\|.$$

That last equation expresses an essential property of orthogonal matrices. When they multiply a vector, the length is not changed. The vector $u(0)$ is just rotated, and that describes the solution to $du/dt = Au$: *It goes around in a circle.*

In this very unusual case, e^{At} can also be recognized directly from the infinite series. Note that $A = \begin{bmatrix} 0 & -1 \\ 1 & 0 \end{bmatrix}$ has $A^2 = -I$, and use this in the series for e^{At}:

$$I + At + \frac{(At)^2}{2} + \frac{(At)^3}{6} + \cdots = \begin{bmatrix} \left(1 - \frac{t^2}{2} + \cdots\right) & \left(-t + \frac{t^3}{6} - \cdots\right) \\ \left(t - \frac{t^3}{6} + \cdots\right) & \left(1 - \frac{t^2}{2} + \cdots\right) \end{bmatrix}$$

$$= \begin{bmatrix} \cos t & -\sin t \\ \sin t & \cos t \end{bmatrix}$$

Example 4 The diffusion equation is stable: $A = \begin{bmatrix} -2 & 1 \\ 1 & -2 \end{bmatrix}$ has $\lambda = -1$ and $\lambda = -3$.

Example 5 If we close off the infinite segments, nothing can escape:

$$\frac{du}{dt} = \begin{bmatrix} -1 & 1 \\ 1 & -1 \end{bmatrix} u \qquad \text{or} \qquad \begin{aligned} dv/dt &= w - v \\ dw/dt &= v - w. \end{aligned}$$

This is a *continuous Markov process*. Instead of moving every year, the particles move every instant. Their total number $v + w$ is constant. That comes from adding the two equations on the right-hand side: the derivative of $v + w$ is zero.

A discrete Markov matrix has its column sums equal to $\lambda_{\max} = 1$. A *continuous* Markov matrix, for differential equations, has its column sums equal to $\lambda_{\max} = 0$. A is a discrete Markov matrix if and only if $B = A - I$ is a continuous Markov matrix. The steady state for both is the eigenvector for $\lambda_{\max}$. It is multiplied by $1^k = 1$ in difference equations and by $e^{0t} = 1$ in differential equations, and it doesn't move.

In the example, the steady state has $v = w$.

Example 6 In nuclear engineering, a reactor is called *critical* when it is neutrally stable; the fission balances the decay. Slower fission makes it stable, or *subcritical*, and eventually it runs down. Unstable fission is a bomb.

Second-Order Equations

The laws of diffusion led to a first-order system $du/dt = Au$. So do a lot of other applications, in chemistry, in biology, and elsewhere, but the most important law of physics does not. It is *Newton's law* $F = ma$, and the acceleration a is a second derivative. Inertial terms produce second-order equations (we have to solve $d^2u/dt^2 = Au$ instead of $du/dt = Au$), and the goal is to understand how this switch to second derivatives alters the solution.* It is optional in linear algebra, but not in physics.

* Fourth derivatives are also possible, in the bending of beams, but nature seems to resist going higher than four.

The comparison will be perfect if we keep the same A:

$$\frac{d^2u}{dt^2} = Au = \begin{bmatrix} -2 & 1 \\ 1 & -2 \end{bmatrix} u. \tag{16}$$

Two initial conditions get the system started—the "displacement" $u(0)$ and the "velocity" $u'(0)$. To match these conditions, there will be $2n$ pure exponential solutions.

Suppose we use ω rather than λ, and write these special solutions as $u = e^{i\omega t}x$. Substituting this exponential into the differential equation, it must satisfy

$$\frac{d^2}{dt^2}(e^{i\omega t}x) = A(e^{i\omega t}x), \qquad \text{or} \qquad -\omega^2 x = Ax. \tag{17}$$

The vector x must be an eigenvector of A, exactly as before. The corresponding eigenvalue is now $-\omega^2$, so the frequency ω is connected to the decay rate λ by the law $-\omega^2 = \lambda$. Every special solution $e^{\lambda t}x$ of the first-order equation leads to *two* special solutions $e^{i\omega t}x$ of the second-order equation, and the two exponents are $\omega = \pm\sqrt{-\lambda}$. This breaks down only when $\lambda = 0$, which has just one square root; if the eigenvector is x, the two special solutions are x and tx.

For a genuine diffusion matrix, the eigenvalues λ are all negative and the frequencies ω are all real: *Pure diffusion is converted into pure oscillation.* The factors $e^{i\omega t}$ produce neutral stability, the solution neither grows or decays, and the total energy stays precisely constant. It just keeps passing around the system. The general solution to $d^2u/dt^2 = Au$, if A has negative eigenvalues $\lambda_1, \ldots, \lambda_n$ and if $\omega_j = \sqrt{-\lambda_j}$, is

$$u(t) = (c_1 e^{i\omega_1 t} + d_1 e^{-\omega_1 t})x_1 + \cdots + (c_n e^{i\omega_n t} + d_n e^{-i\omega_n t})x_n. \tag{18}$$

As always, the constants are found from the initial conditions. This is easier to do (at the expense of one extra formula) by switching from oscillating exponentials to the more familiar sine and cosine:

$$u(t) = (a_1 \cos\omega_1 t + b_1 \sin\omega_1 t)x_1 + \cdots + (a_n \cos\omega_n t + b_n \sin\omega_n t)x_n. \tag{19}$$

The initial displacement $u(0)$ is easy to keep separate: $t = 0$ means that $\sin\omega t = 0$ and $\cos\omega t = 1$, leaving only

$$u(0) = a_1 x_1 + \cdots + a_n x_n, \qquad \text{or} \qquad u(0) = Sa, \qquad \text{or} \qquad a = S^{-1}u(0).$$

Then differentiating $u(t)$ and setting $t = 0$, the b's are determined by the initial velocity: $u'(0) = b_1\omega_1 x_1 + \cdots + b_n\omega_n x_n$. Substituting the a's and b's into the formula for $u(t)$, the equation is solved.

The matrix $A = \begin{bmatrix} -2 & 1 \\ 1 & -2 \end{bmatrix}$ has $\lambda_1 = -1$ and $\lambda_2 = -3$. The frequencies are $\omega_1 = 1$ and $\omega_2 = \sqrt{3}$. If the system starts from rest, $u'(0) = 0$, the terms in $b \sin\omega t$ will disappear:

$$\textbf{Solution from } \boldsymbol{u(0)} = \begin{bmatrix} \mathbf{1} \\ \mathbf{0} \end{bmatrix} \qquad u(t) = \frac{1}{2}\cos t \begin{bmatrix} 1 \\ 1 \end{bmatrix} + \frac{1}{2}\cos\sqrt{3}t \begin{bmatrix} 1 \\ -1 \end{bmatrix}.$$

Physically, two masses are connected to each other and to stationary walls by three identical springs (Figure 5.3). The first mass is held at $v(0) = 1$, the second mass is held at $w(0) = 0$, and at $t = 0$ we let go. Their motion $u(t)$ becomes an average of two pure oscillations, corresponding to the two eigenvectors. In the first mode $x_1 = (1, 1)$, the

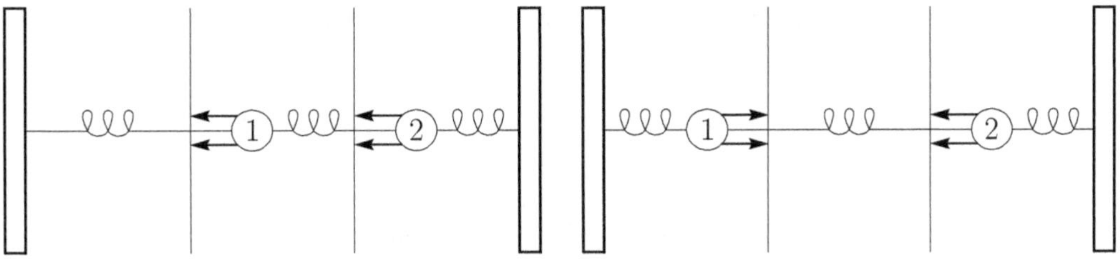

(a) $\omega_1 = 1$, $x_1 = \begin{bmatrix} 1 \\ 1 \end{bmatrix}$ (b) $\omega_2 = \sqrt{3}$, $x_2 = \begin{bmatrix} 1 \\ -1 \end{bmatrix}$

Figure 5.3 The slow and fast modes of oscillation.

masses move together and the spring in the middle is never stretched (Figure 5.3a). The frequency $\omega_1 = 1$ is the same as for a single spring and a single mass. In the faster mode $x_2 = (1, -1)$ with frequency $\sqrt{3}$, the masses move oppositely but with equal speeds. The general solution is a combination of these two normal modes. Our particular solution is half of each.

As time goes on, the motion is "almost periodic." If the ratio ω_1/ω_2 had been a fraction like $2/3$, the masses would eventually return to $u(0) = (1, 0)$ and begin again. A combination of $\sin 2t$ and $\sin 3t$ would have a period of 2π. But $\sqrt{3}$ is irrational. The best we can say is that the masses will come *arbitrarily close* to $(1, 0)$ and also $(0, 1)$. Like a billiard ball bouncing forever on a perfectly smooth table, the total energy is fixed. Sooner or later the masses come near any state with this energy.

Again we cannot leave the problem without drawing a parallel to the continuous case. As the discrete masses and springs merge into a solid rod, the "second differences" given by the $1, -2, 1$ matrix A turn into second derivatives. This limit is described by the celebrated ***wave equation*** $\partial^2 u/\partial t^2 = \partial^2 u/\partial x^2$.

Problem Set 5.4

1. Following the first example in this section, find the eigenvalues and eigenvectors, and the exponential e^{At}, for

$$A = \begin{bmatrix} -1 & 1 \\ 1 & -1 \end{bmatrix}.$$

2. For the previous matrix, write the general solution to $du/dt = Au$, and the specific solution that matches $u(0) = (3, 1)$. What is the *steady state* as $t \to \infty$? (This is a continuous Markov process; $\lambda = 0$ in a differential equation corresponds to $\lambda = 1$ in a difference equation, since $e^{0t} = 1$.)

3. Suppose the time direction is reversed to give the matrix $-A$:

$$\frac{du}{dt} = \begin{bmatrix} 1 & -1 \\ -1 & 1 \end{bmatrix} u \quad \text{with} \quad u_0 = \begin{bmatrix} 3 \\ 1 \end{bmatrix}.$$

Find $u(t)$ and show that it *blows up* instead of decaying as $t \to \infty$. (Diffusion is irreversible, and the heat equation cannot run backward.)

4. If P is a projection matrix, show from the infinite series that

$$e^P \approx I + 1.718P.$$

5. A diagonal matrix like $\Lambda = \begin{bmatrix} 1 & 0 \\ 0 & 2 \end{bmatrix}$ satisfies the usual rule $e^{\Lambda(t+T)} = e^{\Lambda t}e^{\Lambda T}$, because the rule holds for each diagonal entry.

(a) Explain why $e^{A(t+T)} = e^{At}e^{AT}$, using the formula $e^{At} = Se^{\Lambda t}S^{-1}$.
(b) Show that $e^{A+B} = e^A e^B$ is *not true* for matrices, from the example

$$A = \begin{bmatrix} 0 & 0 \\ 1 & 0 \end{bmatrix} \qquad B = \begin{bmatrix} 0 & -1 \\ 0 & 0 \end{bmatrix} \qquad \text{(use series for } e^A \text{ and } e^B\text{).}$$

6. The higher order equation $y'' + y = 0$ can be written as a first-order system by introducing the velocity y' as another unknown:

$$\frac{d}{dt}\begin{bmatrix} y \\ y' \end{bmatrix} = \begin{bmatrix} y' \\ y'' \end{bmatrix} = \begin{bmatrix} y' \\ -y \end{bmatrix}.$$

If this is $du/dt = Au$, what is the 2 by 2 matrix A? Find its eigenvalues and eigenvectors, and compute the solution that starts from $y(0) = 2$, $y'(0) = 0$.

7. Convert $y'' = 0$ to a first-order system $du/dt = Au$:

$$\frac{d}{dt}\begin{bmatrix} y \\ y' \end{bmatrix} = \begin{bmatrix} y' \\ 0 \end{bmatrix} = \begin{bmatrix} 0 & 1 \\ 0 & 0 \end{bmatrix}\begin{bmatrix} y \\ y' \end{bmatrix}.$$

This 2 by 2 matrix A has only one eigenvector and cannot be diagonalized. Compute e^{At} from the series $I + At + \cdots$ and write the solution $e^{At}u(0)$ starting from $y(0) = 3$, $y'(0) = 4$. Check that your (y, y') satisfies $y'' = 0$.

8. Suppose the rabbit population r and the wolf population w are governed by

$$\frac{dr}{dt} = 4r - 2w$$
$$\frac{dw}{dt} = r + w.$$

(a) Is this system stable, neutrally stable, or unstable?
(b) If initially $r = 300$ and $w = 200$, what are the populations at time t?
(c) After a long time, what is the proportion of rabbits to wolves?

9. Decide the stability of $u' = Au$ for the following matrices:

(a) $A = \begin{bmatrix} 2 & 3 \\ 4 & 5 \end{bmatrix}$. (b) $A = \begin{bmatrix} 1 & 2 \\ 3 & -1 \end{bmatrix}$.

(c) $A = \begin{bmatrix} 1 & 1 \\ 1 & -2 \end{bmatrix}$. (d) $A = \begin{bmatrix} -1 & -1 \\ -1 & -1 \end{bmatrix}$.

10. Decide on the stability or instability of $dv/dt = w$, $dw/dt = v$. Is there a solution that decays?

11. From their trace and determinant, at what time t do the following matrices change between stable with real eigenvalues, stable with complex eigenvalues, and unstable?

$$A_1 = \begin{bmatrix} 1 & -1 \\ t & -1 \end{bmatrix}, \qquad A_2 = \begin{bmatrix} 0 & 4-t \\ 1 & -2 \end{bmatrix}, \qquad A_3 = \begin{bmatrix} t & -1 \\ 1 & t \end{bmatrix}.$$

12. Find the eigenvalues and eigenvectors for

$$\frac{du}{dt} = Au = \begin{bmatrix} 0 & 3 & 0 \\ -3 & 0 & 4 \\ 0 & -4 & 0 \end{bmatrix} u.$$

Why do you know, without computing, that e^{At} will be an orthogonal matrix and $\|u(t)\|^2 = u_1^2 + u_2^2 + u_3^2$ will be constant?

13. For the skew-symmetric equation

$$\frac{du}{dt} = Au = \begin{bmatrix} 0 & c & -b \\ -c & 0 & a \\ b & -a & 0 \end{bmatrix} \begin{bmatrix} u_1 \\ u_2 \\ u_3 \end{bmatrix},$$

(a) write out u_1', u_2', u_3' and confirm that $u_1'u_1 + u_2'u_2 + u_3'u_3 = 0$.
(b) deduce that the length $u_1^2 + u_2^2 + u_3^2$ is a constant.
(c) find the eigenvalues of A.

The solution will rotate around the axis $w = (a, b, c)$, because Au is the "cross product" $u \times w$—which is perpendicular to u and w.

14. What are the eigenvalues λ and frequencies ω, and the general solution, of the following equation?

$$\frac{d^2u}{dt^2} = \begin{bmatrix} -5 & 4 \\ 4 & -5 \end{bmatrix} u.$$

15. Solve the second-order equation

$$\frac{d^2u}{dt^2} = \begin{bmatrix} -5 & -1 \\ -1 & -5 \end{bmatrix} u \quad \text{with} \quad u(0) = \begin{bmatrix} 1 \\ 0 \end{bmatrix} \quad \text{and} \quad u'(0) = \begin{bmatrix} 0 \\ 0 \end{bmatrix}.$$

16. In most applications the second-order equation looks like $Mu'' + Ku = 0$, with a *mass matrix* multiplying the second derivatives. Substitute the pure exponential $u = e^{i\omega t}x$ and find the "generalized eigenvalue problem" that must be solved for the frequency ω and the vector x.

17. With a friction matrix F in the equation $u'' + Fu' - Au = 0$, substitute a pure exponential $u = e^{\lambda t}x$ and find a quadratic eigenvalue problem for λ.

18. For equation (16) in the text, with $\omega = 1$ and $\sqrt{3}$, find the motion if the first mass is hit at $t = 0$; $u(0) = (0, 0)$ and $u'(0) = (1, 0)$.

19. Every 2 by 2 matrix with trace zero can be written as

$$A = \begin{bmatrix} a & b + c \\ b - c & -a \end{bmatrix}.$$

Show that its eigenvalues are real exactly when $a^2 + b^2 \geq c^2$.

20. By back-substitution or by computing eigenvectors, solve

$$\frac{du}{dt} = \begin{bmatrix} 1 & 2 & 1 \\ 0 & 3 & 6 \\ 0 & 0 & 4 \end{bmatrix} u \quad \text{with} \quad u(0) = \begin{bmatrix} 1 \\ 0 \\ 1 \end{bmatrix}.$$

21. Find λ's and x's so that $u = e^{\lambda t}x$ solves

$$\frac{du}{dt} = \begin{bmatrix} 4 & 3 \\ 0 & 1 \end{bmatrix} u.$$

What combination $u = c_1 e^{\lambda_1 t}x_1 + c_2 e^{\lambda_2 t}x_2$ starts from $u(0) = (5, -2)$?

22. Solve Problem 21 for $u(t) = (y(t), z(t))$ by back-substitution:

$$\text{First solve } \frac{dz}{dt} = z, \text{ starting from } z(0) = -2.$$

$$\text{Then solve } \frac{dy}{dt} = 4y + 3z, \text{ starting from } y(0) = 5.$$

The solution for y will be a combination of e^{4t} and e^t.

23. Find A to change $y'' = 5y' + 4y$ into a vector equation for $u(t) = (y(t), y'(t))$:

$$\frac{du}{dt} = \begin{bmatrix} y' \\ y'' \end{bmatrix} = \begin{bmatrix} & \\ & \end{bmatrix} \begin{bmatrix} y \\ y' \end{bmatrix} = Au.$$

What are the eigenvalues of A? Find them also by substituting $y = e^{\lambda t}$ into the scalar equation $y'' = 5y' + 4y$.

24. A door is opened between rooms that hold $v(0) = 30$ people and $w(0) = 10$ people. The movement between rooms is proportional to the difference $v - w$:

$$\frac{dv}{dt} = w - v \quad \text{and} \quad \frac{dw}{dt} = v - w.$$

Show that the total $v + w$ is constant (40 people). Find the matrix in $du/dt = Au$, and its eigenvalues and eigenvectors. What are v and w at $t = 1$?

25. Reverse the diffusion of people in Problem 24 to $du/dt = -Au$:

$$\frac{dv}{dt} = v - w \quad \text{and} \quad \frac{dw}{dt} = w - v.$$

The total $v + w$ still remains constant. How are the λ's changed now that A is changed to $-A$? But show that $v(t)$ grows to infinity from $v(0) = 30$.

26. The solution to $y'' = 0$ is a straight line $y = C + Dt$. Convert to a matrix equation:

$$\frac{d}{dt}\begin{bmatrix} y \\ y' \end{bmatrix} = \begin{bmatrix} 0 & 1 \\ 0 & 0 \end{bmatrix} \begin{bmatrix} y \\ y' \end{bmatrix} \text{ has the solution } \begin{bmatrix} y \\ y' \end{bmatrix} = e^{At}\begin{bmatrix} y(0) \\ y'(0) \end{bmatrix}.$$

This matrix A cannot be diagonalized. Find A^2 and compute $e^{At} = I + At + \frac{1}{2}A^2t^2 + \cdots$. Multiply your e^{At} times $(y(0), y'(0))$ to check the straight line $y(t) = y(0) + y'(0)t$.

27. Substitute $y = e^{\lambda t}$ into $y'' = 6y' - 9y$ to show that $\lambda = 3$ is a repeated root. This is trouble; we need a second solution after e^{3t}. The matrix equation is

$$\frac{d}{dt}\begin{bmatrix} y \\ y' \end{bmatrix} = \begin{bmatrix} 0 & 1 \\ -9 & 6 \end{bmatrix} \begin{bmatrix} y \\ y' \end{bmatrix}.$$

Show that this matrix has $\lambda = 3, 3$ and only one line of eigenvectors. *Trouble here too.* Show that the second solution is $y = te^{3t}$.

28. Figure out how to write $my'' + by' + ky = 0$ as a vector equation $Mu' = Au$.

29. (a) Find two familiar functions that solve the equation $d^2y/dt^2 = -y$. Which one starts with $y(0) = 1$ and $y'(0) = 0$?

(b) This second-order equation $y'' = -y$ produces a vector equation $u' = Au$:

$$u = \begin{bmatrix} y \\ y' \end{bmatrix} \qquad \frac{du}{dt} = \begin{bmatrix} y' \\ y'' \end{bmatrix} = \begin{bmatrix} 0 & 1 \\ -1 & 0 \end{bmatrix} \begin{bmatrix} y \\ y' \end{bmatrix} = Au.$$

Put $y(t)$ from part (a) into $u(t) = (y, y')$. This solves Problem 6 again.

30. A particular solution to $du/dt = Au - b$ is $u_p = A^{-1}b$, if A is invertible. The solutions to $du/dt = Au$ give u_n. Find the complete solution $u_p + u_n$ to

(a) $\dfrac{du}{dt} = 2u - 8$. (b) $\dfrac{du}{dt} = \begin{bmatrix} 2 & 0 \\ 0 & 3 \end{bmatrix} u - \begin{bmatrix} 8 \\ 6 \end{bmatrix}$.

31. If c is not an eigenvalue of A, substitute $u = e^{ct}v$ and find v to solve $du/dt = Au - e^{ct}b$. This $u = e^{ct}v$ is a particular solution. How does it break down when c is an eigenvalue?

32. Find a matrix A to illustrate each of the unstable regions in Figure 5.2:

(a) $\lambda_1 < 0$ and $\lambda_2 > 0$.

(b) $\lambda_1 > 0$ and $\lambda_2 > 0$.

(c) Complex λ's with real part $a > 0$.

Problems 33–41 are about the matrix exponential e^{At}.

33. Write five terms of the infinite series for e^{At}. Take the t derivative of each term. Show that you have four terms of Ae^{At}. Conclusion: $e^{At}u(0)$ solves $u' = Au$.

34. The matrix $B = \begin{bmatrix} 0 & -1 \\ 0 & 0 \end{bmatrix}$ has $B^2 = 0$. Find e^{Bt} from a (short) infinite series. Check that the derivative of e^{Bt} is Be^{Bt}.

35. Starting from $u(0)$, the solution at time T is $e^{AT}u(0)$. Go an additional time t to reach $e^{At}\left(e^{AT}u(0)\right)$. This solution at time $t + T$ can also be written as ______. Conclusion: e^{At} times e^{AT} equals ______.

36. Write $A = \begin{bmatrix} 1 & 1 \\ 0 & 0 \end{bmatrix}$ in the form $S\Lambda S^{-1}$. Find e^{At} from $Se^{\Lambda t}S^{-1}$.

37. If $A^2 = A$, show that the infinite series produces $e^{At} = I + (e^t - 1)A$. For $A = \begin{bmatrix} 1 & 1 \\ 0 & 0 \end{bmatrix}$ in Problem 36, this gives $e^{At} =$ ______.

38. Generally e^Ae^B is different from e^Be^A. They are both different from e^{A+B}. Check this using Problems 36–37 and 34:

$$A = \begin{bmatrix} 1 & 1 \\ 0 & 0 \end{bmatrix} \qquad B = \begin{bmatrix} 0 & -1 \\ 0 & 0 \end{bmatrix} \qquad A + B = \begin{bmatrix} 1 & 0 \\ 0 & 0 \end{bmatrix}.$$

39. Write $A = \begin{bmatrix} 1 & 1 \\ 0 & 3 \end{bmatrix}$ as $S\Lambda S^{-1}$. Multiply $Se^{\Lambda t}S^{-1}$ to find the matrix exponential e^{At}. Check $e^{At} = I$ when $t = 0$.

40. Put $A = \begin{bmatrix} 1 & 3 \\ 0 & 0 \end{bmatrix}$ into the infinite series to find e^{At}. First compute A^2:

$$e^{At} = \begin{bmatrix} 1 & 0 \\ 0 & 1 \end{bmatrix} + \begin{bmatrix} t & 3t \\ 0 & 0 \end{bmatrix} + \frac{1}{2}\begin{bmatrix} & \\ & \end{bmatrix} + \cdots = \begin{bmatrix} e^t & \\ 0 & \end{bmatrix}.$$

41. Give two reasons why the matrix exponential e^{At} is never singular:

(a) Write its inverse.

(b) Write its eigenvalues. If $Ax = \lambda x$ then $e^{At}x =$ ______ x.

42. Find a solution $x(t)$, $y(t)$ of the first system that gets large as $t \to \infty$. To avoid this instability a scientist thought of exchanging the two equations!

$$\begin{aligned} dx/dt &= 0x - 4y \\ dy/dt &= -2x + 2y \end{aligned} \quad \text{becomes} \quad \begin{aligned} dy/dt &= -2x + 2y \\ dx/dt &= 0x - 4y. \end{aligned}$$

Now the matrix $\begin{bmatrix} -2 & 2 \\ 0 & -4 \end{bmatrix}$ is stable. It has $\lambda < 0$. Comment on this craziness.

43. From this general solution to $du/dt = Au$, find the matrix A:

$$u(t) = c_1 e^{2t}\begin{bmatrix} 2 \\ 1 \end{bmatrix} + c_2 e^{5t}\begin{bmatrix} 1 \\ 1 \end{bmatrix}.$$

5.5 COMPLEX MATRICES

It is no longer possible to work only with real vectors and real matrices. In the first half of this book, when the basic problem was $Ax = b$, the solution was real when A and b were real. Complex numbers could have been permitted, but would have contributed nothing new. Now we cannot avoid them. A real matrix has real coefficients in $\det(A - \lambda I)$, but the eigenvalues (as in rotations) may be complex.

We now introduce the space $\mathbf{C}^n$ of vectors with n *complex* components. Addition and matrix multiplication follow the same rules as before. ***Length is computed differently***. The old way, the vector in $\mathbf{C}^2$ with components $(1, i)$ would have zero length: $1^2 + i^2 = 0$, not good. The correct length squared is $1^2 + |i|^2 = 2$.

This change to $\|x\|^2 = |x_1|^2 + \cdots + |x_n|^2$ forces a whole series of other changes. The inner product, the transpose, the definitions of symmetric and orthogonal matrices, all need to be modified for complex numbers. The new definitions coincide with the old when the vectors and matrices are real. We have listed these changes in a table at the end of the section, and we explain them as we go.

That table virtually amounts to a dictionary for translating real into complex. We hope it will be useful to the reader. We particularly want to find out about ***symmetric matrices and Hermitian matrices***: *Where are their eigenvalues, and what is special about their eigenvectors*? For practical purposes, those are the most important questions in the theory of eigenvalues. We call attention in advance to the answers:

> **1.** ***Every symmetric matrix (and Hermitian matrix) has real eigenvalues.***
> **2.** ***Its eigenvectors can be chosen to be orthonormal.***

Strangely, to prove that the eigenvalues are real we begin with the opposite possibility—and that takes us to complex numbers, complex vectors, and complex matrices.

Complex Numbers and Their Conjugates

Probably the reader has already met complex numbers; a review is easy to give. The important ideas are the *complex conjugate* $\overline{x}$ and the *absolute value* $|x|$. Everyone knows that whatever i is, it satisfies the equation $i^2 = -1$. It is a pure imaginary number, and so are its multiples ib; b is real. The sum $a + ib$ is a complex number, and it is plotted in a natural way on the complex plane (Figure 5.4).

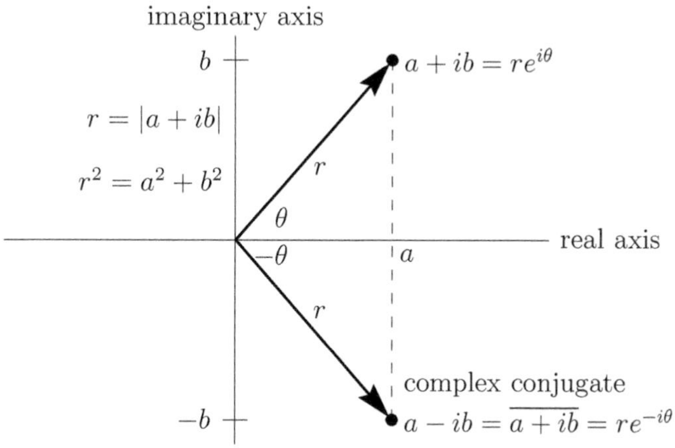

Figure 5.4 The complex plane, with $a + ib = re^{i\theta}$ and its conjugate $a - ib = re^{-i\theta}$.

The real numbers a and the imaginary numbers ib are special cases of complex numbers; they lie on the axes. Two complex numbers are easy to add:

$$\textbf{Complex addition} \qquad (a + ib) + (c + id) = (a + c) + i(b + d).$$

Multiplying $a + ib$ times $c + id$ uses the rule that $i^2 = -1$:

$$\begin{aligned}\textbf{Multiplication} \qquad (a + ib)(c + id) &= ac + ibc + iad + i^2bd \\ &= (ac - bd) + i(bc + ad).\end{aligned}$$

The ***complex conjugate*** of $a + ib$ is the number $a - ib$. *The sign of the imaginary part is reversed.* It is the mirror image across the real axis; any real number is its own conjugate, since $b = 0$. The conjugate is denoted by a bar or a star: $(a + ib)^* = \overline{a + ib} = a - ib$. It has three important properties:

1. The conjugate of a product equals the product of the conjugates:

$$\overline{(a + ib)(c + id)} = (ac - bd) - i(bc + ad) = \overline{(a + ib)}\;\overline{(c + id)}. \qquad (1)$$

2. The conjugate of a sum equals the sum of the conjugates:

$$\overline{(a + c) + i(b + d)} = (a + c) - i(b + d) = \overline{(a + ib)} + \overline{(c + id)}.$$

3. Multiplying any $a + ib$ by its conjugate $a - ib$ produces a real number $a^2 + b^2$:

$$\textbf{Absolute value} \qquad (a + ib)(a - ib) = a^2 + b^2 = r^2. \qquad (2)$$

This distance r is the ***absolute value*** $|a + ib| = \sqrt{a^2 + b^2}$.

Finally, trigonometry connects the sides a and b to the hypotenuse r by $a = r\cos\theta$ and $b = r\sin\theta$. Combining these two equations moves us into polar coordinates:

$$\textbf{Polar form} \qquad a + ib = r(\cos\theta + i\sin\theta) = re^{i\theta}. \tag{3}$$

The most important special case is when $r = 1$. Then $a + ib$ is $e^{i\theta} = \cos\theta + i\sin\theta$. It falls on the ***unit circle*** in the complex plane. As θ varies from 0 to 2π, this number $e^{i\theta}$ circles around zero at the constant radial distance $|e^{i\theta}| = \sqrt{\cos^2\theta + \sin^2\theta} = 1$.

Example 1 $x = 3 + 4i$ times its conjugate $\overline{x} = 3 - 4i$ is the absolute value squared:

$$x\overline{x} = (3+4i)(3-4i) = 25 = |x|^2 \quad \text{so} \quad r = |x| = 5.$$

To divide by $3 + 4i$, multiply numerator and denominator by its conjugate $3 - 4i$:

$$\frac{2+i}{3+4i} = \frac{2+i}{3+4i}\,\frac{3-4i}{3-4i} = \frac{10-5i}{25}.$$

In polar coordinates, multiplication and division are easy:

$re^{i\theta}$ times $Re^{i\alpha}$ has absolute value rR and angle $\theta + \alpha$.
$re^{i\theta}$ divided by $Re^{i\alpha}$ has absolute value r/R and angle $\theta - \alpha$.

Lengths and Transposes in the Complex Case

We return to linear algebra, and make the conversion from real to complex. By definition, *the complex vector space* $\mathbf{C}^n$ *contains all vectors x with n complex components*:

$$\textbf{Complex vector} \qquad x = \begin{bmatrix} x_1 \\ x_2 \\ \vdots \\ x_n \end{bmatrix} \qquad \text{with components } x_j = a_j + ib_j.$$

Vectors x and y are still added component by component. Scalar multiplication cx is now done with complex numbers c. The vectors $v_1, \ldots, v_k$ are linearly *dependent* if some nontrivial combination gives $c_1v_1 + \cdots + c_kv_k = 0$; the c_j may now be complex. The unit coordinate vectors are still in $\mathbf{C}^n$; they are still independent; and they still form a basis. Therefore $\mathbf{C}^n$ is a complex vector space of dimension n.

In the new definition of length, each x_j^2 is replaced by its modulus $|x_j|^2$:

$$\textbf{Length squared} \qquad \|x\|^2 = |x_1|^2 + \cdots + |x_n|^2. \tag{4}$$

Example 2 $x = \begin{bmatrix} 1 \\ i \end{bmatrix}$ and $\|x\|^2 = 2$; $y = \begin{bmatrix} 2+i \\ 2-4i \end{bmatrix}$ and $\|y\|^2 = 25$.

For real vectors there was a close connection between the length and the inner product: $\|x\|^2 = x^{\mathrm{T}}x$. This connection we want to preserve. The inner product must be modified to match the new definition of length, and we *conjugate the first vector in the inner product*. Replacing x by $\overline{x}$, ***the inner product becomes***

$$\textbf{Inner product} \qquad \overline{x}^{\mathrm{T}}y = \overline{x}_1y_1 + \cdots + \overline{x}_ny_n. \tag{5}$$

If we take the inner product of $x = (1+i, 3i)$ with itself, we are back to $\|x\|^2$:

$$\textbf{Length squared} \qquad \overline{x}^{\mathrm{T}}x = \overline{(1+i)}(1+i) + \overline{(3i)}(3i) = 2+9 \quad \text{and} \quad \|x\|^2 = 11.$$

Note that $\overline{y}^{\mathrm{T}}x$ is different from $\overline{x}^{\mathrm{T}}y$; we have to watch the order of the vectors.

This leaves only one more change in notation, condensing two symbols into one. Instead of a bar for the conjugate and a T for the transpose, those are combined into the ***conjugate transpose***. For vectors and matrices, a superscript H (or a star) combines both operations. This matrix $\overline{A}^{\mathrm{T}} = A^{\mathrm{H}} = A^*$ is called "A Hermitian":

$$\textbf{“A Hermitian”} \qquad A^{\mathrm{H}} = \overline{A}^{\mathrm{T}} \quad \text{has entries} \quad (A^{\mathrm{H}})_{ij} = \overline{A_{ji}}. \tag{6}$$

You have to listen closely to distinguish that name from the phrase "A *is* Hermitian," which means that A *equals* A^{H}. If A is an m by n matrix, then A^{H} is n by m:

$$\textbf{Conjugate transpose} \qquad \begin{bmatrix} 2+i & 3i \\ 4-i & 5 \\ 0 & 0 \end{bmatrix}^{\mathrm{H}} = \begin{bmatrix} 2-i & 4+i & 0 \\ -3i & 5 & 0 \end{bmatrix}.$$

This symbol A^{H} gives official recognition to the fact that, with complex entries, it is very seldom that we want only the transpose of A. It is the *conjugate* transpose A^{H} that becomes appropriate, and x^{H} is the row vector $[\overline{x}_1 \ \ldots \ \overline{x}_n]$.

5N **1.** The inner product of x and y is $x^{\mathrm{H}}y$. Orthogonal vectors have $x^{\mathrm{H}}y = 0$.
2. The squared length of x is $\|x\|^2 = x^{\mathrm{H}}x = |x_1|^2 + \cdots + |x_n|^2$.
3. Conjugating $(AB)^{\mathrm{T}} = B^{\mathrm{T}}A^{\mathrm{T}}$ produces $(AB)^{\mathrm{H}} = B^{\mathrm{H}}A^{\mathrm{H}}$.

Hermitian Matrices

We spoke in earlier chapters about symmetric matrices: $A = A^{\mathrm{T}}$. With complex entries, this idea of symmetry has to be extended. The right generalization is not to matrices that equal their transpose, but to ***matrices that equal their conjugate transpose***. These are the Hermitian matrices, and a typical example is A:

$$\textbf{Hermitian matrix} \qquad A = \begin{bmatrix} 2 & 3-3i \\ 3+3i & 5 \end{bmatrix} = A^{\mathrm{H}}. \tag{7}$$

The diagonal entries must be real; they are unchanged by conjugation. Each off-diagonal entry is matched with its mirror image across the main diagonal, and $3-3i$ is the conjugate of $3+3i$. *In every case,* $a_{ij} = \overline{a_{ji}}$.

Our main goal is to establish three basic properties of Hermitian matrices. These properties apply equally well to symmetric matrices. *A real symmetric matrix is certainly Hermitian.* (For real matrices there is no difference between A^{T} and A^{H}.) **The eigenvalues of A are real**—as we now prove.

Property 1 If $A = A^{\mathrm{H}}$, then for all complex vectors x, the number $x^{\mathrm{H}}Ax$ is real.

Every entry of A contributes to $x^{\mathrm{H}}Ax$. Try the 2 by 2 case with $x = (u, v)$:

$$x^{\mathrm{H}}Ax = \begin{bmatrix} \overline{u} & \overline{v} \end{bmatrix} \begin{bmatrix} 2 & 3-3i \\ 3+3i & 5 \end{bmatrix} \begin{bmatrix} u \\ v \end{bmatrix}$$
$$= 2\overline{u}u + 5\overline{v}v + (3-3i)\overline{u}v + (3+3i)u\overline{v}$$
$$= \textbf{real} + \textbf{real} + (\textbf{sum of complex conjugates}).$$

For a proof in general, $(x^{\mathrm{H}}Ax)^{\mathrm{H}}$ is the conjugate of the 1 by 1 matrix $x^{\mathrm{H}}Ax$, but we actually get the same number back again: $(x^{\mathrm{H}}Ax)^{\mathrm{H}} = x^{\mathrm{H}}A^{\mathrm{H}}x^{\mathrm{HH}} = x^{\mathrm{H}}Ax$. So that number must be real.

Property 2 If $A = A^{\mathrm{H}}$, every eigenvalue is real.

Proof Suppose $Ax = \lambda x$. ***The trick is to multiply by*** $\mathbf{x}^{\mathrm{H}}$: $\mathbf{x}^{\mathrm{H}}\mathbf{A}\mathbf{x} = \boldsymbol{\lambda}\mathbf{x}^{\mathrm{H}}\mathbf{x}$. The left-hand side is real by Property 1, and the right-hand side $x^{\mathrm{H}}x = \|x\|^2$ is real and positive, because $x \neq 0$. Therefore $\lambda = x^{\mathrm{H}}Ax/x^{\mathrm{H}}x$ must be real. Our example has $\lambda = 8$ and $\lambda = -1$:

$$|A - \lambda I| = \begin{vmatrix} 2-\lambda & 3-3i \\ 3+3i & 5-\lambda \end{vmatrix} = \lambda^2 - 7\lambda + 10 - |3-3i|^2$$
$$= \lambda^2 - 7\lambda - 8 = (\lambda - 8)(\lambda + 1). \tag{8}$$

■

Note This proof of real eigenvalues looks correct for any real matrix:

False proof $\quad Ax = \lambda x \quad$ gives $\quad x^{\mathrm{T}}Ax = \lambda x^{\mathrm{T}}x, \quad$ so $\quad \lambda = \dfrac{x^{\mathrm{T}}Ax}{x^{\mathrm{T}}x}\quad$ is real.

There must be a catch: *The eigenvector x might be complex.* It is when $A = A^{\mathrm{T}}$ that we can be sure λ and x stay real. More than that, *the eigenvectors are perpendicular*: $x^{\mathrm{T}}y = 0$ in the real symmetric case and $x^{\mathrm{H}}y = 0$ in the complex Hermitian case.

Property 3 Two eigenvectors of a real symmetric matrix or a Hermitian matrix, if they come from different eigenvalues, are orthogonal to one another.

The proof starts with $Ax = \lambda_1 x$, $Ay = \lambda_2 y$, and $A = A^{\mathrm{H}}$:

$$(\lambda_1 x)^{\mathrm{H}}y = (Ax)^{\mathrm{H}}y = x^{\mathrm{H}}Ay = x^{\mathrm{H}}(\lambda_2 y). \tag{9}$$

The outside numbers are $\lambda_1 x^{\mathrm{H}}y = \lambda_2 x^{\mathrm{H}}y$, since the λ's are real. Now we use the assumption $\lambda_1 \neq \lambda_2$, *which forces the conclusion that* $x^{\mathrm{H}}y = 0$. In our example,

$$(A - 8I)x = \begin{bmatrix} -6 & 3-3i \\ 3+3i & -3 \end{bmatrix} \begin{bmatrix} x_1 \\ x_2 \end{bmatrix} = \begin{bmatrix} 0 \\ 0 \end{bmatrix}, \qquad x = \begin{bmatrix} 1 \\ 1+i \end{bmatrix}$$
$$(A + I)y = \begin{bmatrix} 3 & 3-3i \\ 3+3i & 6 \end{bmatrix} \begin{bmatrix} y_1 \\ y_2 \end{bmatrix} = \begin{bmatrix} 0 \\ 0 \end{bmatrix}, \qquad y = \begin{bmatrix} 1-i \\ -1 \end{bmatrix}.$$

These two eigenvectors are orthogonal:

$$x^{\mathrm{H}}y = \begin{bmatrix} 1 & 1-i \end{bmatrix} \begin{bmatrix} 1-i \\ -1 \end{bmatrix} = 0.$$

Of course any multiples x/α and y/β are equally good as eigenvectors. MATLAB picks $\alpha = \|x\|$ and $\beta = \|y\|$, so that x/α and y/β are unit vectors; the eigenvectors are normalized to have length 1. They are now *orthonormal.* If these eigenvectors are chosen to be the columns of S, then we have $S^{-1}AS = \Lambda$ as always. ***The diagonalizing matrix can be chosen with orthonormal columns when*** $A = A^{\mathrm{H}}$.

In case A is real and symmetric, its eigenvalues are real by Property 2. Its unit eigenvectors are orthogonal by Property 3. Those eigenvectors are also real; they solve $(A - \lambda I)x = 0$. *These orthonormal eigenvectors go into an orthogonal matrix* Q, with $Q^{\mathrm{T}}Q = I$ and $Q^{\mathrm{T}} = Q^{-1}$. Then $S^{-1}AS = \Lambda$ becomes special—it is $Q^{-1}AQ = \Lambda$ or $A = Q\Lambda Q^{-1} = Q\Lambda Q^{\mathrm{T}}$. We can state one of the great theorems of linear algebra:

5O A real symmetric matrix can be factored into $A = Q\Lambda Q^{\mathrm{T}}$. Its orthonormal eigenvectors are in the orthogonal matrix Q and its eigenvalues are in Λ.

In geometry or mechanics, this is the *principal axis theorem.* It gives the right choice of axes for an ellipse. Those axes are perpendicular, and they point along the eigenvectors of the corresponding matrix. (Section 6.2 connects symmetric matrices to n-dimensional ellipses.) In mechanics the eigenvectors give the principal directions, along which there is pure compression or pure tension—with no shear.

In mathematics the formula $A = Q\Lambda Q^{\mathrm{T}}$ is known as the *spectral theorem.* If we multiply columns by rows, the matrix A becomes a combination of one-dimensional projections—which are the special matrices xx^{T} of rank 1, multiplied by λ:

$$A = Q\Lambda Q^{\mathrm{T}} = \begin{bmatrix} | & & | \\ x_1 & \cdots & x_n \\ | & & | \end{bmatrix} \begin{bmatrix} \lambda_1 & & \\ & \ddots & \\ & & \lambda_n \end{bmatrix} \begin{bmatrix} \text{---} \; x_1^{\mathrm{T}} \; \text{---} \\ \vdots \\ \text{---} \; x_n^{\mathrm{T}} \; \text{---} \end{bmatrix}$$

$$= \lambda_1 x_1 x_1^{\mathrm{T}} + \lambda_2 x_2 x_2^{\mathrm{T}} + \cdots + \lambda_n x_n x_n^{\mathrm{T}}. \tag{10}$$

Our 2 by 2 example has eigenvalues 3 and 1:

Example 3 $A = \begin{bmatrix} 2 & -1 \\ -1 & 2 \end{bmatrix} = 3\begin{bmatrix} \frac{1}{2} & -\frac{1}{2} \\ -\frac{1}{2} & \frac{1}{2} \end{bmatrix} + \begin{bmatrix} \frac{1}{2} & \frac{1}{2} \\ \frac{1}{2} & \frac{1}{2} \end{bmatrix}$ = **combination of two projections**.

The eigenvectors, with length scaled to 1, are

$$x_1 = \frac{1}{\sqrt{2}}\begin{bmatrix} 1 \\ -1 \end{bmatrix} \quad \text{and} \quad x_2 = \frac{1}{\sqrt{2}}\begin{bmatrix} 1 \\ 1 \end{bmatrix}.$$

Then the matrices on the right-hand side are $x_1x_1^{\mathrm{T}}$ and $x_2x_2^{\mathrm{T}}$—columns times rows—and they are projections onto the line through x_1 and the line through x_2.

All symmetric matrices are combinations of one-dimensional projections—which are symmetric matrices of rank 1.

Remark If A is real and its eigenvalues happen to be real, then its eigenvectors are also real. They solve $(A - \lambda I)x = 0$ and can be computed by elimination. But they will not be orthogonal unless A is symmetric: $A = Q\Lambda Q^{\mathrm{T}}$ leads to $A^{\mathrm{T}} = A$.

If A is real, all complex eigenvalues come in conjugate pairs: $Ax = \lambda x$ and $A\overline{x} = \overline{\lambda}\overline{x}$. *If $a + ib$ is an eigenvalue of a real matrix, so is $a - ib$.* (If $A = A^{\mathrm{T}}$ then $b = 0$.)

Strictly speaking, the spectral theorem $A = Q\Lambda Q^{\mathrm{T}}$ has been proved only when the eigenvalues of A are distinct. Then there are certainly n independent eigenvectors, and A can be safely diagonalized. Nevertheless it is true (see Section 5.6) that *even with repeated eigenvalues, a symmetric matrix still has a complete set of orthonormal eigenvectors*. The extreme case is the identity matrix, which has $\lambda = 1$ repeated n times—and no shortage of eigenvectors.

To finish the complex case we need the analogue of a real orthogonal matrix—and you can guess what happens to the requirement $Q^{\mathrm{T}}Q = I$. The transpose will be replaced by the conjugate transpose. The condition will become $U^{\mathrm{H}}U = I$. The new letter U reflects the new name: ***A complex matrix with orthonormal columns is called a unitary matrix***.

Unitary Matrices

May we propose two analogies? ***A Hermitian (or symmetric) matrix can be compared to a real number. A unitary (or orthogonal) matrix can be compared to a number on the unit circle***—a complex number of absolute value 1. The λ's are real if $A^{\mathrm{H}} = A$, and they are on the unit circle if $U^{\mathrm{H}}U = I$. The eigenvectors can be scaled to unit length and made orthonormal.*

Those statements are not yet proved for unitary (including orthogonal) matrices. Therefore we go directly to the three properties of U that correspond to the earlier Properties 1–3 of A. Remember that U has orthonormal columns:

Unitary matrix $\quad U^{\mathrm{H}}U = I, \qquad UU^{\mathrm{H}} = I, \quad$ and $\quad U^{\mathrm{H}} = U^{-1}.$

This leads directly to Property 1′, that multiplication by U has no effect on inner products, angles, or lengths. The proof is on one line, just as it was for Q:

Property 1′ $(Ux)^{\mathrm{H}}(Uy) = x^{\mathrm{H}}U^{\mathrm{H}}Uy = x^{\mathrm{H}}y$ and lengths are preserved by U:

Length unchanged $\quad \|Ux\|^2 = x^{\mathrm{H}}U^{\mathrm{H}}Ux = \|x\|^2. \qquad (11)$

Property 2′ Every eigenvalue of U has absolute value $|\lambda| = 1$.

This follows directly from $Ux = \lambda x$, by comparing the lengths of the two sides: $\|Ux\| = \|x\|$ by Property 1′, and always $\|\lambda x\| = |\lambda|\|x\|$. Therefore $|\lambda| = 1$.

Property 3′ Eigenvectors corresponding to different eigenvalues are orthonormal.

---

* Later we compare "skew-Hermitian" matrices with pure imaginary numbers, and "normal" matrices with all complex numbers $a + ib$. A nonnormal matrix without orthogonal eigenvectors belongs to none of these classes, and is outside the whole analogy.

Start with $Ux = \lambda_1 x$ and $Uy = \lambda_2 y$, and take inner products by Property 1′:

$$x^{\mathrm{H}}y = (Ux)^{\mathrm{H}}(Uy) = (\lambda_1 x)^{\mathrm{H}}(\lambda_2 y) = \overline{\lambda}_1\lambda_2 x^{\mathrm{H}}y.$$

Comparing the left to the right, $\overline{\lambda}_1\lambda_2 = 1$ or $x^{\mathrm{H}}y = 0$. But Property 2′ is $\overline{\lambda}_1\lambda_1 = 1$, so we cannot also have $\overline{\lambda}_1\lambda_2 = 1$. Thus $x^{\mathrm{H}}y = 0$ and the eigenvectors are orthogonal.

Example 4 $U = \begin{bmatrix} \cos t & -\sin t \\ \sin t & \cos t \end{bmatrix}$ has eigenvalues e^{it} and e^{-it}.

The orthogonal eigenvectors are $x = (1, -i)$ and $y = (1, i)$. (Remember to take conjugates in $x^{\mathrm{H}}y = 1 + i^2 = 0$.) After division by $\sqrt{2}$ they are orthonormal.

Here is the most important *unitary matrix* by far.

Example 5
$$U = \frac{1}{\sqrt{n}}\begin{bmatrix} 1 & 1 & \cdot & 1 \\ 1 & w & \cdot & w^{n-1} \\ \cdot & \cdot & \cdot & \cdot \\ 1 & w^{n-1} & \cdot & w^{(n-1)^2} \end{bmatrix} = \frac{\textbf{Fourier matrix}}{\sqrt{n}}.$$

The complex number w is on the unit circle at the angle $\theta = 2\pi/n$. It equals $e^{2\pi i/n}$. Its powers are spaced evenly around the circle. That spacing assures that the sum of all n powers of w—all the nth roots of 1—is zero. Algebraically, the sum $1 + w + \cdots + w^{n-1}$ is $(w^n - 1)/(w - 1)$. And $w^n - 1$ is zero!

$$\text{row 1 of } U^{\mathrm{H}} \text{ times column 2 of } U \text{ is } \frac{1}{n}(1 + w + w^2 + \cdots + w^{n-1}) = \frac{w^n - 1}{w - 1} = 0.$$

$$\text{row } i \text{ of } U^{\mathrm{H}} \text{ times column } j \text{ of } U \text{ is } \frac{1}{n}(1 + W + W^2 + \cdots + W^{n-1}) = \frac{W^n - 1}{W - 1} = 0.$$

In the second case, $W = w^{j-i}$. Every entry of the original F has absolute value 1. The factor $\sqrt{n}$ shrinks the columns of U into unit vectors. ***The fundamental identity of the finite Fourier transform is $U^{\mathrm{H}}U = I$.***

Thus U is a unitary matrix. Its inverse looks the same except that w is replaced by $w^{-1} = e^{-i\theta} = \overline{w}$. Since U is unitary, its inverse is found by transposing (which changes nothing) and conjugating (which changes w to $\overline{w}$). The inverse of this U is $\overline{U}$. Ux can be computed quickly by the ***Fast Fourier Transform*** as found in Section 3.5.

By Property 1′ of unitary matrices, the length of a vector x is the same as the length of Ux. The energy in state space equals the energy in transform space. The energy is the sum of $|x_j|^2$, and it is also the sum of the energies in the separate frequencies. The vector $x = (1, 0, \ldots, 0)$ contains equal amounts of every frequency component, and its Discrete Fourier Transform $Ux = (1, 1, \ldots, 1)/\sqrt{n}$ also has length 1.

Example 6

$$P = \begin{bmatrix} 0 & 1 & 0 & 0 \\ 0 & 0 & 1 & 0 \\ 0 & 0 & 0 & 1 \\ 1 & 0 & 0 & 0 \end{bmatrix}.$$

This is an orthogonal matrix, so by Property 3′ it must have orthogonal eigenvectors. They are the columns of the Fourier matrix! Its eigenvalues must have absolute value 1.

They are the numbers $1, w, \ldots, w^{n-1}$ (or $1, i, i^2, i^3$ in this 4 by 4 case). It is a real matrix, but its eigenvalues and eigenvectors are complex.

One final note. Skew-Hermitian matrices satisfy $K^{\mathrm{H}} = -K$, just as skew-symmetric matrices satisfy $K^{\mathrm{T}} = -K$. Their properties follow immediately from their close link to Hermitian matrices:

If A is Hermitian then $K = iA$ is skew-Hermitian.

The eigenvalues of K are purely imaginary instead of purely real; we multiply by i. The eigenvectors are not changed. The Hermitian example on the previous pages would lead to

$$K = iA = \begin{bmatrix} 2i & 3+3i \\ -3+3i & 5i \end{bmatrix} = -K^{\mathrm{H}}.$$

The diagonal entries are multiples of i (allowing zero). The eigenvalues are $8i$ and $-i$. The eigenvectors are still orthogonal, and we still have $K = U\Lambda U^{\mathrm{H}}$—with a unitary U instead of a real orthogonal Q, and with $8i$ and $-i$ on the diagonal of Λ.

This section is summarized by a table of parallels between real and complex.

Real versus Complex

$\mathbf{R}^n$ (n real components)	$\leftrightarrow$	$\mathbf{C}^n$ (n complex components)
length: $\|x\|^2 = x_1^2 + \cdots + x_n^2$	$\leftrightarrow$	length: $\|x\|^2 = \lvert x_1\rvert^2 + \cdots + \lvert x_n\rvert^2$
transpose: $A_{ij}^{\mathrm{T}} = A_{ji}$	$\leftrightarrow$	Hermitian transpose: $A_{ij}^{\mathrm{H}} = \overline{A_{ji}}$
$(AB)^{\mathrm{T}} = B^{\mathrm{T}}A^{\mathrm{T}}$	$\leftrightarrow$	$(AB)^{\mathrm{H}} = B^{\mathrm{H}}A^{\mathrm{H}}$
inner product: $x^{\mathrm{T}}y = x_1y_1 + \cdots + x_ny_n$	$\leftrightarrow$	$x^{\mathrm{H}}y = \overline{x}_1y_1 + \cdots + \overline{x}_ny_n$
$(Ax)^{\mathrm{T}}y = x^{\mathrm{T}}(A^{\mathrm{T}}y)$	$\leftrightarrow$	$(Ax)^{\mathrm{H}}y = x^{\mathrm{H}}(A^{\mathrm{H}}y)$
orthogonality: $x^{\mathrm{T}}y = 0$	$\leftrightarrow$	orthogonality: $x^{\mathrm{H}}y = 0$
symmetric matrices: $A^{\mathrm{T}} = A$	$\leftrightarrow$	Hermitian matrices: $A^{\mathrm{H}} = A$
$A = Q\Lambda Q^{-1} = Q\Lambda Q^{\mathrm{T}}$ (real Λ)	$\leftrightarrow$	$A = U\Lambda U^{-1} = U\Lambda U^{\mathrm{H}}$ (real Λ)
skew-symmetric $K^{\mathrm{T}} = -K$	$\leftrightarrow$	skew-Hermitian $K^{\mathrm{H}} = -K$
orthogonal $Q^{\mathrm{T}}Q = I$ or $Q^{\mathrm{T}} = Q^{-1}$	$\leftrightarrow$	unitary $U^{\mathrm{H}}U = I$ or $U^{\mathrm{H}} = U^{-1}$
$(Qx)^{\mathrm{T}}(Qy) = x^{\mathrm{T}}y$ and $\|Qx\| = \|x\|$	$\leftrightarrow$	$(Ux)^{\mathrm{H}}(Uy) = x^{\mathrm{H}}y$ and $\|Ux\| = \|x\|$

The columns, rows, and eigenvectors of Q and U are orthonormal, and every $|\lambda| = 1$

Problem Set 5.5

1. For the complex numbers $3 + 4i$ and $1 - i$,

   (a) find their positions in the complex plane.
   (b) find their sum and product.
   (c) find their conjugates and their absolute values.

   Do the original numbers lie inside or outside the unit circle?

2. What can you say about

(a) the sum of a complex number and its conjugate?
(b) the conjugate of a number on the unit circle?
(c) the product of two numbers on the unit circle?
(d) the sum of two numbers on the unit circle?

3. If $x = 2 + i$ and $y = 1 + 3i$, find $\overline{x}$, $x\overline{x}$, xy, $1/x$, and x/y. Check that the absolute value $|xy|$ equals $|x|$ times $|y|$, and the absolute value $|1/x|$ equals 1 divided by $|x|$.

4. Find a and b for the complex numbers $a + ib$ at the angles $\theta = 30^\circ, 60^\circ, 90^\circ$ on the unit circle. Verify by direct multiplication that the square of the first is the second, and the cube of the first is the third.

5. (a) If $x = re^{i\theta}$ what are x^2, x^{-1}, and $\overline{x}$ in polar coordinates? Where are the complex numbers that have $x^{-1} = \overline{x}$?
(b) At $t = 0$, the complex number $e^{(-1+i)t}$ equals one. Sketch its path in the complex plane as t increases from 0 to 2π.

6. Find the lengths and the inner product of

$$x = \begin{bmatrix} 2 - 4i \\ 4i \end{bmatrix} \quad \text{and} \quad y = \begin{bmatrix} 2 + 4i \\ 4i \end{bmatrix}.$$

7. Write out the matrix A^{H} and compute $C = A^{\mathrm{H}}A$ if

$$A = \begin{bmatrix} 1 & i & 0 \\ i & 0 & 1 \end{bmatrix}.$$

What is the relation between C and C^{H}? Does it hold whenever C is constructed from some $A^{\mathrm{H}}A$?

8. (a) With the preceding A, use elimination to solve $Ax = 0$.
(b) Show that the nullspace you just computed is orthogonal to $\boldsymbol{C}(A^{\mathrm{H}})$ *and not to the usual row space* $\boldsymbol{C}(A^{\mathrm{T}})$. The four fundamental spaces in the complex case are $\boldsymbol{N}(A)$ and $\boldsymbol{C}(A)$ as before, and then $\boldsymbol{N}(A^{\mathrm{H}})$ and $\boldsymbol{C}(A^{\mathrm{H}})$.

9. (a) How is the determinant of A^{H} related to the determinant of A?
(b) Prove that the determinant of any Hermitian matrix is real.

10. (a) How many degrees of freedom are there in a real symmetric matrix, a real diagonal matrix, and a real orthogonal matrix? (The first answer is the sum of the other two, because $A = Q\Lambda Q^{\mathrm{T}}$.)
(b) Show that 3 by 3 Hermitian matrices A and also unitary U have 9 real degrees of freedom (columns of U can be multiplied by any $e^{i\theta}$).

11. Write P, Q and R in the form $\lambda_1 x_1 x_1^{\mathrm{H}} + \lambda_2 x_2 x_2^{\mathrm{H}}$ of the spectral theorem:

$$P = \begin{bmatrix} \frac{1}{2} & \frac{1}{2} \\ \frac{1}{2} & \frac{1}{2} \end{bmatrix}, \quad Q = \begin{bmatrix} 0 & 1 \\ 1 & 0 \end{bmatrix}, \quad R = \begin{bmatrix} 3 & 4 \\ 4 & -3 \end{bmatrix}.$$

12. Give a reason if true or a counterexample if false:

(a) If A is Hermitian, then $A + iI$ is invertible.
(b) If Q is orthogonal, then $Q + \frac{1}{2}I$ is invertible.
(c) If A is real, then $A + iI$ is invertible.

13. Suppose A is a symmetric 3 by 3 matrix with eigenvalues 0, 1, 2.

(a) What properties can be guaranteed for the corresponding unit eigenvectors u, v, w?
(b) In terms of u, v, w, describe the nullspace, left nullspace, row space, and column space of A.
(c) Find a vector x that satisfies $Ax = v + w$. Is x unique?
(d) Under what conditions on b does $Ax = b$ have a solution?
(e) If u, v, w are the columns of S, what are S^{-1} and $S^{-1}AS$?

14. In the list below, which classes of matrices contain A and which contain B?

$$A = \begin{bmatrix} 0 & 1 & 0 & 0 \\ 0 & 0 & 1 & 0 \\ 0 & 0 & 0 & 1 \\ 1 & 0 & 0 & 0 \end{bmatrix} \quad \text{and} \quad B = \frac{1}{4}\begin{bmatrix} 1 & 1 & 1 & 1 \\ 1 & 1 & 1 & 1 \\ 1 & 1 & 1 & 1 \\ 1 & 1 & 1 & 1 \end{bmatrix}.$$

*Orthogonal, invertible, projection, permutation, Hermitian, rank-*1, *diagonalizable, Markov*. Find the eigenvalues of A and B.

15. What is the dimension of the space S of all n by n real symmetric matrices? The spectral theorem says that every symmetric matrix is a combination of n projection matrices. Since the dimension exceeds n, how is this difference explained?

16. Write one significant fact about the eigenvalues of each of the following.

(a) A real symmetric matrix.
(b) A stable matrix: all solutions to $du/dt = Au$ approach zero.
(c) An orthogonal matrix.
(d) A Markov matrix.
(e) A defective matrix (nondiagonalizable).
(f) A singular matrix.

17. Show that if U and V are unitary, so is UV. Use the criterion $U^{\mathrm{H}}U = I$.

18. Show that a unitary matrix has $|\det U| = 1$, but possibly $\det U$ is different from $\det U^{\mathrm{H}}$. Describe all 2 by 2 matrices that are unitary.

19. Find a third column so that U is unitary. How much freedom in column 3?

$$U = \begin{bmatrix} 1/\sqrt{3} & i/\sqrt{2} & \\ 1/\sqrt{3} & 0 & \\ i/\sqrt{3} & 1/\sqrt{2} & \end{bmatrix}.$$

20. Diagonalize the 2 by 2 skew-Hermitian matrix $K = \begin{bmatrix} i & i \\ i & i \end{bmatrix}$, whose entries are all

$\sqrt{-1}$. Compute $e^{Kt} = Se^{\Lambda t}S^{-1}$, and verify that e^{Kt} is unitary. What is the derivative of e^{Kt} at $t = 0$?

21. Describe all 3 by 3 matrices that are simultaneously Hermitian, unitary, and diagonal. How many are there?

22. Every matrix Z can be split into a Hermitian and a skew-Hermitian part, $Z = A+K$, just as a complex number z is split into $a + ib$. The real part of z is half of $z + \bar{z}$, and the "real part" of Z is half of $Z + Z^{\mathrm{H}}$. Find a similar formula for the "imaginary part" K, and split these matrices into $A + K$:

$$Z = \begin{bmatrix} 3+i & 4+2i \\ 0 & 5 \end{bmatrix} \quad \text{and} \quad Z = \begin{bmatrix} i & i \\ -i & i \end{bmatrix}.$$

23. Show that the columns of the 4 by 4 Fourier matrix F in Example 5 are eigenvectors of the permutation matrix P in Example 6.

24. For the permutation of Example 6, write out the *circulant matrix* $C = c_0 I + c_1 P + c_2 P^2 + c_3 P^3$. (Its eigenvector matrix is again the Fourier matrix.) Write out also the four components of the matrix-vector product Cx, which is the *convolution* of $c = (c_0, c_1, c_2, c_3)$ and $x = (x_0, x_1, x_2, x_3)$.

25. For a circulant $C = F\Lambda F^{-1}$, why is it faster to multiply by F^{-1}, then Λ, then F (the convolution rule), than to multiply directly by C?

26. Find the lengths of $u = (1+i, 1-i, 1+2i)$ and $v = (i, i, i)$. Also find $u^{\mathrm{H}}v$ and $v^{\mathrm{H}}u$.

27. Prove that $A^{\mathrm{H}}A$ is always a Hermitian matrix. Compute $A^{\mathrm{H}}A$ and AA^{H}:

$$A = \begin{bmatrix} i & 1 & i \\ 1 & i & i \end{bmatrix}.$$

28. If $Az = 0$, then $A^{\mathrm{H}}Az = 0$. If $A^{\mathrm{H}}Az = 0$, multiply by z^{H} to prove that $Az = 0$. The nullspaces of A and $A^{\mathrm{H}}A$ are ______. $A^{\mathrm{H}}A$ is an invertible Hermitian matrix when the nullspace of A contains only $z =$ ______.

29. When you multiply a Hermitian matrix by a real number c, is cA still Hermitian? If $c = i$, show that iA is skew-Hermitian. The 3 by 3 Hermitian matrices are a subspace, provided that the "scalars" are real numbers.

30. Which classes of matrices does P belong to: orthogonal, invertible, Hermitian, unitary, factorizable into LU, factorizable into QR?

$$P = \begin{bmatrix} 0 & 1 & 0 \\ 0 & 0 & 1 \\ 1 & 0 & 0 \end{bmatrix}.$$

31. Compute P^2, P^3, and P^{100} in Problem 30. What are the eigenvalues of P?

32. Find the unit eigenvectors of P in Problem 30, and put them into the columns of a unitary matrix U. What property of P makes these eigenvectors orthogonal?

33. Write down the 3 by 3 *circulant matrix* $C = 2I + 5P + 4P^2$. It has the same eigenvectors as P in Problem 30. Find its eigenvalues.

34. If U is unitary and Q is a real orthogonal matrix, show that U^{-1} is unitary and also UQ is unitary. Start from $U^{\mathrm{H}}U = I$ and $Q^{\mathrm{T}}Q = I$.

35. Diagonalize A (real λ's) and K (imaginary λ's) to reach $U\Lambda U^{\mathrm{H}}$:

$$A = \begin{bmatrix} 0 & 1-i \\ i+1 & 1 \end{bmatrix} \qquad K = \begin{bmatrix} 0 & -1+i \\ 1+i & i \end{bmatrix}$$

36. Diagonalize this orthogonal matrix to reach $Q = U\Lambda U^{\mathrm{H}}$. Now all λ's are ______:

$$Q = \begin{bmatrix} \cos\theta & -\sin\theta \\ \sin\theta & \cos\theta \end{bmatrix}.$$

37. Diagonalize this unitary matrix V to reach $V = U\Lambda U^{\mathrm{H}}$. Again all $|\lambda| = 1$:

$$V = \frac{1}{\sqrt{3}} \begin{bmatrix} 1 & 1-i \\ 1+i & -1 \end{bmatrix}.$$

38. If $v_1, \ldots, v_n$ is an orthonormal basis for $\mathbf{C}^n$, the matrix with those columns is a ______ matrix. Show that any vector z equals $(v_1^{\mathrm{H}}z)v_1 + \cdots + (v_n^{\mathrm{H}}z)v_n$.

39. The functions e^{-ix} and e^{ix} are orthogonal on the interval $0 \le x \le 2\pi$ because their *complex* inner product is $\int_0^{2\pi}$ ______ $= 0$.

40. The vectors $v = (1, i, 1)$, $w = (i, 1, 0)$ and $z =$ ______ are an orthogonal basis for ______.

41. If $A = R + iS$ is a Hermitian matrix, are the real matrices R and S symmetric?

42. The (complex) dimension of $\mathbf{C}^n$ is ______. Find a nonreal basis for $\mathbf{C}^n$.

43. Describe all 1 by 1 matrices that are Hermitian and also unitary. Do the same for 2 by 2 matrices.

44. How are the eigenvalues of A^{H} (square matrix) related to the eigenvalues of A?

45. If $u^{\mathrm{H}}u = 1$, show that $I - 2uu^{\mathrm{H}}$ is Hermitian and also unitary. The rank-1 matrix uu^{H} is the projection onto what line in $\mathbf{C}^n$?

46. If $A + iB$ is a unitary matrix (A and B are real), show that $Q = \begin{bmatrix} A & -B \\ B & A \end{bmatrix}$ is an orthogonal matrix.

47. If $A + iB$ is a Hermitian matrix (A and B are real), show that $\begin{bmatrix} A & -B \\ B & A \end{bmatrix}$ is symmetric.

48. Prove that the inverse of a Hermitian matrix is again a Hermitian matrix.

49. Diagonalize this matrix by constructing its eigenvalue matrix Λ and its eigenvector matrix S:

$$A = \begin{bmatrix} 2 & 1-i \\ 1+i & 3 \end{bmatrix} = A^{\mathrm{H}}.$$

50. A matrix with orthonormal eigenvectors has the form $A = U\Lambda U^{-1} = U\Lambda U^{\mathrm{H}}$. *Prove that* $AA^{\mathrm{H}} = A^{\mathrm{H}}A$. These are exactly the *normal matrices*.

5.6 SIMILARITY TRANSFORMATIONS

Virtually every step in this chapter has involved the combination $S^{-1}AS$. The eigenvectors of A went into the columns of S, and that made $S^{-1}AS$ a diagonal matrix (called Λ). When A was symmetric, we wrote Q instead of S, choosing the eigenvectors to be orthonormal. In the complex case, when A is Hermitian we write U—it is still the matrix of eigenvectors. Now we look at all combinations $M^{-1}AM$—*formed with any invertible M on the right and its inverse on the left.* The invertible eigenvector matrix S may fail to exist (the defective case), or we may not know it, or we may not want to use it.

First a new word: ***The matrices A and $M^{-1}AM$ are "similar."*** Going from one to the other is a ***similarity transformation***. It is the natural step for differential equations or matrix powers or eigenvalues—just as elimination steps were natural for $Ax = b$. Elimination multiplied A on the left by L^{-1}, but not on the right by L. So U is not similar to A, and the pivots are *not* the eigenvalues.

A whole family of matrices $M^{-1}AM$ is similar to A, and there are two questions:

1. What do these similar matrices $M^{-1}AM$ have in common?
2. With a special choice of M, what special form can be achieved by $M^{-1}AM$?

The final answer is given by the ***Jordan form***, with which the chapter ends.

These combinations $M^{-1}AM$ arise in a differential or difference equation, when a "change of variables" $u = Mv$ introduces the new unknown v:

$$\frac{du}{dt} = Au \quad \text{becomes} \quad M\frac{dv}{dt} = AMv, \quad \text{or} \quad \frac{dv}{dt} = M^{-1}AMv$$

$$u_{n+1} = Au_n \quad \text{becomes} \quad Mv_{n+1} = AMv_n, \quad \text{or} \quad v_{n+1} = M^{-1}AMv_n.$$

The new matrix in the equation is $M^{-1}AM$. In the special case $M = S$, the system is uncoupled because $\Lambda = S^{-1}AS$ is diagonal. The eigenvectors evolve independently. This is the maximum simplification, but other M's are also useful. We try to make $M^{-1}AM$ easier to work with than A.

The family of matrices $M^{-1}AM$ includes A itself, by choosing $M = I$. Any of these similar matrices can appear in the differential and difference equations, by the change $u = Mv$, so they ought to have something in common, and they do: ***Similar matrices share the same eigenvalues***.

5P Suppose that $B = M^{-1}AM$. Then A and B have the **same eigenvalues. Every eigenvector x of A corresponds to an eigenvector $M^{-1}x$ of B.**

Start from $Ax = \lambda x$ and substitute $A = MBM^{-1}$:

$$\textbf{Same eigenvalue} \qquad MBM^{-1}x = \lambda x \quad \text{which is} \quad B(M^{-1}x) = \lambda(M^{-1}x). \qquad (1)$$

The eigenvalue of B is still λ. The eigenvector has changed from x to $M^{-1}x$.

We can also check that $A - \lambda I$ and $B - \lambda I$ have the same determinant:

Product of matrices $\qquad B - \lambda I = M^{-1}AM - \lambda I = M^{-1}(A - \lambda I)M$

Product rule $\qquad \det(B - \lambda I) = \det M^{-1} \det(A - \lambda I) \det M = \det(A - \lambda I).$

The polynomials $\det(A - \lambda I)$ and $\det(B - \lambda I)$ are equal. Their roots—the eigenvalues of A and B—are the same. Here are matrices B similar to A.

Example 1 $A = \begin{bmatrix} 1 & 0 \\ 0 & 0 \end{bmatrix}$ has eigenvalues 1 and 0. Each B is $M^{-1}AM$:

If $M = \begin{bmatrix} 1 & b \\ 0 & 1 \end{bmatrix}$, then $B = \begin{bmatrix} 1 & b \\ 0 & 0 \end{bmatrix}$: triangular with $\lambda = 1$ and 0.

If $M = \begin{bmatrix} 1 & 1 \\ -1 & 1 \end{bmatrix}$, then $B = \begin{bmatrix} \frac{1}{2} & \frac{1}{2} \\ \frac{1}{2} & \frac{1}{2} \end{bmatrix}$: projection with $\lambda = 1$ and 0.

If $M = \begin{bmatrix} a & b \\ c & d \end{bmatrix}$, then $B =$ an arbitrary matrix with $\lambda = 1$ and 0.

In this case we can produce any B that has the correct eigenvalues. It is an easy case, because the eigenvalues 1 and 0 are distinct. The diagonal A was actually Λ, the outstanding member of this family of similar matrices (the *capo*). The Jordan form will worry about repeated eigenvalues and a possible shortage of eigenvectors. All we say now is that every $M^{-1}AM$ has the same number of independent eigenvectors as A (each eigenvector is multiplied by M^{-1}).

The first step is to look at the linear transformations that lie behind the matrices. Rotations, reflections, and projections act on n-dimensional space. The transformation can happen without linear algebra, but linear algebra turns it into matrix multiplication.

Change of Basis = Similarity Transformation

The similar matrix $B = M^{-1}AM$ is closely connected to A, if we go back to linear transformations. Remember the key idea: ***Every linear transformation is represented by a matrix***. The matrix depends on the choice of basis! *If we change the basis by M we change the matrix A to a similar matrix B.*

Similar matrices represent the same transformation T with respect to different bases. The algebra is almost straightforward. Suppose we have a basis $v_1, \ldots, v_n$. The jth column of A comes from applying T to v_j:

$$Tv_j = \text{combination of the basis vectors} = a_{1j}v_1 + \cdots + a_{nj}v_n. \tag{2}$$

For a new basis $V_1, \ldots, V_n$, the new matrix B is constructed in the same way: $TV_j =$ combination of the V's $= b_{1j}V_1 + \cdots + b_{nj}V_n$. But also each V must be a combination of the old basis vectors: $V_j = \sum m_{ij}v_i$. That matrix M is really representing the *identity transformation* (!) when the only thing happening is the change of basis (T is I). The inverse matrix M^{-1} also represents the identity transformation, when the basis is changed from the v's back to the V's. Now the product rule gives the result we want:

5Q The matrices A and B that represent the same linear transformation T with respect to two different bases (the v's and the V's) are ***similar***:

$$\begin{matrix} [T]_{V \text{ to } V} & = & [I]_{v \text{ to } V} & [T]_{v \text{ to } v} & [I]_{V \text{ to } v} \\ B & = & M^{-1} & A & M. \end{matrix} \tag{3}$$

I think an example is the best way to explain $B = M^{-1}AM$. Suppose T is *projection onto the line L at angle θ*. This linear transformation is completely described without the help of a basis. But to represent T by a matrix, we do need a basis. Figure 5.5 offers two choices, the standard basis $v_1 = (1,0)$, $v_2 = (0,1)$ and a basis V_1, V_2 chosen especially for T.

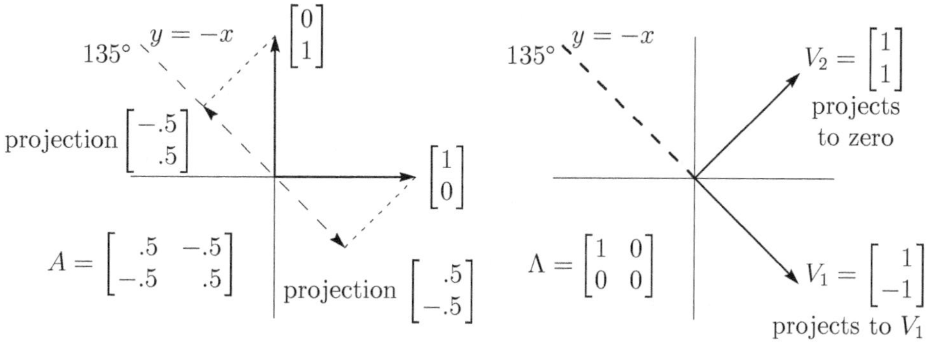

Figure 5.5 Change of basis to make the projection matrix diagonal.

In fact $TV_1 = V_1$ (since V_1 is already on the line L) and $TV_2 = 0$ (since V_2 is perpendicular to the line). In that eigenvector basis, the matrix is diagonal:

$$\textbf{Eigenvector basis} \qquad B = [T]_{V \text{ to } V} = \begin{bmatrix} 1 & 0 \\ 0 & 0 \end{bmatrix}.$$

The other thing is the change of basis matrix M. For that we express V_1 as a combination $v_1 \cos\theta + v_2 \sin\theta$ and put those coefficients into column 1. Similarly V_2 (or IV_2, the transformation is the identity) is $-v_1 \sin\theta + v_2 \cos\theta$, producing column 2:

$$\textbf{Change of basis} \qquad M = [I]_{V \text{ to } v} = \begin{bmatrix} c & -s \\ s & c \end{bmatrix}.$$

The inverse matrix M^{-1} (which is here the transpose) goes from v to V. Combined with B and M, it gives the projection matrix in the standard basis of v's:

$$\textbf{Standard basis} \qquad A = MBM^{-1} = \begin{bmatrix} c^2 & cs \\ cs & s^2 \end{bmatrix}.$$

We can summarize the main point. The way to simplify that matrix A—in fact to diagonalize it—is to find its eigenvectors. They go into the columns of M (or S) and $M^{-1}AM$ is diagonal. The algebraist says the same thing in the language of linear transformations: *Choose a basis consisting of eigenvectors.* The standard basis led to A, which was not simple. The right basis led to B, which was diagonal.

We emphasize again that $M^{-1}AM$ does not arise in solving $Ax = b$. There the basic operation was to multiply A (on the left side only!) by a matrix that subtracts a multiple of one row from another. Such a transformation preserved the nullspace and row space of A; it normally changes the eigenvalues.

Eigenvalues are actually calculated by a sequence of simple similarities. The matrix goes gradually toward a triangular form, and the eigenvalues gradually appear on the main diagonal. (Such a sequence is described in Chapter 7.) This is much better than trying to compute det $(A-\lambda I)$, whose roots should be the eigenvalues. For a large matrix, it is numerically impossible to concentrate all that information into the polynomial and then get it out again.

Triangular Forms with a Unitary M

Our first move beyond the eigenvector matrix $M = S$ is a little bit crazy: Instead of a more general M, we go the other way and *restrict M to be unitary*. $M^{-1}AM$ can achieve a triangular form T under this restriction. The columns of $M = U$ are orthonormal (in the real case, we would write $M = Q$). Unless the eigenvectors of A are orthogonal, a diagonal $U^{-1}AU$ is impossible. But "Schur's lemma" in **5R** is very useful—at least to the theory. (The rest of this chapter is devoted more to theory than to applications. The Jordan form is independent of this triangular form.)

5R There is a unitary matrix $M = U$ such that $U^{-1}AU = T$ is triangular. The eigenvalues of A appear along the diagonal of this similar matrix T.

Proof Every matrix, say 4 by 4, has at least one eigenvalue λ_1. In the worst case, it could be repeated four times. Therefore A has at least one unit eigenvector x_1, which we place in the *first column of U*. At this stage the other three columns are impossible to determine, so we complete the matrix in any way that leaves it unitary, and call it U_1. (The Gram–Schmidt process guarantees that this can be done.) $Ax_1 = \lambda_1 x_1$ in column 1 means that the product $U_1^{-1}AU_1$ starts in the right form:

$$AU_1 = U_1\begin{bmatrix} \lambda_1 & * & * & * \\ 0 & * & * & * \\ 0 & * & * & * \\ 0 & * & * & * \end{bmatrix} \quad \text{leads to} \quad U_1^{-1}AU_1 = \begin{bmatrix} \lambda_1 & * & * & * \\ 0 & * & * & * \\ 0 & * & * & * \\ 0 & * & * & * \end{bmatrix}.$$

Now work with the 3 by 3 submatrix in the lower right-hand corner. It has a unit eigenvector x_2, which becomes the first column of a unitary matrix M_2:

$$\text{If} \quad U_2 = \begin{bmatrix} 1 & 0 & 0 & 0 \\ 0 & & & \\ 0 & & M_2 & \\ 0 & & & \end{bmatrix} \quad \text{then} \quad U_2^{-1}(U_1^{-1}AU_1)U_2 = \begin{bmatrix} \lambda_1 & * & * & * \\ 0 & \lambda_2 & * & * \\ 0 & 0 & * & * \\ 0 & 0 & * & * \end{bmatrix}.$$

At the last step, an eigenvector of the 2 by 2 matrix in the lower right-hand corner goes into a unitary M_3, which is put into the corner of U_3:

$$\textbf{Triangular} \qquad U_3^{-1}(U_2^{-1}U_1^{-1}AU_1U_2)U_3 = \begin{bmatrix} \lambda_1 & * & * & * \\ 0 & \lambda_2 & * & * \\ 0 & 0 & \lambda_3 & * \\ 0 & 0 & 0 & * \end{bmatrix} = T.$$

The product $U = U_1U_2U_3$ is still a unitary matrix, and $U^{-1}AU = T$. ■

This lemma applies to all matrices, with no assumption that A is diagonalizable. We could use it to prove that ***the powers A^k approach zero when all $|\lambda_i| < 1$, and***

the exponentials e^{At} approach zero when all $\mathbf{Re}\,\lambda_i < \mathbf{0}$—even without the full set of eigenvectors which was assumed in Sections 5.3 and 5.4.

Example 2 $A = \begin{bmatrix} 2 & -1 \\ 1 & 0 \end{bmatrix}$ has the eigenvalue $\lambda = 1$ (twice).

The only line of eigenvectors goes through $(1, 1)$. After dividing by $\sqrt{2}$, this is the first column of U, and the triangular $U^{-1}AU = T$ has the eigenvalues on its diagonal:

$$U^{-1}AU = \begin{bmatrix} 1/\sqrt{2} & 1/\sqrt{2} \\ 1/\sqrt{2} & -1/\sqrt{2} \end{bmatrix} \begin{bmatrix} 2 & -1 \\ 1 & 0 \end{bmatrix} \begin{bmatrix} 1/\sqrt{2} & 1/\sqrt{2} \\ 1/\sqrt{2} & -1/\sqrt{2} \end{bmatrix} = \begin{bmatrix} 1 & 2 \\ 0 & 1 \end{bmatrix} = T. \quad (4)$$

Diagonalizing Symmetric and Hermitian Matrices

This triangular form will show that any symmetric or Hermitian matrix—whether its eigenvalues are *distinct or not*—has a complete set of orthonormal eigenvectors. We need a unitary matrix such that $U^{-1}AU$ is *diagonal*. Schur's lemma has just found it. This triangular T must be diagonal, because it is also Hermitian when $A = A^{\mathrm{H}}$:

$$\boldsymbol{T = T^{\mathrm{H}}} \qquad (U^{-1}AU)^{\mathrm{H}} = U^{\mathrm{H}}A^{\mathrm{H}}(U^{-1})^{\mathrm{H}} = U^{-1}AU.$$

The diagonal matrix $U^{-1}AU$ represents a key theorem in linear algebra.

5S (Spectral Theorem) Every real symmetric A can be diagonalized by an orthogonal matrix Q. Every Hermitian matrix can be diagonalized by a unitary U:

$$\textbf{(real)} \quad Q^{-1}AQ = \Lambda \quad \text{or} \quad A = Q\Lambda Q^{\mathrm{T}}$$

$$\textbf{(complex)} \quad U^{-1}AU = \Lambda \quad \text{or} \quad A = U\Lambda U^{\mathrm{H}}$$

The columns of Q (or U) contain orthonormal eigenvectors of A.

Remark 1 In the real symmetric case, the eigenvalues and eigenvectors are real at every step. That produces a *real* unitary U—an orthogonal matrix.

Remark 2 A is the limit of symmetric matrices with *distinct* eigenvalues. As the limit approaches, the eigenvectors stay perpendicular. This can fail if $A \neq A^{\mathrm{T}}$:

$$A(\theta) = \begin{bmatrix} 0 & \cos\theta \\ 0 & \sin\theta \end{bmatrix} \quad \text{has eigenvectors} \quad \begin{bmatrix} 1 \\ 0 \end{bmatrix} \quad \text{and} \quad \begin{bmatrix} \cos\theta \\ \sin\theta \end{bmatrix}.$$

As $\theta \to 0$, the *only* eigenvector of the nondiagonalizable matrix $\begin{bmatrix} 0 & 1 \\ 0 & 0 \end{bmatrix}$ is $\begin{bmatrix} 1 \\ 0 \end{bmatrix}$.

Example 3 The spectral theorem says that this $A = A^{\mathrm{T}}$ can be diagonalized:

$$A = \begin{bmatrix} 0 & 1 & 0 \\ 1 & 0 & 0 \\ 0 & 0 & 1 \end{bmatrix} \quad \text{with repeated eigenvalues} \quad \lambda_1 = \lambda_2 = 1 \text{ and } \lambda_3 = -1.$$

$\lambda = 1$ has a plane of eigenvectors, and we pick an orthonormal pair x_1 and x_2:

$$x_1 = \frac{1}{\sqrt{2}}\begin{bmatrix}1\\1\\0\end{bmatrix} \quad \text{and} \quad x_2 = \begin{bmatrix}0\\0\\1\end{bmatrix}; \quad \text{and} \quad x_3 = \frac{1}{\sqrt{2}}\begin{bmatrix}1\\-1\\0\end{bmatrix} \quad \text{for } \lambda_3 = -1.$$

These are the columns of Q. Splitting $A = Q\Lambda Q^{\mathrm{T}}$ into 3 columns times 3 rows gives

$$A = \begin{bmatrix}0&1&0\\1&0&0\\0&0&1\end{bmatrix} = \lambda_1\begin{bmatrix}\frac{1}{2}&\frac{1}{2}&0\\\frac{1}{2}&\frac{1}{2}&0\\0&0&0\end{bmatrix} + \lambda_2\begin{bmatrix}0&0&0\\0&0&0\\0&0&1\end{bmatrix} + \lambda_3\begin{bmatrix}\frac{1}{2}&-\frac{1}{2}&0\\-\frac{1}{2}&\frac{1}{2}&0\\0&0&0\end{bmatrix}.$$

Since $\lambda_1 = \lambda_2$, those first two projections $x_1x_1^{\mathrm{T}}$ and $x_2x_2^{\mathrm{T}}$ (each of rank 1) combine to give a projection P_1 of rank 2 (onto the plane of eigenvectors). Then A is

$$\begin{bmatrix}0&1&0\\1&0&0\\0&0&1\end{bmatrix} = \lambda_1P_1 + \lambda_3P_3 = (+1)\begin{bmatrix}\frac{1}{2}&\frac{1}{2}&0\\\frac{1}{2}&\frac{1}{2}&0\\0&0&1\end{bmatrix} + (-1)\begin{bmatrix}\frac{1}{2}&-\frac{1}{2}&0\\-\frac{1}{2}&\frac{1}{2}&0\\0&0&0\end{bmatrix}. \qquad (5)$$

Every Hermitian matrix with k different eigenvalues has a ***spectral decomposition*** *into* $A = \lambda_1P_1 + \cdots + \lambda_kP_k$, *where* P_i *is the projection onto the eigenspace for* λ_i. Since there is a full set of eigenvectors, the projections add up to the identity. And since the eigenspaces are orthogonal, two projections produce zero: $P_jP_i = 0$.

We are very close to answering an important question, so we keep going: **For which matrices is $T = \Lambda$?** Symmetric, skew-symmetric, and orthogonal T's are all diagonal! Hermitian, skew-Hermitian, and unitary matrices are also in this class. They correspond to numbers on the *real axis*, the *imaginary axis*, and the *unit circle*. Now we want the whole class, corresponding to all complex numbers. The matrices are called "normal."

5T The matrix N is ***normal*** if it commutes with N^{H}: $NN^{\mathrm{H}} = N^{\mathrm{H}}N$. For such matrices, and no others, the triangular $T = U^{-1}NU$ is the diagonal Λ. Normal matrices are exactly those that have a ***complete set of orthonormal eigenvectors***.

Symmetric and Hermitian matrices are certainly normal: If $A = A^{\mathrm{H}}$, then AA^{H} and $A^{\mathrm{H}}A$ both equal A^2. Orthogonal and unitary matrices are also normal: UU^{H} and $U^{\mathrm{H}}U$ both equal I. Two steps will work for any normal matrix:

1. If N is normal, then so is the triangular $T = U^{-1}NU$:

   $$TT^{\mathrm{H}} = U^{-1}NUU^{\mathrm{H}}N^{\mathrm{H}}U = U^{-1}NN^{\mathrm{H}}U = U^{-1}N^{\mathrm{H}}NU = U^{\mathrm{H}}N^{\mathrm{H}}UU^{-1}NU = T^{\mathrm{H}}T.$$

2. A triangular T that is normal must be diagonal! (See Problems 19–20 at the end of this section.)

Thus, if N is normal, the triangular $T = U^{-1}NU$ must be diagonal. Since T has the same eigenvalues as N, it must be Λ. The eigenvectors of N are the columns of U, and they are orthonormal. That is the good case. We turn now from the best possible matrices (*normal*) to the worst possible (*defective*).

$$\textbf{Normal} \quad N = \begin{bmatrix} 2 & 1 \\ -1 & 2 \end{bmatrix} \qquad\qquad \textbf{Defective} \quad A = \begin{bmatrix} 2 & 1 \\ 0 & 2 \end{bmatrix}.$$

The Jordan Form

This section has done its best while requiring M to be a unitary matrix U. We got $M^{-1}AM$ into a triangular form T. Now we lift this restriction on M. Any matrix is allowed, and the goal is to make $M^{-1}AM$ as *nearly diagonal as possible.*

The result of this supreme effort at diagonalization is the ***Jordan form J***. If A has a full set of eigenvectors, we take $M = S$ and arrive at $J = S^{-1}AS = \Lambda$. Then the Jordan form coincides with the diagonal Λ. This is impossible for a defective (nondiagonalizable) matrix. *For every missing eigenvector, the Jordan form will have a* 1 *just above its main diagonal.* The eigenvalues appear on the diagonal because J is triangular. And distinct eigenvalues can always be decoupled.

It is only a repeated λ that may (or may not!) require an off-diagonal 1 in J.

5U If A has s independent eigenvectors, it is similar to a matrix with s blocks:

$$\textbf{Jordan form} \qquad J = M^{-1}AM = \begin{bmatrix} J_1 & & & \\ & \cdot & & \\ & & \cdot & \\ & & & \cdot \\ & & & & J_s \end{bmatrix}. \tag{6}$$

Each Jordan block J_i is a triangular matrix that has only a single eigenvalue λ_i and only one eigenvector:

$$\textbf{Jordan block} \qquad J_i = \begin{bmatrix} \lambda_i & 1 & & \\ & \lambda_i & \cdot & \\ & & \cdot & 1 \\ & & & \lambda_i \end{bmatrix}. \tag{7}$$

The same λ_i will appear in several blocks, if it has several independent eigenvectors. Two matrices are similar if and only if they share the same Jordan form J.

Many authors have made this theorem the climax of their linear algebra course. Frankly, I think that is a mistake. It is certainly true that not all matrices are diagonalizable, and the Jordan form is the most general case. For that very reason, its construction is both technical and extremely unstable. (A slight change in A can put back all the missing eigenvectors, and remove the off-diagonal 1s.) Therefore the right place for the details is in the appendix, and the best way to start on the Jordan form is to look at some specific and manageable examples.

Example 4 $T = \begin{bmatrix} 1 & 2 \\ 0 & 1 \end{bmatrix}$ and $A = \begin{bmatrix} 2 & -1 \\ 1 & 0 \end{bmatrix}$ and $B = \begin{bmatrix} 1 & 0 \\ 1 & 1 \end{bmatrix}$ all lead to $J = \begin{bmatrix} 1 & 1 \\ 0 & 1 \end{bmatrix}$.

These four matrices have eigenvalues 1 and 1 with only *one eigenvector*—so J consists of *one block*. We now check that. The determinants all equal 1. The traces (the sums down the main diagonal) are 2. The eigenvalues satisfy $1 \cdot 1 = 1$ and $1 + 1 = 2$. For T, B, and J, which are triangular, the eigenvalues are on the diagonal. We want to show that *these matrices are similar*—they all belong to the same family.

(T) From T to J, the job is to change 2 to 1, and a diagonal M will do it:

$$M^{-1}TM = \begin{bmatrix} 1 & 0 \\ 0 & 2 \end{bmatrix} \begin{bmatrix} 1 & 2 \\ 0 & 1 \end{bmatrix} \begin{bmatrix} 1 & 0 \\ 0 & \frac{1}{2} \end{bmatrix} = \begin{bmatrix} 1 & 1 \\ 0 & 1 \end{bmatrix} = J.$$

(B) From B to J, the job is to transpose the matrix. A permutation does that:

$$P^{-1}BP = \begin{bmatrix} 0 & 1 \\ 1 & 0 \end{bmatrix} \begin{bmatrix} 1 & 0 \\ 1 & 1 \end{bmatrix} \begin{bmatrix} 0 & 1 \\ 1 & 0 \end{bmatrix} = \begin{bmatrix} 1 & 1 \\ 0 & 1 \end{bmatrix} = J.$$

(A) From A to J, we go first to T as in equation (4). Then change 2 to 1:

$$U^{-1}AU = \begin{bmatrix} 1 & 2 \\ 0 & 1 \end{bmatrix} = T \qquad \text{and then} \qquad M^{-1}TM = \begin{bmatrix} 1 & 1 \\ 0 & 1 \end{bmatrix} = J.$$

Example 5 $A = \begin{bmatrix} 0 & 1 & 2 \\ 0 & 0 & 1 \\ 0 & 0 & 0 \end{bmatrix}$ and $B = \begin{bmatrix} 0 & 0 & 1 \\ 0 & 0 & 0 \\ 0 & 0 & 0 \end{bmatrix}$.

Zero is a triple eigenvalue for A and B, so it will appear in all their Jordan blocks. There can be a single 3 by 3 block, or a 2 by 2 and a 1 by 1 block, or three 1 by 1 blocks. Then A and B have three possible Jordan forms:

$$J_1 = \begin{bmatrix} \mathbf{0} & \mathbf{1} & \mathbf{0} \\ \mathbf{0} & \mathbf{0} & \mathbf{1} \\ \mathbf{0} & \mathbf{0} & \mathbf{0} \end{bmatrix}, \qquad J_2 = \begin{bmatrix} \mathbf{0} & \mathbf{1} & 0 \\ \mathbf{0} & \mathbf{0} & 0 \\ 0 & 0 & \mathbf{0} \end{bmatrix}, \qquad J_3 = \begin{bmatrix} \mathbf{0} & 0 & 0 \\ 0 & \mathbf{0} & 0 \\ 0 & 0 & \mathbf{0} \end{bmatrix}. \tag{8}$$

The only eigenvector of A is $(1, 0, 0)$. Its Jordan form has only one block, and A must be similar to J_1. The matrix B has the additional eigenvector $(0, 1, 0)$, and its Jordan form is J_2 with two blocks. As for $J_3 =$ *zero matrix*, it is in a family by itself; the only matrix similar to J_3 is $M^{-1}0M = 0$. A count of the eigenvectors will determine J when there is nothing more complicated than a triple eigenvalue.

Example 6 ***Application to difference and differential equations*** (*powers and exponentials*). If A can be diagonalized, the powers of $A = S\Lambda S^{-1}$ are easy: $A^k = S\Lambda^k S^{-1}$. In every case we have Jordan's similarity $A = MJM^{-1}$, so now we need the powers of J:

$$A^k = (MJM^{-1})(MJM^{-1}) \cdots (MJM^{-1}) = MJ^kM^{-1}.$$

J is block-diagonal, and the powers of each block can be taken separately:

$$(J_i)^k = \begin{bmatrix} \lambda & 1 & 0 \\ 0 & \lambda & 1 \\ 0 & 0 & \lambda \end{bmatrix}^k = \begin{bmatrix} \lambda^k & k\lambda^{k-1} & \frac{1}{2}k(k-1)\lambda^{k-2} \\ 0 & \lambda^k & k\lambda^{k-1} \\ 0 & 0 & \lambda^k \end{bmatrix}. \tag{9}$$

This block J_i will enter when λ is a triple eigenvalue with a single eigenvector. Its exponential is in the solution to the corresponding differential equation:

$$\textbf{Exponential} \qquad e^{J_i t} = \begin{bmatrix} e^{\lambda t} & te^{\lambda t} & \frac{1}{2}t^2 e^{\lambda t} \\ 0 & e^{\lambda t} & te^{\lambda t} \\ 0 & 0 & e^{\lambda t} \end{bmatrix}. \tag{10}$$

Here $I + J_i t + (J_i t)^2/2! + \cdots$ produces $1 + \lambda t + \lambda^2 t^2/2! + \cdots = e^{\lambda t}$ on the diagonal.

The third column of this exponential comes directly from solving $du/dt = J_i u$:

$$\frac{d}{dt}\begin{bmatrix} u_1 \\ u_2 \\ u_3 \end{bmatrix} = \begin{bmatrix} \lambda & 1 & 0 \\ 0 & \lambda & 1 \\ 0 & 0 & \lambda \end{bmatrix} \begin{bmatrix} u_1 \\ u_2 \\ u_3 \end{bmatrix} \quad \text{starting from} \quad u_0 = \begin{bmatrix} 0 \\ 0 \\ 1 \end{bmatrix}.$$

This can be solved by back-substitution (since J_i is triangular). The last equation $du_3/dt = \lambda u_3$ yields $u_3 = e^{\lambda t}$. The equation for u_2 is $du_2/dt = \lambda u_2 + u_3$, and its solution is $te^{\lambda t}$. The top equation is $du_1/dt = \lambda u_1 + u_2$, and its solution is $\frac{1}{2}t^2 e^{\lambda t}$. When λ has multiplicity m with only one eigenvector, the extra factor t appears $m-1$ times.

These powers and exponentials of J are a part of the solutions u_k and $u(t)$. The other part is the M that connects the original A to the more convenient matrix J:

$$\begin{aligned} &\text{if} \quad u_{k+1} = Au_k \quad &&\text{then} \quad u_k = A^k u_0 = MJ^k M^{-1} u_0 \\ &\text{if} \quad du/dt = Au \quad &&\text{then} \quad u(t) = e^{At}u(0) = Me^{Jt}M^{-1}u(0). \end{aligned}$$

When M and J are S and Λ (the diagonalizable case) those are the formulas of Sections 5.3 and 5.4. Appendix B returns to the nondiagonalizable case, and shows how the Jordan form can be reached. I hope the following table will be a convenient summary.

Similarity Transformations

1. A is ***diagonalizable***: The columns of S are eigenvectors and $S^{-1}AS = \Lambda$.
2. A is ***arbitrary***: The columns of M include "generalized eigenvectors" of A, and the Jordan form $M^{-1}AM = J$ is *block diagonal*.
3. A is ***arbitrary***: The unitary U can be chosen so that $U^{-1}AU = T$ is *triangular*.
4. A is **normal**, $AA^{\mathrm{H}} = A^{\mathrm{H}}A$: then U can be chosen so that $U^{-1}AU = \Lambda$.

Special cases of normal matrices, all with orthonormal eigenvectors:

(a) If $A = A^{\mathrm{H}}$ is Hermitian, then all λ_i are real.
(b) If $A = A^{\mathrm{T}}$ is real symmetric, then Λ is real and $U = Q$ is orthogonal.
(c) If $A = -A^{\mathrm{H}}$ is skew-Hermitian, then all λ_i are purely imaginary.
(d) If A is orthogonal or unitary, then all $|\lambda_i| = 1$ are on the unit circle.

Problem Set 5.6

1. If B is similar to A and C is similar to B, show that C is similar to A. (Let $B = M^{-1}AM$ and $C = N^{-1}BN$.) Which matrices are similar to I?

2. Describe in words all matrices that are similar to $\begin{bmatrix} 1 & 0 \\ 0 & -1 \end{bmatrix}$, and find two of them.

3. Explain why A is never similar to $A + I$.

4. Find a diagonal M, made up of 1s and -1s, to show that

$$A = \begin{bmatrix} 2 & 1 & & \\ 1 & 2 & 1 & \\ & 1 & 2 & 1 \\ & & 1 & 2 \end{bmatrix} \quad \text{is similar to} \quad B = \begin{bmatrix} 2 & -1 & & \\ -1 & 2 & -1 & \\ & -1 & 2 & -1 \\ & & -1 & 2 \end{bmatrix}.$$

5. Show (if B is invertible) that BA is similar to AB.

6. (a) If $CD = -DC$ (and D is invertible), show that C is similar to $-C$.
(b) Deduce that the eigenvalues of C must come in plus–minus pairs.
(c) Show directly that if $Cx = \lambda x$, then $C(Dx) = -\lambda(Dx)$.

7. Consider any A and a "Givens rotation" M in the 1–2 plane:

$$A = \begin{bmatrix} a & b & c \\ d & e & f \\ g & h & i \end{bmatrix}, \quad M = \begin{bmatrix} \cos\theta & -\sin\theta & 0 \\ \sin\theta & \cos\theta & 0 \\ 0 & 0 & 1 \end{bmatrix}.$$

Choose the rotation angle θ to produce zero in the (3, 1) entry of $M^{-1}AM$.

Note This "zeroing" is not so easy to continue, because the rotations that produce zero in place of d and h will spoil the new zero in the corner. We have to leave one diagonal below the main one, and finish the eigenvalue calculation in a different way. Otherwise, if we could make A diagonal and see its eigenvalues, we would be finding the roots of the polynomial $\det(A - \lambda I)$ by using only the square roots that determine $\cos\theta$—and that is impossible.

8. What matrix M changes the basis $V_1 = (1, 1)$, $V_2 = (1, 4)$ to the basis $v_1 = (2, 5)$, $v_2 = (1, 4)$? The columns of M come from expressing V_1 and V_2 as combinations $\sum m_{ij} v_i$ of the v's.

9. For the same two bases, express the vector (3, 9) as a combination $c_1 V_1 + c_2 V_2$ and also as $d_1 v_1 + d_2 v_2$. Check numerically that M connects c to d: $Mc = d$.

10. Confirm the last exercise: If $V_1 = m_{11} v_1 + m_{21} v_2$ and $V_2 = m_{12} v_1 + m_{22} v_2$, and $m_{11} c_1 + m_{12} c_2 = d_1$ and $m_{21} c_1 + m_{22} c_2 = d_2$, the vectors $c_1 V_1 + c_2 V_2$ and $d_1 v_1 + d_2 v_2$ are the same. This is the "change of basis formula" $Mc = d$.

11. If the transformation T is a reflection across the 45° line in the plane, find its matrix with respect to the standard basis $v_1 = (1, 0)$, $v_2 = (0, 1)$, and also with respect to $V_1 = (1, 1)$, $V_2 = (1, -1)$. Show that those matrices are similar.

12. The *identity transformation* takes every vector to itself: $Tx = x$. Find the corresponding matrix, if the first basis is $v_1 = (1, 2)$, $v_2 = (3, 4)$ and the second basis is $w_1 = (1, 0)$, $w_2 = (0, 1)$. (It is not the identity matrix!)

13. The derivative of $a + bx + cx^2$ is $b + 2cx + 0x^2$.

(a) Write the 3 by 3 matrix D such that

$$D \begin{bmatrix} a \\ b \\ c \end{bmatrix} = \begin{bmatrix} b \\ 2c \\ 0 \end{bmatrix}.$$

(b) Compute D^3 and interpret the results in terms of derivatives.
(c) What are the eigenvalues and eigenvectors of D?

14. Show that every number is an eigenvalue for $Tf(x) = df/dx$, but the transformation $Tf(x) = \int_0^x f(t)\,dt$ has no eigenvalues (here $-\infty < x < \infty$).

15. On the space of 2 by 2 matrices, let T be the transformation that *transposes every matrix*. Find the eigenvalues and "eigenmatrices" for $A^{\mathrm{T}} = \lambda A$.

16. (a) Find an orthogonal Q so that $Q^{-1}AQ = \Lambda$ if

$$A = \begin{bmatrix} 1 & 1 & 1 \\ 1 & 1 & 1 \\ 1 & 1 & 1 \end{bmatrix} \quad \text{and} \quad \Lambda = \begin{bmatrix} 0 & 0 & 0 \\ 0 & 0 & 0 \\ 0 & 0 & 3 \end{bmatrix}.$$

Then find a second pair of orthonormal eigenvectors x_1, x_2 for $\lambda = 0$.
(b) Verify that $P = x_1x_1^{\mathrm{T}} + x_2x_2^{\mathrm{T}}$ is the same for both pairs.

17. Prove that every *unitary* matrix A is diagonalizable, in two steps:

(i) If A is unitary, and U is too, then so is $T = U^{-1}AU$.
(ii) An upper triangular T that is unitary must be diagonal. Thus $T = \Lambda$.

Any unitary matrix A (distinct eigenvalues or not) has a complete set of orthonormal eigenvectors. All eigenvalues satisfy $|\lambda| = 1$.

18. Find a normal matrix ($NN^{\mathrm{H}} = N^{\mathrm{H}}N$) that is not Hermitian, skew-Hermitian, unitary, or diagonal. Show that all permutation matrices are normal.

19. Suppose T is a 3 by 3 upper triangular matrix, with entries t_{ij}. Compare the entries of TT^{H} and $T^{\mathrm{H}}T$, and show that if they are equal, then T must be diagonal. All normal triangular matrices are diagonal.

20. If N is normal, show that $\|Nx\| = \|N^{\mathrm{H}}x\|$ for every vector x. Deduce that the ith row of N has the same length as the ith column. *Note*: If N is also upper triangular, this leads again to the conclusion that it must be diagonal.

21. Prove that a matrix with orthonormal eigenvectors must be normal, as claimed in **5T**: If $U^{-1}NU = \Lambda$, or $N = U\Lambda U^{\mathrm{H}}$, then $NN^{\mathrm{H}} = N^{\mathrm{H}}N$.

22. Find a unitary U and triangular T so that $U^{-1}AU = T$, for

$$A = \begin{bmatrix} 5 & -3 \\ 4 & -2 \end{bmatrix} \quad \text{and} \quad A = \begin{bmatrix} 0 & 1 & 0 \\ 0 & 0 & 0 \\ 1 & 0 & 0 \end{bmatrix}.$$

23. If A has eigenvalues 0, 1, 2, what are the eigenvalues of $A(A - I)(A - 2I)$?

24. (a) Show by direct multiplication that every triangular matrix T, say 3 by 3, satisfies its own characteristic equation: $(T-\lambda_1 I)(T-\lambda_2 I)(T-\lambda_3 I)=0$.
(b) Substituting $U^{-1}AU$ for T, deduce the famous ***Cayley–Hamilton theorem: Every matrix satisfies its own characteristic equation***. For 3 by 3 this is $(A-\lambda_1 I)(A-\lambda_2 I)(A-\lambda_3 I)=0$.

25. The characteristic polynomial of $A=\begin{bmatrix} a & b \\ c & d \end{bmatrix}$ is $\lambda^2-(a+d)\lambda+(ad-bc)$. By direct substitution, verify Cayley–Hamilton: $A^2-(a+d)A+(ad-bc)I=0$.

26. If $a_{ij}=1$ above the main diagonal and $a_{ij}=0$ elsewhere, find the Jordan form (say 4 by 4) by finding all the eigenvectors.

27. Show, by trying for an M and failing, that no two of the three Jordan forms in equation (8) are similar: $J_1 \neq M^{-1}J_2M$, $J_1 \neq M^{-1}J_3M$, and $J_2 \neq M^{-1}J_3M$.

28. Solve $u'=Ju$ by back-substitution, solving first for $u_2(t)$:

$$\frac{du}{dt}=Ju=\begin{bmatrix} 5 & 1 \\ 0 & 5 \end{bmatrix}\begin{bmatrix} u_1 \\ u_2 \end{bmatrix} \quad \text{with initial value } u(0)=\begin{bmatrix} 1 \\ 2 \end{bmatrix}.$$

Notice te^{5t} in the first component $u_1(t)$.

29. Compute A^{10} and e^A if $A=MJM^{-1}$:

$$A=\begin{bmatrix} 14 & 9 \\ -16 & -10 \end{bmatrix}=\begin{bmatrix} 3 & -2 \\ -4 & 3 \end{bmatrix}\begin{bmatrix} 2 & 1 \\ 0 & 2 \end{bmatrix}\begin{bmatrix} 3 & 2 \\ 4 & 3 \end{bmatrix}.$$

30. Show that A and B are similar by finding M so that $B=M^{-1}AM$:

(a) $A=\begin{bmatrix} 1 & 0 \\ 1 & 0 \end{bmatrix}$ and $B=\begin{bmatrix} 0 & 1 \\ 0 & 1 \end{bmatrix}$.

(b) $A=\begin{bmatrix} 1 & 1 \\ 1 & 1 \end{bmatrix}$ and $B=\begin{bmatrix} 1 & -1 \\ -1 & 1 \end{bmatrix}$.

(c) $A=\begin{bmatrix} 1 & 2 \\ 3 & 4 \end{bmatrix}$ and $B=\begin{bmatrix} 4 & 3 \\ 2 & 1 \end{bmatrix}$.

31. Which of these matrices A_1 to A_6 are similar? Check their eigenvalues.

$$\begin{bmatrix} 1 & 0 \\ 0 & 1 \end{bmatrix} \quad \begin{bmatrix} 0 & 1 \\ 1 & 0 \end{bmatrix} \quad \begin{bmatrix} 1 & 1 \\ 0 & 0 \end{bmatrix} \quad \begin{bmatrix} 0 & 0 \\ 1 & 1 \end{bmatrix} \quad \begin{bmatrix} 1 & 0 \\ 1 & 0 \end{bmatrix} \quad \begin{bmatrix} 0 & 1 \\ 0 & 1 \end{bmatrix}.$$

32. There are sixteen 2 by 2 matrices whose entries are 0s and 1s. Similar matrices go into the same family. How many families? How many matrices (total 16) in each family?

33. (a) If x is in the nullspace of A, show that $M^{-1}x$ is in the nullspace of $M^{-1}AM$.
(b) The nullspaces of A and $M^{-1}AM$ have the same (vectors)(basis)(dimension).

34. If A and B have the exactly the same eigenvalues and eigenvectors, does $A=B$? With n independent eigenvectors, we do have $A=B$. Find $A \neq B$ when $\lambda=0,0$ (repeated), but there is only one line of eigenvectors $(x_1,0)$.

Problems 35–39 are about the Jordan form.

35. By direct multiplication, find J^2 and J^3 when

$$J = \begin{bmatrix} c & 1 \\ 0 & c \end{bmatrix}.$$

Guess the form of J^k. Set $k = 0$ to find J^0. Set $k = -1$ to find J^{-1}.

36. If J is the 5 by 5 Jordan block with $\lambda = 0$, find J^2 and count its eigenvectors, and find its Jordan form (two blocks).

37. The text solved $du/dt = Ju$ for a 3 by 3 Jordan block J. Add a fourth equation $dw/dt = 5w + x$. Follow the pattern of solutions for z, y, x to find w.

38. These Jordan matrices have eigenvalues 0, 0, 0, 0. They have two eigenvectors (find them). But the block sizes don't match and J *is not similar to* K:

$$J = \left[\begin{array}{cc|cc} 0 & 1 & 0 & 0 \\ 0 & 0 & 0 & 0 \\ \hline 0 & 0 & 0 & 1 \\ 0 & 0 & 0 & 0 \end{array}\right] \quad \text{and} \quad K = \left[\begin{array}{ccc|c} 0 & 1 & 0 & 0 \\ 0 & 0 & 1 & 0 \\ 0 & 0 & 0 & 0 \\ \hline 0 & 0 & 0 & 0 \end{array}\right].$$

For any matrix M, compare JM with MK. If they are equal, show that M is not invertible. Then $M^{-1}JM = K$ is impossible.

39. Prove in three steps that A^{T} *is always similar to* A (we know that the λ's are the same, the eigenvectors are the problem):

(a) For $A =$ one block, find $M_i =$ permutation so that $M_i^{-1}J_iM_i = J_i^{\mathrm{T}}$.
(b) For $A =$ any J, build M_0 from blocks so that $M_0^{-1}JM_0 = J^{\mathrm{T}}$.
(c) For any $A = MJM^{-1}$: Show that A^{T} is similar to J^{T} and so to J and to A.

40. Which pairs are similar? Choose a, b, c, d to prove that the other pairs aren't:

$$\begin{bmatrix} a & b \\ c & d \end{bmatrix} \quad \begin{bmatrix} b & a \\ d & c \end{bmatrix} \quad \begin{bmatrix} c & d \\ a & b \end{bmatrix} \quad \begin{bmatrix} d & c \\ b & a \end{bmatrix}.$$

41. True or false, with a good reason:

(a) An invertible matrix can't be similar to a singular matrix.
(b) A symmetric matrix can't be similar to a nonsymmetric matrix.
(c) A can't be similar to $-A$ unless $A = 0$.
(d) $A - I$ can't be similar to $A + I$.

42. Prove that AB *has the same eigenvalues as* BA.

43. If A is 6 by 4 and B is 4 by 6, AB and BA have different sizes. Nevertheless,

$$\begin{bmatrix} I & -A \\ 0 & I \end{bmatrix} \begin{bmatrix} AB & 0 \\ B & 0 \end{bmatrix} \begin{bmatrix} I & A \\ 0 & I \end{bmatrix} = \begin{bmatrix} 0 & 0 \\ B & BA \end{bmatrix} = G.$$

(a) What sizes are the blocks of G? They are the same in each matrix.
(b) This equation is $M^{-1}FM = G$, so F and G have the same 10 eigenvalues. F has the eigenvalues of AB plus 4 zeros; G has the eigenvalues of BA plus 6 zeros. ***AB* has the same eigenvalues as *BA* plus ___ zeros.**

44. Why is each of these statements true?

(a) If A is similar to B, then A^2 is similar to B^2.

(b) A^2 and B^2 can be similar when A and B are not similar (try $\lambda = 0, 0$).

(c) $\begin{bmatrix} 3 & 0 \\ 0 & 4 \end{bmatrix}$ is similar to $\begin{bmatrix} 3 & 1 \\ 0 & 4 \end{bmatrix}$.

(d) $\begin{bmatrix} 3 & 0 \\ 0 & 3 \end{bmatrix}$ is not similar to $\begin{bmatrix} 3 & 1 \\ 0 & 3 \end{bmatrix}$.

(e) If we exchange rows 1 and 2 of A, and then exchange columns 1 and 2, **the eigenvalues stay the same.**

Properties of Eigenvalues and Eigenvectors

How are the properties of a matrix reflected in its eigenvalues and eigenvectors? This question is fundamental throughout Chapter 5. A table that organizes the key facts may be helpful. For each class of matrices, here are the special properties of the eigenvalues λ_i and eigenvectors x_i.

Symmetric: $A^T = A$	real λ's	orthogonal $x_i^T x_j = 0$
Orthogonal: $Q^T = Q^{-1}$	all $\lvert\lambda\rvert = 1$	orthogonal $\overline{x}_i^T x_j = 0$
Skew-symmetric: $A^T = -A$	imaginary λ's	orthogonal $\overline{x}_i^T x_j = 0$
Complex Hermitian: $\overline{A}^T = A$	real λ's	orthogonal $\overline{x}_i^T x_j = 0$
Positive definite: $x^T A x > 0$	all $\lambda > 0$	orthogonal
Similar matrix: $B = M^{-1}AM$	$\lambda(B) = \lambda(A)$	$x(B) = M^{-1}x(A)$
Projection: $P = P^2 = P^T$	$\lambda = 1;\ 0$	column space; nullspace
Reflection: $I - 2uu^T$	$\lambda = -1;\ 1, \ldots, 1$	$u; u^\perp$
Rank-1 matrix: uv^T	$\lambda = v^T u;\ 0, \ldots, 0$	$u;\ v^\perp$
Inverse: A^{-1}	$1/\lambda(A)$	eigenvectors of A
Shift: $A + cI$	$\lambda(A) + c$	eigenvectors of A
Stable powers: $A^n \to 0$	all $\lvert\lambda\rvert < 1$	
Stable exponential: $e^{At} \to 0$	all Re $\lambda < 0$	
Markov: $m_{ij} > 0, \sum_{i=1}^n m_{ij} = 1$	$\lambda_{\max} = 1$	steady state $x > 0$
Cyclic permutation: $P^n = I$	$\lambda_k = e^{2\pi ik/n}$	$x_k = \left(1, \lambda_k, \ldots, \lambda_k^{n-1}\right)$
Diagonalizable: $S\Lambda S^{-1}$	diagonal of Λ	columns of S are independent
Symmetric: $Q\Lambda Q^T$	diagonal of Λ (real)	columns of Q are orthonormal
Jordan: $J = M^{-1}AM$	diagonal of J	each block gives 1 eigenvector
Every matrix: $A = U\Sigma V^T$	rank(A) = rank(Σ)	eigenvectors of A^TA, AA^T in V, U

Chapter 5 Review Exercises

5.1 Find the eigenvalues and eigenvectors, and the diagonalizing matrix S, for

$$A = \begin{bmatrix} 1 & 0 \\ 2 & 3 \end{bmatrix} \quad \text{and} \quad B = \begin{bmatrix} 7 & 2 \\ -15 & -4 \end{bmatrix}.$$

5.2 Find the determinants of A and A^{-1} if

$$A = S \begin{bmatrix} \lambda_1 & 2 \\ 0 & \lambda_2 \end{bmatrix} S^{-1}.$$

5.3 If A has eigenvalues 0 and 1, corresponding to the eigenvectors

$$\begin{bmatrix} 1 \\ 2 \end{bmatrix} \quad \text{and} \quad \begin{bmatrix} 2 \\ -1 \end{bmatrix},$$

how can you tell in advance that A is symmetric? What are its trace and determinant? What is A?

5.4 In the previous problem, what will be the eigenvalues and eigenvectors of A^2? What is the relation of A^2 to A?

5.5 Does there exist a matrix A such that the entire family $A + cI$ is invertible for all complex numbers c? Find a real matrix with $A + rI$ invertible for all real r.

5.6 Solve for both initial values and then find e^{At}:

$$\frac{du}{dt} = \begin{bmatrix} 3 & 1 \\ 1 & 3 \end{bmatrix} u \quad \text{if} \quad u(0) = \begin{bmatrix} 1 \\ 0 \end{bmatrix} \quad \text{and if} \quad u(0) = \begin{bmatrix} 0 \\ 1 \end{bmatrix}.$$

5.7 Would you prefer to have interest compounded quarterly at 40% per year, or annually at 50%?

5.8 True or false (with counterexample if false):

(a) If B is formed from A by exchanging two rows, then B is similar to A.
(b) If a triangular matrix is similar to a diagonal matrix, it is already diagonal.
(c) Any two of these statements imply the third: A is Hermitian, A is unitary, $A^2 = I$.
(d) If A and B are diagonalizable, so is AB.

5.9 What happens to the Fibonacci sequence if we go backward in time, and how is F_{-k} related to F_k? The law $F_{k+2} = F_{k+1} + F_k$ is still in force, so $F_{-1} = 1$.

5.10 Find the general solution to $du/dt = Au$ if

$$A = \begin{bmatrix} 0 & -1 & 0 \\ 1 & 0 & -1 \\ 0 & 1 & 0 \end{bmatrix}.$$

Can you find a time T at which the solution $u(T)$ is guaranteed to return to the initial value $u(0)$?

5.11 If P is the matrix that projects $\mathbf{R}^n$ onto a subspace $\mathbf{S}$, explain why every vector in $\mathbf{S}$ is an eigenvector, and so is every vector in $\mathbf{S}^\perp$. What are the eigenvalues? (Note the connection to $P^2 = P$, which means that $\lambda^2 = \lambda$.)

5.12 Show that every matrix of order > 1 is the sum of two singular matrices.

5.13 (a) Show that the matrix differential equation $dX/dt = AX + XB$ has the solution $X(t) = e^{At}X(0)e^{Bt}$.
(b) Prove that the solutions of $dX/dt = AX - XA$ keep the same eigenvalues for all time.

5.14 If the eigenvalues of A are 1 and 3 with eigenvectors $(5, 2)$ and $(2, 1)$, find the solutions to $du/dt = Au$ and $u_{k+1} = Au_k$, starting from $u = (9, 4)$.

5.15 Find the eigenvalues and eigenvectors of

$$A = \begin{bmatrix} 0 & -i & 0 \\ i & 1 & i \\ 0 & -i & 0 \end{bmatrix}.$$

What property do you expect for the eigenvectors, and is it true?

5.16 By trying to solve

$$\begin{bmatrix} a & b \\ c & d \end{bmatrix}\begin{bmatrix} a & b \\ c & d \end{bmatrix} = \begin{bmatrix} 0 & 1 \\ 0 & 0 \end{bmatrix} = A$$

show that A has no square root. Change the diagonal entries of A to 4 and find a square root.

5.17 (a) Find the eigenvalues and eigenvectors of $A = \begin{bmatrix} 0 & 4 \\ \frac{1}{4} & 0 \end{bmatrix}$.
(b) Solve $du/dt = Au$ starting from $u(0) = (100, 100)$.
(c) If $v(t) =$ income to stockbrokers and $w(t) =$ income to client, and they help each other by $dv/dt = 4w$ and $dw/dt = \frac{1}{4}v$, what does the ratio v/w approach as $t \to \infty$?

5.18 True or false, with reason if true and counterexample if false:
(a) For every matrix A, there is a solution to $du/dt = Au$ starting from $u(0) = (1, \ldots, 1)$.
(b) Every invertible matrix can be diagonalized.
(c) Every diagonalizable matrix can be inverted.
(d) Exchanging the rows of a 2 by 2 matrix reverses the signs of its eigenvalues.
(e) If eigenvectors x and y correspond to distinct eigenvalues, then $x^{\mathrm{H}}y = 0$.

5.19 If K is a skew-symmetric matrix, show that $Q = (I - K)(I + K)^{-1}$ is an orthogonal matrix. Find Q if $K = \begin{bmatrix} 0 & 2 \\ -2 & 0 \end{bmatrix}$.

5.20 If $K^{\mathrm{H}} = -K$ (skew-Hermitian), the eigenvalues are imaginary and the eigenvectors are orthogonal.
(a) How do you know that $K - I$ is invertible?
(b) How do you know that $K = U\Lambda U^{\mathrm{H}}$ for a unitary U?

(c) Why is $e^{\Lambda t}$ unitary?
(d) Why is e^{Kt} unitary?

5.21 If M is the diagonal matrix with entries d, d^2, d^3, what is $M^{-1}AM$? What are its eigenvalues in the following case?

$$A = \begin{bmatrix} 1 & 1 & 1 \\ 1 & 1 & 1 \\ 1 & 1 & 1 \end{bmatrix}.$$

5.22 If $A^2 = -I$, what are the eigenvalues of A? If A is a real n by n matrix show that n must be even, and give an example.

5.23 If $Ax = \lambda_1 x$ and $A^{\mathrm{T}} y = \lambda_2 y$ (all real), show that $x^{\mathrm{T}} y = 0$.

5.24 A variation on the Fourier matrix is the "sine matrix":

$$S = \frac{1}{\sqrt{2}} \begin{bmatrix} \sin\theta & \sin 2\theta & \sin 3\theta \\ \sin 2\theta & \sin 4\theta & \sin 6\theta \\ \sin 3\theta & \sin 6\theta & \sin 9\theta \end{bmatrix} \quad \text{with} \quad \theta = \frac{\pi}{4}.$$

Verify that $S^{\mathrm{T}} = S^{-1}$. (The columns are the eigenvectors of the tridiagonal -1, 2, -1 matrix.)

5.25 (a) Find a nonzero matrix N such that $N^3 = 0$.
(b) If $Nx = \lambda x$, show that λ must be zero.
(c) Prove that N (called a "nilpotent" matrix) cannot be symmetric.

5.26 (a) Find the matrix $P = aa^{\mathrm{T}}/a^{\mathrm{T}}a$ that projects any vector onto the line through $a = (2, 1, 2)$.
(b) What is the only nonzero eigenvalue of P, and what is the corresponding eigenvector?
(c) Solve $u_{k+1} = Pu_k$, starting from $u_0 = (9, 9, 0)$.

5.27 Suppose the first row of A is 7, 6 and its eigenvalues are $i, -i$. Find A.

5.28 (a) For which numbers c and d does A have real eigenvalues and orthogonal eigenvectors?

$$A = \begin{bmatrix} 1 & 2 & 0 \\ 2 & d & c \\ 0 & 5 & 3 \end{bmatrix}.$$

(b) For which c and d can we find three orthonormal vectors that are combinations of the columns (don't do it!)?

5.29 If the vectors x_1 and x_2 are in the columns of S, what are the eigenvalues and eigenvectors of

$$A = S \begin{bmatrix} 2 & 0 \\ 0 & 1 \end{bmatrix} S^{-1} \quad \text{and} \quad B = S \begin{bmatrix} 2 & 3 \\ 0 & 1 \end{bmatrix} S^{-1}?$$

5.30 What is the limit as $k \to \infty$ (the Markov steady state) of $\begin{bmatrix} .4 & .3 \\ .6 & .7 \end{bmatrix}^k \begin{bmatrix} a \\ b \end{bmatrix}$?

Chapter

6 Positive Definite Matrices

6.1 MINIMA, MAXIMA, AND SADDLE POINTS

Up to now, we have hardly thought about **the signs of the eigenvalues**. We couldn't ask whether λ was positive before it was known to be real. Chapter 5 established that every symmetric matrix has real eigenvalues. Now we will find a test that can be applied directly to A, without computing its eigenvalues, which will ***guarantee that all those eigenvalues are positive***. The test brings together three of the most basic ideas in the book—*pivots*, *determinants*, and *eigenvalues*.

The signs of the eigenvalues are often crucial. For stability in differential equations, we needed negative eigenvalues so that $e^{\lambda t}$ would decay. The new and highly important problem is to recognize a ***minimum point***. This arises throughout science and engineering and every problem of optimization. The mathematical problem is to move the second derivative test $F'' > 0$ into n dimensions. Here are two examples:

$$F(x,y) = 7 + 2(x+y)^2 - y\sin y - x^3 \qquad f(x,y) = 2x^2 + 4xy + y^2.$$

Does either $F(x,y)$ or $f(x,y)$ have a minimum at the point $x = y = 0$?

Remark 1 The *zero-order terms* $F(0,0) = 7$ and $f(0,0) = 0$ have no effect on the answer. They simply raise or lower the graphs of F and f.

Remark 2 The *linear terms* give a necessary condition: To have any chance of a minimum, the first derivatives must vanish at $x = y = 0$:

$$\frac{\partial F}{\partial x} = 4(x+y) - 3x^2 = 0 \quad \text{and} \quad \frac{\partial F}{\partial y} = 4(x+y) - y\cos y - \sin y = 0$$

$$\frac{\partial f}{\partial x} = 4x + 4y = 0 \quad \text{and} \quad \frac{\partial f}{\partial y} = 4x + 2y = 0. \quad \textit{All zero.}$$

Thus $(x,y) = (0,0)$ is a *stationary point* for both functions. The surface $z = F(x,y)$ is tangent to the horizontal plane $z = 7$, and the surface $z = f(x,y)$ is tangent to the plane $z = 0$. The question is whether the graphs go *above those planes or not*, as we move away from the tangency point $x = y = 0$.

Remark 3 ***The second derivatives at* (0, 0) *are decisive*:**

$$\frac{\partial^2 F}{\partial x^2} = 4 - 6x = 4 \qquad \frac{\partial^2 f}{\partial x^2} = 4$$

$$\frac{\partial^2 F}{\partial x \partial y} = \frac{\partial^2 F}{\partial y \partial x} = 4 \qquad \frac{\partial^2 f}{\partial x \partial y} = \frac{\partial^2 f}{\partial y \partial x} = 4$$

$$\frac{\partial^2 F}{\partial y^2} = 4 + y \sin y - 2 \cos y = 2 \qquad \frac{\partial^2 f}{\partial y^2} = 2.$$

These second derivatives 4, 4, 2 contain the answer. Since they are the same for F and f, they must contain the same answer. The two functions behave in exactly the same way near the origin. ***F has a minimum if and only if f has a minimum***. I am going to show that those functions don't!

Remark 4 The *higher-degree terms* in F have no effect on the question of a *local* minimum, but they can prevent it from being a *global* minimum. In our example the term $-x^3$ must sooner or later pull F toward $-\infty$. For $f(x, y)$, with no higher terms, all the action is at (0, 0).

Every quadratic form $f = ax^2 + 2bxy + cy^2$ *has a stationary point at the origin, where* $\partial f/\partial x = \partial f/\partial y = 0$. A local minimum would also be a global minimum. The surface $z = f(x, y)$ will then be shaped like a bowl, resting on the origin (Figure 6.1). If the stationary point of F is at $x = \alpha$, $y = \beta$, the only change would be to use the second derivatives at α, β:

Quadratic part of *F*

$$f(x, y) = \frac{x^2}{2} \frac{\partial^2 F}{\partial x^2}(\alpha, \beta) + xy \frac{\partial^2 F}{\partial x \partial y}(\alpha, \beta) + \frac{y^2}{2} \frac{\partial^2 F}{\partial y^2}(\alpha, \beta). \tag{1}$$

This $f(x, y)$ behaves near (0, 0) in the same way that $F(x, y)$ behaves near (α, β).

The third derivatives are drawn into the problem when the second derivatives fail to give a definite decision. That happens when the quadratic part is singular. For a true

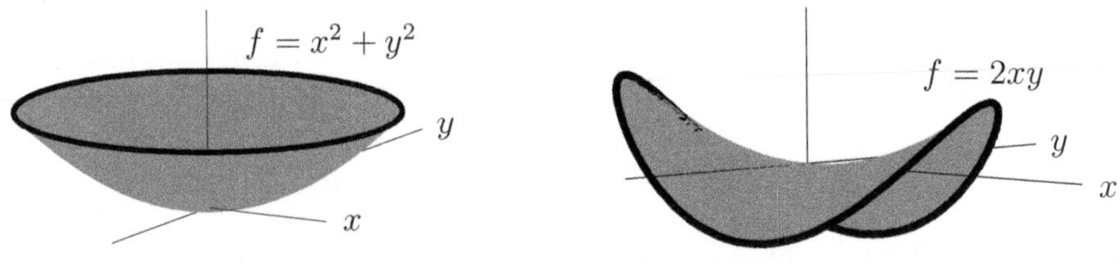

Figure 6.1 A bowl and a saddle: Definite $A = \begin{bmatrix} 1 & 0 \\ 0 & 1 \end{bmatrix}$ and indefinite $A = \begin{bmatrix} 0 & 1 \\ 1 & 0 \end{bmatrix}$.

minimum, f is allowed to vanish *only at* $x = y = 0$. When $f(x, y)$ is strictly positive at all other points (the bowl goes up), it is called ***positive definite***.

Definite versus Indefinite: Bowl versus Saddle

The problem comes down to this: For a function of two variables x and y, what is the correct replacement for the condition $\partial^2 F/\partial x^2 > 0$? With only one variable, the sign of the second derivative decides between a minimum or a maximum. Now we have three second derivatives: F_{xx}, $F_{xy} = F_{yx}$, and F_{yy}. These three numbers (like 4, 4, 2) must determine whether or not F (as well as f) has a minimum.

What conditions on a, b, and c ensure that the quadratic $f(x, y) = ax^2 + 2bxy + cy^2$ is positive definite? One necessary condition is easy:

(i) *If $ax^2 + 2bxy + cy^2$ is positive definite, then necessarily* $\mathbf{a > 0}$.

We look at $x = 1$, $y = 0$, where $ax^2 + 2bxy + cy^2$ is equal to a. This must be positive. Translating back to F, that means that $\partial^2 F/\partial x^2 > 0$. The graph must go up in the x direction. Similarly, fix $x = 0$ and look in the y direction where $f(0, y) = cy^2$:

(ii) *If $f(x, y)$ is positive definite, then necessarily* $\mathbf{c > 0}$.

Do these conditions $a > 0$ and $c > 0$ guarantee that $f(x, y)$ is always positive? The answer is **no**. A large cross term $2bxy$ can pull the graph below zero.

Example 1 $f(x, y) = x^2 - 10xy + y^2$. Here $a = 1$ and $c = 1$ are both positive. But f is not positive definite, because $f(1, 1) = -8$. The conditions $a > 0$ and $c > 0$ ensure that $f(x, y)$ is positive on the x and y axes. But this function is negative on the line $x = y$, because $b = -10$ overwhelms a and c.

Example 2 In our original f the coefficient $2b = 4$ was positive. Does this ensure a minimum? Again the answer is **no**; the sign of b is of no importance! *Even though its second derivatives are positive, $2x^2 + 4xy + y^2$ is not positive definite.* ***Neither F nor f has a minimum at*** $\mathbf{(0, 0)}$ ***because*** $\mathbf{f(1, -1) = 2 - 4 + 1 = -1}$.

It is the size of b, compared to a and c, that must be controlled. We now want a necessary and sufficient condition for positive definiteness. The simplest technique is to complete the square:

Express $f(x, y)$ using squares

$$f = ax^2 + 2bxy + cy^2 = a\left(x + \frac{b}{a}y\right)^2 + \left(c - \frac{b^2}{a}\right)y^2. \quad (2)$$

The first term on the right is never negative, when the square is multiplied by $a > 0$. But this square can be zero, and the second term must then be positive. That term has coefficient $(ac - b^2)/a$. The last requirement for positive definiteness is that this coefficient must be positive:

(iii) *If $ax^2 + 2bxy + cy^2$ stays positive, then necessarily* $\mathbf{ac > b^2}$.

Test for a minimum: The conditions $a > 0$ and $ac > b^2$ are just right. They guarantee $c > 0$. The right side of (2) is positive, and we have found a minimum:

6A $ax^2 + 2bxy + cy^2$ is positive definite if and only if $a > 0$ and $ac > b^2$. Any $F(x, y)$ has a minimum at a point where $\partial F/\partial x = \partial F/\partial y = 0$ with

$$\frac{\partial^2 F}{\partial x^2} > 0 \quad \text{and} \quad \left[\frac{\partial^2 F}{\partial x^2}\right]\left[\frac{\partial^2 F}{\partial y^2}\right] > \left[\frac{\partial^2 F}{\partial x \partial y}\right]^2. \tag{3}$$

Test for a maximum: Since f has a maximum whenever $-f$ has a minimum, we just reverse the signs of a, b, and c. This actually leaves $ac > b^2$ unchanged: The quadratic form is ***negative definite*** if and only if $a < 0$ and $ac > b^2$. The same change applies for a maximum of $F(x, y)$.

Singular case $ac = b^2$: The second term in equation (2) disappears to leave only the first square—which is either ***positive semidefinite***, when $a > 0$, or ***negative semidefinite***, when $a < 0$. The prefix *semi* allows the possibility that f can equal zero, as it will at the point $x = b$, $y = -a$. The surface $z = f(x, y)$ degenerates from a bowl into a valley. For $f = (x + y)^2$, the valley runs along the line $x + y = 0$.

Saddle point $ac < b^2$: In one dimension, $F(x)$ has a minimum or a maximum, or $F'' = 0$. In two dimensions, a very important possibility still remains: *The combination $ac - b^2$ may be negative.* This occurred in both examples, when b dominated a and c. It also occurs if a and c have opposite signs. Then two directions give opposite results—in one direction f increases, in the other it decreases. It is useful to consider two special cases:

Saddle points at (0, 0) $\quad f_1 = 2xy \quad \text{and} \quad f_2 = x^2 - y^2 \quad \text{and} \quad ac - b^2 = -1.$

In the first, $b = 1$ dominates $a = c = 0$. In the second, $a = 1$ and $c = -1$ have opposite sign. The saddles $2xy$ and $x^2 - y^2$ are practically the same; if we turn one through 45° we get the other. They are also hard to draw.

These quadratic forms are ***indefinite***, because they can take either sign. So we have a stationary point that is neither a maximum or a minimum. It is called a ***saddle point***. The surface $z = x^2 - y^2$ goes down in the direction of the y axis, where the legs fit (if you still ride a horse). In case you switched to a car, think of a road going over a mountain pass. The top of the pass is a minimum as you look along the range of mountains, but it is a maximum as you go along the road.

Higher Dimensions: Linear Algebra

Calculus would be enough to find our conditions $F_{xx} > 0$ and $F_{xx}F_{yy} > F_{xy}^2$ for a minimum. But linear algebra is ready to do more, because the second derivatives fit into a symmetric matrix A. The terms ax^2 and cy^2 appear *on the diagonal*. The cross derivative $2bxy$ is split between the same entry b above and below. A quadratic $f(x, y)$

comes directly from a symmetric 2 by 2 matrix!

$$\boldsymbol{x}^{\mathrm{T}}\boldsymbol{A}\boldsymbol{x} \textbf{ in } \mathbf{R}^2 \qquad ax^2 + 2bxy + cy^2 = \begin{bmatrix} x & y \end{bmatrix} \begin{bmatrix} a & b \\ b & c \end{bmatrix} \begin{bmatrix} x \\ y \end{bmatrix}. \tag{4}$$

This identity (please multiply it out) is the key to the whole chapter. It generalizes immediately to n dimensions, and it is a perfect shorthand for studying maxima and minima. When the variables are $x_1, \ldots, x_n$, they go into a column vector x. ***For any symmetric matrix A, the product $\boldsymbol{x}^{\mathrm{T}}\boldsymbol{A}\boldsymbol{x}$ is a pure quadratic form $f(x_1, \ldots, x_n)$***:

$$\boldsymbol{x}^{\mathrm{T}}\boldsymbol{A}\boldsymbol{x} \textbf{ in } \mathbf{R}^n \qquad \begin{bmatrix} x_1 & x_2 & \cdot & x_n \end{bmatrix} \begin{bmatrix} a_{11} & a_{12} & \cdot & a_{1n} \\ a_{21} & a_{22} & \cdot & a_{2n} \\ \cdot & \cdot & \cdot & \cdot \\ a_{n1} & a_{n2} & \cdot & a_{nn} \end{bmatrix} \begin{bmatrix} x_1 \\ x_2 \\ \cdot \\ x_n \end{bmatrix} = \sum_{i=1}^{n} \sum_{j=1}^{n} a_{ij} x_i x_j. \tag{5}$$

The diagonal entries a_{11} to a_{nn} multiply x_1^2 to x_n^2. The pair $a_{ij} = a_{ji}$ combines into $2a_{ij}x_ix_j$. Then $f = a_{11}x_1^2 + 2a_{12}x_1x_2 + \cdots + a_{nn}x_n^2$.

There are no higher-order terms or lower-order terms—only second-order. The function is zero at $x = (0, \ldots, 0)$, and its first derivatives are zero. The tangent is flat; this is a stationary point. We have to decide if $x = 0$ is a minimum or a maximum or a saddle point of the function $f = x^{\mathrm{T}}Ax$.

Example 3 $f = 2x^2 + 4xy + y^2$ and $A = \begin{bmatrix} 2 & 2 \\ 2 & 1 \end{bmatrix} \rightarrow$ *saddle point.*

Example 4 $f = 2xy$ and $A = \begin{bmatrix} 0 & 1 \\ 1 & 0 \end{bmatrix} \rightarrow$ *saddle point.*

Example 5 A is 3 by 3 for $2x_1^2 - 2x_1x_2 + 2x_2^2 - 2x_2x_3 + 2x_3^2$:

$$f = \begin{bmatrix} x_1 & x_2 & x_3 \end{bmatrix} \begin{bmatrix} 2 & -1 & 0 \\ -1 & 2 & -1 \\ 0 & -1 & 2 \end{bmatrix} \begin{bmatrix} x_1 \\ x_2 \\ x_3 \end{bmatrix} \rightarrow \textit{minimum at } (0, 0, 0).$$

Any function $F(x_1, \ldots, x_n)$ is approached in the same way. At a stationary point all first derivatives are zero. A is the **"second-derivative matrix"** with entries $a_{ij} = \partial^2 F/\partial x_i \partial x_j$. This automatically equals $a_{ji} = \partial^2 F/\partial x_j \partial x_i$, so A is symmetric. **Then *F* *has a minimum when the pure quadratic $\boldsymbol{x}^{\mathrm{T}}\boldsymbol{A}\boldsymbol{x}$ is positive definite*.** These second-order terms control F near the stationary point:

$$\textbf{Taylor series} \qquad F(x) = F(0) + x^{\mathrm{T}}(\text{grad } F) + \frac{1}{2}x^{\mathrm{T}}Ax + \text{higher order terms}. \tag{6}$$

At a stationary point, grad $F = (\partial F/\partial x_1, \ldots, \partial F/\partial x_n)$ is a vector of zeros. The second derivatives in $x^{\mathrm{T}}Ax$ take the graph up or down (or saddle). If the stationary point is at x_0 instead of 0, $F(x)$ and all derivatives are computed at x_0. Then x changes to $x - x_0$ on the right-hand side.

The next section contains the tests to decide whether $x^{\mathrm{T}}Ax$ is positive (the bowl goes up from $x = 0$). Equivalently, **the tests decide whether the matrix A is positive definite**—which is the main goal of the chapter.

Problem Set 6.1

1. The quadratic $f = x^2 + 4xy + 2y^2$ has a saddle point at the origin, despite the fact that its coefficients are positive. Write f as a *difference of two squares*.

2. Decide for or against the positive definiteness of these matrices, and write out the corresponding $f = x^{\mathrm{T}}Ax$:

(a) $\begin{bmatrix} 1 & 3 \\ 3 & 5 \end{bmatrix}$. (b) $\begin{bmatrix} 1 & -1 \\ -1 & 1 \end{bmatrix}$. (c) $\begin{bmatrix} 2 & 3 \\ 3 & 5 \end{bmatrix}$. (d) $\begin{bmatrix} -1 & 2 \\ 2 & -8 \end{bmatrix}$.

The determinant in (b) is zero; along what line is $f(x, y) = 0$?

3. If a 2 by 2 symmetric matrix passes the tests $a > 0$, $ac > b^2$, solve the quadratic equation $\det(A - \lambda I) = 0$ and show that both eigenvalues are positive.

4. Decide between a minimum, maximum, or saddle point for the following functions.

(a) $F = -1 + 4(e^x - x) - 5x \sin y + 6y^2$ at the point $x = y = 0$.
(b) $F = (x^2 - 2x) \cos y$, with stationary point at $x = 1$, $y = \pi$.

5. (a) For which numbers b is the matrix $A = \begin{bmatrix} 1 & b \\ b & 9 \end{bmatrix}$ positive definite?
(b) Factor $A = LDL^{\mathrm{T}}$ when b is in the range for positive definiteness.
(c) Find the minimum value of $\frac{1}{2}(x^2 + 2bxy + 9y^2) - y$ for b in this range.
(d) What is the minimum if $b = 3$?

6. Suppose the positive coefficients a and c dominate b in the sense that $a + c > 2b$. Find an example that has $ac < b^2$, so the matrix is not positive definite.

7. (a) What 3 by 3 symmetric matrices A_1 and A_2 correspond to f_1 and f_2?

$$f_1 = x_1^2 + x_2^2 + x_3^2 - 2x_1x_2 - 2x_1x_3 + 2x_2x_3$$

$$f_2 = x_1^2 + 2x_2^2 + 11x_3^2 - 2x_1x_2 - 2x_1x_3 - 4x_2x_3.$$

(b) Show that f_1 is a *single* perfect square and not positive definite. Where is f_1 equal to 0?
(c) Factor A_2 into LL^{T}. Write $f_2 = x^{\mathrm{T}}A_2x$ as a sum of three squares.

8. If $A = \begin{bmatrix} a & b \\ b & c \end{bmatrix}$ is positive definite, test $A^{-1} = \begin{bmatrix} p & q \\ q & r \end{bmatrix}$ for positive definiteness.

9. The quadratic $f(x_1, x_2) = 3(x_1 + 2x_2)^2 + 4x_2^2$ is positive. Find its matrix A, factor it into LDL^{T}, and connect the entries in D and L to 3, 2, 4 in f.

10. If $R = \begin{bmatrix} p & q \\ q & r \end{bmatrix}$, write out R^2 and check that it is positive definite unless R is singular.

11. (a) If $A = \begin{bmatrix} a & b \\ \bar{b} & c \end{bmatrix}$ is Hermitian (*complex* b), find its pivots and determinant.
(b) Complete the square for $x^{\mathrm{H}}Ax$. Now $x^{\mathrm{H}} = \begin{bmatrix} \overline{x}_1 & \overline{x}_2 \end{bmatrix}$ can be complex.

$$a|x_1|^2 + 2\,\mathrm{Re}\, b\overline{x}_1x_2 + c|x_2|^2 = a|x_1 + (b/a)x_2|^2 + \underline{\qquad\quad}|x_2|^2.$$

(c) Show that $a > 0$ and $ac > |b|^2$ ensure that A is positive definite.
(d) Are the matrices $\begin{bmatrix} 1 & 1+i \\ 1-i & 2 \end{bmatrix}$ and $\begin{bmatrix} 3 & 4+i \\ 4-i & 6 \end{bmatrix}$ positive definite?

12. Decide whether $F = x^2y^2 - 2x - 2y$ has a minimum at the point $x = y = 1$ (after showing that the first derivatives are zero at that point).

13. Under what conditions on a, b, c is $ax^2 + 2bxy + cy^2 > x^2 + y^2$ for all x, y?

Problems 14–18 are about tests for positive definiteness.

14. Which of A_1, A_2, A_3, A_4 has two positive eigenvalues? Test $a > 0$ and $ac > b^2$, don't compute the eigenvalues. Find an x so that $x^{\mathrm{T}}A_1x < 0$.

$$A_1 = \begin{bmatrix} 5 & 6 \\ 6 & 7 \end{bmatrix} \quad A_2 = \begin{bmatrix} -1 & -2 \\ -2 & -5 \end{bmatrix} \quad A_3 = \begin{bmatrix} 1 & 10 \\ 10 & 100 \end{bmatrix} \quad A_4 = \begin{bmatrix} 1 & 10 \\ 10 & 101 \end{bmatrix}.$$

15. What is the quadratic $f = ax^2 + 2bxy + cy^2$ for each of these matrices? Complete the square to write f as a sum of one or two squares $d_1(\quad)^2 + d_2(\quad)^2$.

$$A = \begin{bmatrix} 1 & 2 \\ 2 & 9 \end{bmatrix} \quad \text{and} \quad A = \begin{bmatrix} 1 & 3 \\ 3 & 9 \end{bmatrix}.$$

16. Show that $f(x, y) = x^2 + 4xy + 3y^2$ does not have a minimum at $(0, 0)$ even though it has positive coefficients. Write f as a *difference* of squares and find a point (x, y) where f is negative.

17. (*Important*) If A has *independent columns*, then $A^{\mathrm{T}}A$ is square and symmetric and invertible (Section 4.2). ***Rewrite $x^{\mathrm{T}}A^{\mathrm{T}}Ax$ to show why it is positive except when $x = 0$.*** Then $A^{\mathrm{T}}A$ is positive definite.

18. Test to see if $A^{\mathrm{T}}A$ is positive definite in each case:

$$A = \begin{bmatrix} 1 & 2 \\ 0 & 3 \end{bmatrix}, \quad A = \begin{bmatrix} 1 & 1 \\ 1 & 2 \\ 2 & 1 \end{bmatrix}, \quad \text{and} \quad A = \begin{bmatrix} 1 & 1 & 2 \\ 1 & 2 & 1 \end{bmatrix}.$$

19. Find the 3 by 3 matrix A and its pivots, rank, eigenvalues, and determinant:

$$\begin{bmatrix} x_1 & x_2 & x_3 \end{bmatrix} \begin{bmatrix} & & \\ & A & \\ & & \end{bmatrix} \begin{bmatrix} x_1 \\ x_2 \\ x_3 \end{bmatrix} = 4(x_1 - x_2 + 2x_3)^2.$$

20. For $F_1(x, y) = \frac{1}{4}x^4 + x^2y + y^2$ and $F_2(x, y) = x^3 + xy - x$, find the second derivative matrices A_1 and A_2:

$$A = \begin{bmatrix} \partial^2F/\partial x^2 & \partial^2F/\partial x\partial y \\ \partial^2F/\partial y\partial x & \partial^2F/\partial y^2 \end{bmatrix}.$$

A_1 is positive definite, so F_1 is concave up (= convex). Find the minimum point of F_1 and the saddle point of F_2 (look where first derivatives are zero).

21. The graph of $z = x^2 + y^2$ is a bowl opening upward. *The graph* of $z = x^2 - y^2$ *is a saddle*. The graph of $z = -x^2 - y^2$ is a bowl opening downward. What is a test on $F(x, y)$ to have a saddle at $(0, 0)$?

22. Which values of c give a bowl and which give a saddle point for the graph of $z = 4x^2 + 12xy + cy^2$? Describe this graph at the borderline value of c.

6.2 TESTS FOR POSITIVE DEFINITENESS

Which symmetric matrices have the property that $x^{\mathrm{T}}Ax > 0$ for all nonzero vectors x? There are four or five different ways to answer this question, and we hope to find all of them. The previous section began with some hints about the signs of eigenvalues, but that gave place to the tests on a, b, c:

$$A = \begin{bmatrix} a & b \\ b & c \end{bmatrix} \quad \text{is positive definite when} \quad a > 0 \quad \text{and} \quad ac - b^2 > 0.$$

From those conditions, ***both eigenvalues are positive***. Their product $\lambda_1\lambda_2$ is the determinant $ac - b^2 > 0$, so the eigenvalues are either both positive or both negative. They must be positive because their sum is the trace $a + c > 0$.

Looking at a and $ac - b^2$, it is even possible to spot the appearance of the ***pivots***. They turned up when we decomposed $x^{\mathrm{T}}Ax$ into a sum of squares:

$$\textbf{Sum of squares} \qquad ax^2 + 2bxy + cy^2 = a\left(x + \frac{b}{a}y\right)^2 + \frac{ac - b^2}{a}y^2. \qquad (1)$$

Those coefficients a and $(ac - b^2)/a$ are the pivots for a 2 by 2 matrix. For larger matrices the pivots still give a simple test for positive definiteness: $x^{\mathrm{T}}Ax$ stays positive when n independent squares are multiplied by ***positive pivots***.

One more preliminary remark. The two parts of this book were linked by the chapter on determinants. Therefore we ask what part determinants play. ***It is not enough to require that the determinant of A is positive***. If $a = c = -1$ and $b = 0$, then $\det A = 1$ but $A = -I$ = negative definite. The determinant test is applied not only to A itself, giving $ac - b^2 > 0$, but also to the 1 by 1 submatrix a in the upper left-hand corner.

The natural generalization will involve all n of the *upper left submatrices* of A:

$$A_1 = [a_{11}], \quad A_2 = \begin{bmatrix} a_{11} & a_{12} \\ a_{21} & a_{22} \end{bmatrix}, \quad A_3 = \begin{bmatrix} a_{11} & a_{12} & a_{13} \\ a_{21} & a_{22} & a_{23} \\ a_{31} & a_{32} & a_{33} \end{bmatrix}, \ldots, \quad A_n = A.$$

Here is the main theorem on positive definiteness, and a reasonably detailed proof:

6B Each of the following tests is a necessary and sufficient condition for the real symmetric matrix A to be ***positive definite***:

(I) $x^{\mathrm{T}}Ax > 0$ for all nonzero real vectors x.

(II) All the eigenvalues of A satisfy $\lambda_i > 0$.

(III) All the upper left submatrices A_k have positive determinants.

(IV) All the pivots (without row exchanges) satisfy $d_k > 0$.

Proof Condition I defines a positive definite matrix. Our first step shows that each eigenvalue will be positive:

$$\text{If} \quad Ax = \lambda x, \quad \text{then} \quad x^{\mathrm{T}}Ax = x^{\mathrm{T}}\lambda x = \lambda\|x\|^2.$$

A positive definite matrix has positive eigenvalues, since $x^{\mathrm{T}}Ax > 0$.

Now we go in the other direction. If all $\lambda_i > 0$, we have to prove $x^{\mathrm{T}}Ax > 0$ for every vector x (not just the eigenvectors). Since symmetric matrices have a full set of orthonormal eigenvectors, any x is a combination $c_1x_1 + \cdots + c_nx_n$. Then

$$Ax = c_1Ax_1 + \cdots + c_nAx_n = c_1\lambda_1x_1 + \cdots + c_n\lambda_nx_n.$$

Because of the orthogonality $x_i^{\mathrm{T}}x_j = 0$, and the normalization $x_i^{\mathrm{T}}x_i = 1$,

$$\begin{aligned} x^{\mathrm{T}}Ax &= \left(c_1x_1^{\mathrm{T}} + \cdots + c_nx_n^{\mathrm{T}}\right)(c_1\lambda_1x_1 + \cdots + c_n\lambda_nx_n) \\ &= c_1^2\lambda_1 + \cdots + c_n^2\lambda_n. \end{aligned} \tag{2}$$

If every $\lambda_i > 0$, then equation (2) shows that $x^{\mathrm{T}}Ax > 0$. Thus condition II implies condition I.

If condition I holds, so does condition III: The determinant of A is the product of the eigenvalues. And if condition I holds, we already know that these eigenvalues are positive. But we also have to deal with every upper left submatrix A_k. The trick is to look at all nonzero vectors whose last $n-k$ components are zero:

$$x^{\mathrm{T}}Ax = \begin{bmatrix} x_k^{\mathrm{T}} & 0 \end{bmatrix} \begin{bmatrix} A_k & * \\ * & * \end{bmatrix} \begin{bmatrix} x_k \\ 0 \end{bmatrix} = x_k^{\mathrm{T}}A_kx_k > 0.$$

Thus A_k is positive definite. Its eigenvalues (not the same λ_i!) must be positive. Its determinant is their product, so all upper left determinants are positive.

If condition III holds, so does condition IV: According to Section 4.4, the kth pivot d_k is the ratio of $\det A_k$ to $\det A_{k-1}$. If the determinants are all positive, so are the pivots.

If condition IV holds, so does condition I: We are given positive pivots, and must deduce that $x^{\mathrm{T}}Ax > 0$. This is what we did in the 2 by 2 case, by completing the square. The pivots were the numbers outside the squares. To see how that happens for symmetric matrices of any size, we go back to *elimination on a symmetric matrix*: $A = LDL^{\mathrm{T}}$.

Example 1 Positive pivots 2, $\frac{3}{2}$, and $\frac{4}{3}$:

$$A = \begin{bmatrix} 2 & -1 & 0 \\ -1 & 2 & -1 \\ 0 & -1 & 2 \end{bmatrix} = \begin{bmatrix} 1 & 0 & 0 \\ -\frac{1}{2} & 1 & 0 \\ 0 & -\frac{2}{3} & 1 \end{bmatrix} \begin{bmatrix} 2 & & \\ & \frac{3}{2} & \\ & & \frac{4}{3} \end{bmatrix} \begin{bmatrix} 1 & -\frac{1}{2} & 0 \\ 0 & 1 & -\frac{2}{3} \\ 0 & 0 & 1 \end{bmatrix} = LDL^{\mathrm{T}}.$$

I want to split $x^{\mathrm{T}}Ax$ into $x^{\mathrm{T}}LDL^{\mathrm{T}}x$:

$$\text{If } x = \begin{bmatrix} u \\ v \\ w \end{bmatrix}, \text{ then } L^{\mathrm{T}}x = \begin{bmatrix} 1 & -\frac{1}{2} & 0 \\ 0 & 1 & -\frac{2}{3} \\ 0 & 0 & 1 \end{bmatrix} \begin{bmatrix} u \\ v \\ w \end{bmatrix} = \begin{bmatrix} u - \frac{1}{2}v \\ v - \frac{2}{3}w \\ w \end{bmatrix}.$$

So $x^{\mathrm{T}}Ax$ is a sum of squares with the pivots 2, $\frac{3}{2}$, and $\frac{4}{3}$ as coefficients:

$$x^{\mathrm{T}}Ax = (L^{\mathrm{T}}x)^{\mathrm{T}}D(L^{\mathrm{T}}x) = \mathbf{2}\left(u - \frac{\mathbf{1}}{\mathbf{2}}v\right)^2 + \frac{\mathbf{3}}{\mathbf{2}}\left(v - \frac{\mathbf{2}}{\mathbf{3}}w\right)^2 + \frac{\mathbf{4}}{\mathbf{3}}(w)^2.$$

Those positive pivots in D multiply perfect squares to make $x^{\mathrm{T}}Ax$ positive. Thus condition IV implies condition I, and the proof is complete. ■

It is beautiful that elimination and completing the square are actually the same. Elimination removes x_1 from all later equations. Similarly, the first square accounts for all terms in $x^{\mathrm{T}}Ax$ involving x_1. The sum of squares has the pivots outside. *The multipliers* ℓ_{ij} *are inside* ! You can see the numbers $-\frac{1}{2}$ and $-\frac{2}{3}$ inside the squares in the example.

Every diagonal entry a_{ii} *must be positive*. As we know from the examples, however, it is far from sufficient to look only at the diagonal entries.

The pivots d_i are not to be confused with the eigenvalues. For a typical positive definite matrix, they are two completely different sets of positive numbers. In our 3 by 3 example, probably the determinant test is the easiest:

$$\textbf{Determinant test} \qquad \det A_1 = 2, \quad \det A_2 = 3, \quad \det A_3 = \det A = 4.$$

The pivots are the ratios $d_1 = 2$, $d_2 = \frac{3}{2}$, $d_3 = \frac{4}{3}$. Ordinarily the eigenvalue test is the longest computation. For this A we know the λ's are all positive:

$$\textbf{Eigenvalue test} \qquad \lambda_1 = 2 - \sqrt{2}, \quad \lambda_2 = 2, \quad \lambda_3 = 2 + \sqrt{2}.$$

Even though it is the hardest to apply to a single matrix, eigenvalues can be the most useful test for theoretical purposes. ***Each test is enough by itself.***

Positive Definite Matrices and Least Squares

I hope you will allow one more test for positive definiteness. It is already close. We connected positive definite matrices to pivots (Chapter 1), determinants (Chapter 4), and eigenvalues (Chapter 5). Now we see them in the least-squares problems of Chapter 3, coming from the rectangular matrices of Chapter 2.

The rectangular matrix will be R and the least-squares problem will be $Rx = b$. It has m equations with $m \geq n$ (square systems are included). *The least-squares choice* $\widehat{x}$ *is the solution of* $R^{\mathrm{T}}R\widehat{x} = R^{\mathrm{T}}b$. That matrix $A = R^{\mathrm{T}}R$ is not only symmetric but positive definite, as we now show—provided that the n columns of R are linearly independent:

6C The symmetric matrix A is positive definite if and only if

(V) There is a matrix R with independent columns such that $A = R^{\mathrm{T}}R$.

The key is to recognize $x^{\mathrm{T}}Ax$ *as* $x^{\mathrm{T}}R^{\mathrm{T}}Rx = (Rx)^{\mathrm{T}}(Rx)$. This squared length $\|Rx\|^2$ is positive (unless $x = 0$), because R has independent columns. (If x is nonzero then Rx is nonzero.) Thus $x^{\mathrm{T}}R^{\mathrm{T}}Rx > 0$ and $R^{\mathrm{T}}R$ is positive definite.

It remains to find an R for which $A = R^{\mathrm{T}}R$. We have almost done this twice already:

$$\textbf{Elimination} \qquad A = LDL^{\mathrm{T}} = (L\sqrt{D})(\sqrt{D}L^{\mathrm{T}}). \qquad \text{So take } R = \sqrt{D}L^{\mathrm{T}}.$$

This ***Cholesky decomposition*** has the pivots split evenly between L and L^{T}.

$$\textbf{Eigenvalues} \qquad A = Q\Lambda Q^{\mathrm{T}} = (Q\sqrt{\Lambda})(\sqrt{\Lambda}Q^{\mathrm{T}}). \qquad \text{So take } R = \sqrt{\Lambda}Q^{\mathrm{T}}. \tag{3}$$

A third possibility is $R = Q\sqrt{\Lambda}Q^{\mathrm{T}}$, the ***symmetric positive definite square root*** of A. There are many other choices, square or rectangular, and we can see why. If you multiply any R by *a matrix* Q *with orthonormal columns*, then $(QR)^{\mathrm{T}}(QR) = R^{\mathrm{T}}Q^{\mathrm{T}}QR = R^{\mathrm{T}}IR = A$. Therefore QR is another choice.

Applications of positive definite matrices are developed in my earlier book *Introduction to Applied Mathematics* and also the new *Applied Mathematics and Scientific*

Computing (see www.wellesleycambridge.com). We mention that $Ax = \lambda Mx$ arises constantly in engineering analysis. If A and M are positive definite, this generalized problem is parallel to the familiar $Ax = \lambda x$, and $\lambda > 0$. M is a ***mass matrix*** for the *finite element method* in Section 6.4.

Semidefinite Matrices

The tests for semidefiniteness will relax $x^{\mathrm{T}}Ax > 0$, $\lambda > 0$, $d > 0$, and $\det > 0$, to allow zeros to appear. The main point is to see the analogies with the positive definite case.

6D Each of the following tests is a necessary and sufficient condition for a symmetric matrix A to be ***positive semidefinite***:

(I′) $x^{\mathrm{T}}Ax \geq 0$ for all vectors x (this defines positive semidefinite).
(II′) All the eigenvalues of A satisfy $\lambda_i \geq 0$.
(III′) No principal submatrices have negative determinants.
(IV′) No pivots are negative.
(V′) There is a matrix R, possibly with dependent columns, such that $A = R^{\mathrm{T}}R$.

The diagonalization $A = Q\Lambda Q^{\mathrm{T}}$ leads to $x^{\mathrm{T}}Ax = x^{\mathrm{T}}Q\Lambda Q^{\mathrm{T}}x = y^{\mathrm{T}}\Lambda y$. If A has rank r, there are r nonzero λ's and r perfect squares in $y^{\mathrm{T}}\Lambda y = \lambda_1 y_1^2 + \cdots + \lambda_r y_r^2$.

Note The novelty is that condition III′ applies to all the principal submatrices, not only those in the upper left-hand corner. Otherwise, we could not distinguish between two matrices whose upper left determinants were all zero:

$$\begin{bmatrix} 0 & 0 \\ 0 & 1 \end{bmatrix} \text{ is positive semidefinite, and } \begin{bmatrix} 0 & 0 \\ 0 & -1 \end{bmatrix} \text{ is negative semidefinite.}$$

A row exchange comes with the same column exchange to maintain symmetry.

Example 2

$$A = \begin{bmatrix} 2 & -1 & -1 \\ -1 & 2 & -1 \\ -1 & -1 & 2 \end{bmatrix} \quad \text{is positive } \textit{semi}\text{definite, by all five tests:}$$

(I′) $x^{\mathrm{T}}Ax = (x_1 - x_2)^2 + (x_1 - x_3)^2 + (x_2 - x_3)^2 \geq 0$ (zero if $x_1 = x_2 = x_3$).
(II′) The eigenvalues are $\lambda_1 = 0$, $\lambda_2 = \lambda_3 = 3$ (a zero eigenvalue).
(III′) $\det A = 0$ and smaller determinants are positive.

$$\text{(IV}'\text{)} \quad A = \begin{bmatrix} 2 & -1 & -1 \\ -1 & 2 & -1 \\ -1 & -1 & 2 \end{bmatrix} \to \begin{bmatrix} 2 & 0 & 0 \\ 0 & \frac{3}{2} & -\frac{3}{2} \\ 0 & -\frac{3}{2} & \frac{3}{2} \end{bmatrix} \to \begin{bmatrix} 2 & 0 & 0 \\ 0 & \frac{3}{2} & 0 \\ 0 & 0 & \mathbf{0} \end{bmatrix} \quad \text{(missing pivot).}$$

(V′) $A = R^{\mathrm{T}}R$ with dependent columns in R:

$$\begin{bmatrix} 2 & -1 & -1 \\ -1 & 2 & -1 \\ -1 & -1 & 2 \end{bmatrix} = \begin{bmatrix} 1 & -1 & 0 \\ 0 & 1 & -1 \\ -1 & 0 & 1 \end{bmatrix} \begin{bmatrix} 1 & 0 & -1 \\ -1 & 1 & 0 \\ 0 & -1 & 1 \end{bmatrix} \quad (1, 1, 1) \text{ in the nullspace.}$$

Remark The conditions for semidefiniteness could also be deduced from the original conditions I-V for definiteness by the following trick: Add a small multiple of the identity, giving a positive definite matrix $A + \epsilon I$. Then let ϵ approach zero. Since the determinants and eigenvalues depend continuously on ϵ, they will be positive until the very last moment. At $\epsilon = 0$ they must still be nonnegative.

My class often asks about *unsymmetric* positive definite matrices. I never use that term. One reasonable definition is that the symmetric part $\frac{1}{2}(A + A^{\mathrm{T}})$ should be positive definite. That guarantees that *the real parts of the eigenvalues are positive*. But it is not necessary: $A = \begin{bmatrix} 1 & 4 \\ 0 & 1 \end{bmatrix}$ has $\lambda > 0$ but $\frac{1}{2}(A + A^{\mathrm{T}}) = \begin{bmatrix} 1 & 2 \\ 2 & 1 \end{bmatrix}$ is indefinite.

If $Ax = \lambda x$, then $x^{\mathrm{H}}Ax = \lambda x^{\mathrm{H}}x$ and $x^{\mathrm{H}}A^{\mathrm{H}}x = \overline{\lambda}x^{\mathrm{H}}x$.

Adding, $\frac{1}{2}x^{\mathrm{H}}(A + A^{\mathrm{H}})x = (\operatorname{Re}\lambda)x^{\mathrm{H}}x > 0$, so that $\operatorname{Re}\lambda > 0$.

Ellipsoids in *n* Dimensions

Throughout this book, geometry has helped the matrix algebra. A linear equation produced a plane. The system $Ax = b$ gives an intersection of planes. Least squares gives a perpendicular projection. The determinant is the volume of a box. Now, for a positive definite matrix and its $x^{\mathrm{T}}Ax$, we finally get a figure that is curved. It is an *ellipse* in two dimensions, and an *ellipsoid* in n dimensions.

The equation to consider is $x^{\mathrm{T}}Ax = 1$. If A is the identity matrix, this simplifies to $x_1^2 + x_2^2 + \cdots + x_n^2 = 1$. This is the equation of the "unit sphere" in $\mathbf{R}^n$. If $A = 4I$, the sphere gets smaller. The equation changes to $4x_1^2 + \cdots + 4x_n^2 = 1$. Instead of $(1, 0, \ldots, 0)$, it goes through $(\frac{1}{2}, 0, \ldots, 0)$. The center is at the origin, because if x satisfies $x^{\mathrm{T}}Ax = 1$, so does the opposite vector $-x$. The important step is to go from the identity matrix to a *diagonal matrix*:

Ellipsoid $$\text{For } A = \begin{bmatrix} 4 & & \\ & 1 & \\ & & \frac{1}{9} \end{bmatrix}, \text{ the equation is } x^{\mathrm{T}}Ax = 4x_1^2 + x_2^2 + \tfrac{1}{9}x_3^2 = 1.$$

Since the entries are unequal (and positive!) the sphere changes to an ellipsoid.

One solution is $x = \left(\frac{1}{2}, 0, 0\right)$ along the first axis. Another is $x = (0, 1, 0)$. The major axis has the farthest point $x = (0, 0, 3)$. It is like a football or a rugby ball, but not quite—those are closer to $x_1^2 + x_2^2 + \frac{1}{2}x_3^2 = 1$. The two equal coefficients make them circular in the x_1-x_2 plane, and much easier to throw!

Now comes the final step, to allow nonzeros away from the diagonal of A.

Example 3 $A = \begin{bmatrix} 5 & 4 \\ 4 & 5 \end{bmatrix}$ and $x^{\mathrm{T}}Ax = 5u^2 + 8uv + 5v^2 = 1$. That ellipse is centered at $u = v = 0$, but the axes are not so clear. The off-diagonal 4s leave the matrix positive definite, but they rotate the ellipse—its axes no longer line up with the coordinate axes (Figure 6.2). We will show that ***the axes of the ellipse point toward the eigenvectors of A***. Because $A = A^{\mathrm{T}}$, those eigenvectors and axes are orthogonal. The *major* axis of the ellipse corresponds to the *smallest* eigenvalue of A.

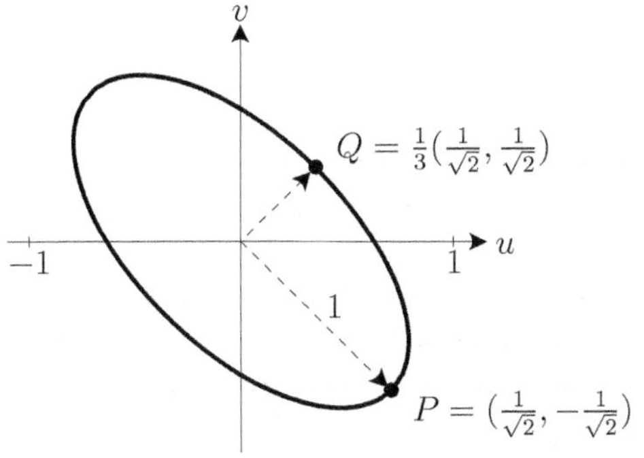

Figure 6.2 The ellipse $x^{\mathrm{T}}Ax = 5u^2 + 8uv + 5v^2 = 1$ and its principal axes.

To locate the ellipse we compute $\lambda_1 = 1$ and $\lambda_2 = 9$. The unit eigenvectors are $(1, -1)/\sqrt{2}$ and $(1, 1)/\sqrt{2}$. Those are at 45° angles with the u-v axes, and they are lined up with the axes of the ellipse. The way to see the ellipse properly is to *rewrite* $x^{\mathrm{T}}Ax = 1$:

New squares $$5u^2 + 8uv + v^2 = \left(\frac{u}{\sqrt{2}} - \frac{v}{\sqrt{2}}\right)^2 + 9\left(\frac{u}{\sqrt{2}} + \frac{v}{\sqrt{2}}\right)^2 = 1. \qquad (4)$$

$\lambda = 1$ and $\lambda = 9$ are outside the squares. The eigenvectors are inside. This is different from completing the square to $5\left(u + \frac{4}{5}v\right)^2 + \frac{9}{5}v^2$, with the *pivots* outside.

The first square equals 1 at $(1/\sqrt{2}, -1/\sqrt{2})$ at the end of the major axis. The minor axis is one-third as long, since we need $\left(\frac{1}{3}\right)^2$ to cancel the 9.

Any ellipsoid $x^{\mathrm{T}}Ax = 1$ can be simplified in the same way. *The key step is to diagonalize $A = Q\Lambda Q^{\mathrm{T}}$.* We straightened the picture by rotating the axes. Algebraically, the change to $y = Q^{\mathrm{T}}x$ produces a sum of squares:

$$x^{\mathrm{T}}Ax = (x^{\mathrm{T}}Q)\Lambda(Q^{\mathrm{T}}x) = y^{\mathrm{T}}\Lambda y = \lambda_1 y_1^2 + \cdots + \lambda_n y_n^2 = 1. \qquad (5)$$

The major axis has $y_1 = 1/\sqrt{\lambda_1}$ along the eigenvector with the smallest eigenvalue.

The other axes are along the other eigenvectors. Their lengths are $1/\sqrt{\lambda_2}, \ldots, 1/\sqrt{\lambda_n}$. Notice that the λ's must be positive—*the matrix must be positive definite*—or these square roots are in trouble. An indefinite equation $y_1^2 - 9y_2^2 = 1$ describes a hyperbola and not an ellipse. A hyperbola is a cross-section through a saddle, and an ellipse is a cross-section through a bowl.

The change from x to $y = Q^{\mathrm{T}}x$ rotates the axes of the space, to match the axes of the ellipsoid. In the y variables we can see that it is an ellipsoid, because the equation becomes so manageable:

6E Suppose $A = Q\Lambda Q^{\mathrm{T}}$ with $\lambda_i > 0$. Rotating $y = Q^{\mathrm{T}}x$ simplifies $x^{\mathrm{T}}Ax = 1$:

$$x^{\mathrm{T}}Q\Lambda Q^{\mathrm{T}}x = 1, \quad y^{\mathrm{T}}\Lambda y = 1, \quad \text{and} \quad \lambda_1 y_1^2 + \cdots + \lambda_n y_n^2 = 1.$$

This is the equation of an ellipsoid. Its axes have lengths $1/\sqrt{\lambda_1}, \ldots, 1/\sqrt{\lambda_n}$ from the center. In the original x-space they point along the eigenvectors of A.

The Law of Inertia

For elimination and eigenvalues, matrices become simpler by elementary operations. The essential thing is to know which properties of the matrix stay unchanged. When a multiple of one row is subtracted from another, the row space, nullspace, rank, and determinant all remain the same. For eigenvalues, the basic operation was a similarity transformation $A \to S^{-1}AS$ (or $A \to M^{-1}AM$). The eigenvalues are unchanged (and also the Jordan form). Now we ask the same question for symmetric matrices: *What are the elementary operations and their invariants for* $x^{\mathrm{T}}Ax$?

The basic operation on a quadratic form is to change variables. A new vector y is related to x by some nonsingular matrix, $x = Cy$. The quadratic form becomes $y^{\mathrm{T}}C^{\mathrm{T}}ACy$. This shows the fundamental operation on A:

$$\textbf{Congruence transformation} \qquad A \to C^{\mathrm{T}}AC \quad \text{for some nonsingular } C. \tag{6}$$

The symmetry of A is preserved, since $C^{\mathrm{T}}AC$ remains symmetric. The real question is, What other properties are shared by A and $C^{\mathrm{T}}AC$? The answer is given by Sylvester's ***law of inertia***.

6F $C^{\mathrm{T}}AC$ has the same number of positive eigenvalues, negative eigenvalues, and zero eigenvalues as A.

The *signs* of the eigenvalues (and not the eigenvalues themselves) are preserved by a congruence transformation. In the proof, we will suppose that A is nonsingular. Then $C^{\mathrm{T}}AC$ is also nonsingular, and there are no zero eigenvalues to worry about. (Otherwise we can work with the nonsingular $A + \epsilon I$ and $A - \epsilon I$, and at the end let $\epsilon \to 0$.)

Proof We want to borrow a trick from topology. Suppose C is linked to an orthogonal matrix Q by a continuous chain of nonsingular matrices $C(t)$. At $t = 0$ and $t = 1$, $C(0) = C$ and $C(1) = Q$. Then the eigenvalues of $C(t)^{\mathrm{T}}AC(t)$ will change gradually, as t goes from 0 to 1, from the eigenvalues of $C^{\mathrm{T}}AC$ to the eigenvalues of $Q^{\mathrm{T}}AQ$. Because $C(t)$ is never singular, *none of these eigenvalues can touch zero* (not to mention cross over it!). Therefore the number of eigenvalues to the right of zero, and the number to the left, is the same for $C^{\mathrm{T}}AC$ as for $Q^{\mathrm{T}}AQ$. And A has exactly the same eigenvalues as the similar matrix $Q^{-1}AQ = Q^{\mathrm{T}}AQ$.

One good choice for Q is to apply Gram–Schmidt to the columns of C. Then $C = QR$, and the chain of matrices is $C(t) = tQ + (1-t)QR$. The family $C(t)$ goes slowly through Gram–Schmidt, from QR to Q. It is invertible, because Q is invertible and the triangular factor $tI + (1-t)R$ has positive diagonal. That ends the proof. ■

Example 4 Suppose $A = I$. Then $C^{\mathrm{T}}AC = C^{\mathrm{T}}C$ is positive definite. Both I and $C^{\mathrm{T}}C$ have n positive eigenvalues, confirming the law of inertia.

Example 5 If $A = \begin{bmatrix} 1 & 0 \\ 0 & -1 \end{bmatrix}$, then $C^{\mathrm{T}}AC$ has a negative determinant:

$$\det C^{\mathrm{T}}AC = (\det C^{\mathrm{T}})(\det A)(\det C) = -(\det C)^2 < 0.$$

Then $C^{\mathrm{T}}AC$ must have one positive and one negative eigenvalue, like A.

Example 6 This application is the important one:

6G For any symmetric matrix A, ***the signs of the pivots agree with the signs of the eigenvalues***. The eigenvalue matrix Λ and the pivot matrix D have the same number of positive entries, negative entries, and zero entries.

We will assume that A allows the symmetric factorization $A = LDL^{\mathrm{T}}$ (without row exchanges). By the law of inertia, A has the same number of positive eigenvalues as D. But the eigenvalues of D are just its diagonal entries (the pivots). Thus the number of positive pivots matches the number of positive eigenvalues of A.

That is both beautiful and practical. It is beautiful because it brings together (for symmetric matrices) two parts of this book that were previously separate: *pivots* and *eigenvalues*. It is also practical, because the pivots can locate the eigenvalues:

A has positive pivots
$A - 2I$ has a negative pivot

$$A = \begin{bmatrix} 3 & 3 & 0 \\ 3 & 10 & 7 \\ 0 & 7 & 8 \end{bmatrix} \qquad A - 2I = \begin{bmatrix} 1 & 3 & 0 \\ 3 & 8 & 7 \\ 0 & 7 & 6 \end{bmatrix}.$$

A has positive eigenvalues, by our test. But we know that $\lambda_{\min}$ *is smaller than* 2, because subtracting 2 dropped it below zero. The next step looks at $A - I$, to see if $\lambda_{\min} < 1$. (It is, because $A - I$ has a negative pivot.) That interval containing λ is cut in half at every step by checking the signs of the pivots.

This was almost the first practical method of computing eigenvalues. It was dominant about 1960, after one important improvement—to make A tridiagonal first. Then the pivots are computed in $2n$ steps instead of $\frac{1}{6}n^3$. Elimination becomes fast, and the search for eigenvalues (by halving the intervals) becomes simple. The current favorite is the QR method in Chapter 7.

The Generalized Eigenvalue Problem

Physics, engineering, and statistics are usually kind enough to produce symmetric matrices in their eigenvalue problems. ***But sometimes $Ax = \lambda x$ is replaced by $Ax = \lambda Mx$.*** *There are two matrices rather than one.*

An example is the motion of two unequal masses in a line of springs:

$$\begin{aligned} m_1\frac{d^2v}{dt^2} + 2v - w &= 0 \\ m_2\frac{d^2w}{dt^2} - v + 2w &= 0 \end{aligned} \quad \text{or} \quad \begin{bmatrix} m_1 & 0 \\ 0 & m_2 \end{bmatrix}\frac{d^2u}{dt^2} + \begin{bmatrix} 2 & -1 \\ -1 & 2 \end{bmatrix}u = 0. \tag{7}$$

When the masses were equal, $m_1 = m_2 = 1$, this was the old system $u'' + Au = 0$. Now it is $Mu'' + Au = 0$, with a *mass matrix* M. The eigenvalue problem arises when we look for exponential solutions $e^{i\omega t}x$:

$$Mu'' + Au = 0 \quad \text{becomes} \quad M(i\omega)^2 e^{i\omega t}x + Ae^{i\omega t}x = 0. \tag{8}$$

Cancelling $e^{i\omega t}$, and writing λ for ω^2, this is an eigenvalue problem:

$$\textbf{Generalized problem } Ax = \lambda Mx \qquad \begin{bmatrix} 2 & -1 \\ -1 & 2 \end{bmatrix}x = \lambda \begin{bmatrix} m_1 & 0 \\ 0 & m_2 \end{bmatrix}x. \tag{9}$$

There is a solution when $A - \lambda M$ is singular. The special choice $M = I$ brings back the usual $\det(A - \lambda I) = 0$. We work out $\det(A - \lambda M)$ with $m_1 = 1$ and $m_2 = 2$:

$$\det \begin{bmatrix} 2-\lambda & -1 \\ -1 & 2-2\lambda \end{bmatrix} = 2\lambda^2 - 6\lambda + 3 = 0 \quad \text{gives} \quad \lambda = \frac{3 \pm \sqrt{3}}{2}.$$

For the eigenvector $x_1 = (\sqrt{3} - 1, 1)$, the two masses oscillate together—but the first mass only moves as far as $\sqrt{3} - 1 \approx .73$. In the faster mode, the components of $x_2 = (1 + \sqrt{3}, -1)$ have opposite signs and the masses move in opposite directions. This time the smaller mass goes much further.

The underlying theory is easier to explain if M is split into $R^{\mathrm{T}}R$. (*M is assumed to be positive definite.*) Then the substitution $y = Rx$ changes

$$Ax = \lambda Mx = \lambda R^{\mathrm{T}}Rx \quad \text{into} \quad AR^{-1}y = \lambda R^{\mathrm{T}}y.$$

Writing C for R^{-1}, and multiplying through by $(R^{\mathrm{T}})^{-1} = C^{\mathrm{T}}$, this becomes a standard eigenvalue problem for the *single* symmetric matrix $C^{\mathrm{T}}AC$:

$$\textbf{Equivalent problem} \qquad C^{\mathrm{T}}ACy = \lambda y. \tag{10}$$

The eigenvalues λ_j are the same as for the original $Ax = \lambda Mx$, and the eigenvectors are related by $y_j = Rx_j$. The properties of $C^{\mathrm{T}}AC$ lead directly to the properties of $Ax = \lambda Mx$, when $A = A^{\mathrm{T}}$ and M is positive definite:

1. The eigenvalues for $Ax = \lambda Mx$ are real, because $C^{\mathrm{T}}AC$ is symmetric.
2. The λ's have the same signs as the eigenvalues of A, by the law of inertia.
3. $C^{\mathrm{T}}AC$ has orthogonal eigenvectors y_j. So the eigenvectors of $Ax = \lambda Mx$ have

$$\textbf{“}\boldsymbol{M}\textbf{-orthogonality”} \qquad x_i^{\mathrm{T}}Mx_j = x_i^{\mathrm{T}}R^{\mathrm{T}}Rx_j = y_i^{\mathrm{T}}y_j = 0. \tag{11}$$

A and M are being *simultaneously diagonalized.* If S has the x_j in its columns, then $S^{\mathrm{T}}AS = \Lambda$ and $S^{\mathrm{T}}MS = I$. This is a *congruence* transformation, with S^{T} on the left, and not a similarity transformation with S^{-1}. The main point is easy to summarize: As long as M is positive definite, the generalized eigenvalue problem $Ax = \lambda Mx$ behaves exactly like $Ax = \lambda x$.

Problem Set 6.2

1. For what range of numbers a and b are the matrices A and B positive definite?

$$A = \begin{bmatrix} a & 2 & 2 \\ 2 & a & 2 \\ 2 & 2 & a \end{bmatrix} \qquad B = \begin{bmatrix} 1 & 2 & 4 \\ 2 & b & 8 \\ 4 & 8 & 7 \end{bmatrix}.$$

2. Decide for or against the positive definiteness of

$$A = \begin{bmatrix} 2 & -1 & -1 \\ -1 & 2 & -1 \\ -1 & -1 & 2 \end{bmatrix}, \quad B = \begin{bmatrix} 2 & -1 & -1 \\ -1 & 2 & 1 \\ -1 & 1 & 2 \end{bmatrix}, \quad C = \begin{bmatrix} 0 & 1 & 2 \\ 1 & 0 & 1 \\ 2 & 1 & 0 \end{bmatrix}^2.$$

3. Construct an *indefinite matrix* with its largest entries on the main diagonal:

$$A = \begin{bmatrix} 1 & b & -b \\ b & 1 & b \\ -b & b & 1 \end{bmatrix} \quad \text{with } |b| < 1 \text{ can have } \det A < 0.$$

4. Show from the eigenvalues that if A is positive definite, so is A^2 and so is A^{-1}.

5. *If A and B are positive definite, then $A+B$ is positive definite.* Pivots and eigenvalues are not convenient for $A + B$. Much better to prove $x^{\mathrm{T}}(A + B)x > 0$.

6. From the pivots, eigenvalues, and eigenvectors of $A = \begin{bmatrix} 5 & 4 \\ 4 & 5 \end{bmatrix}$, write A as $R^{\mathrm{T}}R$ in three ways: $(L\sqrt{D})(\sqrt{D}L^{\mathrm{T}})$, $(Q\sqrt{\Lambda})(\sqrt{\Lambda}Q^{\mathrm{T}})$, and $(Q\sqrt{\Lambda}Q^{\mathrm{T}})(Q\sqrt{\Lambda}Q^{\mathrm{T}})$.

7. If $A = Q\Lambda Q^{\mathrm{T}}$ is symmetric positive definite, then $R = Q\sqrt{\Lambda}Q^{\mathrm{T}}$ is its *symmetric positive definite square root*. Why does R have positive eigenvalues? Compute R and verify $R^2 = A$ for

$$A = \begin{bmatrix} 10 & 6 \\ 6 & 10 \end{bmatrix} \quad \text{and} \quad A = \begin{bmatrix} 10 & -6 \\ -6 & 10 \end{bmatrix}.$$

8. If A is symmetric positive definite and C is nonsingular, prove that $B = C^{\mathrm{T}}AC$ is also symmetric positive definite.

9. If $A = R^{\mathrm{T}}R$ prove the generalized Schwarz inequality $|x^{\mathrm{T}}Ay|^2 \le (x^{\mathrm{T}}Ax)(y^{\mathrm{T}}Ay)$.

10. The ellipse $u^2 + 4v^2 = 1$ corresponds to $A = \begin{bmatrix} 1 & 0 \\ 0 & 4 \end{bmatrix}$. Write the eigenvalues and eigenvectors, and sketch the ellipse.

11. Reduce the equation $3u^2 - 2\sqrt{2}uv + 2v^2 = 1$ to a sum of squares by finding the eigenvalues of the corresponding A, and sketch the ellipse.

12. In three dimensions, $\lambda_1 y_1^2 + \lambda_2 y_2^2 + \lambda_3 y_3^2 = 1$ represents an ellipsoid when all $\lambda_i > 0$. Describe all the different kinds of surfaces that appear in the positive semidefinite case when one or more of the eigenvalues is zero.

13. Write down the five conditions for a 3 by 3 matrix to be *negative definite* ($-A$ is positive definite) with special attention to condition III: How is $\det(-A)$ related to $\det A$?

14. Decide whether the following matrices are positive definite, negative definite, semidefinite, or indefinite:

$$A = \begin{bmatrix} 1 & 2 & 3 \\ 2 & 5 & 4 \\ 3 & 4 & 9 \end{bmatrix}, \quad B = \begin{bmatrix} 1 & 2 & 0 & 0 \\ 2 & 6 & -2 & 0 \\ 0 & -2 & 5 & -2 \\ 0 & 0 & -2 & 3 \end{bmatrix}, \quad C = -B, \quad D = A^{-1}.$$

Is there a real solution to $-x^2 - 5y^2 - 9z^2 - 4xy - 6xz - 8yz = 1$?

15. Suppose A is symmetric positive definite and Q is an orthogonal matrix. True or false:

(a) $Q^{\mathrm{T}}AQ$ is a diagonal matrix.
(b) $Q^{\mathrm{T}}AQ$ is symmetric positive definite.

(c) $Q^{\mathrm{T}}AQ$ has the same eigenvalues as A.
(d) e^{-A} is symmetric positive definite.

16. If A is positive definite and a_{11} is increased, prove from cofactors that the determinant is increased. Show by example that this can fail if A is indefinite.

17. From $A = R^{\mathrm{T}}R$, show for positive definite matrices that $\det A \leq a_{11}a_{22}\cdots a_{nn}$. (The length squared of column j of R is a_{jj}. Use determinant = volume.)

18. (Lyapunov test for stability of M) Suppose $AM + M^{\mathrm{H}}A = -I$ with positive definite A. If $Mx = \lambda x$ show that $\operatorname{Re}\lambda < 0$. (*Hint*: Multiply the first equation by x^{H} and x.)

19. Which 3 by 3 symmetric matrices A produce these functions $f = x^{\mathrm{T}}Ax$? Why is the first matrix positive definite but not the second one?

(a) $f = 2(x_1^2 + x_2^2 + x_3^2 - x_1x_2 - x_2x_3)$.
(b) $f = 2(x_1^2 + x_2^2 + x_3^2 - x_1x_2 - x_1x_3 - x_2x_3)$.

20. Compute the three upper left determinants to establish positive definiteness. Verify that their ratios give the second and third pivots.

$$A = \begin{bmatrix} 2 & 2 & 0 \\ 2 & 5 & 3 \\ 0 & 3 & 8 \end{bmatrix}.$$

21. A positive definite matrix cannot have a zero (or even worse, a negative number) on its diagonal. Show that this matrix fails to have $x^{\mathrm{T}}Ax > 0$:

$$\begin{bmatrix} x_1 & x_2 & x_3 \end{bmatrix} \begin{bmatrix} 4 & 1 & 1 \\ 1 & 0 & 2 \\ 1 & 2 & 5 \end{bmatrix} \begin{bmatrix} x_1 \\ x_2 \\ x_3 \end{bmatrix} \quad \text{is not positive when } (x_1, x_2, x_3) = (\quad,\quad,\quad).$$

22. A diagonal entry a_{jj} of a symmetric matrix cannot be smaller than all the λ's. If it were, then $A - a_{jj}I$ would have ______ eigenvalues and would be positive definite. But $A - a_{jj}I$ has a ______ on the main diagonal.

23. Give a quick reason why each of these statements is true:

(a) Every positive definite matrix is invertible.
(b) The only positive definite projection matrix is $P = I$.
(c) A diagonal matrix with positive diagonal entries is positive definite.
(d) A symmetric matrix with a positive determinant might not be positive definite!

24. For which s and t do A and B have all $\lambda > 0$ (and are therefore positive definite)?

$$A = \begin{bmatrix} s & -4 & -4 \\ -4 & s & -4 \\ -4 & -4 & s \end{bmatrix} \quad \text{and} \quad B = \begin{bmatrix} t & 3 & 0 \\ 3 & t & 4 \\ 0 & 4 & t \end{bmatrix}.$$

25. You may have seen the equation for an ellipse as $\left(\frac{x}{a}\right)^2 + \left(\frac{y}{b}\right)^2 = 1$. What are a and b when the equation is written as $\lambda_1x^2 + \lambda_2y^2 = 1$? The ellipse $9x^2 + 16y^2 = 1$ has half-axes with lengths $a =$ ___ and $b =$ ___.

26. Draw the tilted ellipse $x^2 + xy + y^2 = 1$ and find the half-lengths of its axes from the eigenvalues of the corresponding A.

27. With positive pivots in D, the factorization $A = LDL^{\mathrm{T}}$ becomes $L\sqrt{D}\sqrt{D}L^{\mathrm{T}}$. (Square roots of the pivots give $D = \sqrt{D}\sqrt{D}$.) Then $C = L\sqrt{D}$ yields the ***Cholesky factorization*** $A = CC^{\mathrm{T}}$, which is "symmetrized LU":

$$\text{From} \quad C = \begin{bmatrix} 3 & 0 \\ 1 & 2 \end{bmatrix} \quad \text{find } A. \qquad \text{From} \quad A = \begin{bmatrix} 4 & 8 \\ 8 & 25 \end{bmatrix} \quad \text{find } C.$$

28. In the Cholesky factorization $A = CC^{\mathrm{T}}$, with $C = L\sqrt{D}$, the square roots of the pivots are on the diagonal of C. Find C (lower triangular) for

$$A = \begin{bmatrix} 9 & 0 & 0 \\ 0 & 1 & 2 \\ 0 & 2 & 8 \end{bmatrix} \quad \text{and} \quad A = \begin{bmatrix} 1 & 1 & 1 \\ 1 & 2 & 2 \\ 1 & 2 & 7 \end{bmatrix}.$$

29. The symmetric factorization $A = LDL^{\mathrm{T}}$ means that $x^{\mathrm{T}}Ax = x^{\mathrm{T}}LDL^{\mathrm{T}}x$:

$$\begin{bmatrix} x & y \end{bmatrix} \begin{bmatrix} a & b \\ b & c \end{bmatrix} \begin{bmatrix} x \\ y \end{bmatrix} = \begin{bmatrix} x & y \end{bmatrix} \begin{bmatrix} 1 & 0 \\ b/a & 1 \end{bmatrix} \begin{bmatrix} a & 0 \\ 0 & (ac - b^2)/a \end{bmatrix} \begin{bmatrix} 1 & b/a \\ 0 & 1 \end{bmatrix} \begin{bmatrix} x \\ y \end{bmatrix}.$$

The left-hand side is $ax^2 + 2bxy + cy^2$. The right-hand side is $a\left(x + \frac{b}{a}y\right)^2 +$ ______ y^2. The second pivot completes the square! Test with $a = 2$, $b = 4$, $c = 10$.

30. Without multiplying $A = \begin{bmatrix} \cos\theta & -\sin\theta \\ \sin\theta & \cos\theta \end{bmatrix} \begin{bmatrix} 2 & 0 \\ 0 & 5 \end{bmatrix} \begin{bmatrix} \cos\theta & \sin\theta \\ -\sin\theta & \cos\theta \end{bmatrix}$, find

(a) the determinant of A.
(b) the eigenvalues of A.
(c) the eigenvectors of A.
(d) a reason why A is symmetric positive definite.

31. For the semidefinite matrices

$$A = \begin{bmatrix} 2 & -1 & -1 \\ -1 & 2 & -1 \\ -1 & -1 & 2 \end{bmatrix} \text{ (rank 2)} \quad \text{and} \quad B = \begin{bmatrix} 1 & 1 & 1 \\ 1 & 1 & 1 \\ 1 & 1 & 1 \end{bmatrix} \text{ (rank 1)},$$

write $x^{\mathrm{T}}Ax$ as a sum of two squares and $x^{\mathrm{T}}Bx$ as one square.

32. Apply any three tests to each of the matrices

$$A = \begin{bmatrix} 1 & 1 & 1 \\ 1 & 1 & 1 \\ 1 & 1 & 0 \end{bmatrix} \quad \text{and} \quad B = \begin{bmatrix} 2 & 1 & 2 \\ 1 & 1 & 1 \\ 2 & 1 & 2 \end{bmatrix},$$

to decide whether they are positive definite, positive semidefinite, or indefinite.

33. For $C = \begin{bmatrix} 2 & 0 \\ 0 & -1 \end{bmatrix}$ and $A = \begin{bmatrix} 1 & 1 \\ 1 & 1 \end{bmatrix}$, confirm that $C^{\mathrm{T}}AC$ has eigenvalues of the same signs as A. Construct a chain of nonsingular matrices $C(t)$ linking C to an orthogonal Q. Why is it impossible to construct a nonsingular chain linking C to the identity matrix?

34. If the pivots of a matrix are all greater than 1, are the eigenvalues all greater than 1? Test on the tridiagonal $-1, 2, -1$ matrices.

35. Use the pivots of $A - \frac{1}{2}I$ to decide whether A has an eigenvalue smaller than $\frac{1}{2}$:

$$A - \frac{1}{2}I = \begin{bmatrix} 2.5 & 3 & 0 \\ 3 & 9.5 & 7 \\ 0 & 7 & 7.5 \end{bmatrix}.$$

36. An algebraic proof of the *law of inertia* starts with the orthonormal eigenvectors $x_1, \ldots, x_p$ of A corresponding to eigenvalues $\lambda_i > 0$, and the orthonormal eigenvectors $y_1, \ldots, y_q$ of C^TAC corresponding to eigenvalues $\mu_i < 0$.

(a) To prove that the $p + q$ vectors $x_1, \ldots, x_p, Cy_1, \ldots, Cy_q$ are independent, assume that some combination gives zero:

$$a_1x_1 + \cdots + a_px_p = b_1Cy_1 + \cdots + b_qCy_q \; (= z, \text{say}).$$

Show that $z^TAz = \lambda_1a_1^2 + \cdots + \lambda_pa_p^2 \geq 0$ and $z^TAz = \mu_1b_1^2 + \cdots + \mu_qb_q^2 \leq 0$.

(b) Deduce that the a's and b's are zero (proving linear independence). From that deduce $p + q \leq n$.

(c) The same argument for the $n - p$ negative λ's and the $n - q$ positive μ's gives $n - p + n - q \leq n$. (We again assume no zero eigenvalues—which are handled separately). Show that $p + q = n$, so the number p of positive λ's equals the number $n - q$ of positive μ's—which is the law of inertia.

37. If C is nonsingular, show that A and C^TAC have the same rank. Thus they have the same number of zero eigenvalues.

38. Find by experiment the number of positive, negative, and zero eigenvalues of

$$A = \begin{bmatrix} I & B \\ B^T & 0 \end{bmatrix}$$

when the block B (of order $\frac{1}{2}n$) is nonsingular.

39. Do A and C^TAC always satisfy the law of inertia when C is not square?

40. In equation (9) with $m_1 = 1$ and $m_2 = 2$, verify that the normal modes are M-orthogonal: $x_1^TMx_2 = 0$.

41. Find the eigenvalues and eigenvectors of $Ax = \lambda Mx$:

$$\begin{bmatrix} 6 & -3 \\ -3 & 6 \end{bmatrix} x = \frac{\lambda}{18} \begin{bmatrix} 4 & 1 \\ 1 & 4 \end{bmatrix} x.$$

42. If the symmetric matrices A and M are indefinite, $Ax = \lambda Mx$ might not have real eigenvalues. Construct a 2 by 2 example.

43. A *group* of nonsingular matrices includes AB and A^{-1} if it includes A and B. "Products and inverses stay in the group." Which of these sets are groups? *Positive definite symmetric matrices A, orthogonal matrices Q, all exponentials e^{tA} of a fixed matrix A, matrices P with positive eigenvalues, matrices D with determinant* 1. Invent a group containing only positive definite matrices.

6.3 SINGULAR VALUE DECOMPOSITION

A great matrix factorization has been saved for the end of the basic course. $U\Sigma V^{\mathrm{T}}$ joins with LU from elimination and QR from orthogonalization (Gauss and Gram–Schmidt). Nobody's name is attached; $A = U\Sigma V^{\mathrm{T}}$ is known as the "SVD" or the ***singular value decomposition***. We want to describe it, to prove it, and to discuss its applications—which are many and growing.

The SVD is closely associated with the eigenvalue–eigenvector factorization $Q\Lambda Q^{\mathrm{T}}$ of a positive definite matrix. The eigenvalues are in the diagonal matrix Λ. The eigenvector matrix Q *is orthogonal* ($Q^{\mathrm{T}}Q = I$) because eigenvectors of a symmetric matrix can be chosen to be orthonormal. For most matrices that is not true, and for rectangular matrices it is ridiculous (eigenvalues undefined). But now we allow the Q on the left and the Q^{T} on the right to be *any two orthogonal matrices* U and V^{T}—not necessarily transposes of each other. Then every matrix will split into $A = U\Sigma V^{\mathrm{T}}$.

The diagonal (but rectangular) matrix Σ has eigenvalues from $A^{\mathrm{T}}A$, not from A! Those positive entries (also called sigma) will be $\sigma_1, \ldots, \sigma_r$. They are the ***singular values*** of A. They fill the first r places on the main diagonal of Σ—when A has rank r. The rest of Σ is zero.

With rectangular matrices, the key is almost always to consider $A^{\mathrm{T}}A$ and AA^{T}.

Singular Value Decomposition: Any m by n matrix A can be factored into

$$A = U\Sigma V^{\mathrm{T}} = (\textbf{orthogonal})(\textbf{diagonal})(\textbf{orthogonal})\,.$$

The columns of U (m by m) are eigenvectors of AA^{T}, and the columns of V (n by n) are eigenvectors of $A^{\mathrm{T}}A$. The r singular values on the diagonal of Σ (m by n) are the square roots of the nonzero eigenvalues of both AA^{T} and $A^{\mathrm{T}}A$.

Remark 1 For positive definite matrices, Σ is Λ and $U\Sigma V^{\mathrm{T}}$ is identical to $Q\Lambda Q^{\mathrm{T}}$. For other symmetric matrices, any negative eigenvalues in Λ become positive in Σ. For complex matrices, Σ remains real but U and V become *unitary* (the complex version of orthogonal). We take complex conjugates in $U^{\mathrm{H}}U = I$ and $V^{\mathrm{H}}V = I$ and $A = U\Sigma V^{\mathrm{H}}$.

Remark 2 U and V give orthonormal bases for *all four fundamental subspaces*:

first	r	columns of U:	**column space** of A
last	$m-r$	columns of U:	**left nullspace** of A
first	r	columns of V:	**row space** of A
last	$n-r$	columns of V:	**nullspace** of A

Remark 3 The SVD chooses those bases in an extremely special way. They are more than just orthonormal. *When A multiplies a column v_j of V, it produces σ_j times a column of U*. That comes directly from $AV = U\Sigma$, looked at a column at a time.

Remark 4 Eigenvectors of AA^{T} and $A^{\mathrm{T}}A$ must go into the columns of U and V:

$$AA^{\mathrm{T}} = (U\Sigma V^{\mathrm{T}})(V\Sigma^{\mathrm{T}}U^{\mathrm{T}}) = U\Sigma\Sigma^{\mathrm{T}}U^{\mathrm{T}} \quad \text{and, similarly,} \quad A^{\mathrm{T}}A = V\Sigma^{\mathrm{T}}\Sigma V^{\mathrm{T}}. \tag{1}$$

U must be the eigenvector matrix for AA^{T}. The eigenvalue matrix in the middle is $\Sigma\Sigma^{\mathrm{T}}$—which is m by m with $\sigma_1^2, \ldots, \sigma_r^2$ on the diagonal.

From the $A^TA = V\Sigma^T\Sigma V^T$, the V matrix *must be the eigenvector matrix for* A^TA. The diagonal matrix $\Sigma^T\Sigma$ has the same $\sigma_1^2, \ldots, \sigma_r^2$, but it is n by n.

Remark 5 Here is the reason that $Av_j = \sigma_j u_j$. Start with $A^TAv_j = \sigma_j^2 v_j$:

$$\textbf{Multiply by } \boldsymbol{A} \qquad AA^TAv_j = \sigma_j^2 Av_j \tag{2}$$

This says that Av_j is an eigenvector of AA^T! We just moved parentheses to $(AA^T)(Av_j)$. The length of this eigenvector Av_j is σ_j, because

$$v^TA^TAv_j = \sigma_j^2 v_j^T v_j \quad \text{gives} \quad \|Av_j\|^2 = \sigma_j^2.$$

So the unit eigenvector is $Av_j/\sigma_j = u_j$. **In other words, $AV = U\Sigma$.**

Example 1 This A has only one column: rank $r = 1$. Then Σ has only $\sigma_1 = 3$:

$$\textbf{SVD} \qquad A = \begin{bmatrix} -1 \\ 2 \\ 2 \end{bmatrix} = \begin{bmatrix} -\frac{1}{3} & \frac{2}{3} & \frac{2}{3} \\ \frac{2}{3} & -\frac{1}{3} & \frac{2}{3} \\ \frac{2}{3} & \frac{2}{3} & -\frac{1}{3} \end{bmatrix} \begin{bmatrix} 3 \\ 0 \\ 0 \end{bmatrix} \begin{bmatrix} 1 \end{bmatrix} = U_{3\times3}\,\Sigma_{3\times1}\,V_{1\times1}^T.$$

A^TA is 1 by 1, whereas AA^T is 3 by 3. They both have eigenvalue 9 (whose square root is the 3 in Σ). The two zero eigenvalues of AA^T leave some freedom for the eigenvectors in columns 2 and 3 of U. We kept that matrix orthogonal.

Example 2 Now A has rank 2, and $AA^T = \begin{bmatrix} 2 & -1 \\ -1 & 2 \end{bmatrix}$ with $\lambda = 3$ and 1:

$$\begin{bmatrix} -1 & 1 & 0 \\ 0 & -1 & 1 \end{bmatrix} = U\Sigma V^T = \frac{1}{\sqrt{2}}\begin{bmatrix} -1 & 1 \\ 1 & 1 \end{bmatrix} \begin{bmatrix} \sqrt{3} & 0 & 0 \\ 0 & 1 & 0 \end{bmatrix} \begin{bmatrix} 1 & -2 & 1 \\ -1 & 0 & 1 \\ 1 & 1 & 1 \end{bmatrix} \begin{matrix} /\sqrt{6} \\ /\sqrt{2}. \\ /\sqrt{3} \end{matrix}$$

Notice $\sqrt{3}$ and $\sqrt{1}$. The columns of U are *left* singular vectors (unit eigenvectors of AA^T). The columns of V are *right* singular vectors (unit eigenvectors of A^TA).

Applications of the SVD

We will pick a few important applications, after emphasizing one key point. The SVD is terrific for numerically stable computations, because U and V are orthogonal matrices. They never change the length of a vector. Since $\|Ux\|^2 = x^TU^TUx = \|x\|^2$, multiplication by U cannot destroy the scaling.

Of course Σ could multiply by a large σ or (more commonly) divide by a small σ, and overflow the computer. But still Σ *is as good as possible*. It reveals exactly what is large and what is small. The ratio $\sigma_{\max}/\sigma_{\min}$ is the **condition number** of an invertible n by n matrix. The availability of that information is another reason for the popularity of the SVD. We come back to this in the second application.

1. Image processing Suppose a satellite takes a picture, and wants to send it to Earth. The picture may contain 1000 by 1000 "pixels"—a million little squares, each with a definite color. We can code the colors, and send back 1,000,000 numbers. It is better to find the *essential* information inside the 1000 by 1000 matrix, and send only that.

Suppose we know the SVD. The key is in the singular values (in Σ). Typically, some σ's are significant and others are extremely small. If we keep 20 and throw away 980, then we send only the corresponding 20 columns of U and V. The other 980 columns are multiplied in $U\Sigma V^{\mathrm{T}}$ by the small σ's that are being ignored. *We can do the matrix multiplication as columns times rows*:

$$A = U\Sigma V^{\mathrm{T}} = u_1\sigma_1 v_1^{\mathrm{T}} + u_2\sigma_2 v_2^{\mathrm{T}} + \cdots + u_r\sigma_r v_r^{\mathrm{T}}. \tag{3}$$

Any matrix is the sum of r matrices of rank 1. If only 20 terms are kept, we send 20 times 2000 numbers instead of a million (25 to 1 compression).

The pictures are really striking, as more and more singular values are included. At first you see nothing, and suddenly you recognize everything. The cost is in computing the SVD—this has become much more efficient, but it is expensive for a big matrix.

2. The effective rank The rank of a matrix is the number of independent rows, and the number of independent columns. That can be hard to decide in computations! In exact arithmetic, counting the pivots is correct. Real arithmetic can be misleading—but discarding small pivots is not the answer. Consider the following:

$$\boldsymbol{\epsilon} \textbf{ is small} \qquad \begin{bmatrix} \epsilon & 2\epsilon \\ 1 & 2 \end{bmatrix} \quad \text{and} \quad \begin{bmatrix} \epsilon & 1 \\ 0 & 0 \end{bmatrix} \quad \text{and} \quad \begin{bmatrix} \epsilon & 1 \\ \epsilon & 1+\epsilon \end{bmatrix}.$$

The first has rank 1, although roundoff error will probably produce a second pivot. Both pivots will be small; how many do we ignore? The second has one small pivot, but we cannot pretend that its row is insignificant. The third has two pivots and its rank is 2, but its "effective rank" ought to be 1.

We go to a more stable measure of rank. The first step is to use $A^{\mathrm{T}}A$ or AA^{T}, which are symmetric but share the same rank as A. Their eigenvalues—the singular values squared—are *not* misleading. Based on the accuracy of the data, we decide on a tolerance like 10^{-6} and count the singular values above it—that is the effective rank. The examples above have effective rank 1 (when ϵ is very small).

3. Polar decomposition Every nonzero complex number z is a positive number r times a number $e^{i\theta}$ on the unit circle: $z = re^{i\theta}$. That expresses z in "polar coordinates." If we think of z as a 1 by 1 matrix, r corresponds to a *positive definite matrix* and $e^{i\theta}$ corresponds to an *orthogonal matrix*. More exactly, since $e^{i\theta}$ is complex and satisfies $e^{-i\theta}e^{i\theta} = 1$, it forms a 1 by 1 *unitary matrix*: $U^{\mathrm{H}}U = I$. We take the complex conjugate as well as the transpose, for U^{H}.

The SVD extends this "polar factorization" to matrices of any size:

> Every real square matrix can be factored into $A = QS$, where Q is ***orthogonal*** and S is ***symmetric positive semidefinite***. If A is invertible then S is positive definite.

For proof we just insert $V^{\mathrm{T}}V = I$ into the middle of the SVD:

$$A = U\Sigma V^{\mathrm{T}} = (UV^{\mathrm{T}})(V\Sigma V^{\mathrm{T}}). \tag{4}$$

The factor $S = V\Sigma V^{\mathrm{T}}$ is symmetric and semidefinite (because Σ is). The factor $Q = UV^{\mathrm{T}}$ is an orthogonal matrix (because $Q^{\mathrm{T}}Q = VU^{\mathrm{T}}UV^{\mathrm{T}} = I$). In the complex case, S becomes Hermitian instead of symmetric and Q becomes unitary instead of orthogonal. In the invertible case Σ is definite and so is S.

Example 3 Polar decomposition:

$$A = QS \qquad \begin{bmatrix} 1 & -2 \\ 3 & -1 \end{bmatrix} = \begin{bmatrix} 0 & -1 \\ 1 & 0 \end{bmatrix} \begin{bmatrix} 3 & -1 \\ -1 & 2 \end{bmatrix}.$$

Example 4 Reverse polar decomposition:

$$A = S'Q \qquad \begin{bmatrix} 1 & -2 \\ 3 & -1 \end{bmatrix} = \begin{bmatrix} 2 & 1 \\ 1 & 3 \end{bmatrix} \begin{bmatrix} 0 & -1 \\ 1 & 0 \end{bmatrix}.$$

The exercises show how, in the reverse order, S changes but Q remains the same. Both S and S' are symmetric positive definite because this A is invertible.

Application of $A = QS$: A major use of the polar decomposition is in continuum mechanics (and recently in robotics). In any deformation, it is important to separate stretching from rotation, and that is exactly what QS achieves. The orthogonal matrix Q is a rotation, and possibly a reflection. The material feels no strain. The symmetric matrix S has eigenvalues $\sigma_1, \ldots, \sigma_r$, which are the stretching factors (or compression factors). The diagonalization that displays those eigenvalues is the natural choice of axes—called ***principal axes***: as in the ellipses of Section 6.2. It is S that requires work on the material, and stores up elastic energy.

We note that S^2 is $A^{\mathrm{T}}A$, which is symmetric positive definite when A is invertible. S is the symmetric positive definite square root of $A^{\mathrm{T}}A$, and Q is AS^{-1}. In fact, *A could be rectangular, as long as $A^{\mathrm{T}}A$ is positive definite.* (That is the condition we keep meeting, that A must have independent columns.) In the reverse order $A = S'Q$, the matrix S' is the symmetric positive definite square root of AA^{T}.

4. Least squares For a rectangular system $Ax = b$, the least-squares solution comes from the normal equations $A^{\mathrm{T}}A\widehat{x} = A^{\mathrm{T}}b$. ***If A has dependent columns then $A^{\mathrm{T}}A$ is not invertible and $\widehat{x}$ is not determined***. Any vector in the nullspace could be added to $\widehat{x}$. We can now complete Chapter 3, by choosing a "best" (*shortest*) $\widehat{x}$ for every $Ax = b$.

$Ax = b$ has two possible difficulties: *Dependent rows or dependent columns*. With dependent rows, $Ax = b$ may have no solution. That happens when b is outside the column space of A. Instead of $Ax = b$, we solve $A^{\mathrm{T}}A\widehat{x} = A^{\mathrm{T}}b$. But if A has *dependent columns*, this $\widehat{x}$ will not be unique. We have to choose a particular solution of $A^{\mathrm{T}}A\widehat{x} = A^{\mathrm{T}}b$, and we choose the shortest.

The optimal solution of $Ax = b$ is the minimum length solution of $A^{\mathrm{T}}A\widehat{x} = A^{\mathrm{T}}b$.

That minimum length solution will be called x^+. It is our preferred choice as the best solution to $Ax = b$ (which had no solution), and also to $A^{\mathrm{T}}A\widehat{x} = A^{\mathrm{T}}b$ (which had too many). We start with a diagonal example.

Example 5 A is diagonal, with dependent rows and dependent columns:

$$A\widehat{x} = p \quad \text{is} \quad \begin{bmatrix} \sigma_1 & 0 & 0 & 0 \\ 0 & \sigma_2 & 0 & 0 \\ 0 & 0 & 0 & 0 \end{bmatrix} \begin{bmatrix} \widehat{x}_1 \\ \widehat{x}_2 \\ \widehat{x}_3 \\ \widehat{x}_4 \end{bmatrix} = \begin{bmatrix} b_1 \\ b_2 \\ 0 \end{bmatrix}.$$

The columns all end with zero. In the column space, the closest vector to $b = (b_1, b_2, b_3)$ is $p = (b_1, b_2, 0)$. The best we can do with $Ax = b$ is to solve the first two equations, since the third equation is $0 = b_3$. That error cannot be reduced, but the errors in the first two equations will be zero. Then

$$\widehat{x}_1 = b_1/\sigma_1 \quad \text{and} \quad \widehat{x}_2 = b_2/\sigma_2.$$

Now we face the second difficulty. To make $\widehat{x}$ as short as possible, we choose the totally arbitrary $\widehat{x}_3$ and $\widehat{x}_4$ to be zero. ***The minimum length solution is*** $\boldsymbol{x^+}$:

A^+ is pseudoinverse
$x^+ = A^+b$ is shortest

$$x^+ = \begin{bmatrix} b_1/\sigma_1 \\ b_2/\sigma_2 \\ 0 \\ 0 \end{bmatrix} = \begin{bmatrix} 1/\sigma_1 & 0 & 0 \\ 0 & 1/\sigma_2 & 0 \\ 0 & 0 & 0 \\ 0 & 0 & 0 \end{bmatrix} \begin{bmatrix} b_1 \\ b_2 \\ b_3 \end{bmatrix}. \tag{5}$$

This equation finds x^+, and it also displays *the matrix that produces x^+ from b*. That matrix is the ***pseudoinverse*** A^+ of our diagonal A. Based on this example, we know Σ^+ and x^+ for any diagonal matrix Σ:

$$\Sigma = \begin{bmatrix} \sigma_1 & & & \\ & \ddots & & \\ & & \sigma_r & \\ & & & \end{bmatrix} \qquad \Sigma^+ = \begin{bmatrix} 1/\sigma_1 & & & \\ & \ddots & & \\ & & 1/\sigma_r & \\ & & & \end{bmatrix} \qquad \Sigma^+ b = \begin{bmatrix} b_1/\sigma_1 \\ \vdots \\ b_r/\sigma_r \\ \\ \end{bmatrix}.$$

The matrix Σ is m by n, with r nonzero entries σ_i. Its pseudoinverse Σ^+ is n by m, with r nonzero entries $1/\sigma_i$. **All the blank spaces are zeros**. Notice that $(\Sigma^+)^+$ is Σ again. That is like $(A^{-1})^{-1} = A$, but here A is not invertible.

Now we find x^+ in the general case. We claim that ***the shortest solution x^+ is always in the row space of A***. Remember that any vector $\widehat{x}$ can be split into a row space component x_r and a nullspace component: $\widehat{x} = x_r + x_n$. There are three important points about that splitting:

1. The row space component also solves $A^{\mathrm{T}}A\widehat{x}_r = A^{\mathrm{T}}b$, because $Ax_n = 0$.
2. The components are orthogonal, and they obey Pythagoras's law:

$$\|\widehat{x}\|^2 = \|x_r\|^2 + \|x_n\|^2, \quad \text{so } \widehat{x} \text{ is shortest when } x_n = 0.$$

3. All solutions of $A^{\mathrm{T}}A\widehat{x} = A^{\mathrm{T}}b$ have the same x_r. ***That vector is x^+***.

The fundamental theorem of linear algebra was in Figure 3.4. Every p in the column space comes from one and only one vector x_r in the row space. *All we are doing is to choose that vector, $x^+ = x_r$, as the best solution to $Ax = b$.*

The pseudoinverse in Figure 6.3 starts with b and comes back to x^+. *It inverts A where A is invertible*—between row space and column space. The pseudoinverse knocks out the left nullspace by sending it to zero, and it knocks out the nullspace by choosing x_r as x^+.

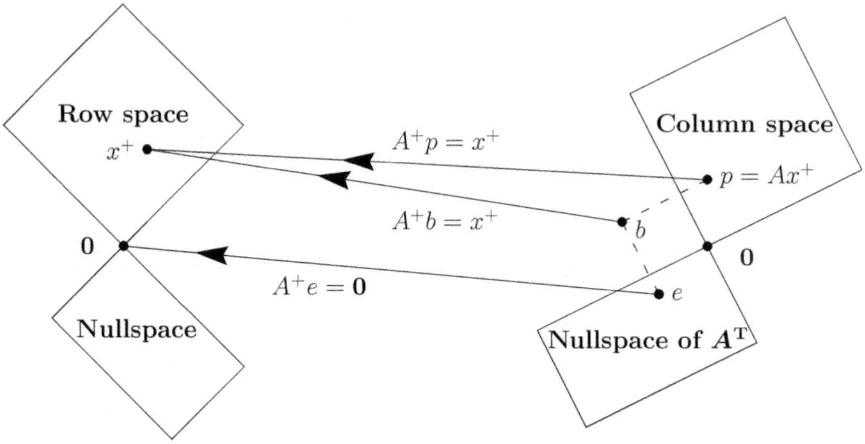

Figure 6.3 The pseudoinverse A^+ inverts A where it can on the column space.

We have not yet shown that there is a matrix A^+ that always gives x^+—but there is. It will be n by m, because it takes b and p in $\mathbf{R}^m$ back to x^+ in $\mathbf{R}^n$. We look at one more example before finding A^+ in general.

Example 6 $Ax = b$ is $-x_1 + 2x_2 + 2x_3 = 18$, with a whole plane of solutions.

According to our theory, the shortest solution should be in the row space of $A = [-1 \;\; 2 \;\; 2]$. The multiple of that row that satisfies the equation is $x^+ = (-2, 4, 4)$. There are longer solutions like $(-2, 5, 3)$, $(-2, 7, 1)$, or $(-6, 3, 3)$, but they all have nonzero components from the nullspace. The matrix that produces x^+ from $b = [18]$ is the pseudoinverse A^+. Whereas A was 1 by 3, this A^+ is 3 by 1:

$$A^+ = \begin{bmatrix} -1 & 2 & 2 \end{bmatrix}^+ = \begin{bmatrix} -\frac{1}{9} \\ \frac{2}{9} \\ \frac{2}{9} \end{bmatrix} \quad \text{and} \quad A^+[18] = \begin{bmatrix} -2 \\ 4 \\ 4 \end{bmatrix}. \tag{6}$$

The row space of A is the column space of A^+. Here is a formula for A^+:

If $A = U\Sigma V^{\mathrm{T}}$ (the SVD), then its pseudoinverse is $A^+ = V\Sigma^+U^{\mathrm{T}}$. (7)

Example 6 had $\sigma = 3$—the square root of the eigenvalue of $AA^{\mathrm{T}} = [9]$. Here it is again with Σ and Σ^+:

$$A = \begin{bmatrix} -1 & 2 & 2 \end{bmatrix} = U\Sigma V^{\mathrm{T}} = \begin{bmatrix} 1 \end{bmatrix} \begin{bmatrix} 3 & 0 & 0 \end{bmatrix} \begin{bmatrix} -\frac{1}{3} & \frac{2}{3} & \frac{2}{3} \\ \frac{2}{3} & -\frac{1}{3} & \frac{2}{3} \\ \frac{2}{3} & \frac{2}{3} & -\frac{1}{3} \end{bmatrix}$$

$$V\Sigma^+U^{\mathrm{T}} = \begin{bmatrix} -\frac{1}{3} & \frac{2}{3} & \frac{2}{3} \\ \frac{2}{3} & -\frac{1}{3} & \frac{2}{3} \\ \frac{2}{3} & \frac{2}{3} & -\frac{1}{3} \end{bmatrix} \begin{bmatrix} \frac{1}{3} \\ 0 \\ 0 \end{bmatrix} \begin{bmatrix} 1 \end{bmatrix} = \begin{bmatrix} -\frac{1}{9} \\ \frac{2}{9} \\ \frac{2}{9} \end{bmatrix} = A^+.$$

The minimum length least-squares solution is $x^+ = A^+b = V\Sigma^+U^{\mathrm{T}}b$.

Proof Multiplication by the orthogonal matrix U^{T} leaves lengths unchanged:

$$\|Ax - b\| = \|U\Sigma V^{\mathrm{T}}x - b\| = \|\Sigma V^{\mathrm{T}}x - U^{\mathrm{T}}b\|.$$

Introduce the new unknown $y = V^{\mathrm{T}}x = V^{-1}x$, which has the same length as x. Then, minimizing $\|Ax - b\|$ is the same as minimizing $\|\Sigma y - U^{\mathrm{T}}b\|$. Now Σ is diagonal and we know the best y^+. It is $y^+ = \Sigma^+ U^{\mathrm{T}}b$, so the best x^+ is Vy^+:

$$\textbf{Shortest solution} \qquad x^+ = Vy^+ = V\Sigma^+U^{\mathrm{T}}b = A^+b.$$

Vy^+ is in the row space, and $A^{\mathrm{T}}Ax^+ = A^{\mathrm{T}}b$ from the **SVD**. ■

Problem Set 6.3

Problems 1–2 compute the SVD of a square singular matrix A.

1. Compute $A^{\mathrm{T}}A$ and its eigenvalues $\sigma_1^2, 0$ and unit eigenvectors v_1, v_2:

$$A = \begin{bmatrix} 1 & 4 \\ 2 & 8 \end{bmatrix}.$$

2. (a) Compute AA^{T} and its eigenvalues $\sigma_1^2, 0$ and unit eigenvectors u_1, u_2.

(b) Choose signs so that $Av_1 = \sigma_1 u_1$ and verify the SVD:

$$\begin{bmatrix} 1 & 4 \\ 2 & 8 \end{bmatrix} = \begin{bmatrix} u_1 & u_2 \end{bmatrix} \begin{bmatrix} \sigma_1 & \\ & 0 \end{bmatrix} \begin{bmatrix} v_1 & v_2 \end{bmatrix}^{\mathrm{T}}.$$

(c) Which four vectors give orthonormal bases for $\boldsymbol{C}(A)$, $\boldsymbol{N}(A)$, $\boldsymbol{C}(A^{\mathrm{T}})$, $\boldsymbol{N}(A^{\mathrm{T}})$?

Problems 3–5 ask for the SVD of matrices of rank 2.

3. Find the SVD from the eigenvectors v_1, v_2 of $A^{\mathrm{T}}A$ and $Av_i = \sigma_i u_i$:

$$\textbf{Fibonacci matrix} \qquad A = \begin{bmatrix} 1 & 1 \\ 1 & 0 \end{bmatrix}.$$

4. Use the SVD part of the MATLAB demo **eigshow** (or Java on the course page `web.mit.edu/18.06`) to find the same vectors v_1 and v_2 graphically.

5. Compute $A^{\mathrm{T}}A$ and AA^{T}, and their eigenvalues and unit eigenvectors, for

$$A = \begin{bmatrix} 1 & 1 & 0 \\ 0 & 1 & 1 \end{bmatrix}.$$

Multiply the three matrices $U\Sigma V^{\mathrm{T}}$ to recover A.

Problems 6–13 bring out the underlying ideas of the SVD.

6. Suppose $u_1, \ldots, u_n$ and $v_1, \ldots, v_n$ are orthonormal bases for $\mathbf{R}^n$. Construct the matrix A that transforms each v_j into u_j to give $Av_1 = u_1, \ldots, Av_n = u_n$.

7. Construct the matrix with rank 1 that has $Av = 12u$ for $v = \frac{1}{2}(1, 1, 1, 1)$ and $u = \frac{1}{3}(2, 2, 1)$. Its only singular value is $\sigma_1 =$ ___.

8. Find $U\Sigma V^{\mathrm{T}}$ if A has orthogonal columns $w_1, \ldots, w_n$ of lengths $\sigma_1, \ldots, \sigma_n$.

9. Explain how $U\Sigma V^{\mathrm{T}}$ expresses A as a sum of r rank-1 matrices in equation (3):

$$A = \sigma_1 u_1 v_1^{\mathrm{T}} + \cdots + \sigma_r u_r v_r^{\mathrm{T}}.$$

10. Suppose A is a 2 by 2 symmetric matrix with unit eigenvectors u_1 and u_2. If its eigenvalues are $\lambda_1 = 3$ and $\lambda_2 = -2$, what are U, Σ, and V^{T}?

11. Suppose A is invertible (with $\sigma_1 > \sigma_2 > 0$). Change A by as small a matrix as possible to produce a *singular* matrix A_0. Hint: U and V do not change:

$$\text{Find } A_0 \text{ from} \quad A = \begin{bmatrix} u_1 & u_2 \end{bmatrix} \begin{bmatrix} \sigma_1 & \\ & \sigma_2 \end{bmatrix} \begin{bmatrix} v_1 & v_2 \end{bmatrix}^{\mathrm{T}}.$$

12. (a) If A changes to $4A$, what is the change in the SVD?
(b) What is the SVD for A^{T} and for A^{-1}?

13. Why doesn't the SVD for $A + I$ just use $\Sigma + I$?

14. Find the SVD and the pseudoinverse 0^+ of the m by n *zero matrix.*

15. Find the SVD and the pseudoinverse $V\Sigma^+U^{\mathrm{T}}$ of

$$A = \begin{bmatrix} 1 & 1 & 1 & 1 \end{bmatrix}, \quad B = \begin{bmatrix} 0 & 1 & 0 \\ 1 & 0 & 0 \end{bmatrix}, \quad \text{and} \quad C = \begin{bmatrix} 1 & 1 \\ 0 & 0 \end{bmatrix}.$$

16. If an m by n matrix Q has orthonormal columns, what is Q^+?

17. Diagonalize $A^{\mathrm{T}}A$ to find its positive definite square root $S = V\Sigma^{1/2}V^{\mathrm{T}}$ and its polar decomposition $A = QS$:

$$A = \frac{1}{\sqrt{10}} \begin{bmatrix} 10 & 6 \\ 0 & 8 \end{bmatrix}.$$

18. What is the minimum-length least-squares solution $x^+ = A^+b$ to the following?

$$Ax = \begin{bmatrix} 1 & 0 & 0 \\ 1 & 0 & 0 \\ 1 & 1 & 1 \end{bmatrix} \begin{bmatrix} C \\ D \\ E \end{bmatrix} = \begin{bmatrix} 0 \\ 2 \\ 2 \end{bmatrix}.$$

You can compute A^+, or find the general solution to $A^{\mathrm{T}}A\widehat{x} = A^{\mathrm{T}}b$ and choose the solution that is in the row space of A. This problem fits the best plane $C + Dt + Ez$ to $b = 0$ *and also* $b = 2$ at $t = z = 0$ (and $b = 2$ at $t = z = 1$).

19. (a) If A has independent columns, its left-inverse $(A^{\mathrm{T}}A)^{-1}A^{\mathrm{T}}$ is A^+.
(b) If A has independent rows, its right-inverse $A^{\mathrm{T}}(AA^{\mathrm{T}})^{-1}$ is A^+.

In both cases, verify that $x^+ = A^+b$ is in the row space, and $A^{\mathrm{T}}Ax^+ = A^{\mathrm{T}}b$.

20. Split $A = U\Sigma V^{\mathrm{T}}$ into its reverse polar decomposition QS'.

21. Is $(AB)^+ = B^+A^+$ always true for pseudoinverses? I believe not.

22. Removing zero rows of U leaves $A = \underline{L}\,\underline{U}$, where the r columns of $\underline{L}$ span the column space of A and the r rows of $\underline{U}$ span the row space. Then A^+ has the explicit formula $\underline{U}^{\mathrm{T}}(\underline{U}\,\underline{U}^{\mathrm{T}})^{-1}(\underline{L}^{\mathrm{T}}\underline{L})^{-1}\underline{L}^{\mathrm{T}}$.

Why is A^+b in the row space with $\underline{U}^{\mathrm{T}}$ at the front? Why does $A^{\mathrm{T}}AA^+b = A^{\mathrm{T}}b$, so that $x^+ = A^+b$ satisfies the normal equation as it should?

23. Explain why AA^+ and A^+A are projection matrices (and therefore symmetric). What fundamental subspaces do they project onto?

6.4 MINIMUM PRINCIPLES

In this section we escape for the first time from linear equations. The unknown x will not be given as the solution to $Ax = b$ or $Ax = \lambda x$. Instead, the vector x will be determined by a minimum principle.

It is astonishing how many natural laws can be expressed as minimum principles. Just the fact that heavy liquids sink to the bottom is a consequence of minimizing their potential energy. And when you sit on a chair or lie on a bed, the springs adjust themselves so that the energy is minimized. A straw in a glass of water looks bent because light reaches your eye as quickly as possible. Certainly there are more highbrow examples: The fundamental principle of structural engineering is the minimization of total energy.*

We have to say immediately that these "energies" are nothing but *positive definite quadratic functions*. And the derivative of a quadratic is linear. We get back to the familiar linear equations, when we set the first derivatives to zero. Our first goal in this section is ***to find the minimum principle that is equivalent to $Ax = b$, and the minimization equivalent to $Ax = \lambda x$***. We will be doing in finite dimensions exactly what the theory of optimization does in a continuous problem, where "first derivatives = 0" gives a differential equation. In every problem, we are free to solve the linear equation or minimize the quadratic.

The first step is straightforward: We want to find the "parabola" $P(x)$ whose minimum occurs when $Ax = b$. If A is just a scalar, that is easy to do:

$$\text{The graph of} \quad P(x) = \frac{1}{2}Ax^2 - bx \quad \text{has zero slope when} \quad \frac{dP}{dx} = Ax - b = 0.$$

This point $x = A^{-1}b$ will be a minimum if A is positive. Then the parabola $P(x)$ opens upward (Figure 6.4). In more dimensions this parabola turns into a parabolic bowl (a paraboloid). To assure a minimum of $P(x)$, not a maximum or a saddle point, A must be positive definite!

6H If A is symmetric positive definite, then $P(x) = \frac{1}{2}x^{\mathrm{T}}Ax - x^{\mathrm{T}}b$ reaches its minimum at the point where $Ax = b$. At that point $P_{\min} = -\frac{1}{2}b^{\mathrm{T}}A^{-1}b$.

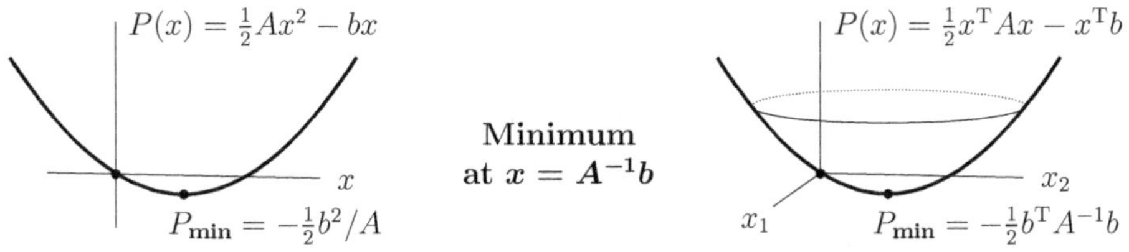

Figure 6.4 The graph of a positive quadratic $P(x)$ is a parabolic bowl.

* I am convinced that plants and people also develop in accordance with minimum principles. Perhaps civilization is based on a law of least action. There must be new laws (and minimum principles) to be found in the social sciences and life sciences.

Proof Suppose $Ax = b$. For any vector y, we show that $P(y) \geq P(x)$:

$$\begin{aligned} P(y) - P(x) &= \frac{1}{2}y^{\mathrm{T}}Ay - y^{\mathrm{T}}b - \frac{1}{2}x^{\mathrm{T}}Ax + x^{\mathrm{T}}b \\ &= \frac{1}{2}y^{\mathrm{T}}Ay - y^{\mathrm{T}}Ax + \frac{1}{2}x^{\mathrm{T}}Ax \quad (\text{set } b = Ax) \\ &= \frac{1}{2}(y-x)^{\mathrm{T}}A(y-x). \end{aligned} \tag{1}$$

This can't be negative since A is positive definite—and it is zero only if $y - x = 0$. At all other points $P(y)$ is larger than $P(x)$, so the minimum occurs at x. ■

Example 1 Minimize $P(x) = x_1^2 - x_1x_2 + x_2^2 - b_1x_1 - b_2x_2$. The usual approach, by calculus, is to set the partial derivatives to zero. This gives $Ax = b$:

$$\begin{aligned} \partial P/\partial x_1 &= 2x_1 - x_2 - b_1 = 0 \\ \partial P/\partial x_2 &= -x_1 + 2x_2 - b_2 = 0 \end{aligned} \quad \text{means} \quad \begin{bmatrix} 2 & -1 \\ -1 & 2 \end{bmatrix} \begin{bmatrix} x_1 \\ x_2 \end{bmatrix} = \begin{bmatrix} b_1 \\ b_2 \end{bmatrix}. \tag{2}$$

Linear algebra recognizes this $P(x)$ as $\frac{1}{2}x^{\mathrm{T}}Ax - x^{\mathrm{T}}b$, and knows immediately that $Ax = b$ gives the minimum. Substitute $x = A^{-1}b$ into $P(x)$:

$$\textbf{Minimum value} \qquad P_{\min} = \frac{1}{2}(A^{-1}b)^{\mathrm{T}}A(A^{-1}b) - (A^{-1}b)^{\mathrm{T}}b = -\frac{1}{2}b^{\mathrm{T}}A^{-1}b. \tag{3}$$

In applications, $\frac{1}{2}x^{\mathrm{T}}Ax$ is the internal energy and $-x^{\mathrm{T}}b$ is the external work. The system automatically goes to $x = A^{-1}b$, where the total energy $P(x)$ is a minimum.

Minimizing with Constraints

Many applications add extra equations $Cx = d$ on top of the minimization problem. These equations are **constraints**. We minimize $P(x)$ subject to the extra requirement $Cx = d$. Usually x can't satisfy n equations $Ax = b$ and also ℓ extra constraints $Cx = d$. We have too many equations and we need ℓ more unknowns.

Those new unknowns $y_1, \ldots, y_\ell$ are called **Lagrange multipliers**. They build the constraint into a function $L(x, y)$. This was the brilliant insight of Lagrange:

$$L(x, y) = P(x) + \mathbf{y}^{\mathrm{T}}(\mathbf{C}\mathbf{x} - \mathbf{d}) = \frac{1}{2}x^{\mathrm{T}}Ax - x^{\mathrm{T}}b + x^{\mathrm{T}}C^{\mathrm{T}}y - y^{\mathrm{T}}d.$$

That term in L is chosen exactly so that $\partial L/\partial y = 0$ brings back $Cx = d$. When we set the derivatives of L to zero, we have $n + \ell$ equations for $n + \ell$ unknowns x and y:

$$\begin{array}{lll} \textbf{Constrained} & \partial L/\partial x = 0: & Ax + C^{\mathrm{T}}y = b \\ \textbf{minimization} & \partial L/\partial y = 0: & Cx \qquad\quad = d \end{array} \tag{4}$$

The first equations involve the mysterious unknowns y. You might well ask what they represent. Those "dual unknowns" y tell how much the constrained minimum $P_{C/\min}$ (which only allows x when $Cx = d$) exceeds the unconstrained $P_{\min}$ (allowing all x):

$$\textbf{Sensitivity of minimum} \qquad P_{C/\min} = P_{\min} + \frac{1}{2}y^{\mathrm{T}}(CA^{-1}b - d) \geq P_{\min}. \tag{5}$$

Example 2 Suppose $P(x_1, x_2) = \frac{1}{2}x_1^2 + \frac{1}{2}x_2^2$. Its smallest value is certainly $P_{\min} = 0$. This unconstrained problem has $n = 2$, $A = I$, and $b = 0$. So the minimizing equation $Ax = b$ just gives $x_1 = 0$ and $x_2 = 0$.

Now add one constraint $c_1x_1 + c_2x_2 = d$. This puts x on a line in the x_1-x_2 plane. The old minimizer $x_1 = x_2 = 0$ is not on the line. The Lagrangian function $L(x, y) = \frac{1}{2}x_1^2 + \frac{1}{2}x_2^2 + y(c_1x_1 + c_2x_2 - d)$ has $n + \ell = 2 + 1$ partial derivatives:

$$\begin{aligned} \partial L/\partial x_1 &= 0 & \qquad x_1 + c_1 y &= 0 \\ \partial L/\partial x_2 &= 0 & x_2 + c_2 y &= 0 \\ \partial L/\partial y &= 0 & c_1x_1 + c_2x_2 &= d. \end{aligned} \tag{6}$$

Substituting $x_1 = -c_1y$ and $x_2 = -c_2y$ into the third equation gives $-c_1^2y - c_2^2y = d$.

$$\textbf{Solution} \qquad y = \frac{-d}{c_1^2 + c_2^2} \qquad x_1 = \frac{c_1 d}{c_1^2 + c_2^2} \qquad x_2 = \frac{c_2 d}{c_1^2 + c_2^2}. \tag{7}$$

The constrained minimum of $P = \frac{1}{2}x^{\mathrm{T}}x$ is reached at that solution point:

$$P_{C/\min} = \frac{1}{2}x_1^2 + \frac{1}{2}x_2^2 = \frac{1}{2}\frac{c_1^2d^2 + c_2^2d^2}{\left(c_1^2 + c_2^2\right)^2} = \frac{1}{2}\frac{d^2}{c_1^2 + c_2^2}. \tag{8}$$

This equals $-\frac{1}{2}yd$ as predicted in equation (5), since $b = 0$ and $P_{\min} = 0$.

Figure 6.5 shows what problem the linear algebra has solved, if the constraint keeps x on a line $2x_1 - x_2 = 5$. We are looking for **the closest point to (0, 0) on this line**. The solution is $x = (2, -1)$. We expect this shortest vector x to be perpendicular to the line, and we are right.

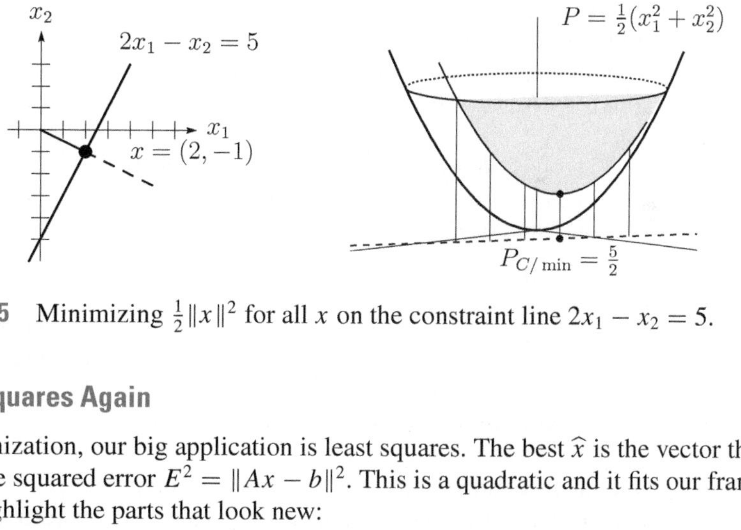

Figure 6.5 Minimizing $\frac{1}{2}\|x\|^2$ for all x on the constraint line $2x_1 - x_2 = 5$.

Least Squares Again

In minimization, our big application is least squares. The best $\widehat{x}$ is the vector that minimizes the squared error $E^2 = \|Ax - b\|^2$. This is a quadratic and it fits our framework! I will highlight the parts that look new:

$$\textbf{Squared error} \qquad E^2 = (Ax - b)^{\mathrm{T}}(Ax - b) = x^{\mathrm{T}}\boldsymbol{A}^{\mathrm{T}}\boldsymbol{A}\,x - 2x^{\mathrm{T}}\boldsymbol{A}^{\mathrm{T}}\boldsymbol{b} + \boldsymbol{b}^{\mathrm{T}}\boldsymbol{b}. \tag{9}$$

Compare with $\frac{1}{2}x^{\mathrm{T}}Ax - x^{\mathrm{T}}b$ at the start of the section, which led to $Ax = b$:

[A changes to $\boldsymbol{A}^{\mathrm{T}}\boldsymbol{A}$] [$b$ changes to $\boldsymbol{A}^{\mathrm{T}}\boldsymbol{b}$] [$\boldsymbol{b}^{\mathrm{T}}\boldsymbol{b}$ is added].

The constant $b^{\mathrm{T}}b$ raises the whole graph—this has no effect on the best $\widehat{x}$. The other two changes, A to $A^{\mathrm{T}}A$ and b to $A^{\mathrm{T}}b$, give a new way to reach the least-squares equation (normal equation). The minimizing equation $Ax = b$ changes into the

$$\textbf{Least-squares equation} \qquad A^{\mathrm{T}}A\widehat{x} = A^{\mathrm{T}}b\,. \tag{10}$$

Optimization needs a whole book. We stop while it is pure linear algebra.

The Rayleigh Quotient

Our second goal is to find a minimization problem equivalent to $Ax = \lambda x$. That is not so easy. The function to minimize cannot be a quadratic, or its derivative would be linear—and the eigenvalue problem is nonlinear (λ times x). The trick that succeeds is to divide one quadratic by another one:

$$\textbf{Rayleigh quotient} \qquad \text{Minimize} \quad R(x) = \frac{x^{\mathrm{T}}Ax}{x^{\mathrm{T}}x}.$$

6I Rayleigh's Principle: The minimum value of the Rayleigh quotient is the smallest eigenvalue λ_1. $R(x)$ reaches that minimum at the first eigenvector x_1 of A:

$$\textbf{Minimum where } \boldsymbol{Ax_1 = \lambda x_1} \qquad R(x_1) = \frac{x_1^{\mathrm{T}}Ax_1}{x_1^{\mathrm{T}}x_1} = \frac{x_1^{\mathrm{T}}\lambda_1 x_1}{x_1^{\mathrm{T}}x_1} = \lambda_1.$$

If we keep $x^{\mathrm{T}}Ax = 1$, then $R(x)$ is a minimum when $x^{\mathrm{T}}x = \|x\|^2$ is as large as possible. We are looking for the point on the ellipsoid $x^{\mathrm{T}}Ax = 1$ farthest from the origin—the vector x of greatest length. From our earlier description of the ellipsoid, its longest axis points along the first eigenvector. So $R(x)$ is a minimum at x_1.

Algebraically, we can diagonalize the symmetric A by an orthogonal matrix: $Q^{\mathrm{T}}AQ = \Lambda$. Then set $x = Qy$ and the quotient becomes simple:

$$R(x) = \frac{(Qy)^{\mathrm{T}}A(Qy)}{(Qy)^{\mathrm{T}}(Qy)} = \frac{y^{\mathrm{T}}\Lambda y}{y^{\mathrm{T}}y} = \frac{\boldsymbol{\lambda_1 y_1^2 + \cdots + \lambda_n y_n^2}}{\boldsymbol{y_1^2 + \cdots + y_n^2}}. \tag{11}$$

The minimum of R is λ_1, at the point where $y_1 = 1$ and $y_2 = \cdots = y_n = 0$:

$$\textbf{At all points} \qquad \lambda_1\left(y_1^2 + y_2^2 + \cdots + y_n^2\right) \le \left(\lambda_1 y_1^2 + \lambda_2 y_2^2 + \cdots + \lambda_n y_n^2\right).$$

The Rayleigh quotient in equation (11) is ***never below*** $\boldsymbol{\lambda_1}$ and ***never above*** $\boldsymbol{\lambda_n}$ (the largest eigenvalue). Its minimum is at the eigenvector x_1 and its maximum is at x_n:

$$\textbf{Maximum where } \boldsymbol{Ax_n = \lambda_n x_n} \qquad R(x_n) = \frac{x_n^{\mathrm{T}}Ax_n}{x_n^{\mathrm{T}}x_n} = \frac{x_n^{\mathrm{T}}\lambda_n x_n}{x_n^{\mathrm{T}}x_n} = \lambda_n.$$

One small yet important point: The Rayleigh quotient equals a_{11}, when the trial vector is $x = (1, 0, \ldots, 0)$. So a_{11} (on the main diagonal) is between λ_1 and λ_n. You can see this in Figure 6.6, where the horizontal distance to the ellipse (where $a_{11}x^2 = 1$) is between the shortest distance and the longest distance:

$$\frac{1}{\sqrt{\lambda_n}} \le \frac{1}{\sqrt{a_{11}}} \le \frac{1}{\sqrt{\lambda_1}} \quad \text{which is} \quad \lambda_1 \le a_{11} \le \lambda_n.$$

The diagonal entries of any symmetric matrix are between $\boldsymbol{\lambda_1}$ ***and*** $\boldsymbol{\lambda_n}$. We drew Figure 6.6 for a 2 by 2 positive definite matrix to see it clearly.

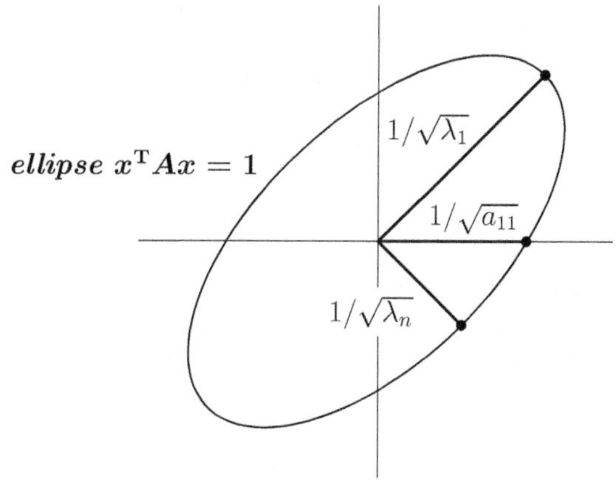

Figure 6.6 The farthest $x = x_1/\sqrt{\lambda_1}$ and the closest $x = x_n/\sqrt{\lambda_n}$ both give $x^TAx = x^T\lambda x = 1$. Those are the major and minor axes of the ellipse.

Intertwining of the Eigenvalues

The intermediate eigenvectors $x_2, \ldots, x_{n-1}$ are ***saddle points*** of the Rayleigh quotient (zero derivatives, but not minima or maxima). The difficulty with saddle points is that we have no idea whether $R(x)$ is above or below them. That makes the intermediate eigenvalues $\lambda_2, \ldots, \lambda_{n-1}$ harder to estimate.

For this optional topic, the key is to find a constrained minimum or maximum. The constraints come from the basic property of symmetric matrices: x_j is perpendicular to the other eigenvectors.

6J The minimum of $R(x)$ subject to $x^Tx_1 = 0$ is λ_2. The minimum of $R(x)$ subject to any other constraint $x^Tv = 0$ is not above λ_2:

$$\lambda_2 = \min_{x^Tx_1=0} R(x) \quad \text{and} \quad \lambda_2 \geq \min_{x^Tv=0} R(x). \tag{12}$$

This "maximin principle" makes λ_2 the *maximum over all v of the minimum* of $R(x)$ with $x^Tv = 0$. That offers a way to estimate λ_2 without knowing λ_1.

Example 3 Throw away the last row and column of any symmetric matrix:

$$\begin{matrix}\lambda_1(A) = 2-\sqrt{2}\\ \lambda_2(A) = 2\\ \lambda_3(A) = 2+\sqrt{2}\end{matrix} \qquad A = \begin{bmatrix} 2 & -1 & 0\\ -1 & 2 & -1\\ 0 & -1 & 2\end{bmatrix} \text{ becomes } B = \begin{bmatrix} 2 & -1\\ -1 & 2\end{bmatrix} \quad \begin{matrix}\lambda_1(B) = 1\\ \lambda_2(B) = 3.\end{matrix}$$

The second eigenvalue $\lambda_2(A) = 2$ is above the lowest eigenvalue $\lambda_1(B) = 1$. The lowest eigenvalue $\lambda_1(A) = 2 - \sqrt{2}$ is *below* $\lambda_1(B)$. So $\lambda_1(B)$ is caught between.

This example chose $v = (0, 0, 1)$ so the constraint $x^Tv = 0$ knocked out the third component of x (thereby reducing A to B).

The complete picture is an ***intertwining of eigenvalues***:

$$\lambda_1(A) \le \lambda_1(B) \le \lambda_2(A) \le \lambda_2(B) \le \cdots \le \lambda_{n-1}(B) \le \lambda_n(A). \tag{13}$$

This has a natural interpretation for an ellipsoid, when it is cut by a plane through the origin. The cross section is an ellipsoid of one lower dimension. The major axis of this cross section cannot be longer than the major axis of the whole ellipsoid: $\lambda_1(B) \ge \lambda_1(A)$. But the major axis of the cross section is *at least as long as the second axis* of the original ellipsoid: $\lambda_1(B) \le \lambda_2(A)$. Similarly the minor axis of the cross section is smaller than the original second axis, and larger than the original minor axis: $\lambda_2(A) \le \lambda_2(B) \le \lambda_3(A)$.

You can see the same thing in mechanics. When springs and masses are oscillating, suppose one mass is held at equilibrium. Then the lowest frequency is increased, but not above λ_2. The highest frequency is decreased, but not below λ_{n-1}.

We close with three remarks. I hope your intuition says that they are correct.

Remark 1 The **maximin principle** extends to j-dimensional subspaces S_j:

$$\textbf{Maximum of minimum} \qquad \lambda_{j+1} = \max_{\text{all } S_j} \left[\min_{x \perp S_j} R(x) \right]. \tag{14}$$

Remark 2 There is also a **minimax principle** for λ_{n-j}:

$$\textbf{Minimum of maximum} \qquad \lambda_{n-j} = \min_{\text{all } S_j} \left[\max_{x \perp S_j} R(x) \right]. \tag{15}$$

If $j = 1$, we are maximizing $R(x)$ over one constraint $x^{\mathrm{T}}v = 0$. That maximum is between the unconstrained λ_{n-1} and λ_n. The toughest constraint makes x perpendicular to the top eigenvector $v = x_n$. Then the best x is the next eigenvector x_{n-1}. The "minimum of the maximum" is λ_{n-1}.

Remark 3 For the generalized problem $Ax = \lambda Mx$, the same principles hold if M is positive definite. In the Rayleigh quotient, $x^{\mathrm{T}}x$ becomes $x^{\mathrm{T}}Mx$:

$$\textbf{Rayleigh quotient} \qquad \text{Minimizing} \quad R(x) = \frac{x^{\mathrm{T}}Ax}{x^{\mathrm{T}}Mx} \quad \text{gives} \quad \lambda_1(M^{-1}A). \tag{16}$$

Even for *unequal* masses in an oscillating system ($M \ne I$), holding one mass at equilibrium will raise the lowest frequency and lower the highest frequency.

Problem Set 6.4

1. Consider the system $Ax = b$ given by

$$\begin{bmatrix} 2 & -1 & 0 \\ -1 & 2 & -1 \\ 0 & -1 & 2 \end{bmatrix} \begin{bmatrix} x_1 \\ x_2 \\ x_3 \end{bmatrix} = \begin{bmatrix} 4 \\ 0 \\ 4 \end{bmatrix}.$$

Construct the corresponding quadratic $P(x_1, x_2, x_3)$, compute its partial derivatives $\partial P/\partial x_i$, and verify that they vanish exactly at the desired solution.

2. Complete the square in $P = \frac{1}{2}x^{\mathrm{T}}Ax - x^{\mathrm{T}}b = \frac{1}{2}(x - A^{-1}b)^{\mathrm{T}}A(x - A^{-1}b) + \text{constant}$. This constant equals $P_{\min}$ because the term before it is never negative. (Why?)

3. Find the minimum, if there is one of $P_1 = \frac{1}{2}x^2 + xy + y^2 - 3y$ and $P_2 = \frac{1}{2}x^2 - 3y$. What matrix A is associated with P_2?

4. (Review) Another quadratic that certainly has its minimum at $Ax = b$ is

$$Q(x) = \frac{1}{2}\|Ax - b\|^2 = \frac{1}{2}x^{\mathrm{T}}A^{\mathrm{T}}Ax - x^{\mathrm{T}}A^{\mathrm{T}}b + \frac{1}{2}b^{\mathrm{T}}b.$$

Comparing Q with P, and ignoring the constant $\frac{1}{2}b^{\mathrm{T}}b$, what system of equations do we get at the minimum of Q? What are these equations called in the theory of least squares?

5. For any symmetric matrix A, compute the ratio $R(x)$ for the special choice $x = (1, \ldots, 1)$. How is the sum of all entries a_{ij} related to λ_1 and λ_n?

6. With $A = \begin{bmatrix} 2 & -1 \\ -1 & 2 \end{bmatrix}$, find a choice of x that gives a smaller $R(x)$ than the bound $\lambda_1 \le 2$ that comes from the diagonal entries. What is the minimum value of $R(x)$?

7. If B is positive definite, show from the Rayleigh quotient that the smallest eigenvalue of $A + B$ is larger than the smallest eigenvalue of A.

8. If λ_1 and μ_1 are the smallest eigenvalues of A and B, show that the smallest eigenvalue θ_1 of $A + B$ is at least as large as $\lambda_1 + \mu_1$. (Try the corresponding eigenvector x in the Rayleigh quotients.)

Note Problems 7 and 8 are perhaps the most typical and most important results that come easily from Rayleigh's principle, but only with great difficulty from the eigenvalue equations themselves.

9. If B is positive definite, show from the minimax principle (12) that the *second* smallest eigenvalue is increased by adding $B : \lambda_2(A + B) > \lambda_2(A)$.

10. If you throw away *two* rows and columns of A, what inequalities do you expect between the smallest eigenvalue μ of the new matrix and the original λ's?

11. Find the minimum values of

$$R(x) = \frac{x_1^2 - x_1x_2 + x_2^2}{x_1^2 + x_2^2} \quad \text{and} \quad R(x) = \frac{x_1^2 - x_1x_2 + x_2^2}{2x_1^2 + x_2^2}.$$

12. Prove from equation (11) that $R(x)$ is never larger than the largest eigenvalue λ_n.

13. The minimax principle for λ_j involves j-dimensional subspaces S_j:

Equivalent to equation (15) $$\lambda_j = \min_{S_j} \left[\max_{x \text{ in } S_j} R(x) \right].$$

(a) If λ_j is positive, infer that every S_j contains a vector x with $R(x) > 0$.
(b) Deduce that S_j contains a vector $y = C^{-1}x$ with $y^{\mathrm{T}}C^{\mathrm{T}}ACy/y^{\mathrm{T}}y > 0$.
(c) Conclude that the jth eigenvalue of $C^{\mathrm{T}}AC$, from *its* minimax principle, is also positive—proving again the *law of inertia* in Section 6.2.

14. Show that the smallest eigenvalue λ_1 of $Ax = \lambda Mx$ is not larger than the ratio a_{11}/m_{11} of the corner entries.

15. Which particular subspace S_2 in Problem 13 gives the minimum value λ_2? In other words, over which S_2 is the maximum of $R(x)$ equal to λ_2?

16. (Recommended) From the zero submatrix decide the signs of the n eigenvalues:

$$A = \begin{bmatrix} 0 & \cdot & 0 & 1 \\ \cdot & \cdot & 0 & 2 \\ 0 & 0 & 0 & \cdot \\ 1 & 2 & \cdot & n \end{bmatrix}.$$

17. (Constrained minimum) Suppose the unconstrained minimum $x = A^{-1}b$ happens to satisfy the constraint $Cx = d$. Verify that equation (5) correctly gives $P_{C/\min} = P_{\min}$; the correction term is zero.

6.5 THE FINITE ELEMENT METHOD

There were two main ideas in the preceding section on minimum principles:

(i) Solving $Ax = b$ is equivalent to minimizing $P(x) = \frac{1}{2}x^{\mathrm{T}}Ax - x^{\mathrm{T}}b$.
(ii) Solving $Ax = \lambda_1 x$ is equivalent to minimizing $R(x) = x^{\mathrm{T}}Ax/x^{\mathrm{T}}x$.

Now we try to explain how these ideas can be applied.

The story is a long one, because these principles have been known for more than a century. In engineering problems like plate bending, or physics problems like the ground state (eigenfunction) of an atom, minimization was used to get a rough approximation to the true solution. The approximations *had* to be rough; the computers were human. The principles (i) and (ii) were there, but they could not be implemented.

Obviously the computer was going to bring about a revolution. It was the method of finite differences that jumped ahead, because it is easy to "discretize" a differential equation. Already in Section 1.7, derivatives were replaced by differences. The physical region is covered by a mesh, and $u'' = f(x)$ became $u_{j+1} - 2u_j + u_{j-1} = h^2 f_j$. The 1950s brought new ways to solve systems $Au = f$ that are very large and very sparse—algorithms and hardware are both much faster now.

What we did not fully recognize was that even finite differences become incredibly complicated for real engineering problems, like the stresses on an airplane. *The real difficulty is not to solve the equations, but to set them up.* For an irregular region we piece the mesh together from triangles or quadrilaterals or tetrahedra. Then we need a systematic way to approximate the underlying physical laws. The computer has to help not only in the solution of $Au = f$ and $Ax = \lambda x$, but in its formulation.

You can guess what happened. The old methods came back, with a new idea and a new name. The new name is the ***finite element method***. The new idea uses more of the power of the computer—in constructing a discrete approximation, solving it, and displaying the results—than any other technique in scientific computation.* If the basic idea is simple, the applications can be complicated. For problems on this scale, the one

* Please forgive this enthusiasm; I know the method may not be immortal.

undebatable point is their cost—I am afraid a billion dollars would be a conservative estimate of the expense so far. I hope some readers will be vigorous enough to master the finite element method and put it to good use.

Trial Functions

Starting from the classical ***Rayleigh–Ritz principle***, I will introduce the new idea of finite elements. The equation can be $-u'' = f(x)$ with boundary conditions $u(0) = u(1) = 0$. This problem is *infinite-dimensional* (the vector b is replaced by a function f, and the matrix A becomes $-d^2/dx^2$). We can write down the energy whose minimum is required, replacing inner products $v^{\mathrm{T}} f$ by integrals of $v(x)f(x)$:

$$\textbf{Total energy} \quad P(v) = \frac{1}{2}v^{\mathrm{T}}Av - v^{\mathrm{T}}f = \frac{1}{2}\int_0^1 v(x)(-v''(x))\,dx - \int_0^1 v(x)f(x)\,dx. \quad (1)$$

$P(v)$ is to be minimized over all functions $v(x)$ that satisfy $v(0) = v(1) = 0$. ***The function that gives the minimum will be the solution $u(x)$***. The differential equation has been converted to a minimum principle, and it only remains to integrate by parts:

$$\int_0^1 v(-v'')\,dx = \int_0^1 (v')^2\,dx - [vv']_{x=0}^{x=1} \quad \text{so} \quad P(v) = \int_0^1 \left[\frac{1}{2}(v'(x))^2 + v(x)f(x)\right] dx.$$

The term vv' is zero at both limits, because v is. Now $\int (v'(x))^2\,dx$ is *positive* like $x^{\mathrm{T}}Ax$. We are guaranteed a minimum.

To compute the minimum exactly is equivalent to solving the differential equation exactly. *The Rayleigh–Ritz principle produces an n-dimensional problem by choosing only n trial functions $V_1(x), \ldots, V_n(x)$.* From all combinations $V = y_1V_1(x) + \cdots + y_nV_n(x)$, we look for the particular combination (call it U) that minimizes $P(V)$. This is the key idea, to minimize over a subspace of V's instead of over all possible $v(x)$. The function that gives the minimum is $U(x)$. We hope and expect that $U(x)$ is near the correct $u(x)$.

Substituting V for v, the quadratic turns into

$$P(V) = \frac{1}{2}\int_0^1 (y_1V_1'(x) + \cdots + y_nV_n'(x))^2\,dx - \int_0^1 (y_1V_1(x) + \cdots + y_nV_n(x))f(x)\,dx. \quad (2)$$

The trial functions V are chosen in advance. That is the key step! The unknowns $y_1, \ldots, y_n$ go into a vector y. Then $P(V) = \frac{1}{2}y^{\mathrm{T}}Ay - y^{\mathrm{T}}b$ is recognized as one of the quadratics we are accustomed to. The matrix entries A_{ij} are $\int V_i'V_j'\,dx$ = coefficient of y_iy_j. The components b_j are $\int V_jf\,dx$. We can certainly find the minimum of $\frac{1}{2}y^{\mathrm{T}}Ay - y^{\mathrm{T}}b$ by solving $Ay = b$. Therefore the Rayleigh-Ritz method has three steps:

1. *Choose the trial functions $V_1, \ldots, V_n$.*
2. *Compute the coefficients A_{ij} and b_j.*
3. *Solve $Ay = b$ to find $U(x) = y_1V_1(x) + \cdots + y_nV_n(x)$.*

Everything depends on step 1. Unless the functions $V_j(x)$ are extremely simple, the other steps will be virtually impossible. And unless some combination of the V_j is close to the true solution $u(x)$, those steps will be useless. To combine both computability and accuracy, ***the key idea that makes finite elements successful is the use of piecewise polynomials as the trial functions $V(x)$***.

Linear Finite Elements

The simplest and most widely used finite element is **piecewise linear**. Place nodes at the interior points $x_1 = h, x_2 = 2h, \ldots, x_n = nh$, just as for finite differences. Then V_j is the "hat function" that equals 1 at the node x_j, and zero at all the other nodes (Figure 6.7a). It is concentrated in a small interval around its node, and it is zero everywhere else (including $x = 0$ and $x = 1$). Any combination $y_1V_1 + \cdots + y_nV_n$ must have the value y_j at node j (the other V's are zero there), so its graph is easy to draw (Figure 6.7b).

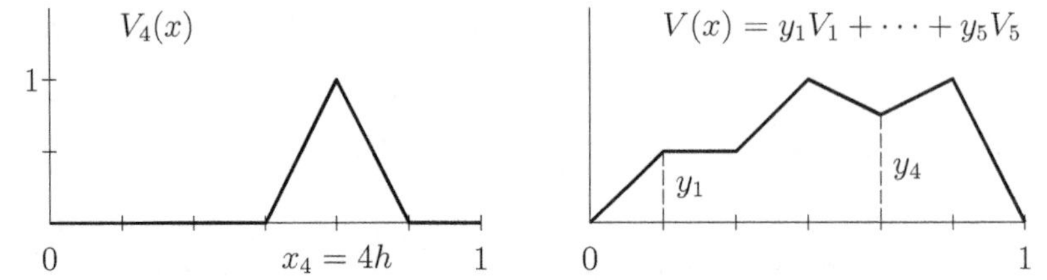

Figure 6.7 Hat functions and their linear combinations.

Step 2 computes the coefficients $A_{ij} = \int V_i'V_j'\,dx$ in the "stiffness matrix" A. The slope V_j' equals $1/h$ in the small interval to the left of x_j, and $-1/h$ in the interval to the right. *If these "double intervals" do not overlap, the product* $V_i'V_j'$ *is zero and* $A_{ij} = 0$. Each hat function overlaps itself and only two neighbors:

$$\textbf{Diagonal} \quad i = j \quad A_{ii} = \int V_i'V_i'\,dx = \int \left(\frac{1}{h}\right)^2 dx + \int \left(-\frac{1}{h}\right)^2 dx = \frac{2}{h}.$$

$$\textbf{Off-diagonal} \quad i = j \pm 1 \quad A_{ij} = \int V_i'V_j'\,dx = \int \left(\frac{1}{h}\right)\left(\frac{-1}{h}\right) dx = \frac{-1}{h}.$$

Then the stiffness matrix is actually tridiagonal:

$$\textbf{Stiffness matrix} \qquad A = \frac{1}{h}\begin{bmatrix} 2 & -1 & & & \\ -1 & 2 & -1 & & \\ & -1 & 2 & -1 & \\ & & -1 & 2 & -1 \\ & & & -1 & 2 \end{bmatrix}.$$

This looks just like finite differences! It has led to a thousand discussions about the relation between these two methods. More complicated finite elements—polynomials of higher degree, defined on triangles or quadrilaterals for partial differential equations—also produce sparse matrices A. You could think of finite elements as a systematic way to construct accurate difference equations on irregular meshes. The essential thing is the *simplicity* of these piecewise polynomials. Inside every element, their slopes are easy to find and to integrate.

The components b_j on the right side are new. Instead of just the value of f at x_j, as for finite differences, they are now an average of f around that point: $b_j = \int V_j f\,dx$. Then, in step 3, we solve the tridiagonal system $Ay = b$, which gives the coefficients in the minimizing trial function $U = y_1V_1 + \cdots + y_nV_n$. Connecting all these heights y_j by a broken line, we have the approximate solution $U(x)$.

Example 1 $-u'' = 2$ with $u(0) = u(1) = 0$, and solution $u(x) = x - x^2$.

The approximation will use three intervals and two hat functions, with $h = \frac{1}{3}$. The matrix A is 2 by 2. The right side requires integration of the hat function times $f(x) = 2$. That produces twice the area $\frac{1}{3}$ under the hat:

$$A = 3\begin{bmatrix} 2 & -1 \\ -1 & 2 \end{bmatrix} \quad \text{and} \quad b = \begin{bmatrix} \frac{2}{3} \\ \frac{2}{3} \end{bmatrix}.$$

The solution to $Ay = b$ is $y = (\frac{2}{9}, \frac{2}{9})$. The best $U(x)$ is $\frac{2}{9}V_1 + \frac{2}{9}V_2$, which equals $\frac{2}{9}$ at the mesh points. *This agrees with the exact solution* $u(x) = x - x^2 = \frac{1}{3} - \frac{1}{9}$.

In a more complicated example, the approximation will not be exact at the nodes. But it is remarkably close. The underlying theory is explained in the author's book *An Analysis of the Finite Element Method* (see www.wellesleycambridge.com) written jointly with George Fix. Other books give more detailed applications, and the subject of finite elements has become an important part of engineering education. It is treated in *Introduction to Applied Mathematics*, and also in my new book *Applied Mathematics and Scientific Computing*. There we discuss partial differential equations, where the method really comes into its own.

Eigenvalue Problems

The Rayleigh–Ritz idea—to minimize over a finite-dimensional family of V's in place of all admissible v's—is also useful for eigenvalue problems. The true minimum of the Rayleigh quotient is the fundamental frequency λ_1. Its approximate minimum Λ_1 will be larger—because the class of trial functions is restricted to the V's. This step was completely natural and inevitable: to apply the new finite element ideas to this long-established variational form of the eigenvalue problem.

The best example of an eigenvalue problem has $u(x) = \sin \pi x$ and $\lambda_1 = \pi^2$:

$$\textbf{Eigenfunction } \boldsymbol{u(x)} \qquad -u'' = \lambda u, \quad \text{with} \quad u(0) = u(1) = 0.$$

That function $\sin \pi x$ minimizes the Rayleigh quotient $v^{\mathrm{T}}Av/v^{\mathrm{T}}v$:

$$\textbf{Rayleigh quotient} \qquad R(v) = \frac{\int_0^1 v(x)(-v''(x))\,dx}{\int_0^1 (v(x))^2\,dx} = \frac{\int_0^1 (v'(x))^2\,dx}{\int_0^1 (v(x))^2\,dx}.$$

This is a ratio of potential to kinetic energy, and they are in balance at the eigenvector. Normally this eigenvector would be unknown, and to approximate it we admit only the trial candidates $V = y_1V_1 + \cdots + y_nV_n$:

$$R(V) = \frac{\int_0^1 (y_1V_1' + \cdots + y_nV_n')^2\,dx}{\int_0^1 (y_1V_1 + \cdots + y_nV_n)^2\,dx} = \frac{y^{\mathrm{T}}Ay}{y^{\mathrm{T}}My}.$$

Now we face a matrix problem: Minimize $y^{\mathrm{T}}Ay/y^{\mathrm{T}}My$. With $M = I$, this leads to the standard eigenvalue problem $Ay = \lambda y$. But our matrix M will be tridiagonal, because neighboring hat functions overlap. It is exactly this situation that brings in the *generalized eigenvalue problem*. **The minimum value Λ_1 will be the smallest eigenvalue of $Ay = \lambda My$.** That Λ_1 will be close to (and above) π^2. The eigenvector y will give the approximation $U = y_1V_1 + \cdots + y_nV_n$ to the eigenfunction.

As in the static problem, the method can be summarized in three steps: (1) choose the V_j, (2) compute A and M, and (3) solve $Ay = \lambda My$. I don't know why that costs a billion dollars.

Problem Set 6.5

1. Use three hat functions, with $h = \frac{1}{4}$, to solve $-u'' = 2$ with $u(0) = u(1) = 0$. Verify that the approximation U matches $u = x - x^2$ at the nodes.

2. Solve $-u'' = x$ with $u(0) = u(1) = 0$. Then solve approximately with two hat functions and $h = \frac{1}{3}$. Where is the largest error?

3. Suppose $-u'' = 2$, with the boundary condition $u(1) = 0$ changed to $u'(1) = 0$. This "natural" condition on u' need not be imposed on the trial functions V. With $h = \frac{1}{3}$, there is an extra *half-hat* V_3, which goes from 0 to 1 between $x = \frac{2}{3}$ and $x = 1$. Compute $A_{33} = \int (V_3')^2\,dx$ and $f_3 = \int 2V_3\,dx$. Solve $Ay = f$ for the finite element solution $y_1V_1 + y_2V_2 + y_3V_3$.

4. Solve $-u'' = 2$ with a single hat function, but place its node at $x = \frac{1}{4}$ instead of $x = \frac{1}{2}$. (Sketch this function V_1.) With boundary conditions $u(0) = u(1) = 0$, compare the finite element approximation with the true $u = x - x^2$.

5. *Galerkin's method* starts with the differential equation (say $-u'' = f(x)$) instead of the energy P. The trial solution is still $u = y_1V_1 + y_2V_2 + \cdots + y_nV_n$, and the y's are chosen to make the difference between $-u''$ and f orthogonal to every V_j:

$$\textbf{Galerkin} \quad \int (-y_1V_1'' - y_2V_2'' - \cdots - y_nV_n'')V_j\,dx = \int f(x)V_j(x)\,dx.$$

Integrate the left side by parts to reach $Ay = f$, proving that *Galerkin gives the same A and f as Rayleigh–Ritz for symmetric problems.*

6. A basic identity for quadratics shows $y = A^{-1}b$ as minimizing:

$$P(y) = \frac{1}{2}y^{\mathrm{T}}Ay - y^{\mathrm{T}}b = \frac{1}{2}(y - A^{-1}b)^{\mathrm{T}}A(y - A^{-1}b) - \frac{1}{2}b^{\mathrm{T}}A^{-1}b.$$

The minimum over a *subspace* of trial functions is at the y *nearest to* $A^{-1}b$. (That makes the first term on the right as small as possible; it is the key to convergence of U to u.) If $A = I$ and $b = (1, 0, 0)$, which multiple of $V = (1, 1, 1)$ gives the smallest value of $P(y) = \frac{1}{2}y^{\mathrm{T}}y - y_1$?

7. For a single hat function $V(x)$ centered at $x = \frac{1}{2}$, compute $A = \int (V')^2\,dx$ and $M = \int V^2\,dx$. In the 1 by 1 eigenvalue problem, is $\lambda = A/M$ larger or smaller than the true eigenvalue $\lambda = \pi^2$?

8. For the hat functions V_1 and V_2 centered at $x = h = \frac{1}{3}$ and $x = 2h = \frac{2}{3}$, compute the 2 by 2 mass matrix $M_{ij} = \int V_iV_j\,dx$, and solve the eigenvalue problem $Ax = \lambda Mx$.

9. What is the mass matrix $M_{ij} = \int V_iV_j\,dx$ for n hat functions with $h = \frac{1}{n+1}$?

Chapter

7 Computations with Matrices

7.1 INTRODUCTION

One aim of this book is to explain the useful parts of matrix theory. In comparison with older texts in abstract linear algebra, the underlying theory has not been radically changed. One of the best things about the subject is that the theory is really essential for the applications. What is different is the *change in emphasis* which comes with a new point of view. Elimination becomes more than just a way to find a basis for the row space, and the Gram–Schmidt process is not just a proof that every subspace has an orthonormal basis. Instead, we really *need* these algorithms. And we need a convenient description, $A = LU$ or $A = QR$, of what they do.

This chapter will take a few more steps in the same direction. I suppose these steps are governed by computational necessity, rather than by elegance, and I don't know whether to apologize for that; it makes them sound very superficial, and that is wrong. They deal with the oldest and most fundamental problems of the subject, $Ax = b$ and $Ax = \lambda x$, but they are continually changing and improving. In numerical analysis there is a survival of the fittest, and we want to describe some ideas that have survived so far. They fall into three groups:

1. **Techniques for Solving $Ax = b$.** Elimination is a perfect algorithm, except when the particular problem has special properties—as almost every problem has. Section 7.4 will concentrate on the property of *sparseness*, when most of the entries in A are zero. We develop ***iterative rather than direct methods*** for solving $Ax = b$. An iterative method is "self-correcting," and never reaches the exact answer. The object is to get close more quickly than elimination. In some problems, that can be done; in many others, elimination is safer and faster if it takes advantage of the zeros. The competition is far from over, and we will identify the *spectral radius* that controls the speed of convergence to $x = A^{-1}b$.

2. **Techniques for Solving $Ax = \lambda x$.** The eigenvalue problem is one of the outstanding successes of numerical analysis. It is clearly defined, its importance is obvious, but until recently no one knew how to solve it. Dozens of algorithms have been suggested, and everything depends on the size and the properties of A (and on the number of eigenvalues that are wanted). You can ask LAPACK for an eigenvalue subroutine, without knowing its contents, but it is better to know. We have chosen two or three ideas that have superseded almost all of their predecessors: ***the QR algorithm***, the family of "***power methods***," and the preprocessing of a symmetric matrix to make it ***tridiagonal***.

The first two methods are iterative, and the last is direct. It does its job in a finite number of steps, but it does not end up with the eigenvalues themselves. This produces a much simpler matrix to use in the iterative steps.

3. The Condition Number of a Matrix. Section 7.2 attempts to measure the "sensitivity" of a problem: If A and b are slightly changed, how great is the effect on $x = A^{-1}b$? Before starting on that question, we need a way to measure A and the change ΔA. The length of a vector is already defined, and now we need the ***norm of a matrix***. Then the ***condition number***, and the sensitivity of A will follow from multiplying the norms of A and A^{-1}. *The matrices in this chapter are square.*

7.2 MATRIX NORM AND CONDITION NUMBER

An error and a blunder are very different things. An error is a small mistake, probably unavoidable even by a perfect mathematician or a perfect computer. A blunder is much more serious, and larger by at least an order of magnitude. When the computer rounds off a number after 16 bits, that is an error. But when a problem is so excruciatingly sensitive that this roundoff error completely changes the solution, then almost certainly someone has committed a blunder. Our goal in this section is to analyze the effect of errors, so that blunders can be avoided.

We are actually continuing a discussion that began in Chapter 1 with

$$A = \begin{bmatrix} 1 & 1 \\ 1 & 1.0001 \end{bmatrix} \quad \text{and} \quad B = \begin{bmatrix} 0.0001 & 1 \\ 1 & 1 \end{bmatrix}.$$

We claimed that B is well-conditioned, and not particularly sensitive to roundoff—except that if Gaussian elimination is applied in a stupid way, the matrix becomes completely vulnerable. It is a blunder to accept .0001 as the first pivot, and we must insist on a larger and safer choice by exchanging the rows of B. When "partial pivoting" is built into the elimination algorithm, the computer automatically looks for the *largest pivot*. Then the natural resistance to roundoff error is no longer compromised.

How do we measure this natural resistance, and decide whether a matrix is well-conditioned or ill-conditioned? If there is a small change in b or in A, how large a change does that produce in the solution x?

We begin with *a change in the right-hand side*, from b to $b + \delta b$. This error might come from experimental data or from roundoff. We may suppose that δb is small, but its direction is outside our control. The solution is changed from x to $x + \delta x$:

$$\textbf{Error equation} \qquad A(x + \delta x) = b + \delta b, \qquad \text{so, by subtraction} \qquad A(\delta x) = \delta b. \qquad (1)$$

An error δb leads to $\delta x = A^{-1}\delta b$. There will be a large change in the solution x when A^{-1} is large—A is nearly singular. The change in x is especially large when δb points in the direction that is amplified most by A^{-1}.

Suppose A is symmetric and its eigenvalues are positive: $0 < \lambda_1 \le \cdots \le \lambda_n$. Any vector δb is a combination of the corresponding unit eigenvectors $x_1, \ldots, x_n$. The worst error δx, coming from A^{-1}, is in the direction of the first eigenvector x_1:

$$\textbf{Worst error} \qquad \text{If} \quad \delta b = \epsilon x_1, \quad \text{then} \quad \delta x = \frac{\delta b}{\lambda_1}. \qquad (2)$$

The error $\|\delta b\|$ ***is amplified by*** $1/\lambda_1$***, which is the largest eigenvalue of*** A^{-1}***.*** This amplification is greatest when λ_1 is near zero, and A is *nearly singular*.

Measuring sensitivity entirely by λ_1 has a serious drawback. Suppose we multiply all the entries of A by 1000; then λ_1 will be multiplied by 1000 and the matrix will look much less singular. This offends our sense of fair play; such a simple rescaling cannot make an ill-conditioned matrix well. It is true that δx will be 1000 times smaller, but so will the solution $x = A^{-1}b$. The relative error $\|\delta x\|/\|x\|$ will be the same. Dividing by $\|x\|$ normalizes the problem against a trivial change of scale. At the same time there is a normalization for δb; our problem is to compare the ***relative change*** $\|\delta b\|/\|b\|$ with the ***relative error*** $\|\delta x\|/\|x\|$.

The worst case is when $\|\delta x\|$ is large—with δb in the direction of the eigenvector x_1—and when $\|x\|$ is small. The true solution x should be as small as possible compared to the true b. This means that *the original problem* $Ax = b$ *should be at the other extreme*, in the direction of the last eigenvector x_n: if $b = x_n$, then $x = A^{-1}b = b/\lambda_n$.

It is this combination, $b = x_n$ and $\delta b = \epsilon x_1$, that makes the relative error as large as possible. These are the extreme cases in the following inequalities:

7A For a positive definite matrix, the solution $x = A^{-1}b$ and the error $\delta x = A^{-1}\delta b$ always satisfy

$$\|x\| \geq \frac{\|b\|}{\lambda_{\max}} \quad \text{and} \quad \|\delta x\| \leq \frac{\|\delta b\|}{\lambda_{\min}} \quad \text{and} \quad \frac{\|\delta x\|}{\|x\|} \leq \frac{\lambda_{\max}}{\lambda_{\min}} \frac{\|\delta b\|}{\|b\|}. \tag{3}$$

The ratio $c = \lambda_{\max}/\lambda_{\min}$ is the ***condition number*** of a positive definite matrix A.

Example 1 The eigenvalues of A are approximately $\lambda_1 = 10^{-4}/2$ and $\lambda_2 = 2$:

$$A = \begin{bmatrix} 1 & 1 \\ 1 & 1.0001 \end{bmatrix} \quad \text{has condition number about } c = 4 \cdot 10^4.$$

We must expect a violent change in the solution from ordinary changes in the data. Chapter 1 compared the equations $Ax = b$ and $Ax' = b'$:

$$\begin{aligned} u + v &= 2 \\ u + 1.0001v &= 2 \end{aligned} \qquad \begin{aligned} u + v &= 2 \\ u + 1.0001v &= 2.0001. \end{aligned}$$

The right-hand sides are changed only by $\|\delta b\| = .0001 = 10^{-4}$. At the same time, the solution goes from $u = 2$, $v = 0$ to $u = v = 1$. This is a relative error of

$$\frac{\|\delta x\|}{\|x\|} = \frac{\|(-1, 1)\|}{\|(2, 0)\|} = \frac{\sqrt{2}}{2}, \quad \text{which equals} \quad 2 \cdot 10^4 \frac{\|\delta b\|}{\|b\|}.$$

Without having made any special choice of the perturbation, there was a relatively large change in the solution. Our x and δb make 45° angles with the worst cases, which accounts for the missing 2 between $2 \cdot 10^4$ and the extreme possibility $c = 4 \cdot 10^4$.

If $A = I$ or even if $A = I/10$, its condition number is $c = \lambda_{\max}/\lambda_{\min} = 1$. By comparison, *the determinant is a terrible measure of ill-conditioning*. It depends not only on the scaling but also on the order n; if $A = I/10$, then the determinant of A is 10^{-n}. In fact, this "nearly singular" matrix is as well-conditioned as possible.

Example 2 The n by n finite difference matrix A has $\lambda_{\max} \approx 4$ and $\lambda_{\min} \approx \pi^2/n^2$:

$$A = \begin{bmatrix} 2 & -1 & & & \\ -1 & 2 & -1 & & \\ & -1 & 2 & \cdot & \\ & & \cdot & \cdot & -1 \\ & & & -1 & 2 \end{bmatrix}.$$

The condition number is approximately $c(A) = \frac{1}{2}n^2$, and this time the dependence on the order n is genuine. The better we approximate $-u'' = f$, by increasing the number of unknowns, the harder it is to compute the approximation. At a certain crossover point, an increase in n will actually produce a poorer answer.

Fortunately for the engineer, this crossover occurs where the accuracy is already pretty good. Working in single precision, a typical computer might make roundoff errors of order 10^{-9}. With $n = 100$ unknowns and $c = 5000$, the error is amplified at most to be of order 10^{-5}—which is still more accurate than any ordinary measurements. But there will be trouble with 10,000 unknowns, or with a $1, -4, 6, -4, 1$ approximation to $d^4u/dx^4 = f(x)$—for which the condition number grows as n^4.*

Unsymmetric Matrices

Our analysis so far has applied to symmetric matrices with positive eigenvalues. We could easily drop the positivity assumption, and use absolute values $|\lambda|$. But to go beyond symmetry, as we certainly want to do, there will have to be a major change. This is easy to see for the very unsymmetric matrices

$$A = \begin{bmatrix} 1 & 100 \\ 0 & 1 \end{bmatrix} \quad \text{and} \quad A^{-1} = \begin{bmatrix} 1 & -100 \\ 0 & 1 \end{bmatrix}. \tag{4}$$

The eigenvalues all equal one, but the proper condition number is *not* $\lambda_{\max}/\lambda_{\min} = 1$. The relative change in x is *not* bounded by the relative change in b. Compare

$$x = \begin{bmatrix} 0 \\ 1 \end{bmatrix} \quad \text{when} \quad b = \begin{bmatrix} 100 \\ 1 \end{bmatrix}; \quad x' = \begin{bmatrix} 100 \\ 0 \end{bmatrix} \quad \text{when} \quad b' = \begin{bmatrix} 100 \\ 0 \end{bmatrix}.$$

A 1% change in b has produced a hundredfold change in x; the amplification factor is 100^2. Since c represents an upper bound, the condition number must be at least 10,000. The difficulty here is that a large off-diagonal entry in A means an equally large entry in A^{-1}. Expecting A^{-1} to get smaller as A gets bigger is often wrong.

For a proper definition of the condition number, we look back at equation (3). We were trying to make x small and $b = Ax$ large. When A is not symmetric, *the maximum of $\|Ax\|/\|x\|$ may be found at a vector x that is not one of the eigenvectors.* This maximum is an excellent measure of the size of A. It is the ***norm*** of A.

---

* The usual rule of thumb, experimentally verified, is that the computer can lose $\log c$ decimal places to the roundoff errors in Gaussian elimination.

7B The ***norm*** of A is the number $\|A\|$ defined by

$$\|A\| = \max_{x\neq 0} \frac{\|Ax\|}{\|x\|}. \tag{5}$$

In other words, $\|A\|$ bounds the "amplifying power" of the matrix:

$$\|Ax\| \leq \|A\|\|x\| \qquad \text{for all vectors } x. \tag{6}$$

The matrices A and A^{-1} in equation (4) have norms somewhere between 100 and 101. They can be calculated exactly, but first we want to complete the connection between norms and condition numbers. Because $b = Ax$ and $\delta x = A^{-1}\delta b$, equation (6) gives

$$\|b\| \leq \|A\|\|x\| \qquad \text{and} \qquad \|\delta x\| \leq \|A^{-1}\|\|\delta b\|. \tag{7}$$

This is the replacement for equation (3), when A is not symmetric. In the symmetric case, $\|A\|$ is the same as $\lambda_{\max}$, and $\|A^{-1}\|$ is the same as $1/\lambda_{\min}$. *The correct replacement for $\lambda_{\max}/\lambda_{\min}$ is the product $\|A\|\|A^{-1}\|$*—which is the condition number.

7C The ***condition number*** of A is $c = \|A\|\|A^{-1}\|$. The relative error satisfies

$$\boldsymbol{\delta x \text{ from } \delta b} \qquad \frac{\|\delta x\|}{\|x\|} \leq c\,\frac{\|\delta b\|}{\|b\|} \qquad \text{directly from equation (7).} \tag{8}$$

If we perturb the matrix A instead of the right-hand side b, then

$$\boldsymbol{\delta x \text{ from } \delta A} \qquad \frac{\|\delta x\|}{\|x+\delta x\|} \leq c\,\frac{\|\delta A\|}{\|A\|} \qquad \text{from equation (10) below.} \tag{9}$$

What is remarkable is that the same condition number appears in equation (9), when the matrix itself is perturbed: If $Ax = b$ and $(A + \delta A)(x + \delta x) = b$, then by subtraction

$$A\delta x + \delta A(x + \delta x) = 0, \qquad \text{or} \qquad \delta x = -A^{-1}(\delta A)(x + \delta x).$$

Multiplying by δA amplifies a vector by no more than $\|\delta A\|$, and multiplying by A^{-1} amplifies by no more than $\|A^{-1}\|$. Then $\|\delta x\| < \|A^{-1}\|\|\delta A\|\|x + \delta x\|$, which is

$$\frac{\|\delta x\|}{\|x+\delta x\|} \leq \|A^{-1}\|\|\delta A\| = c\,\frac{\|\delta A\|}{\|A\|}. \tag{10}$$

These inequalities mean that roundoff error comes from two sources. One is the *natural sensitivity* of the problem, measured by c. The other is the actual error δb or δA. This was the basis of Wilkinson's error analysis. Since elimination actually produces approximate factors L' and U', it solves the equation with the wrong matrix $A + \delta A = L'U'$ instead of the right matrix $A = LU$. He proved that partial pivoting controls δA—so *the burden of the roundoff error is carried by the condition number c.*

A Formula for the Norm

The norm of A measures the largest amount by which any vector (eigenvector or not) is amplified by matrix multiplication: $\|A\| = \max(\|Ax\|/\|x\|)$. The norm of the identity matrix is 1. To compute the norm, square both sides to reach the symmetric $A^{\mathrm{T}}A$:

$$\|A\|^2 = \max \frac{\|Ax\|^2}{\|x\|^2} = \max \frac{x^{\mathrm{T}}A^{\mathrm{T}}Ax}{x^{\mathrm{T}}x}. \tag{11}$$

7D $\|A\|$ is the square root of the largest eigenvalue of $A^{\mathrm{T}}A$: $\|A\|^2 = \lambda_{\max}(A^{\mathrm{T}}A)$. The vector that A amplifies the most is the corresponding eigenvector of $A^{\mathrm{T}}A$:

$$\frac{x^{\mathrm{T}}A^{\mathrm{T}}Ax}{x^{\mathrm{T}}x} = \frac{x^{\mathrm{T}}(\lambda_{\max}x)}{x^{\mathrm{T}}x} = \lambda_{\max}(A^{\mathrm{T}}A) = \|A\|^2. \tag{12}$$

Figure 7.1 shows an unsymmetric matrix with eigenvalues $\lambda_1 = \lambda_2 = 1$ and norm $\|A\| = 1.618$. In this case A^{-1} has the same norm. The farthest and closest points Ax on the ellipse come from eigenvectors x of $A^{\mathrm{T}}A$, not of A.

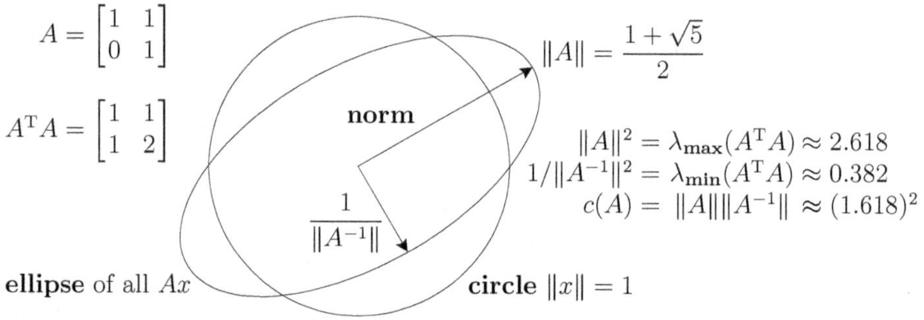

Figure 7.1 The norms of A and A^{-1} come from the longest and shortest Ax.

Note 1 The norm and condition number are not actually computed in practice, only estimated. There is not time to solve an eigenvalue problem for $\lambda_{\max}(A^{\mathrm{T}}A)$.

Note 2 In the least-squares equation $A^{\mathrm{T}}Ax = A^{\mathrm{T}}b$, the condition number $c(A^{\mathrm{T}}A)$ is the *square* of $c(A)$. Forming $A^{\mathrm{T}}A$ can turn a healthy problem into a sick one. It may be necessary to orthogonalize A by Gram–Schmidt, instead of computing with $A^{\mathrm{T}}A$.

Note 3 The ***singular values*** of A in the SVD are *the square roots of the eigenvalues of* $A^{\mathrm{T}}A$. By equation (12), another formula for the norm is $\|A\| = \sigma_{\max}$. The orthogonal U and V leave lengths unchanged in $\|Ax\| = \|U\Sigma V^{\mathrm{T}}x\|$. So the largest $\|Ax\|/\|x\|$ comes from the largest σ in the diagonal matrix Σ.

Note 4 Roundoff error also enters $Ax = \lambda x$. What is the condition number of the eigenvalue problem? *The condition number of the diagonalizing S measures the sensitivity of the eigenvalues.* If μ is an eigenvalue of $A + E$, then its distance from one of the eigenvalues of A is

$$|\mu - \lambda| \le \|S\|\,\|S^{-1}\|\,\|E\| = c(S)\|E\|. \tag{13}$$

With orthonormal eigenvectors and $S = Q$, the eigenvalue problem is perfectly conditioned: $c(Q) = 1$. The change $\delta\lambda$ in the eigenvalues is no greater than the change δA. Therefore the best case is when A is symmetric, or more generally when $AA^{\mathrm{T}} = A^{\mathrm{T}}A$. Then A is a normal matrix; its diagonalizing S is an orthogonal Q (Section 5.6).

If x_k is the kth column of S and y_k is the kth row of S^{-1}, then λ_k changes by

$$\delta\lambda_k = y_k E x_k + \text{terms of order } \|E\|^2. \tag{14}$$

In practice, $y_k E x_k$ is a realistic estimate of $\delta\lambda$. The idea in every good algorithm is to keep the error matrix E as small as possible—usually by insisting, as in the next section, on orthogonal matrices at every step of the computation of λ.

Problem Set 7.2

1. For an orthogonal matrix Q, show that $\|Q\| = 1$ and also $c(Q) = 1$. Orthogonal matrices (and their multiples αQ) are the only perfectly conditioned matrices.

2. Which "famous" inequality gives $\|(A+B)x\| \le \|Ax\| + \|Bx\|$, and why does it follow from equation (5) that $\|A+B\| \le \|A\| + \|B\|$?

3. Explain why $\|ABx\| \le \|A\|\,\|B\|\,\|x\|$, and deduce from equation (5) that $\|AB\| \le \|A\|\,\|B\|$. Show that this also implies $c(AB) \le c(A)c(B)$.

4. For the positive definite $A = \begin{bmatrix} 2 & -1 \\ -1 & 2 \end{bmatrix}$, compute $\|A^{-1}\| = 1/\lambda_1$, $\|A\| = \lambda_2$, and $c(A) = \lambda_2/\lambda_1$. Find a right-hand side b and a perturbation δb so that the error is the worst possible, $\|\delta x\|/\|x\| = c\|\delta b\|/\|b\|$.

5. Show that if λ is any eigenvalue of A, $Ax = \lambda x$, then $|\lambda| \le \|A\|$.

6. The matrices in equation (4) have norms between 100 and 101. Why?

7. Comparing the eigenvalues of $A^{\mathrm{T}}A$ and AA^{T}, prove that $\|A\| = \|A^{\mathrm{T}}\|$.

8. For a positive definite A, the Cholesky decomposition is $A = LDL^{\mathrm{T}} = R^{\mathrm{T}}R$, where $R = \sqrt{D}L^{\mathrm{T}}$. Show directly from equation (12) that the condition number of $c(R)$ is the square root of $c(A)$. Elimination without row exchanges cannot hurt a positive definite matrix, since $c(A) = c(R^{\mathrm{T}})c(R)$.

9. Show that $\max|\lambda|$ is not a true norm, by finding 2 by 2 counterexamples to $\lambda_{\max}(A+B) \le \lambda_{\max}(A) + \lambda_{\max}(B)$ and $\lambda_{\max}(AB) \le \lambda_{\max}(A)\lambda_{\max}(B)$.

10. Show that the eigenvalues of $B = \begin{bmatrix} 0 & A \\ A^{\mathrm{T}} & 0 \end{bmatrix}$ are $\pm\sigma_i$, the singular values of A. *Hint*: Try B^2.

11. (a) Do A and A^{-1} have the same condition number c?

(b) In parallel with the upper bound (8) on the error, prove a lower bound:

$$\frac{\|\delta x\|}{\|x\|} \ge \frac{1}{c}\frac{\|\delta b\|}{\|b\|}. \qquad \text{(Consider } A^{-1}b = x \text{ instead of } Ax = b.\text{)}$$

12. Find the norms $\lambda_{\max}$ and condition numbers $\lambda_{\max}/\lambda_{\min}$ of these positive definite matrices:

$$\begin{bmatrix} 100 & 0 \\ 0 & 2 \end{bmatrix} \quad \begin{bmatrix} 2 & 1 \\ 1 & 2 \end{bmatrix} \quad \begin{bmatrix} 3 & 1 \\ 1 & 1 \end{bmatrix}.$$

13. Find the norms and condition numbers from the square roots of $\lambda_{\max}(A^{\mathrm{T}}A)$ and $\lambda_{\min}(A^{\mathrm{T}}A)$:

$$\begin{bmatrix} -2 & 0 \\ 0 & 2 \end{bmatrix} \quad \begin{bmatrix} 1 & 1 \\ 0 & 0 \end{bmatrix} \quad \begin{bmatrix} 1 & 1 \\ -1 & 1 \end{bmatrix}.$$

14. Prove that the condition number $\|A\|\,\|A^{-1}\|$ is at least 1.

15. Why is I the only symmetric positive definite matrix that has $\lambda_{\max} = \lambda_{\min} = 1$? Then the only matrices with $\|A\| = 1$ and $\|A^{-1}\| = 1$ must have $A^{\mathrm{T}}A = I$. They are ______ matrices.

16. Orthogonal matrices have norm $\|Q\| = 1$. If $A = QR$, show that $\|A\| \le \|R\|$ and also $\|R\| \le \|A\|$. Then $\|A\| = \|Q\|\,\|R\|$. Find an example of $A = LU$ with $\|A\| < \|L\|\|U\|$.

17. (Suggested by Moler and Van Loan) Compute $b - Ay$ and $b - Az$ when

$$b = \begin{bmatrix} .217 \\ .254 \end{bmatrix} \quad A = \begin{bmatrix} .780 & .563 \\ .913 & .659 \end{bmatrix} \quad y = \begin{bmatrix} .341 \\ -.087 \end{bmatrix} \quad z = \begin{bmatrix} .999 \\ -1.0 \end{bmatrix}.$$

Is y closer than z to solving $Ax = b$? Answer in two ways: Compare the *residual* $b - Ay$ to $b - Az$. Then compare y and z to the true $x = (1, -1)$. Sometimes we want a small residual, sometimes a small δx.

Problems 18–20 are about vector norms other than the usual $\|x\| = \sqrt{x \cdot x}$.

18. The "ℓ^1 norm" is $\|x\|_1 = |x_1| + \cdots + |x_n|$. The "$\ell^\infty$ norm" is $\|x\|_\infty = \max |x_i|$. Compute $\|x\|$, $\|x\|_1$, and $\|x\|_\infty$ for the vectors

$$x = (1, 1, 1, 1, 1) \quad \text{and} \quad x = (.1, .7, .3, .4, .5).$$

19. Prove that $\|x\|_\infty \le \|x\| \le \|x\|_1$. Show from the Schwarz inequality that the ratios $\|x\|/\|x\|_\infty$ and $\|x\|_1/\|x\|$ are never larger than $\sqrt{n}$. Which vector $(x_1, \ldots, x_n)$ gives ratios equal to $\sqrt{n}$?

20. All vector norms must satisfy the *triangle inequality*. Prove that

$$\|x + y\|_\infty \le \|x\|_\infty + \|y\|_\infty \quad \text{and} \quad \|x + y\|_1 \le \|x\|_1 + \|y\|_1.$$

21. Compute the exact inverse of the Hilbert matrix A by elimination. Then compute A^{-1} again by rounding all numbers to three figures:

$$\text{In MATLAB: } A = \text{hilb}(3) = \begin{bmatrix} 1 & \frac{1}{2} & \frac{1}{3} \\ \frac{1}{2} & \frac{1}{3} & \frac{1}{4} \\ \frac{1}{3} & \frac{1}{4} & \frac{1}{5} \end{bmatrix}.$$

22. For the same A, compute $b = Ax$ for $x = (1, 1, 1)$ and $x = (0, 6, -3.6)$. A small change Δb produces a large change Δx.

23. Compute $\lambda_{\max}$ and $\lambda_{\min}$ for the 8 by 8 Hilbert matrix $a_{ij} = 1/(i+j-1)$. If $Ax = b$ with $\|b\| = 1$, how large can $\|x\|$ be? If b has roundoff error less than 10^{-16}, how large an error can this cause in x?

24. If you know L, U, Q, and R, is it faster to solve $LUx = b$ or $QRx = b$?

25. Choosing the largest available pivot in each column (partial pivoting), factor each A into $PA = LU$:

$$A = \begin{bmatrix} 1 & 0 \\ 2 & 2 \end{bmatrix} \quad \text{and} \quad A = \begin{bmatrix} 1 & 0 & 1 \\ 2 & 2 & 0 \\ 0 & 2 & 0 \end{bmatrix}.$$

26. Find the LU factorization of $A = \begin{bmatrix} \epsilon & 1 \\ 1 & 1 \end{bmatrix}$. On your computer, solve by elimination when $\epsilon = 10^{-3}, 10^{-6}, 10^{-9}, 10^{-12}, 10^{-15}$:

$$\begin{bmatrix} \epsilon & 1 \\ 1 & 1 \end{bmatrix} \begin{bmatrix} x_1 \\ x_2 \end{bmatrix} = \begin{bmatrix} 1+\epsilon \\ 2 \end{bmatrix}.$$

The true x is $(1, 1)$. Make a table to show the error for each ϵ. Exchange the two equations and solve again—the errors should almost disappear.

7.3 COMPUTATION OF EIGENVALUES

There is no one best way to find the eigenvalues of a matrix. But there are certainly some terrible ways which should never be tried, and also some ideas that do deserve a permanent place. We begin by describing one very rough and ready approach, the ***power method***, whose convergence properties are easy to understand. We added a graphic animation (with sound) to the course page *web.mit.edu/18.06*, to show the power method in action.

We move steadily toward a more sophisticated algorithm, which starts by making a symmetric matrix tridiagonal and ends by making it virtually diagonal. That second step is done by repeating Gram–Schmidt, so it is known as the ***QR method***.

The ordinary power method operates on the principle of a difference equation. It starts with an initial guess u_0 and then successively forms $u_1 = Au_0$, $u_2 = Au_1$, and in general $u_{k+1} = Au_k$. Each step is a matrix–vector multiplication. After k steps it produces $u_k = A^k u_0$, although the matrix A^k will never appear. The essential thing is that multiplication by A should be easy—if the matrix is large, it had better be sparse—because convergence to the eigenvector is often very slow. Assuming A has a full set of eigenvectors $x_1, \ldots, x_n$, the vector u_k will be given by the usual formula:

Eigenvectors weighted by λ^k $\qquad u_k = c_1\lambda_1^k x_1 + \cdots + c_n\lambda_n^k x_n.$

Suppose the largest eigenvalue λ_n is all by itself; there is no other eigenvalue of the same magnitude, and $|\lambda_1| \le \cdots \le |\lambda_{n-1}| < |\lambda_n|$. Then as long as the initial guess u_0 contained *some* component of the eigenvector x_n, so that $c_n \ne 0$, this component will gradually dominate in u_k:

$$\frac{u_k}{\lambda_n^k} = c_1\left(\frac{\lambda_1}{\lambda_n}\right)^k x_1 + \cdots + c_{n-1}\left(\frac{\lambda_{n-1}}{\lambda_n}\right)^k x_{n-1} + c_n x_n. \tag{1}$$

The vectors u_k point more and more accurately toward the direction of x_n. Their convergence factor is the ratio $r = |\lambda_{n-1}|/|\lambda_n|$. It is just like convergence to a steady state, for a Markov matrix, except now λ_n may not equal 1. The scaling factor λ_n^k in equation (1) prevents u_k from growing very large or very small, in case $|\lambda_n| > 1$ or $|\lambda_n| < 1$.

Often we can just divide each u_k by its first component α_k before taking the next step. With this simple scaling, the power method $u_{k+1} = Au_k/\alpha_k$ converges to a multiple of x_n. ***The scaling factors α_k will approach λ_n.***

Example 1 The u_k approach the eigenvector $\begin{bmatrix} 2/3 \\ 1/3 \end{bmatrix} = \begin{bmatrix} .667 \\ .333 \end{bmatrix}$ when $A = \begin{bmatrix} .9 & .2 \\ .1 & .8 \end{bmatrix}$ is the matrix of population shifts in Section 1.3:

$$u_0 = \begin{bmatrix} 1 \\ 0 \end{bmatrix}, \quad u_1 = \begin{bmatrix} .9 \\ .1 \end{bmatrix}, \quad u_2 = \begin{bmatrix} .83 \\ .17 \end{bmatrix}, \quad u_3 = \begin{bmatrix} .781 \\ .219 \end{bmatrix}, \quad u_4 = \begin{bmatrix} .747 \\ .253 \end{bmatrix}.$$

If $r = |\lambda_{n-1}|/|\lambda_n|$ is close to 1, then convergence is very slow. In many applications $r > .9$, which means that more than 20 iterations are needed to achieve one more digit. (The example had $r = .7$, and it was still slow.) If $r = 1$, which means $|\lambda_{n-1}| = |\lambda_n|$, then convergence will probably not occur at all. That happens (in the applet with sound) for a complex conjugate pair $\lambda_{n-1} = \overline{\lambda}_n$. There are several ways to get around this limitation, and we shall describe three of them:

1. The ***block power method*** works with several vectors at once, in place of u_k. If we multiply p orthonormal vectors by A, and then apply Gram–Schmidt to orthogonalize them again—that is a single step of the method—the convergence ratio becomes $r' = |\lambda_{n-p}|/|\lambda_n|$. We will obtain approximations to p different eigenvalues and their eigenvectors.
2. The ***inverse power method*** operates with A^{-1} instead of A. A single step is $v_{k+1} = A^{-1}v_k$, which means that we solve the linear system $Av_{k+1} = v_k$ (and save the factors L and U!). Now we converge to the *smallest eigenvalue* λ_1 and its eigenvector x_1, provided $|\lambda_1| < |\lambda_2|$. Often it is λ_1 that is wanted in the applications, and then inverse iteration is an automatic choice.
3. The ***shifted inverse power method*** is best of all. Replace A by $A - \alpha I$. Each eigenvalue is shifted by α, and the convergence factor for the inverse method will change to $r'' = |\lambda_1 - \alpha|/|\lambda_2 - \alpha|$. If α is a good approximation to λ_1, r'' will be very small and the convergence is enormously accelerated. Each step of the method solves $(A - \alpha I)w_{k+1} = w_k$:

$$w_k = \frac{c_1x_1}{(\lambda_1 - \alpha)^k} + \frac{c_2x_2}{(\lambda_2 - \alpha)^k} + \cdots + \frac{c_nx_n}{(\lambda_n - \alpha)^k}.$$

When α is close to λ_1, the first term dominates after only one or two steps. If λ_1 has already been computed by another algorithm (such as QR), then α is this computed value. One standard procedure is to factor $A - \alpha I$ into LU and to solve $Ux_1 = (1, 1, \ldots, 1)$ by back-substitution.

If λ_1 is not already approximated, the shifted inverse power method has to generate its own choice of α. We can vary $\alpha = \alpha_k$ at every step if we want to, so $(A - \alpha_k I)w_{k+1} = w_k$.

When A is symmetric, a very accurate choice is the ***Rayleigh quotient***:

$$\text{shift by} \quad \alpha_k = R(w_k) = \frac{w_k^{\mathrm{T}} A w_k}{w_k^{\mathrm{T}} w_k}.$$

This quotient $R(x)$ has a minimum at the true eigenvector x_1. Its graph is like the bottom of a parabola, so the error $\lambda_1 - \alpha_k$ is roughly the square of the error in the eigenvector. The convergence factors $|\lambda_1 - \alpha_k|/|\lambda_2 - \alpha_k|$ are themselves converging to zero. Then these Rayleigh quotient shifts give *cubic convergence* of α_k to λ_1.*

Tridiagonal and Hessenberg Forms

The power method is reasonable only for a matrix that is large and sparse. When too many entries are nonzero, this method is a mistake. Therefore we ask whether there is any simple way *to create zeros*. That is the goal of the following paragraphs.

It should be said that after computing a similar matrix $Q^{-1}AQ$ with more zeros than A, we do not intend to go back to the power method. There are much more powerful variants, and the best of them seems to be the QR algorithm. (The shifted inverse power method has its place at the very end, in finding the eigenvector.) The first step is to produce quickly as many zeros as possible, using an orthogonal matrix Q. If A is symmetric, then so is $Q^{-1}AQ$. No entry can become dangerously large because Q preserves lengths.

To go from A to $Q^{-1}AQ$, there are two main possibilities: We can produce one zero at every step (as in elimination), or we can work with a whole column at once. For a single zero, it is easy to use a plane rotation as illustrated in equation (7), found near the end of this section, that has $\cos\theta$ and $\sin\theta$ in a 2 by 2 block. Then we could cycle through all the entries below the diagonal, choosing at each step a rotation θ that will produce a zero; this is ***Jacobi's method***. It fails to diagonalize A after a finite number of rotations, since the zeros from early steps will be destroyed when later zeros are created.

To preserve the zeros and stop, we have to settle for less than a triangular form. ***The Hessenberg form accepts one nonzero diagonal below the main diagonal***. If a Hessenberg matrix is symmetric, it only has three nonzero diagonals.

A series of rotations in the right planes will produce the required zeros. Householder found a new way to accomplish exactly the same thing. A ***Householder transformation*** is a reflection matrix determined by one vector v:

$$\textbf{Householder matrix} \qquad H = I - 2\frac{vv^{\mathrm{T}}}{\|v\|^2}.$$

Often v is normalized to become a unit vector $u = v/\|v\|$, and then H becomes $I - 2uu^{\mathrm{T}}$.

---

* Linear convergence means that every step multiplies the error by a fixed factor $r < 1$. Quadratic convergence means that the error is squared at every step, as in Newton's method $x_{k+1} - x_k = -f(x_k)/f'(x_k)$ for solving $f(x) = 0$. Cubic convergence takes 10^{-1} to 10^{-3} to 10^{-9}.

In either case H is both *symmetric* and *orthogonal*:

$$H^{\mathrm{T}}H = (I - 2uu^{\mathrm{T}})(I - 2uu^{\mathrm{T}}) = I - 4uu^{\mathrm{T}} + 4uu^{\mathrm{T}}uu^{\mathrm{T}} = I.$$

Thus $H = H^{\mathrm{T}} = H^{-1}$. Householder's plan was to produce zeros with these matrices, and its success depends on the following identity $Hx = -\sigma z$:

7E Suppose z is the column vector $(1, 0, \dots, 0)$, $\sigma = \|x\|$, and $v = x + \sigma z$. Then $Hx = -\sigma z = (-\sigma, 0, \dots, 0)$. The vector Hx ends in zeros as desired.

The proof is to compute Hx and reach $-\sigma z$:

$$\begin{aligned} Hx = x - \frac{2vv^{\mathrm{T}}x}{\|v\|^2} &= x - (x + \sigma z)\frac{2(x + \sigma z)^{\mathrm{T}}x}{(x + \sigma z)^{\mathrm{T}}(x + \sigma z)} \\ &= x - (x + \sigma z) \qquad (\text{because } x^{\mathrm{T}}x = \sigma^2) \\ &= -\sigma z. \end{aligned} \tag{2}$$

This identity can be used right away, on the first column of A. The final $Q^{-1}AQ$ is allowed one nonzero diagonal below the main diagonal (Hessenberg form). Therefore *only the entries strictly below the diagonal will be involved*:

$$x = \begin{bmatrix} a_{21} \\ a_{31} \\ \vdots \\ a_{n1} \end{bmatrix}, \quad z = \begin{bmatrix} 1 \\ 0 \\ \vdots \\ 0 \end{bmatrix}, \quad Hx = \begin{bmatrix} -\sigma \\ 0 \\ \vdots \\ 0 \end{bmatrix}. \tag{3}$$

At this point Householder's matrix H is only of order $n - 1$, so it is embedded into the lower right-hand corner of a full-size matrix U_1:

$$U_1 = \begin{bmatrix} 1 & 0 & 0 & 0 & 0 \\ 0 & & & & \\ 0 & & H & & \\ 0 & & & & \\ 0 & & & & \end{bmatrix} = U_1^{-1}, \quad \text{and} \quad U_1^{-1}AU_1 = \begin{bmatrix} a_{11} & * & * & * & * \\ -\sigma & * & * & * & * \\ \mathbf{0} & * & * & * & * \\ \mathbf{0} & * & * & * & * \\ \mathbf{0} & * & * & * & * \end{bmatrix}.$$

The first stage is complete, and $U_1^{-1}AU_1$ has the required first column. At the second stage, x consists of the last $n - 2$ entries in the second column (three bold stars). Then H_2 is of order $n - 2$. When it is embedded in U_2, it produces

$$U_2 = \begin{bmatrix} 1 & 0 & 0 & 0 & 0 \\ 0 & 1 & 0 & 0 & 0 \\ 0 & 0 & & & \\ 0 & 0 & & H_2 & \\ 0 & 0 & & & \end{bmatrix} = U_2^{-1}, \quad U_2^{-1}(U_1^{-1}AU_1)U_2 = \begin{bmatrix} * & * & * & * & * \\ * & * & * & * & * \\ \mathbf{0} & * & * & * & * \\ \mathbf{0} & \mathbf{0} & * & * & * \\ \mathbf{0} & \mathbf{0} & * & * & * \end{bmatrix}.$$

U_3 will take care of the third column. For a 5 by 5 matrix, the Hessenberg form is achieved (it has six zeros). In general Q is the product of all the matrices $U_1U_2 \cdots U_{n-2}$, and the number of operations required to compute it is of order n^3.

Example 2 (to change $a_{13} = a_{31}$ to zero)

$$A = \begin{bmatrix} 1 & 0 & 1 \\ 0 & 1 & 1 \\ 1 & 1 & 0 \end{bmatrix}, \qquad x = \begin{bmatrix} 0 \\ 1 \end{bmatrix}, \quad v = \begin{bmatrix} 1 \\ 1 \end{bmatrix}, \qquad H = \begin{bmatrix} 0 & -1 \\ -1 & 0 \end{bmatrix}.$$

Embedding H into Q, the result $Q^{-1}AQ$ is tridiagonal:

$$Q = \begin{bmatrix} 1 & 0 & 0 \\ 0 & 0 & -1 \\ 0 & -1 & 0 \end{bmatrix}, \qquad Q^{-1}AQ = \begin{bmatrix} 1 & -1 & \mathbf{0} \\ -1 & 0 & 1 \\ \mathbf{0} & 1 & 1 \end{bmatrix}.$$

$Q^{-1}AQ$ is a matrix that is ready to reveal its eigenvalues—the QR algorithm is ready to begin—but we digress for a moment to mention two other applications of these same Householder matrices H.

1. *The Gram–Schmidt factorization* $A = QR$. Remember that R is to be upper triangular. We no longer have to accept an extra nonzero diagonal below the main one, since no matrices are multiplying on the right to spoil the zeros. The first step in constructing Q is to work with the whole first column of A:

$$x = \begin{bmatrix} a_{11} \\ a_{21} \\ \vdots \\ a_{n1} \end{bmatrix}, \qquad z = \begin{bmatrix} 1 \\ 0 \\ \vdots \\ 0 \end{bmatrix}, \qquad v = x + \|x\|z, \qquad H_1 = I - 2\frac{vv^{\mathrm{T}}}{\|v\|^2}.$$

The first column of H_1A equals $-\|x\|z$. It is zero below the main diagonal, and it is the first column of R. The second step works with the second column of H_1A, from the pivot on down, and produces an H_2H_1A which is zero below that pivot. (The whole algorithm is like elimination, but slightly slower.) The result of $n-1$ steps is an upper triangular R, but the matrix that records the steps is not a lower triangular L. Instead it is the product $Q = H_1H_2 \cdots H_{n-1}$, which can be stored in this factored form (keep only the v's) and never computed explicitly. That completes Gram–Schmidt.

2. *The singular value decomposition* $U^{\mathrm{T}}AV = \Sigma$. The diagonal matrix Σ has the same shape as A, and its entries (the singular values) are the square roots of the eigenvalues of $A^{\mathrm{T}}A$. Since Householder transformations can only *prepare* for the eigenvalue problem, we cannot expect them to produce Σ. Instead, they stably produce a *bidiagonal matrix*, with zeros everywhere except along the main diagonal and the one above.

The first step toward the SVD is exactly as in QR above: x is the first column of A, and H_1x is zero below the pivot. The next step is to multiply on the right by an $H^{(1)}$ which will produce zeros as indicated along the first row:

$$A \to H_1A = \begin{bmatrix} * & * & * & * \\ 0 & * & * & * \\ 0 & * & * & * \end{bmatrix} \to H_1AH^{(1)} = \begin{bmatrix} * & * & \mathbf{0} & \mathbf{0} \\ \mathbf{0} & * & * & * \\ \mathbf{0} & * & * & * \end{bmatrix}. \tag{4}$$

Then two final Householder transformations quickly achieve the bidiagonal form:

$$H_2H_1AH^{(1)} = \begin{bmatrix} * & * & 0 & 0 \\ 0 & * & * & * \\ 0 & 0 & * & * \end{bmatrix} \quad \text{and} \quad H_2H_1AH^{(1)}H^{(2)} = \begin{bmatrix} * & * & \mathbf{0} & \mathbf{0} \\ \mathbf{0} & * & * & \mathbf{0} \\ \mathbf{0} & \mathbf{0} & * & * \end{bmatrix}.$$

The *QR* Algorithm for Computing Eigenvalues

The algorithm is almost magically simple. It starts with A_0, factors it by Gram–Schmidt into Q_0R_0, and then *reverses the factors*: $A_1 = R_0Q_0$. This new matrix A_1 is *similar* to the original one because $Q_0^{-1}A_0Q_0 = Q_0^{-1}(Q_0R_0)Q_0 = A_1$. So the process continues with no change in the eigenvalues:

$$\textbf{All } \boldsymbol{A_k} \textbf{ are similar} \qquad A_k = Q_kR_k \qquad \text{and then} \qquad A_{k+1} = R_kQ_k. \tag{5}$$

This equation describes the *unshifted QR algorithm*, and almost always A_k approaches a triangular form. Its diagonal entries approach its eigenvalues, which are also the eigenvalues of A_0. If there was already some processing to obtain a tridiagonal form, then A_0 is connected to the absolutely original A by $Q^{-1}AQ = A_0$.

As it stands, the QR algorithm is good but not very good. To make it special, it needs two refinements: We must allow shifts to $A_k - \alpha_k I$, and we must ensure that the QR factorization at each step is very quick.

1. The Shifted Algorithm. If the number α_k is close to an eigenvalue, the step in equation (5) should be shifted immediately by α_k (which changes Q_k and R_k):

$$A_k - \alpha_k I = Q_kR_k \qquad \text{and then} \qquad A_{k+1} = R_kQ_k + \alpha_k I. \tag{6}$$

This matrix A_{k+1} is similar to A_k (always the same eigenvalues):

$$Q_k^{-1}A_kQ_k = Q_k^{-1}(Q_kR_k + \alpha_k I)Q_k = A_{k+1}.$$

What happens in practice is that the (n, n) entry of A_k—the one in the lower right-hand corner—is the first to approach an eigenvalue. That entry is the simplest and most popular choice for the shift α_k. Normally this produces quadratic convergence, and in the symmetric case even cubic convergence, to the smallest eigenvalue. After three or four steps of the shifted algorithm, the matrix A_k looks like this:

$$A_k = \left[\begin{array}{ccc|c} * & * & * & * \\ * & * & * & * \\ 0 & * & * & * \\ \hline 0 & 0 & \epsilon & \lambda_1' \end{array}\right], \qquad \text{with } \epsilon \ll 1.$$

We accept the computed λ_1' as a very close approximation to the true λ_1. To find the next eigenvalue, the QR algorithm continues with the smaller matrix (3 by 3, in the illustration) in the upper left-hand corner. Its subdiagonal elements will be somewhat reduced by the first QR steps, and another two steps are sufficient to find λ_2. This gives a systematic procedure for finding all the eigenvalues. In fact, ***the QR method is now***

completely described. It only remains to catch up on the eigenvectors—that is a single inverse power step—and to use the zeros that Householder created.

2. When A_0 is tridiagonal or Hessenberg, each QR step is very fast. The Gram–Schmidt process (factoring into QR) takes $O(n^3)$ operations for a full matrix A. For a Hessenberg matrix this becomes $O(n^2)$, and for a tridiagonal matrix it is $O(n)$. Fortunately, each new A_k is again in Hessenberg or tridiagonal form:

$$\textbf{Q_0 is Hessenberg} \qquad Q_0 = A_0 R_0^{-1} = \begin{bmatrix} * & * & * & * \\ * & * & * & * \\ 0 & * & * & * \\ 0 & 0 & * & * \end{bmatrix} \begin{bmatrix} * & * & * & * \\ 0 & * & * & * \\ 0 & 0 & * & * \\ 0 & 0 & 0 & * \end{bmatrix}.$$

You can easily check that this multiplication leaves Q_0 with the same three zeros as A_0. *Hessenberg times triangular is Hessenberg.* So is triangular times Hessenberg:

$$\textbf{A_1 is Hessenberg} \qquad A_1 = R_0 Q_0 = \begin{bmatrix} * & * & * & * \\ 0 & * & * & * \\ 0 & 0 & * & * \\ 0 & 0 & 0 & * \end{bmatrix} \begin{bmatrix} * & * & * & * \\ * & * & * & * \\ 0 & * & * & * \\ 0 & 0 & * & * \end{bmatrix}.$$

The symmetric case is even better, since $A_1 = Q_0^{-1} A_0 Q_0 = Q_0^{\mathrm{T}} A_0 Q_0$ stays symmetric. By the reasoning just completed, A_1 is also Hessenberg. So A_1 must be *tridiagonal*. The same applies to $A_2, A_3, \ldots$, and *every QR step begins with a tridiagonal matrix.*

The last point is the factorization itself, producing the Q_k and R_k from each A_k (or really from $A_k - \alpha_k I$). We may use Householder again, but it is simpler to annihilate each subdiagonal element in turn by a "plane rotation" P_{ij}. The first is P_{21}:

$$\textbf{Rotation to kill a_{21}} \qquad P_{21} A_k = \begin{bmatrix} \cos\theta & -\sin\theta & & \\ \sin\theta & \cos\theta & & \\ & & 1 & \\ & & & 1 \end{bmatrix} \begin{bmatrix} a_{11} & * & * & * \\ a_{21} & * & * & * \\ 0 & * & * & * \\ 0 & 0 & * & * \end{bmatrix} \qquad (7)$$

The (2, 1) entry in this product is $a_{11}\sin\theta + a_{21}\cos\theta$, and we choose the angle θ that makes this combination zero. The next rotation P_{32} is chosen in a similar way, to remove the (3, 2) entry of $P_{32}P_{21}A_k$. After $n-1$ rotations, we have R_0:

$$\textbf{Triangular factor} \qquad R_k = P_{nn-1} \cdots P_{32} P_{21} A_k. \qquad (8)$$

Books on numerical linear algebra give more information about this remarkable algorithm in scientific computing. We mention one more method—***Arnoldi*** in ARPACK—for large sparse matrices. It orthogonalizes the Krylov sequence x, Ax, A^2x, ... by Gram–Schmidt. If you need the eigenvalues of a large matrix, don't use $\det(A - \lambda I)$!

Problem Set 7.3

1. For the matrix $A = \begin{bmatrix} 2 & -1 \\ -1 & 2 \end{bmatrix}$, with eigenvalues $\lambda_1 = 1$ and $\lambda_2 = 3$, apply the power method $u_{k+1} = Au_k$ three times to the initial guess $u_0 = \begin{bmatrix} 1 \\ 0 \end{bmatrix}$. What is the limiting vector u_∞?

2. For the same A and the initial guess $u_0 = \begin{bmatrix} 3 \\ 4 \end{bmatrix}$, compare three inverse power steps to one shifted step with $\alpha = u_0^{\mathrm{T}} A u_0 / u_0^{\mathrm{T}} u_0$:

$$u_{k+1} = A^{-1} u_k = \frac{1}{3} \begin{bmatrix} 2 & 1 \\ 1 & 2 \end{bmatrix} u_k \quad \text{or} \quad u = (A - \alpha I)^{-1} u_0.$$

The limiting vector u_∞ is now a multiple of the other eigenvector $(1, 1)$.

3. Explain why $|\lambda_n / \lambda_{n-1}|$ controls the convergence of the usual power method. Construct a matrix A for which this method *does not converge*.

4. The Markov matrix $A = \begin{bmatrix} .9 & .3 \\ .1 & .7 \end{bmatrix}$ has $\lambda = 1$ and .6, and the power method $u_k = A^k u_0$ converges to $\begin{bmatrix} .75 \\ .25 \end{bmatrix}$. Find the eigenvectors of A^{-1}. What does the inverse power method $u_{-k} = A^{-k} u_0$ converge to (after you multiply by $.6^k$)?

5. Show that for any two different vectors of the same length, $\|x\| = \|y\|$, the Householder transformation with $v = x - y$ gives $Hx = y$ and $Hy = x$.

6. Compute $\sigma = \|x\|$, $v = x + \sigma z$, and $H = I - 2vv^{\mathrm{T}} / v^{\mathrm{T}} v$. Verify $Hx = -\sigma z$:

$$x = \begin{bmatrix} 3 \\ 4 \end{bmatrix} \quad \text{and} \quad z = \begin{bmatrix} 1 \\ 0 \end{bmatrix}.$$

7. Using Problem 6, find the tridiagonal HAH^{-1} that is similar to

$$A = \begin{bmatrix} 1 & 3 & 4 \\ 3 & 1 & 0 \\ 4 & 0 & 0 \end{bmatrix}.$$

8. Show that starting from $A_0 = \begin{bmatrix} 2 & -1 \\ -1 & 2 \end{bmatrix}$, the unshifted QR algorithm produces only the modest improvement $A_1 = \frac{1}{5} \begin{bmatrix} 14 & -3 \\ -3 & 6 \end{bmatrix}$.

9. Apply to the following matrix A a single QR step with the shift $\alpha = a_{22}$—which in this case means without shift, since $a_{22} = 0$. Show that the off-diagonal entries go from $\sin\theta$ to $-\sin^3\theta$, which is *cubic convergence*.

$$A = \begin{bmatrix} \cos\theta & \sin\theta \\ \sin\theta & 0 \end{bmatrix}.$$

10. Check that the tridiagonal $A = \begin{bmatrix} 0 & 1 \\ 1 & 0 \end{bmatrix}$ is left unchanged by the QR algorithm. It is one of the (rare) counterexamples to convergence (so we shift).

11. Show by induction that, without shifts, $(Q_0 Q_1 \cdots Q_k)(R_k \cdots R_1 R_0)$ is exactly the QR factorization of A_{k+1}. This identity connects QR to the power method and leads to an explanation of its convergence. If $|\lambda_1| > |\lambda_2| > \cdots > |\lambda_n|$, these eigenvalues will gradually appear on the main diagonal.

12. Choose $\sin\theta$ and $\cos\theta$ in the rotation P to triangularize A, and find R:

$$P_{21} A = \begin{bmatrix} \cos\theta & -\sin\theta \\ \sin\theta & \cos\theta \end{bmatrix} \begin{bmatrix} 1 & -1 \\ 3 & 5 \end{bmatrix} = \begin{bmatrix} * & * \\ 0 & * \end{bmatrix} = R.$$

13. Choose $\sin\theta$ and $\cos\theta$ to make $P_{21}AP_{21}^{-1}$ triangular (same A). What are the eigenvalues?

14. When A is multiplied by P_{ij} (plane rotation), which entries are changed? When $P_{ij}A$ is multiplied on the right by P_{ij}^{-1}, which entries are changed now?

15. How many multiplications and how many additions are used to compute PA? (A careful organization of all the rotations gives $\frac{2}{3}n^3$ multiplications and additions, the same as for QR by reflectors and twice as many as for LU.)

16. (Turning a robot hand) A robot produces any 3 by 3 rotation A from plane rotations around the x, y, and z axes. If $P_{32}P_{31}P_{21}A = I$, the three robot turns are in $A = P_{21}^{-1}P_{31}^{-1}P_{32}^{-1}$. The three angles are ***Euler angles***. Choose the first θ so that

$$P_{21}A = \begin{bmatrix} \cos\theta & -\sin\theta & 0 \\ \sin\theta & \cos\theta & 0 \\ 0 & 0 & 1 \end{bmatrix} \frac{1}{3} \begin{bmatrix} -1 & 2 & 2 \\ 2 & -1 & 2 \\ 2 & 2 & -1 \end{bmatrix} \quad \text{is zero in the } (2, 1) \text{ position.}$$

7.4 ITERATIVE METHODS FOR $Ax = b$

In contrast to eigenvalues, for which there was no choice, we do not absolutely need an iterative method to solve $Ax = b$. Gaussian elimination will reach the solution x in a finite number of steps ($n^3/3$ for a full matrix, less than that for the large matrices we actually meet). Often that number is reasonable. When it is enormous, we may have to settle for an approximate x that can be obtained more quickly—and it is no use to go part way through elimination and then stop.

Our goal is to describe methods that start from any initial guess x_0, and produce an improved approximation x_{k+1} from the previous x_k. We can stop when we want to.

An iterative method is easy to invent, by ***splitting the matrix A***. If $A = S - T$, then the equation $Ax = b$ is the same as $Sx = Tx + b$. Therefore we can try

$$\textbf{Iteration from } \boldsymbol{x_k} \textbf{ to } \boldsymbol{x_{k+1}} \qquad Sx_{k+1} = Tx_k + b. \tag{1}$$

There is no guarantee that this method is any good. A successful splitting $S - T$ satisfies two different requirements:

1. The new vector x_{k+1} should be *easy to compute*. Therefore S should be a simple (and invertible!) matrix; it may be diagonal or triangular.
2. The sequence x_k should *converge* to the true solution x. If we subtract the iteration in equation (1) from the true equation $Sx = Tx + b$, the result is a formula involving only the errors $e_k = x - x_k$:

$$\textbf{Error equation} \qquad Se_{k+1} = Te_k. \tag{2}$$

This is just a difference equation. It starts with the initial error e_0, and after k steps it produces the new error $e_k = (S^{-1}T)^k e_0$. The question of convergence is exactly the same as the question of stability: $x_k \to x$ exactly when $e_k \to 0$.

7F The iterative method in equation (1) is ***convergent*** if and only if every eigenvalue of $S^{-1}T$ satisfies $|\lambda| < 1$. Its rate of convergence depends on the maximum size of $|\lambda|$:

$$\textbf{Spectral radius "rho"} \qquad \rho(S^{-1}T) = \max_i |\lambda_i|. \tag{3}$$

Remember that a typical solution to $e_{k+1} = S^{-1}Te_k$ is a combination of eigenvectors:

$$\textbf{Error after } \boldsymbol{k} \textbf{ steps} \qquad e_k = c_1\lambda_1^k x_1 + \cdots + c_n\lambda_n^k x_n. \tag{4}$$

The largest $|\lambda_i|$ will eventually be dominant, so the spectral radius $\rho = |\lambda_{max}|$ will govern the rate at which e_k converges to zero. We certainly need $\rho < 1$.

Requirements **1** and **2** above are conflicting. We could achieve immediate convergence with $S = A$ and $T = 0$; the first and only step of the iteration would be $Ax_1 = b$. In that case the error matrix $S^{-1}T$ is zero, its eigenvalues and spectral radius are zero, and the rate of convergence (usually defined as $-\log \rho$) is infinite. But $Ax_1 = b$ may be hard to solve; that was the reason for a splitting. A simple choice of S can often succeed, and we start with three possibilities:

1. S = diagonal part of A (**Jacobi's method**).
2. S = triangular part of A (**Gauss–Seidel method**).
3. S = combination of 1 and 2 (**successive overrelaxation** or SOR).

S is also called a ***preconditioner***, and its choice is crucial in numerical analysis.

Example 1 **(Jacobi)** Here S is the diagonal part of A:

$$A = \begin{bmatrix} 2 & -1 \\ -1 & 2 \end{bmatrix}, \quad S = \begin{bmatrix} 2 & \\ & 2 \end{bmatrix}, \quad T = \begin{bmatrix} 0 & 1 \\ 1 & 0 \end{bmatrix}, \quad S^{-1}T = \begin{bmatrix} 0 & \frac{1}{2} \\ \frac{1}{2} & 0 \end{bmatrix}.$$

If the components of x are v and w, the Jacobi step $Sx_{k+1} = Tx_k + b$ is

$$\begin{aligned} 2v_{k+1} &= w_k + b_1 \\ 2w_{k+1} &= v_k + b_2, \end{aligned} \qquad \text{or} \qquad \begin{bmatrix} v \\ w \end{bmatrix}_{k+1} = \begin{bmatrix} 0 & \frac{1}{2} \\ \frac{1}{2} & 0 \end{bmatrix} \begin{bmatrix} v \\ w \end{bmatrix}_k + \begin{bmatrix} b_1/2 \\ b_2/2 \end{bmatrix}.$$

The decisive matrix $S^{-1}T$ has eigenvalues $\pm\frac{1}{2}$, which means that the error is cut in half (one more binary digit becomes correct) at every step. In this example, which is much too small to be typical, the convergence is fast.

For a larger matrix A, there is a very practical difficulty. **The Jacobi iteration requires us to keep all components of $\boldsymbol{x_k}$ until the calculation of $\boldsymbol{x_{k+1}}$ is complete.** A much more natural idea, which requires only half as much storage, is to start using each component of the new x_{k+1} as soon as it is computed; x_{k+1} takes the place of x_k a component at a time. Then x_k can be destroyed as fast as x_{k+1} is created. The first component remains as before:

$$\textbf{New } \boldsymbol{x_1} \qquad a_{11}(x_1)_{k+1} = (-a_{12}x_2 - a_{13}x_3 - \cdots - a_{1n}x_n)_k + b_1.$$

The next step operates immediately with this new value of x_1, to find $(x_2)_{k+1}$:

$$\textbf{New } \boldsymbol{x_2} \qquad a_{22}(x_2)_{k+1} = -a_{21}(x_1)_{k+1} + (-a_{23}x_3 - \cdots - a_{2n}x_n)_k + b_2.$$

And the last equation in the iteration step will use new values exclusively:

$$\textbf{New } \boldsymbol{x_n} \qquad a_{nn}(x_n)_{k+1} = (-a_{n1}x_1 - a_{n2}x_2 - \cdots - a_{nn-1}x_{n-1})_{k+1} + b_n.$$

This is called the ***Gauss–Seidel method***, even though it was apparently unknown to Gauss and not recommended by Seidel. That is a surprising bit of history, because it is not a bad method. When the terms in x_{k+1} are moved to the left-hand side, *S is seen as the lower triangular part of A*. On the right-hand side, T is strictly upper triangular.

Example 2 **(Gauss–Seidel)** Here $S^{-1}T$ has smaller eigenvalues:

$$A = \begin{bmatrix} 2 & -1 \\ -1 & 2 \end{bmatrix}, \quad S = \begin{bmatrix} 2 & 0 \\ -1 & 2 \end{bmatrix}, \quad T = \begin{bmatrix} 0 & 1 \\ 0 & 0 \end{bmatrix}, \quad S^{-1}T = \begin{bmatrix} 0 & \frac{1}{2} \\ 0 & \frac{1}{4} \end{bmatrix}.$$

A single Gauss–Seidel step takes the components v_k and w_k into

$$\begin{aligned} 2v_{k+1} &= w_k + b_1 \\ 2w_{k+1} &= v_{k+1} + b_2, \end{aligned} \quad \text{or} \quad \begin{bmatrix} 2 & 0 \\ -1 & 2 \end{bmatrix} x_{k+1} = \begin{bmatrix} 0 & 1 \\ 0 & 0 \end{bmatrix} x_k + b.$$

The eigenvalues of $S^{-1}T$ are $\frac{1}{4}$ and 0. The error is divided by 4 every time, so *a single Gauss–Seidel step is worth two Jacobi steps*. Since both methods require the same number of operations—we just use the new value instead of the old, and actually save on storage—the Gauss–Seidel method is better.

This rule holds in many applications, even though there are examples in which Jacobi converges and Gauss–Seidel fails (or conversely). The symmetric case is straightforward: When all $a_{ii} > 0$, Gauss–Seidel converges if and only if A is positive definite.

It was discovered during the years of hand computation (probably by accident) that convergence is faster if we go *beyond* the Gauss–Seidel correction $x_{k+1} - x_k$. Roughly speaking, those approximations stay on the same side of the solution x. An ***overrelaxation factor ω*** moves us closer to the solution. With $\omega = 1$, we recover Gauss–Seidel; with $\omega > 1$, the method is known as ***successive overrelaxation*** (SOR). The optimal choice of ω never exceeds 2. It is often in the neighborhood of 1.9.

To describe overrelaxation, let D, L, and U be the parts of A on, below, and above the diagonal, respectively. (This splitting has nothing to do with the $A = LDU$ of elimination. In fact we now have $A = L + D + U$.) The Jacobi method has $S = D$ on the left-hand side and $T = -L - U$ on the right-hand side. Gauss–Seidel chose $S = D + L$ and $T = -U$. To accelerate the convergence, we move to

$$\textbf{Overrelaxation} \qquad [D + \omega L]x_{k+1} = [(1 - \omega)D - \omega U]x_k + \omega b. \tag{5}$$

Regardless of ω, the matrix on the left is lower triangular and the one on the right is upper triangular. Therefore x_{k+1} can still replace x_k, component by component, as soon as it is computed. A typical step is

$$a_{ii}(x_i)_{k+1} = a_{ii}(x_i)_k + \omega[(-a_{i1}x_1 - \cdots - a_{ii-1}x_{i-1})_{k+1} + (-a_{ii}x_i - \cdots - a_{in}x_n)_k + b_i].$$

If the old guess x_k happened to coincide with the true solution x, then the new guess x_{k+1} would stay the same, and the quantity in brackets would vanish.

Example 3 **(SOR)** For the same $A = \begin{bmatrix} 2 & -1 \\ -1 & 2 \end{bmatrix}$, each overrelaxation step is

$$\begin{bmatrix} 2 & 0 \\ -\omega & 2 \end{bmatrix} x_{k+1} = \begin{bmatrix} 2(1-\omega) & \omega \\ 0 & 2(1-\omega) \end{bmatrix} x_k + \omega b.$$

If we divide by ω, these two matrices are the S and T in the splitting $A = S - T$; the iteration is back to $Sx_{k+1} = Tx_k + b$. The crucial matrix $L = S^{-1}T$ is

$$L = \begin{bmatrix} 2 & 0 \\ -\omega & 2 \end{bmatrix}^{-1} \begin{bmatrix} 2(1-\omega) & \omega \\ 0 & 2(1-\omega) \end{bmatrix} = \begin{bmatrix} 1-\omega & \frac{1}{2}\omega \\ \frac{1}{2}\omega(1-\omega) & 1-\omega+\frac{1}{4}\omega^2 \end{bmatrix}.$$

The optimal ω makes the largest eigenvalue of L (its spectral radius) as small as possible. *The whole point of overrelaxation is to discover this optimal ω.* The product of the eigenvalues equals $\det L = \det T / \det S$:

$$\lambda_1 \lambda_2 = \det L = (1-\omega)^2.$$

Always $\det S = \det D$ because L lies below the diagonal, and $\det T = \det(1-\omega)D$ because U lies above the diagonal. Their product is $\det L = (1-\omega)^n$. (This explains why we never go as far as $\omega = 2$. The product of the eigenvalues would be too large, and the iteration could not converge.) We also get a clue to the behavior of the eigenvalues: *At the optimal ω the two eigenvalues are equal. They must both equal $\omega - 1$ so their product will match* $\det L$. This value of ω is easy to compute, because the sum of the eigenvalues always agrees with the sum of the diagonal entries (the trace of L):

$$\textbf{Optimal } \omega \qquad \lambda_1 + \lambda_2 = (\omega_{\text{opt}} - 1) + (\omega_{\text{opt}} - 1) = 2 - 2\omega_{\text{opt}} + \frac{1}{4}\omega_{\text{opt}}^2. \tag{6}$$

This quadratic equation gives $\omega_{\text{opt}} = 4(2 - \sqrt{3}) \approx 1.07$. The two equal eigenvalues are approximately $\omega - 1 = .07$, which is a major reduction from the Gauss–Seidel value $\lambda = \frac{1}{4}$ at $\omega = 1$. In this example, the right choice of ω has again doubled the rate of convergence, because $\left(\frac{1}{4}\right)^2 \approx .07$. If ω is further increased, the eigenvalues become a complex conjugate pair—both have $|\lambda| = \omega - 1$, which is now increasing with ω.

The discovery that such an improvement could be produced so easily, almost as if by magic, was the starting point for 20 years of enormous activity in numerical analysis. The first problem was solved in Young's 1950 thesis—a simple formula for the optimal ω. The key step was to connect the eigenvalues λ of L to the eigenvalues μ of the original Jacobi matrix $D^{-1}(-L-U)$. That connection is expressed by

$$\textbf{Formula for } \omega \qquad (\lambda + \omega - 1)^2 = \lambda \omega^2 \mu^2. \tag{7}$$

This is valid for a wide class of finite difference matrices, and if we take $\omega = 1$ (Gauss–Seidel) it yields $\lambda^2 = \lambda\mu^2$. Therefore $\lambda = 0$ and $\lambda = \mu^2$ as in Example 2, where $\mu = \pm\frac{1}{2}$ and $\lambda = 0$, $\lambda = \frac{1}{4}$. All the matrices in Young's class have eigenvalues μ that occur in plus–minus pairs, and the corresponding λ are 0 and μ^2. So Gauss–Seidel doubles the Jacobi rate of convergence.

The important problem is to choose ω so that $\lambda_{\max}$ will be minimized. Fortunately, Young's equation (7) is exactly our 2 by 2 example! The best ω makes the two roots λ both equal to $\omega - 1$:

$$(\omega - 1) + (\omega - 1) = 2 - 2\omega + \mu^2\omega^2, \quad \text{or} \quad \omega = \frac{2(1 - \sqrt{1 - \mu^2})}{\mu^2}.$$

For a large matrix, this pattern will be repeated for a number of different pairs $\pm\mu_i$—and we can only make a single choice of ω. The largest μ gives the largest value of ω and of $\lambda = \omega - 1$. Since our goal is to make $\lambda_{\max}$ as small as possible, that extremal pair specifies the best choice ω_{opt}:

$$\textbf{Optimal } \boldsymbol{\omega} \qquad \omega_{\text{opt}} = \frac{2(1 - \sqrt{1 - \mu_{\max}^2})}{\mu_{\max}^2} \quad \text{and} \quad \lambda_{\max} = \omega_{\text{opt}} - 1. \tag{8}$$

7G The splittings of the $-1, 2, -1$ matrix of order n yield these eigenvalues of B:

Jacobi ($S = 0, 2, 0$ matrix): $S^{-1}T$ has $|\lambda|_{\max} = \cos\dfrac{\pi}{n+1}$

Gauss–Seidel ($S = -1, 2, 0$ matrix): $S^{-1}T$ has $|\lambda|_{\max} = \left(\cos\dfrac{\pi}{n+1}\right)^2$

SOR (with the best ω): $|\lambda|_{\max} = \left(\cos\dfrac{\pi}{n+1}\right)^2 \Big/ \left(1 + \sin\dfrac{\pi}{n+1}\right)^2.$

This can only be appreciated by an example. Suppose A is of order 21, which is very moderate. Then $h = \frac{1}{22}$, $\cos\pi h = .99$, and the Jacobi method is slow; $\cos^2\pi h = .98$ means that even Gauss–Seidel will require a great many iterations. But since $\sin\pi h = \sqrt{.02} = .14$, the optimal overrelaxation method will have the convergence factor

$$\lambda_{\max} = \frac{.86}{1.14} = .75, \quad \text{with} \quad \omega_{\text{opt}} = 1 + \lambda_{\max} = 1.75.$$

The error is reduced by 25% at every step, and ***a single SOR step is the equivalent of 30 Jacobi steps***: $(.99)^{30} = .75$.

That is a striking result from such a simple idea. Its real applications are not in one-dimensional problems like $-u_{xx} = f$. A tridiagonal system $Ax = b$ is already easy. It is for partial differential equations that overrelaxation (and other ideas) will be important. Changing to $-u_{xx} - u_{yy} = f$ leads to the "five-point scheme." The entries $-1, 2, -1$ in the x direction combine with $-1, 2, -1$ in the y direction to give a main diagonal of $+4$ and four off-diagonal entries of -1. *The matrix A does not have a small bandwidth!* There is no way to number the N^2 mesh points in a square so that each point stays close to all four of its neighbors. That is the true ***curse of dimensionality***, and parallel computers will partly relieve it.

If the ordering goes a row at a time, every point must wait a whole row for the neighbor above it to turn up. The "five-point matrix" has bandwidth N:

$-1, 2, -1$ in x and y
gives $-1, -1, 4, -1, -1$

$A =$ 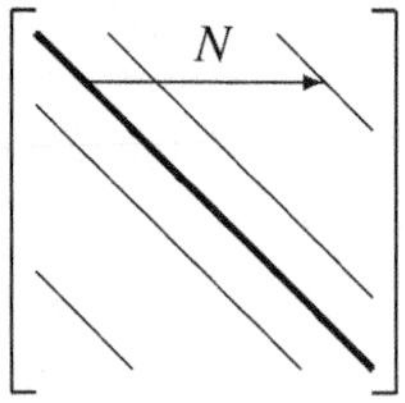

This matrix has had more attention, and been attacked in more different ways, than any other linear equation $Ax = b$. The trend now is back to direct methods, based on an idea of Golub and Hockney; certain special matrices will fall apart when they are dropped the right way. (It is comparable to the Fast Fourier Transform.) Before that came the iterative methods of ***alternating direction***, in which the splitting separated the tridiagonal matrix in the x direction from the one in the y direction. A recent choice is $S = L_0U_0$, in which small entries of the true L and U are set to zero while factoring A. It is called ***incomplete*** $\boldsymbol{LU}$ and it can be terrific.

We cannot close without mentioning the ***conjugate gradient method***, which looked dead but is suddenly very much alive (Problem 33 gives the steps). It is direct rather than iterative, but unlike elimination, it can be stopped part way. And needless to say, a completely new idea may still appear and win. But it seems fair to say that it was the change from .99 to .75 that revolutionized the solution of $Ax = b$.

Problem Set 7.4

1. This matrix has eigenvalues $2 - \sqrt{2}$, 2, and $2 + \sqrt{2}$:

$$A = \begin{bmatrix} 2 & -1 & 0 \\ -1 & 2 & -1 \\ 0 & -1 & 2 \end{bmatrix}.$$

Find the Jacobi matrix $D^{-1}(-L-U)$ and the Gauss–Seidel matrix $(D+L)^{-1}(-U)$ and their eigenvalues, and the numbers ω_{opt} and $\lambda_{\max}$ for SOR.

2. For this n by n matrix, describe the Jacobi matrix $J = D^{-1}(-L - U)$:

$$A = \begin{bmatrix} 2 & -1 & & \\ -1 & \cdot & \cdot & \\ & \cdot & \cdot & -1 \\ & & -1 & 2 \end{bmatrix}.$$

Show that the vector $x_1 = (\sin \pi h, \sin 2\pi h, \ldots, \sin n\pi h)$ is an eigenvector of J with eigenvalue $\lambda_1 = \cos \pi h = \cos \pi/(n+1)$.

3. In Problem 2, show that $x_k = (\sin k\pi h, \sin 2k\pi h, \ldots, \sin nk\pi h)$ is an eigenvector of A. Multiply x_k by A to find the corresponding eigenvalue α_k. Verify that in the 3 by 3 case these eigenvalues are $2 - \sqrt{2}$, 2, $2 + \sqrt{2}$.

Note The eigenvalues of the Jacobi matrix $J = \frac{1}{2}(-L - U) = I - \frac{1}{2}A$ are $\lambda_k = 1 - \frac{1}{2}\alpha_k = \cos k\pi h$. They occur in plus–minus pairs and $\lambda_{\max}$ is $\cos \pi h$.

Problems 4–5 require Gershgorin's "circle theorem": *Every eigenvalue of A lies in at least one of the circles $C_1, \ldots, C_n$, where C_i has its center at the diagonal entry a_{ii}. Its radius $r_i = \sum_{j \neq i} |a_{ij}|$ is equal to the absolute sum along the rest of the row.*

Proof Suppose x_i is the largest component of x. Then $Ax = \lambda x$ leads to

$$(\lambda - a_{ii})x_i = \sum_{j \neq i} a_{ij}x_j, \qquad \text{or} \qquad |\lambda - a_{ii}| \leq \sum_{j \neq i} |a_{ij}| \frac{|x_j|}{|x_i|} \leq \sum_{j \neq i} |a_{ij}| = r_i. \qquad \blacksquare$$

4. The matrix

$$A = \begin{bmatrix} 3 & 1 & 1 \\ 0 & 4 & 1 \\ 2 & 2 & 5 \end{bmatrix}$$

is called *diagonally dominant* because every $|a_{ii}| > r_i$. Show that zero cannot lie in any of the circles, and conclude that A is nonsingular.

5. Write the Jacobi matrix J for the diagonally dominant A of Problem 4, and find the three Gershgorin circles for J. Show that all the radii satisfy $r_i < 1$, and that the Jacobi iteration converges.

6. The true solution to $Ax = b$ is slightly different from the elimination solution to $LUx_0 = b$; $A - LU$ misses zero because of roundoff. One strategy is to do everything in double precision, but a better and faster way is *iterative refinement*: Compute only one vector $r = b - Ax_0$ in double precision, solve $LUy = r$, and add the correction y to x_0. Problem: Multiply $x_1 = x_0 + y$ by LU, write the result as a splitting $Sx_1 = Tx_0 + b$, and explain why T is extremely small. This single step brings us almost exactly to x.

7. For a general 2 by 2 matrix

$$A = \begin{bmatrix} a & b \\ c & d \end{bmatrix},$$

find the Jacobi iteration matrix $S^{-1}T = -D^{-1}(L + U)$ and its eigenvalues μ_i. Find also the Gauss–Seidel matrix $-(D + L)^{-1}U$ and its eigenvalues λ_i, and decide whether $\lambda_{\max} = \mu^2_{\max}$.

8. Change $Ax = b$ to $x = (I - A)x + b$. What are S and T for this splitting? What matrix $S^{-1}T$ controls the convergence of $x_{k+1} = (I - A)x_k + b$?

9. If λ is an eigenvalue of A, then ______ is an eigenvalue of $B = I - A$. The real eigenvalues of B have absolute value less than 1 if the real eigenvalues of A lie between ______ and ______.

10. Show why the iteration $x_{k+1} = (I - A)x_k + b$ does not converge for $A = \begin{bmatrix} 2 & -1 \\ -1 & 2 \end{bmatrix}$.

11. Why is the norm of B^k never larger than $\|B\|^k$? Then $\|B\| < 1$ guarantees that the powers B^k approach zero (convergence). This is no surprise, since $|\lambda|_{\max}$ is below $\|B\|$.

12. If A is singular, then all splittings $A = S - T$ must fail. From $Ax = 0$, show that $S^{-1}Tx = x$. So this matrix $B = S^{-1}T$ has $\lambda = 1$ and fails.

13. Change the 2s to 3s and find the eigenvalues of $S^{-1}T$ for both methods:

$$\textbf{(J)} \quad \begin{bmatrix} 3 & 0 \\ 0 & 3 \end{bmatrix} x_{k+1} = \begin{bmatrix} 0 & 1 \\ 1 & 0 \end{bmatrix} x_k + b \qquad \textbf{(GS)} \quad \begin{bmatrix} 3 & 0 \\ -1 & 3 \end{bmatrix} x_{k+1} = \begin{bmatrix} 0 & 1 \\ 0 & 0 \end{bmatrix} x_k + b.$$

Does $|\lambda|_{\max}$ for Gauss–Seidel equal $|\lambda|^2_{\max}$ for Jacobi?

14. Write a computer code (MATLAB or other) for Gauss–Seidel. You can define S and T from A, or set up the iteration loop directly from the entries a_{ij}. Test it on the -1, 2, -1 matrices A of order 10, 20, 50, with $b = (1, 0, \ldots, 0)$.

15. The **SOR** splitting matrix S is the same as for Gauss–Seidel except that the diagonal is divided by ω. Write a program for **SOR** on an n by n matrix. Apply it with $\omega = 1$, 1.4, 1.8, 2.2 when A is the $-1, 2, -1$ matrix of order 10.

16. When $A = A^{\mathrm{T}}$, the *Arnoldi-Lanczos method* finds orthonormal q's so that $Aq_j = b_{j-1}q_{j-1} + a_jq_j + b_jq_{j+1}$ (with $q_0 = 0$). Multiply by q_j^{T} to find a formula for a_j. The equation says that $AQ = QT$ where T is a ______ matrix.

17. What bound on $|\lambda|_{\max}$ does Gershgorin give for these matrices (see Problem 4)? What are the three Gershgorin circles that contain all the eigenvalues?

$$A = \begin{bmatrix} .3 & .3 & .2 \\ .3 & .2 & .4 \\ .2 & .4 & .1 \end{bmatrix} \qquad A = \begin{bmatrix} 2 & -1 & 0 \\ -1 & 2 & -1 \\ 0 & -1 & 2 \end{bmatrix}.$$

The key point for large matrices is that matrix-vector multiplication is much faster than matrix-matrix multiplication. A crucial construction starts with a vector b and computes Ab, $A^2b, \ldots$ (but never A^2!). The first N vectors span the Nth ***Krylov subspace***. They are the columns of the ***Krylov matrix*** $\boldsymbol{K_N}$:

$$K_N = \begin{bmatrix} b & Ab & A^2b & \cdots & A^{N-1}b \end{bmatrix}.$$

The Arnoldi-Lanczos iteration orthogonalizes the columns of K_N, and the conjugate gradient iteration solves $Ax = b$ when A is symmetric positive definite.

Arnoldi Iteration	**Conjugate Gradient Iteration**	
$q_1 = b/\|b\|$	$x_0 = 0,\ r_0 = b,\ p_0 = r_0$	
for $n = 1$ to $N-1$	for $n = 1$ to N	
$v = Aq_n$	$\alpha_n = (r_{n-1}^{\mathrm{T}}r_{n-1})/(p_{n-1}^{\mathrm{T}}Ap_{n-1})$	step length x_{n-1} to x_n
for $j = 1$ to n	$x_n = x_{n-1} + \alpha_n p_{n-1}$	approximate solution
$h_{jn} = q_j^{\mathrm{T}}v$	$r_n = r_{n-1} - \alpha_n Ap_{n-1}$	new residual $b - Ax_n$
$v = v - h_{jn}q_j$	$\beta_n = (r_n^{\mathrm{T}}r_n)/(r_{n-1}^{\mathrm{T}}r_{n-1})$	improvement this step
$h_{n+1,n} = \|v\|$	$p_n = r_n + \beta_n p_{n-1}$	next search direction
$q_{n+1} = v/h_{n+1,n}$	*Note: Only* 1 *matrix–vector multiplication* Aq *and* Ap	

18. In Arnoldi, show that q_2 is orthogonal to q_1. The Arnoldi method is Gram–Schmidt orthogonalization applied to the Krylov matrix: $K_N = Q_N R_N$. The eigenvalues of $Q_N^{\mathrm{T}} A Q_N$ are often very close to those of A, even for $N \ll n$. The *Lanczos iteration* is Arnoldi for symmetric matrices (all coded in ARPACK).

19. In conjugate gradients, show that r_1 is orthogonal to r_0 (orthogonal residuals), and $p_1^{\mathrm{T}} A p_0 = 0$ (search directions are A-orthogonal). The iteration solves $Ax = b$ by minimizing the error $e^{\mathrm{T}} A e$ in the Krylov subspace. It is a fantastic algorithm.

Chapter

8 Linear Programming and Game Theory

8.1 LINEAR INEQUALITIES

Algebra is about equations, and analysis is often about inequalities. The line between them has always seemed clear. But I have realized that this chapter is a counterexample: ***linear programming is about inequalities***, but it is unquestionably a part of linear algebra. It is also extremely useful—business decisions are more likely to involve linear programming than determinants or eigenvalues.

There are three ways to approach the underlying mathematics: intuitively through the geometry, computationally through the simplex method, or algebraically through duality. These approaches are developed in Sections 8.1, 8.2, and 8.3. Then Section 8.4 is about problems (like marriage) in which the solution is an integer. Section 8.5 discusses poker and other matrix games. The MIT students in *Bringing Down the House* counted high cards to win at blackjack (Las Vegas follows fixed rules, and a true matrix game involves random strategies).

Section 8.3 has something new in this fourth edition. The simplex method is now in a lively competition with a completely different way to do the computations, called an **interior point method**. The excitement began when Karmarkar claimed that his version was 50 times faster than the simplex method. (His algorithm, outlined in 8.2, was one of the first to be patented—something we then believed impossible, and not really desirable.) That claim brought a burst of research into methods that approach the solution from the "interior" where all inequalities are strict: $x \geq 0$ becomes $x > 0$. The result is now a great way to get help from the dual problem in solving the primal problem.

One key to this chapter is to see the geometric meaning of ***linear inequalities***. An inequality divides n-dimensional space into a ***halfspace*** in which the inequality is satisfied, and a halfspace in which it is not. A typical example is $x + 2y \geq 4$. The boundary between the two halfspaces is the line $x + 2y = 4$, where the inequality is "tight." Figure 8.1 would look almost the same in three dimensions. The boundary becomes a plane like $x + 2y + z = 4$, and above it is the halfspace $x + 2y + z \geq 4$. In n dimensions, the "plane" has dimension $n - 1$.

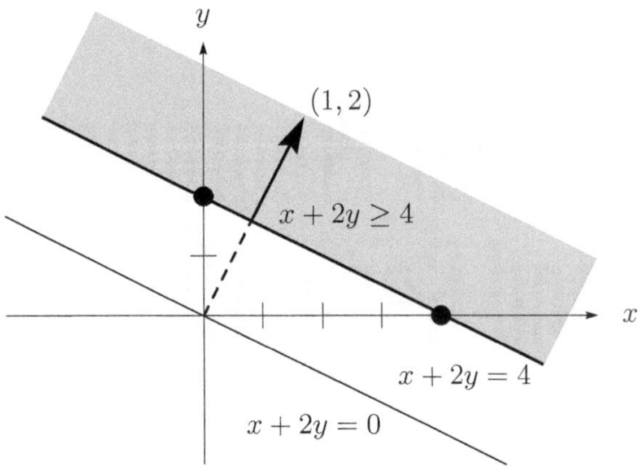

Figure 8.1 Equations give lines and planes. Inequalities give halfspaces.

Another constraint is fundamental to linear programming: x and y are required to be ***nonnegative***. This pair of inequalities $x \geq 0$ and $y \geq 0$ produces two more halfspaces. Figure 8.2 is bounded by the coordinate axes: $x \geq 0$ admits all points to the right of $x = 0$, and $y \geq 0$ is the halfspace above $y = 0$.

The Feasible Set and the Cost Function

The important step is to impose all three inequalities at once. They combine to give the shaded region in Figure 8.2. This ***feasible set*** is the *intersection* of the three halfspaces $x + 2y \geq 4$, $x \geq 0$, and $y \geq 0$. A feasible set is composed of the solutions to a family of linear inequalities like $Ax \geq b$ (the intersection of m halfspaces). When we also require that every component of x is nonnegative (the vector inequality $x \geq 0$), this adds n more halfspaces. The more constraints we impose, the smaller the feasible set.

It can easily happen that a feasible set is bounded or even empty. If we switch our example to the halfspace $x + 2y \leq 4$, keeping $x \geq 0$ and $y \geq 0$, we get the small triangle OAB. By combining both inequalities $x + 2y \geq 4$ and $x + 2y \leq 4$, the set shrinks to a line where $x + 2y = 4$. If we add a contradictory constraint like $x + 2y \leq -2$, the feasible set is empty.

The algebra of linear inequalities (or feasible sets) is one part of our subject. But linear programming has another essential ingredient: It looks for *the feasible point that maximizes or minimizes a certain* ***cost function*** like $2x + 3y$. The problem in linear programming is to find the point that ***lies in the feasible set and minimizes the cost***.

The problem is illustrated by the geometry of Figure 8.2. The family of costs $2x + 3y$ gives a family of parallel lines. The minimum cost comes when the first line intersects the feasible set. That intersection occurs at B, where $x^* = 0$ and $y^* = 2$; the minimum cost is $2x^* + 3y^* = 6$. The vector (0, 2) is ***feasible*** because it lies in the feasible set, it is ***optimal*** because it minimizes the cost function, and the minimum cost 6 is the ***value*** of the program. We denote optimal vectors by an asterisk.

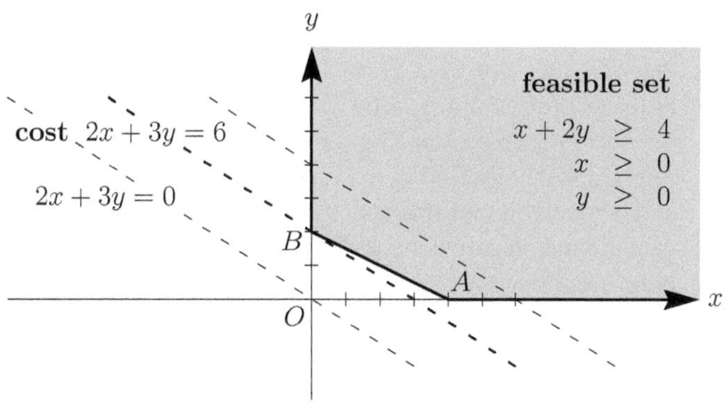

Figure 8.2 The feasible set with flat sides, and the costs $2x + 3y$, touching at B.

The optimal vector occurs at a corner of the feasible set. This is guaranteed by the geometry, because the lines that give the cost function (or the planes, when we get to more unknowns) move steadily up until they intersect the feasible set. The first contact must occur along its boundary! The "simplex method" will go from one corner of the feasible set to the next until it finds the corner with lowest cost. In contrast, "interior point methods" approach that optimal solution from ***inside*** the feasible set.

Note With a different cost function, the intersection might not be just a single point. If the cost happened to be $x + 2y$, the whole edge between B and A would be optimal. The minimum cost is $x^* + 2y^*$, which equals 4 for all these optimal vectors. On our feasible set, the maximum problem would have no solution ! The cost can go arbitrarily high and the maximum cost is infinite.

Every linear programming problem falls into one of three possible categories:

1. The feasible set is *empty.*
2. The cost function is *unbounded* on the feasible set.
3. The cost reaches its *minimum* (or maximum) on the feasible set: *the good case.*

The empty and unbounded cases should be very uncommon for a genuine problem in economics or engineering. We expect a solution.

Slack Variables

There is a simple way to change the inequality $x + 2y \geq 4$ to an equation. Just introduce the difference as a ***slack variable*** $w = x + 2y - 4$. This is our equation! The old constraint $x + 2y \geq 4$ is converted into $w \geq 0$, which matches perfectly the other inequality constraints $x \geq 0$, $y \geq 0$. Then we have only equations and simple nonnegativity constraints on x, y, w. The variables w that "take up the slack" are now included in the vector unknown x:

Primal problem ***Minimize cx subject to*** $Ax = b$ ***and*** $x \geq \mathbf{0}$.

The row vector c contains the costs; in our example, $c = [2 \quad 3 \quad 0]$. The condition $x \geq 0$ puts the problem into the nonnegative part of $\mathbf{R}^n$. Those inequalities cut back on the solutions to $Ax = b$. Elimination is in danger, and a completely new idea is needed.

The Diet Problem and Its Dual

Our example with cost $2x + 3y$ can be put into words. It illustrates the "diet problem" in linear programming, with two sources of protein—say steak and peanut butter. Each pound of peanut butter gives a unit of protein, and each steak gives two units. At least four units are required in the diet. Therefore a diet containing x pounds of peanut butter and y steaks is constrained by $x + 2y \geq 4$, as well as by $x \geq 0$ and $y \geq 0$. (We cannot have negative steak or peanut butter.) This is the feasible set, and the problem is to minimize the cost. If a pound of peanut butter costs \$2 and a steak is \$3, then the cost of the whole diet is $2x + 3y$. Fortunately, the optimal diet is two steaks: $x^* = 0$ and $y^* = 2$.

Every linear program, including this one, has a ***dual***. If the original problem is a minimization, its dual is a maximization. ***The minimum in the given "primal problem" equals the maximum in its dual.*** This is the key to linear programming, and it will be explained in Section 8.3. Here we stay with the diet problem and try to interpret its dual.

In place of the shopper, who buys enough protein at minimal cost, the dual problem is faced by a druggist. *Protein pills* compete with steak and peanut butter. Immediately we meet the two ingredients of a typical linear program: The druggist maximizes the pill price p, but that price is subject to linear constraints. Synthetic protein must not cost more than the protein in peanut butter (\$2 a unit) or the protein in steak (\$3 for two units). The price must be nonnegative or the druggist will not sell. Since four units of protein are required, the income to the druggist will be $4p$:

Dual problem ***Maximize*** $\mathbf{4p}$***, subject to*** $p \leq 2$, $2p \leq 3$, ***and*** $p \geq 0$.

In this example the dual is easier to solve than the primal; it has only one unknown p. The constraint $2p \leq 3$ is the tight one that is really active, and the maximum price of synthetic protein is $p = \$1.50$. The maximum revenue is $4p = \$6$, and the shopper ends up paying the same for natural and synthetic protein. That is the duality theorem: ***maximum equals minimum***.

Typical Applications

The next section will concentrate on solving linear programs. This is the time to describe two practical situations in which we *minimize or maximize a linear cost function subject to linear constraints.*

1. Production Planning. Suppose General Motors makes a profit of \$200 on each Chevrolet, \$300 on each Buick, and \$500 on each Cadillac. These get 20, 17, and 14 miles per gallon, respectively, and Congress insists that the average car must get 18. The plant can assemble a Chevrolet in 1 minute, a Buick in 2 minutes, and a Cadillac in 3 minutes. What is the maximum profit in 8 hours (480 minutes)?

Problem *Maximize the profit* $200x + 300y + 500z$ *subject to*

$$20x + 17y + 14z \geq 18(x + y + z), \quad x + 2y + 3z \leq 480, \quad x, y, z \geq 0.$$

2. **Portfolio Selection.** Federal bonds pay 5%, municipals pay 6%, and junk bonds pay 9%. We can buy amounts x, y, z not exceeding a total of \$100,000. The problem is to maximize the interest, with two constraints:

(i) no more than \$20,000 can be invested in junk bonds, and
(ii) the portfolio's average quality must be no lower than municipals, so $x \geq z$.

Problem *Maximize* $5x + 6y + 9z$ *subject to*

$$x + y + z \leq 100{,}000, \quad z \leq 20{,}000, \quad z \leq x, \quad x, y, z \geq 0.$$

The three inequalities give three slack variables, with new equations like $w = x - z$ and inequalities $w \geq 0$.

Problem Set 8.1

1. Sketch the feasible set with constraints $x + 2y \geq 6$, $2x + y \geq 6$, $x \geq 0$, $y \geq 0$. What points lie at the three "corners" of this set?

2. (Recommended) On the preceding feasible set, what is the minimum value of the cost function $x + y$? Draw the line $x + y =$ constant that first touches the feasible set. What points minimize the cost functions $3x + y$ and $x - y$?

3. Show that the feasible set constrained by $2x + 5y \leq 3$, $-3x + 8y \leq -5$, $x \geq 0$, $y \geq 0$, is empty.

4. Show that the following problem is feasible but unbounded, so it has no optimal solution: Maximize $x + y$, subject to $x \geq 0$, $y \geq 0$, $-3x + 2y \leq -1$, $x - y \leq 2$.

5. Add a single inequality constraint to $x \geq 0$, $y \geq 0$ such that the feasible set contains only one point.

6. What shape is the feasible set $x \geq 0$, $y \geq 0$, $z \geq 0$, $x + y + z = 1$, and what is the maximum of $x + 2y + 3z$?

7. Solve the portfolio problem at the end of the preceding section.

8. In the feasible set for the General Motors problem, the nonnegativity $x, y, z \geq 0$ leaves an eighth of three-dimensional space (the positive octant). How is this cut by the two planes from the constraints, and what shape is the feasible set? How do its corners show that, with only these two constraints, there will be only two kinds of cars in the optimal solution?

9. (Transportation problem) Suppose Texas, California, and Alaska each produce a million barrels of oil; 800,000 barrels are needed in Chicago at a distance of 1000, 2000, and 3000 miles from the three producers, respectively; and 2,200,000 barrels are needed in New England 1500, 3000, and 3700 miles away. If shipments cost one unit for each barrel-mile, what linear program with five equality constraints must be solved to minimize the shipping cost?

8.2 THE SIMPLEX METHOD

This section is about linear programming with n unknowns $x \geq 0$ and m constraints $Ax \geq b$. In the previous section we had two variables, and one constraint $x + 2y \geq 4$. The full problem is not hard to explain, and not easy to solve.

The best approach is to put the problem into matrix form. We are given A, b, and c:

1. an m by n matrix A,
2. a column vector b with m components, and
3. a row vector c (**cost vector**) with n components.

To be "feasible," the vector x must satisfy $x \geq 0$ and $Ax \geq b$. The optimal vector x^* is the *feasible vector of least cost*—and the cost is $cx = c_1x_1 + \cdots + c_nx_n$.

Minimum problem *Minimize the cost cx, subject to $x \geq 0$ and $Ax \geq b$.*

The condition $x \geq 0$ restricts x to the positive quadrant in n-dimensional space. In $\mathbf{R}^2$ it is a quarter of the plane; it is an eighth of $\mathbf{R}^3$. A random vector has one chance in 2^n of being nonnegative. $Ax \geq b$ produces m additional halfspaces, and the feasible vectors meet all of the $m+n$ conditions. In other words, x lies in the intersection of $m+n$ halfspaces. This **feasible set** has flat sides; it may be unbounded, and it may be empty.

The cost function cx brings to the problem a family of parallel planes. One plane $cx = 0$ goes through the origin. The planes $cx =$ constant give all possible costs. As the cost varies, these planes sweep out the whole n-dimensional space. *The optimal x^* (lowest cost) occurs at the point where **the planes first touch the feasible set**.*

Our aim is to compute x^*. We could do it (in principle) by finding all the corners of the feasible set, and computing their costs. In practice this is impossible. There could be billions of corners, and we cannot compute them all. Instead we turn to the ***simplex method***, one of the most celebrated ideas in computational mathematics. It was developed by Dantzig as a systematic way to solve linear programs, and either by luck or genius it is an astonishing success. The steps of the simplex method are summarized later, and first we try to explain them.

The Geometry: Movement Along Edges

I think it is the geometric explanation that gives the method away. Phase I simply locates one corner of the feasible set. ***The heart of the method goes from corner to corner along the edges of the feasible set***. At a typical corner there are n edges to choose from. Some edges lead away from the optimal but unknown x^*, and others lead gradually toward it. Dantzig chose an edge that leads to a new corner with a *lower cost*. There is no possibility of returning to anything more expensive. Eventually a special corner is reached, from which all edges go the wrong way: The cost has been minimized. That corner is the optimal vector x^*, and the method stops.

The next problem is to turn the ideas of *corner* and *edge* into linear algebra. **A corner is the meeting point of n different planes**. Each plane is given by one equation—just as three planes (front wall, side wall, and floor) produce a corner in three dimensions. Each corner of the feasible set comes from turning n of the $n + m$ inequalities $Ax \geq b$ and $x \geq 0$ into equations, and finding the intersection of these n planes.

One possibility is to choose the n equations $x_1 = 0, \ldots, x_n = 0$, and end up at the origin. Like all the other possible choices, *this intersection point will only be a genuine corner if it also satisfies the m remaining inequality constraints*. Otherwise it is not even in the feasible set, and is a complete fake. Our example with $n = 2$ variables and $m = 2$ constraints has six intersections, illustrated in Figure 8.3. Three of them are actually corners P, Q, R of the feasible set. They are the vectors $(0, 6)$, $(2, 2)$, and $(6, 0)$. One of them must be the optimal vector (unless the minimum cost is $-\infty$). The other three, including the origin, are fakes.

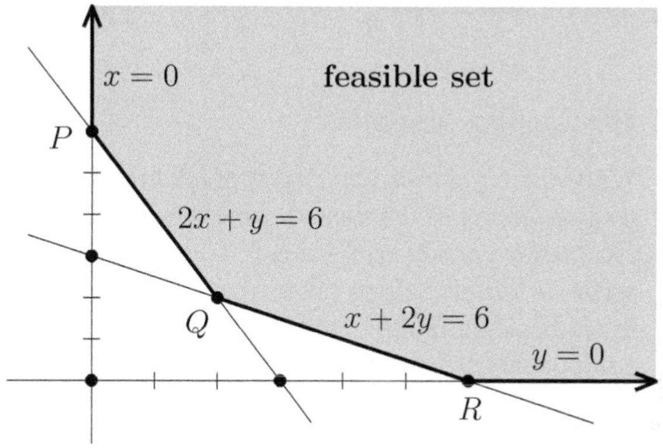

Figure 8.3 The corners P, Q, R, and the edges of the feasible set.

In general there are $(n+m)!/n!m!$ possible intersections. That counts the number of ways to choose n plane equations out of $n + m$. The size of that binomial coefficient makes computing all corners totally impractical for large m and n. It is the task of Phase I either to find one genuine corner or to establish that the feasible set is empty. We continue on the assumption that a corner has been found.

Suppose one of the n intersecting planes is removed. **The points that satisfy the remaining $n - 1$ equations form an edge that comes out of the corner**. This edge is the intersection of the $n - 1$ planes. To stay in the feasible set, only one direction is allowed along each edge. But we do have a choice of n different edges, and Phase II must make that choice.

To describe this phase, rewrite $Ax \geq b$ in a form completely parallel to the n simple constraints $x_j \geq 0$. This is the role of the ***slack variables*** $w = Ax - b$. The constraints $Ax \geq b$ are translated into $w_1 \geq 0, \ldots, w_m \geq 0$, with one slack variable for every row of A. The equation $w = Ax - b$, or $Ax - w = b$, goes into matrix form:

Slack variables give *m* equations $$\begin{bmatrix} A & -I \end{bmatrix} \begin{bmatrix} x \\ w \end{bmatrix} = b.$$

The feasible set is governed by these m equations and the $n + m$ simple inequalities $x \geq 0$, $w \geq 0$. We now have ***equality constraints and nonnegativity***.

The simplex method notices no difference between x and w, so we simplify:

$$\begin{bmatrix} A & -I \end{bmatrix} \text{ is renamed } A \qquad \begin{bmatrix} x \\ w \end{bmatrix} \text{ is renamed } x \qquad \begin{bmatrix} c & 0 \end{bmatrix} \text{ is renamed } c.$$

The equality constraints are now $Ax = b$. The $n + m$ inequalities become just $x \geq 0$. The only trace left of the slack variable w is in the fact that the new matrix A is m by $n+m$, and the new x has $n+m$ components. We keep this much of the original notation, leaving m and n unchanged as a reminder of what happened. The problem has become: ***Minimize cx, subject to x ≥ 0 and Ax = b.***

Example 1 The problem in Figure 8.3 has constraints $x + 2y \geq 6$, $2x + y \geq 6$, and cost $x + y$. The new system has four unknowns (x, y, and two slack variables):

$$A = \begin{bmatrix} 1 & 2 & -1 & 0 \\ 2 & 1 & 0 & -1 \end{bmatrix} \qquad b = \begin{bmatrix} 6 \\ 6 \end{bmatrix} \qquad c = \begin{bmatrix} 1 & 1 & 0 & 0 \end{bmatrix}.$$

The Simplex Algorithm

With equality constraints, the simplex method can begin. ***A corner is now a point where n components of the new vector x*** (the old x and w) ***are zero***. These n components of x are the *free variables* in $Ax = b$. The remaining m components are the *basic variables* or *pivot variables*. Setting the n free variables to zero, the m equations $Ax = b$ determine the m basic variables. This "basic solution" x will be a genuine corner if its m nonzero components are *positive*. Then x belongs to the feasible set.

> **8A** The ***corners of the feasible set*** are the ***basic feasible solutions*** of $Ax = b$. A solution is *basic* when n of its $m + n$ components are zero, and it is *feasible* when it satisfies $x \geq 0$. Phase I of the simplex method finds one basic feasible solution. Phase II moves step by step to the optimal x^*.

The corner point P in Figure 8.3 is the intersection of $x = 0$ with $2x + y - 6 = 0$.

Corner **(0, 6, 6, 0)**
Basic **(two zeros)**
Feasible **(positive nonzeros)**

$$Ax = \begin{bmatrix} 1 & 2 & -1 & 0 \\ 2 & 1 & 0 & -1 \end{bmatrix} \begin{bmatrix} 0 \\ 6 \\ 6 \\ 0 \end{bmatrix} = \begin{bmatrix} 6 \\ 6 \end{bmatrix} = b.$$

Which corner do we go to next? We want to move along an edge to an adjacent corner. Since the two corners are neighbors, $m - 1$ basic variables will remain basic. *Only one of the* 6s *will become free* (zero). At the same time, *one variable will move up from zero to become basic*. The other $m - 1$ basic components (in this case, the other 6) will change but stay positive. The choice of edge (see Example 2 below) decides which variable leaves the basis and which one enters. The basic variables are computed by solving $Ax = b$. The free components of x are set to zero.

Example 2 An entering variable and a leaving variable move us to a new corner.

$$\text{Minimize} \quad 7x_3 - x_4 - 3x_5 \quad \text{subject to} \quad \begin{aligned} x_1 \qquad + x_3 + 6x_4 + 2x_5 &= 8 \\ x_2 + x_3 \qquad\quad + 3x_5 &= 9. \end{aligned}$$

Start from the corner at which $x_1 = 8$ and $x_2 = 9$ are the basic variables. At that corner $x_3 = x_4 = x_5 = 0$. This is feasible, but the zero cost may not be minimal. It would be foolish to make x_3 positive, because its cost coefficient is $+7$ and we are trying to lower the cost. We choose x_5 because it has the most negative cost coefficient -3. ***The entering variable will be x_5.***

With x_5 entering the basis, x_1 or x_2 must leave. In the first equation, increase x_5 and decrease x_1 while keeping $x_1 + 2x_5 = 8$. Then x_1 will be down to zero when x_5 reaches 4. The second equation keeps $x_2 + 3x_5 = 9$. Here x_5 can only increase as far as 3. To go further would make x_2 negative, so ***the leaving variable is x_2***. The new corner has $x = (2, 0, 0, 0, 3)$. *The cost is down to -9.*

Quick Way In $Ax = b$, the right sides divided by the coefficients of the entering variable are $\frac{8}{2}$ and $\frac{9}{3}$. The smallest ratio $\frac{9}{3}$ tells which variable hits zero first, and must leave. We consider only positive ratios, because if the coefficient of x_5 were -3, then increasing x_5 would actually *increase* x_2. (At $x_5 = 10$ the second equation would give $x_2 = 39$.) ***The ratio $\frac{9}{3}$ says that the second variable leaves***. It also gives $x_5 = 3$.

If all coefficients of x_5 had been negative, this would be an *unbounded* case: we can make x_5 arbitrarily large, and bring the cost down toward $-\infty$.

The current step ends at the new corner $x = (2, 0, 0, 0, 3)$. The next step will only be easy if the basic variables x_1 and x_5 stand by themselves (as x_1 and x_2 originally did). Therefore, we "pivot" by substituting $x_5 = \frac{1}{3}(9 - x_2 - x_3)$ into the cost function and the first equation. The new problem, starting from the new corner, is:

$$\begin{array}{ll} \text{Minimize the cost} & 7x_3 - x_4 - (9 - x_2 - x_3) = x_2 + 8x_3 - x_4 - 9 \\ \text{with constraints} & x_1 - \frac{2}{3}x_2 + \frac{1}{3}x_3 + 6x_4 \qquad = 2 \\ & \qquad \frac{1}{3}x_2 + \frac{1}{3}x_3 \qquad + x_5 = 3. \end{array}$$

The next step is now easy. The only negative coefficient -1 in the cost makes x_4 the entering variable. The ratios of $\frac{2}{6}$ and $\frac{3}{0}$, the right sides divided by the x_4 column, make x_1 the leaving variable. The new corner is $x^* = (0, 0, 0, \frac{1}{3}, 3)$. The new cost $-9\frac{1}{3}$ is the minimum.

In a large problem, a departing variable might reenter the basis later on. But the cost keeps going down—except in a degenerate case—so the m basic variables can't be the same as before. No corner is ever revisited! The simplex method must end at the optimal corner (or at $-\infty$ if the cost turns out to be unbounded). What is remarkable is the speed at which x^* is found.

Summary The cost coefficients $7, -1, -3$ at the first corner and $1, 8, -1$ at the second corner decided the entering variables. (These numbers go into r, the crucial vector defined below. When they are all positive we stop.) The ratios decided the leaving variables.

Remark on Degeneracy A corner is *degenerate* if more than the usual n components of x are zero. More than n planes pass through the corner, so a basic variable happens to vanish. The ratios that determine the leaving variable will include zeros, and the basis might change without actually moving from the corner. In theory, we could stay at a corner and cycle forever in the choice of basis.

Fortunately, cycling does not occur. It is so rare that commercial codes ignore it. Unfortunately, degeneracy is extremely common in applications—if you print the cost after each simplex step you see it repeat several times before the simplex method finds a good edge. Then the cost decreases again.

The Tableau

Each simplex step involves decisions followed by row operations—the entering and leaving variables have to be chosen, and they have to be made to come and go. One way to organize the step is to fit A, b, c into a large matrix, or ***tableau***:

$$\textbf{Tableau is } m+1 \textbf{ by } m+n+1 \qquad T = \begin{bmatrix} A & b \\ c & 0 \end{bmatrix}.$$

At the start, the basic variables may be mixed with the free variables. Renumbering if necessary, *suppose that* $x_1, \dots, x_m$ *are the basic (nonzero) variables at the current corner*. The first m columns of A form a square matrix B (the *basis matrix* for that corner). The last n columns give an m by n matrix N. The cost vector c splits into $[\, c_B \quad c_N \,]$, and the unknown x into (x_B, x_N).

At the corner, the free variables are $x_N = 0$. There, $Ax = b$ turns into $Bx_B = b$:

$$\textbf{Tableau at corner} \qquad T = \left[\begin{array}{c:c:c} B & N & b \\ \hdashline c_B & c_N & 0 \end{array}\right] \quad x_N = 0 \quad x_B = B^{-1}b \quad \textbf{cost} = c_B B^{-1} b.$$

The basic variables will stand alone when elimination multiplies by B^{-1}:

$$\textbf{Reduced tableau} \qquad T' = \left[\begin{array}{c:c:c} I & B^{-1}N & B^{-1}b \\ \hdashline c_B & c_N & 0 \end{array}\right].$$

To reach the ***fully reduced row echelon form*** $R = \mathrm{rref}(T)$, subtract c_B times the top block row from the bottom row:

$$\textbf{Fully reduced} \qquad R = \left[\begin{array}{c:c:c} I & B^{-1}N & B^{-1}b \\ \hdashline 0 & \boldsymbol{c_N - c_B B^{-1} N} & -c_B B^{-1} b \end{array}\right].$$

Let me review the meaning of each entry in this tableau, and also call attention to Example 3 (following, with numbers). Here is the algebra:

$$\textbf{Constraints} \quad x_B + B^{-1}Nx_N = B^{-1}b \qquad \textbf{Corner} \quad x_B = B^{-1}b, \ x_N = 0. \tag{1}$$

The cost $c_Bx_B + c_Nx_N$ has been turned into

$$\textbf{Cost} \quad cx = (c_N - c_B B^{-1} N)x_N + c_B B^{-1} b \quad \textbf{Cost at this corner} = c_B B^{-1} b. \tag{2}$$

Every important quantity appears in the fully reduced tableau R. We can decide whether the corner is optimal by looking at $r = c_N - c_B B^{-1} N$ in the middle of the bottom row. **If any entry in r is negative, the cost can still be reduced**. We can make rx_N negative, at the start of equation (2), by increasing a component of x_N. That will be our next step. But if $r \geq 0$, the best corner has been found. This is the ***stopping test***, or ***optimality condition***:

> **8B** The corner is optimal when $r = c_N - c_B B^{-1} N \geq 0$. Its cost is $c_B B^{-1} b$. Negative components of r correspond to edges on which the cost goes down. **The entering variable x_i corresponds to the most negative component of r.**

The components of r are the ***reduced costs***—the cost in c_N to use a free variable *minus what it saves*. Computing r is called ***pricing out*** the variables. If the direct cost (in c_N) is less than the saving (from reducing basic variables), then $r_i < 0$, and it will pay to increase that free variable.

Suppose the most negative reduced cost is r_i. Then the ith component of x_N is the ***entering variable***, which increases from zero to a positive value α at the next corner (the end of the edge).

As x_i is increased, other components of x may decrease (to maintain $Ax = b$). The x_k that reaches zero first becomes the ***leaving variable***—it changes from basic to free. *We reach the next corner when a component of x_B drops to zero.*

That new corner is feasible because we still have $x \geq 0$. It is basic because we again have n zero components. The ith component of x_N went from zero to α. The kth component of x_B dropped to zero (the other components of x_B remain positive). The leaving x_k that drops to zero is the one that gives the minimum ratio in equation (3):

8C Suppose x_i is the entering variable and u is column i of N:

$$\textbf{At new corner} \qquad x_i = \alpha = \text{smallest ratio } \frac{(B^{-1}b)_j}{(B^{-1}u)_j} = \frac{(B^{-1}b)_k}{(B^{-1}u)_k}. \tag{3}$$

This minimum is taken only over positive components of $B^{-1}u$. The kth column of the old B leaves the basis (x_k becomes 0) and the new column u enters.

$B^{-1}u$ is the column of $B^{-1}N$ in the reduced tableau R, above the most negative entry in the bottom row r. If $B^{-1}u \leq 0$, the next corner is infinitely far away and the minimal cost is $-\infty$ (this doesn't happen here). Our example will go from the corner P to Q, and begin again at Q.

Example 3 The original cost function $x + y$ and constraints $Ax = b = (6, 6)$ give

$$\begin{bmatrix} A & b \\ c & 0 \end{bmatrix} = \left[\begin{array}{cccc:c} 1 & 2 & -1 & 0 & 6 \\ 2 & 1 & 0 & -1 & 6 \\ \hdashline 1 & 1 & 0 & 0 & 0 \end{array}\right].$$

At the corner P in Figure 8.3, $x = 0$ intersects $2x + y = 6$. To be organized, we exchange columns 1 and 3 to put basic variables before free variables:

$$\textbf{Tableau at } \boldsymbol{P} \qquad T = \left[\begin{array}{cc:cc:c} -1 & 2 & 1 & 0 & 6 \\ 0 & 1 & 2 & -1 & 6 \\ \hdashline 0 & 1 & 1 & 0 & 0 \end{array}\right].$$

Then, elimination multiplies the first row by -1, to give a unit pivot, and uses the second row to produce zeros in the second column:

$$\textbf{Fully reduced at } \boldsymbol{P} \qquad R = \left[\begin{array}{cc:cc:c} 1 & 0 & 3 & -2 & 6 \\ 0 & 1 & 2 & -1 & 6 \\ \hdashline 0 & 0 & -1 & 1 & -6 \end{array}\right].$$

Look first at $\boldsymbol{r = [\,-1 \quad 1\,]}$ in the bottom row. It has a negative entry in column 3, so the third variable will enter the basis. The current corner P and its cost $+6$ are not optimal. The column above that negative entry is $B^{-1}u = (3, 2)$; its ratios with the last column are $\frac{6}{3}$ and $\frac{6}{2}$. Since the first ratio is smaller, the first unknown w (and the first column of the tableau) is pushed out of the basis. We move along the feasible set from corner P to corner Q in Figure 8.3.

The new tableau exchanges columns 1 and 3, and pivoting by elimination gives

$$\left[\begin{array}{cc|cc|c} 3 & 0 & 1 & -2 & 6 \\ 2 & 1 & 0 & -1 & 6 \\ \hline -1 & 0 & 0 & 1 & -6 \end{array}\right] \rightarrow \left[\begin{array}{cc|cc|c} 1 & 0 & \frac{1}{3} & -\frac{2}{3} & 2 \\ 0 & 1 & -\frac{2}{3} & \frac{1}{3} & 2 \\ \hline 0 & 0 & \frac{1}{3} & \frac{1}{3} & -4 \end{array}\right].$$

In that new tableau at Q, $r = \left[\frac{1}{3} \;\; \frac{1}{3}\right]$ is positive. **The stopping test is passed**. The corner $x = y = 2$ and its cost $+4$ are optimal.

The Organization of a Simplex Step

The geometry of the simplex method is now expressed in algebra—"corners" are "basic feasible solutions." The vector r and the ratio α are decisive. Their calculation is the heart of the simplex method, and it can be organized in three different ways:

1. In a tableau, as above.
2. By updating B^{-1} when column u taken from N replaces column k of B.
3. By computing $B = LU$, and updating these LU factors instead of B^{-1}.

This list is really a brief history of the simplex method. In some ways, the most fascinating stage was the first—the *tableau*—which dominated the subject for so many years. For most of us it brought an aura of mystery to linear programming, chiefly because it managed to avoid matrix notation almost completely (by the skillful device of writing out all matrices in full !). For computational purposes (except for small problems in textbooks), the day of the tableau is over.

To see why, remember that after the most negative coefficient in r indicates which column u will enter the basis, none of the other columns above r will be used. *It was a waste of time to compute them.* In a larger problem, hundreds of columns would be computed time and time again, just waiting for their turn to enter the basis. It makes the theory clear to do the eliminations so completely and reach R. But in practice this cannot be justified.

It is quicker, and in the end simpler, to see what calculations are really necessary. Each simplex step exchanges a column of N for a column of B. Those columns are decided by r and α. This step begins with the current basis matrix B and the current solution $x_B = B^{-1}b$.

A Step of the Simplex Method

1. Compute the row vector $\lambda = c_B B^{-1}$ and the reduced costs $r = c_N - \lambda N$.
2. If $r \geq 0$, stop: the current solution is optimal. Otherwise, if r_i is the most negative component, choose u = column i of N to enter the basis.
3. Compute the ratios of $B^{-1}b$ to $B^{-1}u$, admitting only positive components of $B^{-1}u$. (If $B^{-1}u < 0$, the minimal cost is $-\infty$.) When the smallest ratio occurs at component k, the kth column of the current B will leave.
4. Update B, B^{-1}, or LU, and the solution $x_B = B^{-1}b$. Return to step **1**.

This is sometimes called the ***revised simplex method*** to distinguish it from the operations on a tableau. It is really the simplex method itself, boiled down.

This discussion is finished once we decide how to compute steps **1**, **3**, and **4**:

$$\lambda = c_B B^{-1}, \quad v = B^{-1}u, \quad \text{and} \quad x_B = B^{-1}b. \tag{4}$$

The most popular way is to work directly with B^{-1}, calculating it explicitly at the first corner. At succeeding corners, the pivoting step is simple. When column k of the identity matrix is replaced by u, column k of B^{-1} is replaced by $v = B^{-1}u$. To recover the identity matrix, elimination will multiply the old B^{-1} by

$$E^{-1} = \begin{bmatrix} 1 & & v_1 & & \\ & \cdot & \cdot & & \\ & & v_k & & \\ & & \cdot & \cdot & \\ & & v_n & & 1 \end{bmatrix}^{-1} = \begin{bmatrix} 1 & & -v_1/v_k & & \\ & \cdot & \cdot & & \\ & & 1/v_k & & \\ & & \cdot & \cdot & \\ & & -v_n/v_k & & 1 \end{bmatrix} \tag{5}$$

Many simplex codes use the ***product form of the inverse***, which saves these simple matrices E^{-1} instead of directly updating B^{-1}. When needed, they are applied to b and c_B. At regular intervals (maybe every 40 simplex steps), B^{-1} is recomputed and the E^{-1} are erased. Equation (5) is checked in Problem 9 at the end of this section.

A newer approach uses the ordinary methods of numerical linear algebra, regarding equation (4) as three equations sharing the same matrix B:

$$\lambda B = c_B, \quad Bv = u, \quad Bx_B = b. \tag{6}$$

The usual factorization $B = LU$ (or $PB = LU$, with row exchanges for stability) leads to the three solutions. L and U can be updated instead of recomputed.

One question remains: *How many simplex steps do we have to take*? This is impossible to answer in advance. Experience shows that the method touches only about $3m/2$ different corners, which means an operation count of about m^2n. That is comparable to ordinary elimination for $Ax = b$, and is the reason for the simplex method's success. But mathematics shows that the path length cannot always be bounded by any fixed multiple or power of m. The worst feasible sets (Klee and Minty invented a lopsided cube) can force the simplex method to try every corner—at exponential cost.

It was ***Khachian's method*** that showed that linear programming could be solved in polynomial time.* His algorithm stayed *inside* the feasible set, and captured x^* in a series of shrinking ellipsoids. Linear programming is in the nice class ***P***, not in the dreaded class ***NP*** (like the traveling salesman problem). For ***NP*** problems it is believed (but not proved) that all deterministic algorithms must take exponentially long to finish, in the worst case.

All this time, the simplex method was doing the job—in an *average* time that is now proved (for variants of the usual method) to be polynomial. For some reason, hidden in

* The number of operations is bounded by powers of m and n, as in elimination. For integer programming and factoring into primes, all known algorithms can take exponentially long. The celebrated conjecture "$P \neq NP$" says that such problems cannot have polynomial algorithms.

the geometry of many-dimensional polyhedra, bad feasible sets are rare and the simplex method is lucky.

Karmarkar's Method

We come now to the most sensational event in the recent history of linear programming. Karmarkar proposed a method based on two simple ideas, and in his experiments it defeated the simplex method. The choice of problem and the details of the code are both crucial, and the debate is still going on. But Karmarkar's ideas were so natural, and fit so perfectly into the framework of applied linear algebra, that they can be explained in a few paragraphs.

The first idea is to start from a point ***inside the feasible set***—we will suppose it is $x^0 = (1, 1, \ldots, 1)$. Since the cost is cx, the best *cost-reducing direction* is toward $-c$. Normally that takes us off the feasible set; moving in that direction does not maintain $Ax = b$. If $Ax^0 = b$ and $Ax^1 = b$, then $\Delta x = x^1 - x^0$ has to satisfy $A\Delta x = 0$. ***The step Δx must lie in the nullspace of A.*** Therefore we *project* $-c$ onto the nullspace, to find the feasible direction closest to the best direction. This is the natural but expensive step in Karmarkar's method.

The step Δx is a multiple of the projection $-Pc$. The longer the step, the more the cost is reduced—but we cannot go out of the feasible set. The multiple of $-Pc$ is chosen so that x^1 is close to, but a *little inside*, the boundary at which a component of x reaches zero.

That completes the first idea—the projection that gives the *steepest feasible descent*. The second step needs a new idea, since to continue in the same direction is useless.

Karmarkar's suggestion is to ***transform x^1 back to $(1, 1, \ldots, 1)$ at the center***. His change of variables was nonlinear, but the simplest transformation is just a ***rescaling*** by a diagonal matrix D. Then we have room to move. The rescaling from x to $X = D^{-1}x$ changes the constraint and the cost:

$$Ax = b \text{ becomes } ADX = b \qquad\qquad c^{\mathrm{T}}x \text{ becomes } c^{\mathrm{T}}DX.$$

Therefore *the matrix AD takes the place of A, and the vector $c^{\mathrm{T}}D$ takes the place of c^{T}*. The second step projects the new c onto the nullspace of the new A. All the work is in this projection, to solve the weighted normal equations:

$$(AD^2A^{\mathrm{T}})y = AD^2c. \qquad (7)$$

The normal way to compute y is by elimination. Gram–Schmidt will orthogonalize the columns of DA^{T}, which can be expensive (although it makes the rest of the calculation easy). The favorite for large sparse problems is the ***conjugate gradient method***, which gives the exact answer y more slowly than elimination, but you can go part way and then stop. In the middle of elimination you cannot stop.

Like other new ideas in scientific computing, Karmarkar's method succeeded on some problems and not on others. The underlying idea was analyzed and improved. Newer **interior point methods** (staying inside the feasible set) are a major success—mentioned in the next section. And the simplex method remains tremendously valuable, like the whole subject of linear programming—which was discovered centuries after $Ax = b$, but shares the fundamental ideas of linear algebra. The most far-reaching of those ideas is duality, which comes next.

Problem Set 8.2

1. Minimize $x_1 + x_2 - x_3$, subject to

$$\begin{aligned} 2x_1 - 4x_2 + x_3 + x_4 \quad &= 4 \\ 3x_1 + 5x_2 + x_3 \quad + x_5 &= 2. \end{aligned}$$

Which of x_1, x_2, x_3 should enter the basis, and which of x_4, x_5 should leave? Compute the new pair of basic variables, and find the cost at the new corner.

2. After the preceding simplex step, prepare for and decide on the next step.

3. In Example 3, suppose the cost is $3x + y$. With rearrangement, the cost vector is $c = (0, 1, 3, 0)$. Show that $r \geq 0$ and, therefore, that corner P is optimal.

4. Suppose the cost function in Example 3 is $x - y$, so that after rearrangement $c = (0, -1, 1, 0)$ at the corner P. Compute r and decide which column u should enter the basis. Then compute $B^{-1}u$ and show from its sign that you will never meet another corner. We are climbing the y-axis in Figure 8.3, and $x - y$ goes to $-\infty$.

5. Again in Example 3, change the cost to $x + 3y$. Verify that the simplex method takes you from P to Q to R, and that the corner R is optimal.

6. *Phase I finds a basic feasible solution to* $Ax = b$ (a corner). After changing signs to make $b \geq 0$, consider the auxiliary problem of minimizing $w_1 + w_2 + \cdots + w_m$, subject to $x \geq 0$, $w \geq 0$, $Ax + w = b$. Whenever $Ax = b$ has a nonnegative solution, the minimum cost in this problem will be zero—with $w^* = 0$.

   (a) Show that, for this new problem, the corner $x = 0$, $w = b$ is both basic and feasible. Therefore *its* Phase I is already set, and the simplex method can proceed to find the optimal pair x^*, w^*. If $w^* = 0$, then x^* is the required corner in the original problem.

   (b) With $A = [\,1 \quad -1\,]$ and $b = [3]$, write out the auxiliary problem, its Phase I vector $x = 0$, $w = b$, and its optimal vector. Find the corner of the feasible set $x_1 - x_2 = 3$, $x_1 \geq x_2 \geq 0$, and draw a picture of this set.

7. If we wanted to maximize instead of minimize the cost (with $Ax = b$ and $x \geq 0$), what would be the stopping test on r, and what rules would choose the column of N to make basic and the column of B to make free?

8. Minimize $2x_1 + x_2$, subject to $x_1 + x_2 \geq 4$, $x_1 + 3x_2 \geq 12$, $x_1 - x_2 \geq 0$, $x \geq 0$.

9. Verify the inverse in equation (5), and show that BE has $Bv = u$ in its kth column. Then BE is the correct basis matrix for the next stop, $E^{-1}B^{-1}$ is its inverse, and E^{-1} updates the basis matrix correctly.

10. Suppose we want to minimize $cx = x_1 - x_2$, subject to

$$\begin{aligned} 2x_1 - 4x_2 + x_3 \quad &= 6 \\ 3x_1 + 6x_2 \quad + x_4 &= 12 \end{aligned} \qquad (\text{all } x_1, x_2, x_3, x_4 \geq 0).$$

Starting from $x = (0, 0, 6, 12)$, should x_1 or x_2 be increased from its current value of zero? How far can it be increased until the equations force x_3 or x_4 down to zero? At that point, what is the new x?

11. For the matrix $P = I - A^{\mathrm{T}}(AA^{\mathrm{T}})^{-1}A$, show that if x is in the nullspace of A, then $Px = x$. The nullspace stays unchanged under this projection.

12. (a) Minimize the cost $c^{\mathrm{T}}x = 5x_1 + 4x_2 + 8x_3$ on the plane $x_1 + x_2 + x_3 = 3$, by testing the vertices P, Q, R, where the triangle is cut off by the requirement $x \geq 0$.

(b) Project $c = (5, 4, 8)$ onto the nullspace of $A = [\,1 \quad 1 \quad 1\,]$, and find the maximum step s that keeps $e - sPc$ nonnegative.

8.3 THE DUAL PROBLEM

Elimination can solve $Ax = b$, but the four fundamental subspaces showed that a different and deeper understanding is possible. It is exactly the same for linear programming. The mechanics of the simplex method will solve a linear program, but duality is really at the center of the underlying theory. Introducing the dual problem is an elegant idea, and at the same time fundamental for the applications. We shall explain as much as we understand.

The theory begins with the given *primal problem*:

Primal (P) *Minimize cx, subject to $x \geq 0$ and $Ax \geq b$.*

The dual problem starts from the same A, b, and c, and reverses everything. In the primal, c is in the cost function and b is in the constraint. In the dual, b and c are switched. The dual unknown y is a *row vector* with m components, and the feasible set has $yA \leq c$ instead of $Ax \geq b$.

In short, the dual of a minimum problem is a maximum problem. Now $y \geq 0$:

Dual (D) *Maximize yb, subject to $y \geq 0$ and $yA \leq c$.*

The dual of *this* problem is the original minimum problem. There is complete symmetry between the primal and dual problems. The simplex method applies equally well to a maximization—anyway, both problems get solved at once.

I have to give you some interpretation of all these reversals. They conceal a competition between the minimizer and the maximizer. In the diet problem, the minimizer has n foods (peanut butter and steak, in Section 8.1). They enter the diet in the (nonnegative) amounts $x_1, \ldots, x_n$. The constraints represent *m required vitamins*, in place of the one earlier constraint of sufficient protein. The entry a_{ij} measures the ith vitamin in the jth food, and the ith row of $Ax \geq b$ forces the diet to include at least b_i of that vitamin. If c_j is the cost of the jth food, then $c_1x_1 + \cdots + c_nx_n = cx$ is the cost of the diet. That cost is to be minimized.

In the dual, the druggist is selling vitamin pills at prices $y_i \geq 0$. Since food j contains vitamins in the amounts a_{ij}, the druggist's price for the vitamin equivalent cannot exceed the grocer's price c_j. That is the jth constraint in $yA \leq c$. Working within this constraint on vitamin prices, the druggist can sell the required amount b_i of each vitamin for a total income of $y_1b_1 + \cdots + y_mb_m = yb$—to be maximized.

The feasible sets for the primal and dual problems look completely different. The first is a subset of $\mathbf{R}^n$, marked out by $x \geq 0$ and $Ax \geq b$. The second is a subset of $\mathbf{R}^m$, determined by $y \geq 0$ and A^{T} and c. The whole theory of linear programming hinges on the relation between primal and dual. Here is the fundamental result:

8D Duality Theorem When both problems have feasible vectors, they have optimal x^* and y^*. **The minimum cost cx^* equals the maximum income y^*b.**

If optimal vectors do not exist, there are two possibilities: Either both feasible sets are empty, or one is empty and the other problem is unbounded (the maximum is $+\infty$ or the minimum is $-\infty$).

The duality theorem settles the competition between the grocer and the druggist. *The result is always a tie.* We will find a similar "minimax theorem" in game theory. The customer has no economic reason to prefer vitamins over food, even though the druggist guarantees to match the grocer on every food—and even undercuts on expensive foods (like peanut butter). We will show that expensive foods are kept out of the optimal diet, so the outcome can be (and is) a tie.

This may seem like a total stalemate, but I hope you will not be fooled. The optimal vectors contain the crucial information. In the primal problem, x^* tells the purchaser what to buy. In the dual, y^* fixes the natural prices (***shadow prices***) at which the economy should run. Insofar as our linear model reflects the true economy, x^* and y^* represent the essential decisions to be made.

We want to prove that $cx^* = y^*b$. It may seem obvious that the druggist can raise the vitamin prices y^* to meet the grocer, but only one thing is truly clear: Since each food can be replaced by its vitamin equivalent, with no increase in cost, all adequate food diets must cost at least as much as vitamins. This is only a one-sided inequality, *druggist's price $\leq$ grocer's price*. It is called ***weak duality***, and it is easy to prove for any linear program and its dual:

8E If x and y are feasible in the primal and dual problems, then $yb \leq cx$.

Proof Since the vectors are feasible, they satisfy $Ax \geq b$ and $yA \leq c$. Because feasibility also includes $x \geq 0$ and $y \geq 0$, we can take inner products without spoiling those inequalities (multiplying by negative numbers would reverse them):

$$yAx \geq yb \quad \text{and} \quad yAx \leq cx. \tag{1}$$

Since the left-hand sides are identical, we have weak duality $yb \leq cx$. ∎

This one-sided inequality prohibits the possibility that both problems are unbounded. If yb is arbitrarily large, a feasible x would contradict $yb \leq cx$. Similarly, if cx can go down to $-\infty$, the dual cannot admit a feasible y.

Equally important, any vectors that achieve $yb = cx$ must be optimal. At that point the grocer's price equals the druggist's price. We recognize an optimal food diet and optimal vitamin prices by the fact that the consumer has nothing to choose:

8F If the vectors x and y are feasible and $cx = yb$, then x and y are optimal.

Since no feasible y can make yb larger than cx, our y that achieves this value is optimal. Similarly, any x that achieves the cost $cx = yb$ must be an optimal x^*.

We give an example with two foods and two vitamins. Note how A^{T} appears when we write out the dual, since $yA \le c$ for row vectors means $A^{\mathrm{T}}y^{\mathrm{T}} \le c^{\mathrm{T}}$ for columns.

Primal Minimize $x_1 + 4x_2$ subject to $x_1 \ge 0,\ x_2 \ge 0$

$$2x_1 + x_2 \ge 6$$
$$5x_1 + 3x_2 \ge 7.$$

Dual Maximize $6y_1 + 7y_2$ subject to $y_1 \ge 0,\ y_2 \ge 0$

$$2y_1 + 5y_2 \le 1$$
$$y_1 + 3x_2 \le 4.$$

Solution $x_1 = 3$ and $x_2 = 0$ are feasible, with cost $x_1 + 4x_2 = 3$. In the dual, $y_1 = \frac{1}{2}$ and $y_2 = 0$ give the same value $6y_1 + 7y_2 = 3$. These vectors must be optimal.

Please look closely to see what actually happens at the moment when $yb = cx$. Some of the inequality constraints are **tight**, meaning that equality holds. Other constraints are loose, and the key rule makes economic sense:

(i) The diet has $x_j^* = 0$ when food j is priced *above* its vitamin equivalent.
(ii) The price is $y_i^* = 0$ when vitamin i is *oversupplied* in the diet x^*.

In the example, $x_2 = 0$ because the second food is too expensive. Its price exceeds the druggist's price, since $y_1 + 3y_2 \le 4$ is a strict inequality $\frac{1}{2} + 0 < 4$. Similarly, the diet required seven units of the second vitamin, but actually supplied $5x_1 + 3x_2 = 15$. So we found $y_2 = 0$, and that vitamin is a *free good*. You can see how the duality has become complete.

These ***optimality conditions*** are easy to understand in matrix terms. From equation (1) we want $y^*Ax^* = y^*b$ at the optimum. Feasibility requires $Ax^* \ge b$, and we look for any components *in which equality fails*. This corresponds to a vitamin that is oversupplied, so its price is $y_i^* = 0$.

At the same time, we have $y^*A \le c$. All strict inequalities (expensive foods) correspond to $x_j^* = 0$ (omission from the diet). That is the key to $y^*Ax^* = cx^*$, which we need. These are the ***complementary slackness conditions*** of linear programming, and the ***Kuhn–Tucker conditions*** of nonlinear programming:

8G The optimal vectors x^* and y^* satisfy **complementary slackness**:

$$\text{If } (Ax^*)_i > b_i \quad \text{then} \quad y_i^* = 0 \qquad\qquad \text{If } (y^*A)_j < c_j \quad \text{then} \quad x_j^* = 0. \tag{2}$$

Let me repeat the proof. Any feasible vectors x and y satisfy weak duality:

$$yb \le y(Ax) = (yA)x \le cx. \tag{3}$$

We need equality, and there is only one way in which y^*b can equal $y^*(Ax^*)$. *Any time $b_i < (Ax^*)_i$, the factor y_i^* that multiplies these components must be zero.*

Similarly, feasibility gives $yAx \leq cx$. We get equality only when the second slackness condition is fulfilled. If there is an overpricing $(y^*A)_j < c_j$, it must be canceled through multiplication by $x_j^* = 0$. This leaves us with $y^*b = cx^*$ in equation (3). This equality guarantees the optimality of x^* and y^*.

The Proof of Duality

The one-sided inequality $yb \leq cx$ was easy to prove; it gave a quick test for optimal vectors (they turn it into an equality); and now it has given the slackness conditions in equation (2). The only thing it has not done is to show that $y^*b = cx^*$ is really possible. Until those optimal vectors are actually produced, the duality theorem is not complete.

To produce y^* we return to the simplex method—which has already computed x^*. Our problem is to show that the method stopped in the right place for the dual problem (even though it was constructed to solve the primal). Recall that the m inequalities $Ax \geq b$ were changed to equations by introducing the slack variables $w = Ax - b$:

$$\textbf{Primal feasibility} \qquad \begin{bmatrix} A & -I \end{bmatrix} \begin{bmatrix} x \\ w \end{bmatrix} = b \quad \text{and} \quad \begin{bmatrix} x \\ w \end{bmatrix} \geq 0. \tag{4}$$

Every simplex step picked m columns of the long matrix $[\,A \quad -I\,]$ to be basic, and shifted them (theoretically) to the front. This produced $[\,B \quad N\,]$. The same shift reordered the long cost vector $[\,c \quad 0\,]$ into $[\,c_B \quad c_N\,]$. The stopping condition, which brought the simplex method to an end, was $r = c_N - c_B B^{-1} N \geq 0$.

This condition $r \geq 0$ was finally met, since the number of corners is finite. At that moment the cost was as low as possible:

$$\textbf{Minimum cost} \qquad cx^* = \begin{bmatrix} c_B & c_N \end{bmatrix} \begin{bmatrix} B^{-1}b \\ 0 \end{bmatrix} = c_B B^{-1} b. \tag{5}$$

If we can choose $y^* = c_B B^{-1}$ in the dual, we certainly have $y^*b = cx^*$. The minimum and maximum will be equal. We have to show that this y^* satisfies the dual constraints $yA \leq c$ and $y \geq 0$:

$$\textbf{Dual feasibility} \qquad y\begin{bmatrix} A & -I \end{bmatrix} \leq \begin{bmatrix} c & 0 \end{bmatrix}. \tag{6}$$

When the simplex method reshuffles the long matrix and vector to put the basic variables first, this rearranges the constraints in equation (6) into

$$y\begin{bmatrix} B & N \end{bmatrix} \leq \begin{bmatrix} c_B & c_N \end{bmatrix}. \tag{7}$$

For $y^* = c_B B^{-1}$, the first half is an equality and the second half is $c_B B^{-1} N \leq c_N$. This is the stopping condition $r \geq 0$ that we know to be satisfied! Therefore our y^* is feasible, and *the duality theorem is proved.* By locating the critical m by m matrix B, which is nonsingular as long as degeneracy is forbidden, the simplex method has produced the optimal y^* as well as x^*.

Shadow Prices

In calculus, everybody knows the condition for a maximum or a minimum: *The first derivatives are zero.* But this is completely changed by constraints. The simplest example is the line $y = x$. Its derivative is never zero, calculus looks useless, and the largest y is certain to occur at the end of the interval. That is exactly the situation in linear programming! There are more variables, and an interval is replaced by a feasible set, but still the maximum is always found at a corner of the feasible set (with only m nonzero components).

The problem in linear programming is to locate that corner. For this, calculus is not completely helpless. Far from it, because "Lagrange multipliers" will bring back zero derivatives at the maximum and minimum. *The dual variables y are exactly the Lagrange multipliers.* And they answer the key question: **How does the minimum cost $cx^* = y^*b$ change, if we change b or c?**

This is a question in ***sensitivity analysis***. It allows us to squeeze extra information out of the dual problem. For an economist or an executive, these questions about ***marginal cost*** are the most important.

If we allow large changes in b or c, the solution behaves in a very jumpy way. As the price of eggs increases, there will be a point at which they disappear from the diet. The variable x_{egg} will jump from basic to free. To follow it properly, we would have to introduce "parametric" programming. But if the changes are small, ***the corner that was optimal remains optimal***. The choice of basic variables does not change; B and N stay the same. Geometrically, we shifted the feasible set a little (by changing b), and we tilted the planes that come up to meet it (by changing c). When these changes are small, contact occurs at the same (slightly moved) corner.

At the end of the simplex method, when the right basic variables are known, the corresponding m columns of A make up the basis matrix B. At that corner, a shift of size Δb changes the minimum cost by $y^*\Delta b$. ***The dual solution y^* gives the rate of change of minimum cost*** (its derivative) ***with respect to changes in b***. The components of y^* are the ***shadow prices***. If the requirement for a vitamin goes up by Δ, and the druggist's price is y_1^*, then the diet cost (from druggist or grocer) will go up by $y_1^*\Delta$. In the case that y_1^* is zero, that vitamin is a *free good* and the small change has no effect. The diet already contained more than b_1.

We now ask a different question. Suppose we insist that the diet contain some *small* edible amount of egg. The condition $x_{\text{egg}} \geq 0$ is changed to $x_{\text{egg}} \geq \delta$. How does this change the cost?

If eggs were in the diet x^*, there is no change. But if $x^*_{\text{egg}} = 0$, it will cost extra to add in the amount δ. The increase will not be the full price $c_{\text{egg}}\delta$, since we can cut down on other foods. The ***reduced cost*** of eggs is their own price, *minus* the price we are paying for the equivalent in cheaper foods. To compute it we return to equation (2) of Section 8.2:

$$\text{cost} = (c_N - c_B B^{-1}N)x_N + c_B B^{-1}b = rx_N + c_B B^{-1}b.$$

If egg is the first free variable, then increasing the first component of x_N to δ will increase the cost by $r_1\delta$. *The real cost of egg is r_1.* This is the change in diet cost as the zero lower bound (nonnegativity constraint) moves upwards. We know that $r \geq 0$, and economics tells us the same thing: The reduced cost of eggs cannot be negative or they would have entered the diet.

Interior Point Methods

The simplex method moves along edges of the feasible set, eventually reaching the optimal corner x^*. Interior point methods start ***inside*** the feasible set (where the constraints are all *in*equalities). These methods hope to move more directly to x^* (and also find y^*). When they are very close to the answer, they stop.

One way to stay inside is to put a barrier at the boundary. Add an extra cost in the form of a logarithm that blows up when any variable x or any slack variable $w = Ax - b$ touches zero. The number θ is a small parameter to be chosen:

$$\textbf{Barrier problem } \boldsymbol{P(\theta)} \qquad \text{Minimize} \quad cx - \theta\left(\sum_1^n \ln x_i + \sum_1^m \ln w_i\right). \tag{8}$$

This cost is nonlinear (but linear programming is already nonlinear, from inequalities). The notation is simpler if the long vector (x, w) is renamed x and $[A \;\; -I]$ is renamed A. The primal constraints are now $x \geq 0$ and $Ax = b$. The sum of $\ln x_i$ in the barrier now goes to $m + n$.

The dual constraints are $yA \leq c$. (We don't need $y \geq 0$ when we have $Ax = b$ in the primal.) The slack variable is $s = c - yA$, with $s \geq 0$. What are the Kuhn–Tucker conditions for x and y to be the optimal x^* and y^*? Along with the constraints we require duality: $cx^* = y^*b$.

Including the barrier gives an *approximate problem* $P(\theta)$. For its Kuhn–Tucker optimality conditions, the derivative of $\ln x_i$ gives $1/x_i$. If we create a diagonal matrix X from those positive numbers x_i, and use $e = [1 \;\; \ldots \;\; 1]$ for the row vector of $n + m$ ones, then optimality in $P(\theta)$ is as follows:

$$\textbf{Primal (column vectors)} \qquad Ax = b \text{ with } x \geq 0 \tag{9a}$$

$$\textbf{Dual (row vectors)} \qquad yA + \theta e X^{-1} = c \tag{9b}$$

As $\theta \to 0$, we expect those optimal x and y to approach x^* and y^* for the original no-barrier problem, and $\theta e X^{-1}$ will stay nonnegative. The plan is to solve equations (9a–9b) with smaller and smaller barriers, given by the size of θ.

In reality, those nonlinear equations are approximately solved by Newton's method (which means they are linearized). The nonlinear term is $s = \theta e X^{-1}$. To avoid $1/x_i$, rewrite that as $sX = \theta e$. Creating the diagonal matrix S from s, this is $eSX = \theta e$. If we change e, y, c, and s to column vectors, and transpose, optimality now has three parts:

$$\textbf{Primal} \qquad Ax = b, \; x \geq 0. \tag{10a}$$

$$\textbf{Dual} \qquad A^{\mathrm{T}}y + s = c. \tag{10b}$$

$$\textbf{Nonlinear} \qquad XSe - \theta e = 0. \tag{10c}$$

Newton's method takes a step Δx, Δy, Δs from the current x, y, s. (Those solve equations (10a) and (10b), but not (10c).) By ignoring the second-order term $\Delta X \Delta S e$, the corrections come from linear equations!

$$A\,\Delta x = 0. \tag{11a}$$

$$\textbf{Newton step} \qquad A^{\mathrm{T}}\Delta y + \Delta s = 0. \tag{11b}$$

$$S\,\Delta x + X\,\Delta s = \theta e - XSe. \tag{11c}$$

Robert Freund's notes for his MIT class pin down the (quadratic) convergence rate and the computational complexity of this algorithm. Regardless of the dimensions m and n, the duality gap sx is generally below 10^{-8} after 20–80 Newton steps. This algorithm is used almost "as is" in commercial interior-point software, and for a large class of nonlinear optimization problems as well.

The Theory of Inequalities

There is more than one way to study duality. We quickly proved $yb \le cx$, and then used the simplex method to get equality. This was a *constructive proof*; x^* and y^* were actually computed. Now we look briefly at a different approach, which omits the simplex algorithm and looks more directly at the geometry. I think the key ideas will be just as clear (in fact, probably clearer) if we omit some of the details.

The best illustration of this approach came in the Fundamental Theorem of Linear Algebra. The problem in Chapter 2 was to find b in the column space of A. After elimination and the four subspaces, this solvability question was answered in a completely different way by Problem 11 in Section 3.1:

8H $Ax = b$ has a solution ***or*** there is a y such that $yA = 0$ and $yb \ne 0$.

This is the ***theorem of the alternative***, because to find both x and y is impossible: If $Ax = b$ then $yAx = yb \ne 0$, and this contradicts $yAx = 0x = 0$. In the language of subspaces, either b is in the column space, or it has a component sticking into the left nullspace. That component is the required y.

For inequalities, we want to find a theorem of exactly the same kind. Start with the same system $Ax = b$, but add the constraint $x \ge 0$. When does there exist a ***nonnegative solution*** to $Ax = b$?

In Chapter 2, b was anywhere in the column space. Now we allow only *nonnegative* combinations, and the b's no longer fill out a subspace. Instead, they fill a cone-shaped region. For n columns in $\mathbf{R}^m$, the cone becomes an open-ended pyramid. Figure 8.4 has four vectors in $\mathbf{R}^2$, and A is 2 by 4. If b lies in this cone, there is a nonnegative solution to $Ax = b$; otherwise not.

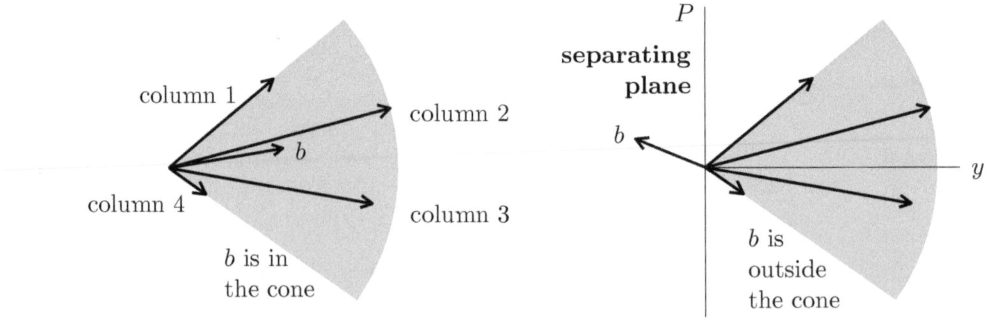

Figure 8.4 The cone of nonnegative combinations of the columns: $b = Ax$ with $x \ge 0$. When b is outside the cone, it is separated by a hyperplane (perpendicular to y).

What is the alternative if b lies outside the cone? Figure 8.4 also shows a "separating hyperplane," which has the vector b on one side and the whole cone on the other side. The plane consists of all vectors perpendicular to a fixed vector y. The angle between y and b is greater than 90°, so $yb < 0$. The angle between y and every column of A is less than 90°, so $yA \geq 0$. This is the alternative we are looking for. This *theorem of the separating hyperplane* is fundamental to mathematical economics.

8I $Ax = b$ has a **nonnegative** solution ***or*** there is a y with $yA \geq 0$ and $yb < 0$.

Example 1 The nonnegative combinations of the columns of $A = I$ fill the positive quadrant $b \geq 0$. For every other b, the alternative must hold for some y:

$$\textbf{Not in cone} \qquad \text{If } b = \begin{bmatrix} 2 \\ -3 \end{bmatrix}, \ \text{then } y = \begin{bmatrix} 0 & 1 \end{bmatrix} \ \text{gives } yI \geq 0 \ \text{but } yb = -3.$$

The x-axis, perpendicular to $y = [\,0 \quad 1\,]$, separates b from the cone = quadrant.

Here is a curious pair of alternatives. It is impossible for a subspace S and its orthogonal complement $S^\perp$ both to contain positive vectors. Their inner product would be positive, not zero. But S might be the x-axis and $S^\perp$ the y-axis, in which case they contain the "semipositive" vectors $[\,1 \quad 0\,]$ and $[\,0 \quad 1\,]$. This slightly weaker alternative does work: *Either S contains a positive vector $x > 0$, or $S^\perp$ contains a nonzero $y \geq 0$.* When S and $S^\perp$ are perpendicular lines in the plane, one or the other must enter the first quadrant. I can't see this clearly in three or four dimensions.

For linear programming, the important alternatives come when the constraints are inequalities. When is the feasible set empty (no x)?

8J $Ax \geq b$ has a solution $x \geq 0$ ***or*** there is a $y \leq 0$ with $yA \geq 0$ and $yb < 0$.

Proof The slack variables $w = Ax - b$ change $Ax \geq b$ into an equation. Use 8I:

$$\textbf{First alternative} \qquad \begin{bmatrix} A & -I \end{bmatrix} \begin{bmatrix} x \\ w \end{bmatrix} = b \quad \text{for some} \quad \begin{bmatrix} x \\ w \end{bmatrix} \geq 0.$$

$$\textbf{Second alternative} \qquad y \begin{bmatrix} A & -I \end{bmatrix} \geq \begin{bmatrix} 0 & 0 \end{bmatrix} \quad \text{for some } y \text{ with} \quad yb < 0. \qquad \blacksquare$$

It is this result that leads to a "nonconstructive proof" of the duality theorem.

Problem Set 8.3

1. What is the dual of the following problem: Minimize $x_1 + x_2$, subject to $x_1 \geq 0$, $x_2 \geq 0$, $2x_1 \geq 4$, $x_1 + 3x_2 \geq 11$? Find the solution to both this problem and its dual, and verify that minimum equals maximum.

2. What is the dual of the following problem: Maximize y_2, subject to $y_1 \geq 0$, $y_2 \geq 0$, $y_1 + y_2 \leq 3$? Solve both this problem and its dual.

3. Suppose A is the identity matrix (so that $m = n$), and the vectors b and c are nonnegative. Explain why $x^* = b$ is optimal in the minimum problem, find y^*

in the maximum problem, and verify that the two values are the same. If the first component of b is negative, what are x^* and y^*?

4. Construct a 1 by 1 example in which $Ax \geq b$, $x \geq 0$ is unfeasible, and the dual problem is unbounded.

5. Starting with the 2 by 2 matrix $A = \begin{bmatrix} 1 & 0 \\ 0 & -1 \end{bmatrix}$, choose b and c so that both of the feasible sets $Ax \geq b$, $x \geq 0$ and $yA \leq c$, $y \geq 0$ are empty.

6. If all entries of A, b, and c are positive, show that both the primal and the dual are feasible.

7. Show that $x = (1, 1, 1, 0)$ and $y = (1, 1, 0, 1)$ are feasible in the primal and dual, with

$$A = \begin{bmatrix} 0 & 0 & 1 & 0 \\ 0 & 1 & 0 & 0 \\ 1 & 1 & 1 & 1 \\ 1 & 0 & 0 & 1 \end{bmatrix}, \quad b = \begin{bmatrix} 1 \\ 1 \\ 1 \\ 1 \end{bmatrix}, \quad c = \begin{bmatrix} 1 \\ 1 \\ 1 \\ 3 \end{bmatrix}.$$

Then, after computing cx and yb, explain how you know they are optimal.

8. Verify that the vectors in the previous exercise satisfy the complementary slackness conditions in equation (2), and find the one slack inequality in both the primal and the dual.

9. Suppose that $A = \begin{bmatrix} 1 & 0 \\ 0 & 1 \end{bmatrix}$, $b = \begin{bmatrix} 1 \\ -1 \end{bmatrix}$, and $c = \begin{bmatrix} 1 \\ 1 \end{bmatrix}$. Find the optimal x and y, and verify the complementary slackness conditions (as well as $yb = cx$).

10. If the primal problem is constrained by equations instead of inequalities—*Minimize cx subject to $Ax = b$ and $x \geq 0$*—then the requirement $y \geq 0$ is left out of the dual: *Maximize yb subject to $yA \leq c$*. Show that the one-sided inequality $yb \leq cx$ still holds. Why was $y \geq 0$ needed in equation (1) but not here? This weak duality can be completed to full duality.

11. (a) Without the simplex method, minimize the cost $5x_1 + 3x_2 + 4x_3$, subject to $x_1 + x_2 + x_3 \geq 1$, $x_1 \geq 0$, $x_2 \geq 0$, $x_3 \geq 0$.
(b) What is the shape of the feasible set?
(c) What is the dual problem, and what is its solution y?

12. If the primal has a unique optimal solution x^*, and then c is changed a little, explain why x^* still remains the optimal solution.

13. Write the dual of the following problem: Maximize $x_1 + x_2 + x_3$ subject to $2x_1 + x_2 \leq 4$, $x_3 \leq 6$. What are the optimal x^* and y^* (if they exist!)?

14. If $A = \begin{bmatrix} 1 & 1 \\ 0 & 1 \end{bmatrix}$, describe the cone of nonnegative combinations of the columns. If b lies inside that cone, say $b = (3, 2)$, what is the feasible vector x? If b lies outside, say $b = (0, 1)$, what vector y will satisfy the alternative?

15. In three dimensions, can you find a set of six vectors whose cone of nonnegative combinations fills the whole space? What about four vectors?

16. Use 8H to show that the following equation has no solution, because the alternative holds:

$$\begin{bmatrix} 2 & 2 \\ 4 & 4 \end{bmatrix} x = \begin{bmatrix} 1 \\ 1 \end{bmatrix}.$$

17. Use 8I to show that there is no solution $x \geq 0$ (the alternative holds):

$$\begin{bmatrix} 1 & 3 & -5 \\ 1 & -4 & -7 \end{bmatrix} x = \begin{bmatrix} 2 \\ 3 \end{bmatrix}.$$

18. Show that the alternatives in 8J ($Ax \geq b$, $x \geq 0$, $yA \geq 0$, $yb < 0$, $y \leq 0$) cannot both hold. *Hint*: yAx.

8.4 NETWORK MODELS

Some linear problems have a structure that makes their solution very quick. Band matrices have all nonzeros close to the main diagonal, and $Ax = b$ is easy to solve. In linear programming, we are interested in the special class for which A is an ***incidence matrix***. Its entries are -1 or $+1$ or (mostly) zero, and pivot steps involve only additions and subtractions. Much larger problems than usual can be solved.

Networks enter all kinds of applications. Traffic through an intersection satisfies Kirchhoff's current law: flow in equals flow out. For gas and oil, network programming has designed pipeline systems that are millions of dollars cheaper than the intuitive (not optimized) designs. Scheduling pilots and crews and airplanes has become a significant problem in applied mathematics! We even solve the ***marriage problem***—to maximize the number of marriages when brides have a veto. That may not be the real problem, but it is the one that network programming solves.

The problem in Figure 8.5 is to ***maximize the flow from the source to the sink***. The flows cannot exceed the capacities marked on the edges, and the directions given by the arrows cannot be reversed. The flow on the two edges into the sink cannot exceed $6 + 1 = 7$. Is this total of 7 achievable? What is the ***maximal flow*** from left to right?

The unknowns are the flows x_{ij} from node i to node j. The capacity constraints are $x_{ij} \leq c_{ij}$. The flows are nonnegative: $x_{ij} \geq 0$ going with the arrows. By maximizing the return flow x_{61} (dotted line), we maximize the total flow into the sink.

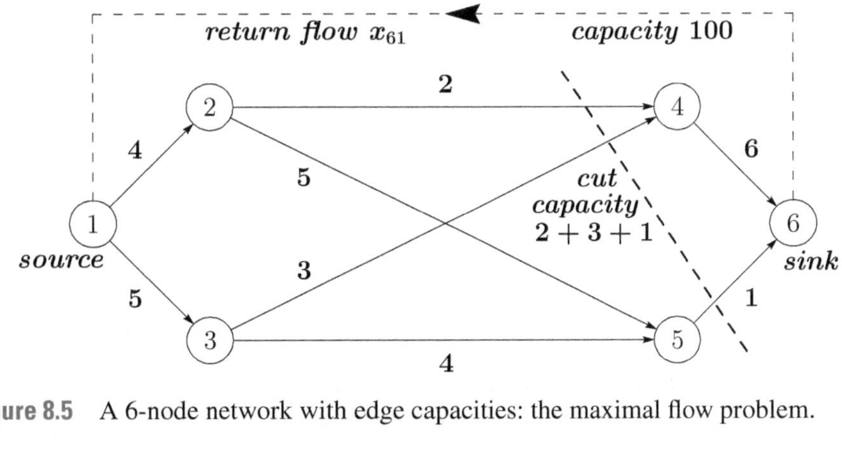

Figure 8.5 A 6-node network with edge capacities: the maximal flow problem.

Another constraint is still to be heard from. It is the "conservation law," that *the flow into each node equals the flow out*. That is Kirchhoff's current law:

$$\textbf{Current law} \qquad \sum_i x_{ij} - \sum_k x_{jk} = 0 \quad \text{for} \quad j = 1, 2, \ldots, 6. \tag{1}$$

The flows x_{ij} enter node j from earlier nodes i. The flows x_{jk} leave node j to later nodes k. The balance in equation (1) can be written as $Ax = 0$, where A is a *node–edge incidence matrix* (the transpose of Section 2.5). A has a row for every node and a $+1, -1$ column for every edge:

$$\textbf{Incidence Matrix} \qquad A = \begin{bmatrix} 1 & 1 & & & & & & & -1 \\ -1 & & 1 & 1 & & & & & \\ & -1 & & & 1 & 1 & & & \\ & & -1 & & -1 & & 1 & & \\ & & & -1 & & -1 & & 1 & \\ & & & & & & -1 & -1 & 1 \end{bmatrix} \begin{matrix} \textbf{node } 1 \\ 2 \\ 3 \\ 4 \\ 5 \\ 6 \end{matrix}$$

$$\textbf{edge} \quad 12 \quad 13 \quad 24 \quad 25 \quad 34 \quad 35 \quad 46 \quad 56 \quad 61$$

Maximal Flow **Maximize x_{61} subject to $Ax = 0$ and $0 \le x_{ij} \le c_{ij}$.**

A flow of 2 can go on the path 1-2-4-6-1. A flow of 3 can go along 1-3-4-6-1. An additional flow of 1 can take the lowest path 1-3-5-6-1. The total is 6, and *no more is possible*. How do you prove that the maximal flow is 6 and not 7?

Trial and error is convincing, but mathematics is conclusive: The key is to find a ***cut*** in the network, across which all capacities are filled. That cut separates nodes 5 and 6 from the others. The edges that go forward across the cut have total capacity $2 + 3 + 1 = 6$—and no more can get across! Weak duality says that every cut gives a bound to the total flow, and full duality says that the cut of smallest capacity (*the minimal cut*) is filled by the maximal flow.

8K ***Max flow–min cut theorem.*** The maximal flow in a network equals the total capacity across the minimal cut.

A "cut" splits the nodes into two groups S and T (source in S and sink in T). Its capacity is the sum of the capacities of all edges crossing the cut (from S to T). Several cuts might have the same capacity. Certainly the total flow can never be greater than the total capacity across the minimal cut. The problem, here and in all of duality, is to show that equality is achieved by the right flow and the right cut.

Proof that max flow = min cut Suppose a flow is maximal. Some nodes might still be reached from the source by additional flow, without exceeding any capacities. Those nodes go with the source into the set S. The sink must lie in the remaining set T, or it could have received more flow! Every edge across the cut must be filled, or extra flow could have gone further forward to a node in T. Thus the maximal flow does fill this cut to capacity, and equality has been achieved. ∎

This suggests a way to construct the maximal flow: Check whether any path has unused capacity. If so, add flow along that "augmenting path." Then compute the remaining capacities and decide whether the sink is cut off from the source, or additional flow is possible. If you label each node in S by the previous node that flow could come from, you can backtrack to find the path for extra flow.

The Marriage Problem

Suppose we have four women and four men. Some of those sixteen couples are compatible, others regrettably are not. When is it possible to find a ***complete matching***, with everyone married? If linear algebra can work in 20-dimensional space, it can certainly handle the trivial problem of marriage.

There are two ways to present the problem—in a matrix or on a graph. The matrix contains $a_{ij} = 0$ if the ith woman and jth man are not compatible, and $a_{ij} = 1$ if they are willing to try. Thus row i gives the choices of the ith woman, and column j corresponds to the jth man:

Compatibility matrix $$A = \begin{bmatrix} 1 & 0 & 0 & 0 \\ 1 & 1 & 1 & 0 \\ 0 & 0 & 0 & 1 \\ 0 & 0 & 0 & 1 \end{bmatrix}$$ has 6 compatible pairs.

The left graph in Figure 8.6 shows two possible marriages. Ignoring the source s and sink t, it has four women on the left and four men on the right. *The edges correspond to the* 1*s in the matrix*, and the capacities are 1 marriage. There is no edge between the first woman and fourth man, because the matrix has $a_{14} = 0$.

It might seem that node M_2 can't be reached by more flow—but that is not so! The extra flow on the right goes backward to cancel an existing marriage. This extra flow makes 3 marriages, which is maximal. The minimal cut is crossed by 3 edges.

A complete matching (if it is possible) is a set of four 1s in the matrix. They would come from four different rows and four different columns, since bigamy is not allowed. It is like finding a *permutation matrix* within the nonzero entries of A. On the graph, this means four edges with no nodes in common. The maximal flow is less than 4 exactly when a complete matching is impossible.

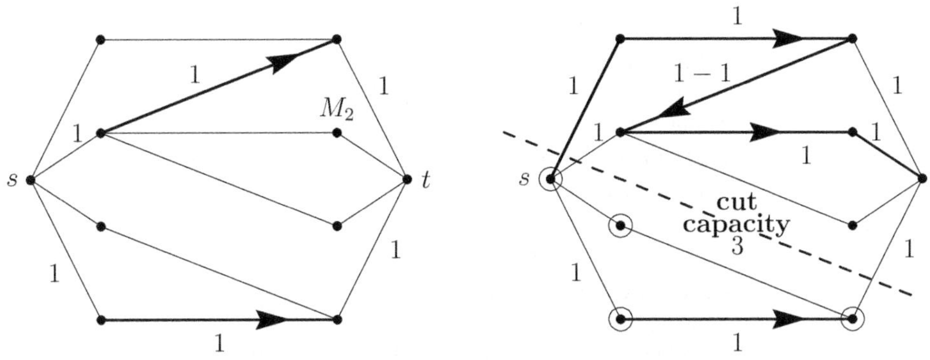

Figure 8.6 Two marriages on the left, three (maximum) on the right. The third is created by adding two new marriages and one divorce (backward flow).

In our example the maximal flow is 3, not 4. The marriages 1–1, 2–2, 4–4 are allowed (and several other sets of three marriages), but there is no way to reach four. The minimal cut on the right separates the two women at the bottom from the three men at the top. The two women have only one man left to choose—not enough. The capacity across the cut is only 3.

Whenever there is a subset of k women who among them like fewer than k men, a complete matching is impossible.

That test is decisive. The same impossibility can be expressed in different ways:

1. **(For Chess)** It is impossible to put four rooks on squares with 1s in A, so that no rook can take any other rook.

2. **(For Marriage Matrices)** The 1s in the matrix can be covered by three horizontal or vertical lines. That equals the maximum number of marriages.

3. **(For Linear Algebra)** Every matrix with the same zeros as A is singular.

Remember that the determinant is a sum of $4! = 24$ terms. Each term uses all four rows and columns. The zeros in A make all 24 terms zero.

A block of zeros is preventing a complete matching! The 2 by 3 submatrix in rows 3, 4 and columns 1, 2, 3 of A is entirely zero. The general rule for an n by n matrix is that ***a p by q block of zeros prevents a matching if*** $p + q > n$. Here women 3, 4 could marry only the man 4. If p women can marry only $n - q$ men and $p > n - q$ (which is the same as a zero block with $p + q > n$), then a complete matching is impossible.

The mathematical problem is to prove the following: ***If every set of p women does like at least p men, a complete matching is possible. That is Hall's condition.*** No block of zeros is too large. Each woman must like at least one man, each two women must between them like at least two men, and so on, to $p = n$.

8L A complete matching is possible if (and only if) Hall's condition holds.

The proof is simplest if the capacities are n, instead of 1, on all edges across the middle. The capacities out of the source and into the sink are still 1. If the maximal flow is n, all those edges from the source and into the sink are filled—and the flow produces n marriages. When a complete matching is impossible, and the maximal flow is below n, some cut must be responsible.

That cut will have capacity below n, so no middle edges cross it. Suppose p nodes on the left and r nodes on the right are in the set S with the source. The capacity across that cut is $n - p$ from the source to the remaining women, and r from these men to the sink. Since the cut capacity is below n, *the p women like only the r men* and no others. But the capacity $n - p + r$ is below n exactly when $p > r$, and Hall's condition fails.

Spanning Trees and the Greedy Algorithm

A fundamental network model is the ***shortest path problem***—in which the edges have *lengths* instead of capacities. We want the shortest path from source to sink. If the edges are telephone lines and the lengths are delay times, we are finding the quickest route for a call. If the nodes are computers, we are looking for the perfect message-passing protocol.

A closely related problem finds the ***shortest spanning tree***—a set of $n - 1$ edges connecting all the nodes of the network. Instead of getting quickly between a source and a sink, we are now minimizing the cost of connecting *all* the nodes. There are no loops, because the cost to close a loop is unnecessary. *A spanning tree connects the nodes without loops*, and we want the shortest one. Here is one possible algorithm:

1. *Start from any node s and repeat the following step:*
Add the shortest edge that connects the current tree to a new node.

In Figure 8.7, the edge lengths would come in the order 1, 2, 7, 4, 3, 6. The last step skips the edge of length 5, which closes a loop. The total length is 23—but is it minimal? We accepted the edge of length 7 very early, and the second algorithm holds out longer.

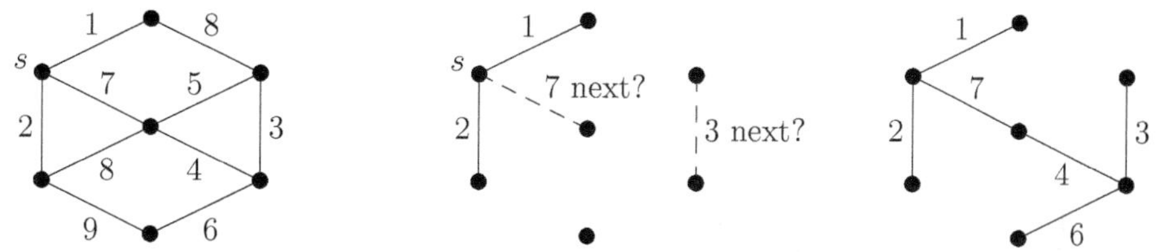

Figure 8.7 A network and a shortest spanning tree of length 23.

2. *Accept edges in increasing order of length, rejecting edges that complete a loop.*

Now the edges come in the order 1, 2, 3, 4, 6 (again rejecting 5), and 7. They are the same edges—although that will not always happen. Their total length is the same—and that *does* always happen. ***The spanning tree problem is exceptional, because it can be solved in one pass.***

In the language of linear programming, we are finding the optimal corner first. The spanning tree problem is being solved like back-substitution, with *no false steps*. This general approach is called the ***greedy algorithm***. Here is another greedy idea:

3. *Build trees from all n nodes, by repeating the following step:*
Select any tree and add the minimum-length edge going out from that tree.

The steps depend on the selection order of the trees. To stay with the same tree is algorithm **1**. To take the lengths in order is algorithm **2**. To sweep through all the trees in turn is a new algorithm. It sounds so easy, but for a large problem the data structure becomes critical. With a thousand nodes, there might be nearly a million edges, and you don't want to go through that list a thousand times.

Further Network Models

There are important problems related to matching that are almost as easy:

1. The ***optimal assignment problem***: a_{ij} measures the value of applicant i in job j. Assign jobs to maximize the total value—the sum of the a_{ij} on assigned jobs. (If all a_{ij} are 0 or 1, this is the marriage problem.)

2. The ***transportation problem***: Given supplies at n points and demands at n markets, choose shipments x_{ij} from suppliers to markets that minimize the total cost $\sum C_{ij}x_{ij}$. (If all supplies and demands are 1, this is the optimal assignment problem—sending one person to each job.)
3. ***Minimum cost flow***: Now the routes have capacities c_{ij} as well as costs C_{ij}, mixing the maximal flow problem with the transportation problem. What is the cheapest flow, subject to capacity constraints?

A fascinating part of this subject is the development of algorithms. Instead of a theoretical proof of duality, we use *breadth-first search or depth-first search* to find the optimal assignment or the cheapest flow. It is like the simplex method, in starting from a feasible flow (a corner) and adding a new flow (to move to the next corner). The algorithms are special because network problems involve incidence matrices.

The technique of ***dynamic programming*** rests on a simple idea: If a path from source to sink is optimal, then *each part of the path must be optimal*. The solution is built backwards from the sink, with a multistage decision process. At each stage, the distance to the sink is the minimum of a new distance plus an old distance:

Bellman equation $\quad \boldsymbol{x}\text{-}\boldsymbol{t}$ distance $=$ minimum over y of $(\boldsymbol{x}\text{-}\boldsymbol{y} + \boldsymbol{y}\text{-}\boldsymbol{t}$ distances).

I wish there were space for more about networks. They are simple but beautiful.

Problem Set 8.4

1. In Figure 8.5, add 3 to every capacity. Find by inspection the maximal flow and minimal cut.

2. Find a maximal flow and minimal cut for the following network:

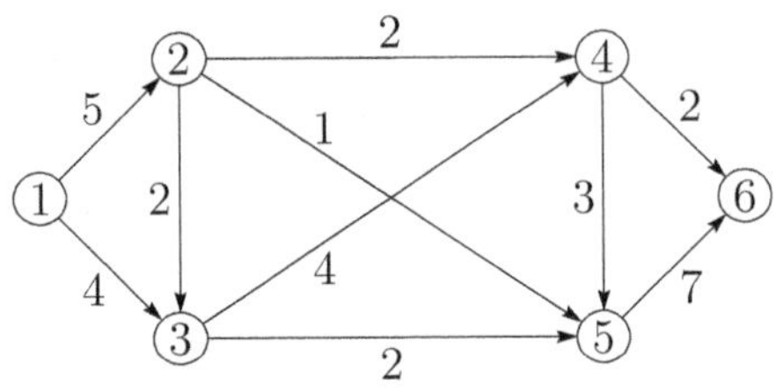

3. If you could increase the capacity of any one pipe in the network above, which change would produce the largest increase in the maximal flow?

4. Draw a 5-node network with capacity $|i - j|$ between node i and node j. Find the largest possible flow from node 1 to node 4.

5. In a graph, the maximum number of paths from s to t with no common edges equals the minimum number of edges whose removal disconnects s from t. Relate this to the max flow–min cut theorem.

6. Find a maximal set of marriages (a complete matching, if possible) for

$$A = \begin{bmatrix} 0 & 0 & 1 & 0 & 0 \\ 1 & 1 & 0 & 1 & 1 \\ 0 & 1 & 1 & 0 & 1 \\ 0 & 0 & 1 & 1 & 0 \\ 0 & 0 & 0 & 1 & 0 \end{bmatrix} \quad \text{and} \quad B = \begin{bmatrix} 1 & 1 & 0 & 0 & 0 \\ 0 & 1 & 0 & 1 & 0 \\ 0 & 0 & 1 & 0 & 1 \\ 1 & 1 & 1 & 0 & 0 \\ 1 & 0 & 0 & 0 & 0 \end{bmatrix}.$$

Sketch the network for B, with heavier lines on the edges in your matching.

7. For the matrix A in Problem 6, which rows violate Hall's condition—by having all their 1s in too few columns? Which p by q submatrix of zeros has $p + q > n$?

8. How many lines (horizontal and vertical) are needed to cover all the 1s in A in Problem 6? For any matrix, explain why weak duality is true: If k marriages are possible, then it takes at least k lines to cover all the 1s.

9. (a) Suppose every row and every column contains exactly two 1s. Prove that a complete matching is possible. (Show that the 1s cannot be covered by less than n lines.)

(b) Find an example with two *or more* 1s in each row and column, for which a complete matching is impossible.

10. If a 7 by 7 matrix has 15 1s, prove that it allows at least 3 marriages.

11. For *infinite* sets, a complete matching may be impossible even if Hall's condition is passed. If the first row is all 1s and then every $a_{i\,i-1} = 1$, show that any p rows have 1s in at least p columns—and yet there is no complete matching.

12. If Figure 8.5 shows lengths instead of capacities, find the shortest path from s to t, and a minimal spanning tree.

13. Apply algorithms 1 and 2 to find a shortest spanning tree for the network of Problem 2.

14. (a) Why does the greedy algorithm work for the spanning tree problem?

(b) Show by example that the greedy algorithm could fail to find the shortest path from s to t, by starting with the shortest edge.

15. If A is the 5 by 5 matrix with 1s just above and just below the main diagonal, find

(a) a set of rows with 1s in too few columns.

(b) a set of columns with 1s in too few rows.

(c) a p by q submatrix of zeros with $p + q > 5$.

(d) four lines that cover all the 1s.

16. The maximal flow problem has slack variables $w_{ij} = c_{ij} - x_{ij}$ for the difference between capacities and flows. State the problem of Figure 8.5 as a linear program.

8.5 GAME THEORY

The best way to explain a ***two-person zero-sum game*** is to give an example. It has two players X and Y, and the rules are the same for every turn:

X holds up one hand or two, and so does Y. If they make the same decision, Y wins \$10. If they make opposite decisions, X wins \$10 for one hand and \$20 for two:

Payoff matrix (payments to X)
$$A = \begin{bmatrix} -10 & 20 \\ 10 & -10 \end{bmatrix} \begin{matrix} \text{one hand by } Y \\ \text{two hands by } Y \end{matrix}$$
$$\begin{matrix} \text{one hand} & \text{two hands} \\ \text{by } X & \text{by } X \end{matrix}$$

If X does the same thing every time, Y will copy him and win. Similarly Y cannot stick to a single strategy, or X will do the opposite. Both players must use a ***mixed strategy***, and the choice at every turn must be independent of the previous turns. If there is some historical pattern, the opponent can take advantage of it. Even the strategy "stay with the same choice until you lose" is obviously fatal. After enough plays, your opponent would know exactly what to expect.

In a mixed strategy, X can put up one hand with frequency x_1 and both hands with frequency $x_2 = 1 - x_1$. At every turn this decision is random. Similarly Y can pick probabilities y_1 and $y_2 = 1 - y_1$. None of these probabilities should be 0 or 1; otherwise the opponent adjusts and wins. If they equal $\frac{1}{2}$, Y would be losing \$20 too often. (He would lose \$20 a quarter of the time, \$10 another quarter of the time, and win \$10 half the time—an average loss of \$2.50. This is more than necessary.) But the more Y moves toward a pure two-hand strategy, the more X will move toward one hand.

The fundamental problem is *to find the best mixed strategies*. Can X choose probabilities x_1 and x_2 that present Y with no reason to move his own strategy (and vice versa)? Then the average payoff will have reached a ***saddle point***: It is a maximum as far as X is concerned, and a minimum as far as Y is concerned. To find such a saddle point is to solve the game.

X is combining the two columns with weights x_1 and $1 - x_1$ to produce a new "mixed" column. Weights $\frac{3}{5}$ and $\frac{2}{5}$ would produce this column:

$$\textbf{Mixed column} \qquad \frac{3}{5}\begin{bmatrix} -10 \\ 10 \end{bmatrix} + \frac{2}{5}\begin{bmatrix} 20 \\ -10 \end{bmatrix} = \begin{bmatrix} 2 \\ 2 \end{bmatrix}.$$

***Against this mixed strategy, Y will always lose* \$2**. This does not mean that all strategies are optimal for Y! If Y is lazy and stays with one hand, X will change and start winning \$20. Then Y will change, and then X again. Finally, since we assume they are both intelligent, they settle down to optimal mixtures. Y will combine the *rows* with weights y_1 and $1 - y_1$, trying to produce a new row which is as *small* as possible:

$$\textbf{Mixed row} \qquad y_1\begin{bmatrix} -10 & 20 \end{bmatrix} + (1 - y_1)\begin{bmatrix} 10 & -10 \end{bmatrix} = \begin{bmatrix} 10 - 20y_1 & -10 + 30y_1 \end{bmatrix}.$$

The right mixture makes the two components equal, at $y_1 = \frac{2}{5}$. Then both components equal 2; the mixed row becomes $[2 \quad 2]$. ***With this strategy Y cannot lose more than* \$2.**

Y has minimized the maximum loss, and that *minimax* agrees with the *maximin* found by X. The *value of the game* is minimax = maximin = \$2.

The optimal mixture of rows might not always have equal entries! Suppose X is allowed a third strategy of holding up three hands to win \$60 when Y puts up one hand and \$80 when Y puts up two. The payoff matrix becomes

$$A = \begin{bmatrix} -10 & 20 & 60 \\ 10 & -10 & 80 \end{bmatrix}.$$

X will choose the three-hand strategy (column 3) every time, and win at least \$60. At the same time, Y always chooses the first row; the maximum loss is \$60. We still have maximin = minimax = \$60, but the saddle point is over in the corner.

In Y's optimal mixture of rows, which was purely row 1, \$60 appears only in the column actually used by X. In X's optimal mixture of columns, which was column 3, \$60 appears in the row that enters Y's best strategy. This rule corresponds exactly to the *complementary slackness condition* of linear programming.

Matrix Games

The most general "m by n matrix game" is exactly like our example. X has n possible moves (columns of A). Y chooses from the m rows. The entry a_{ij} is the payment when X chooses column j and Y chooses row i. A negative entry means a payment to Y. This is a ***zero-sum game***. Whatever one player loses, the other wins.

X is free to choose any mixed strategy $x = (x_1, \dots, x_n)$. These x_i give the frequencies for the n columns and they add to 1. At every turn X uses a random device to produce strategy i with frequency x_i. Y chooses a vector $y = (y_1, \dots, y_m)$, also with $y_i \geq 0$ and $\sum y_i = 1$, which gives the frequencies for selecting rows.

A single play of the game is random. On the average, the combination of column j for X and row i for Y will turn up with probability $x_j y_i$. When it does come up, the payoff is a_{ij}. The expected payoff to X from this combination is $a_{ij} x_j y_i$, and ***the total expected payoff from each play of the same game is*** $\sum \sum a_{ij} x_j y_i = yAx$:

$$yAx = \begin{bmatrix} y_1 & \cdots & y_m \end{bmatrix} \begin{bmatrix} a_{11} & a_{12} & \cdots & a_{1n} \\ \vdots & \vdots & & \vdots \\ a_{m1} & a_{m2} & \cdots & a_{mn} \end{bmatrix} \begin{bmatrix} x_1 \\ x_2 \\ \vdots \\ x_n \end{bmatrix} \begin{aligned} &= a_{11}x_1y_1 + \cdots + a_{mn}x_ny_m \\ &= \textbf{average payoff}. \end{aligned}$$

It is this payoff yAx that X wants to maximize and Y wants to minimize.

Example 1 Suppose A is the n by n identity matrix, $A = I$. The expected payoff becomes $yIx = x_1y_1 + \cdots + x_ny_n$. X is hoping to hit on the same choice as Y, to win $a_{ii} =$ \$1. Y is trying to evade X, to pay $a_{ij} =$ \$0. If X chooses any column more often than another, Y can escape more often. *The optimal mixture is* $x^* = (1/n, 1/n, \dots, 1/n)$. Similarly Y cannot overemphasize any row—the optimal mixture is $y^* = (1/n, 1/n, \dots, 1/n)$. The probability that both will choose strategy i is $(1/n)^2$, and the sum over i is the expected payoff to X. The total value of the game is n times $(1/n)^2$, or $1/n$:

$$y^*Ax^* = \begin{bmatrix} 1/n & \cdots & 1/n \end{bmatrix} \begin{bmatrix} 1 & & \\ & \ddots & \\ & & 1 \end{bmatrix} \begin{bmatrix} 1/n \\ \vdots \\ 1/n \end{bmatrix} = \left(\frac{1}{n}\right)^2 + \cdots + \left(\frac{1}{n}\right)^2 = \frac{1}{n}.$$

As n increases, Y has a better chance to escape. The value $1/n$ goes down.

The symmetric matrix $A = I$ did not make the game fair. *A skew-symmetric matrix, $A^{\mathrm{T}} = -A$, means a completely fair game.* Then a choice of strategy j by X and i by Y wins a_{ij} for X, and a choice of j by Y and i by X wins the same amount for Y (because $a_{ji} = -a_{ij}$). The optimal strategies x^* and y^* must be the same, and the expected payoff must be $y^*Ax^* = 0$. The value of the game, when $A^{\mathrm{T}} = -A$, is zero. But the strategy is still to be found.

Example 2

$$\textbf{Fair game} \qquad A = \begin{bmatrix} 0 & -1 & -1 \\ 1 & 0 & -1 \\ 1 & 1 & 0 \end{bmatrix}.$$

In words, X and Y both choose a number between 1 and 3. The smaller choice wins \$1. (If X chooses 2 and Y chooses 3, the payoff is $a_{32} = \$1$; if they choose the same number, we are on the diagonal and nobody wins.) Neither player can choose a strategy involving 2 or 3. The pure strategies $x^* = y^* = (1, 0, 0)$ are optimal—both players choose 1 every time. The value is $y^*Ax^* = a_{11} = 0$.

The matrix that leaves all decisions unchanged has mn equal entries, say α. This simply means that X wins an additional amount α at every turn. The value of the game is increased by α, but there is no reason to change x^* and y^*.

The Minimax Theorem

Put yourself in the place of X, who chooses the mixed strategy $x = (x_1, \ldots, x_n)$. Y will eventually recognize that strategy and choose y to *minimize* the payment yAx. An intelligent player X will select x^* to ***maximize this minimum***:

$$\textbf{\textit{X} wins at least} \qquad \min_y yAx^* = \max_x \min_y yAx. \tag{1}$$

Player Y does the opposite. For any chosen strategy y, X will *maximize* yAx. Therefore Y will choose the mixture y^* that ***minimizes this maximum***:

$$\textbf{\textit{Y} loses no more than} \qquad \max_x y^*Ax = \min_y \max_x yAx. \tag{2}$$

I hope you see what the key result will be, if it is true. We want the amount in equation (1) that X is guaranteed to win to equal the amount in equation (2) that Y must be satisfied to lose. Then the game will be solved: X can only lose by moving from x^* and Y can only lose by moving from y^*. The existence of this saddle point was proved by von Neumann:

8M For any matrix A, the minimax over all strategies equals the maximin:

Minimax theorem $$\max_x \min_y yAx = \min_y \max_x yAx = \text{value of the game.} \qquad (3)$$

If the maximum on the left is attained at x^*, and the minimum on the right is attained at y^*, this is a saddle point from which nobody wants to move:

$$y^*Ax \le y^*Ax^* \le yAx^* \quad \text{for all } x \text{ and } y. \qquad (4)$$

At this saddle point, x^* is at least as good as any other x (since $y^*Ax \le y^*Ax^*$). And the second player Y could only pay more by leaving y^*.

As in duality theory, *maximin* $\le$ *minimax* is easy. We combine the definition in equation (1) of x^* and the definition in equation (2) of y^*:

$$\max_x \min_y yAx = \min_y yAx^* \le y^*Ax^* \le \max_x y^*Ax = \min_y \max_x yAx. \qquad (5)$$

This only says that if X can guarantee to win at least α, and Y can guarantee to lose no more than β, then $\alpha \le \beta$. The achievement of von Neumann was to prove that $\alpha = \beta$. The minimax theorem means that equality must hold throughout equation (5).

For us, the striking thing about the proof is that *it uses exactly the same mathematics as the theory of linear programming*. X and Y are playing "dual" roles. They are both choosing strategies from the "feasible set" of probability vectors: $x_i \ge 0, \sum x_i = 1, y_i \ge 0, \sum y_i = 1$. What is amazing is that even von Neumann did not immediately recognize the two theories as the same. (He proved the minimax theorem in 1928, linear programming began before 1947, and Gale, Kuhn, and Tucker published the first proof of duality in 1951—based on von Neumann's notes!) We are reversing history by deducing the minimax theorem from duality.

Briefly, the minimax theorem can be proved as follows. Let b be the column vector of m 1s, and c be the row vector of n 1s. These linear programs are dual:

(P) minimize cx
subject to $Ax \ge b, x \ge 0$

(D) maximize yb
subject to $yA \le c, y \ge 0$.

To make sure that both problems are feasible, add a large number α to all entries of A. This cannot affect the optimal strategies, since every payoff goes up by α. For the resulting matrix, which we still denote by A, $y = 0$ is feasible in the dual and any large x is feasible in the primal.

The duality theorem of linear programming guarantees optimal x^* and y^* with $cx^* = y^*b$. Because of the 1s in b and c, this means that $\sum x_i^* = \sum y_i^* = S$. Division by S changes the sums to 1—and *the resulting mixed strategies x^*/S and y^*/S are optimal*. For any other strategies x and y,

$$Ax^* \ge b \quad \text{implies} \quad yAx^* \ge yb = 1 \quad \text{and} \quad y^*A \le c \quad \text{implies} \quad y^*Ax \le cx = 1.$$

The main point is that $y^*Ax \le 1 \le yAx^*$. Dividing by S, this says that player X cannot win more than $1/S$ against the strategy y^*/S, and player Y cannot lose less than $1/S$ against x^*/S. Those strategies give maximin $=$ minimax $= 1/S$.

Real Games

This completes the theory, but it leaves a natural question: Which ordinary games are actually equivalent to "matrix games"? ***Do chess and bridge and poker fit into von Neumann's theory?***

I think chess does not fit very well, for two reasons. A strategy for black must include a decision on how to respond to white's first play, and second play, and so on to the end of the game. X and Y have billions of pure strategies. I do not see much of a role for chance. If white can find a winning strategy or if black can find a drawing strategy—neither has ever been found—that would effectively end the game of chess. You could play it like tic-tac-toe, but the excitement would go away.

Bridge does contain some deception—as in a finesse. It counts as a matrix game, but m and n are again fantastically big. Perhaps separate parts of bridge could be analyzed for an optimal strategy. The same is true in baseball, where the pitcher and batter try to outguess each other on the choice of pitch. (Or the catcher tries to guess when the runner will steal. A pitchout every time will walk the batter, so there must be an optimal frequency—depending on the base runner and on the situation.) Again a small part of the game could be isolated and analyzed.

On the other hand, *blackjack is not a matrix game* (in a casino) because the house follows fixed rules. My friend Ed Thorp found a winning strategy by counting high cards—forcing more shuffling and more decks at Las Vegas. There was no element of chance, and no mixed strategy x^*. The best-seller *Bringing Down the House* tells how MIT students made a lot of money (while not doing their homework).

There is also the ***Prisoner's Dilemma***, in which two accomplices are separately offered the same deal: Confess and you are free, provided your accomplice does not confess (the accomplice then gets 10 years). If both confess, each gets 6 years. If neither confesses, only a minor crime (2 years each) can be proved. What to do? The temptation to confess is very great, although if they could depend on each other they would hold out. This is not a zero-sum game; both can lose.

One example of a matrix game is ***poker***. Bluffing is essential, and to be effective it has to be unpredictable. (If your opponent finds a pattern, you lose.) The probabilities for and against bluffing will depend on the cards that are seen, and on the bets. In fact, the number of alternatives again makes it impractical to find an absolutely optimal strategy x^*. A good poker player must come pretty close to x^*, and we can compute it exactly if we accept the following enormous simplification of the game:

X is dealt a jack or a king, with equal probability, and Y always gets a queen. X can fold and lose the \$1 ante, or bet an additional \$2. If X bets, Y can fold and lose \$1, or match the extra \$2 and see if X is bluffing. Then the higher card wins the \$3 from the opponent. So Y has two possibilities, reacting to X (who has four strategies):

Strategies for Y	(Row 1)	If X bets, Y folds.
	(Row 2)	If X bets, Y matches the extra \$2.

Strategies for X	(1) Bet the extra \$2 on a king and fold on a jack.
	(2) Bet the extra \$2 in either case (bluffing).
	(3) Fold in either case, and lose \$1 (foolish).
	(4) Fold on a king and bet on a jack (foolish).

The payoff matrix A requires a little patience to compute:

$a_{11} = 0$: X loses \$1 half the time on a jack and wins on a king (Y folds).

$a_{21} = 1$: Both bets X loses \$1 half the time and wins \$3 half the time.

$a_{12} = 1$: X bets and Y folds (the bluff succeeds).

$a_{11} = 0$: X wins \$3 with the king and loses \$3 with the jack (the bluff fails).

$$\textbf{Poker payoff matrix} \qquad A = \begin{bmatrix} 0 & 1 & -1 & 0 \\ 1 & 0 & -1 & -2 \end{bmatrix}.$$

The optimal strategy for X is to bluff half the time, $x^* = \left(\frac{1}{2}, \frac{1}{2}, 0, 0\right)$. The underdog Y must choose $y^* = \left(\frac{1}{2}, \frac{1}{2}\right)$. The value of the game is fifty cents to X.

That is a strange way to end this book, by teaching you how to play watered-down poker (blackjack pays a lot better). But I guess even poker has its place within linear algebra and its applications. I hope you have enjoyed the book.

Problem Set 8.5

1. How will the optimal strategies in the game that opens this section be affected if the \$20 is increased to \$70? What is the value (the average win for X) of this new game?

2. With payoff matrix $A = \begin{bmatrix} 1 & 2 \\ 3 & 4 \end{bmatrix}$, explain the calculation by X of the maximin and by Y of the minimax. What strategies x^* and y^* are optimal?

3. If a_{ij} is the largest entry in its row and the smallest in its column, why will X always choose column j and Y always choose row i (regardless of the rest of the matrix)? Show that the preceding problem had such an entry, and then construct an A without one.

4. Compute Y's best strategy by weighting the rows of $A = \begin{bmatrix} 3 & 4 & 1 \\ 2 & 0 & 3 \end{bmatrix}$ with y and $1 - y$. X will concentrate on the largest of the components $3y + 2(1 - y)$, $4y$, and $y + 3(1 - y)$. Find the largest of those three (depending on y) and then find the y^* between 0 and 1 that makes this largest component as small as possible.

5. With the same A as in Problem 4, find the best strategy for X. Show that X uses only the two columns (the first and third) that meet at the minimax point in the graph.

6. Find both optimal strategies, and the value, if

$$A = \begin{bmatrix} 1 & 0 & -1 \\ -2 & -1 & 2 \end{bmatrix}.$$

7. Suppose $A = \begin{bmatrix} a & b \\ c & d \end{bmatrix}$. What weights x_1 and $1 - x_1$ will give a column of the form $[u \quad u]^{\mathrm{T}}$, and what weights y_1 and $1 - y_1$ on the two rows will give a new row $[v \quad v]$? Show that $u = v$.

8. Find x^*, y^*, and the value v for

$$A = \begin{bmatrix} 1 & 0 & 0 \\ 0 & 2 & 0 \\ 0 & 0 & 3 \end{bmatrix}.$$

9. Compute

$$\min_{\substack{y_i \geq 0 \\ y_1 + y_2 = 1}} \quad \max_{\substack{x_i \geq 0 \\ x_1 + x_2 = 1}} \quad (x_1 y_1 + x_2 y_2).$$

10. Explain each of the inequalities in equation (5). Then, once the minimax theorem has turned them into equalities, derive (again in words) the saddle point equations (4).

11. Show that $x^* = \left(\frac{1}{2}, \frac{1}{2}, 0, 0\right)$ and $y^* = \left(\frac{1}{2}, \frac{1}{2}\right)$ are optimal strategies in our simplified version of poker, by computing yAx^* and y^*Ax and verifying the conditions (4) for a saddle point.

12. Has it been proved that no chess strategy always wins for black? This is certainly true when the players are given two moves at a time; if black had a winning strategy, white could move a knight out and back and then follow that strategy, leading to the impossible conclusion that both would win.

13. If X chooses a prime number and simultaneously Y guesses whether it is odd or even (with gain or loss of \$1), who has the advantage?

14. If X is a quarterback, with the choice of run or pass, and Y can defend against a run or a pass, suppose the payoff (in yards) is

$$A = \begin{bmatrix} 2 & 8 \\ 6 & -6 \end{bmatrix} \begin{matrix} \text{defense against run} \\ \text{defense against pass.} \end{matrix}$$
$$\qquad \text{run} \quad \text{pass}$$

What are the optimal strategies and the average gain on each play?

Appendix

A Intersection, Sum, and Product of Spaces

1. The Intersection of Two Vector Spaces

New questions arise from considering two subspaces **V** and **W**, not just one. We look first at the vectors that belong to *both* subspaces. This "intersection" $\mathbf{V} \cap \mathbf{W}$ is a subspace of those subspaces:

> If **V** and **W** are subspaces of one vector space, so is their ***intersection*** $\mathbf{V} \cap \mathbf{W}$. **The vectors belonging to both V and W form a subspace.**

Suppose x and y are vectors in **V** and also in **W**. Because **V** and **W** are vector spaces in their own right, $x + y$ and cx are in **V** and in **W**. ***The results of addition and scalar multiplication stay within the intersection.***

Two planes through the origin (or two "hyperplanes" in $\mathbf{R}^n$) meet in a subspace. The intersection of several subspaces, or infinitely many, is again a subspace.

Example 1 The intersection of two *orthogonal* subspaces **V** and **W** is the one-point subspace $\mathbf{V} \cap \mathbf{W} = \{0\}$. Only the zero vector is orthogonal to itself.

Example 2 Suppose **V** and **W** are the spaces of n by n upper and lower triangular matrices. The intersection $\mathbf{V} \cap \mathbf{W}$ is the set of *diagonal matrices*—belonging to both triangular subspaces. Adding diagonal matrices, or multiplying by c, leaves a diagonal matrix.

Example 3 Suppose **V** is the nullspace of A, and **W** is the nullspace of B. Then $\mathbf{V} \cap \mathbf{W}$ is the smaller nullspace of the larger matrix C:

$$\textbf{Intersection of nullspaces} \qquad N(A) \cap N(B) \textbf{ is the nullspace of } C = \begin{bmatrix} A \\ B \end{bmatrix}.$$

$Cx = 0$ requires both $Ax = 0$ and $Bx = 0$. So x has to be in both nullspaces.

2. The Sum of Two Vector Spaces

Usually, after discussing the intersection of two sets, it is natural to look at their union. With vector spaces, this is not natural. *The union* $\mathbf{V} \cup \mathbf{W}$ *of two subspaces will not in general be a subspace.* If $\mathbf{V}$ and $\mathbf{W}$ are the x-axis and the y-axis in the plane, the two axes together are not a subspace. The sum of $(1, 0)$ and $(0, 1)$ is not on either axis.

We do want to combine $\mathbf{V}$ and $\mathbf{W}$. In place of their union we turn to their sum.

DEFINITION If $\mathbf{V}$ and $\mathbf{W}$ are both subspaces of a given space, so is their ***sum***. $\mathbf{V} + \mathbf{W}$ contains all combinations $v + w$, where v is in $\mathbf{V}$ and w is in $\mathbf{W}$.

$\mathbf{V} + \mathbf{W}$ is the smallest vector space that contains both $\mathbf{V}$ and $\mathbf{W}$. The sum of the x-axis and the y-axis is the whole x-y plane. So is the sum of any two different lines, *perpendicular or not*. If $\mathbf{V}$ is the x-axis and $\mathbf{W}$ is the 45° line $x = y$, then any vector like $(5, 3)$ can be split into $v + w = (2, 0) + (3, 3)$. Thus $\mathbf{V} + \mathbf{W}$ is all of $\mathbf{R}^2$.

Example 4 Suppose $\mathbf{V}$ and $\mathbf{W}$ are orthogonal complements in $\mathbf{R}^n$. Then their sum is $\mathbf{V} + \mathbf{W} = \mathbf{R}^n$. Every x is the sum of its projections in $\mathbf{V}$ and $\mathbf{W}$.

Example 5 If $\mathbf{V}$ is the space of upper triangular matrices, and $\mathbf{W}$ is the space of lower triangular matrices, then $\mathbf{V} + \mathbf{W}$ is the space of *all* matrices. Every n by n matrix can be written as the sum of an upper and a lower triangular matrix—in many ways, because the diagonals are not uniquely determined.

These triangular subspaces have dimension $n(n + 1)/2$. The space $\mathbf{V} + \mathbf{W}$ of all matrices has dimension n^2. The space $\mathbf{V} \cap \mathbf{W}$ of diagonal matrices has dimension n. Formula (8) below becomes $n^2 + n = n(n + 1)/2 + n(n + 1)/2$.

Example 6 If $\mathbf{V}$ is the column space of A, and $\mathbf{W}$ is the column space of B, then $\mathbf{V} + \mathbf{W}$ ***is the column space of the larger matrix*** $[A \quad B]$. The dimension of $\mathbf{V} + \mathbf{W}$ may be less than the combined dimensions of $\mathbf{V}$ and $\mathbf{W}$ (because those two spaces might overlap):

$$\textbf{Sum of column spaces} \qquad \dim(\mathbf{V} + \mathbf{W}) = \text{rank of } [A \quad B]. \tag{6}$$

The computation of $\mathbf{V} \cap \mathbf{W}$ *is more subtle.* For the intersection of column spaces, a good method is to put bases for $\mathbf{V}$ and $\mathbf{W}$ in the columns of A and B. The nullspace of $[A \quad B]$ leads to $\mathbf{V} \cap \mathbf{W}$ (see Problem 9). *Those spaces have the same dimension* (the nullity of $[A \quad B]$). Combining with $\dim(\mathbf{V} + \mathbf{W})$ gives

$$\dim(\mathbf{V} + \mathbf{W}) + \dim(\mathbf{V} \cap \mathbf{W}) = \text{rank of } [A \quad B] + \text{nullity of } [A \quad B]. \tag{7}$$

We know that the rank plus the nullity (counting pivot columns plus free columns) always equals the total number of columns. When $[A \quad B]$ has $k + \ell$ columns, with $k = \dim \mathbf{V}$ and $\ell = \dim \mathbf{W}$, we reach a neat conclusion:

$$\textbf{Dimension formula} \quad \dim(\mathbf{V} + \mathbf{W}) + \dim(\mathbf{V} \cap \mathbf{W}) = \dim(\mathbf{V}) + \dim(\mathbf{W}). \tag{8}$$

Not a bad formula. The overlap of $\mathbf{V}$ and $\mathbf{W}$ is in $\mathbf{V} \cap \mathbf{W}$.

3. The Cartesian Product of Two Vector Spaces

If $\mathbf{V}$ has dimension n, and $\mathbf{W}$ has dimension q, their Cartesian product $\mathbf{V} \times \mathbf{W}$ has dimension $n + q$.

DEFINITION $\mathbf{V} \times \mathbf{W}$ ***contains all pairs of vectors*** $\boldsymbol{x} = (\boldsymbol{v}, \boldsymbol{w})$.

Adding (v, w) to (v^*, w^*) in this product space gives $(v + v^*, w + w^*)$. Multiplying by c gives (cv, cw). All operations in $\mathbf{V} \times \mathbf{W}$ are a component at a time.

Example 7 The Cartesian product of $\mathbf{R}^2$ and $\mathbf{R}^3$ is very much like $\mathbf{R}^5$. A typical vector x in $\mathbf{R}^2 \times \mathbf{R}^3$ is $((1, 2), (4, 6, 5))$: one vector from $\mathbf{R}^2$ and one from $\mathbf{R}^3$. That looks like $(1, 2, 4, 6, 5)$ in $\mathbf{R}^5$.

Cartesian products go naturally with *block matrices*. From $\mathbf{R}^5$ to $\mathbf{R}^5$, we have ordinary 5 by 5 matrices. On the product space $\mathbf{R}^2 \times \mathbf{R}^3$, the natural form of a matrix is a 5 by 5 block matrix M:

$$M = \begin{bmatrix} \mathbf{R}^2 \text{ to } \mathbf{R}^2 & \mathbf{R}^3 \text{ to } \mathbf{R}^2 \\ \mathbf{R}^2 \text{ to } \mathbf{R}^3 & \mathbf{R}^3 \text{ to } \mathbf{R}^3 \end{bmatrix} = \begin{bmatrix} 2 \text{ by } 2 & 2 \text{ by } 3 \\ 3 \text{ by } 2 & 3 \text{ by } 3 \end{bmatrix} = \begin{bmatrix} A & B \\ C & D \end{bmatrix}.$$

Matrix–vector multiplication produces $(Av + Bw, Cv + Dw)$. Not too fascinating.

4. The Tensor Product of Two Vector Spaces

Somehow we want a product space that has dimension n *times* q. **The vectors in this "tensor product" (denoted $\otimes$) will look like n by q matrices**. For the tensor product $\mathbf{R}^2 \otimes \mathbf{R}^3$, the vectors will look like 2 by 3 matrices. The dimension of $\mathbf{R}^2 \times \mathbf{R}^3$ is 5, but the dimension of $\mathbf{R}^2 \otimes \mathbf{R}^3$ is going to be 6.

Start with $v = (1, 2)$ and $w = (4, 6, 5)$ in $\mathbf{R}^2$ and $\mathbf{R}^3$. The Cartesian product just puts them next to each other as (v, w). The tensor product combines v and w into the ***rank 1 matrix*** $\boldsymbol{vw}^{\mathrm{T}}$:

$$\textbf{Column times row} \qquad v \otimes w = vw^{\mathrm{T}} = \begin{bmatrix} 1 \\ 2 \end{bmatrix} \begin{bmatrix} 4 & 6 & 5 \end{bmatrix} = \begin{bmatrix} 4 & 6 & 5 \\ 8 & 12 & 10 \end{bmatrix}.$$

All the special matrices vw^{T} belong to the tensor product $\mathbf{R}^2 \otimes \mathbf{R}^3$. The product space is *spanned* by those vectors $v \otimes w$. Combinations of rank-1 matrices give *all* 2 by 3 matrices, so the dimension of $\mathbf{R}^2 \otimes \mathbf{R}^3$ is 6. Abstractly: The tensor product $\mathbf{V} \otimes \mathbf{W}$ is identified with the space of linear transformations from $\mathbf{V}$ to $\mathbf{W}$.

If $\mathbf{V}$ is only a line in $\mathbf{R}^2$, and $\mathbf{W}$ is only a line in $\mathbf{R}^3$, then $\mathbf{V} \otimes \mathbf{W}$ is only a "line in matrix space." The dimensions are now $1 \times 1 = 1$. All the rank-1 matrices vw^{T} will be multiples of one matrix.

Basis for the Tensor Product. When $\mathbf{V}$ is $\mathbf{R}^2$ and $\mathbf{W}$ is $\mathbf{R}^3$, we have a standard basis for all 2 by 3 matrices (a six-dimensional space):

$$\textbf{Basis} \qquad \begin{bmatrix} 1 & 0 & 0 \\ 0 & 0 & 0 \end{bmatrix} \begin{bmatrix} 0 & 1 & 0 \\ 0 & 0 & 0 \end{bmatrix} \begin{bmatrix} 0 & 0 & 1 \\ 0 & 0 & 0 \end{bmatrix} \begin{bmatrix} 0 & 0 & 0 \\ 1 & 0 & 0 \end{bmatrix} \begin{bmatrix} 0 & 0 & 0 \\ 0 & 1 & 0 \end{bmatrix} \begin{bmatrix} 0 & 0 & 0 \\ 0 & 0 & 1 \end{bmatrix}.$$

That basis for $\mathbf{R}^2 \otimes \mathbf{R}^3$ was constructed in a natural way. I started with the standard basis $v_1 = (1, 0)$ and $v_2 = (0, 1)$ for $\mathbf{R}^2$. Those were combined with the basis vectors $w_1 = (1, 0, 0)$, $w_2 = (0, 1, 0)$, and $w_3 = (0, 0, 1)$ in $\mathbf{R}^3$. Each pair $v_i \otimes w_j$ corresponds to one of the six basis vectors (2 by 3 matrices above) in the tensor product $\mathbf{V} \otimes \mathbf{W}$. This construction succeeds for subspaces too:

Basis: Suppose $\mathbf{V}$ and $\mathbf{W}$ are subspaces of $\mathbf{R}^m$ and $\mathbf{R}^p$ with bases $v_1, \ldots, v_n$ and $w_1, \ldots, w_q$. Then the nq rank-1 matrices $v_i w_j^{\mathrm{T}}$ are a basis for $\mathbf{V} \otimes \mathbf{W}$.

$\mathbf{V} \otimes \mathbf{W}$ is an nq-dimensional subspace of m by p matrices. An algebraist would match this matrix construction to the abstract definition of $\mathbf{V} \otimes \mathbf{W}$. Then tensor products can go beyond the specific case of column vectors.

5. The Kronecker Product $A \otimes B$ of Two Matrices

An m by n matrix A transforms any vector v in $\mathbf{R}^n$ to a vector Av in $\mathbf{R}^m$. Similarly, a p by q matrix B transforms w to Bw. The two matrices together transform vw^{T} to $Avw^{\mathrm{T}}B^{\mathrm{T}}$. This is a linear transformation (of tensor products) and it must come from a matrix.

What is the size of that matrix $A \otimes B$? It takes the nq-dimensional space $\mathbf{R}^n \otimes \mathbf{R}^q$ to the mp-dimensional space $\mathbf{R}^m \otimes \mathbf{R}^p$. Therefore the matrix has shape mp by nq. We will write this Kronecker product (also called tensor product) as a block matrix:

Kronecker product
***mp* rows, *nq* columns**

$$A \otimes B = \begin{bmatrix} a_{11}B & a_{12}B & \cdots & a_{1n}B \\ a_{21}B & a_{22}B & \cdots & a_{2n}B \\ \cdot & \cdot & \cdots & \cdot \\ a_{m1}B & a_{m2}B & \cdots & a_{mn}B \end{bmatrix}. \tag{9}$$

Notice the special structure of this matrix ! A lot of important block matrices have that Kronecker form. They often come from two-dimensional applications, where A is a "matrix in the x-direction" and B is acting in the y-direction (examples below). If A and B are square, so $m = n$ and $p = q$, then the big matrix $A \otimes B$ is also square.

Example 8 **(Finite differences in the *x* and *y* directions)** Laplace's partial differential equation $-\partial^2 u/\partial x^2 - \partial^2 u/\partial y^2 = 0$ is replaced by finite differences, to find values for u on a two-dimensional grid. Differences in the x-direction add to differences in the y-direction, connecting five neighboring values of u:

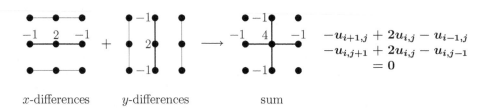

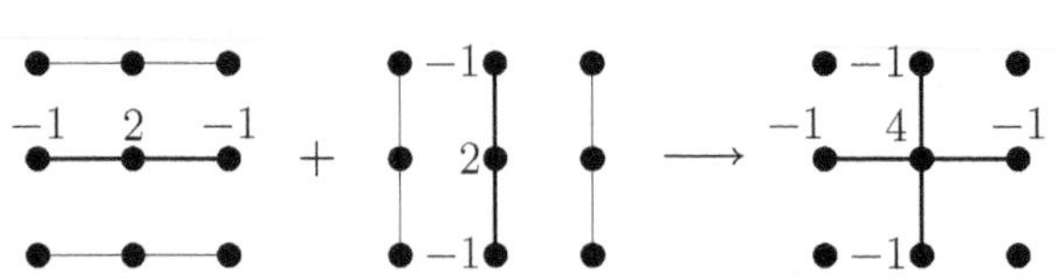

$$\begin{aligned} -u_{i+1,j} + 2u_{i,j} - u_{i-1,j} \\ -u_{i,j+1} + 2u_{i,j} - u_{i,j-1} \\ = 0 \end{aligned}$$

x-differences y-differences   sum

A 5-point equation is centered at each of the nine meshpoints. The 9 by 9 matrix (call it A_{2D}) is constructed from the 3 by 3 "1D" matrix for differences along a line:

$$\textbf{Difference matrix in one direction} \quad A = \begin{bmatrix} 2 & -1 & 0 \\ -1 & 2 & -1 \\ 0 & -1 & 2 \end{bmatrix} \quad \textbf{Identity matrix in other direction} \quad I = \begin{bmatrix} 1 & 0 & 0 \\ 0 & 1 & 0 \\ 0 & 0 & 1 \end{bmatrix}.$$

Kronecker products produce three 1D differences along three lines, up or across:

$$\textbf{One direction} \qquad A \otimes I = \begin{bmatrix} 2I & -I & 0 \\ -I & 2I & -I \\ 0 & -I & 2I \end{bmatrix}.$$

$$\textbf{Other direction} \qquad I \otimes A = \begin{bmatrix} A & 0 & 0 \\ 0 & A & 0 \\ 0 & 0 & A \end{bmatrix}.$$

$$\textbf{Both directions} \qquad A_{2D} = (A \otimes I) + (I \otimes A) = \begin{bmatrix} A+2I & -I & 0 \\ -I & A+2I & -I \\ 0 & -I & A+2I \end{bmatrix}.$$

The sum $(A \otimes I) + (I \otimes A)$ is the 9 by 9 matrix for Laplace's five-point difference equation (Section 1.7 was for 1D and Section 7.4 mentioned 2D). The middle row of this 9 by 9 matrix shows all five nonzeros from the five-point molecule:

$$\textbf{Away from boundary} \qquad \text{Row 5 of } A_{2D} = [0 \ \ -1 \ \ 0 \quad -1 \ \ 4 \ \ -1 \quad 0 \ \ -1 \ \ 0].$$

Example 9 **(The Fourier matrix in 2D)** The one-dimensional Fourier matrix F is the most important complex matrix in the world. The Fast Fourier Transform in Section 3.5 is a quick way to multiply by that matrix F. So the FFT transforms "time domain to frequency domain" for a 1D audio signal. **For images we need the 2D transform**:

$$\textbf{Fourier matrix in 2D} \qquad F_{2D} = F \otimes F = \begin{array}{l}\textbf{Transform along each row,} \\ \textbf{then down each column}\end{array}$$

The image is a two-dimensional array of pixel values. It is transformed by F_{2D} into a two-dimensional array of Fourier coefficients. That array can be compressed and transmitted and stored. Then the *inverse transform* brings us back from Fourier coefficients to pixel values. We need to know the inverse rule for Kronecker products:

The inverse of the matrix $A \otimes B$ is the matrix $A^{-1} \otimes B^{-1}$.

The FFT also speeds up the 2D inverse transform! We just invert in one direction followed by the other direction. We are adding $\sum\sum c_{k\ell}e^{ikx}e^{i\ell y}$ over k and then ℓ.

The Laplace difference matrix $A_{2D} = (A \otimes I) + (I \otimes A)$ has no simple inverse formula. That is why the equation $A_{2D}u = b$ has been studied so carefully. One of the fastest methods is to diagonalize A_{2D} by using its eigenvector matrix (which is the Fourier sine matrix $S \otimes S$, very similar to F_{2D}). The eigenvalues of A_{2D} come immediately from the eigenvalues of A_{1D}:

> The n^2 eigenvalues of $(A \otimes I) + (I \otimes B)$ are all the sums $\lambda_i(A) + \lambda_j(B)$.
> The n^2 eigenvalues of $A \otimes B$ are all the products $\lambda_i(A)\,\lambda_j(B)$.

If A and B are n by n, the determinant of $A \otimes B$ (the product of its eigenvalues) is $(\det A)^n(\det B)^n$. The trace of $A \otimes B$ is (trace A)(trace B). This appendix illustrates both "pure linear algebra" and its crucial applications!

Problem Set A

1. Suppose $\mathbf{S}$ and $\mathbf{T}$ are subspaces of $\mathbf{R}^{13}$, with $\dim \mathbf{S} = 7$ and $\dim \mathbf{T} = 8$.
   (a) What is the largest possible dimension of $\mathbf{S} \cap \mathbf{T}$?
   (b) What is the smallest possible dimension of $\mathbf{S} \cap \mathbf{T}$?
   (c) What is the smallest possible dimension of $\mathbf{S} + \mathbf{T}$?
   (d) What is the largest possible dimension of $\mathbf{S} + \mathbf{T}$?

2. What are the intersections of the following pairs of subspaces?
   (a) The x-y plane and the y-z plane in $\mathbf{R}^3$.
   (b) The line through $(1, 1, 1)$ and the plane through $(1, 0, 0)$ and $(0, 1, 1)$.
   (c) The zero vector and the whole space $\mathbf{R}^3$.
   (d) The plane S perpendicular to $(1, 1, 0)$ and perpendicular to $(0, 1, 1)$ in $\mathbf{R}^3$.

   What are the *sums* of those pairs of subspaces?

3. Within the space of all 4 by 4 matrices, let $\mathbf{V}$ be the subspace of *tridiagonal* matrices and $\mathbf{W}$ the subspace of *upper triangular* matrices. Describe the subspace $\mathbf{V}+\mathbf{W}$, whose members are the upper Hessenberg matrices. What is $\mathbf{V} \cap \mathbf{W}$? Verify formula (8).

4. If $\mathbf{V} \cap \mathbf{W}$ contains only the zero vector, then equation (8) becomes $\dim(\mathbf{V} + \mathbf{W}) = \dim \mathbf{V} + \dim \mathbf{W}$. Check this when $\mathbf{V}$ is the row space of A, $\mathbf{W}$ is the nullspace of A, and the matrix A is m by n of rank r. What are the dimensions?

5. Give an example in $\mathbf{R}^3$ for which $\mathbf{V} \cap \mathbf{W}$ contains only the zero vector, but $\mathbf{V}$ is not orthogonal to $\mathbf{W}$.

6. If $\mathbf{V} \cap \mathbf{W} = \{0\}$, then $\mathbf{V} + \mathbf{W}$ is called the *direct sum* of $\mathbf{V}$ and $\mathbf{W}$, with the special notation $\mathbf{V} \oplus \mathbf{W}$. If $\mathbf{V}$ is spanned by $(1, 1, 1)$ and $(1, 0, 1)$, choose a subspace $\mathbf{W}$ so that $\mathbf{V} \oplus \mathbf{W} = \mathbf{R}^3$. Explain why any vector x in the direct sum $\mathbf{V} \oplus \mathbf{W}$ can be written in one *and only one* way as $x = v + w$ (with v in $\mathbf{V}$ and w in $\mathbf{W}$).

7. Find a basis for the sum $\mathbf{V} + \mathbf{W}$ of the space $\mathbf{V}$ spanned by $v_1 = (1, 1, 0, 0)$, $v_2 = (1, 0, 1, 0)$ and the space $\mathbf{W}$ spanned by $w_1 = (0, 1, 0, 1)$, $w_2 = (0, 0, 1, 1)$. Find also the dimension of $\mathbf{V} \cap \mathbf{W}$ and a basis for it.

8. Prove from equation (8) that $\operatorname{rank}(A + B) \le \operatorname{rank}(A) + \operatorname{rank}(B)$.

9. **The intersection $C(A) \cap C(B)$ matches the nullspace of $[A \;\; B]$.** Each $y = Ax_1 = Bx_2$ in the column spaces of both A and B matches $x = (x_1, -x_2)$ in the nullspace, because $[A \;\; B]x = Ax_1 - Bx_2 = 0$. Check that $y = (6, 3, 6)$ matches

$x = (1, 1, -2, -3)$, and find the intersection $\boldsymbol{C}(A) \cap \boldsymbol{C}(B)$, for

$$A = \begin{bmatrix} 1 & 5 \\ 3 & 0 \\ 2 & 4 \end{bmatrix} \qquad B = \begin{bmatrix} 3 & 0 \\ 0 & 1 \\ 0 & 2 \end{bmatrix}.$$

10. Multiply $A \otimes B$ times $A^{-1} \otimes B^{-1}$ to get $AA^{-1} \otimes BB^{-1} = I \otimes I = I_{2\text{D}}$.

11. What is the 4 by 4 Fourier matrix $F_{2\text{D}} = F \otimes F$ for $F = \begin{bmatrix} 1 & 1 \\ 1 & -1 \end{bmatrix}$?

12. Suppose $Ax = \lambda(A)x$ and $By = \lambda(B)y$. Form a long column vector z with n^2 components, $x_1 y$, then $x_2 y$, and eventually $x_n y$. Show that z is an eigenvector for $(A \otimes I)z = \lambda(A)z$ and $(A \otimes B)z = \lambda(A)\lambda(B)z$.

13. What would be the seven-point Laplace matrix for $-u_{xx} - u_{yy} - u_{zz} = 0$? This "three-dimensional" matrix is built from Kronecker products using I and $A_{1\text{D}}$.

Appendix

B The Jordan Form

Given a square matrix A, we want to choose M so that $M^{-1}AM$ is as nearly diagonal as possible. In the simplest case, A has a complete set of eigenvectors and they become the columns of M—otherwise known as S. The Jordan form is $J = M^{-1}AM = \Lambda$; it is constructed entirely from 1 by 1 blocks $J_i = \lambda_i$, and the goal of a diagonal matrix is completely achieved. In the more general and more difficult case, some eigenvectors are missing and a diagonal form is impossible. That case is now our main concern.

We repeat the theorem that is to be proved:

If a matrix A has s linearly independent eigenvectors, then it is similar to a matrix J that is in ***Jordan form***, with s square blocks on the diagonal:

$$J = M^{-1}AM = \begin{bmatrix} J_1 & & \\ & \ddots & \\ & & J_s \end{bmatrix}.$$

Each block has one eigenvector, one eigenvalue, and 1s just above the diagonal:

$$J_i = \begin{bmatrix} \lambda_i & 1 & & \\ & \cdot & \cdot & \\ & & \cdot & 1 \\ & & & \lambda_i \end{bmatrix}.$$

An example of such a Jordan matrix is

$$J = \begin{bmatrix} 8 & 1 & 0 & 0 & 0 \\ 0 & 8 & 0 & 0 & 0 \\ 0 & 0 & 0 & 1 & 0 \\ 0 & 0 & 0 & 0 & 0 \\ 0 & 0 & 0 & 0 & 0 \end{bmatrix} = \begin{bmatrix} \begin{bmatrix} 8 & 1 \\ 0 & 8 \end{bmatrix} & & \\ & \begin{bmatrix} 0 & 1 \\ 0 & 0 \end{bmatrix} & \\ & & [0] \end{bmatrix} = \begin{bmatrix} J_1 & & \\ & J_2 & \\ & & J_3 \end{bmatrix}.$$

The double eigenvalue $\lambda = 8$ has only a single eigenvector, in the first coordinate direction $e_1 = (1, 0, 0, 0, 0)$; as a result, $\lambda = 8$ appears only in a single block J_1. The triple eigenvalue $\lambda = 0$ has two eigenvectors, e_3 and e_5, which correspond to the two Jordan blocks J_2 and J_3. If A had 5 eigenvectors, all blocks would be 1 by 1 and J would be diagonal.

The key question is this: *If A is some other 5 by 5 matrix, under what conditions will its Jordan form be this same J? When will there exist an M such that $M^{-1}AM = J$?* As a first requirement, any similar matrix A must share the same eigenvalues 8, 8, 0, 0, 0. But the diagonal matrix with these eigenvalues is not similar to J—and our question really concerns the eigenvectors.

To answer it, we rewrite $M^{-1}AM = J$ in the simpler form $AM = MJ$:

$$A\begin{bmatrix} & & & & \\ x_1 & x_2 & x_3 & x_4 & x_5 \\ & & & & \end{bmatrix} = \begin{bmatrix} & & & & \\ x_1 & x_2 & x_3 & x_4 & x_5 \\ & & & & \end{bmatrix}\begin{bmatrix} 8 & 1 & & & \\ 0 & 8 & & & \\ & & 0 & 1 & \\ & & 0 & 0 & \\ & & & & 0 \end{bmatrix}.$$

Carrying out the multiplications a column at a time,

$$Ax_1 = 8x_1 \quad \text{and} \quad Ax_2 = 8x_2 + x_1 \tag{10}$$

$$Ax_3 = 0x_3 \quad \text{and} \quad Ax_4 = 0x_4 + x_3 \quad \text{and} \quad Ax_5 = 0x_5. \tag{11}$$

Now we can recognize the conditions on A. It must have three genuine eigenvectors, just as J has. The one with $\lambda = 8$ will go into the first column of M, exactly as it would have gone into the first column of S: $Ax_1 = 8x_1$. The other two, which will be named x_3 and x_5, go into the third and fifth columns of M: $Ax_3 = Ax_5 = 0$. Finally there must be two other special vectors, the *generalized eigenvectors* x_2 and x_4. We think of x_2 as belonging to a ***string of vectors***, headed by x_1 and described by equation (10). In fact, x_2 is the only other vector in the string, and the corresponding block J_1 is of order 2. Equation (11) describes *two different strings*, one in which x_4 follows x_3, and another in which x_5 is alone; the blocks J_2 and J_3 are 2 by 2 and 1 by 1.

The search for the Jordan form of A becomes a search for these strings of vectors, each one headed by an eigenvector: For every i,

$$\text{either} \qquad Ax_i = \lambda_i x_i \qquad \text{or} \qquad Ax_i = \lambda_i x_i + x_{i-1}. \tag{12}$$

The vectors x_i go into the columns of M, and each string produces a single block in J. Essentially, we have to show how these strings can be constructed for every matrix A. Then if the strings match the particular equations (10) and (11), our J will be the Jordan form of A.

I think that Filippov's idea makes the construction as clear and simple as possible.* It proceeds by mathematical induction, starting from the fact that every 1 by 1 matrix is already in its Jordan form. We may assume that the construction is achieved for all matrices of order less than n—this is the "induction hypothesis"—and then explain the steps for a matrix of order n. There are three steps, and after a general description we apply them to a specific example.

Step 1 If we assume A is singular, then its column space has dimension $r < n$. Looking only within this smaller space, the induction hypothesis guarantees that a Jordan form is possible—there must be r independent vectors w_i in the column space such that

$$\text{either} \qquad Aw_i = \lambda_i w_i \qquad \text{or} \qquad Aw_i = \lambda_i w_i + w_{i-1}. \tag{13}$$

Step 2 Suppose the nullspace and the column space of A have an intersection of dimension p. Of course, every vector in the nullspace is an eigenvector corresponding to $\lambda = 0$. Therefore, there must have been p strings in step 1 that started from this eigenvalue, and we are interested in the vectors w_i that come at the

* A. F. Filippov, A short proof of the reduction to Jordan form, Moscow Univ. Math. Bull., volume 26 (1971) pp. 70–71.

end of these strings. Each of these p vectors is in the column space, so each one is a combination of the columns of A: $w_i = Ay_i$ for some y_i.

Step 3 The nullspace always has dimension $n - r$. Therefore, independent from its p-dimensional intersection with the column space, it must contain $n - r - p$ additional basis vectors z_i lying *outside* that intersection.

Now we put these steps together to give Jordan's theorem:

> The r vectors w_i, the p vectors y_i, and the $n - r - p$ vectors z_i form Jordan strings for the matrix A, and these vectors are linearly independent. They go into the columns of M, and $J = M^{-1}AM$ is in Jordan form.

If we want to renumber these vectors as $x_1, \ldots, x_n$, and match them to equation (12), then each y_i should be inserted immediately after the w_i it came from; it completes a string in which $\lambda_i = 0$. The z's come at the very end, each one alone in its own string; again the eigenvalue is zero, since the z's lie in the nullspace. The blocks with nonzero eigenvalues are already finished at step 1, the blocks with zero eigenvalues grow by one row and column at step 2, and step 3 contributes any 1 by 1 blocks $J_i = [0]$.

Now we try an example, and to stay close to the previous pages we take the eigenvalues to be 8, 8, 0, 0, 0:

$$A = \begin{bmatrix} 8 & 0 & 0 & 8 & 8 \\ 0 & 0 & 0 & 8 & 8 \\ 0 & 0 & 0 & 0 & 0 \\ 0 & 0 & 0 & 0 & 0 \\ 0 & 0 & 0 & 0 & 8 \end{bmatrix}.$$

Step 1 The column space has dimension $r = 3$, and is spanned by the coordinate vectors e_1, e_2, e_5. To look within this space we ignore the third and fourth rows and columns of A; what is left has eigenvalues 8, 8, 0, and its Jordan form comes from the vectors

$$w_1 = \begin{bmatrix} 8 \\ 0 \\ 0 \\ 0 \\ 0 \end{bmatrix}, \qquad w_2 = \begin{bmatrix} 0 \\ 1 \\ 0 \\ 0 \\ 1 \end{bmatrix}, \qquad w_3 = \begin{bmatrix} 0 \\ 8 \\ 0 \\ 0 \\ 0 \end{bmatrix}.$$

The w_i are in the column space, they complete the string for $\lambda = 8$, and they start the string for $\lambda = 0$:

$$Aw_1 = 8w_1, \qquad Aw_2 = 8w_2 + w_1, \qquad Aw_3 = 0w_3. \tag{14}$$

Step 2 The nullspace of A contains e_2 and e_3, so its intersection with the column space is spanned by e_2. Therefore $p = 1$ and, as expected, there is one string in equation (14) corresponding to $\lambda = 0$. The vector w_3 comes at the end (as well as the beginning) of that string, and $w_3 = A(e_4 - e_1)$. Therefore $y = e_4 - e_1$.

Step 3 The example has $n - r - p = 5 - 3 - 1 = 1$, and $z = e_3$ is in the nullspace but outside the column space. It will be this z that produces a 1 by 1 block in J.

If we assemble all five vectors, the full strings are

$$Aw_1 = 8w_1, \quad Aw_2 = 8w_2 + w_1, \quad Aw_3 = 0w_3, \quad Ay = 0y + w_3, \quad Az = 0z.$$

Comparing with equations (10) and (11), we have a perfect match—the Jordan form of our example will be exactly the J we wrote earlier. Putting the five vectors into the columns of M must give $AM = MJ$, or $M^{-1}AM = J$:

$$M = \begin{bmatrix} 8 & 0 & 0 & -1 & 0 \\ 0 & 1 & 8 & 0 & 0 \\ 0 & 0 & 0 & 0 & 1 \\ 0 & 0 & 0 & 1 & 0 \\ 0 & 1 & 0 & 0 & 0 \end{bmatrix}.$$

We are sufficiently trustful of mathematics (or sufficiently lazy) not to multiply out $M^{-1}AM$.

In Filippov's construction, the only technical point is to verify the independence of the whole collection w_i, y_i, and z_i. Therefore, we assume that some combination is zero:

$$\sum c_i w_i + \sum d_i y_i + \sum g_i z_i = 0. \tag{15}$$

Multiplying by A, and using equations (13) for the w_i as well as $Az_i = 0$,

$$\sum c_i \begin{bmatrix} \lambda_i w_i \\ \text{or} \\ \lambda_i w_i + w_{i-1} \end{bmatrix} + \sum d_i Ay_i = 0. \tag{16}$$

The Ay_i are the special w_i at the ends of strings corresponding to $\lambda_i = 0$, so they cannot appear in the first sum. (They are multiplied by zero in $\lambda_i w_i$.) Since equation (16) is some combination of the w_i, which were independent by the induction hypothesis—they supplied the Jordan form within the column space—we conclude that *each d_i must be zero*. Returning to equation (15), this leaves $\sum c_i w_i = -\sum g_i z_i$, and the left-hand side is in the column space. Since the z's were independent of that space, each g_i must be zero. Finally, $\sum c_i w_i = 0$, and the independence of the w_i produces $c_i = 0$.

If the original A had not been singular, the three steps would have been applied instead to $A' = A - cI$. (The constant c is chosen to make A' singular, and it can be any one of the eigenvalues of A.) The algorithm puts A' into its Jordan form $M^{-1}A'M = J'$ by producing the strings x_i from the w_i, y_i and z_i. Then the Jordan form for A uses the same strings and the same M:

$$M^{-1}AM = M^{-1}A'M + M^{-1}cM = J' + cI = J.$$

This completes the proof that every A is similar to some Jordan matrix J. Except for a reordering of the blocks, ***it is similar to only one such J***; there is a unique Jordan form for A. Thus, the set of all matrices is split into a number of families, with the following property: *All the matrices in the same family have the same Jordan form, and they are all similar to each other* (and to J), *but no matrices in different families are similar.* In every family, J is the most beautiful—if you like matrices to be nearly diagonal. With this classification into families, we stop.

Example 1

$$A = \begin{bmatrix} 0 & 1 & 2 \\ 0 & 0 & 1 \\ 0 & 0 & 0 \end{bmatrix} \quad \text{with } \lambda = 0, 0, 0.$$

This matrix has rank $r = 2$ and only one eigenvector. Within the column space, there is a single string w_1, w_2, which happens to coincide with the last two columns:

$$A\begin{bmatrix}1\\0\\0\end{bmatrix} = 0 \qquad \text{and} \qquad A\begin{bmatrix}2\\1\\0\end{bmatrix} = \begin{bmatrix}1\\0\\0\end{bmatrix},$$

or

$$Aw_1 = 0 \qquad \text{and} \qquad Aw_2 = 0w_2 + w_1.$$

The nullspace lies entirely within the column space, and it is spanned by w_1. Therefore $p = 1$ in step 2, and the vector y comes from the equation

$$Ay = w_2 = \begin{bmatrix}2\\1\\0\end{bmatrix}, \qquad \text{whose solution is} \qquad y = \begin{bmatrix}0\\0\\1\end{bmatrix}.$$

Finally, the string w_1, w_2, y goes into the matrix M:

$$M = \begin{bmatrix}1&2&0\\0&1&0\\0&0&1\end{bmatrix}, \qquad \text{and} \qquad M^{-1}AM = \begin{bmatrix}0&1&0\\0&0&1\\0&0&0\end{bmatrix} = J.$$

Application to $du/dt = Au$

As always, we simplify the problem by uncoupling the unknowns. This uncoupling is complete only when there is a full set of eigenvectors, and $u = Sv$; the best change of variables in the present case is $u = Mv$. This produces the new equation $M\,dv/dt = AMv$, or $dv/dt = Jv$, which is as simple as the circumstances allow. It is coupled only by the off-diagonal 1s within each Jordan block. In the preceding example, which has a single block, $du/dt = Au$ becomes

$$\frac{dv}{dt} = \begin{bmatrix}0&1&0\\0&0&1\\0&0&0\end{bmatrix}v \qquad \text{or} \qquad \begin{aligned} da/dt &= b\\ db/dt &= c\\ dc/dt &= 0\end{aligned} \qquad \text{or} \qquad \begin{aligned} a &= a_0 + b_0t + c_0t^2/2\\ b &= \phantom{a_0 + {}} b_0 + c_0t\\ c &= \phantom{a_0 + b_0 + {}} c_0.\end{aligned}$$

The system is solved by working upward from the last equation, and a new power of t enters at every step. (An ℓ by ℓ block has powers as high as $t^{\ell-1}$.) The exponentials of J, in this case and in the earlier 5 by 5 example, are

$$e^{Jt} = \begin{bmatrix}1&t&t^2/2\\0&1&t\\0&0&1\end{bmatrix} \qquad \text{and} \qquad \begin{bmatrix}e^{8t}&te^{8t}&0&0&0\\0&e^{8t}&0&0&0\\0&0&1&t&0\\0&0&0&1&0\\0&0&0&0&1\end{bmatrix}.$$

You can see how the coefficients of a, b, and c appear in the first exponential. And in the second example, you can identify all five of the "special solutions" to $du/dt = Au$. Three of them are the pure exponentials $u_1 = e^{8t}x_1$, $u_3 = e^{0t}x_3$, and $u_5 = e^{0t}x_5$, formed as usual from the three eigenvectors of A. The other two involve the generalized eigenvectors x_2 and x_4:

$$u_2 = e^{8t}(tx_1 + x_2) \qquad \text{and} \qquad u_4 = e^{0t}(tx_3 + x_4). \tag{17}$$

The most general solution to $du/dt = Au$ is a combination $c_1u_1 + \cdots + c_5u_5$, and the combination that matches u_0 at time $t = 0$ is again

$$u_0 = c_1x_1 + \cdots + c_5x_5, \qquad \text{or} \qquad u_0 = Mc, \qquad \text{or} \qquad c = M^{-1}u_0.$$

This only means that $u = Me^{Jt}M^{-1}u_0$, and that the S and Λ in the old formula $Se^{\Lambda t}S^{-1}u_0$ have been replaced by M and J.

Problem Set B

1. Find the Jordan forms (in three steps!) of

$$A = \begin{bmatrix} 1 & 1 \\ 1 & 1 \end{bmatrix} \quad \text{and} \quad B = \begin{bmatrix} 0 & 1 & 2 \\ 0 & 0 & 0 \\ 0 & 0 & 0 \end{bmatrix}.$$

2. Show that the special solution u_2 in equation (17) does satisfy $du/dt = Au$, exactly because of the string $Ax_1 = 8x_1$, $Ax_2 = 8x_2 + x_1$.

3. For the matrix B in Problem 1, use $Me^{Jt}M^{-1}$ to compute the exponential e^{Bt}, and compare it with the power series $I + Bt + (Bt)^2/2! + \cdots$.

4. Show that each Jordan block J_i is similar to its transpose, $J_i^{\mathrm{T}} = P^{-1}J_iP$, using the permutation matrix P with 1s along the cross-diagonal (lower left to upper right). Deduce that every matrix is similar to its transpose.

5. Find "by inspection" the Jordan forms of

$$A = \begin{bmatrix} 1 & 2 & 3 \\ 0 & 4 & 5 \\ 0 & 0 & 6 \end{bmatrix} \quad \text{and} \quad B = \begin{bmatrix} 1 & 1 \\ -1 & -1 \end{bmatrix}.$$

6. Find the Jordan form J and the matrix M for A and B (B has eigenvalues 1, 1, 1, -1). What is the solution to $du/dt = Au$, and what is e^{At}?

$$A = \begin{bmatrix} 0 & 0 & 1 & 0 & 0 \\ 0 & 0 & 0 & 1 & 0 \\ 0 & 0 & 0 & 0 & 1 \\ 0 & 0 & 0 & 0 & 0 \\ 0 & 0 & 0 & 0 & 0 \end{bmatrix} \quad \text{and} \quad B = \begin{bmatrix} 1 & -1 & 0 & -1 \\ 0 & 2 & 0 & 1 \\ -2 & 1 & -1 & 1 \\ 2 & -1 & 2 & 0 \end{bmatrix}.$$

7. Suppose that $A^2 = A$. Show that its Jordan form $J = M^{-1}AM$ satisfies $J^2 = J$. Since the diagonal blocks stay separate, this means $J_i^2 = J_i$ for each block; show by direct computation that J_i can only be a 1 by 1 block, $J_i = [0]$ or $J_i = [1]$. Thus, A is similar to a diagonal matrix of 0s and 1s.

Note This is a typical case of our closing theorem: *The matrix A can be diagonalized if and only if the product $(A - \lambda_1 I)(A - \lambda_2 I)\cdots(A - \lambda_p I)$, without including any repetitions of the λ's, is zero.* One extreme case is a matrix with distinct eigenvalues; the Cayley–Hamilton theorem says that with n factors $A - \lambda I$ we always get zero. The other extreme is the identity matrix, also diagonalizable ($p = 1$ and $A - I = 0$). The nondiagonalizable matrix $A = \begin{bmatrix} 1 & 1 \\ 0 & 1 \end{bmatrix}$ satisfies not $(A - I) = 0$ but only $(A - I)^2 = 0$—an equation with a repeated root.

Solutions to Selected Exercises

Problem Set 1.2, page 9

1. The lines intersect at $(x, y) = (3, 1)$. Then $3(\text{column } 1) + 1(\text{column } 2) = (4, 4)$.

3. These "planes" intersect in a line in four-dimensional space. The fourth plane normally intersects that line in a point. An inconsistent equation like $u + w = 5$ leaves no solution (no intersection).

5. The two points on the plane are $(1, 0, 0, 0)$ and $(0, 1, 0, 0)$.

7. Solvable for $(3, 5, 8)$ and $(1, 2, 3)$; not solvable for $b = (3, 5, 7)$ or $b = (1, 2, 2)$.

9. Column $3 = 2(\text{column } 2) - \text{column } 1$. If $b = (0, 0, 0)$, then $(u, v, w) = (c, -2c, c)$.

11. Both $a = 2$ and $a = -2$ give a line of solutions. All other a give $x = 0$, $y = 0$.

13. The row picture has two lines meeting at $(4, 2)$. The column picture has $4(1, 1) + 2(-2, 1) = 4(\text{column } 1) + 2(\text{column } 2) = \text{right-hand side } (0, 6)$.

15. The row picture shows four *lines*. The column picture is in *four*-dimensional space. No solution unless the right-hand side is a combination of *the two columns*.

17. If x, y, z satisfy the first two equations, they also satisfy the third equation. The line **L** of solutions contains $v = (1, 1, 0)$, $w = \left(\frac{1}{2}, 1, \frac{1}{2}\right)$, and $u = \frac{1}{2}v + \frac{1}{2}w$, and all combinations $cv + dw$ with $c + d = 1$.

19. Column $3 = \text{column } 1$; solutions $(x, y, z) = (1, 1, 0)$ or $(0, 1, 1)$ and you can add any multiple of $(-1, 0, 1)$; $b = (4, 6, c)$ needs $c = 10$ for solvability.

21. The second plane and row 2 of the matrix and all columns of the matrix are changed. The solution is not changed.

23. $u = 0$, $v = 0$, $w = 1$, because $1(\text{column } 3) = b$.

Problem Set 1.3, page 15

1. Multiply by $\ell = \frac{10}{2} = 5$, and subtract to find $2x + 3y = 1$ and $-6y = 6$. Pivots $2, -6$.

3. Subtract $-\frac{1}{2}$ times equation 1 (or add $\frac{1}{2}$ times equation 1). The new second equation is $3y = 3$. Then $y = 1$ and $x = 5$. If the right-hand side changes sign, so does the solution: $(x, y) = (-5, -1)$.

5. $6x + 4y$ is 2 times $3x + 2y$. There is no solution unless the right-hand side is $2 \cdot 10 = 20$. Then all points on the line $3x + 2y = 10$ are solutions, including $(0, 5)$ and $(4, -1)$.

7. If $a = 2$, elimination must fail. The equations have no solution. If $a = 0$, elimination stops for a row exchange. Then $3y = -3$ gives $y = -1$ and $4x + 6y = 6$ gives $x = 3$.

9. $6x - 4y$ is 2 times $(3x - 2y)$. Therefore, we need $b_2 = 2b_1$. Then there will be infinitely many solutions. The columns $(3, 6)$ and $(-2, -4)$ are on the same line.

11. $\begin{aligned} 2x - 3y &= 3 \\ y + z &= 1 \\ 2y - 3z &= 2 \end{aligned}$ gives $\begin{aligned} 2x - 3y &= 3 \\ y + z &= 1 \\ -5z &= 0 \end{aligned}$ and $\begin{aligned} x &= 3 \\ y &= 1 \\ z &= 0 \end{aligned}$ Subtract $2 \times$ row 1 from row 2; Subtract $1 \times$ row 1 from row 3; Subtract $2 \times$ row 2 from row 3.

13. The second pivot position will contain $-2-b$. If $b=-2$, we exchange with row 3. If $b=-1$ (singular case), the second equation is $-y-z=0$. A solution is $(1,1,-1)$.

15. If row 1 = row 2, then row 2 is zero after the first step; exchange the zero row with row 3 and there is no *third* pivot. If column 1 = column 2, there is no *second* pivot.

17. Row 2 becomes $3y-4z=5$, then row 3 becomes $(q+4)z=t-5$. If $q=-4$, the system is singular — no third pivot. Then, if $t=5$, the third equation is $0=0$. Choosing $z=1$, the equation $3y-4z=5$ gives $y=3$ and equation 1 gives $x=-9$.

19. The system is singular if row 3 is a *combination of rows* 1 *and* 2. From the end view, the three planes form a triangle. This happens if rows $1+2=$ row 3 on the left-hand side but not the right-hand side: for example, $x+y+z=0$, $x-2y-z=1$, $2x-y=9$. No two planes are parallel, but still no solution.

21. The fifth pivot is $\frac{6}{5}$. The nth pivot is $\frac{(n+1)}{n}$.

23. Triangular system $\begin{cases} u + v + w = 2 \\ 2v + 2w = -2 \\ 2w = 2 \end{cases}$ Solution $\begin{aligned} u &= 3 \\ v &= -2 \\ w &= 1 \end{aligned}$.

25. $(u,v,w)=(3/2,1/2,-3)$. Change to $+1$ would make the system singular (2 equal columns).

27. $a=0$ requires a row exchange, but the system is nonsingular: $a=2$ makes it singular (one pivot, infinity of solutions); $a=-2$ makes it singular (one pivot, no solution).

29. The second term $bc+ad$ is $(a+b)(c+d)-ac-bd$ (only 1 additional multiplication).

31. Elimination fails for $a=2$ (equal columns), $a=4$ (equal rows), $a=0$ (zero column).

Problem Set 1.4, page 26

1. $\begin{bmatrix}17\\4\\17\end{bmatrix}, \begin{bmatrix}5\\-2\\3\end{bmatrix}, \begin{bmatrix}2\\4\end{bmatrix}$. With sides to (2, 1) and (0, 3), the parallelogram goes to (2, 4).

3. Inner products 54 and 0, column times row gives $\begin{bmatrix}3 & 5 & 1\\-6 & -10 & -2\\21 & 35 & 7\end{bmatrix}$.

5. $Ax=(0,0,0)$, so $x=(2,1,1)$ is a solution; other solutions are $cx=(2c,c,c)$.

7. Examples: Diagonal $\begin{bmatrix}1&0&0\\0&2&0\\0&0&7\end{bmatrix}$, symmetric $\begin{bmatrix}1&3&4\\3&2&0\\4&0&7\end{bmatrix}$, triangular $\begin{bmatrix}1&3&4\\0&2&0\\0&0&7\end{bmatrix}$,

skew-symmetric $\begin{bmatrix}0&3&4\\-3&0&0\\-4&0&0\end{bmatrix}$.

9. (a) a_{11} (b) $\ell_{i1} = a_{i1}/a_{11}$ (c) new a_{ij} is $a_{ij} - \dfrac{a_{i1}}{a_{11}}a_{1j}$
(d) second pivot $a_{22} - \dfrac{a_{21}}{a_{11}}a_{12}$.

11. The coefficients of rows of B are 2, 1, 4 from A. The first row of AB is $[6\ \ 3]$.

13. $A = \begin{bmatrix} 0 & 1 \\ -1 & 0 \end{bmatrix}$, $B = \begin{bmatrix} 0 & 1 \\ 0 & 0 \end{bmatrix}$, $C = \begin{bmatrix} 0 & 1 \\ 1 & 0 \end{bmatrix}$, $D = A$, $E = F = \begin{bmatrix} 1 & -1 \\ 1 & -1 \end{bmatrix}$.

15. $AB_1 = B_1A$ gives $b = c = 0$. $AB_2 = B_2A$ gives $a = d$. So $A = aI$.

17. $A(A+B) + B(A+B)$, $(A+B)(B+A)$, $A^2 + AB + BA + B^2$ always equal $(A+B)^2$.

19. $\begin{bmatrix} a & b \\ c & d \end{bmatrix}\begin{bmatrix} p & q \\ r & s \end{bmatrix} = \begin{bmatrix} a \\ c \end{bmatrix}[p\ \ q] + \begin{bmatrix} b \\ d \end{bmatrix}[r\ \ s] = \begin{bmatrix} ap+br & aq+bs \\ cp+dr & cq+ds \end{bmatrix}$.

21. $A^n = A$; $B^n = \begin{bmatrix} 1 & 0 \\ 0 & (-1)^n \end{bmatrix}$, $C = \begin{bmatrix} 0 & 0 \\ 0 & 0 \end{bmatrix}$ = zero matrix.

23. $E_{32}E_{21}b = (1, -5, -35)$ but $E_{21}E_{32}b = (1, -5, \mathbf{0})$. Then row 3 feels no effect from row 1.

25. Changing a_{33} from 7 to 11 will change the third pivot from 5 to 9. Changing a_{33} from 7 to 2 will change the pivot from 5 to *no pivot*.

27. To reverse E_{31}, *add* 7 times row 1 to row 3. The matrix is $R_{31} = \begin{bmatrix} 1 & 0 & 0 \\ 0 & 1 & 0 \\ 7 & 0 & 1 \end{bmatrix}$.

29. $E_{13} = \begin{bmatrix} 1 & 0 & 1 \\ 0 & 1 & 0 \\ 0 & 0 & 1 \end{bmatrix}$; $\begin{bmatrix} 1 & 0 & 1 \\ 0 & 1 & 0 \\ 1 & 0 & 1 \end{bmatrix}$; $E_{31}E_{13} = \begin{bmatrix} 2 & 0 & 1 \\ 0 & 1 & 0 \\ 1 & 0 & 1 \end{bmatrix}$. Test on the identity matrix!

31. E_{21} has $\ell_{21} = -\frac{1}{2}$, E_{32} has $\ell_{32} = -\frac{2}{3}$, E_{43} has $\ell_{43} = -\frac{3}{4}$. Otherwise the E's match I.

33. $\begin{aligned} a + b + c &= 4 \\ a + 2b + 4c &= 8 \\ a + 3b + 9c &= 14 \end{aligned}$ gives $\begin{aligned} a &= 2 \\ b &= 1. \\ c &= 1 \end{aligned}$

35. (a) Each column is E times a column of B.
(b) $EB = \begin{bmatrix} 1 & 0 \\ 1 & 1 \end{bmatrix}\begin{bmatrix} 1 & 2 & 4 \\ 1 & 2 & 4 \end{bmatrix} = \begin{bmatrix} 1 & 2 & 4 \\ 2 & 4 & 8 \end{bmatrix}$.
Rows of EB are combinations of rows of B, so they are multiples of $[1\ \ 2\ \ 4]$.

37. (row 3) $\cdot\, x$ is $\sum a_{3j}x_j$, and $(A^2)_{11}$ = (row 1) $\cdot$ (column 1) $= \sum a_{1j}a_{j1}$.

39. $BA = 3I$ is 5 by 5, $AB = 5I$ is 3 by 3, $ABD = 5D$ is 3 by 1, ABD: No, $A(B+C)$: No.

41. (a) $B = 4I$. (b) $B = 0$. (c) $B = \begin{bmatrix} 0 & 0 & 1 \\ 0 & 1 & 0 \\ 1 & 0 & 0 \end{bmatrix}$.
(d) Every row of B is 1, 0, 0.

43. (a) mn (every entry). (b) mnp. (c) n^3 (this is n^2 dot products).

45. $\begin{bmatrix} 1 \\ 2 \\ 2 \end{bmatrix}\begin{bmatrix} 3 & 3 & 0 \end{bmatrix} + \begin{bmatrix} 0 \\ 4 \\ 1 \end{bmatrix}\begin{bmatrix} 1 & 2 & 1 \end{bmatrix} = \begin{bmatrix} 3 & 3 & 0 \\ 6 & 6 & 0 \\ 6 & 6 & 0 \end{bmatrix} + \begin{bmatrix} 0 & 0 & 0 \\ 4 & 8 & 4 \\ 1 & 2 & 1 \end{bmatrix} = \begin{bmatrix} 3 & 3 & 0 \\ 10 & 14 & 4 \\ 7 & 8 & 1 \end{bmatrix}$.

47. A times B is $A \begin{bmatrix} | & | & | \\ | & | & | \end{bmatrix}, \begin{bmatrix} \rule{1em}{0.5pt} \\ \rule{1em}{0.5pt} \end{bmatrix} B, \begin{bmatrix} \rule{1em}{0.5pt} \\ \rule{1em}{0.5pt} \end{bmatrix} \begin{bmatrix} | & | & | \\ | & | & | \end{bmatrix}, \begin{bmatrix} | & | & | \\ | & | & | \end{bmatrix} \begin{bmatrix} \rule{1em}{0.5pt} \\ \rule{1em}{0.5pt} \end{bmatrix}.$

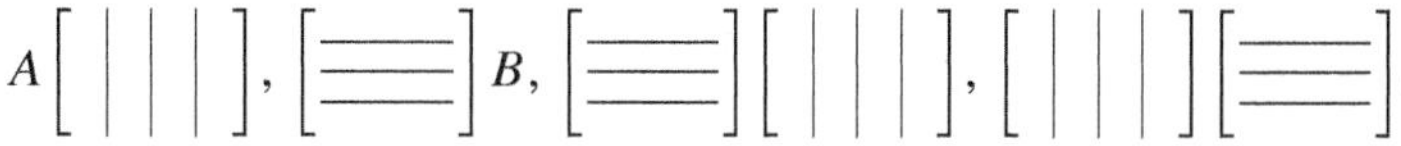

49. The $(2, 2)$ block $S = D - CA^{-1}B$ is the **Schur complement**: blocks in $d - (cb/a)$.

51. A times $X = [x_1 \ x_2 \ x_3]$ will be the identity matrix $I = [Ax_1 \ Ax_2 \ Ax_3]$.

53. $\begin{bmatrix} a+b & a+b \\ c+d & c+d \end{bmatrix}$ agrees with $\begin{bmatrix} a+c & b+d \\ a+c & b+d \end{bmatrix}$ when $b = c$ and $a = d$.

55. $2x + 3y + z + 5t = 8$ is $Ax = b$ with the 1 by 4 matrix $A = [2 \ 3 \ 1 \ 5]$. The solutions x fill a 3D "plane" in four dimensions.

57. The dot product $[1 \ 4 \ 5] \begin{bmatrix} x \\ y \\ z \end{bmatrix} = (1 \text{ by } 3)(3 \text{ by } 1)$ is zero for points (x, y, z) on a

plane $x + 4y + 5z = 0$ in three dimensions. The columns of A are one-dimensional vectors.

59. $A * v = [3 \ 4 \ 5]'$ and $v' * v = 50$; $v * A$ gives an error message.

61. $M = \begin{bmatrix} 8 & 3 & 4 \\ 1 & 5 & 9 \\ 6 & 7 & 2 \end{bmatrix} = \begin{bmatrix} 5+u & 5-u+v & 5-v \\ 5-u-v & 5 & 5+u+v \\ 5+v & 5+u-v & 5-u \end{bmatrix}$;

$M_3(1, 1, 1) = (15, 15, 15)$; $M_4(1, 1, 1, 1) = (34, 34, 34, 34)$ because the numbers 1 to 16 add to 136, which is 4(34).

Problem Set 1.5, page 39

1. U is nonsingular when no entry on the main diagonal is zero.

3. $\begin{bmatrix} 1 & 0 & 0 \\ 2 & 1 & 0 \\ -1 & -1 & 1 \end{bmatrix} \begin{bmatrix} 1 & 0 & 0 \\ -2 & 1 & 0 \\ -1 & 1 & 1 \end{bmatrix} = \begin{bmatrix} 1 & 0 & 0 \\ 0 & 1 & 0 \\ 0 & 0 & 1 \end{bmatrix};$ $\begin{bmatrix} 1 & 0 & 0 \\ -2 & 1 & 0 \\ -1 & 1 & 1 \end{bmatrix} \begin{bmatrix} 1 & 0 & 0 \\ 2 & 1 & 0 \\ -1 & -1 & 1 \end{bmatrix} = I$ also.

$(E^{-1}F^{-1}G^{-1})(GFE) = E^{-1}F^{-1}FE = E^{-1}E = I;$ also $(GFE)(E^{-1}F^{-1}G^{-1}) = I.$

5. $LU = \begin{bmatrix} 1 & 0 & 0 \\ 0 & 1 & 0 \\ 3 & 0 & 1 \end{bmatrix} \begin{bmatrix} 2 & 3 & 3 \\ 0 & 5 & 7 \\ 0 & 0 & -1 \end{bmatrix};$ after elimination, $\begin{bmatrix} 2 & 3 & 3 \\ 0 & 5 & 7 \\ 0 & 0 & -1 \end{bmatrix} \begin{bmatrix} u \\ v \\ w \end{bmatrix} = \begin{bmatrix} 2 \\ 2 \\ -1 \end{bmatrix}.$

7. $FGH = \begin{bmatrix} 1 & 0 & 0 & 0 \\ 2 & 1 & 0 & 0 \\ 0 & 2 & 1 & 0 \\ 0 & 0 & 2 & 1 \end{bmatrix};$ $HGF = \begin{bmatrix} 1 & 0 & 0 & 0 \\ 2 & 1 & 0 & 0 \\ 4 & 2 & 1 & 0 \\ 8 & 4 & 2 & 1 \end{bmatrix}.$

9. (a) Nonsingular when $d_1 d_2 d_3 \neq 0$. (b) Suppose $d_3 \neq 0$: Solve $Lc = b$ going

downward: $Lc = b$ gives $c = \begin{bmatrix} 0 \\ 0 \\ 1 \end{bmatrix}$. Then $\begin{bmatrix} d_1 & -d_1 & 0 \\ 0 & d_2 & -d_2 \\ 0 & 0 & d_3 \end{bmatrix} \begin{bmatrix} u \\ v \\ w \end{bmatrix} = \begin{bmatrix} 0 \\ 0 \\ 1 \end{bmatrix}$ gives

$x = \begin{bmatrix} 1/d_3 \\ 1/d_3 \\ 1/d_3 \end{bmatrix}.$

11. $Lc = b$ going downward gives $c = \begin{bmatrix} 2 \\ -2 \\ 0 \end{bmatrix}$; $Ux = c$ upward gives $x = \begin{bmatrix} 5 \\ -2 \\ 0 \end{bmatrix}$.

13. Permutation rows 2 and 3 $\begin{bmatrix} 1 & 0 & 0 \\ 0 & 0 & 1 \\ 0 & 1 & 0 \end{bmatrix}$, $\begin{bmatrix} u \\ v \\ w \end{bmatrix} = \begin{bmatrix} 2 \\ -3 \\ 4 \end{bmatrix}$;

permutation rows 1 and 2 $\begin{bmatrix} 0 & 1 & 0 \\ 1 & 0 & 0 \\ 0 & 0 & 0 \end{bmatrix}$, $\begin{bmatrix} u \\ v \\ w \end{bmatrix} = \begin{bmatrix} 1 \\ -1 \\ 1 \end{bmatrix}$.

15. $PA = LDU$ is $\begin{bmatrix} 0 & 1 & 0 \\ 1 & 0 & 0 \\ 0 & 0 & 1 \end{bmatrix} \begin{bmatrix} 0 & 1 & 1 \\ 1 & 0 & 1 \\ 2 & 3 & 4 \end{bmatrix} = \begin{bmatrix} 1 & 0 & 0 \\ 0 & 1 & 0 \\ 2 & 3 & 1 \end{bmatrix} \begin{bmatrix} 1 & 0 & 0 \\ 0 & 1 & 0 \\ 0 & 0 & -1 \end{bmatrix} \begin{bmatrix} 1 & 0 & 1 \\ 0 & 1 & 1 \\ 0 & 0 & 1 \end{bmatrix}$;

$PA = LDU$ is $\begin{bmatrix} 1 & 0 & 0 \\ 0 & 0 & 1 \\ 0 & 1 & 0 \end{bmatrix} \begin{bmatrix} 1 & 2 & 1 \\ 2 & 4 & 2 \\ 1 & 1 & 1 \end{bmatrix} = \begin{bmatrix} 1 & 0 & 0 \\ 1 & 1 & 0 \\ 2 & 0 & 1 \end{bmatrix} \begin{bmatrix} 1 & 0 & 0 \\ 0 & -1 & 0 \\ 0 & 0 & 0 \end{bmatrix} \begin{bmatrix} 1 & 2 & 1 \\ 0 & 1 & 0 \\ 0 & 0 & 0 \end{bmatrix}$.

17. L becomes $\begin{bmatrix} 1 & 0 & 0 \\ 1 & 1 & 0 \\ 2 & 0 & 1 \end{bmatrix}$. MATLAB and other codes use $PA = LU$.

19. $a = 4$ leads to a row exchange; $3b + 10a = 40$ leads to a singular matrix; $c = 0$ leads to a row exchange; $c = 3$ leads to a singular matrix.

21. $\ell_{31} = 1$ and $\ell_{32} = 2$ ($\ell_{33} = 1$): reverse steps to recover $x + 3y + 6z = 11$ from $Ux = c$: 1 times $(x + y + z = 5)$ + 2 times $(y + 2z = 2)$ + 1 times $(z = 2)$ gives $x + 3y + 6z = 11$.

23.
$$\begin{bmatrix} 1 & & \\ 0 & 1 & \\ 0 & -2 & 1 \end{bmatrix} \begin{bmatrix} 1 & & \\ -2 & 1 & \\ 0 & 0 & 1 \end{bmatrix} A = \begin{bmatrix} 1 & 1 & 1 \\ 0 & 2 & 3 \\ 0 & 0 & -6 \end{bmatrix} = U.$$

$$A = \begin{bmatrix} 1 & 0 & 0 \\ 2 & 1 & 0 \\ 0 & 2 & 1 \end{bmatrix} U = E_{21}^{-1} E_{32}^{-1} U = LU.$$

25. 2 by 2: $d = 0$ not allowed;

$$\begin{bmatrix} 1 & 1 & 0 \\ 1 & 1 & 2 \\ 1 & 2 & 1 \end{bmatrix} = \begin{bmatrix} 1 & & \\ \ell & 1 & \\ m & n & 1 \end{bmatrix} \begin{bmatrix} d & e & g \\ & f & h \\ & & i \end{bmatrix}$$

$d = 1$, $e = 1$, then $\ell = 1$
$f = 0$ is not allowed
no pivot in row 2.

27. $A = \begin{bmatrix} 2 & 4 & 8 \\ 0 & 3 & 9 \\ 0 & 0 & 7 \end{bmatrix}$ has $L = I$ and $D = \begin{bmatrix} 2 & & \\ & 3 & \\ & & 7 \end{bmatrix}$; $A = LU$ has $U = A$ (pivots on the diagonal); $A = LDU$ has $U = D^{-1}A = \begin{bmatrix} 1 & 2 & 4 \\ 0 & 1 & 3 \\ 0 & 0 & 1 \end{bmatrix}$ with 1s on the diagonal.

29. $\begin{bmatrix} a & a & a & a \\ a & b & b & b \\ a & b & c & c \\ a & b & c & d \end{bmatrix} = \begin{bmatrix} 1 & & & \\ 1 & 1 & & \\ 1 & 1 & 1 & \\ 1 & 1 & 1 & 1 \end{bmatrix} \begin{bmatrix} a & a & a & a \\ & b-a & b-a & b-a \\ & & c-b & c-b \\ & & & d-c \end{bmatrix}$. Need $\begin{matrix} a \neq 0 \\ b \neq a \\ c \neq b \\ d \neq c. \end{matrix}$

31. $\begin{bmatrix} 1 & & \\ 1 & 1 & \\ 0 & 1 & 1 \end{bmatrix} \begin{bmatrix} 1 & 1 & 0 \\ & 1 & 1 \\ & & 1 \end{bmatrix} = LIU;\ \begin{bmatrix} a & a & 0 \\ a & a+b & b \\ 0 & b & b+c \end{bmatrix} = (\text{same } L) \begin{bmatrix} a & & \\ & b & \\ & & c \end{bmatrix}$ (same U).

33. $\begin{bmatrix} 1 & 0 & 0 \\ 1 & 1 & 0 \\ 1 & 1 & 1 \end{bmatrix} c = \begin{bmatrix} 4 \\ 5 \\ 6 \end{bmatrix}$ gives $c = \begin{bmatrix} 4 \\ 1 \\ 1 \end{bmatrix}$. $\begin{bmatrix} 1 & 1 & 1 \\ 0 & 1 & 1 \\ 0 & 0 & 1 \end{bmatrix} x = \begin{bmatrix} 4 \\ 1 \\ 1 \end{bmatrix}$ gives $x = \begin{bmatrix} 3 \\ 0 \\ 1 \end{bmatrix}$. $A = LU$.

35. The 2 by 2 upper submatrix B has the first two pivots 2, 7. Reason: Elimination on A starts in the upper left corner with elimination on B.

37. $\begin{bmatrix} 1 & 1 & 1 & 1 & 1 \\ 1 & 2 & 3 & 4 & 5 \\ 1 & 3 & 6 & 10 & 15 \\ 1 & 4 & 10 & 20 & 35 \\ 1 & 5 & 15 & 35 & 70 \end{bmatrix}$

$$= \begin{bmatrix} 1 & & & & \\ 1 & 1 & & & \\ 1 & 2 & 1 & & \\ 1 & 3 & 3 & 1 & \\ 1 & 4 & 6 & 4 & 1 \end{bmatrix} \begin{bmatrix} 1 & 1 & 1 & 1 & 1 \\ & 1 & 2 & 3 & 4 \\ & & 1 & 3 & 6 \\ & & & 1 & 4 \\ & & & & 1 \end{bmatrix}.$$

Pascal's triangle in L and U. MATLAB's lu code will wreck the pattern. chol does no row exchanges for symmetric matrices with positive pivots.

39. Each new *right-hand side* costs only n^2 steps compared to $n^3/3$ for full elimination $A\backslash b$.

41. 2 exchanges; 3 exchanges; 50 exchanges and then 51.

43. $P = \begin{bmatrix} 0 & 1 & 0 \\ 0 & 0 & 1 \\ 1 & 0 & 0 \end{bmatrix}$; $P_1 = \begin{bmatrix} 1 & 0 & 0 \\ 0 & 0 & 1 \\ 0 & 1 & 0 \end{bmatrix}$ and $P_2 = \begin{bmatrix} 0 & 0 & 1 \\ 0 & 1 & 0 \\ 1 & 0 & 0 \end{bmatrix}$ (P_2 gives a column exchange).

45. There are $n!$ permutation matrices of order n. Eventually two powers of P *must be the same*: If $P^r = P^s$ then $P^{r-s} = I$. Certainly $r - s \leq n!$

$$P = \begin{bmatrix} P_2 & \\ & P_3 \end{bmatrix} \text{ is 5 by 5 with } P_2 = \begin{bmatrix} 0 & 1 \\ 1 & 0 \end{bmatrix},\ P_3 = \begin{bmatrix} 0 & 1 & 0 \\ 0 & 0 & 1 \\ 1 & 0 & 0 \end{bmatrix}, \text{ and } P^6 = I.$$

47. The solution is $x = (1, 1, \ldots, 1)$. Then $x = Px$.

Problem Set 1.6, page 52

1. $A_1^{-1} = \begin{bmatrix} 0 & \frac{1}{3} \\ \frac{1}{2} & 0 \end{bmatrix}$; $A_2^{-1} = \begin{bmatrix} \frac{1}{2} & 0 \\ -1 & \frac{1}{2} \end{bmatrix}$; $A_3^{-1} = \begin{bmatrix} \cos\theta & \sin\theta \\ -\sin\theta & \cos\theta \end{bmatrix}$.

3. $A^{-1} = BC^{-1}$; $A^{-1} = U^{-1}L^{-1}P$.

5. $A(AB) = \text{(move parentheses)} = (A^2)(B) = I$.

7. $\begin{bmatrix} \sqrt{3}/2 & 1/2 \\ 1/2 & -\sqrt{3}/2 \end{bmatrix}, \begin{bmatrix} -\sqrt{3}/2 & 1/2 \\ 1/2 & \sqrt{3}/2 \end{bmatrix}, \begin{bmatrix} 0 & 1 \\ 1 & 0 \end{bmatrix}$ all have $A^2 = I$.

9. If row 3 of A^{-1} were (a, b, c, d), then $A^{-1}A = I$ would give $2a = 0$, $a + 3b = 0$, $4a + 8b = 1$. This has no solution.

11. (a) $\begin{bmatrix} 1 & 0 \\ 0 & 1 \end{bmatrix} + \begin{bmatrix} -1 & 0 \\ 0 & -1 \end{bmatrix} = \begin{bmatrix} 0 & 0 \\ 0 & 0 \end{bmatrix}$. (b) $\begin{bmatrix} 1 & 0 \\ 0 & 0 \end{bmatrix} + \begin{bmatrix} 0 & 0 \\ 0 & 1 \end{bmatrix} = \begin{bmatrix} 1 & 0 \\ 0 & 1 \end{bmatrix}$.

(c) $\begin{bmatrix} 1 & 0 \\ 0 & 1 \end{bmatrix} + \begin{bmatrix} 0 & 1 \\ -1 & 0 \end{bmatrix} = \begin{bmatrix} 1 & 1 \\ -1 & 1 \end{bmatrix}$; $(B^{-1} + A^{-1})^{-1} = B(A + B)^{-1}A$.

13. $A^{\mathrm{T}}B = 8$; $B^{\mathrm{T}}A = 8$; $AB^{\mathrm{T}} = \begin{bmatrix} 6 & 6 \\ 2 & 2 \end{bmatrix}$; $BA^{\mathrm{T}} = \begin{bmatrix} 6 & 2 \\ 6 & 2 \end{bmatrix}$.

15. (a) $n(n + 1)/2$ entries on and above diagonal. (b) $(n - 1)n/2$ entries above diagonal.

17. (a) The inverse of a lower (upper) triangular matrix is still lower (upper) triangular. Multiplying lower (upper) triangular matrices gives a lower (upper) triangular matrix. (b) The main diagonals of $L_1^{-1}L_2D_2$ and $D_1U_1U_2^{-1}$ are the same as those of D_2 and D_1 respectively. $L_1^{-1}L_2D_2 = D_1U_1U_2^{-1}$, so we have $D_1 = D_2$. By comparing the off-diagonals of $L_1^{-1}L_2D_2 = D_1U_1U_2^{-1}$, both matrices must be diagonal. $L_1^{-1}L_2D_2 = D_2$, $D_1U_1U_2^{-1} = D_1$, D_1 is invertible so $L_1^{-1}L_2 = I$, $U_1U_2^{-1} = I$. Then $L_1 = L_2$, $U_1 = U_2$.

19. $\begin{bmatrix} 1 & 0 & 0 \\ 3 & 1 & 0 \\ 5 & 1 & 1 \end{bmatrix} \begin{bmatrix} 1 & 0 & 0 \\ 0 & 3 & 0 \\ 0 & 0 & 2 \end{bmatrix} \begin{bmatrix} 1 & 3 & 5 \\ 0 & 1 & 1 \\ 0 & 0 & 1 \end{bmatrix}$;

$$\begin{bmatrix} 1 & 0 \\ b/a & 1 \end{bmatrix} \begin{bmatrix} a & 0 \\ 0 & d - (b^2/a) \end{bmatrix} \begin{bmatrix} 1 & b/a \\ 0 & 1 \end{bmatrix} = LDL^{\mathrm{T}}.$$

21. From $B(I - AB) = (I - BA)B$ we get $(I - BA)^{-1} = B(I - AB)^{-1}B^{-1}$, an explicit inverse provided B and $I - AB$ are invertible. *Second approach*: If $I - BA$ is not invertible, then $BAx = x$ for some nonzero x. Therefore $ABAx = Ax$, or $ABy = y$, and $I - AB$ could not be invertible. (Note that $y = Ax$ is nonzero, from $BAx = x$.)

23. $\begin{bmatrix} x \\ y \end{bmatrix} = \begin{bmatrix} .5 \\ -.2 \end{bmatrix}$, $\begin{bmatrix} t \\ z \end{bmatrix} = \begin{bmatrix} -.2 \\ .1 \end{bmatrix}$ so $A^{-1} = \dfrac{1}{10}\begin{bmatrix} 5 & -2 \\ -2 & 1 \end{bmatrix}$.

25. (a) In $Ax = (1, 0, 0)$, equation 1 + equation 2 − equation 3 is $0 = 1$. (b) The right-hand sides must satisfy $b_1 + b_2 = b_3$. (c) Row 3 becomes a row of zeros—no third pivot.

27. If B exchanges rows 1 and 2 of A, then B^{-1} exchanges *columns* 1 and 2 of A^{-1}.

29. If A has a column of zeros, so does BA. So $BA = I$ is impossible. There is no A^{-1}.

31. $\begin{bmatrix} 1 & & \\ & 1 & \\ & -1 & 1 \end{bmatrix} \begin{bmatrix} 1 & & \\ & 1 & \\ -1 & & 1 \end{bmatrix} \begin{bmatrix} 1 & & \\ -1 & 1 & \\ & & 1 \end{bmatrix} = \begin{bmatrix} 1 & & \\ -1 & 1 & \\ 0 & -1 & 1 \end{bmatrix} = E$;

then $\begin{bmatrix} 1 & & \\ 1 & 1 & \\ 1 & 1 & 1 \end{bmatrix}$ is $L = E^{-1}$, after reversing the order of these 3 elementary matrices and changing -1 to $+1$.

33. A $*$ ones(4,1) gives the zero vector, so A cannot be invertible.

35. $\begin{bmatrix}1&3&1&0\\2&7&0&1\end{bmatrix}\to\begin{bmatrix}1&3&1&0\\0&1&-2&1\end{bmatrix}\to\begin{bmatrix}1&0&7&-3\\0&1&-2&1\end{bmatrix}=[I\quad A^{-1}]$;

$\begin{bmatrix}1&3&1&0\\3&8&0&1\end{bmatrix}\to\begin{bmatrix}1&0&-8&3\\0&1&3&-1\end{bmatrix}=[I\quad A^{-1}]$.

37. $\begin{bmatrix}1&a&b&1&0&0\\0&1&c&0&1&0\\0&0&1&0&0&1\end{bmatrix}\to\begin{bmatrix}1&a&0&1&0&-b\\0&1&0&0&1&-c\\0&0&1&0&0&1\end{bmatrix}$

$\to\begin{bmatrix}1&0&0&1&-a&ac-b\\0&1&0&0&1&-c\\0&0&1&0&0&1\end{bmatrix}$.

39. $\begin{bmatrix}2&2&0&1\\0&2&1&0\end{bmatrix}\to\begin{bmatrix}2&0&-1&1\\0&2&1&0\end{bmatrix}\to\begin{bmatrix}1&0&-1/2&1/2\\0&1&1/2&0\end{bmatrix}=[I\quad A^{-1}]$.

41. Not invertible for $c=7$ (equal columns), $c=2$ (equal rows), $c=0$ (zero column).

43. $A^{-1}=\begin{bmatrix}1&1&0&0\\0&1&1&0\\0&0&1&1\\0&0&0&1\end{bmatrix}$. The 5 by 5 A^{-1} also has 1s on the diagonal and super-diagonal.

45. $\begin{bmatrix}I&0\\-C&I\end{bmatrix}$, $\begin{bmatrix}A^{-1}&0\\-D^{-1}CA^{-1}&D^{-1}\end{bmatrix}$, and $\begin{bmatrix}-D&I\\I&0\end{bmatrix}$.

47. For $Ax=b$ with A = ones(4, 4) = singular matrix and b = ones(4, 1), A\b will pick $x=(1,0,0,0)$ and pinv(A) $*$ b will pick the shortest solution $x=(1,1,1,1)/4$.

49. $A^{\mathrm T}=\begin{bmatrix}1&9\\0&3\end{bmatrix}$, $A^{-1}=\begin{bmatrix}1&0\\-3&1/3\end{bmatrix}$, $(A^{-1})^{\mathrm T}=(A^{\mathrm T})^{-1}=\begin{bmatrix}1&-3\\0&1/3\end{bmatrix}$; $A^{\mathrm T}=A$ and then $A^{-1}=\dfrac{1}{c^2}\begin{bmatrix}0&c\\c&-1\end{bmatrix}=(A^{-1})^{\mathrm T}=(A^{\mathrm T})^{-1}$.

51. $\left((AB)^{-1}\right)^{\mathrm T}=(B^{-1}A^{-1})^{\mathrm T}=(A^{-1})^{\mathrm T}(B^{-1})^{\mathrm T}$; $(U^{-1})^{\mathrm T}$ is *lower* triangular.

53. (a) $x^{\mathrm T}Ay=a_{22}=5$. (b) $x^{\mathrm T}A=[4\quad 5\quad 6]$. (c) $Ay=\begin{bmatrix}2\\5\end{bmatrix}$.

55. $(Px)^{\mathrm T}(Py)=x^{\mathrm T}P^{\mathrm T}Py=x^{\mathrm T}y$ because $P^{\mathrm T}P=I$; usually $Px\cdot y=x\cdot P^{\mathrm T}y\neq x\cdot Py$:

$$\begin{bmatrix}0&1&0\\0&0&1\\1&0&0\end{bmatrix}\begin{bmatrix}1\\2\\3\end{bmatrix}\cdot\begin{bmatrix}1\\1\\2\end{bmatrix}\neq\begin{bmatrix}1\\2\\3\end{bmatrix}\cdot\begin{bmatrix}0&1&0\\0&0&1\\1&0&0\end{bmatrix}\begin{bmatrix}1\\1\\2\end{bmatrix}.$$

57. $PAP^{\mathrm T}$ recovers the symmetry.

59. (a) The transpose of $R^{\mathrm T}AR$ is $R^{\mathrm T}A^{\mathrm T}R^{\mathrm{TT}}=R^{\mathrm T}AR=n$ by n.
(b) $(R^{\mathrm T}R)_{jj}=$ (column j of R) $\cdot$ (column j of R) $=$ length squared of column j.

61. Total currents are $A^{\mathrm{T}}y = \begin{bmatrix} 1 & 0 & 1 \\ -1 & 1 & 0 \\ 0 & -1 & -1 \end{bmatrix} \begin{bmatrix} y_{BC} \\ y_{CS} \\ y_{BS} \end{bmatrix} = \begin{bmatrix} y_{BC} + y_{BS} \\ -y_{BC} + y_{CS} \\ -y_{CS} - y_{BS} \end{bmatrix}$.

Either way $(Ax)^{\mathrm{T}}y = x^{\mathrm{T}}(A^{\mathrm{T}}y) = x_B y_{BC} + x_B y_{BS} - x_C y_{BC} + x_C y_{CS} - x_S y_{CS} - x_S y_{BS}$.

63. $Ax \cdot y$ is the *cost* of inputs, whereas $x \cdot A^{\mathrm{T}}y$ is the *value* of outputs.

65. These are groups: Lower triangular with diagonal 1s, diagonal invertible D, and permutations P. Two more: Even permutations, all nonsingular matrices.

67. Reordering the rows and/or columns of $\begin{bmatrix} a & b \\ c & d \end{bmatrix}$ will move entry a, not giving $\begin{bmatrix} a & c \\ b & d \end{bmatrix}$.

69. Random matrices are almost surely invertible.

71. The $-1, 2, -1$ matrix in Section 1.7 has $A = LDL^{\mathrm{T}}$ with $\ell_{i,i-1} = 1 - \frac{1}{i}$.

Problem Set 1.7, page 63

1. $\begin{bmatrix} 2 & -1 & & \\ -1 & 2 & -1 & \\ & -1 & 2 & -1 \\ & & -1 & 2 \end{bmatrix}$

$= \begin{bmatrix} 1 & & & \\ -\frac{1}{2} & 1 & & \\ & -\frac{2}{3} & 1 & \\ & & -\frac{3}{4} & 1 \end{bmatrix} \begin{bmatrix} 2 & & & \\ & \frac{3}{2} & & \\ & & \frac{4}{3} & \\ & & & \frac{5}{4} \end{bmatrix} \begin{bmatrix} 1 & -\frac{1}{2} & & \\ & 1 & -\frac{2}{3} & \\ & & 1 & -\frac{3}{4} \\ & & & 1 \end{bmatrix} = LDL^{\mathrm{T}}$ det $= 5$.

3. $A_0 = \begin{bmatrix} 1 & -1 & & & \\ -1 & 2 & -1 & & \\ & -1 & 2 & -1 & \\ & & -1 & 2 & -1 \\ & & & -1 & 1 \end{bmatrix}$. Each row adds to 1, so $A_0 \begin{bmatrix} c \\ c \\ c \\ c \\ c \end{bmatrix} = \begin{bmatrix} 0 \\ 0 \\ 0 \\ 0 \\ 0 \end{bmatrix}$.

5. $(u_1, u_2, u_3) = (\pi^2/8, 0, -\pi^2/8)$ instead of the true values $(1, 0, -1)$.

7. $H^{-1} = \begin{bmatrix} 9 & -36 & 30 \\ -36 & 192 & -180 \\ 30 & -180 & 180 \end{bmatrix}$.

9. The 10 by 10 Hilbert matrix is very ill-conditioned.

11. A large pivot is multiplied by less than 1 in eliminating each entry below it. An extreme case, with multipliers $= 1$ and pivots $= \frac{1}{2}, \frac{1}{2}, 4$, is $A = \begin{bmatrix} 1/2 & 1/2 & 1 \\ -1/2 & 0 & 1 \\ -1/2 & -1 & 1 \end{bmatrix}$.

Problem Set 2.1, page 73

1. (a) The set of all (u, v), where u and v are ratios p/q of integers. (b) The set of all (u, v), where $u = 0$ or $v = 0$.

3. $\boldsymbol{C}(A)$ is the x-axis; $\boldsymbol{N}(A)$ is the line through $(1, 1)$; $\boldsymbol{C}(B)$ is $\mathbf{R}^2$; $\boldsymbol{N}(B)$ is the line through $(-2, 1, 0)$; $\boldsymbol{C}(C)$ is the point $(0, 0)$ in $\mathbf{R}^2$; the nullspace $\boldsymbol{N}(C)$ is $\mathbf{R}^3$.

5. Broken rules: (a) 7, 8 (b) 1 (c) 1, 2, 8.

7. (b), (d), (e) are subspaces. Can't multiply by -1 in (a) and (c). Can't add in (f).

9. The sum of two nonsingular matrices may be singular $(A + (-A))$. The sum of two singular matrices may be nonsingular.

11. (a) One possibility: The matrices cA form a subspace not containing B.
(b) Yes: the subspace must contain $A - B = I$.
(c) The subspace of matrices whose main diagonal is all zero.

13. If $(f + g)(x)$ is the usual $f(g(x))$, then $(g + f)x$ is $g(f(x))$, which is different. In rule 2 both sides are $f(g(h(x)))$. Rule 4 is broken because there might be no inverse function $f^{-1}(x)$ such that $f(f^{-1}(x)) = x$. If the inverse function exists, it will be the vector $-f$.

15. The sum of $(4, 0, 0)$ and $(0, 4, 0)$ is not on the plane; it has $x + y - 2z = 8$.

17. (a) The subspaces of $\mathbf{R}^2$ are $\mathbf{R}^2$ itself, lines through $(0, 0)$, and the point $(0, 0)$. (b) The subspaces of $\mathbf{R}^4$ are $\mathbf{R}^4$ itself, three-dimensional planes $n \cdot v = 0$, two-dimensional subspaces ($n_1 \cdot v = 0$ and $n_2 \cdot v = 0$), one-dimensional lines through $(0, 0, 0, 0)$, and $(0, 0, 0, 0)$ alone.

19. The smallest subspace containing **P** and **L** is either **P** or $\mathbf{R}^3$.

21. The column space of A is the x-axis = all vectors $(x, 0, 0)$. The column space of B is the x-y plane = all vectors $(x, y, 0)$. The column space of C is the line of vectors $(x, 2x, 0)$.

23. A combination of the columns of C is also a combination of the columns of A (same column space; B has a different column space).

25. The extra column b enlarges the column space, unless b is *already in* that space:

$$[A \;\; b] = \begin{bmatrix} 1 & 0 & 1 \\ 0 & 0 & 1 \end{bmatrix} \quad \begin{matrix} \text{(larger column space)} \\ \text{(no solution to } Ax = b). \end{matrix}$$

$$\begin{bmatrix} 1 & 0 & 1 \\ 0 & 1 & 1 \end{bmatrix} \quad \begin{matrix} (b \text{ already in column space}) \\ (Ax = b \text{ has a solution}). \end{matrix}$$

27. Column space $= \mathbf{R}^8$. Every b is a combination of the columns, since $Ax = b$ is solvable.

29. $A = \begin{bmatrix} 1 & 1 & 0 \\ 1 & 0 & 0 \\ 0 & 1 & 0 \end{bmatrix}$ or $\begin{bmatrix} 1 & 1 & 2 \\ 1 & 0 & 1 \\ 0 & 1 & 1 \end{bmatrix}$; $A = \begin{bmatrix} 1 & 2 & 0 \\ 2 & 4 & 0 \\ 3 & 6 & 0 \end{bmatrix}$ (columns on 1 line).

31. $\mathbf{R}^2$ contains vectors with *two* components—they don't belong to $\mathbf{R}^3$.

Problem Set 2.2, page 85

1. $x + y + z = 1, x + y + z = 0$. Changing 1 to 0, $(x, y, z) = c(-1, 1, 0) + d(-1, 0, 1)$.

3. Echelon form $U = \begin{bmatrix} 0 & 1 & 0 & 3 \\ 0 & 0 & 0 & 0 \end{bmatrix}$; free variables x_1, x_3, x_4; special solutions $(1, 0, 0, 0)$, $(0, 0, 1, 0)$, and $(0, -3, 0, 1)$. Consistent when $b_2 = 2b_1$. Complete solution $(0, b_1, 0, 0)$ plus any combination of special solutions.

5. $\begin{bmatrix} u \\ v \\ w \end{bmatrix} = \begin{bmatrix} -2v-3 \\ v \\ 2 \end{bmatrix} = v\begin{bmatrix} -2 \\ 1 \\ 0 \end{bmatrix} + \begin{bmatrix} -3 \\ 0 \\ 2 \end{bmatrix}$; no solution!

7. $c = 7$ allows $u = 1, v = 1, w = 0$. The column space is a plane.

9. (a) $x = x_2\begin{bmatrix} -2 \\ 1 \\ 0 \\ 0 \end{bmatrix} + x_4\begin{bmatrix} 2 \\ 0 \\ -2 \\ 1 \end{bmatrix}$, for any x_2, x_4. Row-reduced $R = \begin{bmatrix} 1 & 2 & 0 & -2 \\ 0 & 0 & 1 & 2 \\ 0 & 0 & 0 & 0 \end{bmatrix}$.

(b) Complete solution $x = \begin{bmatrix} a-3b \\ 0 \\ b \\ 0 \end{bmatrix} + x_2\begin{bmatrix} -2 \\ 1 \\ 0 \\ 0 \end{bmatrix} + x_4\begin{bmatrix} 2 \\ 0 \\ -2 \\ 1 \end{bmatrix}$, for any x_2, x_4.

11. $\begin{bmatrix} 1 & 1 \\ 1 & 1 \end{bmatrix}\begin{bmatrix} x_1 \\ x_2 \end{bmatrix} = \begin{bmatrix} 1 \\ 0 \end{bmatrix}$ has nullspace = line through $(-1, 1)$ but no solution. Any

$b = \begin{bmatrix} c \\ c \end{bmatrix}$ has many particular solutions to $Ax_p = b$.

13. $R = \begin{bmatrix} 1 & 1 & 1 & 1 \\ 0 & 0 & 0 & 0 \\ 0 & 0 & 0 & 0 \end{bmatrix}$; $R = \begin{bmatrix} 1 & 0 & 1 & 0 \\ 0 & 1 & 0 & 1 \\ 0 & 0 & 0 & 0 \\ 0 & 0 & 0 & 0 \end{bmatrix}$; $R = \begin{bmatrix} 1 & -1 & 1 & -1 \\ 0 & 0 & 0 & 0 \\ 0 & 0 & 0 & 0 \end{bmatrix}$. (a) $r = 1$. (b) $r = 2$. (c) $r = 1$.

15. A nullspace matrix $N = \begin{bmatrix} -F \\ I \end{bmatrix}$ is n by $n - r$.

17. I think this is true.

19. The special solutions are the columns of $N = \begin{bmatrix} -2 & -3 \\ -4 & -5 \\ 1 & 0 \\ 0 & 1 \end{bmatrix}$ and $N = \begin{bmatrix} 1 & 0 \\ 0 & -2 \\ 0 & 1 \end{bmatrix}$.

21. The r pivot columns of A form an m by r submatrix of rank r, so that matrix A^* has r independent pivot rows, giving an r by r invertible submatrix of A. (The pivot rows of A^* and A are the same, since elimination is done in the same order—we just don't see for A^* the "free" columns of zeros that appear for A.)

23. $(uv^{\mathrm{T}})(wz^{\mathrm{T}}) = u(v^{\mathrm{T}}w)z^{\mathrm{T}}$ has rank 1 unless $v^{\mathrm{T}}w = 0$.

25. We are given $AB = I$ which has rank n. Then $\operatorname{rank}(AB) \le \operatorname{rank}(A)$ forces $\operatorname{rank}(A) = n$.

27. If $R = EA$ and the same $R = E^*B$, then $B = (E^*)^{-1}EA$. (To get B, reduce A to R and then invert steps back to B.) B is an *invertible* matrix times A, when they share the same R.

29. Since R starts with r independent rows, R^{T} starts with r independent columns (and then zeros). So *its* reduced echelon form is $\begin{bmatrix} I & 0 \\ 0 & 0 \end{bmatrix}$ where I is r by r.

31. If $c = 1$, $R = \begin{bmatrix} 1 & 1 & 2 & 2 \\ 0 & 0 & 0 & 0 \\ 0 & 0 & 0 & 0 \end{bmatrix}$ has x_2, x_3, x_4 free.

If $c \neq 1$, $R = \begin{bmatrix} 1 & 0 & 2 & 2 \\ 0 & 1 & 0 & 0 \\ 0 & 0 & 0 & 0 \end{bmatrix}$ has x_3, x_4 free.

Special solutions in $N = \begin{bmatrix} -1 & -2 & -2 \\ 1 & 0 & 0 \\ 0 & 1 & 0 \\ 0 & 0 & 1 \end{bmatrix}$ $(c = 1)$ and $N = \begin{bmatrix} -2 & -2 \\ 0 & 0 \\ 1 & 0 \\ 0 & 1 \end{bmatrix}$ $(c \neq 1)$.

If $c = 1$, $R = \begin{bmatrix} 0 & 1 \\ 0 & 0 \end{bmatrix}$ has x_1 free; if $c = 2$, $R = \begin{bmatrix} 1 & -2 \\ 0 & 0 \end{bmatrix}$ has x_2 free; $R = I$ if $c \neq 1, 2$.
Special solutions in $N = \begin{bmatrix} 1 \\ 0 \end{bmatrix}$ $(c = 1)$ or $N = \begin{bmatrix} 2 \\ 1 \end{bmatrix}$ $(c = 2)$ or $N = 2$ by 0 *empty matrix.*

33. $x_{\text{complete}} = \begin{bmatrix} -2 \\ 0 \\ 1 \end{bmatrix} + x_2 \begin{bmatrix} -3 \\ 1 \\ 0 \end{bmatrix}$; $x_{\text{complete}} = \begin{bmatrix} 1/2 \\ 0 \\ 1/2 \\ 0 \end{bmatrix} + x_2 \begin{bmatrix} -3 \\ 1 \\ 0 \\ 0 \end{bmatrix} + x_4 \begin{bmatrix} 0 \\ 0 \\ -2 \\ 1 \end{bmatrix}$.

35. (a) Solvable if $b_2 = 2b_1$ and $3b_1 - 3b_3 + b_4 = 0$. Then $x = \begin{bmatrix} 5b_1 - 2b_3 \\ b_3 - 2b_1 \end{bmatrix}$ (no free variables). (b) Solvable if $b_2 = 2b_1$ and $3b_1 - 3b_3 + b_4 = 0$.
Then $x = \begin{bmatrix} 5b_1 - 2b_3 \\ b_3 - 2b_1 \\ 0 \end{bmatrix} + x_3 \begin{bmatrix} -1 \\ -1 \\ 1 \end{bmatrix}$.

37. A 1 by 3 system has at least two free variables.

39. (a) The particular solution x_p is always multiplied by 1. (b) Any solution can be x_p. (c) $\begin{bmatrix} 3 & 3 \\ 3 & 3 \end{bmatrix} \begin{bmatrix} x \\ y \end{bmatrix} = \begin{bmatrix} 6 \\ 6 \end{bmatrix}$. Then $\begin{bmatrix} 1 \\ 1 \end{bmatrix}$ is shorter (length $\sqrt{2}$) than $\begin{bmatrix} 2 \\ 0 \end{bmatrix}$. (d) The "homogeneous" solution in the nullspace is $x_n = 0$ when A is invertible.

41. Multiply x_p by 2, same x_n; $\begin{bmatrix} x \\ X \end{bmatrix}_p$ is $\begin{bmatrix} x_p \\ 0 \end{bmatrix}$, special solutions also include the columns of $\begin{bmatrix} -I \\ I \end{bmatrix}$; x_p and the special solutions are not changed.

43. For A, $q = 3$ gives rank 1, every other q gives rank 2. For B, $q = 6$ gives rank 1, every other q gives rank 2.

45. (a) $r < m$, always $r \leq n$. (b) $r = m, r < n$. (c) $r < m, r = n$. (d) $r = m = n$.

47. $R = \begin{bmatrix} 1 & 0 & 0 & \mathbf{0} \\ 0 & 0 & 1 & \mathbf{0} \\ 0 & 0 & 0 & \mathbf{0} \end{bmatrix}$ and $x_n = \begin{bmatrix} 0 \\ 1 \\ 0 \end{bmatrix}$; $\begin{bmatrix} 1 & 0 & 0 & \mathbf{-1} \\ 0 & 0 & 1 & \mathbf{2} \\ 0 & 0 & 0 & \mathbf{5} \end{bmatrix}$: no solution because of row 3.

49. $A = \begin{bmatrix} 1 & 1 \\ 0 & 2 \\ 0 & 3 \end{bmatrix}$; B can't exist since two equations in three unknowns can't have one solution.

51. A has rank $4 - 1 = 3$; the complete solution to $Ax = 0$ is $x = (2, 3, 1, 0)$.

$$R = \begin{bmatrix} 1 & 0 & -2 & 0 \\ 0 & 1 & -3 & 0 \\ 0 & 0 & 0 & 1 \end{bmatrix} \text{ with } -2, -3 \text{ in the free column.}$$

53. (a) False. (b) True. (c) True (only n columns). (d) True (only m rows).

55. $U = \begin{bmatrix} 0 & 1 & 1 & 1 & 1 & 1 & 1 \\ 0 & 0 & 0 & 1 & 1 & 1 & 1 \\ 0 & 0 & 0 & 0 & 1 & 1 & 1 \\ 0 & 0 & 0 & 0 & 0 & 0 & 0 \end{bmatrix}$ and $R = \begin{bmatrix} 0 & 1 & 1 & 0 & 0 & 1 & 1 \\ 0 & 0 & 0 & 1 & 0 & 1 & 1 \\ 0 & 0 & 0 & 0 & 1 & 1 & 1 \\ 0 & 0 & 0 & 0 & 0 & 0 & 0 \end{bmatrix}$ (R doesn't come from this U).

57. If column 1 = column 5, then x_5 is a free variable. Its special solution is $(-1, 0, 0, 0, 1)$.

59. Column 5 is sure to have no pivot since it is a combination of earlier columns, and x_5 is free. With four pivots in the other columns, the special solution is $(1, 0, 1, 0, 1)$. The nullspace contains all multiples of $(1, 0, 1, 0, 1)$ (a line in $\mathbf{R}^5$).

61. $A = \begin{bmatrix} 1 & 0 & 0 & -4 \\ 0 & 1 & 0 & -3 \\ 0 & 0 & 1 & -2 \end{bmatrix}$.

63. This construction is impossible: two pivot columns, two free variables, only three columns.

65. $A = \begin{bmatrix} 0 & 1 \\ 0 & 0 \end{bmatrix}$.

67. R is most likely to be I; R is most likely to be I with fourth row of zeros.

69. Any zero rows come after these rows: $R = [1 \ \ -2 \ \ -3]$, $R = \begin{bmatrix} 1 & 0 & 0 \\ 0 & 1 & 0 \end{bmatrix}$, $R = I$.

Problem Set 2.3, page 98

1. $\begin{bmatrix} 1 & 1 & 1 \\ 0 & 1 & 1 \\ 0 & 0 & 1 \end{bmatrix} \begin{bmatrix} c_1 \\ c_2 \\ c_3 \end{bmatrix} = 0$ gives $c_3 = c_2 = c_1 = 0$. But $v_1 + v_2 - 4v_3 + v_4 = 0$ (dependent).

3. If $a = 0$ then column 1 = 0; if $d = 0$ then b(column 1) − a(column 2) = 0; if $f = 0$ then all columns end in zero (all are perpendicular to $(0, 0, 1)$, all in the xy plane, must be dependent).

5. (a) $\begin{bmatrix}1&2&3\\3&1&2\\2&3&1\end{bmatrix} \to \begin{bmatrix}1&2&3\\0&-5&-7\\0&-1&-5\end{bmatrix}$

$\to \begin{bmatrix}1&2&3\\0&-5&-7\\0&0&-18/5\end{bmatrix}$: invertible $\Rightarrow$ independent columns (could have used rows).

(b) $\begin{bmatrix}1&2&-3\\-3&1&2\\2&-3&1\end{bmatrix} \to \begin{bmatrix}1&2&-3\\0&7&-7\\0&0&0\end{bmatrix}; A\begin{bmatrix}1\\1\\1\end{bmatrix} = \begin{bmatrix}0\\0\\0\end{bmatrix}$, columns add to 0 (could use rows).

7. The sum $v_1 - v_2 + v_3 = 0$ because $(w_2 - w_3) - (w_1 - w_3) + (w_1 - w_2) = 0$.

9. (a) The four vectors are the columns of a 3 by 4 matrix A with at least one free variable, so $Ax = 0$. (b) Dependent if $[v_1 \;\; v_2]$ has rank 0 or 1.
(c) $0v_1 + c(0, 0, 0) = 0$ has a nonzero solution (take any $c \neq 0$).

11. (a) Line in $\mathbf{R}^3$. (b) Plane in $\mathbf{R}^3$. (c) Plane in $\mathbf{R}^3$. (d) All of $\mathbf{R}^3$.

13. All dimensions are 2. The row spaces of A and U are the same.

15. $v = \frac{1}{2}(v + w) + \frac{1}{2}(v - w)$ and $w = \frac{1}{2}(v + w) - \frac{1}{2}(v - w)$. The two pairs *span* the same space. They are a basis when v and w are *independent*.

17. If elimination produces one or more zero rows, the rows of A are linearly dependent; for example in Problem 16 $\begin{bmatrix}1&1&0&0\\1&0&1&0\\0&0&1&1\\0&1&0&1\end{bmatrix} \to \begin{bmatrix}1&1&0&0\\0&-1&1&0\\0&0&1&1\\0&0&1&1\end{bmatrix}$

$$\to \begin{bmatrix}1&1&0&0\\0&-1&1&0\\0&0&1&1\\0&0&0&0\end{bmatrix}.$$

19. The n independent vectors span a space of dimension n. They are a *basis* for that space. If they are the columns of A then m is *not less* than n $(m \geq n)$.

21. $\boldsymbol{C}(U)$: Any bases for $\mathbf{R}^2$; $\boldsymbol{N}(U)$: (row 1 and row 2) or (row 1 and row 1 + row 2).

23. Independent columns $\Rightarrow$ rank n. Columns span $\mathbf{R}^m \Rightarrow$ rank m. Columns are basis for $\mathbf{R}^m \Rightarrow$ rank $= m = n$.

25. (a) The only solution is $x = 0$ because *the columns are independent.* (b) $Ax = b$ is solvable because *the columns span* $\mathbf{R}^5$.

27. Columns 1 and 2 are bases for the (different) column spaces of A and U; rows 1 and 2 are bases for the (equal) row spaces; $(1, -1, 1)$ is a basis for the (equal) nullspaces.

29. $\text{rank}(A) = 2$ if $c = 0$ and $d = 2$; $\text{rank}(B) = 2$ except when $c = d$ or $c = -d$.

31. Let $v_1 = (1, 0, 0, 0), \ldots, v_4 = (0, 0, 0, 1)$ be the coordinate vectors. If $\mathbf{W}$ is the line through $(1, 2, 3, 4)$, none of the v's are in $\mathbf{W}$.

33. (a) If it were not a basis, we could add more independent vectors, which would exceed the given dimension k. (b) If it were not a basis, we could delete some vectors, leaving less than the given dimension k.

35. (a) False, might be no solution. (b) True, 7 vectors in $\mathbf{R}^5$ are dependent.

37. (a) $\begin{bmatrix}1&0&0\\0&0&0\\0&0&0\end{bmatrix}$, $\begin{bmatrix}0&0&0\\0&1&0\\0&0&0\end{bmatrix}$, $\begin{bmatrix}0&0&0\\0&0&0\\0&0&1\end{bmatrix}$. (b) Add $\begin{bmatrix}0&1&0\\1&0&0\\0&0&0\end{bmatrix}$, $\begin{bmatrix}0&0&1\\0&0&0\\1&0&0\end{bmatrix}$, $\begin{bmatrix}0&0&0\\0&0&1\\0&1&0\end{bmatrix}$. (c) $\begin{bmatrix}0&1&0\\-1&0&0\\0&0&0\end{bmatrix}$, $\begin{bmatrix}0&0&1\\0&0&0\\-1&0&0\end{bmatrix}$, $\begin{bmatrix}0&0&0\\0&0&1\\0&-1&0\end{bmatrix}$ are a basis for all $A = -A^{\mathrm{T}}$.

39. $y(0) = 0$ requires $A + B + C = 0$. One basis is $\cos x - \cos 2x$ and $\cos x - \cos 3x$.

41. $y_1(x)$, $y_2(x)$, $y_3(x)$ can be x, $2x$, $3x$ (dim 1) or x, $2x$, x^2 (dim 2) or x, x^2, x^3 (dim 3).

43. $$\begin{bmatrix}1&&\\&1&\\&&1\end{bmatrix} = \begin{bmatrix}&1&\\1&&\\&&1\end{bmatrix} - \begin{bmatrix}&1&\\&&1\\1&&\end{bmatrix} + \begin{bmatrix}&&1\\&1&\\1&&\end{bmatrix} + \begin{bmatrix}1&&\\&&1\\&1&\end{bmatrix} - \begin{bmatrix}&&1\\1&&\\&1&\end{bmatrix}.$$

Check the $(1, 1)$ entry, then $(3, 2)$, then $(3, 3)$, then $(1, 2)$ to show that those five P's are independent. Four conditions on the nine entries make all row sums and column sums equal: row sum 1 = row sum 2 = row sum 3 = column sum 1 = column sum 2 (= column sum 3 is automatic because sum of all rows = sum of all columns).

45. If the 5 by 5 matrix $[A\ \ b]$ is invertible, b is not a combination of the columns of A. If $[A\ \ b]$ is singular, and A has independent columns, b *is* a combination of those columns.

Problem Set 2.4, page 110

1. False, we only know dimensions are equal. Left nullspace has smaller dim $= m - r$.

3. $\boldsymbol{C}(A)$: $r = 2$, $(1, 0, 1)$ $(0, 1, 0)$; $\boldsymbol{N}(A)$: $n - r = 2$, $(2, -1, 1, 0)$, $(-1, 0, 0, 1)$;
$\boldsymbol{C}(A^{\mathrm{T}})$: $r = 2$, $(1, 2, 0, 1)$, $(0, 1, 1, 0)$; $\boldsymbol{N}(A^{\mathrm{T}})$: $m - r = 1$, $(-1, 0, 1)$;
$\boldsymbol{C}(U)$: $(1, 0, 0)$, $(0, 1, 0)$; $\boldsymbol{N}(U)$: $(2, -1, 1, 0)$, $(-1, 0, 0, 0)$;
$\boldsymbol{C}(U^{\mathrm{T}})$: $(1, 2, 0, 1)$, $(0, 1, 1, 0)$; $\boldsymbol{N}(A^{\mathrm{T}})$: $(0, 0, 1)$.

5. A times every column of B is zero, so $\boldsymbol{C}(B)$ is contained in the nullspace $\boldsymbol{N}(A)$.

7. From $Ax = 0$, the row space and the nullspace must be orthogonal. See Chapter 3.

9. $[1\ \ 2\ \ 4]$; $\begin{bmatrix}1&2&4\\2&4&8\\3&6&12\end{bmatrix}$ has the same nullspace.

11. If $Ax = 0$ has a nonzero solution, then $r < n$ and $\boldsymbol{C}(A^{\mathrm{T}})$ is smaller than $\mathbf{R}^n$. So $A^{\mathrm{T}}y = f$ is not solvable for some f. Example: $A = [1\ \ 1]$ and $f = (1, 2)$.

13. $d = bc/a$; the only pivot is a.

15. With independent columns: rank n; nullspace = $\{0\}$; row space is $\mathbf{R}^n$; *left* inverse.

17. $A = [1\ \ 1\ \ 0]$; $B = [0\ \ 0\ \ 1]$.

19. No—for example, all invertible n by n matrices have the same four subspaces.

21. (a) $\begin{bmatrix}1 & 0\\1 & 0\\0 & 1\end{bmatrix}$. (b) Impossible: dimensions $1+1 \neq 3$. (c) $[1 \quad 1]$.

(d) $\begin{bmatrix}-9 & -3\\3 & 1\end{bmatrix}$. (e) Impossible: Row space $=$ column space requires $m = n$. Then $m - r = n - r$.

23. Invertible A: row space basis $=$ column space basis $= (1,0,0), (0,1,0), (0,0,1)$; nullspace and left nullspace bases are empty. B: row space basis $(1,0,0,1,0,0)$, $(0,1,0,0,1,0)$, and $(0,0,1,0,0,1)$; column space basis $(1,0,0), (0,1,0), (0,0,1)$; nullspace basis $(-1,0,0,1,0,0)$, $(0,-1,0,0,1,0)$, and $(0,0,-1,0,0,1)$; left nullspace basis is empty.

25. (a) Same row space and nullspace. Therefore rank (dimension of row space) is the same. (b) Same column space and left nullspace. Same rank (dimension of column space).

27. (a) No solution means that $r < m$. Always $r \leq n$. Can't compare m and n. (b) If $m - r > 0$, the nullspace of A^{T} contains a nonzero vector.

29. Row space basis $(1,2,3,4)$, $(0,1,2,3)$, $(0,0,1,2)$; nullspace basis $(0,1,-2,1)$; column space basis $(1,0,0)$, $(0,1,0)$, $(0,0,1)$; left nullspace has empty basis.

31. If $Av = 0$ and v is a row of A then $v \cdot v = 0$. Only $v = 0$ is in both spaces.

33. Row 3 $-$ 2 (row 2) $+$ row 1 $=$ zero row, so the vectors $c(1,-2,1)$ are in the left nullspace. The same vectors happen to be in the nullspace.

35. (a) u and w span $\boldsymbol{C}(A)$. (b) v and z span $\boldsymbol{C}(A^{\mathrm{T}})$. (c) rank < 2 if u and w are dependent or v and z are dependent. (d) The rank of $uv^{\mathrm{T}} + wz^{\mathrm{T}}$ is 2.

37. (a) True (same rank). (b) False ($A = [1 \quad 0]$). (c) False (A can be invertible and also unsymmetric). (d) True.

39. $a_{11} = 1, a_{12} = 0, a_{13} = 1, a_{22} = 0, a_{32} = 1, a_{31} = 0, a_{23} = 1, a_{33} = 0, a_{21} = 1$ (not unique).

41. Rank $r = n$ means nullspace $=$ zero vector and $x_n = 0$.

Problem Set 2.5, page 122

1. $A = \begin{bmatrix}1 & -1 & 0\\0 & 1 & -1\\1 & 0 & -1\end{bmatrix}$; $\boldsymbol{N}(A)$ contains multiples of $\begin{bmatrix}1\\1\\1\end{bmatrix}$; $\boldsymbol{N}(A^{\mathrm{T}})$ contains multiples of $\begin{bmatrix}1\\1\\-1\end{bmatrix}$.

3. The entries in each row add to zero. Therefore, any combination will have that same property: $f_1 + f_2 + f_3 = 0$; $A^{\mathrm{T}}y = f \Rightarrow y_1 + y_3 = f_1, -y_1 + y_2 = f_2, -y_2 - y_3 = f_3 \Rightarrow f_1 + f_2 + f_3 = 0$. It means that the total current entering from outside is zero.

5. $\begin{bmatrix} c_1+c_3 & -c_1 & -c_3 \\ -c_1 & c_1+c_2 & -c_2 \\ -c_3 & -c_2 & c_2+c_3 \end{bmatrix}$; $\begin{bmatrix} c_1+c_3 & -c_1 \\ -c_1 & c_1+c_2 \end{bmatrix}$ has pivots c_1+c_3, $\dfrac{c_1c_3+c_1c_2+c_2c_3}{c_1+c_3}$.

7. Conditions on b are $b_1+b_4-b_5=0$, $b_3-b_4+b_6=0$, $b_2-b_5+b_6=0$.

9. $\begin{bmatrix} 3 & -1 & -1 & -1 \\ -1 & 3 & -1 & -1 \\ -1 & -1 & 3 & -1 \\ -1 & -1 & -1 & 3 \end{bmatrix}$, $\begin{bmatrix} c_1+c_2+c_5 & -c_1 & -c_2 & -c_5 \\ -c_1 & c_1+c_3+c_4 & -c_3 & -c_4 \\ -c_2 & -c_3 & c_2+c_3+c_6 & -c_6 \\ -c_5 & -c_4 & -c_6 & c_4+c_5+c_6 \end{bmatrix}$.

Those c's that connect to node j will appear in row j.

11. $\begin{bmatrix} 1 & 0 & 0 & 0 & -1 & 1 & 0 \\ 0 & \frac{1}{2} & 0 & 0 & -1 & 0 & 1 \\ 0 & 0 & \frac{1}{2} & 0 & 0 & 1 & 0 \\ 0 & 0 & 0 & 1 & 0 & 0 & -1 \\ -1 & -1 & 0 & 0 & 0 & 0 & 0 \\ 1 & 0 & 1 & 0 & 0 & 0 & 0 \\ 0 & 1 & 0 & -1 & 0 & 0 & 0 \end{bmatrix} \begin{bmatrix} y_1 \\ y_2 \\ y_3 \\ y_4 \\ x_1 \\ x_2 \\ x_3 \end{bmatrix} = \begin{bmatrix} 0 \\ 0 \\ 0 \\ 0 \\ f_1 \\ f_2 \\ f_3 \end{bmatrix}$; $x = \begin{bmatrix} -4 \\ -\frac{5}{3} \\ -\frac{14}{3} \\ 0 \end{bmatrix}$; $y = \begin{bmatrix} -\frac{7}{3} \\ \frac{4}{3} \\ \frac{10}{3} \\ \frac{14}{3} \end{bmatrix}$.

13. There are 20 choices of 3 edges out of 6 because "6 choose 3" $= \dfrac{6!}{3!3!} = 20$. Four choices give triangles, leaving 16 spanning trees.

15. I think it is already built in.

17. 9 nodes $-$ 12 edges $+$ 4 loops $= 1$; 7 nodes $-$ 12 edges $+$ 6 loops $= 1$.

19. $x = (1,1,1,1)$ gives $Ax = 0$; then $A^{\mathrm{T}}Ax = 0$; rank is again $n-1$.

21. $M = \begin{bmatrix} 0 & 1 & 1 & 1 \\ 1 & 0 & 1 & 1 \\ 1 & 1 & 0 & 1 \\ 1 & 1 & 1 & 0 \end{bmatrix}$ and

$M^2 = \begin{bmatrix} 3 & 2 & 2 & 2 \\ 2 & 3 & 2 & 2 \\ 2 & 2 & 3 & 2 \\ 2 & 2 & 2 & 3 \end{bmatrix}$. $(M^2)_{ij} = a_{i1}a_{1j} + \cdots + a_{in}a_{nj}$ and we get $a_{ik}a_{kj} = 1$ when there is a 2-step path i to k to j. Notice 3 paths from a node to itself.

Problem Set 2.6, page 133

1. Rotation $\begin{bmatrix} 0 & -1 \\ 0 & 0 \end{bmatrix}$; $\begin{bmatrix} 0 & 0 \\ 0 & 0 \end{bmatrix}$.

3. $\|Ax\|^2 = 1$ always produces an ellipse.

5. They are transformed to $(1,3)$, $(2,6)$, $(-1,-3)$. The x-axis turns; vertical lines shift up/down but stay vertical.

7. Second derivative matrix $\begin{bmatrix} 0 & 0 & 2 & 0 \\ 0 & 0 & 0 & 6 \\ 0 & 0 & 0 & 0 \\ 0 & 0 & 0 & 0 \end{bmatrix}$. The nullspace is spanned by $(1,0,0,0)$ and $(0,1,0,0)$, which gives linear P_1. Second derivatives of linear functions are zero. The column space is accidentally the same as the nullspace, because second derivatives of cubics are linear.

9. e^t and e^{-t} are a basis for the solutions of $u'' = u$.

11. $\begin{bmatrix} \cos\theta & -\sin\theta \\ \sin\theta & \cos\theta \end{bmatrix} \begin{bmatrix} \cos\theta & -\sin\theta \\ \sin\theta & \cos\theta \end{bmatrix} = \begin{bmatrix} 1 & 0 \\ 0 & 1 \end{bmatrix}$ so $H^2 = I$.

13. (a) Yes. (b) Yes. We don't need parentheses $(AB)C$ or $A(BC)$ for ABC!

15. $A = \begin{bmatrix} 1 & 0 & 0 & 0 \\ 0 & 0 & 1 & 0 \\ 0 & 1 & 0 & 0 \\ 0 & 0 & 0 & 1 \end{bmatrix}$ and $A^2 = I$; the double transpose of a matrix gives the matrix itself. Note $A_{23} = 1$ because transpose of matrix 2 is matrix 3.

17. $A = \begin{bmatrix} 0 & 0 & 0 \\ 1 & 0 & 0 \\ 0 & 1 & 0 \\ 0 & 0 & 1 \end{bmatrix}$; $B = \begin{bmatrix} 0 & 1 & 0 & 0 \\ 0 & 0 & 1 & 0 \\ 0 & 0 & 0 & 1 \end{bmatrix}$; $AB = \begin{bmatrix} 0 & 0 & 0 & 0 \\ 0 & 1 & 0 & 0 \\ 0 & 0 & 1 & 0 \\ 0 & 0 & 0 & 1 \end{bmatrix}$; $BA = \begin{bmatrix} 1 & 0 & 0 \\ 0 & 1 & 0 \\ 0 & 0 & 1 \end{bmatrix}$.

19. (a) is invertible with $T^{-1}(y) = y^{1/3}$; (c) is invertible with $T^{-1}(y) = y - 11$.

21. With $w = 0$, linearity gives $T(v+0) = T(v) + T(0)$. Thus $T(0) = 0$. With $c = -1$, linearity gives $T(-0) = -T(0)$. Certainly $T(-0) = T(0)$. Thus $T(0) = 0$.

23. $S(T(v)) = S(v) = v$.

25. (b) and (c) are linear, (a) fails $T(2v) = 2T(v)$, (d) fails $T(v+w) = T(v) + T(w)$.

27. $T(T(v)) = (v_3, v_1, v_2)$; $T^3(v) = v$; $T^{100}(v) = T(T^{99}(v)) = T(v)$.

29. (a) $T(1,0) = 0$. (b) $(0,0,1)$ is not in the range. (c) $T(0,1) = 0$.

31. Associative law gives $A(M_1 + M_2) = AM_1 + AM_2$. Distributive law over c's gives $A(cM) = c(AM)$.

33. No matrix A gives $A \begin{bmatrix} 0 & 0 \\ 1 & 0 \end{bmatrix} = \begin{bmatrix} 0 & 1 \\ 0 & 0 \end{bmatrix}$. To professors: The matrix space has dimension 4. Linear transformations on that space must come from 4 by 4 matrices (16 parameters). Those multiplications by A in Problems 31 and 32 were special transformations with only 4 parameters.

35. $T(I) = 0$ but $M = \begin{bmatrix} 0 & b \\ 0 & 0 \end{bmatrix} = T(M)$; these fill the range. $M = \begin{bmatrix} a & 0 \\ c & d \end{bmatrix}$ in the kernel.

37. (a) $M = \begin{bmatrix} r & s \\ t & u \end{bmatrix}$. (b) $N = \begin{bmatrix} a & b \\ c & d \end{bmatrix}^{-1}$. (c) $ad = bc$.

39. Reorder basis by *permutation matrix*; change lengths by *positive diagonal matrix*.

41. $\begin{bmatrix} 1 & a & a^2 \\ 1 & b & b^2 \\ 1 & c & c^2 \end{bmatrix} \begin{bmatrix} A \\ B \\ C \end{bmatrix} = \begin{bmatrix} 4 \\ 5 \\ 6 \end{bmatrix}$; Vandermonde determinant $= (b-a)(c-a)(c-b)$; the points a, b, c must be different, and then determinant $\neq 0$ (interpolation is possible).

43. If T is not invertible, then $T(v_1), \ldots, T(v_n)$ will not be a basis. Then we couldn't choose $w_i = T(v_i)$ as output basis.

45. $S(T(v)) = (-1, 2)$ but $S(v) = (-2, 1)$ and $T(S(v)) = (1, -2)$. So $TS \neq ST$.

47. The Hadamard matrix H has orthogonal columns of length 2. So the inverse of H is $H^{\mathrm{T}}/4 = H/4$.

49. False: the n nonzero vectors would have to be independent.

Problem Set 3.1, page 148

1. $\|x\| = \sqrt{21}$; $\|y\| = 3\sqrt{2}$; $x^{\mathrm{T}}y = 0$.

3. $(x_2/x_1)(y_2/y_1) = -1$ means that $x_1y_1 + x_2y_2 = 0$, so $x^{\mathrm{T}}y = 0$.

5. v_1 and v_3 are orthogonal, also v_2 and v_3.

7. $x = (-2, 1, 0)$; $y = (-1, -1, 1)$; the row $z = (1, 2, 1)$ is orthogonal to the nullspace.

9. The orthogonal complement is the line through $(-1, -1, 1)$ and $(0, 0, 0)$.

11. If $A^{\mathrm{T}}y = 0$, then $y^{\mathrm{T}}b = y^{\mathrm{T}}Ax = (y^{\mathrm{T}}A)x = 0$, which contradicts $y^{\mathrm{T}}b \neq 0$.

13. The figure splits any y in $\mathbf{R}^m$ into column space part + left nullspace part.

15. No such matrix, because $(1, 2, 1)^{\mathrm{T}}(1, -2, 1) \neq 0$.

17. The matrix with the basis for $\mathbf{V}$ as its rows. Then the nullspace is $\mathbf{V}^{\perp} = \mathbf{W}$.

19. (a) If $\mathbf{V}$ and $\mathbf{W}$ are lines in $\mathbf{R}^3$, $\mathbf{V}^{\perp}$ and $\mathbf{W}^{\perp}$ are intersecting planes. (b) $\mathbf{V}$.

21. $(1, 2, -1)$ is perpendicular to $\mathbf{P}$. $A = \begin{bmatrix} 1 & 1 & 3 \\ 0 & 1 & 2 \end{bmatrix}$ has $\boldsymbol{N}(A) = \mathbf{P}$; $B = [1 \quad 2 \quad -1]$ has row space $= \mathbf{P}$.

23. $A = \begin{bmatrix} 1 & 1 \\ 2 & 2 \end{bmatrix}$ has subspaces = four lines; $(1, 1)$ orthogonal to $(-1, 1)$, $(1, 2)$ orthogonal to $(-2, 1)$. Always row space $\perp$ nullspace.

25. (a) $\begin{bmatrix} 1 & 2 & -3 \\ 2 & -3 & 1 \\ -3 & 5 & -2 \end{bmatrix}$. (b) $\begin{bmatrix} 2 \\ -3 \\ 5 \end{bmatrix}$ is not orthogonal to $\begin{bmatrix} 1 \\ 1 \\ 1 \end{bmatrix}$. (c) $\begin{bmatrix} 1 \\ 1 \\ 1 \end{bmatrix}$ in $\boldsymbol{C}(A)$ and $\begin{bmatrix} 1 \\ 0 \\ 0 \end{bmatrix}$ in $\boldsymbol{N}(A^{\mathrm{T}})$ is impossible: not perpendicular. (d) $A = \begin{bmatrix} 1 & -1 \\ 1 & -1 \end{bmatrix}$ has $A^2 = 0$. (e) $(1, 1, 1)$ will be in the nullspace and row space; no such matrix.

27. (a) If $Ax = b$ has a solution and $A^{\mathrm{T}}y = 0$, then $b^{\mathrm{T}}y = (Ax)^{\mathrm{T}}y = 0$.
(b) b is not in the column space; so, not perpendicular to all y in the left nullspace.

29. $x = x_r + x_n$, where x_r is in the row space and x_n is in the nullspace. Then $Ax_n = 0$ and $Ax = Ax_r + Ax_n = Ax_r$. All vectors Ax are combinations of the columns of A. If $x = (1, 0)$, then $x_r = (1/2, 1/2)$.

31. (a) For a symmetric matrix, the column space and row space are the same.
(b) x is in the nullspace and z is in the column space = row space: so these "eigenvectors" have $x^{\mathrm{T}}z = 0$.

33. x splits into $x_r + x_n = (1, -1) + (1, 1) = (2, 0)$.

35. $Ax = B\widehat{x}$ means that $[\,A \quad B\,]\begin{bmatrix} x \\ -\widehat{x}\end{bmatrix} = 0$. Three homogeneous equations in four unknowns always have a nonzero solution. Here $x = (3, 1)$ and $\widehat{x} = (1, 0)$, and $Ax = B\widehat{x} = (5, 6, 5)$ is in both column spaces. Two planes in $\mathbf{R}^3$ (through zero) must intersect in a line at least!

37. $A^{\mathrm{T}}y = 0$ gives $(Ax)^{\mathrm{T}}y = x^{\mathrm{T}}A^{\mathrm{T}}y = 0$. Then $y \perp Ax$ and $\boldsymbol{N}(A^{\mathrm{T}}) \perp \boldsymbol{C}(A)$.

39. $\mathbf{S}^{\perp}$ is the nullspace of $A = \begin{bmatrix} 1 & 5 & 1 \\ 2 & 2 & 2 \end{bmatrix}$. Therefore $\mathbf{S}^{\perp}$ is a *subspace* even if $\mathbf{S}$ is not.

41. If $\mathbf{V}$ is all of $\mathbf{R}^4$, then $\mathbf{V}^{\perp}$ contains only the *zero vector*. Then $(\mathbf{V}^{\perp})^{\perp} = \mathbf{R}^4 = \mathbf{V}$.

43. $(1, 1, 1, 1)$ is a basis for $\mathbf{P}^{\perp}$. $A = [1 \quad 1 \quad 1 \quad 1]$ has the plane $\mathbf{P}$ as its nullspace.

45. Column 1 of A^{-1} is orthogonal to the space spanned by the 2nd, ..., nth rows of A.

47. $A = \begin{bmatrix} 2 & 2 & -1 \\ -1 & 2 & 2 \\ 2 & -1 & 2 \end{bmatrix}$,

$A^{\mathrm{T}}A = 9I$ is *diagonal*: $(A^{\mathrm{T}}A)_{ij} = (\text{column } i \text{ of } A)\cdot(\text{column } j)$.

49. (a) $(1, -1, 0)$ is in both planes. Normal vectors are perpendicular, planes still intersect! (b) Need *three* orthogonal vectors to span the whole orthogonal complement in $\mathbf{R}^5$. (c) Lines can meet without being orthogonal.

51. When $AB = 0$, the column space of B is contained in the nullspace of A. Therefore the dimension of $\boldsymbol{C}(B) \le$ dimension of $\boldsymbol{N}(A)$. This means $\text{rank}(B) \le 4 - \text{rank}(A)$.

Problem Set 3.2, page 157

1. (a) $(x + y)/2 \ge \sqrt{xy}$ (arithmetic mean $\ge$ geometric mean of x and y).
(b) $\|x+y\|^2 \le (\|x\|+\|y\|)^2$ means that $(x+y)^{\mathrm{T}}(x+y) \le \|x\|^2+2\|x\|\,\|y\|+\|y\|^2$. The left-hand side is $x^{\mathrm{T}}x + 2x^{\mathrm{T}}y + y^{\mathrm{T}}y$. After cancelling this is $x^{\mathrm{T}}y \le \|x\|\,\|y\|$.

3. $p = (10/3, 10/3, 10/3)$; $(5/9, 10/9, 10/9)$.

5. $\cos\theta = 1/\sqrt{n}$ so $\theta = \arccos(1/\sqrt{n})$; $P = \begin{bmatrix} 1 \\ \vdots \\ 1 \end{bmatrix} [1/n \quad \cdots \quad 1/n] = \text{all entries } \dfrac{1}{n}$.

7. Choose $b = (1, \ldots, 1)$; equality if $a_1 = \cdots = a_n$ (then a is parallel to b).

9. $P^2 = \dfrac{aa^{\mathrm{T}}aa^{\mathrm{T}}}{a^{\mathrm{T}}aa^{\mathrm{T}}a} = \dfrac{a(a^{\mathrm{T}}a)a^{\mathrm{T}}}{(a^{\mathrm{T}}a)(a^{\mathrm{T}}a)} = \dfrac{aa^{\mathrm{T}}}{a^{\mathrm{T}}a} = P$.

11. (a) $P = \begin{bmatrix} \frac{1}{10} & \frac{3}{10} \\ \frac{3}{10} & \frac{9}{10} \end{bmatrix}$; $P_2 = I - P_1 = \begin{bmatrix} \frac{9}{10} & -\frac{3}{10} \\ -\frac{3}{10} & \frac{1}{10} \end{bmatrix}$. (b) $P_1 + P_2 = \begin{bmatrix} 1 & 0 \\ 0 & 1 \end{bmatrix}$;

$P_1P_2 = \begin{bmatrix} 0 & 0 \\ 0 & 0 \end{bmatrix}$. The sum of the projections onto two perpendicular lines gives the vector itself. The projection onto one line and then a perpendicular line gives the zero vector.

13. $\text{Trace} = \dfrac{a_1a_1}{a^{\mathrm{T}}a} + \cdots + \dfrac{a_na_n}{a^{\mathrm{T}}a} = \dfrac{a^{\mathrm{T}}a}{a^{\mathrm{T}}a} = 1$.

15. $\|Ax\|^2 = (Ax)^T(Ax) = xA^TAx$, $\|A^Tx\|^2 = (A^Tx)^T(A^Tx) = xAA^Tx$. If $A^TA = AA^T$, then $\|Ax\| = \|A^Tx\|$. (These matrices are called *normal*.)

17. (a) $a^Tb/a^Ta = 5/3$; $p = (5/3, 5/3, 5/3)$; $e = (-2/3, 1/3, 1/3)$ has $e^Ta = 0$. (b) $a^Tb/a^Ta = -1$; $p = (1, 3, 1) = b$ and $e = (0, 0, 0)$.

19. $P_1 = \frac{1}{3}\begin{bmatrix}1&1&1\\1&1&1\\1&1&1\end{bmatrix} = P_1^2$ and $P_1b = \frac{1}{3}\begin{bmatrix}5\\5\\5\end{bmatrix}$. $P_2 = \frac{1}{11}\begin{bmatrix}1&3&1\\3&9&3\\1&3&1\end{bmatrix}$ and

$$P_2b = \begin{bmatrix}1\\3\\1\end{bmatrix}.$$

21. $P_1 = \frac{1}{9}\begin{bmatrix}1&-2&-2\\-2&4&4\\-2&4&4\end{bmatrix}$, $P_2 = \frac{1}{9}\begin{bmatrix}4&4&-2\\4&4&-2\\-2&-2&1\end{bmatrix}$.

$P_1P_2 =$ zero matrix because $a_1 \perp a_2$.

23. $P_1 + P_2 + P_3$

$$= \frac{1}{9}\begin{bmatrix}1&-2&-2\\-2&4&4\\-2&4&4\end{bmatrix} + \frac{1}{9}\begin{bmatrix}4&4&-2\\4&4&-2\\-2&-2&1\end{bmatrix} + \frac{1}{9}\begin{bmatrix}4&-2&4\\-2&1&-2\\4&-2&4\end{bmatrix} = I.$$

25. Since A is invertible, $P = A(A^TA)^{-1}A^T = AA^{-1}(A^T)^{-1}A^T = I$: project onto all of $\mathbf{R}^2$.

Problem Set 3.3, page 170

1. $\widehat{x} = 2$; $E^2 = (10 - 3x)^2 + (5 - 4x)^2$ is minimized; $(4, -3)^T(3, 4) = 0$.

3. $\widehat{x} = \begin{bmatrix}\frac{1}{3}\\\frac{1}{3}\end{bmatrix}$; $p = \begin{bmatrix}\frac{1}{3}\\\frac{1}{3}\\\frac{2}{3}\end{bmatrix}$; $b - p = \begin{bmatrix}\frac{2}{3}\\\frac{2}{3}\\-\frac{2}{3}\end{bmatrix}$ is perpendicular to both columns.

5. $b = 4, 5, 9$ at $t = -1, 0, 1$; the best line is $6 + (5/2)t$; $p = (7/2, 6, 17/2)$.

7. $P = A(A^TA)^{-1}A^T = \begin{bmatrix}1&1/2&0\\1/2&1/2&-1/2\\0&-1/2&1\end{bmatrix}$.

9. (a) $P^T = (P^TP)^T = P$. Then $P = P^TP = P^2$. (b) P projects onto the space $\mathbf{Z} = \{0\}$.

11. $P + Q = I$, $PQ = 0$, transpose to $QP = 0$, so $(P - Q)(P - Q) = P - 0 - 0 + Q = I$.

13. Best line $61/35 - (36/35)t$; $p = (133/35, 95/35, 61/35, -11/35)$ from $C + Dt$.

15. $H^2 = (I - 2P)^2 = I - 4P + 4P^2 = I - 4P + 4P = I$. Two reflections give I.

17. Projection onto $x + y = 0$ = Projection onto $(-1, 1) = \begin{bmatrix}1/2&-1/2\\-1/2&1/2\end{bmatrix}$.

19. Projection matrix onto row space would be $A^T(AA^T)^{-1}A$ if the rows were independent.

21. Best line is $\begin{bmatrix} a_1^{\mathrm{T}}a_1 & -a_1^{\mathrm{T}}a_2 \\ -a_1^{\mathrm{T}}a_2 & a_2^{\mathrm{T}}a_2 \end{bmatrix} \begin{bmatrix} \widehat{x}_1 \\ \widehat{x}_2 \end{bmatrix} = \begin{bmatrix} a_1^{\mathrm{T}}b \\ -a_2^{\mathrm{T}}b \end{bmatrix}; \widehat{x} = \begin{bmatrix} 2 \\ 1 \end{bmatrix}$.

23. $C = (A^{\mathrm{T}}A)^{-1}A^{\mathrm{T}}b$, $A^{\mathrm{T}} = [1 \cdots 1]$, $b = (y_1, \ldots, y_m)^{\mathrm{T}}$ then

$$C = \frac{A^{\mathrm{T}}b}{A^{\mathrm{T}}A} = \frac{y_1 + \cdots + y_m}{m}.$$

25. $A = \begin{bmatrix} 1 & -1 & 1 \\ 1 & 0 & 0 \\ 1 & 1 & 1 \\ 1 & 2 & 4 \end{bmatrix}; x = \begin{bmatrix} C \\ D \\ E \end{bmatrix}; b = \begin{bmatrix} 2 \\ 0 \\ -3 \\ -5 \end{bmatrix}$.

27. (a) $a^{\mathrm{T}}a = m$, $a^{\mathrm{T}}b = b_1 + \cdots + b_m$. Therefore $\widehat{x}$ is the mean of the b's. (b) The variance is $\|e\|^2 = \sum_{i=1}^{m}(b_i - \widehat{x})^2$. (c) $p = (3, 3, 3)$, $e = (-2, -1, 3)$, $p^{\mathrm{T}}e = 0$.

$$P = \frac{1}{3}\begin{bmatrix} 1 & 1 & 1 \\ 1 & 1 & 1 \\ 1 & 1 & 1 \end{bmatrix}.$$

29. $(\widehat{x} - x)(\widehat{x} - x)^{\mathrm{T}} = (A^{\mathrm{T}}A)^{-1}A^{\mathrm{T}}[(b - Ax)(b - Ax)^{\mathrm{T}}]A(A^{\mathrm{T}}A)^{-1}$. For independent errors, substituting $(b - Ax)(b - Ax)^{\mathrm{T}} = \sigma^2 I$ gives the *covariance matrix* $(A^{\mathrm{T}}A)^{-1}A^{\mathrm{T}}\sigma^2 A(A^{\mathrm{T}}A)^{-1}$. This simplifies to $\sigma^2(A^{\mathrm{T}}A)^{-1}$: neat formula for the covariance matrix.

31. $\frac{1}{10}b_{10} + \frac{\mathbf{9}}{\mathbf{10}}\widehat{x}_9 = \frac{1}{10}(b_1 + \cdots + b_{10})$.

33. $\begin{bmatrix} 1 & 0 \\ 1 & 1 \\ 1 & 3 \\ 1 & 4 \end{bmatrix} \begin{bmatrix} C \\ D \end{bmatrix} = \begin{bmatrix} 0 \\ 8 \\ 8 \\ 20 \end{bmatrix}$. Change right side to $p = \begin{bmatrix} 1 \\ 5 \\ 13 \\ 17 \end{bmatrix}; \widehat{x} = \begin{bmatrix} 1 \\ 4 \end{bmatrix}$ solves $A\widehat{x} = p$.

35. Closest parabola: $\begin{bmatrix} 1 & 0 & 0 \\ 1 & 1 & 1 \\ 1 & 3 & 9 \\ 1 & 4 & 16 \end{bmatrix} \begin{bmatrix} C \\ D \\ E \end{bmatrix} = \begin{bmatrix} 0 \\ 8 \\ 8 \\ 20 \end{bmatrix}$.

$$A^{\mathrm{T}}A\widehat{x} = \begin{bmatrix} 4 & 8 & 26 \\ 8 & 26 & 92 \\ 26 & 92 & 338 \end{bmatrix} \begin{bmatrix} \widehat{C} \\ \widehat{D} \\ \widehat{E} \end{bmatrix} = \begin{bmatrix} 36 \\ 112 \\ 400 \end{bmatrix}.$$

37. (a) The best line is $x = 1 + 4t$, which goes through the center point $(\widehat{t}, \widehat{b}) = (2, 9)$.
(b) From the first equation: $Cm + D\sum t_i = \sum b_i$. Divide by m to get $C + D\widehat{t} = \widehat{b}$.

39. $\widehat{x}_W = \dfrac{w_1^2 b_1 + \cdots + w_m^2 b_m}{w_1^2 + \cdots + w_m^2}$.

41. $\widehat{x}_W = (1/21, 4/7)$; $A\widehat{x}_W = (1/21, 13/21, 25/21)$,
$b - A\widehat{x}_W = (-1/21, 8/21, -4/21)$, $(A\widehat{x}_W)W^{\mathrm{T}}W(b - A\widehat{x}_W) = 0$.

Problem Set 3.4, page 185

1. (a) $-4 = C - 2D$, $-3 = C - D$, $-1 = C + D$, $0 = C + 2D$. (b) Best line $-2 + t$ goes through all 4 points; $E^2 = 0$. (c) b is in the column space.

3. Projection on a_3: $(-2/3, 1/3, -2/3)$; the sum is b itself; notice that $a_1a_1^{\mathrm{T}}, a_2a_2^{\mathrm{T}}, a_3a_3^{\mathrm{T}}$ are projections onto three orthogonal directions. Their sum is projection onto the whole space and should be the identity.

5. $(I-2uu^{\mathrm{T}})^{\mathrm{T}}(I-2uu^{\mathrm{T}}) = I-4uu^{\mathrm{T}}+4uu^{\mathrm{T}}uu^{\mathrm{T}} = I$; $Q = \begin{bmatrix} \frac{1}{2} & -\frac{1}{2} & \frac{1}{2} & \frac{1}{2} \\ -\frac{1}{2} & \frac{1}{2} & \frac{1}{2} & \frac{1}{2} \\ \frac{1}{2} & \frac{1}{2} & \frac{1}{2} & -\frac{1}{2} \\ \frac{1}{2} & \frac{1}{2} & -\frac{1}{2} & \frac{1}{2} \end{bmatrix}$.

7. $(x_1q_1 + \cdots + x_nq_n)^{\mathrm{T}}(x_1q_1 + \cdots + x_nq_n) = x_1^2 + \cdots + x_n^2 \Rightarrow \|b\|^2 = b^{\mathrm{T}}b = x_1^2 + \cdots + x_n^2$.

9. The combination closest to q_3 is $0q_1 + 0q_2$.

11. Q is upper triangular: column 1 has $q_{11} = \pm 1$; by orthogonality column 2 must be $(0, \pm 1, 0, \ldots)$; by orthogonality column 3 is $(0, 0, \pm 1, \ldots)$; and so on.

13. $A = \begin{bmatrix} 0 & 0 & 1 \\ 0 & 1 & 1 \\ 1 & 1 & 1 \end{bmatrix} = \begin{bmatrix} 0 & 0 & 1 \\ 0 & 1 & 0 \\ 1 & 0 & 0 \end{bmatrix} \begin{bmatrix} 1 & 1 & 1 \\ 0 & 1 & 1 \\ 0 & 0 & 1 \end{bmatrix} = QR.$

15. $q_1 = \begin{bmatrix} 1/3 \\ 2/3 \\ -2/3 \end{bmatrix}$, $q_2 = \begin{bmatrix} 2/3 \\ 1/3 \\ 2/3 \end{bmatrix}$, $q_3 = \begin{bmatrix} -2/3 \\ 2/3 \\ 1/3 \end{bmatrix}$ is in the left nullspace;
$\widehat{x} = \begin{bmatrix} q_1^{\mathrm{T}}b \\ q_2^{\mathrm{T}}b \end{bmatrix} = \begin{bmatrix} 1 \\ 2 \end{bmatrix}$.

17. $R\widehat{x} = Q^{\mathrm{T}}b$ gives $\begin{bmatrix} 3 & 3 \\ 0 & \sqrt{2} \end{bmatrix} \begin{bmatrix} \widehat{x} \end{bmatrix} = \begin{bmatrix} 5/3 \\ 0 \end{bmatrix}$ and $\widehat{x} = \begin{bmatrix} 5/9 \\ 0 \end{bmatrix}$.

19. $C^* - (q_2^{\mathrm{T}}C^*)\, q_2$ is $c - (q_1^{\mathrm{T}}c)\, q_1 - (q_2^{\mathrm{T}}c)\, q_2$ because $q_2^{\mathrm{T}}q_1 = 0$.

21. By orthogonality, the closest functions are $0 \sin 2x = 0$ and $0 + 0x = 0$.

23. $a_0 = 1/2$, $a_1 = 0$, $b_1 = 2/\pi$.

25. The closest line is $y = 1/3$ (horizontal since $(x, x^2) = 0$).

27. $(1/\sqrt{2}, -1/\sqrt{2}, 0, 0)$, $(1/\sqrt{6}, 1/\sqrt{6}, 2/\sqrt{6}, 0)$,
$(-1/2\sqrt{3}, -1/2\sqrt{3}, 1/2\sqrt{3}, -1/\sqrt{3})$.

29. $A = a = (1, -1, 0, 0)$; $B = b - p = \left(\frac{1}{2}, \frac{1}{2}, -1, 0\right)$; $C = c - p_A - p_B = \left(\frac{1}{3}, \frac{1}{3}, \frac{1}{3}, -1\right)$. Notice the pattern in those orthogonal vectors A, B, C. Next, $(1, 1, 1, 1)/4$.

31. (a) True. (b) True. $Qx = x_1q_1 + x_2q_2$. $\|Qx\|^2 = x_1^2 + x_2^2$ because $q_1^{\mathrm{T}}q_2 = 0$.

Problem Set 3.5, page 196

1. $F^2 = \begin{bmatrix} 4 & 0 & 0 & 0 \\ 0 & 0 & 0 & 4 \\ 0 & 0 & 4 & 0 \\ 0 & 4 & 0 & 0 \end{bmatrix}$, $F^4 = \begin{bmatrix} 16 & 0 & 0 & 0 \\ 0 & 16 & 0 & 0 \\ 0 & 0 & 16 & 0 \\ 0 & 0 & 0 & 16 \end{bmatrix} = 4^2 I$.

3. The submatrix is F_3.

5. $e^{ix} = -1$ for $x = (2k+1)\pi$, $e^{i\theta} = i$ for $\theta = 2k\pi + \pi/2$, k is integer.

7. $c = (1, 0, 1, 0)$.

9. (a) $y = F$ times $(1, 0, 0, 0) =$ column zero of $F = (1, 1, 1, 1)$.
(b) $c = (1, 1, 1, 1)/4$.

11. $$c = \begin{bmatrix}1\\0\\1\\0\end{bmatrix} \rightarrow \begin{matrix}c_{\text{even}} =\\ c_{\text{odd}} =\end{matrix} \begin{bmatrix}1\\1\\0\\0\end{bmatrix} \rightarrow \begin{matrix}y' =\\ y'' =\end{matrix} \begin{bmatrix}2\\0\\0\\0\end{bmatrix} \rightarrow y = \begin{bmatrix}2\\0\\2\\0\end{bmatrix}.$$

13. $c_0 = (f_0 + f_1 + f_2 + f_3)/4$, $c_1 = (f_0 - if_1 - f_2 + if_3)/4$, $c_2 = (f_0 - f_1 + f_2 - f_3)/4$, $c_3 = (f_0 + if_1 - f_2 - if_3)/4$; f odd means $f_0 = 0$, $f_2 = 0$, $f_3 = -f_1$. Then $c_0 = 0$, $c_2 = 0$, $c_3 = -c_1$, so c is also odd.

15. $$F^{-1} = \begin{bmatrix}1 & & & \\ & & 1 & \\ & 1 & & \\ & & & 1\end{bmatrix} \frac{1}{2} \begin{bmatrix}1 & 1 & & \\ 1 & i^2 & & \\ & & 1 & 1 \\ & & 1 & i^2\end{bmatrix} \frac{1}{2} \begin{bmatrix}1 & & 1 & \\ & 1 & & 1 \\ 1 & & -1 & \\ & -i & & i\end{bmatrix} = \frac{1}{4} F^{\mathrm{H}}.$$

17. $$D = \begin{bmatrix}1 & & \\ & e^{2\pi i/6} & \\ & & e^{4\pi i/6}\end{bmatrix} \text{ and } F_3 = \begin{bmatrix}1 & 1 & 1 \\ 1 & e^{2\pi i/3} & e^{4\pi i/3} \\ 1 & e^{4\pi i/3} & e^{2\pi i/3}\end{bmatrix}.$$

19. $\Lambda = \operatorname{diag}(1, i, i^2, i^3)$; $P = \begin{bmatrix}0 & 1 & 0 \\ 0 & 0 & 1 \\ 1 & 0 & 0\end{bmatrix}$ and P^{T} lead to $\lambda^3 - 1 = 0$.

21. Eigenvalues $e_0 = 2 - 1 - 1 = 0$, $e_1 = 2 - i - i^3 = 2$, $e_2 = 2 - (-1) - (-1) = 4$, $e_3 = 2 - i^3 - i^9 = 2$. Check trace $0 + 2 + 4 + 2 = 8$.

23. The four components are $(c_0 + c_2) + (c_1 + c_3)$; then $(c_0 - c_2) + i(c_1 - c_3)$; then $(c_0 + c_2) - (c_1 + c_3)$; then $(c_0 - c_2) - i(c_1 - c_3)$. These steps are the **FFT**!

Problem Set 4.2, page 206

1. $\det(2A) = 8$ and $\det(-A) = (-1)^4 \det A = \frac{1}{2}$ and $\det(A^2) = \frac{1}{4}$ and $\det(A^{-1}) = 2$.

3. The row operations leave $\det A$ unchanged by Rule 5. Then multiplying a row by -1 (Rule 3) gives the row exchange rule: $\det B = -\det A$.

5. For the first matrix, two row exchanges will produce the identity matrix. The second matrix needs three row exchanges to reach I.

7. $\det A = 0$ (singular); $\det U = 16$; $\det U^{\mathrm{T}} = 16$; $\det U^{-1} = 1/16$; $\det M = 16$ (2 exchanges).

9. The new determinant is $(1 - m\ell)(ad - bc)$.

11. If $|\det Q|$ is not 1 then $\det Q^n = (\det Q)^n$ would blow up or approach zero. But Q^n remains an orthogonal matrix. So $\det Q$ must be 1 or -1.

13. (a) Rule 3 (factoring -1 from each row) gives $\det(K^{\mathrm{T}}) = (-1)^3 \det K$. Then $-\det K = \det K^{\mathrm{T}} = \det K$ gives $\det K = 0$.

(b) $\begin{bmatrix} 0 & 0 & 0 & 1 \\ 0 & 0 & 1 & 0 \\ 0 & -1 & 0 & 0 \\ -1 & 0 & 0 & 0 \end{bmatrix}$ has det $= 1$.

15. Adding every column of A to the first column makes it a zero column, so det $A = 0$. If every row of A adds to 1, then every row of $A - I$ adds to 0 and $\det(A - I) = 0$. But det A need not be 1: $A = \begin{bmatrix} \frac{1}{2} & \frac{1}{2} \\ \frac{1}{2} & \frac{1}{2} \end{bmatrix}$ has $\det(A - I) = 0$, but $\det A = 0 \neq 1$.

17. $\det(A) = 10$, $\det(A^{-1}) = \frac{1}{10}$, $\det(A - \lambda I) = \lambda^2 - 7\lambda + 10 = 0$ for $\lambda = 5$ and $\lambda = 2$.

19. Taking determinants gives $(\det C)(\det D) = (-1)^n(\det D)(\det C)$. For n even the reasoning fails (because $(-1)^n = +1$) and the conclusion is wrong.

21. $\det(A^{-1}) = \det \begin{bmatrix} \dfrac{d}{ad-bc} & \dfrac{-b}{ad-bc} \\ \dfrac{-c}{ad-bc} & \dfrac{a}{ad-bc} \end{bmatrix} = \dfrac{ad-bc}{(ad-bc)^2} = \dfrac{1}{ad-bc}$.

23. Determinant $= 36$ and determinant $= 5$.

25. $\det(L) = 1$, $\det(U) = -6$, $\det(A) = -6$, $\det(U^{-1}L^{-1}) = -\frac{1}{6}$, and $\det(U^{-1}L^{-1}A) = 1$.

27. Row 3 − row 2 = row 2 − row 1 so A is singular.

29. A is rectangular so $\det(A^{\mathrm{T}}A) \neq (\det A^{\mathrm{T}})(\det A)$: these are not defined.

31. The Hilbert determinants are $1, 8 \times 10^{-2}, 4.6 \times 10^{-4}, 1.6 \times 10^{-7}, 3.7 \times 10^{-12}, 5.4 \times 10^{-18}, 4.8 \times 10^{-25}, 2.7 \times 10^{-33}, 9.7 \times 10^{-43}, 2.2 \times 10^{-53}$. Pivots are ratios of determinants, so the tenth pivot is near $10^{-53}/10^{-43} = 10^{-10}$: very small.

33. The largest determinants of 0–1 matrices for $n = 1, 2, \ldots,$ are 1, 1, 2, 3, 5, 9, 32, 56, 144, 320, on the web at *www.mathworld.wolfram.com/HadamardsMaximumDeterminantProblem.html* and also in the "On-Line Encyclopedia of Integer Sequences": *www.research.att.com*. With −1s and 1s, the largest 4 by 4 determinant (see Hadamard in index) is 16.

35. $\det(I + M) = 1 + a + b + c + d$. Subtract row 4 from rows 1, 2, and 3. Then subtract a(row 1)$+b$(row 2)$+c$(row 3) from row 4. This leaves a triangular matrix with 1, 1, 1, and $1 + a + b + c + d$ on its diagonal.

Problem Set 4.3, page 215

1. (a) $a_{12}a_{21}a_{34}a_{43} = 1$; *even*, so $\det A = 1$.
(b) $b_{13}b_{22}b_{31}b_{14} = 18$; *odd*, so $\det B = -18$.

3. (a) True (product rule). (b) False (all 1s).
(c) False (det [1 1 0; 0 1 1; 1 0 1] = 2).

5. The 1, 1 cofactor is F_{n-1}. The 1, 2 cofactor has a 1 in column 1, with cofactor F_{n-2}. Multiply by $(-1)^{1+2}$ and also -1 to find $F_n = F_{n-1} + F_{n-2}$. So the determinants are Fibonacci numbers, except F_n is the usual F_{n-1}.

7. Cofactor expansion: det $= 4(3) - 4(1) + 4(-4) - 4(1) = -12$.

9. (a) $(n-1)n!$ (each term $n-1$). (b) $\left(1 + \dfrac{1}{2!} + \cdots + \dfrac{1}{(n-1)!}\right) n!$.
(c) $\dfrac{1}{3}(n^3 + 2n - 3)$.

11. $\begin{bmatrix} 0 & A \\ -B & I \end{bmatrix} \begin{bmatrix} I & 0 \\ B & I \end{bmatrix} = \begin{bmatrix} AB & A \\ 0 & I \end{bmatrix}$, $\det \begin{bmatrix} I & 0 \\ B & I \end{bmatrix} = 1 \Rightarrow \det \begin{bmatrix} 0 & A \\ -B & I \end{bmatrix} =$
$\det \begin{bmatrix} AB & A \\ 0 & I \end{bmatrix} = \det(AB)$. Test $A = [1 \quad 2]$, $B = \begin{bmatrix} 1 \\ 2 \end{bmatrix}$, $\det \begin{bmatrix} 0 & A \\ -B & I \end{bmatrix} = 5 =$
$\det(AB)$; $A = \begin{bmatrix} 1 \\ 2 \end{bmatrix}$, $B = [1 \quad 2]$, $\det \begin{bmatrix} 0 & A \\ -B & I \end{bmatrix} = 0 = \det(AB)$. Singular:
$\operatorname{rank}(AB) \le \operatorname{rank}(A) \le n < m$.

13. $\det A = 1 + 18 + 12 - 9 - 4 - 6 = 12$, so rows are independent; $\det B = 0$, so rows are dependent (row 1 + row 2 = row 3); $\det C = -1$, C has independent rows.

15. Each of the six terms in $\det A$ is zero; the rank is at most 2; column 2 has no pivot.

17. $a_{11}a_{23}a_{32}a_{44}$ has $-$, $a_{14}a_{23}a_{32}a_{41}$ has $+$, so $\det A = 0$;
$\det B = 2 \cdot 4 \cdot 4 \cdot 2 - 1 \cdot 4 \cdot 4 \cdot 1 = 48$.

19. (a) If $a_{11} = a_{22} = a_{33} = 0$ then four terms are sure zeros.
(b) Fifteen terms are zero.

21. Some term $a_{1\alpha}a_{2\beta} \cdots a_{n\omega}$ in the big formula is not zero! Move rows $1, 2, \ldots, n$ into rows $\alpha, \beta, \ldots, \omega$. Then these nonzero a's will be on the main diagonal.

23. $4!/2 = 12$ even permutations; $\det(I + P_{\text{even}}) = 16$ or 4 or 0 (16 comes from $I + I$).

25. $C = \begin{bmatrix} 3 & 2 & 1 \\ 2 & 4 & 2 \\ 1 & 2 & 3 \end{bmatrix}$ and $AC^{\mathrm{T}} = \begin{bmatrix} 4 & 0 & 0 \\ 0 & 4 & 0 \\ 0 & 0 & 4 \end{bmatrix} = 4I$. Therefore $A^{-1} = \dfrac{1}{4}C^{\mathrm{T}}$.

27. $|B_n| = |A_n| - |A_{n-1}| = (n+1) - n = 1$.

29. We must choose 1s from columns 2 and 1, columns 4 and 3, and so on. Therefore n must be even to have $\det A_n \neq 0$. The number of exchanges is $\frac{1}{2}n$ so $C_n = (-1)^{n/2}$.

31. $S_1 = 3$, $S_2 = 8$, $S_3 = 21$. The rule looks like every second number in Fibonacci's sequence $\ldots, 3, 5, 8, 13, 21, 34, 55, \ldots$ so the guess is $S_4 = 55$. The five nonzero terms in the big formula for S_4 are (with 3s where Problem 39 has 2s) $81 + 1 - 9 - 9 - 9 = 55$.

33. Changing 3 to 2 in the corner reduces the determinant F_{2n+2} by 1 times the cofactor of that corner entry. This cofactor is the determinant of S_{n-1} (one size smaller), which is F_{2n}. Therefore changing 3 to 2 changes the determinant to $F_{2n+2} - F_{2n}$, which is F_{2n+1}.

35. (a) Every $\det L = 1$; $\det U_k = \det A_k = 2, 6, -6$ for $k = 1, 2, 3$.
(b) Pivots $5, \frac{6}{5}, \frac{7}{6}$.

37. The six terms are correct. Row 1 $-$ 2 row 2 + row 3 = 0, so the matrix is singular.

39. The five nonzero terms in $\det A = 5$ are

$$(2)(2)(2)(2) + (-1)(-1)(-1)(-1) - (-1)(-1)(2)(2) - (2)(2)(-1)(-1) - (2)(-1)(-1)(2).$$

41. With $a_{11} = 1$, the $-1, 2, -1$ matrix has det $= 1$ and inverse $(A^{-1})_{ij} = n + 1 - \max(i, j)$.

43. Subtracting 1 from the n, n entry subtracts its cofactor C_{nn} from the determinant. That cofactor is $C_{nn} = 1$ (smaller Pascal matrix). Subtracting 1 from 1 leaves 0.

Problem Set 4.4, page 225

1. $\det A = 20; C^{\mathrm{T}} = \begin{bmatrix} 20 & -10 & -12 \\ 0 & 5 & 0 \\ 0 & 0 & 4 \end{bmatrix}; AC^{\mathrm{T}} = 20I; A^{-1} = \dfrac{1}{20}\begin{bmatrix} 20 & -10 & -12 \\ 0 & 5 & 0 \\ 0 & 0 & 4 \end{bmatrix}.$

3. $(x, y) = (d/(ad - bc), -c/(ad - bc)); (x, y, z) = (3, -1, -2).$

5. (a) The area of that parallelogram is det $\begin{bmatrix} 2 & 2 \\ -1 & 3 \end{bmatrix}$, so the triangle ABC has area $\frac{1}{2}4 = 2$. (b) The triangle $A'B'C'$ has the same area; it is just moved to the origin.

7. The pivots of A are 2, 3, 6 from determinants 2, 6, 36; the pivots of B are 2, 3, 0.

9. (a) P^2 takes $(1, 2, 3, 4, 5)$ to $(3, 2, 5, 4, 1)$.
(b) P^{-1} takes $(1, 2, 3, 4, 5)$ to $(3, 4, 5, 2, 1)$.

11. The powers of P are all permutation matrices, so eventually one of those matrices must be repeated. If P^r is the same as P^s, then $P^{r-s} = I$.

13. (a) $\det A = 3$, $\det B_1 = -6$, $\det B_2 = 3$, so $x_1 = -6/3 = -2$ and $x_2 = 3/3 = 1$.
(b) $|A| = 4$, $|B_1| = 3$, $|B_2| = -2$, $|B_3| = 1$. So $x_1 = \frac{3}{4}$ and $x_2 = -\frac{1}{2}$ and $x_3 = \frac{1}{4}$.

15. (a) $x_1 = \frac{3}{0}$ and $x_2 = \frac{-2}{0}$: no solution (b) $x_1 = \frac{0}{0}$ and $x_2 = \frac{0}{0}$: *undetermined.*

17. If the first column in A is also the right-hand side b then $\det A = \det B_1$. Both B_2 and B_3 are singular, since a column is repeated. Therefore $x_1 = |B_1|/|A| = 1$ and $x_2 = x_3 = 0$.

19. If all cofactors $= 0$ (even in a single row or column), then $\det A = 0$ (no inverse). $A = \begin{bmatrix} 1 & 1 \\ 1 & 1 \end{bmatrix}$ has no zero cofactors but it is not invertible.

21. If $\det A = 1$ and we know the cofactors, then $C^{\mathrm{T}} = A^{-1}$ and also $\det A^{-1} = 1$. Since A is the inverse of A^{-1}, A must be the cofactor matrix for C.

23. Knowing C, Problem 22 gives $\det A = (\det C)^{\frac{1}{n-1}}$ with $n = 4$. So we can construct $A^{-1} = C^{\mathrm{T}}/\det A$ using the known cofactors. Invert to find A.

25. (a) Cofactors $C_{21} = C_{31} = C_{32} = 0$.
(b) $C_{12} = C_{21}, C_{31} = C_{13}, C_{32} = C_{23}$ make S^{-1} symmetric.

27. (a) Area $\begin{vmatrix} 3 & 2 \\ 1 & 4 \end{vmatrix} = 10$. (b) Triangle area $= 5$. (c) Triangle area $= 5$.

29. (a) Area $\frac{1}{2}\begin{vmatrix} 2 & 1 & 1 \\ 3 & 4 & 1 \\ 0 & 5 & 1 \end{vmatrix} = 5$. (b) $5 +$ new triangle area $\frac{1}{2}\begin{vmatrix} 2 & 1 & 1 \\ 0 & 5 & 1 \\ -1 & 0 & 1 \end{vmatrix} = 5 + 7 = 12$.

31. The edges of the hypercube have length $\sqrt{1+1+1+1} = 2$. The volume $\det H$ is $2^4 = 16$. ($H/2$ has orthonormal columns. Then $\det(H/2) = 1$ leads again to $\det H = 16$.)

33. 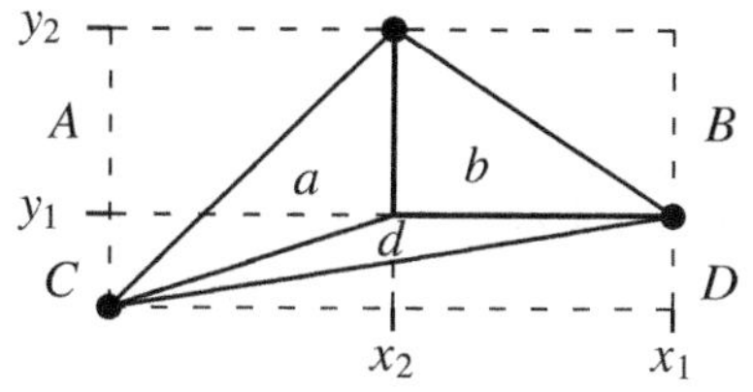

$x_1y_2 - x_2y_1 =$ rectangles $A+B+D$ (not C).

Areas from same bases same heights: rectangle $A = 2$(triangle a), rectangle $B = 2$(triangle b), rectangle $D = 2$(triangle d).

So triangles $a + b + d = \frac{1}{2}(x_1y_2 - x_2y_1)$.

Check an example with $(a, b) = (3, 2)$, $(c, d) = (1, 4)$, and area $= 10$. The line from $(0, e)$ in step 3 has slope c/a and equation $y = e + cx/a$. Step 3 works because (b, d) is on that line! $d = e + cb/a$ is true, since $ad - bc =$ area ae at step 2.

35. The n-dimensional cube has 2^n corners, $n2^{n-1}$ edges, and $2n$ faces of dimension $n-1$. The cube whose edges are the rows of $2I$ has volume 2^n.

37. $J = r$. The columns are orthogonal and their lengths are 1 and r.

39. $\begin{vmatrix} \partial r/\partial x & \partial r/\partial y \\ \partial\theta/\partial x & \partial\theta/\partial y \end{vmatrix} = \begin{vmatrix} \cos\theta & \sin\theta \\ (-\sin\theta)/r & (\cos\theta)/r \end{vmatrix} = \dfrac{1}{r}.$

41. $S = (2, 1, -1)$ gives a parallelogram, whose area is the length of a cross product: $\|PQ \times PS\| = \|(-2, -2, -1)\| = 3$. This comes also from a determinant! The other four corners could be $(0, 0, 0)$, $(0, 0, 2)$, $(1, 2, 2)$, $(1, 1, 0)$. The volume of the tilted box is $|\det| = 1$.

43. $\det \begin{bmatrix} x & y & z \\ 3 & 2 & 1 \\ 1 & 2 & 3 \end{bmatrix} = 0 = 7x - 5y + z$; plane contains the two vectors.

45. VISA has the five reversals VI, VS, VA, IA, SA. And AVIS has the two reversals VI and VS. Since $5 - 2$ is odd, VISA and AVIS have opposite parity.

Problem Set 5.1, page 240

1. $\lambda = 2$ and $\lambda = 3$, trace $= 5$, determinant $= 6$.

3. $\lambda = -5$ and $\lambda = -4$; both λ's are reduced by 7, with unchanged eigenvectors.

5. $\lambda = 3$, $\lambda = 1$, $\lambda = 0$, with eigenvectors $(1, 0, 0)$, $(2, -1, 0)$, $(3, -2, 1)$; trace $= 4$, det $= 0$. $\lambda = 2$, $\lambda = 2$, $\lambda = -2$, with eigenvectors $(1, 1, 1)$, $(0, 1, 0)$, $(1, 0, -1)$; trace $= 2$, det $= -8$.

7. $Ax = \lambda x$ gives $(A - 7I)x = (\lambda - 7)x$; $Ax = \lambda x$ gives $x = \lambda A^{-1}x$, so $A^{-1}x = (1/\lambda)x$.

9. The coefficient of $(-\lambda)^{n-1}$ in $(\lambda_1 - \lambda)\cdots(\lambda_n - \lambda)$ is $\lambda_1 + \cdots + \lambda_n$. In $\det(A - \lambda I)$, a term that includes an off-diagonal a_{ij} excludes both $a_{ii} - \lambda$ and $a_{jj} - \lambda$. Such a term doesn't involve $(-\lambda)^{n-1}$. So the coefficient of $(-\lambda)^{n-1}$ in $\det(A - \lambda I)$ must come from the product down the main diagonal. That coefficient is $a_{11} + \cdots + a_{nn} = \lambda_1 + \cdots + \lambda_n$.

11. Transpose $A - \lambda I$: $\det(A - \lambda I) = \det(A - \lambda I)^{\mathrm{T}} = \det(A^{\mathrm{T}} - \lambda I)$.

13. The eigenvalues of A are 1, 2, 3, 7, 8, 9.

15. $\operatorname{rank}(A) = 1$, $\lambda = 0, \ldots, 0, n$ (trace n); $\operatorname{rank}(C) = 2$, $\lambda = 0, \ldots, n/2, -n/2$ (trace 0).

17. The third row contains 6, 5, 4.

19. A and A^2 and A^∞ all have the same eigenvectors. The eigenvalues are 1 and 0.5 for A, 1 and 0.25 for A^2, 1 and 0 for A^∞. Therefore A^2 is halfway between A and A^∞.

21. $\lambda_1 = 4$ and $\lambda_2 = -1$ (check trace and determinant) with $x_1 = (1, 2)$ and $x_2 = (2, -1)$. A^{-1} has the same eigenvectors as A, with eigenvalues $1/\lambda_1 = 1/4$ and $1/\lambda_2 = -1$.

23. (a) Multiply Ax to see λx which reveals λ. (b) Solve $(A - \lambda I)x = 0$ to find x.

25. (a) $Pu = (uu^{\mathrm{T}})u = u(u^{\mathrm{T}}u) = u$, so $\lambda = 1$. (b) $Pv = (uu^{\mathrm{T}})v = u(u^{\mathrm{T}}v) = 0$, so $\lambda = 0$. (c) $x_1 = (-1, 1, 0, 0)$, $x_2 = (-3, 0, 1, 0)$, $x_3 = (-5, 0, 0, 1)$ are orthogonal to u, so they are eigenvectors of P with $\lambda = 0$.

27. $\lambda^3 - 1 = 0$ gives $\lambda = 1$ and $\lambda = \frac{1}{2}(-1 \pm i\sqrt{3})$; the three eigenvalues are $1, 1, -1$.

29. (a) rank = 2. (b) $\det(B^{\mathrm{T}}B) = 0$. *Not* (c). (d) $(B + I)^{-1}$ has $(\lambda + 1)^{-1} = 1, \frac{1}{2}, \frac{1}{3}$.

31. $a = 0,\ b = 9,\ c = 0$ multiply $1, \lambda, \lambda^2$ in $\det(A - \lambda I) = 9\lambda - \lambda^3$: $A =$ *companion matrix.*

33. $\begin{bmatrix} 0 & 0 \\ 1 & 0 \end{bmatrix}, \begin{bmatrix} 0 & 1 \\ 0 & 0 \end{bmatrix}, \begin{bmatrix} -1 & 1 \\ -1 & 1 \end{bmatrix}$. Always $A^2 =$ zero matrix if $\lambda = 0, 0$ (Cayley–Hamilton).

35. $Ax = c_1\lambda_1 x_1 + \cdots + c_n\lambda_n x_n$ equals $Bx = c_1\lambda_1 x_1 + \cdots + c_n\lambda_n x_n$ for all x. So $A = B$.

37. $\begin{bmatrix} a & b \\ c & d \end{bmatrix}\begin{bmatrix} 1 \\ 1 \end{bmatrix} = \begin{bmatrix} a+b \\ c+d \end{bmatrix} = (a+b)\begin{bmatrix} 1 \\ 1 \end{bmatrix}$; $\lambda_2 = d - b$ to produce trace $= a + d$.

39. We need $\lambda^3 = 1$ but not $\lambda = 1$ (to avoid I). With $\lambda_1 = e^{2\pi i/3}$ and $\lambda_2 = e^{-2\pi i/3}$, the determinant will be $\lambda_1\lambda_2 = 1$ and the trace is $\lambda_1 + \lambda_2 = \cos\frac{2\pi}{3} + i\sin\frac{2\pi}{3} + \cos\frac{2\pi}{3} - i\sin\frac{2\pi}{3} = -1$. One matrix with this trace -1 and determinant 1 is $A = \begin{bmatrix} -1 & 1 \\ -1 & 0 \end{bmatrix}$.

Problem Set 5.2, page 250

1. $\begin{bmatrix} 1 & 1 \\ 1 & 1 \end{bmatrix} = \begin{bmatrix} 1 & 1 \\ 1 & -1 \end{bmatrix}\begin{bmatrix} 2 & 0 \\ 0 & 0 \end{bmatrix}\begin{bmatrix} 1 & 1 \\ 1 & -1 \end{bmatrix}^{-1}$;

$\begin{bmatrix} 2 & 1 \\ 0 & 0 \end{bmatrix} = \begin{bmatrix} 1 & 1 \\ 0 & -2 \end{bmatrix}\begin{bmatrix} 2 & 0 \\ 0 & 0 \end{bmatrix}\begin{bmatrix} 1 & 1 \\ 0 & -2 \end{bmatrix}^{-1}$.

3. $\lambda = 0, 0, 3$; the third column of S is a multiple of $\begin{bmatrix} 1 \\ 1 \\ 1 \end{bmatrix}$ and the other columns are on the plane orthogonal to it.

5. A_1 and A_3 cannot be diagonalized. They have only one line of eigenvectors.

7. $A = \begin{bmatrix} 3 & 1 \\ 1 & -1 \end{bmatrix}\begin{bmatrix} 5 & 0 \\ 0 & 1 \end{bmatrix}\begin{bmatrix} 3 & 1 \\ 1 & -1 \end{bmatrix}^{-1}$ gives $A^{100} = \begin{bmatrix} 3 & 1 \\ 1 & -1 \end{bmatrix}\begin{bmatrix} 5^{100} & 0 \\ 0 & 1 \end{bmatrix}\begin{bmatrix} 3 & 1 \\ 1 & -1 \end{bmatrix}^{-1} =$

$\frac{1}{4}\begin{bmatrix} 3 \cdot 5^{100} + 1 & 3 \cdot 5^{100} - 3 \\ 5^{100} - 1 & 5^{100} + 3 \end{bmatrix}$.

9. $\text{trace}(AB) = \text{trace}(BA) = aq + bs + cr + dt$. Then $\text{trace}(AB - BA) = 0$ (always). So $AB - BA = I$ is impossible for matrices, since I does not have trace zero.

11. (a) True; $\det A = 2 \neq 0$. (b) False; $\begin{bmatrix} 1 & 1 & 1 \\ 0 & 1 & 1 \\ 0 & 0 & 2 \end{bmatrix}$. (c) False; $\begin{bmatrix} 1 & 0 & 0 \\ 0 & 1 & 0 \\ 0 & 0 & 2 \end{bmatrix}$ is diagonal!

13. $A = \begin{bmatrix} 1 & 1 \\ 1 & -1 \end{bmatrix} \begin{bmatrix} 9 & 0 \\ 0 & 1 \end{bmatrix} \begin{bmatrix} 1 & 1 \\ 1 & -1 \end{bmatrix}^{-1}$; $\begin{bmatrix} 2 & 1 \\ 1 & 2 \end{bmatrix}$; four square roots.

15. $\begin{bmatrix} 1 & 2 \\ 0 & 3 \end{bmatrix} = \begin{bmatrix} 1 & 1 \\ 0 & 1 \end{bmatrix} \begin{bmatrix} 1 & 0 \\ 0 & 3 \end{bmatrix} \begin{bmatrix} 1 & -1 \\ 0 & 1 \end{bmatrix}$; $\begin{bmatrix} 1 & 1 \\ 2 & 2 \end{bmatrix} = \begin{bmatrix} 1 & 1 \\ -1 & 2 \end{bmatrix} \begin{bmatrix} 0 & 0 \\ 0 & 3 \end{bmatrix} \begin{bmatrix} \frac{2}{3} & -\frac{1}{3} \\ \frac{1}{3} & \frac{1}{3} \end{bmatrix}$.

17. $A = \begin{bmatrix} 1 & 1 \\ 0 & 1 \end{bmatrix} \begin{bmatrix} 2 & 0 \\ 0 & 5 \end{bmatrix} \begin{bmatrix} 1 & -1 \\ 0 & 1 \end{bmatrix} = \begin{bmatrix} 2 & 3 \\ 0 & 5 \end{bmatrix}$.

19. (a) False: don't know λ's. (b) True. (c) True. (d) False: need eigenvectors of S!

21. The columns of S are multiples of (2, 1) and (0, 1) in either order. Same for A^{-1}.

23. A and B have $\lambda_1 = 1$ and $\lambda_2 = 1$. $A + B$ has $\lambda_1 = 1, \lambda_2 = 3$. Eigenvalues of $A + B$ *are not equal* to eigenvalues of A plus eigenvalues of B.

25. (a) True. (b) False. (c) False (A might have 2 or 3 independent eigenvectors).

27. $A = \begin{bmatrix} 8 & 3 \\ -3 & 2 \end{bmatrix}$ (or other), $A = \begin{bmatrix} 9 & 4 \\ -4 & 1 \end{bmatrix}$, $A = \begin{bmatrix} 10 & 5 \\ -5 & 0 \end{bmatrix}$; only eigenvectors are $(c, -c)$.

29. $S\Lambda^k S^{-1}$ approaches zero if and only if every $|\lambda| < 1$; $B^k \to 0$ from $\lambda = .9$ and $\lambda = .3$.

31. $\Lambda = \begin{bmatrix} .9 & 0 \\ 0 & .3 \end{bmatrix}$, $S = \begin{bmatrix} 3 & -3 \\ 1 & 1 \end{bmatrix}$; $B^{10} \begin{bmatrix} 3 \\ 1 \end{bmatrix} = (.9)^{10} \begin{bmatrix} 3 \\ 1 \end{bmatrix}$, $B^{10} \begin{bmatrix} 3 \\ -1 \end{bmatrix} = (.3)^{10} \begin{bmatrix} 3 \\ -1 \end{bmatrix}$, $B^{10} \begin{bmatrix} 6 \\ 0 \end{bmatrix}$ = sum of those two.

33. $B^k = \begin{bmatrix} 1 & 1 \\ 0 & -1 \end{bmatrix} \begin{bmatrix} 3 & 0 \\ 0 & 2 \end{bmatrix}^k \begin{bmatrix} 1 & 1 \\ 0 & -1 \end{bmatrix} = \begin{bmatrix} 3^k & 3^k - 2^k \\ 0 & 2^k \end{bmatrix}$.

35. $\text{trace}\, AB = (aq + bs) + (cr + dt) = (qa + rc) + (sb + td) = \text{trace}\, BA$. Proof for diagonalizable case: the trace of $S\Lambda S^{-1}$ is the trace of $(\Lambda S^{-1})S = \Lambda$, which is *the sum of the* λ*'s*.

37. The A's form a subspace, since cA and $A_1 + A_2$ have the same S. When $S = I$, the A's give the subspace of diagonal matrices. Dimension 4.

39. Two problems: The nullspace and column space can overlap, so x could be in both. There may not be r independent eigenvectors in the column space.

41. $A = \begin{bmatrix} 1 & 1 \\ 1 & 0 \end{bmatrix}$ has $A^2 = \begin{bmatrix} 2 & 1 \\ 1 & 1 \end{bmatrix}$, and $A^2 - A - I$ = zero matrix confirms Cayley–Hamilton.

43. By **5F**, B has the same eigenvectors $(1, 0)$ and $(0, 1)$ as A, so B is also diagonal. The equations $AB - BA = \begin{bmatrix} a & b \\ 2c & 2d \end{bmatrix} - \begin{bmatrix} a & 2b \\ c & 2d \end{bmatrix} = \begin{bmatrix} 0 & 0 \\ 0 & 0 \end{bmatrix}$ are $-b = 0$ and $c = 0$: rank 2.

45. A has $\lambda_1 = 1$ and $\lambda_2 = .4$ with $x_1 = (1, 2)$ and $x_2 = (1, -1)$. A^∞ has $\lambda_1 = 1$ and $\lambda_2 = 0$ (same eigenvectors). A^{100} has $\lambda_1 = 1$ and $\lambda_2 = (.4)^{100}$, which is near zero. So A^{100} is very near A^∞.

Problem Set 5.3, page 262

1. The Fibonacci numbers start even, odd, odd. Then *odd* + *odd* = *even*. The next two are odd (from odd + even and even + odd). Then repeat *odd* + *odd* = *even*.

3. $A^2 = \begin{bmatrix} 2 & 1 \\ 1 & 1 \end{bmatrix}$, $A^3 = \begin{bmatrix} 3 & 2 \\ 2 & 1 \end{bmatrix}$, $A^4 = \begin{bmatrix} 5 & 3 \\ 3 & 2 \end{bmatrix}$; $F_{20} = 6765$.

5. $A = S\Lambda S^{-1} = \begin{bmatrix} 1 & 1 \\ 1 & 0 \end{bmatrix} = \dfrac{1}{\lambda_1 - \lambda_2} \begin{bmatrix} \lambda_1 & \lambda_2 \\ 1 & 1 \end{bmatrix} \begin{bmatrix} \lambda_1 & 0 \\ 0 & \lambda_2 \end{bmatrix} \begin{bmatrix} 1 & -\lambda_2 \\ -1 & \lambda_1 \end{bmatrix}$ (notice S^{-1}).

$$S\Lambda^k S^{-1} = \frac{1}{\lambda_1 - \lambda_2} \begin{bmatrix} \lambda_1 & \lambda_2 \\ 1 & 1 \end{bmatrix} \begin{bmatrix} \lambda_1^k & 0 \\ 0 & \lambda_2^k \end{bmatrix} \begin{bmatrix} 1 & -\lambda_2 \\ -1 & \lambda_1 \end{bmatrix} \begin{bmatrix} 1 \\ 0 \end{bmatrix} = \begin{bmatrix} - - - - - - \\ (\lambda_1^k - \lambda_2^k)/(\lambda_1 - \lambda_2) \end{bmatrix}.$$

7. Direct addition $L_k + L_{k+1}$ gives $L_0, \ldots, L_{10}$ as 2, 1, 3, 4, 7, 11, 18, 29, 47, 76, 123. My calculator gives $\lambda_1^{10} = (1.618\ldots)^{10} = 122.991\ldots$, which rounds off to $L_{10} = 123$.

9. The Markov transition matrix is $\begin{bmatrix} \frac{7}{12} & \frac{1}{6} & 0 \\ \frac{1}{6} & \frac{1}{2} & 0 \\ \frac{1}{4} & \frac{1}{3} & 1 \end{bmatrix}$. Fractions $\frac{7}{12}, \frac{1}{2}, 1$ don't move.

11. (a) $\lambda = 0, (1, 1, -2)$. (b) $\lambda = 1$ and -0.2. (c) limit $(3, 4, 4)$ = eigenvector for $\lambda = 1$.

13. (a) $\begin{matrix} 0 \le a \le 1 \\ 0 \le b \le 1. \end{matrix}$

(b) $$u_k = \begin{bmatrix} b/(1-a) & 1 \\ 1 & -1 \end{bmatrix} \begin{bmatrix} 1^k & 0 \\ 0 & (a-b)^k \end{bmatrix} \begin{bmatrix} b/(1-a) & 1 \\ 1 & -1 \end{bmatrix}^{-1} \begin{bmatrix} 1 \\ 1 \end{bmatrix}$$
$$= \begin{bmatrix} \dfrac{2b}{b-a+1} - \dfrac{1-a-b}{b-a+1}(a-b)^k \\ \dfrac{2(1-a)}{b-a+1} - \dfrac{1-a-b}{b-a+1}(a-b)^k \end{bmatrix}.$$

(c) $u_k \to \begin{bmatrix} \dfrac{2b}{b-a+1} \\ \dfrac{2(1-a)}{b-a+1} \end{bmatrix}$ if $|a - b| < 1$; $\begin{matrix} a = 1/3 \\ b = -1/3 \end{matrix}$ not Markov.

15. The components of Ax add to $x_1 + x_2 + x_3$ (each column adds to 1 and nobody is lost). The components of λx add to $\lambda(x_1 + x_2 + x_3)$. If $\lambda \neq 1$, $x_1 + x_2 + x_3$ must be zero.

17. $\begin{bmatrix} \alpha & \alpha \\ \alpha & \alpha \end{bmatrix}$ is unstable for $|\alpha| > 1/2$, and stable for $|\alpha| < 1/2$. Neutral for $\alpha = \pm 1/2$.

19. $A^2 = \begin{bmatrix} 0 & 0 & 2 \\ 0 & 0 & 0 \\ 0 & 0 & 0 \end{bmatrix}$ and $A^3 = 0$. So $(I - A)^{-1} = I + A + A^2 = \begin{bmatrix} 1 & 1 & 2 \\ 0 & 1 & 1 \\ 0 & 0 & 1 \end{bmatrix}$.

21. If A is increased, then more goods are consumed in production and the expansion must be slower. Mathematically, $Ax \geq tx$ remains true if A is increased; $t_{\max}$ goes up.

23. $\begin{bmatrix} 3 & 2 \\ 2 & 3 \end{bmatrix} = \frac{1}{2}\begin{bmatrix} 1 & -1 \\ 1 & 1 \end{bmatrix}\begin{bmatrix} 5 & 0 \\ 0 & 1 \end{bmatrix}\begin{bmatrix} 1 & 1 \\ -1 & 1 \end{bmatrix}$ and $A^k = \frac{1}{2}\begin{bmatrix} 1 & -1 \\ 1 & 1 \end{bmatrix}\begin{bmatrix} 5^k & 0 \\ 0 & 1 \end{bmatrix}\begin{bmatrix} 1 & 1 \\ -1 & 1 \end{bmatrix}$.

25. $R = S\sqrt{\Lambda}S^{-1} = \begin{bmatrix} 2 & 1 \\ 1 & 2 \end{bmatrix}$ has $R^2 = A$. $\sqrt{B}$ would have $\lambda = \sqrt{9}$ and $\lambda = \sqrt{-1}$, so its trace is not real. Note that $\begin{bmatrix} -1 & 0 \\ 0 & -1 \end{bmatrix}$ can have $\sqrt{-1} = i$ and $-i$, and real square root $\begin{bmatrix} 0 & 1 \\ -1 & 0 \end{bmatrix}$.

27. $A = S\Lambda_1 S^{-1}$ and $B = S\Lambda_2 S^{-1}$. Diagonal matrices always give $\Lambda_1\Lambda_2 = \Lambda_2\Lambda_1$. Then $AB = BA$, from $S\Lambda_1 S^{-1} S\Lambda_2 S^{-1} = S\Lambda_1\Lambda_2 S^{-1} = S\Lambda_2\Lambda_1 S^{-1} = S\Lambda_2 S^{-1} S\Lambda_1 S^{-1} = BA$.

29. B has $\lambda = i$ and $-i$, so B^4 has $\lambda^4 = 1$ and 1; C has $\lambda = (1 \pm \sqrt{3}i)/2 = \exp(\pm\pi i/3)$, so $\lambda^3 = -1$ and -1. Then $C^3 = -I$ and $C^{1024} = -C$.

Problem Set 5.4, page 275

1. $\lambda_1 = -2$ and $\lambda_2 = 0$; $x_1 = (1, -1)$ and $x_2 = (1, 1)$;
$e^{At} = \frac{1}{2}\begin{bmatrix} e^{-2t} + 1 & -e^{-2t} + 1 \\ -e^{-2t} + 1 & e^{-2t} + 1 \end{bmatrix}$.

3. $u(t) = \begin{bmatrix} e^{2t} + 2 \\ -e^{2t} + 2 \end{bmatrix}$; as $t \to \infty$, $e^{2t} \to +\infty$.

5. (a) $e^{A(t+T)} = Se^{\Lambda(t+T)}S^{-1} = Se^{\Lambda t}e^{\Lambda T}S^{-1} = Se^{\Lambda t}S^{-1}Se^{\Lambda T}S^{-1} = e^{At}e^{AT}$.

(b) $e^A = I + A = \begin{bmatrix} 1 & 0 \\ 1 & 1 \end{bmatrix}$, $e^B = I + B = \begin{bmatrix} 1 & -1 \\ 0 & 1 \end{bmatrix}$, $A + B = \begin{bmatrix} 0 & -1 \\ 1 & 0 \end{bmatrix}$ gives $e^{A+B} = \begin{bmatrix} \cos 1 & -\sin 1 \\ \sin 1 & \cos 1 \end{bmatrix}$ from Example 3 in the text, at $t = 1$. This matrix is different from $e^A e^B$.

7. $e^{At} = I + At = \begin{bmatrix} 1 & t \\ 0 & 1 \end{bmatrix}$; $e^{\Lambda t}u(0) = \begin{bmatrix} 4t + 3 \\ 4 \end{bmatrix}$.

9. (a) $\lambda_1 = \frac{7+\sqrt{57}}{2}$, $\lambda_2 = \frac{7-\sqrt{57}}{2}$, $\operatorname{Re}\lambda_1 > 0$, unstable. (b) $\lambda_1 = \sqrt{7}$, $\lambda_2 = -\sqrt{7}$, $\operatorname{Re}\lambda_1 > 0$, unstable (c) $\lambda_1 = \frac{-1+\sqrt{13}}{2}$, $\lambda_2 = \frac{-1-\sqrt{13}}{2}$, $\operatorname{Re}\lambda_1 > 0$, unstable (d) $\lambda_1 = 0$, $\lambda_2 = -2$, neutrally stable.

11. A_1 is unstable for $t < 1$, neutrally stable for $t \geq 1$. A_2 is unstable for $t < 4$, neutrally stable at $t = 4$, stable with real λ for $4 < t \leq 5$, and stable with complex λ for $t > 5$. A_3 is unstable for all $t > 0$, because the trace is $2t$.

13. (a) $u_1' = cu_2 - bu_3$, $u_2' = -cu_1 + au_3$, $u_3' = bu_1 - au_2$ gives $u_1'u_1 + u_2'u_2 + u_3'u_3 = 0$. (b) Because e^{At} is an orthogonal matrix, $\|u(t)\|^2 = \|e^{At}u(0)\|^2 = \|u(0)\|^2$ is constant. (c) $\lambda = 0$ and $\pm(\sqrt{a^2+b^2+c^2})i$. Skew-symmetric matrices have pure imaginary λ's.

15. $u(t) = \frac{1}{2}\cos 2t \begin{bmatrix} 1 \\ -1 \end{bmatrix} + \frac{1}{2}\cos\sqrt{6}t \begin{bmatrix} 1 \\ 1 \end{bmatrix}$.

17. $Ax = \lambda Fx + \lambda^2 x$ or $(A - \lambda F - \lambda^2 I)x = 0$.

19. Eigenvalues are real when $(\text{trace})^2 - 4\det \geq 0 \Rightarrow -4(-a^2 - b^2 + c^2) \geq 0 \Rightarrow a^2 + b^2 \geq c^2$.

21. $u_1 = e^{4t}\begin{bmatrix} 1 \\ 0 \end{bmatrix}$, $u_2 = e^t \begin{bmatrix} 1 \\ -1 \end{bmatrix}$. If $u(0) = (5, -2)$, then $u(t) = 3e^{4t}\begin{bmatrix} 1 \\ 0 \end{bmatrix} + 2e^t\begin{bmatrix} 1 \\ -1 \end{bmatrix}$.

23. $\begin{bmatrix} y' \\ y'' \end{bmatrix} = \begin{bmatrix} 0 & 1 \\ 4 & 5 \end{bmatrix}\begin{bmatrix} y \\ y' \end{bmatrix}$. Then $\lambda = \frac{1}{2}(5 \pm \sqrt{41})$.

25. $\lambda_1 = 0$ and $\lambda_2 = 2$. Now $v(t) = 20 + 10e^{2t} \to \infty$ as $t \to \infty$.

27. $A = \begin{bmatrix} 0 & 1 \\ -9 & 6 \end{bmatrix}$ has trace 6, det 9, $\lambda = 3$ and 3, with only one independent eigenvector $(1, 3)$. That gives $y = ce^{3t}$, $y' = 3e^{3t}$. Also te^{3t} solves $y'' = 6y' - 9y$.

29. $y(t) = \cos t$ starts at $y(0) = 1$ and $y'(0) = 0$. The vector equation has $u = (y, y') = (\cos t, -\sin t)$.

31. Substituting $u = e^{ct}v$ gives $ce^{ct}v = Ae^{ct}v - e^{ct}b$, or $(A - cI)v = b$, or $v = (A - cI)^{-1}b =$ particular solution. If c is an eigenvalue, then $A - cI$ is not invertible: this v fails.

33. $de^{At}/dt = A + A^2t + \frac{1}{2}A^3t^2 + \frac{1}{6}A^4t^3 + \cdots = A(I + At + \frac{1}{2}A^2t^2 + \frac{1}{6}A^3t^3 + \cdots) = Ae^{At}$.

35. The solution at time $t + T$ is also $e^{A(t+T)}u(0)$. Thus e^{At} times e^{AT} equals $e^{A(t+T)}$.

37. If $A^2 = A$ then $e^{At} = I + At + \frac{1}{2}At^2 + \frac{1}{6}At^3 + \cdots = I + (e^t - 1)A$

$= \begin{bmatrix} 1 & 0 \\ 0 & 1 \end{bmatrix} + \begin{bmatrix} e^t - 1 & e^t - 1 \\ 0 & 0 \end{bmatrix} = \begin{bmatrix} e^t & e^t - 1 \\ 0 & 1 \end{bmatrix}$.

39. $A = \begin{bmatrix} 1 & 1 \\ 0 & 3 \end{bmatrix} = \begin{bmatrix} 1 & 1 \\ 2 & 0 \end{bmatrix}\begin{bmatrix} 3 & 0 \\ 0 & 1 \end{bmatrix}\begin{bmatrix} 0 & \frac{1}{2} \\ 1 & -\frac{1}{2} \end{bmatrix}$, then $e^{At} = \begin{bmatrix} e^t & \frac{1}{2}(e^{3t} - e^t) \\ 0 & e^{3t} \end{bmatrix} = I$ at $t = 0$.

41. (a) The inverse of e^{At} is e^{-At}. (b) If $Ax = \lambda x$ then $e^{At}x = e^{\lambda t}x$ and $e^{\lambda t} \neq 0$.

43. $\lambda = 2$ and 5 with eigenvectors $\begin{bmatrix} 2 \\ 1 \end{bmatrix}$ and $\begin{bmatrix} 1 \\ 1 \end{bmatrix}$. Then $A = S\Lambda S^{-1} = \begin{bmatrix} -1 & 6 \\ -3 & 8 \end{bmatrix}$.

Problem Set 5.5, page 288

1. (b) sum $= 4 + 3i$; product $= 7 + i$. (c) $\overline{3 + 4i} = 3 - 4i$; $\overline{1 - i} = 1 + i$; $|3 + 4i| = 5$; $|1 - i| = \sqrt{2}$. Both numbers lie *outside* the unit circle.

3. $\overline{x} = 2 - i$, $x\overline{x} = 5$, $xy = -1 + 7i$, $1/x = 2/5 - (1/5)i$, $x/y = 1/2 - (1/2)i$; check that $|xy| = \sqrt{50} = |x||y|$ and $|1/x| = 1/\sqrt{5} = 1/|x|$.

5. (a) $x^2 = r^2e^{i2\theta}$, $x^{-1} = (1/r)e^{-i\theta}$, $\overline{x} = re^{-i\theta}$; $x^{-1} = \overline{x}$ gives $|x|^2 = 1$: on the unit circle.

7. $C = \begin{bmatrix} 1 & -i \\ -i & 0 \\ 0 & 1 \end{bmatrix} \begin{bmatrix} 1 & i & 0 \\ i & 0 & 1 \end{bmatrix} = \begin{bmatrix} 2 & i & -i \\ -i & 1 & 0 \\ i & 0 & 1 \end{bmatrix}$, $C^{\mathrm{H}} = C$ because $(A^{\mathrm{H}}A)^{\mathrm{H}} = A^{\mathrm{H}}A$.

9. (a) $\det A^{\mathrm{T}} = \det A$ but $\det A^{\mathrm{H}} = \overline{\det A}$. (b) $A^{\mathrm{H}} = A$ gives $\overline{\det A} = \det A = \text{real}$.

11. $P: \lambda_1 = 0,\ \lambda_2 = 1,\ x_1 = \begin{bmatrix} 1/\sqrt{2} \\ -1/\sqrt{2} \end{bmatrix},\ x_2 = \begin{bmatrix} 1/\sqrt{2} \\ 1/\sqrt{2} \end{bmatrix}$; $Q: \lambda_1 = 1,\ \lambda_2 = -1,\ x_1 = \begin{bmatrix} 1/\sqrt{2} \\ 1/\sqrt{2} \end{bmatrix},\ x_2 = \begin{bmatrix} 1/\sqrt{2} \\ -1/\sqrt{2} \end{bmatrix}$; $R: \lambda_1 = 5,\ \lambda_2 = -5,\ x_1 = \begin{bmatrix} 2/\sqrt{5} \\ 1/\sqrt{5} \end{bmatrix},\ x_2 = \begin{bmatrix} 1/\sqrt{5} \\ -2/\sqrt{5} \end{bmatrix}$.

13. (a) u, v, w are orthogonal to each other. (b) The nullspace is spanned by u; the left nullspace is the same as the nullspace; the row space is spanned by v and w; the column space is the same as the row space. (c) $x = v + \frac{1}{2}w$; not unique, we can add any multiple of u to x. (d) Need $b^{\mathrm{T}}u = 0$. (e) $S^{-1} = S^{\mathrm{T}}$; $S^{-1}AS = \operatorname{diag}(0, 1, 2)$.

15. The dimension of S is $n(n+1)/2$, not n. Every symmetric matrix A is a combination of n projections, but the projections change as A changes. There is no basis of n fixed projection matrices, in the space **S** of symmetric matrices.

17. $(UV)^{\mathrm{H}}(UV) = V^{\mathrm{H}}U^{\mathrm{H}}UV = V^{\mathrm{H}}IV = I$. So UV is unitary.

19. The third column of U can be $(1, -2, i)/\sqrt{6}$, multiplied by any number $e^{i\theta}$.

21. A has $+1$ or -1 in each diagonal entry; eight possibilities.

23. Columns of Fourier matrix U are eigenvectors of P because $PU = \operatorname{diag}(1, w, w^2, w^3)U$ (and $w = i$).

25. n^2 steps for direct C times x; only $n \log n$ steps for F and F^{-1} by FFT (and n for Λ).

27. $A^{\mathrm{H}}A = \begin{bmatrix} 2 & 0 & 1+i \\ 0 & 2 & 1+i \\ 1-i & 1-i & 2 \end{bmatrix}$ and $AA^{\mathrm{H}} = \begin{bmatrix} 3 & 1 \\ 1 & 3 \end{bmatrix}$ are *Hermitian* matrices.

$(A^{\mathrm{H}}A)^{\mathrm{H}} = A^{\mathrm{H}}A^{\mathrm{HH}} = A^{\mathrm{H}}A$ again.

29. cA is still Hermitian for real c; $(iA)^{\mathrm{H}} = -iA^{\mathrm{H}} = -iA$ is skew-Hermitian.

31. $P^2 = \begin{bmatrix} 0 & 0 & 1 \\ 1 & 0 & 0 \\ 0 & 1 & 0 \end{bmatrix}$, $P^3 = I$, $P^{100} = P^{99}P = P$; $\lambda = $ cube roots of $1 = 1$, $e^{2\pi i/3}$, $e^{4\pi i/3}$.

33. $C = \begin{bmatrix} 2 & 5 & 4 \\ 4 & 2 & 5 \\ 5 & 4 & 2 \end{bmatrix} = 2 + 5P + 4P^2$ has $\lambda(C) = \begin{Bmatrix} 2+5+4 \\ 2 + 5e^{2\pi i/3} + 4e^{4\pi i/3} \\ 2 + 5e^{4\pi i/3} + 4e^{8\pi i/3} \end{Bmatrix}$.

35. $A = \dfrac{1}{\sqrt{3}} \begin{bmatrix} 1 & -1+i \\ 1+i & 1 \end{bmatrix} \begin{bmatrix} 2 & 0 \\ 0 & -1 \end{bmatrix} \dfrac{1}{\sqrt{3}} \begin{bmatrix} 1 & 1-i \\ -1-i & 1 \end{bmatrix}$.

$K = (iA^{\mathrm{T}}) = \dfrac{1}{\sqrt{3}} \begin{bmatrix} 1 & -1-i \\ 1-i & 1 \end{bmatrix} \begin{bmatrix} 2i & 0 \\ 0 & -i \end{bmatrix} \dfrac{1}{\sqrt{3}} \begin{bmatrix} 1 & 1+i \\ -1+i & 1 \end{bmatrix}$.

37. $V = \frac{1}{L}\begin{bmatrix} 1+\sqrt{3} & -1+i \\ 1+i & 1+\sqrt{3} \end{bmatrix}\begin{bmatrix} 1 & 0 \\ 0 & -1 \end{bmatrix}\frac{1}{L}\begin{bmatrix} 1+\sqrt{3} & 1-i \\ -1-i & 1+\sqrt{3} \end{bmatrix}$ with $L^2 = 6+2\sqrt{3}$.
$V = V^{\mathrm{H}}$ gives real λ, unitary gives $|\lambda| = 1$, then trace zero gives $\lambda = 1, -1$.

39. Don't multiply e^{-ix} times e^{ix}; conjugate the first, then $\int_0^{2\pi} e^{2ix}\,dx = [e^{2ix}/2i]_0^{2\pi} = 0$.

41. $R + iS = (R+iS)^{\mathrm{H}} = R^{\mathrm{T}} - iS^{\mathrm{T}}$; R is symmetric but S is skew-symmetric.

43. $[1]$ and $[-1]$; $\begin{bmatrix} a & b+ic \\ b-ic & -a \end{bmatrix}$ with $a^2+b^2+c^2 = 1$.

45. $(I - 2uu^{\mathrm{H}})^{\mathrm{H}} = I - 2uu^{\mathrm{H}}$; $(I-2uu^{\mathrm{H}})^2 = I - 4uu^{\mathrm{H}} + 4u(u^{\mathrm{H}}u)u^{\mathrm{H}} = I$; the matrix uu^{H} projects onto the line through u.

47. We are given $A + iB = (A+iB)^{\mathrm{H}} = A^{\mathrm{T}} - iB^{\mathrm{T}}$. Then $A = A^{\mathrm{T}}$ and $B = -B^{\mathrm{T}}$.

49. $A = \begin{bmatrix} 1-i & 1-i \\ -1 & 2 \end{bmatrix}\begin{bmatrix} 1 & 0 \\ 0 & 4 \end{bmatrix}\frac{1}{6}\begin{bmatrix} 2+2i & -2 \\ 1+i & 2 \end{bmatrix} = S\Lambda S^{-1}$. Real eigenvalues 1 and 4.

Problem Set 5.6, page 302

1. $C = N^{-1}BN = N^{-1}M^{-1}AMN = (MN)^{-1}A(MN)$; only $M^{-1}IM = I$ is similar to I.

3. If $\lambda_1, \ldots, \lambda_n$ are eigenvalues of A, then $\lambda_1 + 1, \ldots, \lambda_n + 1$ are eigenvalues of $A + I$. So A and $A + I$ never have the same eigenvalues, and can't be similar.

5. If B is invertible, then $BA = B(AB)B^{-1}$ is similar to AB.

7. The $(3, 1)$ entry of $M^{-1}AM$ is $g\cos\theta + h\sin\theta$, which is zero if $\tan\theta = -g/h$.

9. The coefficients are $c_1 = 1$, $c_2 = 2$, $d_1 = 1$, $d_2 = 1$; check $Mc = d$.

11. The reflection matrix with basis v_1 and v_2 is $A = \begin{bmatrix} 0 & 1 \\ 1 & 0 \end{bmatrix}$. The basis V_1 and V_2 (same reflection!) gives $B = \begin{bmatrix} 1 & 0 \\ 0 & -1 \end{bmatrix}$. If $M = \begin{bmatrix} 1 & 1 \\ 1 & -1 \end{bmatrix}$ then $A = MBM^{-1}$.

13. (a) $D = \begin{bmatrix} 0 & 1 & 0 \\ 0 & 0 & 2 \\ 0 & 0 & 0 \end{bmatrix}$. (b) $D^3 = \begin{bmatrix} 0 & 0 & 0 \\ 0 & 0 & 0 \\ 0 & 0 & 0 \end{bmatrix}$ = third derivative matrix. The third derivatives of 1, x, and x^2 are zero, so $D^3 = 0$. (c) $\lambda = 0$ (triple); only one independent eigenvector $(1, 0, 0)$.

15. The eigenvalues are $1, 1, 1, -1$. Eigenmatrices $\begin{bmatrix} 1 & 0 \\ 0 & 0 \end{bmatrix}, \begin{bmatrix} 0 & 1 \\ 1 & 0 \end{bmatrix}, \begin{bmatrix} 0 & 0 \\ 0 & 1 \end{bmatrix}, \begin{bmatrix} 0 & 1 \\ -1 & 0 \end{bmatrix}$.

17. (a) $TT^{\mathrm{H}} = U^{-1}AUU^{\mathrm{H}}A^{\mathrm{H}}(U^{-1})^{\mathrm{H}} = I$. (b) If T is triangular and unitary, then its diagonal entries (the eigenvalues) must have absolute value 1. Then all off-diagonal entries are zero because the columns are to be unit vectors.

19. The 1, 1 entries of $T^{\mathrm{H}}T = TT^{\mathrm{H}}$ give $|t_{11}|^2 = |t_{11}|^2 + |t_{12}|^2 + |t_{13}|^2$ so $t_{12} = t_{13} = 0$. Comparing the 2, 2 entries of $T^{\mathrm{H}}T = TT^{\mathrm{H}}$ gives $t_{23} = 0$. So T must be diagonal.

21. If $N = U\Lambda U^{-1}$, then $NN^{\mathrm{H}} = U\Lambda U^{-1}(U^{-1})^{\mathrm{H}}\Lambda^{\mathrm{H}}U^{\mathrm{H}}$ is equal to $U\Lambda\Lambda^{\mathrm{H}}U^{\mathrm{H}}$. This is the same as $U\Lambda^{\mathrm{H}}\Lambda U^{\mathrm{H}} = (U\Lambda U^{-1})^{\mathrm{H}}(U\Lambda U^{-1}) = N^{\mathrm{H}}N$. So N is normal.

23. The eigenvalues of $A(A-I)(A-2I)$ are 0, 0, 0.

25. Always $\begin{bmatrix} a^2+bc & ab+bd \\ ac+cd & bc+d^2 \end{bmatrix} - (a+d)\begin{bmatrix} a & b \\ c & d \end{bmatrix} + (ad-bc)\begin{bmatrix} 1 & 0 \\ 0 & 1 \end{bmatrix} = \begin{bmatrix} 0 & 0 \\ 0 & 0 \end{bmatrix}!$

27. $M^{-1}J_3M = 0$, so the last two inequalities are easy. Trying for $MJ_1 = J_2M$ forces the first column of M to be zero, so M cannot be invertible. Cannot have $J_1 = M^{-1}J_2M$.

29. $A^{10} = 2^{10}\begin{bmatrix} 61 & 45 \\ -80 & -59 \end{bmatrix}$; $e^A = e^2\begin{bmatrix} 13 & 9 \\ -16 & -11 \end{bmatrix}$.

31. $\begin{bmatrix} 1 & 1 \\ 0 & 0 \end{bmatrix}, \begin{bmatrix} 0 & 0 \\ 1 & 1 \end{bmatrix}, \begin{bmatrix} 1 & 0 \\ 1 & 0 \end{bmatrix}, \begin{bmatrix} 0 & 1 \\ 0 & 1 \end{bmatrix}$ are similar; $\begin{bmatrix} 1 & 0 \\ 0 & 1 \end{bmatrix}$ by itself and $\begin{bmatrix} 0 & 1 \\ 1 & 0 \end{bmatrix}$ by itself.

33. (a) $(M^{-1}AM)(M^{-1}x) = M^{-1}(Ax) = M^{-1}0 = 0$. (b) The nullspaces of A and of $M^{-1}AM$ have the same *dimension*. Different vectors and different bases.

35. $J^2 = \begin{bmatrix} c^2 & 2c \\ 0 & c^2 \end{bmatrix}$, $J^3 = \begin{bmatrix} c^3 & 3c^2 \\ 0 & c^3 \end{bmatrix}$, $J^k = \begin{bmatrix} c^k & kc^{k-1} \\ 0 & c^k \end{bmatrix}$; $J^0 = I$, $J^{-1} = \begin{bmatrix} c^{-1} & -c^{-2} \\ 0 & c^{-1} \end{bmatrix}$.

37. $w(t) = \left(w(0) + tx(0) + \frac{1}{2}t^2y(0) + \frac{1}{6}t^3z(0)\right)e^{5t}$.

39. (a) Choose M_i = reverse diagonal matrix to get $M_i^{-1}J_iM_i = M_i^{\mathrm{T}}$ in each block (b) M_0 has those blocks M_i on its diagonal to get $M_0^{-1}JM_0 = J^{\mathrm{T}}$.
(c) $A^{\mathrm{T}} = (M^{-1})^{\mathrm{T}}J^{\mathrm{T}}M^{\mathrm{T}}$ is $(M^{-1})^{\mathrm{T}}M_0^{-1}JM_0M^{\mathrm{T}} = (MM_0M^{\mathrm{T}})^{-1}A(MM_0M^{\mathrm{T}})$, and A^{T} is similar to A.

41. (a) True: One has $\lambda = 0$, the other doesn't. (b) False. Diagonalize a nonsymmetric matrix and Λ is symmetric. (c) False: $\begin{bmatrix} 0 & 1 \\ -1 & 0 \end{bmatrix}$ and $\begin{bmatrix} 0 & -1 \\ 1 & 0 \end{bmatrix}$ are similar.
(d) True: All eigenvalues of $A+I$ are increased by 1, thus different from the eigenvalues of A.

43. Diagonals 6 by 6 and 4 by 4; AB has all the same eigenvalues as BA plus $6-4$ zeros.

Problem Set 6.1, page 316

1. $ac - b^2 = 2 - 4 = -2 < 0$; $x^2 + 4xy + 2y^2 = (x+2y)^2 - 2y^2$ (difference of squares).

3. $\det(A - \lambda I) = \lambda^2 - (a+c)\lambda + ac - b^2 = 0$ gives $\lambda_1 = ((a+c) + \sqrt{(a-c)^2 + b^2})/2$ and $\lambda_2 = ((a+c) - \sqrt{(a-c)^2 + 4b^2})/2)$; $\lambda_1 > 0$ is a sum of positive numbers; $\lambda_2 > 0$ because $(a+c)^2 > (a-c)^2 + 4b^2$ reduces to $ac > b^2$. Better way: product $\lambda_1\lambda_2 = ac - b^2$.

5. (a) Positive definite when $-3 < b < 3$.
(b) $\begin{bmatrix} 1 & b \\ b & 9 \end{bmatrix} = \begin{bmatrix} 1 & 0 \\ b & 1 \end{bmatrix}\begin{bmatrix} 1 & 0 \\ 0 & 9-b^2 \end{bmatrix}\begin{bmatrix} 1 & b \\ 0 & 1 \end{bmatrix}$. (c) The minimum is $-\dfrac{1}{2(9-b^2)}$ when $\begin{bmatrix} 1 & b \\ b & 9 \end{bmatrix}\begin{bmatrix} x \\ y \end{bmatrix} = \begin{bmatrix} 0 \\ 1 \end{bmatrix}$, which is $\begin{bmatrix} x \\ y \end{bmatrix} = \dfrac{1}{9-b^2}\begin{bmatrix} -b \\ 1 \end{bmatrix}$. (d) No minimum, let $y \to \infty$, $x = -3y$, then $x - y$ approaches $-\infty$.

7. (a) $A_1 = \begin{bmatrix} 1 & -1 & -1 \\ -1 & 1 & 1 \\ -1 & 1 & 1 \end{bmatrix}$ and $A_2 = \begin{bmatrix} 1 & -1 & -1 \\ -1 & 2 & -2 \\ -1 & -2 & 11 \end{bmatrix}$.

(b) $f_1 = (x_1 - x_2 - x_3)^2 = 0$ when $x_1 - x_2 - x_3 = 0$.

(c) $f_2 = (x_1 - x_2 - x_3)^2 + (x_2 - 3x_3)^2 + x_3^2$; $L = \begin{bmatrix} 1 & 0 & 0 \\ -1 & 1 & 0 \\ -1 & -3 & 1 \end{bmatrix}$.

9. $A = \begin{bmatrix} 3 & 6 \\ 6 & 16 \end{bmatrix} = \begin{bmatrix} 1 & 0 \\ 2 & 1 \end{bmatrix} \begin{bmatrix} 3 & 0 \\ 0 & 4 \end{bmatrix} \begin{bmatrix} 1 & 2 \\ 0 & 1 \end{bmatrix}$; the coefficients of the squares are the pivots in D, whereas the coefficients inside the squares are columns of L.

11. (a) Pivots are a and $c - |b|^2/a$ and $\det A = ac - |b|^2$. (b) Multiply $|x_2|^2$ by $(c - |b|^2/a)$. (c) Now $x^{\mathrm{H}}Ax$ is a sum of squares. (d) $\det = -1$ (indefinite) and $\det = +1$ (positive definite).

13. $a > 1$ and $(a-1)(c-1) > b^2$. This means that $A - I$ is positive definite.

15. $f(x, y) = x^2 + 4xy + 9y^2 = (x + 2y)^2 + 5y^2$; $f(x, y) = x^2 + 6xy + 9y^2 = (x + 3y)^2$.

17. $x^{\mathrm{T}}A^{\mathrm{T}}Ax = (Ax)^{\mathrm{T}}(Ax) =$ length squared $= 0$ only if $Ax = 0$. Since A has independent columns, this only happens when $x = 0$.

19. $A = \begin{bmatrix} 4 & -4 & 8 \\ -4 & 4 & -8 \\ 8 & -8 & 16 \end{bmatrix}$ has only one pivot $= 4$, rank $= 1$, eigenvalues $24, 0, 0$, $\det A = 0$.

21. $ax^2 + 2bxy + cy^2$ has a saddle point at $(0, 0)$ if $ac < b^2$. The matrix is *indefinite* ($\lambda < 0$ and $\lambda > 0$).

Problem Set 6.2, page 326

1. A is positive definite for $a > 2$. B is never positive definite: notice $\begin{bmatrix} 1 & 4 \\ 4 & 7 \end{bmatrix}$.

3. $\det A = -2b^3 - 3b^2 + 1$ is negative at (and near) $b = \frac{2}{3}$.

5. If $x^{\mathrm{T}}Ax > 0$ and $x^{\mathrm{T}}Bx > 0$ for any $x \neq 0$, then $x^{\mathrm{T}}(A + B)x > 0$; condition (I).

7. Positive λ's because R is symmetric and $\sqrt{\Lambda} > 0$. $R = \begin{bmatrix} 3 & 1 \\ 1 & 3 \end{bmatrix}$; $R = \begin{bmatrix} 3 & -1 \\ -1 & 3 \end{bmatrix}$.

9. $|x^{\mathrm{T}}Ay|^2 = |x^{\mathrm{T}}R^{\mathrm{T}}Ry|^2 = |(Rx)^{\mathrm{T}}Ry|^2 \le$ (by the ordinary Schwarz inequality) $\|Rx\|^2\|Ry\|^2 = (x^{\mathrm{T}}R^{\mathrm{T}}Rx)(y^{\mathrm{T}}R^{\mathrm{T}}Ry) = (x^{\mathrm{T}}Ax)(y^{\mathrm{T}}Ay)$.

11. $A = \begin{bmatrix} 3 & -\sqrt{2} \\ -\sqrt{2} & 2 \end{bmatrix}$ has $\lambda = 1$ and 4, axes $1 \begin{bmatrix} 1 \\ \sqrt{2} \end{bmatrix}$ and $\frac{1}{2} \begin{bmatrix} \sqrt{2} \\ -1 \end{bmatrix}$ along eigenvectors.

13. *Negative definite matrices*: (I) $x^{\mathrm{T}}Ax < 0$ for all nonzero vectors x. (II) All the eigenvalues of A satisfy $\lambda_i < 0$. (III) $\det A_1 < 0$, $\det A_2 > 0$, $\det A_3 < 0$.

(IV) All the pivots (without row exchanges) satisfy $d_i < 0$. (V) There is a matrix R with independent columns such that $A = -R^{\mathrm{T}}R$.

15. False (Q must contain eigenvectors of A); True (same eigenvalues as A); True ($Q^{\mathrm{T}}AQ = Q^{-1}AQ$ is similar to A); True (eigenvalues of e^{-A} are $e^{-\lambda} > 0$).

17. Start from a_{jj} = (row j of R^{T})(column j of R) = length squared of column j of R. Then $\det A = (\det R)^2$ = (volume of the R parallelepiped)$^2 \le$ product of the lengths squared of all the columns of R. This product is $a_{11}a_{22}\cdots a_{nn}$.

19. $A = \begin{bmatrix} 2 & -1 & 0 \\ -1 & 2 & -1 \\ 0 & -1 & 2 \end{bmatrix}$ has pivots $2, \frac{3}{2}, \frac{4}{3}$; $A = \begin{bmatrix} 2 & -1 & -1 \\ -1 & 2 & -1 \\ -1 & -1 & 2 \end{bmatrix}$ is singular;

$$A\begin{bmatrix} 1 \\ 1 \\ 1 \end{bmatrix} = \begin{bmatrix} 0 \\ 0 \\ 0 \end{bmatrix}.$$

21. $x^{\mathrm{T}}Ax$ is not positive when $(x_1, x_2, x_3) = (0, 1, 0)$ because of the zero on the diagonal.

23. (a) Positive definite requires positive determinant (also: all $\lambda > 0$). (b) All projection matrices except I are singular. (c) The diagonal entries of D are its eigenvalues. (d) The negative definite matrix $-I$ has det $= +1$ when n is even.

25. $\lambda_1 = 1/a^2$ and $\lambda_2 = 1/b^2$, so $a = 1/\sqrt{\lambda_1}$ and $b = 1/\sqrt{\lambda_2}$. The ellipse $9x^2 + 16y^2 = 1$ has axes with half-lengths $a = \frac{1}{3}$ and $b = \frac{1}{4}$.

27. $A = \begin{bmatrix} 9 & 3 \\ 3 & 5 \end{bmatrix} = \begin{bmatrix} 3 & 0 \\ 1 & 2 \end{bmatrix}\begin{bmatrix} 3 & 1 \\ 0 & 2 \end{bmatrix}$; $C = \begin{bmatrix} 2 & 0 \\ 4 & 3 \end{bmatrix}$ has $CC^{\mathrm{T}} = \begin{bmatrix} 4 & 8 \\ 8 & 25 \end{bmatrix}$.

29. $ax^2 + 2bxy + cy^2 = a\left(x + \frac{b}{a}y\right)^2 + \frac{ac-b^2}{a}y^2$; $2x^2 + 8xy + 10y^2 = 2(x+2y)^2 + 2y^2$.

31. $x^{\mathrm{T}}Ax = 2\left(x_1 - \frac{1}{2}x_2 - \frac{1}{2}x_3\right)^2 + \frac{3}{2}(x_2 - x_3)^2$; $x^{\mathrm{T}}Bx = (x_1 + x_2 + x_3)^2$. B has one pivot.

33. A and $C^{\mathrm{T}}AC$ have $\lambda_1 > 0$, $\lambda_2 = 0$. $C(t) = tQ + (1-t)QR$, $Q = \begin{bmatrix} 1 & 0 \\ 0 & -1 \end{bmatrix}$, $R = \begin{bmatrix} 2 & 0 \\ 0 & 1 \end{bmatrix}$; C has one positive and one negative eigenvalue, but I has two positive eigenvalues.

35. The pivots of $A - \frac{1}{2}I$ are 2.5, 5.9, -0.81, so one eigenvalue of $A - \frac{1}{2}I$ is negative. Then A has an eigenvalue smaller than $\frac{1}{2}$.

37. $\operatorname{rank}(C^{\mathrm{T}}AC) \le \operatorname{rank} A$, but also $\operatorname{rank}(C^{\mathrm{T}}AC) \ge \operatorname{rank}((C^{\mathrm{T}})^{-1}C^{\mathrm{T}}ACC^{-1}) = \operatorname{rank} A$.

39. No. If C is not square, $C^{\mathrm{T}}AC$ is not the same size matrix as A.

41. $\det\begin{bmatrix} 6 - 4\lambda/18 & -3 - \lambda/18 \\ -3 - \lambda/18 & 6 - 4\lambda/18 \end{bmatrix} = 0$ gives $\lambda_1 = 54$, $\lambda_2 = \dfrac{54}{5}$.

Eigenvectors $\begin{bmatrix} 1 \\ -1 \end{bmatrix}, \begin{bmatrix} 1 \\ 1 \end{bmatrix}$.

43. *Groups*: orthogonal matrices; e^{tA} for all t; all matrices with det $= 1$. If A is positive definite, the group of all powers A^k contains only positive definite matrices.

Problem Set 6.3, page 337

1. $A^{\mathrm{T}}A = \begin{bmatrix} 5 & 20 \\ 20 & 80 \end{bmatrix}$ has only $\sigma_1^2 = 85$ with $v_1 = \begin{bmatrix} 1/\sqrt{17} \\ 4/\sqrt{17} \end{bmatrix}$, so $v_2 = \begin{bmatrix} 4/\sqrt{17} \\ -1/\sqrt{17} \end{bmatrix}$.

3. $A^{\mathrm{T}}A = \begin{bmatrix} 2 & 1 \\ 1 & 1 \end{bmatrix}$ has eigenvalues $\sigma_1^2 = \dfrac{3+\sqrt{5}}{2}$ and $\sigma_2^2 = \dfrac{3-\sqrt{5}}{2}$.

Since $A = A^{\mathrm{T}}$, the eigenvectors of $A^{\mathrm{T}}A$ are the same as for A. Since $\lambda_2 = \frac{1}{2}(1-\sqrt{5})$ is *negative*, $\sigma_1 = \lambda_1$ but $\sigma_2 = -\lambda_2$. The unit eigenvectors are the same as in Section 6.2 for A, except for the effect of this minus sign (because we need $Av_2 = \sigma_2 u_2$):

$$u_1 = v_1 = \begin{bmatrix} \lambda_1/\sqrt{1+\lambda_1^2} \\ 1/\sqrt{1+\lambda_1^2} \end{bmatrix} \text{ and } u_2 = -v_2 = \begin{bmatrix} \lambda_2/\sqrt{1+\lambda_2^2} \\ 1/\sqrt{1+\lambda_2^2} \end{bmatrix}.$$

5. $AA^{\mathrm{T}} = \begin{bmatrix} 2 & 1 \\ 1 & 2 \end{bmatrix}$ has $\sigma_1^2 = 3$ with $u_1 = \begin{bmatrix} 1/\sqrt{2} \\ 1/\sqrt{2} \end{bmatrix}$ and $\sigma_2^2 = 1$ with $u_2 = \begin{bmatrix} 1/\sqrt{2} \\ -1/\sqrt{2} \end{bmatrix}$.

$A^{\mathrm{T}}A = \begin{bmatrix} 1 & 1 & 0 \\ 1 & 2 & 1 \\ 0 & 1 & 1 \end{bmatrix}$ has $\sigma_1^2 = 3$ with $v_1 = \begin{bmatrix} 1/\sqrt{6} \\ 2/\sqrt{6} \\ 1/\sqrt{6} \end{bmatrix}$, $\sigma_2^2 = 1$ with $v_2 = \begin{bmatrix} 1/\sqrt{2} \\ 0 \\ -1/\sqrt{2} \end{bmatrix}$,

and nullvector $v_3 = \begin{bmatrix} 1/\sqrt{3} \\ -1/\sqrt{3} \\ 1/\sqrt{3} \end{bmatrix}$.

Then $\begin{bmatrix} 1 & 1 & 0 \\ 0 & 1 & 1 \end{bmatrix} = [u_1 \quad u_2] \begin{bmatrix} \sqrt{3} & 0 & 0 \\ 0 & 1 & 0 \end{bmatrix} [v_1 \quad v_2 \quad v_3]^{\mathrm{T}}$.

7. $A = 12\,uv^{\mathrm{T}}$ has one singular value $\sigma_1 = 12$.

9. Multiply $U\Sigma V^{\mathrm{T}}$ using columns (of U) times rows (of ΣV^{T}).

11. To make A singular, the smallest change sets its smallest singular value σ_2 to zero.

13. The singular values of $A + I$ are not $\sigma_j + 1$. They come from eigenvalues of $(A+I)^{\mathrm{T}}(A+I)$.

15. $A^+ = \begin{bmatrix} \frac{1}{4} \\ \frac{1}{4} \\ \frac{1}{4} \\ \frac{1}{4} \end{bmatrix}$, $B = \begin{bmatrix} 0 & 1 \\ 1 & 0 \end{bmatrix} \begin{bmatrix} 1 & 0 & 0 \\ 0 & 1 & 0 \end{bmatrix} \begin{bmatrix} 1 & 0 & 0 \\ 0 & 1 & 0 \\ 0 & 0 & 1 \end{bmatrix}$, $B^+ = \begin{bmatrix} 0 & 1 \\ 1 & 0 \\ 0 & 0 \end{bmatrix}$, $C^+ = \begin{bmatrix} \frac{1}{2} & 0 \\ \frac{1}{2} & 0 \end{bmatrix}$.

A^+ is the right-inverse of A; B^+ is the left-inverse of B.

17. $A^{\mathrm{T}}A = \begin{bmatrix} 10 & 6 \\ 6 & 10 \end{bmatrix} = \dfrac{1}{2}\begin{bmatrix} 1 & -1 \\ 1 & 1 \end{bmatrix}\begin{bmatrix} 4 & 0 \\ 0 & 16 \end{bmatrix}\begin{bmatrix} 1 & 1 \\ -1 & 1 \end{bmatrix}$, take square roots of 4 and 16 to obtain $S = \dfrac{1}{2}\begin{bmatrix} 1 & -1 \\ 1 & 1 \end{bmatrix}\begin{bmatrix} 2 & 0 \\ 0 & 4 \end{bmatrix}\begin{bmatrix} 1 & 1 \\ -1 & 1 \end{bmatrix} = \begin{bmatrix} 3 & 1 \\ 1 & 3 \end{bmatrix}$ and $Q = AS^{-1} = \dfrac{1}{\sqrt{10}}\begin{bmatrix} 3 & 1 \\ -1 & 3 \end{bmatrix}$.

19. (a) With independent columns, the row space is all of $\mathbf{R}^n$; check $(A^{\mathrm{T}}A)A^+b = A^{\mathrm{T}}b$. (b) $A^{\mathrm{T}}(AA^{\mathrm{T}})^{-1}b$ is in the row space because A^{T} times any vector is in that space; now $(A^{\mathrm{T}}A)A^+b = A^{\mathrm{T}}AA^{\mathrm{T}}(AA^{\mathrm{T}})^{-1}b = A^{\mathrm{T}}b$. Both cases give $A^{\mathrm{T}}Ax^+ = A^{\mathrm{T}}b$.

21. Take $A = \begin{bmatrix} 1 & 1 \\ 0 & 0 \end{bmatrix}$ and $B = \begin{bmatrix} 0 & 0 \\ 1 & 1 \end{bmatrix}$. Then $AB = \begin{bmatrix} 1 & 1 \\ 0 & 0 \end{bmatrix}$. From C^+ in Problem 15 we have $A^+ = \begin{bmatrix} \frac{1}{2} & 0 \\ \frac{1}{2} & 0 \end{bmatrix}$, $B^+ = \begin{bmatrix} 0 & \frac{1}{2} \\ 0 & \frac{1}{2} \end{bmatrix} = (AB)^+$, and $(AB)^+ \neq B^+A^+$.

23. $A = Q_1 \Sigma Q_2^{\mathrm{T}} \Rightarrow A^+ = Q_2 \Sigma^+ Q_1^{\mathrm{T}} \Rightarrow AA^+ = Q_1 \Sigma \Sigma^+ Q_1^{\mathrm{T}}$. Squaring gives $(AA^+)^2 = Q_1 \Sigma \Sigma^+ \Sigma \Sigma^+ Q_1^{\mathrm{T}} = Q_1 \Sigma \Sigma^+ Q_1^{\mathrm{T}}$. So we have projections: $(AA^+)^2 = AA^+ = (AA^+)^{\mathrm{T}}$ and similarly for A^+A. AA^+ and A^+A project onto the column space and row space of A.

Problem Set 6.4, page 344

1. $P(x) = x_1^2 - x_1x_2 + x_2^2 - x_2x_3 + x_3^2 - 4x_1 - 4x_3$ has $\partial P/\partial x_1 = 2x_1 - x_2 - 4$, $\partial P/\partial x_2 = -x_1 + 2x_2 - x_3$, and $\partial P/\partial x_3 = -x_2 + 2x_3 - 4$.

3. $\partial P_1/\partial x = x + y = 0$ and $\partial P_1/\partial y = x + 2y - 3 = 0$ give $x = -3$ and $y = 3$. P_2 has no minimum (let $y \to \infty$). It is associated with the semidefinite matrix $\begin{bmatrix} 1 & 0 \\ 0 & 0 \end{bmatrix}$.

5. Put $x = (1, \ldots, 1)$ in Rayleigh's quotient (the denominator becomes n). Since $R(x)$ is always between λ_1 and λ_n, we get $n\lambda_1 \le x^{\mathrm{T}}Ax = \textit{sum of all } a_{ij} \le n\lambda_n$.

7. Since $x^{\mathrm{T}}Bx > 0$ for all nonzero vectors x, $x^{\mathrm{T}}(A+B)x$ will be larger than $x^{\mathrm{T}}Ax$. So the Rayleigh quotient is larger for $A+B$ (in fact all n eigenvalues are increased).

9. Since $x^{\mathrm{T}}Bx > 0$, the Rayleigh quotient for $A+B$ is larger than the quotient for A.

11. The smallest eigenvalues in $Ax = \lambda x$ and $Ax = \lambda Mx$ are $\frac{1}{2}$ and $(3 - \sqrt{3})/4$.

13. (a) $\lambda_j = \min_{S_j}[\max_{x \text{ in } S_j} R(x)] > 0$ means that every S_j contains a vector x with $R(x) > 0$. (b) $y = C^{-1}x$ gives quotient $\overline{R}(y) = \dfrac{y^{\mathrm{T}}C^{\mathrm{T}}ACy}{y^{\mathrm{T}}y} = \dfrac{x^{\mathrm{T}}Ax}{x^{\mathrm{T}}x} = R(x) > 0$.

15. The extreme subspace S_2 is spanned by the eigenvectors x_1 and x_2.

17. If $Cx = C(A^{-1}b)$ equals d then $CA^{-1}b - d$ is zero in the correction term in equation (5).

Problem Set 6.5, page 350

1. $Ay = b$ is $4\begin{bmatrix} 2 & -1 & 0 \\ -1 & 2 & -1 \\ 0 & -1 & 2 \end{bmatrix}\begin{bmatrix} 3/16 \\ 4/16 \\ 3/16 \end{bmatrix} = b = \begin{bmatrix} 1/2 \\ 1/2 \\ 1/2 \end{bmatrix}$. The linear finite element $U = \frac{3}{16}V_1 + \frac{4}{16}V_2 + \frac{3}{16}V_3$ equals the exact $u = \frac{3}{16}, \frac{4}{16}, \frac{3}{16}$ at the nodes $x = \frac{1}{4}, \frac{1}{2}, \frac{3}{4}$.

3. $A_{33} = 3$, $b_3 = \frac{1}{3}$. Then $A = 3\begin{bmatrix} 2 & -1 & 0 \\ -1 & 2 & -1 \\ 0 & -1 & 1 \end{bmatrix}$, $b = \dfrac{1}{3}\begin{bmatrix} 2 \\ 2 \\ 1 \end{bmatrix}$, $Ay = b$ gives $y = \dfrac{1}{9}\begin{bmatrix} 5 \\ 8 \\ 9 \end{bmatrix}$.

5. Integrate by parts: $\int_0^1 -V_i''V_j\,dx = \int_0^1 V_i'V_j'\,dx - \left[V_i'V_j\right]_{x=0}^{x=1} = \int_0^1 V_i'V_j'\,dx =$ same A_{ij}.

7. $A = 4$, $M = \frac{1}{3}$. Their ratio 12 (Rayleigh quotient on the subspace of multiples of $V(x)$) is *larger* than the true eigenvalue $\lambda = \pi^2$.

9. The mass matrix M is $h/6$ times the 1, 4, 1 tridiagonal matrix.

Problem Set 7.2, page 357

1. If Q is orthogonal, its norm is $\|Q\| = \max \|Qx\|/\|x\| = 1$ because Q preserves length: $\|Qx\| = \|x\|$ for every x. Also Q^{-1} is orthogonal and has norm one, so $c(Q) = 1$.

3. $\|ABx\| \le \|A\|\|Bx\|$, by the definition of the norm of A, and then $\|Bx\| \le \|B\|\|x\|$. Dividing by $\|x\|$ and maximizing, $\|AB\| \le \|A\|\|B\|$. The same is true for the inverse, $\|B^{-1}A^{-1}\| \le \|B^{-1}\|\|A^{-1}\|$; $c(AB) \le c(A)c(B)$ by multiplying these inequalities.

5. In the definition $\|A\| = \max \|Ax\|/\|x\|$, choose x to be the particular eigenvector in question; $\|Ax\| = |\lambda|\|x\|$, so the ratio is $|\lambda|$ and *maximum* ratio is *at least* $|\lambda|$.

7. $A^{\mathrm{T}}A$ and AA^{T} have the same eigenvalues, since $A^{\mathrm{T}}Ax = \lambda x$ gives $AA^{\mathrm{T}}(Ax) = A(A^{\mathrm{T}}Ax) = \lambda(Ax)$. Equality of the largest eigenvalues means $\|A\| = \|A^{\mathrm{T}}\|$.

9. $A = \begin{bmatrix} 0 & 1 \\ 0 & 0 \end{bmatrix}$, $B = \begin{bmatrix} 0 & 0 \\ 1 & 0 \end{bmatrix}$, $\lambda_{\max}(A+B) > \lambda_{\max}(A) + \lambda_{\max}(B)$ (since $1 > 0 + 0$), and $\lambda_{\max}(AB) > \lambda_{\max}(A)\lambda_{\max}(B)$. So $\lambda_{\max}(A)$ is not a norm.

11. (a) Yes, $c(A) = \|A\|\,\|A^{-1}\| = c(A^{-1})$, since $(A^{-1})^{-1}$ is A again. (b) $A^{-1}b = x$ leads to $\dfrac{\|\delta b\|}{\|b\|} \le \|A\|\,\|A^{-1}\|\dfrac{\|\delta x\|}{\|x\|}$. This is $\dfrac{\|\delta x\|}{\|x\|} \ge \dfrac{1}{c}\dfrac{\|\delta b\|}{\|b\|}$.

13. $\|A\| = 2$ and $c = 1$; $\|A\| = \sqrt{2}$ and c is infinite (singular !); $\|A\| = \sqrt{2}$ and $c = 1$.

15. If $\lambda_{\max} = \lambda_{\min} = 1$, then all $\lambda_i = 1$ and $A = SIS^{-1} = I$. The only matrices with $\|A\| = \|A^{-1}\| = 1$ are *orthogonal matrices*, because $A^{\mathrm{T}}A$ has to be I.

17. The residual $b - Ay = (10^{-7}, 0)$ is much smaller than $b - Az = (.0013, .0016)$. But z is much closer to the solution than y.

19. $x_1^2 + \cdots + x_n^2$ is not smaller than $\max(x_i^2) = (\|x\|_\infty)^2$ and not larger than $(|x_1| + \cdots + |x_n|)^2$, which is $(\|x\|_1)^2$. Certainly $x_1^2 + \cdots + x_n^2 \le n \max(x_i^2)$, so $\|x\| \le \sqrt{n}\|x\|_\infty$. Choose $y = (\operatorname{sign} x_1, \operatorname{sign} x_2, \ldots, \operatorname{sign} x_n)$ to get $x \cdot y = \|x\|_1$. By Schwarz, this is at most $\|x\|\,\|y\| = \sqrt{n}\|x\|$. Choose $x = (1, 1, \ldots, 1)$ for maximum ratios $\sqrt{n}$.

21. The exact inverse of the 3 by 3 Hilbert matrix is $A^{-1} = \begin{bmatrix} 9 & -36 & 30 \\ -36 & 192 & -180 \\ 30 & -180 & 180 \end{bmatrix}$.

23. The largest $\|x\| = \|A^{-1}b\|$ is $1/\lambda_{\min}$; the largest error is $10^{-16}/\lambda_{\min}$.

25. Exchange $\begin{bmatrix} 1 & 0 \\ 2 & 2 \end{bmatrix}$ to $\begin{bmatrix} 2 & 2 \\ 1 & 0 \end{bmatrix} \to \begin{bmatrix} 2 & 2 \\ 0 & -1 \end{bmatrix} = U$ with $P = \begin{bmatrix} 0 & 1 \\ 1 & 0 \end{bmatrix}$ and

$$L = \begin{bmatrix} 1 & 0 \\ .5 & 1 \end{bmatrix}. \; A \to \begin{bmatrix} 2 & 2 & 0 \\ 1 & 0 & 1 \\ 0 & 2 & 0 \end{bmatrix} \to \begin{bmatrix} 2 & 2 & 0 \\ 0 & -1 & 1 \\ 0 & 2 & 0 \end{bmatrix} \to \begin{bmatrix} 2 & 2 & 0 \\ 0 & 2 & 0 \\ 0 & -1 & 1 \end{bmatrix} \to$$

$$\begin{bmatrix} 2 & 2 & 0 \\ 0 & 2 & 0 \\ 0 & 0 & 1 \end{bmatrix} = U. \text{ Then } PA = LU \text{ with } P = \begin{bmatrix} 0 & 1 & 0 \\ 0 & 0 & 1 \\ 1 & 0 & 0 \end{bmatrix} \text{ and } L = \begin{bmatrix} 1 & 0 & 0 \\ 0 & 1 & 0 \\ .5 & -.5 & 1 \end{bmatrix}.$$

Problem Set 7.3, page 365

1. $u_0 = \begin{bmatrix} 1 \\ 0 \end{bmatrix}, u_1 = \begin{bmatrix} 2 \\ -1 \end{bmatrix}, u_2 = \begin{bmatrix} 5 \\ -4 \end{bmatrix}, u_3 = \begin{bmatrix} 14 \\ -13 \end{bmatrix}; u_\infty = \dfrac{1}{\sqrt{2}} \begin{bmatrix} 1 \\ -1 \end{bmatrix}$ normalized to unit vector.

3. $u_k/\lambda_1^k = c_1x_1 + c_2x_2(\lambda_2/\lambda_1)^k + \cdots + c_nx_n(\lambda_n/\lambda_1)^k \to c_1x_1$ if all ratios $|\lambda_i/\lambda_1| < 1$. The largest ratio controls, when k is large. $A = \begin{bmatrix} 0 & 1 \\ 1 & 0 \end{bmatrix}$ has $|\lambda_2| = |\lambda_1|$ and no convergence.

5. $Hx = x - (x-y)\dfrac{2(x-y)^{\mathrm{T}}x}{(x-y)^{\mathrm{T}}(x-y)} = x - (x-y) = y$. Then $H(Hx) = Hy$ is $x = Hy$.

7. $U = \begin{bmatrix} 1 & 0 \\ 0 & H \end{bmatrix} \begin{bmatrix} 1 & 0 & 0 \\ 0 & -\frac{3}{5} & -\frac{4}{5} \\ 0 & -\frac{4}{5} & \frac{3}{5} \end{bmatrix} = U^{-1}$ and then $U^{-1}AU = \begin{bmatrix} 1 & -5 & 0 \\ -5 & \frac{9}{25} & \frac{12}{25} \\ 0 & \frac{12}{25} & \frac{16}{25} \end{bmatrix}$.

9. $\begin{bmatrix} \cos\theta & \sin\theta \\ \sin\theta & 0 \end{bmatrix} = QR = \begin{bmatrix} \cos\theta & -\sin\theta \\ \sin\theta & \cos\theta \end{bmatrix} \begin{bmatrix} 1 & \cos\theta\sin\theta \\ 0 & -\sin^2\theta \end{bmatrix}$.

Then $RQ = \begin{bmatrix} c(1+s^2) & -s^3 \\ -s^3 & -s^2c \end{bmatrix}$.

11. *Assume* that $(Q_0 \cdots Q_{k-1})(R_{k-1} \cdots R_0)$ is the QR factorization of A^k (certainly true if $k = 1$). By construction, $A_{k+1} = R_kQ_k$, so $R_k = A_{k+1}Q_k^{\mathrm{T}} = (Q_k^{\mathrm{T}} \cdots Q_0^{\mathrm{T}}AQ_0 \cdots Q_k)Q_k^{\mathrm{T}}$. Postmultiplying by $(R_{k-1} \cdots R_0)$, the assumption gives $R_k \cdots R_0 = Q_k^{\mathrm{T}} \cdots Q_0^{\mathrm{T}}A^{k+1}$. After moving the Q's to the left-hand side, this is the required result for A^{k+1}.

13. A has eigenvalues 4 and 2. Put one unit eigenvector in row 1 of P: it is either $\dfrac{1}{\sqrt{2}}\begin{bmatrix} 1 & -1 \\ 1 & 1 \end{bmatrix}$ and $PAP^{-1} = \begin{bmatrix} 2 & -4 \\ 0 & 4 \end{bmatrix}$ or $\dfrac{1}{\sqrt{10}}\begin{bmatrix} 1 & -3 \\ 3 & 1 \end{bmatrix}$ and $PAP^{-1} = \begin{bmatrix} 4 & -4 \\ 0 & 2 \end{bmatrix}$.

15. $P_{ij}A$ uses $4n$ multiplications (2 for each entry in rows i and j). By factoring out $\cos\theta$, the entries 1 and $\pm\tan\theta$ need only $2n$ multiplications, which leads to $\frac{2}{3}n^3$ for *PR*.

Problem Set 7.4, page 372

1. $D^{-1}(-L-U) = \begin{bmatrix} 0 & \frac{1}{2} & 0 \\ \frac{1}{2} & 0 & \frac{1}{2} \\ 0 & \frac{1}{2} & 0 \end{bmatrix}$, eigenvalues $\mu = 0, \pm 1/\sqrt{2}$; $(D+L)^{-1}(-U) = \begin{bmatrix} 1 & \frac{1}{2} & 0 \\ 0 & \frac{1}{4} & \frac{1}{2} \\ 0 & \frac{1}{8} & \frac{1}{4} \end{bmatrix}$, eigenvalues $0, 0, 1/2$; $\omega_{\text{opt}} = 4 - 2\sqrt{2}$, reducing $\lambda_{\max}$ to $3 - 2\sqrt{2} \approx 0.2$.

3. $Ax_k = (2 - 2\cos k\pi h)x_k$; $Jx_k = \frac{1}{2}(\sin 2k\pi h, \sin 3k\pi h + \sin k\pi h, \ldots) = (\cos k\pi h)x_k$. For $h = \dfrac{1}{4}$, A has eigenvalues $2 - 2\cos\dfrac{\pi}{4} = \mathbf{2 - \sqrt{2}}$, $2 - \cos\dfrac{\pi}{2} = \mathbf{2}$, $2 - \cos\dfrac{3\pi}{4} = \mathbf{2 + \sqrt{2}}$.

5. $J = D^{-1}(L+U) = -\begin{bmatrix} 0 & \frac{1}{3} & \frac{1}{3} \\ 0 & 0 & \frac{1}{4} \\ \frac{2}{5} & \frac{2}{5} & 0 \end{bmatrix}$; the three circles have radius $r_1 = \dfrac{2}{3}$, $r_2 = \dfrac{1}{4}$, $r_3 = \dfrac{4}{5}$. Their centers are at zero, so all $|\lambda_i| \le 4/5 < 1$.

7. $-D^{-1}(L+U) = \begin{bmatrix} 0 & -b/a \\ -c/d & 0 \end{bmatrix}$ has $\mu = \pm\left(\dfrac{bc}{ad}\right)^{1/2}$; $-(D+L)^{-1}U = \begin{bmatrix} 0 & -b/a \\ 0 & bc/ad \end{bmatrix}$, $\lambda = 0, bc/ad$; $\lambda_{\max}$ does equal $\mu^2_{\max}$.

9. If $Ax = \lambda x$, then $(I - A)x = (1 - \lambda)x$. Real eigenvalues of $B = I - A$ have $|1 - \lambda| < 1$, provided that λ is between 0 and 2.

11. Always $\|AB\| \le \|A\|\|B\|$. Choose $A = B$ to find $\|B^2\| \le \|B\|^2$. Then choose $A = B^2$ to find $\|B^3\| \le \|B^2\|\|B\| \le \|B\|^3$. Continue (or use induction). Since $\|B\| \ge \max|\lambda(B)|$, it is no surprise that $\|B\| < 1$ gives convergence.

13. Jacobi has $S^{-1}T = \frac{1}{3}\begin{bmatrix} 0 & 1 \\ 1 & 0 \end{bmatrix}$ with $|\lambda|_{\max} = \frac{1}{3}$. Gauss–Seidel has $S^{-1}T = \begin{bmatrix} 0 & \frac{1}{3} \\ 0 & \frac{1}{9} \end{bmatrix}$ with $|\lambda|_{\max} = \frac{1}{9} = (|\lambda|_{\max}$ for Jacobi$)^2$.

15. Successive overrelaxation (SOR) in MATLAB.

17. The maximum row sums give all $|\lambda| \le .9$ and $|\lambda| \le 4$. The circles around diagonal entries give tighter bounds. First A: The circle $|\lambda - .2| \le .7$ contains the other circles $|\lambda - .3| \le .5$ and $|\lambda - .1| \le .6$ and all three eigenvalues. Second A: The circle $|\lambda - 2| \le 2$ contains the circle $|\lambda - 2| \le 1$ and all three eigenvalues $2 + \sqrt{2}$, 2, and $2 - \sqrt{2}$.

19. $r_1 = b - \alpha_1 Ab = b - (b^{\mathrm{T}}b/b^{\mathrm{T}}Ab)Ab$ is orthogonal to $r_0 = b$: *the residuals $r = b - Ax$ are orthogonal at each step*. To show that p_1 is orthogonal to $Ap_0 = Ab$, simplify p_1 to cP_1: $P_1 = \|Ab\|^2 b - (b^{\mathrm{T}}Ab)Ab$ and $c = b^{\mathrm{T}}b/(b^{\mathrm{T}}Ab)^2$. Certainly $(Ab)^{\mathrm{T}}P_1 = 0$, because $A^{\mathrm{T}} = A$. (That simplification put α_1 into $p_1 = b - \alpha_1 Ab + (b^{\mathrm{T}}b - 2\alpha_1 b^{\mathrm{T}}Ab + \alpha_1^2\|Ab\|^2)b/b^{\mathrm{T}}b$. For a good discussion see *Numerical Linear Algebra* by Trefethen and Bau.)

Problem Set 8.1, page 381

1. The corners are at (0, 6), (2, 2), (6, 0); see Figure 8.3.

3. The constraints give $3(2x + 5y) + 2(-3x + 8y) \le 9 - 10$, or $31y \le -1$. Can't have $y \ge 0$.

5. $x \ge 0$, $y \ge 0$, with added constraint that $x + y \le 0$ admits only the point (0, 0).

7. x (5% bonds) $= z$ (9% bonds) $=$ 20,000 and y (6% bonds) $=$ 60,000.

9. The cost to be minimized is $1000x + 2000y + 3000z + 1500u + 3000v + 3700w$. The amounts x, y, z to Chicago and u, v, w to New England satisfy $x + u = 1{,}000{,}000$; $y + v = 1{,}000{,}000$; $z + w = 1{,}000{,}000$; $x + y + z = 800{,}000$; $u + v + w = 2{,}200{,}000$.

Problem Set 8.2, page 391

1. At present $x_4 = 4$ and $x_5 = 2$ are in the basis, and the cost is zero. The entering variable should be x_3, to reduce the cost. The leaving variable should be x_5, since $2/1$ is less than $4/1$. With x_3 and x_4 in the basis, the constraints give $x_3 = 2$, $x_4 = 2$, and the cost is now $x_1 + x_2 - x_3 = -2$.

3. The "reduced costs" are $r = [1 \quad 1]$, so change is not good and the corner is optimal.

5. At P, $r = [-5 \quad 3]$; then at Q, $r = \begin{bmatrix} \frac{5}{3} & -\frac{1}{3} \end{bmatrix}$; R is optimal because $r \geq 0$.

7. For a maximum problem the stopping test becomes $r \leq 0$. If this fails, and the ith component is the largest, then that column of N enters the basis; the rule **8C** for the vector leaving the basis is the same.

9. $BE = B[\cdots v \cdots] = [\cdots u \cdots]$, since $Bv = u$. So E is the correct matrix.

11. If $Ax = 0$, then $Px = x - A^{\mathrm{T}}(AA^{\mathrm{T}})^{-1}Ax = x$.

Problem Set 8.3, page 399

1. Maximize $4y_1 + 11y_2$, with $y_1 \geq 0$, $y_2 \geq 0$, $2y_1 + y_2 \leq 1$, $3y_2 \leq 1$; the primal has $x_1^* = 2$, $x_2^* = 3$, the dual has $y_1^* = \frac{1}{3}$, $y_2^* = \frac{1}{3}$, *cost* $= 5$.

3. The dual maximizes yb, with $y \geq c$. Therefore $x = b$ and $y = c$ are feasible, and give the same value cb for the cost in the primal and dual; by **8F** they must be optimal. If $b_1 < 0$, then the optimal x^* is changed to $(0, b_2, \ldots, b_n)$ and $y^* = (0, c_2, \ldots, c_n)$.

5. $b = [0 \quad 1]^{\mathrm{T}}$ and $c = [-1 \quad 0]$.

7. Since $cx = 3 = yb$, x and y are optimal by **8F**.

9. $x^* = [1 \quad 0]^{\mathrm{T}}$, $y^* = [1 \quad 0]$, with $y^*b = 1 = cx^*$. The second inequalities in both $Ax^* \geq b$ and $y^*A \leq c$ are strict, so the second components of y^* and x^* are zero.

11. (a) $x_1^* = 0$, $x_2^* = 1$, $x_3^* = 0$, $c^{\mathrm{T}}x = 3$. (b) It is the first quadrant with the tetrahedron in the corner cut off. (c) Maximize y_1, subject to $y_1 \geq 0$, $y_1 \leq 5$, $y_1 \leq 3$, $y_1 \leq 4$; $y_1^* = 3$.

13. Here $c = [1 \quad 1 \quad 1]$ with $A = \begin{bmatrix} 2 & 1 & 0 \\ 0 & 0 & 1 \end{bmatrix}$. No constraint $x \geq 0$ so the dual will have equality $yA = c$ (or $A^{\mathrm{T}}y = c^{\mathrm{T}}$). That gives $2y_1 = 1$ and $y_1 = 1$ and $y_2 = 2$ and *no feasible solution*. So the primal must have ∞ as maximum: $x_1 = -N$ and $x_2 = 2N$ and $x_3 = 0$ give Cost $= x_1 + x_2 + x_3 = N$ (arbitrarily large).

15. The columns of $\begin{bmatrix} 1 & 0 & 0 & -1 & 0 & 0 \\ 0 & 1 & 0 & 0 & -1 & 0 \\ 0 & 0 & 1 & 0 & 0 & -1 \end{bmatrix}$ or $\begin{bmatrix} 1 & 0 & 0 & -1 \\ 0 & 1 & 0 & -1 \\ 0 & 0 & 1 & -1 \end{bmatrix}$.

17. Take $y = [1 \quad -1]$; then $yA \geq 0$, $yb < 0$.

Problem Set 8.4, page 406

1. The maximal flow is 13, with the minimal cut separating node 6 from the other nodes.

3. Increasing the capacity of pipes from node 4 to node 6 or node 4 to node 5 will produce the largest increase in the maximal flow. The maximal flow increases from 8 to 9.

5. Assign capacities = 1 to all edges. The maximum number of disjoint paths from s to t then equals the maximum flow. The minimum number of edges whose removal disconnects s from t is the minimum cut. Then max flow = min cut.

7. Rows $1, 4,$ and 5 violate Hall's condition; the 3 by 3 submatrix coming from rows 1, 4, 5, and columns 1, 2, 5 has $3 + 3 > 5$.

9. (a) The matrix has $2n$ 1s which cannot be covered by less than n lines because each line covers exactly two 1s. It takes n lines; there must be a complete matching.

(b) $\begin{bmatrix} 1 & 1 & 1 & 1 & 1 \\ 1 & 0 & 0 & 0 & 1 \\ 1 & 0 & 0 & 0 & 1 \\ 1 & 0 & 0 & 0 & 1 \\ 1 & 1 & 1 & 1 & 1 \end{bmatrix}$. The 1s can be covered with four lines; five marriages are not possible.

11. If each $m + 1$ marries the only acceptable man m, there is no one for #1 to marry (even though all are acceptable to #1).

13. Algorithm 1 gives 1–3, 3–2, 2–5, 2–4, 4–6, and algorithm 2 gives 2–5, 4–6, 2–4, 3–2, 1–3. These are equal-length shortest spanning trees.

15. (a) Rows $1, 3, 5$ only have 1s in columns 2 and 4. (b) Columns $1, 3, 5$ (in rows 2, 4). (c) Zero submatrix from rows $1, 3, 5$ and columns $1, 3, 5$. (d) Rows 2, 4 and columns 2, 4 cover all 1s.

Problem Set 8.5, page 413

1. $-10x_1 + 70(1-x_1) = 10x_1 - 10(1-x_1)$, or $x_1 = \frac{4}{5}$, $x_2 = \frac{1}{5}$; $-10y_1 + 10(1-y_1) = 70y_1 - 10(1-y_1)$, or $y_1 = \frac{1}{5}$, $y_2 = \frac{4}{5}$; average payoff $yAx = 6$.

3. If X chooses column j, Y will choose its smallest entry a_{ij} (in row i). X will not move, since this is the largest entry in that row. In Problem 2, $a_{12} = 2$ was an equilibrium of this kind. If we exchange the 2 and 4 below it, no entry has this property, and mixed strategies are required.

5. The best strategy for X combines the two lines to produce a horizontal line, guaranteeing this height of $7/3$. The combination is $\frac{2}{3}(3y + 2(1-y)) + \frac{1}{3}(y + 3(1-y)) = 7/3$, so X chooses the columns with frequencies $\frac{2}{3}$, 0, $\frac{1}{3}$.

7. For columns, we want $x_1a + (1-x_1)b = x_1c + (1-x_1)d = u$, so $x_1(a-b-c+d) = d-b$. For rows, $y_1a + (1-y_1)c = y_1b + (1-y_1)d = v$ exchanges b and c. Compare u with v:

$$u = x_1(a-b) + b = \frac{(a-b)(d-b)}{a-b-c+d} + b = \frac{ad-bc}{a-b-c+d} = \text{same after } b \leftrightarrow c = v.$$

9. The inner maximum is the larger of y_1 and y_2; x concentrates on that one. Subject to $y_1 + y_2 = 1$, the minimum of the *larger* y is $\frac{1}{2}$. Notice $A = I$.

11. $Ax^* = \begin{bmatrix} \frac{1}{2} & \frac{1}{2} \end{bmatrix}^{\mathrm{T}}$ and $yAx^* = \frac{1}{2}y_1 + \frac{1}{2}y_2 = \frac{1}{2}$ for all strategies of Y; $y^*A = \begin{bmatrix} \frac{1}{2} & \frac{1}{2} & -1 & -1 \end{bmatrix}$ and $y^*Ax = \frac{1}{2}x_1 + \frac{1}{2}x_2 - x_3 - x_4$, which cannot exceed $\frac{1}{2}$; in between is $y^*Ax^* = \frac{1}{2}$.

13. Value 0 (fair game). X chooses 2 or 3, y chooses odd or even: $x^* = y^* = \left(\frac{1}{2}, \frac{1}{2}\right)$.

Problem Set A, page 420

1. (a) Largest dim $(\mathbf{S} \cap \mathbf{T}) = 7$ when $\mathbf{S} \subset \mathbf{T}$. (b) Smallest dim $(\mathbf{S} \cap \mathbf{T}) = 2$.
(c) Smallest dim $(\mathbf{S} + \mathbf{T}) = 8$ when $\mathbf{S} \subset \mathbf{T}$.
(d) Largest dim $(\mathbf{S} + \mathbf{T}) = 13$ (all of $\mathbf{R}^{13}$).

3. $\mathbf{V} + \mathbf{W}$ and $\mathbf{V} \cap \mathbf{W}$ contain $\begin{bmatrix} a_{11} & a_{12} & a_{13} & a_{14} \\ a_{21} & a_{22} & a_{23} & a_{24} \\ 0 & a_{32} & a_{33} & a_{34} \\ 0 & 0 & a_{43} & a_{44} \end{bmatrix}$ and $\begin{bmatrix} a_{11} & a_{12} & 0 & 0 \\ 0 & a_{22} & a_{23} & 0 \\ 0 & 0 & a_{23} & a_{34} \\ 0 & 0 & 0 & a_{44} \end{bmatrix}$.
dim $(\mathbf{V} + \mathbf{W}) = 13$ and dim $(\mathbf{V} \cap \mathbf{W}) = 7$; add to get $20 = \dim \mathbf{V} + \dim \mathbf{W}$.

5. The lines through $(1, 1, 1)$ and $(1, 1, 2)$ have $\mathbf{V} \cap \mathbf{W} = \{0\}$.

7. One basis for $\mathbf{V} + \mathbf{W}$ is v_1, v_2, w_1; dim $(\mathbf{V} \cap \mathbf{W}) = 1$ with basis $(0, 1, -1, 0)$.

9. The intersection of column spaces is the line through $y = (6, 3, 6)$:

$$y = \begin{bmatrix} 1 & 5 \\ 3 & 0 \\ 2 & 4 \end{bmatrix} \begin{bmatrix} 1 \\ 1 \end{bmatrix} = \begin{bmatrix} 3 & 0 \\ 0 & 1 \\ 0 & 2 \end{bmatrix} \begin{bmatrix} 2 \\ 3 \end{bmatrix} \text{ matches } [A \quad B]x = \begin{bmatrix} 1 & 5 & 3 & 0 \\ 3 & 0 & 0 & 1 \\ 2 & 4 & 0 & 2 \end{bmatrix} \begin{bmatrix} 1 \\ 1 \\ -2 \\ -3 \end{bmatrix} = 0.$$

The column spaces have dimension 2. Their sum and intersection give $3+1 = 2+2$.

11. $$F_2 \otimes F_2 = \begin{bmatrix} F_2 & F_2 \\ F_2 & -F_2 \end{bmatrix} = \begin{bmatrix} 1 & 1 & 1 & 1 \\ 1 & -1 & 1 & -1 \\ 1 & 1 & -1 & -1 \\ 1 & -1 & -1 & 1 \end{bmatrix}.$$

13. $A_{3D} = (A_{1D} \otimes I \otimes I) + (I \otimes A_{1D} \otimes I) + (I \otimes I \otimes A_{1D})$.

Problem Set B, page 427

1. $J = \begin{bmatrix} 2 & 0 \\ 0 & 0 \end{bmatrix}$ (A is diagonalizable); $J = \begin{bmatrix} 0 & 1 & 0 \\ 0 & 0 & 0 \\ 0 & 0 & 0 \end{bmatrix}$ (eigenvectors $(1, 0, 0)$ and $(2, -1, 0)$).

3. $e^{Bt} = \begin{bmatrix} 1 & t & 2t \\ 0 & 1 & 0 \\ 0 & 0 & 0 \end{bmatrix} = I + Bt$ since $B^2 = 0$. Also $e^{Jt} = I + Jt$.

5. $J = \begin{bmatrix} 1 & 0 & 0 \\ 0 & 4 & 0 \\ 0 & 0 & 6 \end{bmatrix}$ (distinct eigenvalues); $J = \begin{bmatrix} 0 & 1 \\ 0 & 0 \end{bmatrix}$ (B has $\lambda = 0, 0$ but rank 1).

Matrix Factorizations

1. $A = LU = \begin{pmatrix}\text{lower triangular } L\\ \text{1s on the diagonal}\end{pmatrix}\begin{pmatrix}\text{upper triangular } U\\ \text{pivots on the diagonal}\end{pmatrix}.$

   Requirements: No row exchanges, as Gaussian elimination reduces A to U.

2. $A = LDU = \begin{pmatrix}\text{lower triangular } L\\ \text{1s on the diagonal}\end{pmatrix}\begin{pmatrix}\text{pivot matrix}\\ D \text{ is diagonal}\end{pmatrix}\begin{pmatrix}\text{upper triangular } U\\ \text{1s on the diagonal}\end{pmatrix}.$

   Requirements: No row exchanges. The pivots in D are divided out to leave 1s in U. If A is symmetric, then U is L^{T} and $A = LDL^{\mathrm{T}}$.

3. $PA = LU$ (permutation matrix P to avoid zeros in the pivot positions).
   Requirements: A is invertible. Then P, L, U are invertible. P does the row exchanges in advance. Alternative: $A = L_1 P_1 U_1$.

4. $EA = R$ (m by m invertible E)(any A) = rref(A).
   Requirements: None ! *The reduced row echelon form* R has r pivot rows and pivot columns. The only nonzero in a pivot column is the unit pivot. The last $m - r$ rows of E are a basis for the left nullspace of A, and the first r columns of E^{-1} are a basis for the column space of A.

5. $A = CC^{\mathrm{T}}$ = (lower triangular matrix C)(transpose is upper triangular).
   Requirements: A is symmetric and positive definite (all n pivots in D are positive). This *Cholesky factorization* has $C = L\sqrt{D}$.

6. $A = QR$ = (orthonormal columns in Q)(upper triangular R).
   Requirements: A has independent columns. Those are *orthogonalized* in Q by the Gram–Schmidt process. If A is square, then $Q^{-1} = Q^{\mathrm{T}}$.

7. $A = S\Lambda S^{-1}$ = (eigenvectors in S)(eigenvalues in Λ)(left eigenvectors in S^{-1}).
   Requirements: A must have n linearly independent eigenvectors.

8. $A = Q\Lambda Q^{\mathrm{T}}$ = (orthogonal matrix Q)(real eigenvalue matrix Λ)(Q^{T} is Q^{-1}).
   Requirements: A is *symmetric*. This is the Spectral Theorem.

9. $A = MJM^{-1}$ = (generalized eigenvectors in M)(Jordan blocks in J)(M^{-1}).
   Requirements: A is any square matrix. *Jordan form* J has a block for each independent eigenvector of A. Each block has one eigenvalue.

10. $A = U\Sigma V^{\mathrm{T}} = \begin{pmatrix}\text{orthogonal}\\ U \text{ is } m \times m\end{pmatrix}\begin{pmatrix}m \times n \text{ matrix } \Sigma\\ \sigma_1, \ldots, \sigma_r \text{ on diagonal}\end{pmatrix}\begin{pmatrix}\text{orthogonal}\\ V \text{ is } n \times n\end{pmatrix}.$

Requirements: None. This *singular value decomposition* (SVD) has the eigenvectors of AA^{T} in U and of $A^{\mathrm{T}}A$ in V; $\sigma_i = \sqrt{\lambda_i(A^{\mathrm{T}}A)} = \sqrt{\lambda_i(AA^{\mathrm{T}})}$.

11. $\boldsymbol{A^+ = V\Sigma^+U^{\mathrm{T}}} = \begin{pmatrix}\text{orthogonal}\\ n\times n\end{pmatrix}\begin{pmatrix}\text{diagonal } n\times m\\ 1/\sigma_1,\ldots,1/\sigma_r\end{pmatrix}\begin{pmatrix}\text{orthogonal}\\ m\times m\end{pmatrix}.$

Requirements: None. The *pseudoinverse* has A^+A = projection onto row space of A and AA^+ = projection onto column space. The shortest least-squares solution to $Ax = b$ is $\widehat{x} = A^+b$. This solves $A^{\mathrm{T}}A\widehat{x} = A^{\mathrm{T}}b$.

12. $\boldsymbol{A = QH}$ = (orthogonal matrix Q)(symmetric positive definite matrix H).
Requirements: A is invertible. This *polar decomposition* has $H^2 = A^{\mathrm{T}}A$. The factor H is semidefinite if A is singular. The reverse polar decomposition $A = KQ$ has $K^2 = AA^{\mathrm{T}}$. Both have $Q = UV^{\mathrm{T}}$ from the SVD.

13. $\boldsymbol{A = U\Lambda U^{-1}}$ = (unitary U)(eigenvalue matrix Λ)($U^{-1} = U^{\mathrm{H}} = \overline{U}^{\mathrm{T}}$).
Requirements: A is *normal*: $A^{\mathrm{H}}A = AA^{\mathrm{H}}$. Its orthonormal (and possibly complex) eigenvectors are the columns of U. Complex λ's unless $A = A^{\mathrm{H}}$.

14. $\boldsymbol{A = UTU^{-1}}$ = (unitary U)(triangular T with λ's on diagonal)($U^{-1} = U^{\mathrm{H}}$).
Requirements: *Schur triangularization* of any square A. There is a matrix U with orthonormal columns that makes $U^{-1}AU$ triangular.

15. $\boldsymbol{F_n} = \begin{bmatrix} I & D\\ I & -D\end{bmatrix}\begin{bmatrix}\boldsymbol{F_{n/2}} & \\ & \boldsymbol{F_{n/2}}\end{bmatrix}\begin{bmatrix}\text{even–odd}\\ \text{permutation}\end{bmatrix}$ = one step of the **FFT**.

Requirements: F_n = Fourier matrix with entries w^{jk} where $w^n = 1$, $w = e^{2\pi i/n}$. Then $\boldsymbol{F_n\overline{F}_n} = nI$. D has $1, w, w^2, \ldots$ on its diagonal. For $n = 2^\ell$ the *Fast Fourier Transform* has $\frac{1}{2}n\ell$ multiplications from ℓ stages of D's.

Glossary: A Dictionary for Linear Algebra

Adjacency matrix of a graph Square matrix with $a_{ij} = 1$ when there is an edge from node i to node j; otherwise $a_{ij} = 0$. $A = A^{\mathrm{T}}$ for an undirected graph.

Affine transformation $T(v) = Av + v_0 =$ linear transformation plus shift.

Associative Law $(AB)C = A(BC)$ Parentheses can be removed to leave ABC.

Augmented matrix $[A \quad b]$ $Ax = b$ is solvable when b is in the column space of A; then $[A \quad b]$ has the same rank as A. Elimination on $[A \quad b]$ keeps equations correct.

Back substitution Upper triangular systems are solved in reverse order x_n to x_1.

Basis for V Independent vectors $v_1, \ldots, v_d$ whose linear combinations give every v in **V**. A vector space has many bases!

Big formula for n by n determinants $\det(A)$ is a sum of $n!$ terms, one term for each permutation P of the columns. That term is the product $a_{1\alpha} \cdots a_{n\omega}$ down the diagonal of the reordered matrix, times $\det(P) = \pm 1$.

Block matrix A matrix can be partitioned into matrix blocks, by cuts between rows and/or between columns. **Block multiplication** of AB is allowed if the block shapes permit (the columns of A and rows of B must be in matching blocks).

Cayley–Hamilton Theorem $p(\lambda) = \det(A - \lambda I)$ has $p(A) =$ *zero matrix*.

Change of basis matrix M The old basis vectors v_j are combinations $\sum m_{ij} w_i$ of the new basis vectors. The coordinates of $c_1 v_1 + \cdots + c_n v_n = d_1 w_1 + \cdots + d_n w_n$ are related by $d = Mc$. (For $n = 2$, set $v_1 = m_{11} w_1 + m_{21} w_2$, $v_2 = m_{12} w_1 + m_{22} w_2$.)

Characteristic equation $\det(A - \lambda I) = 0$ The n roots are the eigenvalues of A.

Cholesky factorization $A = CC^{\mathrm{T}} = (L\sqrt{D})(L\sqrt{D})^{\mathrm{T}}$ for positive definite A.

Circulant matrix C Constant diagonals wrap around as in cyclic shift S. Every circulant is $c_0 I + c_1 S + \cdots + c_{n-1} S^{n-1}$. $Cx =$ **convolution** $c * x$. Eigenvectors in F.

Cofactor C_{ij} Remove row i and column j; multiply the determinant by $(-1)^{i+j}$.

Column picture of $Ax = b$ The vector b becomes a combination of the columns of A. The system is solvable only when b is in the column space $\boldsymbol{C}(A)$.

Column space $C(A)$ Space of all combinations of the columns of A.

Commuting matrices $AB = BA$ If diagonalizable, they share n eigenvectors.

Companion matrix Put $c_1, \ldots, c_n$ in row n and put $n - 1$ 1s along diagonal 1. Then $\det(A - \lambda I) = \pm(c_1 + c_2\lambda + c_3\lambda^2 + \cdots)$.

Complete solution $x = x_p + x_n$ to $Ax = b$ (Particular x_p) + (x_n in nullspace).

Complex conjugate $\bar{z} = a - ib$ for any complex number $z = a + ib$. Then $z\bar{z} = |z|^2$.

Condition number cond$(A) = \kappa(A) = \|A\|\|A^{-1}\| = \sigma_{\max}/\sigma_{\min}$ In $Ax = b$, the relative change $\|\delta x\|/\|x\|$ is less than cond(A) times the relative change $\|\delta b\|/\|b\|$. Condition numbers measure the *sensitivity* of the output to change in the input.

Conjugate Gradient Method A sequence of steps to solve positive definite $Ax = b$ by minimizing $\frac{1}{2}x^{\mathrm{T}}Ax - x^{\mathrm{T}}b$ over growing Krylov subspaces.

Covariance matrix Σ When random variables x_i have mean = average value = 0, their covariances Σ_{ij} are the averages of $x_i x_j$. With means $\bar{x}_i$, the matrix $\Sigma =$ mean of $(x - \bar{x})(x - \bar{x})^{\mathrm{T}}$ is positive (semi)definite; it is diagonal if the x_i are independent.

Cramer's Rule for $Ax = b$ B_j has b replacing column j of A, and $x_j = |B_j|/|A|$.

Cross product $u \times v$ in $\mathbf{R}^3$ Vector perpendicular to u and v, length $\|u\|\|v\||\sin\theta|$ = parallelogram area, computed as the "determinant" of $[i \ \ j \ \ k;\ u_1 \ \ u_2 \ \ u_3;\ v_1 \ \ v_2 \ \ v_3]$.

Cyclic shift S Permutation with $s_{21} = 1, s_{32} = 1, \ldots$, finally $s_{1n} = 1$. Its eigenvalues are nth roots $e^{2\pi ik/n}$ of 1; eigenvectors are columns of the Fourier matrix F.

Determinant $|A| = \det(A)$ Defined by $\det I = 1$, sign reversal for row exchange, and linearity in each row. Then $|A| = 0$ when A is singular. Also $|AB| = |A||B|$, $|A^{-1}| = 1/|A|$, and $|A^{\mathrm{T}}| = |A|$. The big formula for $\det(A)$ has a sum of $n!$ terms, the cofactor formula uses determinants of size $n-1$, volume of box $= |\det(A)|$.

Diagonal matrix D $d_{ij} = 0$ if $i \neq j$. **Block-diagonal**: zero outside square blocks D_{ii}.

Diagonalizable matrix A Must have n independent eigenvectors (in the columns of S; automatic with n different eigenvalues). Then $S^{-1}AS = \Lambda$ = eigenvalue matrix.

Diagonalization $\Lambda = S^{-1}AS$ Λ = eigenvalue matrix and S = eigenvector matrix. A must have n independent eigenvectors to make S invertible. All $A^k = S\Lambda^k S^{-1}$.

Dimension of vector space $\dim(\mathbf{V})$ = number of vectors in any basis for $\mathbf{V}$.

Distributive Law $A(B+C) = AB + AC$ Add then multiply, or multiply then add.

Dot product $x^{\mathrm{T}}y = x_1y_1 + \cdots + x_ny_n$ Complex dot product is $\overline{x}^{\mathrm{T}}y$. Perpendicular vectors have zero dot product. $(AB)_{ij}$ = (row i of A) $\cdot$ (column j of B).

Echelon matrix U The first nonzero entry (the pivot) in each row comes after the pivot in the previous row. All zero rows come last.

Eigenvalue λ and eigenvector x $Ax = \lambda x$ with $x \neq 0$, so $\det(A - \lambda I) = 0$.

Eigshow Graphical 2 by 2 eigenvalues and singular values (MATLAB or Java).

Elimination A sequence of row operations that reduces A to an upper triangular U or to the reduced form $R = \mathrm{rref}(A)$. Then $A = LU$ with multipliers ℓ_{ij} in L, or $PA = LU$ with row exchanges in P, or $EA = R$ with an invertible E.

Elimination matrix = Elementary matrix E_{ij} The identity matrix with an extra $-\ell_{ij}$ in the i, j entry ($i \neq j$). Then $E_{ij}A$ subtracts ℓ_{ij} times row j of A from row i.

Ellipse (or ellipsoid) $x^{\mathrm{T}}Ax = 1$ A must be positive definite; the axes of the ellipse are eigenvectors of A, with lengths $1/\sqrt{\lambda}$. (For $\|x\| = 1$ the vectors $y = Ax$ lie on the ellipse $\|A^{-1}y\|^2 = y^{\mathrm{T}}(AA^{\mathrm{T}})^{-1}y = 1$ displayed by eigshow; axis lengths σ_i.)

Exponential $e^{At} = I + At + (At)^2/2! + \cdots$ has derivative Ae^{At}; $e^{At}u(0)$ solves $u' = Au$.

Factorization $A = LU$ If elimination takes A to U *without row exchanges*, then the lower triangular L with multipliers ℓ_{ij} (and $\ell_{ii} = 1$) brings U back to A.

Fast Fourier Transform (FFT) A factorization of the Fourier matrix F_n into $\ell = \log_2 n$ matrices S_i times a permutation. Each S_i needs only $n/2$ multiplications, so F_nx and $F_n^{-1}c$ can be computed with $n\ell/2$ multiplications. Revolutionary.

Fibonacci numbers $0, 1, 1, 2, 3, 5, \ldots$ satisfy $F_n = F_{n-1} + F_{n-2} = (\lambda_1^n - \lambda_2^n)/(\lambda_1 - \lambda_2)$. Growth rate $\lambda_1 = \left(1 + \sqrt{5}\right)/2$ is the largest eigenvalue of the Fibonacci matrix $\begin{bmatrix} 1 & 1 \\ 1 & 0 \end{bmatrix}$.

Four fundamental subspaces of A $C(A), N(A), C(A^{\mathrm{T}}), N(A^{\mathrm{T}})$.

Fourier matrix F Entries $F_{jk} = e^{2\pi ijk/n}$ give orthogonal columns $\overline{F}^{\mathrm{T}}F = nI$. Then $y = Fc$ is the (inverse) Discrete Fourier Transform $y_j = \sum c_k e^{2\pi ijk/n}$.

Free columns of A Columns without pivots; combinations of earlier columns.

Free variable x_i Column i has no pivot in elimination. We can give the $n - r$ free variables any values, then $Ax = b$ determines the r pivot variables (if solvable!).

Full column rank $r = n$ Independent columns, $N(A) = \{0\}$, no free variables.

Full row rank $r = m$ Independent rows, at least one solution to $Ax = b$, column space is all of $\mathbf{R}^m$. *Full rank* means full column rank or full row rank.

Fundamental Theorem The nullspace $N(A)$ and row space $C(A^{\mathrm{T}})$ are orthogonal complements (perpendicular subspaces of $\mathbf{R}^n$ with dimensions r and $n - r$) from $Ax = 0$. Applied to A^{T}, the column space $C(A)$ is the orthogonal complement of $N(A^{\mathrm{T}})$.

Gauss–Jordan method Invert A by row operations on $[A \ \ I]$ to reach $[I \ \ A^{-1}]$.

Gram–Schmidt orthogonalization $A = QR$ Independent columns in A, orthonormal columns in Q. Each column q_j of Q is a combination of the first j columns of A (and conversely, so R is upper triangular). Convention: $\mathrm{diag}(R) > 0$.

Graph G Set of n nodes connected pairwise by m edges. A **complete graph** has all $n(n-1)/2$ edges between nodes. A **tree** has only $n - 1$ edges and no closed loops.

A **directed graph** has a direction arrow specified on each edge.

Hankel matrix H Constant along each antidiagonal; h_{ij} depends on $i + j$.

Hermitian matrix $A^{\mathrm{H}} = \overline{A}^{\mathrm{T}} = A$ Complex analog of a symmetric matrix: $\overline{a_{ji}} = a_{ij}$.

Hessenberg matrix H Triangular matrix with one extra nonzero adjacent diagonal.

Hilbert matrix hilb(n) Entries $H_{ij} = 1/(i + j - 1) = \int_0^1 x^{i-1}x^{j-1}dx$. Positive definite but extremely small $\lambda_{\min}$ and large condition number.

Hypercube matrix P_L^2 Row $n + 1$ counts corners, edges, faces, ..., of a cube in $\mathbf{R}^n$.

Identity matrix I (or I_n) Diagonal entries $= 1$, off-diagonal entries $= 0$.

Incidence matrix of a directed graph The m by n edge–node incidence matrix has a row for each edge (node i to node j), with entries -1 and 1 in columns i and j.

Indefinite matrix A symmetric matrix with eigenvalues of both signs ($+$ and $-$).

Independent vectors $v_1, \ldots, v_k$ No combination $c_1v_1 + \cdots + c_kv_k =$ zero vector unless all $c_i = 0$. If the v's are the columns of A, the only solution to $Ax = 0$ is $x = 0$.

Inverse matrix A^{-1} Square matrix with $A^{-1}A = I$ and $AA^{-1} = I$. No inverse if $\det A = 0$ and $\operatorname{rank}(A) < n$, and $Ax = 0$ for a nonzero vector x. The inverses of AB and A^{T} are $B^{-1}A^{-1}$ and $(A^{-1})^{\mathrm{T}}$. Cofactor formula $(A^{-1})_{ij} = C_{ji}/\det A$.

Iterative method A sequence of steps intended to approach the desired solution.

Jordan form $J = M^{-1}AM$ If A has s independent eigenvectors, its "generalized" eigenvector matrix M gives $J = \operatorname{diag}(J_1, \ldots, J_s)$. The block J_k is $\lambda_k I_k + N_k$ where N_k has 1s on diagonal 1. Each block has one eigenvalue λ_k and one eigenvector $(1, 0, \ldots, 0)$.

Kirchhoff's Laws *Current law*: net current (in minus out) is zero at each node. *Voltage law*: Potential differences (voltage drops) add to zero around any closed loop.

Kronecker product (tensor product) $A \otimes B$ Blocks $a_{ij}B$, eigenvalues $\lambda_p(A)\lambda_q(B)$.

Krylov subspace $K_j(A, b)$ The subspace spanned by $b, Ab, \ldots, A^{j-1}b$. Numerical methods approximate $A^{-1}b$ by x_j with residual $b - Ax_j$ in this subspace. A good basis for K_j requires only multiplication by A at each step.

Least-squares solution $\widehat{x}$ The vector $\widehat{x}$ that minimizes the error $\|e\|^2$ solves $A^{\mathrm{T}}A\widehat{x} = A^{\mathrm{T}}b$. Then $e = b - A\widehat{x}$ is orthogonal to all columns of A.

Left inverse A^+ If A has full column rank n, then $A^+ = (A^{\mathrm{T}}A)^{-1}A^{\mathrm{T}}$ has $A^+A = I_n$.

Left nullspace $N(A^{\mathrm{T}})$ Nullspace of $A^{\mathrm{T}} =$ "left nullspace" of A because $y^{\mathrm{T}}A = 0^{\mathrm{T}}$.

Length $\|x\|$ Square root of $x^{\mathrm{T}}x$ (Pythagoras in n dimensions).

Linear combination $cv + dw$ or $\sum c_jv_j$ Vector addition and scalar multiplication.

Linear transformation T Each vector v in the input space transforms to $T(v)$ in the output space, and linearity requires $T(cv + dw) = c\,T(v) + d\,T(w)$. Examples: Matrix multiplication Av, differentiation in function space.

Linearly dependent $v_1, \ldots, v_n$ A combination other than all $c_i = 0$ gives $\sum c_iv_i = 0$.

Lucas numbers $L_n = 2, 1, 3, 4, \ldots,$ satisfy $L_n = L_{n-1} + L_{n-2} = \lambda_1^n + \lambda_2^n$, with eigenvalues $\lambda_1, \lambda_2 = (1 \pm \sqrt{5})/2$ of the Fibonacci matrix $\begin{bmatrix} 1 & 1 \\ 1 & 0 \end{bmatrix}$. Compare $L_0 = 2$ with Fibonacci.

Markov matrix M All $m_{ij} \geq 0$ and each column sum is 1. Largest eigenvalue $\lambda = 1$. If $m_{ij} > 0$, the columns of M^k approach the steady-state eigenvector $Ms = s > 0$.

Matrix multiplication AB The i, j entry of AB is (row i of A) $\cdot$ (column j of B) $= \sum a_{ik}b_{kj}$. By columns: column j of $AB = A$ times column j of B. By rows: row i of A multiplies B. Columns times rows: $AB =$ sum of (column k)(row k). All these equivalent definitions come from the rule that AB times x equals A times Bx.

Minimal polynomial of A The lowest-degree polynomial with $m(A) =$ zero matrix. The roots of m are eigenvalues, and $m(\lambda)$ divides $\det(A - \lambda I)$.

Multiplication $Ax = x_1$(column 1) $+ \cdots + x_n$(column n) $=$ combination of columns.

Multiplicities AM and GM The algebraic multiplicity AM of an eigenvalue λ is the number of times λ appears as a root of $\det(A - \lambda I) = 0$. The geometric multiplicity GM is the number of independent eigenvectors ($=$ dimension of the eigenspace for λ).

Multiplier ℓ_{ij} The pivot row j is multiplied by ℓ_{ij} and subtracted from row i to eliminate the i, j entry: $\ell_{ij} =$ (entry to eliminate)/(jth pivot).

Network A directed graph that has constants $c_1, \ldots, c_m$ associated with the edges.

Nilpotent matrix N Some power of N is the zero matrix, $N^k = 0$. The only eigenvalue is $\lambda = 0$ (repeated n times). Examples: triangular matrices with zero diagonal.

Norm $\|A\|$ of a matrix The "ℓ^2 norm" is the maximum ratio $\|Ax\|/\|x\| = \sigma_{\max}$. Then $\|Ax\| \le \|A\|\|x\|$, $\|AB\| \le \|A\|\|B\|$, and $\|A+B\| \le \|A\| + \|B\|$. **Frobenius norm** $\|A\|_F^2 = \sum\sum a_{ij}^2$; ℓ^1 and ℓ^∞ norms are largest column and row sums of $|a_{ij}|$.

Normal equation $A^{\mathrm{T}}A\widehat{x} = A^{\mathrm{T}}b$ Gives the least-squares solution to $Ax = b$ if A has full rank n. The equation says that (columns of A) $\cdot$ $(b - A\widehat{x}) = 0$.

Normal matrix N $NN^{\mathrm{T}} = N^{\mathrm{T}}N$, leads to orthonormal (complex) eigenvectors.

Nullspace matrix N The columns of N are the $n - r$ special solutions to $As = 0$.

Nullspace $N(A)$ Solutions to $Ax = 0$. Dimension $n - r =$ (# columns) $-$ rank.

Orthogonal matrix Q Square matrix with orthonormal columns, so $Q^{\mathrm{T}}Q = I$ implies $Q^{\mathrm{T}} = Q^{-1}$. Preserves length and angles, $\|Qx\| = \|x\|$ and $(Qx)^{\mathrm{T}}(Qy) = x^{\mathrm{T}}y$. All $|\lambda| = 1$, with orthogonal eigenvectors. Examples: Rotation, reflection, permutation.

Orthogonal subspaces Every v in $\mathbf{V}$ is orthogonal to every w in $\mathbf{W}$.

Orthonormal vectors $q_1, \ldots, q_n$ Dot products are $q_i^{\mathrm{T}}q_j = 0$, if $i \ne j$ and $q_i^{\mathrm{T}}q_i = 1$. The matrix Q with these orthonormal columns has $Q^{\mathrm{T}}Q = I$. If $m = n$, then $Q^{\mathrm{T}} = Q^{-1}$ and $q_1, \ldots, q_n$ is an **orthonormal basis** for $\mathbf{R}^n$: every $v = \sum (v^{\mathrm{T}}q_j)q_j$.

Outer product uv^{T} column times row = rank-1 matrix.

Partial pivoting In elimination, the jth pivot is chosen as the largest available entry (in absolute value) in column j. Then all multipliers have $|\ell_{ij}| \le 1$. Roundoff error is controlled (depending on the *condition number* of A).

Particular solution x_p Any solution to $Ax = b$; often x_p has free variables $= 0$.

Pascal matrix $P_S = \text{pascal}(n)$ The symmetric matrix with binomial entries $\binom{i+j-2}{i-1}$. $P_S = P_L P_U$ all contain Pascal's triangle with det $= 1$ (see index for more properties).

Permutation matrix P There are $n!$ orders of $1, \ldots, n$; the $n!$ P's have the rows of I in those orders. PA puts the rows of A in the same order. P is a product of row exchanges P_{ij}; P is *even* or *odd* (det $P = 1$ or -1) based on the number of exchanges.

Pivot columns of A Columns that contain pivots after row reduction; not combinations of earlier columns. The pivot columns are a basis for the column space.

Pivot d The first nonzero entry when a row is used in elimination.

Plane (or hyperplane) in $\mathbf{R}^n$ Solutions to $a^{\mathrm{T}}x = 0$ give the plane (dimension $n - 1$) perpendicular to $a \ne 0$.

Polar decomposition $A = QH$ Orthogonal Q, positive (semi)definite H.

Positive definite matrix A Symmetric matrix with positive eigenvalues and positive pivots. Definition: $x^{\mathrm{T}}Ax > 0$ unless $x = 0$.

Projection matrix P onto subspace $\mathbf{S}$ Projection $p = Pb$ is the closest point to b in $\mathbf{S}$, error $e = b - Pb$ is perpendicular to $\mathbf{S}$. $P^2 = P = P^{\mathrm{T}}$, eigenvalues are 1 or 0, eigenvectors are in $\mathbf{S}$ or $\mathbf{S}^{\perp}$. If columns of A = basis for $\mathbf{S}$, then $P = A(A^{\mathrm{T}}A)^{-1}A^{\mathrm{T}}$.

Projection $p = a(a^{\mathrm{T}}b/a^{\mathrm{T}}a)$ onto the line through a $P = aa^{\mathrm{T}}/a^{\mathrm{T}}a$ has rank 1.

Pseudoinverse A^+ (Moore–Penrose inverse) The n by m matrix that "inverts" A from column space back to row space, with $N(A^+) = N(A^{\mathrm{T}})$. A^+A and AA^+ are the projection matrices onto the row space and column space. Rank(A^+) = rank(A).

Random matrix rand(n) or randn(n) MATLAB creates a matrix with random entries, uniformly distributed on [0 1] for rand, and standard normal distribution for randn.

Rank 1 matrix $A = uv^{\mathrm{T}} \ne 0$ Column and row spaces = lines cu and cv.

Rank $r(A)$ Equals number of pivots = dimension of column space = dimension of row space.

Rayleigh quotient $q(x) = x^{\mathrm{T}}Ax/x^{\mathrm{T}}x$ For $A = A^T$, $\lambda_{\min} \le q(x) \le \lambda_{\max}$. Those extremes are reached at the eigenvectors x for $\lambda_{\min}(A)$ and $\lambda_{\max}(A)$.

Reduced row echelon form $R = \text{rref}(A)$ Pivots = 1; zeros above and below pivots; r nonzero rows of R give a basis for the row space of A.

Reflection matrix $Q = I - 2uu^{\mathrm{T}}$ The unit vector u is reflected to $Qu = -u$. All vectors x in the plane $u^{\mathrm{T}}x = 0$ are unchanged because $Qx = x$. The "Householder matrix" has $Q^{\mathrm{T}} = Q^{-1} = Q$.

Right inverse A^+ If A has full row rank m, then $A^+ = A^{\mathrm{T}}(AA^{\mathrm{T}})^{-1}$ has $AA^+ = I_m$.

Rotation matrix $R = \begin{bmatrix} \cos\theta & -\sin\theta \\ \sin\theta & \cos\theta \end{bmatrix}$ rotates the plane by θ, and $R^{-1} = R^{\mathrm{T}}$ rotates back by $-\theta$. Orthogonal matrix, eigenvalues $e^{i\theta}$ and $e^{-i\theta}$, eigenvectors $(1, \pm i)$.

Row picture of $Ax = b$ Each equation gives a plane in $\mathbf{R}^n$; planes intersect at x.

Row space $C(A^T)$ All combinations of rows of A. Column vectors by convention.

Saddle point of $f(x_1, \ldots, x_n)$ A point where the first derivatives of f are zero and the second derivative matrix ($\partial^2 f/\partial x_i \partial x_j$ = **Hessian matrix**) is indefinite.

Schur complement $S = D - CA^{-1}B$ Appears in block elimination on $\begin{bmatrix} A & B \\ C & D \end{bmatrix}$.

Schwarz inequality $|v \cdot w| \le \|v\| \, \|w\|$ Then $|v^T Aw|^2 \le (v^T Av)(w^T Aw)$ if $A = C^T C$.

Semidefinite matrix A (Positive) semidefinite means symmetric with $x^T Ax \ge 0$ for all vectors x. Then all eigenvalues $\lambda \ge 0$; no negative pivots.

Similar matrices A and B $B = M^{-1}AM$ has the same eigenvalues as A.

Simplex method for linear programming The minimum cost vector x^* is found by moving from corner to lower-cost corner along the edges of the feasible set (where the constraints $Ax = b$ and $x \ge 0$ are satisfied). Minimum cost at a corner!

Singular matrix A A square matrix that has no inverse: $\det(A) = 0$.

Singular Value Decomposition (SVD) $A = U\Sigma V^T$ = (orthogonal U) times (diagonal Σ) times (orthogonal V^T) First r columns of U and V are orthonormal bases of $C(A)$ and $C(A^T)$, with $Av_i = \sigma_i u_i$ and singular value $\sigma_i > 0$. Last columns of U and V are orthonormal bases of the nullspaces of A^T and A.

Skew-symmetric matrix K The transpose is $-K$, since $K_{ij} = -K_{ji}$. Eigenvalues are pure imaginary, eigenvectors are orthogonal, e^{Kt} is an orthogonal matrix.

Solvable system $Ax = b$ The right side b is in the column space of A.

Spanning set $v_1, \ldots, v_m$ for V Every vector in **V** is a combination of $v_1, \ldots, v_m$.

Special solutions to $As = 0$ One free variable is $s_i = 1$, other free variables $= 0$.

Spectral theorem $A = Q\Lambda Q^T$ Real symmetric A has real λ_i and orthonormal q_i, with $Aq_i = \lambda_i q_i$. In mechanics, the q_i give the *principal axes*.

Spectrum of A The set of eigenvalues $\{\lambda_1, \ldots, \lambda_n\}$. **Spectral radius** $= |\lambda_{\max}|$.

Standard basis for $\mathbf{R}^n$ Columns of n by n identity matrix (written i, j, k in $\mathbf{R}^3$).

Stiffness matrix K When x gives the movements of the nodes in a discrete structure, Kx gives the internal forces. Often $K = A^T CA$, where C contains spring constants from Hooke's Law and Ax = stretching (strains) from the movements x.

Subspace S of V Any vector space inside **V**, including **V** and **Z** = {zero vector}.

Sum V + W of subspaces Space of all (v in **V**) + (w in **W**). **Direct sum**: dim(**V** + **W**) = dim **V** + dim **W**, when **V** and **W** share only the zero vector.

Symmetric factorizations $A = LDL^T$ and $A = Q\Lambda Q^T$ The number of positive pivots in D and positive eigenvalues in Λ is the same.

Symmetric matrix A The transpose is $A^T = A$, and $a_{ij} = a_{ji}$. A^{-1} is also symmetric. All matrices of the form $R^T R$ and LDL^T and $Q\Lambda Q^T$ are symmetric. Symmetric matrices have real eigenvalues in Λ and orthonormal eigenvectors in Q.

Toeplitz matrix T Constant-diagonal matrix, so t_{ij} depends only on $j - i$. Toeplitz matrices represent linear time-invariant filters in signal processing.

Trace of A Sum of diagonal entries = sum of eigenvalues of A. Tr AB = Tr BA.

Transpose matrix A^T Entries $A^T_{ij} = A_{ji}$. A^T is n by m, $A^T A$ is square, symmetric, positive semidefinite. The transposes of AB and A^{-1} are $B^T A^T$ and $(A^T)^{-1}$.

Triangle inequality $\|u + v\| \le \|u\| + \|v\|$ For matrix norms, $\|A + B\| \le \|A\| + \|B\|$.

Tridiagonal matrix T $t_{ij} = 0$ if $|i - j| > 1$. T^{-1} has rank 1 above and below diagonal.

Unitary matrix $U^H = \overline{U}^T = U^{-1}$ Orthonormal columns (complex analog of Q).

Vandermonde matrix V $Vc = b$ gives the polynomial $p(x) = c_0 + \cdots + c_{n-1}x^{n-1}$ with $p(x_i) = b_i$ at n points. $V_{ij} = (x_i)^{j-1}$, and $\det V$ = product of $(x_k - x_i)$ for $k > i$.

Vector addition $v + w = (v_1 + w_1, \ldots, v_n + w_n)$ = diagonal of parallelogram.

Vector space V Set of vectors such that all combinations $cv + dw$ remain in **V**. Eight required rules are given in Section 2.1 for $cv + dw$.

Vector v in $\mathbf{R}^n$ Sequence of n real numbers $v = (v_1, \ldots, v_n)$ = point in $\mathbf{R}^n$.

Volume of box The rows (or columns) of A generate a box with volume $|\det(A)|$.

Wavelets $w_{jk}(t)$ or vectors w_{jk} Rescale and shift the time axis to create $w_{jk}(t) = w_{00}(2^j t - k)$. Vectors from $w_{00} = (1, 1, -1, -1)$ would be $(1, -1, 0, 0)$ and $(0, 0, 1, -1)$.

MATLAB Teaching Codes

cofactor	Compute the n by n matrix of cofactors.
cramer	Solve the system $Ax = b$ by Cramer's Rule.
deter	Matrix determinant computed from the pivots in $PA = LU$.
eigen2	Eigenvalues, eigenvectors, and $\det(A - \lambda I)$ for 2 by 2 matrices.
eigshow	Graphical demonstration of eigenvalues and singular values.
eigval	Eigenvalues and their multiplicity as roots of $\det(A - \lambda I) = 0$.
eigvec	Compute as many linearly independent eigenvectors as possible.
elim	Reduction of A to row echelon form R by an invertible E.
findpiv	Find a pivot for Gaussian elimination (used by **plu**).
fourbase	Construct bases for all four fundamental subspaces.
grams	Gram–Schmidt orthogonalization of the columns of A.
house	2 by 12 matrix giving corner coordinates of a house.
inverse	Matrix inverse (if it exists) by Gauss–Jordan elimination.
leftnull	Compute a basis for the left nullspace.
linefit	Plot the least squares fit to m given points by a line.
lsq	Least-squares solution to $Ax = b$ from $A^{\mathrm{T}}A\widehat{x} = A^{\mathrm{T}}b$.
normal	Eigenvalues and orthonormal eigenvectors when $A^{\mathrm{T}}A = AA^{\mathrm{T}}$.
nulbasis	Matrix of special solutions to $Ax = 0$ (basis for nullspace).
orthcomp	Find a basis for the orthogonal complement of a subspace.
partic	Particular solution of $Ax = b$, with all free variables zero.
plot2d	Two-dimensional plot for the house figures.
plu	Rectangular $PA = LU$ factorization with row exchanges.
poly2str	Express a polynomial as a string.
project	Project a vector b onto the column space of A.
projmat	Construct the projection matrix onto the column space of A.
randperm	Construct a random permutation.
rowbasis	Compute a basis for the row space from the pivot rows of R.
samespan	Test whether two matrices have the same column space.
signperm	Determinant of the permutation matrix with rows ordered by p.
slu	LU factorization of a square matrix using *no row exchanges*.
slv	Apply **slu** to solve the system $Ax = b$ allowing no row exchanges.
splu	Square $PA = LU$ factorization *with row exchanges*.
splv	The solution to a square, invertible system $Ax = b$.
symmeig	Compute the eigenvalues and eigenvectors of a symmetric matrix.
tridiag	Construct a tridiagonal matrix with constant diagonals a, b, c.

These Teaching Codes are directly available from the Linear Algebra Home Page: `http://web.mit.edu/18.06/www`.

They were written in MATLAB, and translated into Maple and Mathematica.

Index

L

M

N

Linear Algebra in a Nutshell

(A is n by n)

Nonsingular	Singular
A is invertible.	A is not invertible.
The columns are independent.	The columns are dependent.
The rows are independent.	The rows are dependent.
The determinant is not zero.	The determinant is zero.
$Ax = 0$ has one solution $x = 0$.	$Ax = 0$ has infinitely many solutions.
$Ax = b$ has one solution $x = A^{-1}b$.	$Ax = b$ has no solution or infinitely many.
A has n (nonzero) pivots.	A has $r < n$ pivots.
A has full rank $r = n$.	A has rank $r < n$.
The reduced row echelon form is $R = I$.	R has at least one zero row.
The column space is all of $\mathbf{R}^n$.	The column space has dimension $r < n$.
The row space is all of $\mathbf{R}^n$.	The row space has dimension $r < n$.
All eigenvalues are nonzero.	Zero is an eigenvalue of A.
$A^{\mathrm{T}}A$ is symmetric positive definite.	$A^{\mathrm{T}}A$ is only semidefinite.
A has n (positive) singular values.	A has $r < n$ singular values.

Each line of the singular column can be made quantitative using r.

SECOND-ORDER LINEAR DIFFERENTIAL EQUATIONS

A **second-order linear differential equation** has the form

$$\boxed{1} \qquad P(x)\frac{d^2y}{dx^2} + Q(x)\frac{dy}{dx} + R(x)y = G(x)$$

where P, Q, R, and G are continuous functions. Equations of this type arise in the study of the motion of a spring. In *Additional Topics: Applications of Second-Order Differential Equations* we will further pursue this application as well as the application to electric circuits.

In this section we study the case where $G(x) = 0$, for all x, in Equation 1. Such equations are called **homogeneous** linear equations. Thus, the form of a second-order linear homogeneous differential equation is

$$\boxed{2} \qquad P(x)\frac{d^2y}{dx^2} + Q(x)\frac{dy}{dx} + R(x)y = 0$$

If $G(x) \neq 0$ for some x, Equation 1 is **nonhomogeneous** and is discussed in *Additional Topics: Nonhomogeneous Linear Equations*.

Two basic facts enable us to solve homogeneous linear equations. The first of these says that if we know two solutions y_1 and y_2 of such an equation, then the **linear combination** $y = c_1y_1 + c_2y_2$ is also a solution.

> **3 Theorem** If $y_1(x)$ and $y_2(x)$ are both solutions of the linear homogeneous equation (2) and c_1 and c_2 are any constants, then the function
>
> $$y(x) = c_1y_1(x) + c_2y_2(x)$$
>
> is also a solution of Equation 2.

Proof Since y_1 and y_2 are solutions of Equation 2, we have

$$P(x)y_1'' + Q(x)y_1' + R(x)y_1 = 0$$

and

$$P(x)y_2'' + Q(x)y_2' + R(x)y_2 = 0$$

Therefore, using the basic rules for differentiation, we have

$$\begin{aligned}
&P(x)y'' + Q(x)y' + R(x)y \\
&\qquad = P(x)(c_1y_1 + c_2y_2)'' + Q(x)(c_1y_1 + c_2y_2)' + R(x)(c_1y_1 + c_2y_2) \\
&\qquad = P(x)(c_1y_1'' + c_2y_2'') + Q(x)(c_1y_1' + c_2y_2') + R(x)(c_1y_1 + c_2y_2) \\
&\qquad = c_1[P(x)y_1'' + Q(x)y_1' + R(x)y_1] + c_2[P(x)y_2'' + Q(x)y_2' + R(x)y_2] \\
&\qquad = c_1(0) + c_2(0) = 0
\end{aligned}$$

Thus, $y = c_1y_1 + c_2y_2$ is a solution of Equation 2. ■

The other fact we need is given by the following theorem, which is proved in more advanced courses. It says that the general solution is a linear combination of two **linearly independent** solutions y_1 and y_2. This means that neither y_1 nor y_2 is a constant multiple of the other. For instance, the functions $f(x) = x^2$ and $g(x) = 5x^2$ are linearly dependent, but $f(x) = e^x$ and $g(x) = xe^x$ are linearly independent.

4 Theorem If y_1 and y_2 are linearly independent solutions of Equation 2, and $P(x)$ is never 0, then the general solution is given by

$$y(x) = c_1y_1(x) + c_2y_2(x)$$

where c_1 and c_2 are arbitrary constants.

Theorem 4 is very useful because it says that if we know *two* particular linearly independent solutions, then we know *every* solution.

In general, it is not easy to discover particular solutions to a second-order linear equation. But it is always possible to do so if the coefficient functions P, Q, and R are constant functions, that is, if the differential equation has the form

$$ay'' + by' + cy = 0 \tag{5}$$

where a, b, and c are constants and $a \neq 0$.

It's not hard to think of some likely candidates for particular solutions of Equation 5 if we state the equation verbally. We are looking for a function y such that a constant times its second derivative y'' plus another constant times y' plus a third constant times y is equal to 0. We know that the exponential function $y = e^{rx}$ (where r is a constant) has the property that its derivative is a constant multiple of itself: $y' = re^{rx}$. Furthermore, $y'' = r^2e^{rx}$. If we substitute these expressions into Equation 5, we see that $y = e^{rx}$ is a solution if

$$ar^2e^{rx} + bre^{rx} + ce^{rx} = 0$$

or

$$(ar^2 + br + c)e^{rx} = 0$$

But e^{rx} is never 0. Thus, $y = e^{rx}$ is a solution of Equation 5 if r is a root of the equation

$$ar^2 + br + c = 0 \tag{6}$$

Equation 6 is called the **auxiliary equation** (or **characteristic equation**) of the differential equation $ay'' + by' + cy = 0$. Notice that it is an algebraic equation that is obtained from the differential equation by replacing y'' by r^2, y' by r, and y by 1.

Sometimes the roots r_1 and r_2 of the auxiliary equation can be found by factoring. In other cases they are found by using the quadratic formula:

$$r_1 = \frac{-b + \sqrt{b^2 - 4ac}}{2a} \qquad r_2 = \frac{-b - \sqrt{b^2 - 4ac}}{2a} \tag{7}$$

We distinguish three cases according to the sign of the discriminant $b^2 - 4ac$.

CASE I □ $b^2 - 4ac > 0$

In this case the roots r_1 and r_2 of the auxiliary equation are real and distinct, so $y_1 = e^{r_1x}$ and $y_2 = e^{r_2x}$ are two linearly independent solutions of Equation 5. (Note that e^{r_2x} is not a constant multiple of e^{r_1x}.) Therefore, by Theorem 4, we have the following fact.

8 If the roots r_1 and r_2 of the auxiliary equation $ar^2 + br + c = 0$ are real and unequal, then the general solution of $ay'' + by' + cy = 0$ is

$$y = c_1e^{r_1x} + c_2e^{r_2x}$$

■■ In Figure 1 the graphs of the basic solutions $f(x) = e^{2x}$ and $g(x) = e^{-3x}$ of the differential equation in Example 1 are shown in black and red, respectively. Some of the other solutions, linear combinations of f and g, are shown in blue.

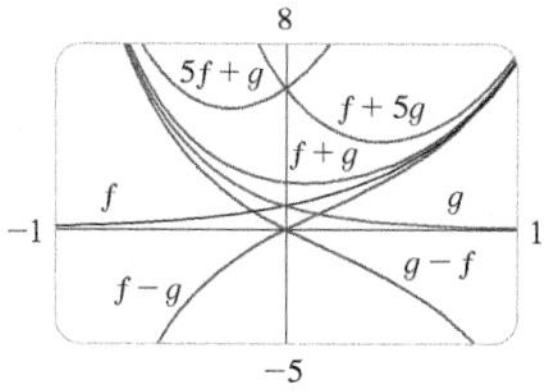

FIGURE 1

EXAMPLE 1 Solve the equation $y'' + y' - 6y = 0$.

SOLUTION The auxiliary equation is

$$r^2 + r - 6 = (r - 2)(r + 3) = 0$$

whose roots are $r = 2, -3$. Therefore, by (8) the general solution of the given differential equation is

$$y = c_1 e^{2x} + c_2 e^{-3x}$$

We could verify that this is indeed a solution by differentiating and substituting into the differential equation. ■

EXAMPLE 2 Solve $3\dfrac{d^2y}{dx^2} + \dfrac{dy}{dx} - y = 0$.

SOLUTION To solve the auxiliary equation $3r^2 + r - 1 = 0$ we use the quadratic formula:

$$r = \frac{-1 \pm \sqrt{13}}{6}$$

Since the roots are real and distinct, the general solution is

$$y = c_1 e^{(-1+\sqrt{13})x/6} + c_2 e^{(-1-\sqrt{13})x/6}$$ ■

CASE II □ $b^2 - 4ac = 0$

In this case $r_1 = r_2$; that is, the roots of the auxiliary equation are real and equal. Let's denote by r the common value of r_1 and r_2. Then, from Equations 7, we have

9 $$r = -\frac{b}{2a} \qquad \text{so} \qquad 2ar + b = 0$$

We know that $y_1 = e^{rx}$ is one solution of Equation 5. We now verify that $y_2 = xe^{rx}$ is also a solution:

$$\begin{aligned} ay_2'' + by_2' + cy_2 &= a(2re^{rx} + r^2xe^{rx}) + b(e^{rx} + rxe^{rx}) + cxe^{rx} \\ &= (2ar + b)e^{rx} + (ar^2 + br + c)xe^{rx} \\ &= 0(e^{rx}) + 0(xe^{rx}) = 0 \end{aligned}$$

The first term is 0 by Equations 9; the second term is 0 because r is a root of the auxiliary equation. Since $y_1 = e^{rx}$ and $y_2 = xe^{rx}$ are linearly independent solutions, Theorem 4 provides us with the general solution.

10 If the auxiliary equation $ar^2 + br + c = 0$ has only one real root r, then the general solution of $ay'' + by' + cy = 0$ is

$$y = c_1 e^{rx} + c_2 xe^{rx}$$

EXAMPLE 3 Solve the equation $4y'' + 12y' + 9y = 0$.

SOLUTION The auxiliary equation $4r^2 + 12r + 9 = 0$ can be factored as

$$(2r + 3)^2 = 0$$

■■ Figure 2 shows the basic solutions $f(x) = e^{-3x/2}$ and $g(x) = xe^{-3x/2}$ in Example 3 and some other members of the family of solutions. Notice that all of them approach 0 as $x \to \infty$.

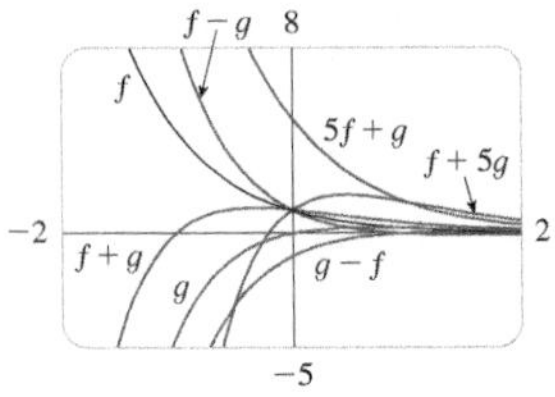

FIGURE 2

so the only root is $r = -\frac{3}{2}$. By (10) the general solution is

$$y = c_1 e^{-3x/2} + c_2 x e^{-3x/2}$$ ■

CASE III ▫ $b^2 - 4ac < 0$

In this case the roots r_1 and r_2 of the auxiliary equation are complex numbers. (See *Additional Topics: Complex Numbers* for information about complex numbers.) We can write

$$r_1 = \alpha + i\beta \qquad r_2 = \alpha - i\beta$$

where α and β are real numbers. [In fact, $\alpha = -b/(2a)$, $\beta = \sqrt{4ac - b^2}/(2a)$.] Then, using Euler's equation

$$e^{i\theta} = \cos\theta + i\sin\theta$$

from *Additional Topics: Complex Numbers*, we write the solution of the differential equation as

$$\begin{aligned} y &= C_1 e^{r_1 x} + C_2 e^{r_2 x} = C_1 e^{(\alpha + i\beta)x} + C_2 e^{(\alpha - i\beta)x} \\ &= C_1 e^{\alpha x}(\cos\beta x + i\sin\beta x) + C_2 e^{\alpha x}(\cos\beta x - i\sin\beta x) \\ &= e^{\alpha x}[(C_1 + C_2)\cos\beta x + i(C_1 - C_2)\sin\beta x] \\ &= e^{\alpha x}(c_1\cos\beta x + c_2\sin\beta x) \end{aligned}$$

where $c_1 = C_1 + C_2$, $c_2 = i(C_1 - C_2)$. This gives all solutions (real or complex) of the differential equation. The solutions are real when the constants c_1 and c_2 are real. We summarize the discussion as follows.

11 If the roots of the auxiliary equation $ar^2 + br + c = 0$ are the complex numbers $r_1 = \alpha + i\beta$, $r_2 = \alpha - i\beta$, then the general solution of $ay'' + by' + cy = 0$ is

$$y = e^{\alpha x}(c_1\cos\beta x + c_2\sin\beta x)$$

■■ Figure 3 shows the graphs of the solutions in Example 4, $f(x) = e^{3x}\cos 2x$ and $g(x) = e^{3x}\sin 2x$, together with some linear combinations. All solutions approach 0 as $x \to -\infty$.

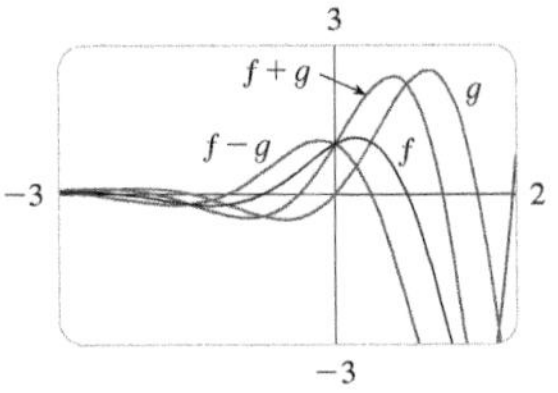

FIGURE 3

EXAMPLE 4 Solve the equation $y'' - 6y' + 13y = 0$.

SOLUTION The auxiliary equation is $r^2 - 6r + 13 = 0$. By the quadratic formula, the roots are

$$r = \frac{6 \pm \sqrt{36 - 52}}{2} = \frac{6 \pm \sqrt{-16}}{2} = 3 \pm 2i$$

By (11) the general solution of the differential equation is

$$y = e^{3x}(c_1\cos 2x + c_2\sin 2x)$$ ■

INITIAL-VALUE AND BOUNDARY-VALUE PROBLEMS

An **initial-value problem** for the second-order Equation 1 or 2 consists of finding a solution y of the differential equation that also satisfies initial conditions of the form

$$y(x_0) = y_0 \qquad y'(x_0) = y_1$$

where y_0 and y_1 are given constants. If P, Q, R, and G are continuous on an interval and $P(x) \neq 0$ there, then a theorem found in more advanced books guarantees the existence and uniqueness of a solution to this initial-value problem. Examples 5 and 6 illustrate the technique for solving such a problem.

EXAMPLE 5 Solve the initial-value problem

$$y'' + y' - 6y = 0 \qquad y(0) = 1 \qquad y'(0) = 0$$

■ ■ Figure 4 shows the graph of the solution of the initial-value problem in Example 5. Compare with Figure 1.

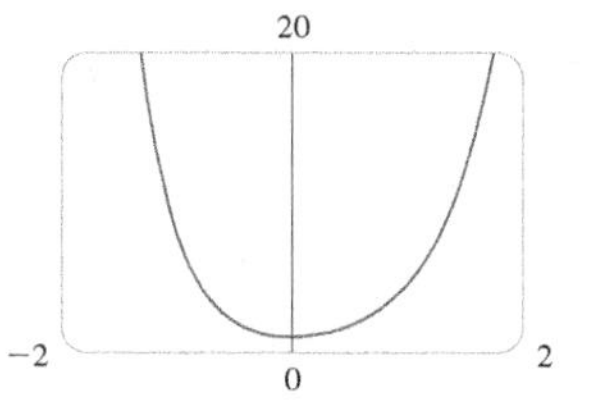

FIGURE 4

SOLUTION From Example 1 we know that the general solution of the differential equation is

$$y(x) = c_1e^{2x} + c_2e^{-3x}$$

Differentiating this solution, we get

$$y'(x) = 2c_1e^{2x} - 3c_2e^{-3x}$$

To satisfy the initial conditions we require that

12 $$y(0) = c_1 + c_2 = 1$$

13 $$y'(0) = 2c_1 - 3c_2 = 0$$

From (13) we have $c_2 = \frac{2}{3}c_1$ and so (12) gives

$$c_1 + \tfrac{2}{3}c_1 = 1 \qquad c_1 = \tfrac{3}{5} \qquad c_2 = \tfrac{2}{5}$$

Thus, the required solution of the initial-value problem is

$$y = \tfrac{3}{5}e^{2x} + \tfrac{2}{5}e^{-3x}$$ ■

EXAMPLE 6 Solve the initial-value problem

$$y'' + y = 0 \qquad y(0) = 2 \qquad y'(0) = 3$$

■ ■ The solution to Example 6 is graphed in Figure 5. It appears to be a shifted sine curve and, indeed, you can verify that another way of writing the solution is

$$y = \sqrt{13}\sin(x + \phi) \quad \text{where } \tan\phi = \tfrac{2}{3}$$

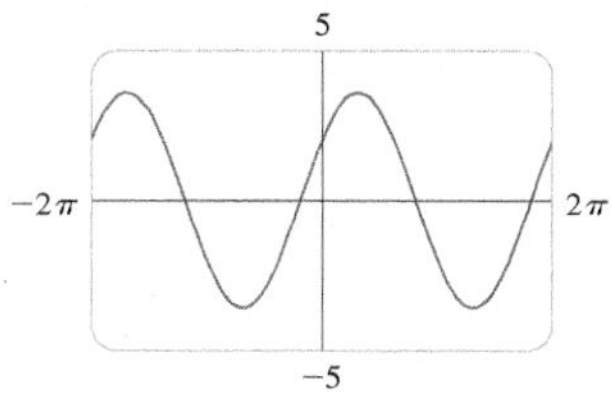

FIGURE 5

SOLUTION The auxiliary equation is $r^2 + 1 = 0$, or $r^2 = -1$, whose roots are $\pm i$. Thus $\alpha = 0$, $\beta = 1$, and since $e^{0x} = 1$, the general solution is

$$y(x) = c_1\cos x + c_2\sin x$$

Since $$y'(x) = -c_1\sin x + c_2\cos x$$

the initial conditions become

$$y(0) = c_1 = 2 \qquad y'(0) = c_2 = 3$$

Therefore, the solution of the initial-value problem is

$$y(x) = 2\cos x + 3\sin x$$ ■

A **boundary-value problem** for Equation 1 consists of finding a solution y of the differential equation that also satisfies boundary conditions of the form

$$y(x_0) = y_0 \qquad y(x_1) = y_1$$

In contrast with the situation for initial-value problems, a boundary-value problem does not always have a solution.

EXAMPLE 7 Solve the boundary-value problem

$$y'' + 2y' + y = 0 \qquad y(0) = 1 \qquad y(1) = 3$$

SOLUTION The auxiliary equation is

$$r^2 + 2r + 1 = 0 \qquad \text{or} \qquad (r + 1)^2 = 0$$

whose only root is $r = -1$. Therefore, the general solution is

$$y(x) = c_1e^{-x} + c_2xe^{-x}$$

■■ Figure 6 shows the graph of the solution of the boundary-value problem in Example 7.

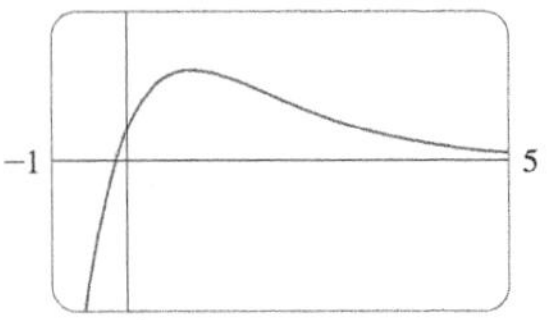

FIGURE 6

The boundary conditions are satisfied if

$$y(0) = c_1 = 1$$

$$y(1) = c_1 e^{-1} + c_2 e^{-1} = 3$$

The first condition gives $c_1 = 1$, so the second condition becomes

$$e^{-1} + c_2 e^{-1} = 3$$

Solving this equation for c_2 by first multiplying through by e, we get

$$1 + c_2 = 3e \qquad \text{so} \qquad c_2 = 3e - 1$$

Thus, the solution of the boundary-value problem is

$$y = e^{-x} + (3e - 1)xe^{-x}$$ ■

Summary: Solutions of $ay'' + by' + c = 0$

Roots of $ar^2 + br + c = 0$	General solution
r_1, r_2 real and distinct	$y = c_1 e^{r_1 x} + c_2 e^{r_2 x}$
$r_1 = r_2 = r$	$y = c_1 e^{rx} + c_2 x e^{rx}$
r_1, r_2 complex: $\alpha \pm i\beta$	$y = e^{\alpha x}(c_1 \cos \beta x + c_2 \sin \beta x)$

EXERCISES

A Click here for answers. S Click here for solutions.

1–13 ■ Solve the differential equation.

1. $y'' - 6y' + 8y = 0$

2. $y'' - 4y' + 8y = 0$

3. $y'' + 8y' + 41y = 0$

4. $2y'' - y' - y = 0$

5. $y'' - 2y' + y = 0$

6. $3y'' = 5y'$

7. $4y'' + y = 0$

8. $16y'' + 24y' + 9y = 0$

9. $4y'' + y' = 0$

10. $9y'' + 4y = 0$

11. $\dfrac{d^2y}{dt^2} - 2\dfrac{dy}{dt} - y = 0$

12. $\dfrac{d^2y}{dt^2} - 6\dfrac{dy}{dt} + 4y = 0$

13. $\dfrac{d^2y}{dt^2} + \dfrac{dy}{dt} + y = 0$

14–16 ■ Graph the two basic solutions of the differential equation and several other solutions. What features do the solutions have in common?

14. $6\dfrac{d^2y}{dx^2} - \dfrac{dy}{dx} - 2y = 0$

15. $\dfrac{d^2y}{dx^2} - 8\dfrac{dy}{dx} + 16y = 0$

16. $\dfrac{d^2y}{dx^2} - 2\dfrac{dy}{dx} + 5y = 0$

17–24 ■ Solve the initial-value problem.

17. $2y'' + 5y' + 3y = 0, \quad y(0) = 3, \quad y'(0) = -4$

18. $y'' + 3y = 0, \quad y(0) = 1, \quad y'(0) = 3$

19. $4y'' - 4y' + y = 0, \quad y(0) = 1, \quad y'(0) = -1.5$

20. $2y'' + 5y' - 3y = 0, \quad y(0) = 1, \quad y'(0) = 4$

21. $y'' + 16y = 0, \quad y(\pi/4) = -3, \quad y'(\pi/4) = 4$

22. $y'' - 2y' + 5y = 0, \quad y(\pi) = 0, \quad y'(\pi) = 2$

23. $y'' + 2y' + 2y = 0, \quad y(0) = 2, \quad y'(0) = 1$

24. $y'' + 12y' + 36y = 0, \quad y(1) = 0, \quad y'(1) = 1$

25–32 ■ Solve the boundary-value problem, if possible.

25. $4y'' + y = 0, \quad y(0) = 3, \quad y(\pi) = -4$

26. $y'' + 2y' = 0, \quad y(0) = 1, \quad y(1) = 2$

27. $y'' - 3y' + 2y = 0, \quad y(0) = 1, \quad y(3) = 0$

28. $y'' + 100y = 0, \quad y(0) = 2, \quad y(\pi) = 5$

29. $y'' - 6y' + 25y = 0, \quad y(0) = 1, \quad y(\pi) = 2$

30. $y'' - 6y' + 9y = 0, \quad y(0) = 1, \quad y(1) = 0$

31. $y'' + 4y' + 13y = 0, \quad y(0) = 2, \quad y(\pi/2) = 1$

32. $9y'' - 18y' + 10y = 0, \quad y(0) = 0, \quad y(\pi) = 1$

33. Let L be a nonzero real number.
(a) Show that the boundary-value problem $y'' + \lambda y = 0$, $y(0) = 0$, $y(L) = 0$ has only the trivial solution $y = 0$ for the cases $\lambda = 0$ and $\lambda < 0$.
(b) For the case $\lambda > 0$, find the values of λ for which this problem has a nontrivial solution and give the corresponding solution.

34. If a, b, and c are all positive constants and $y(x)$ is a solution of the differential equation $ay'' + by' + cy = 0$, show that $\lim_{x \to \infty} y(x) = 0$.

ANSWERS

S Click here for solutions.

1. $y = c_1 e^{4x} + c_2 e^{2x}$ **3.** $y = e^{-4x}(c_1 \cos 5x + c_2 \sin 5x)$

5. $y = c_1 e^{x} + c_2 x e^{x}$ **7.** $y = c_1 \cos(x/2) + c_2 \sin(x/2)$

9. $y = c_1 + c_2 e^{-x/4}$ **11.** $y = c_1 e^{(1+\sqrt{2})t} + c_2 e^{(1-\sqrt{2})t}$

13. $y = e^{-t/2}[c_1 \cos(\sqrt{3}t/2) + c_2 \sin(\sqrt{3}t/2)]$

15.

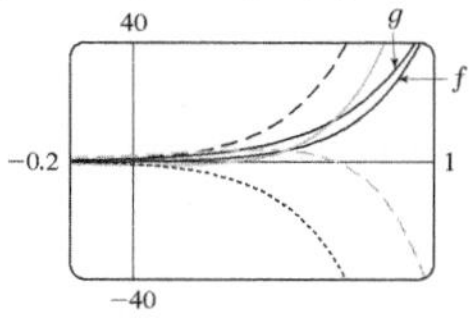

All solutions approach 0 as $x \to -\infty$ and approach $\pm\infty$ as $x \to \infty$.

17. $y = 2e^{-3x/2} + e^{-x}$

19. $y = e^{x/2} - 2xe^{x/2}$

21. $y = 3 \cos 4x - \sin 4x$

23. $y = e^{-x}(2 \cos x + 3 \sin x)$

25. $y = 3 \cos(\frac{1}{2}x) - 4 \sin(\frac{1}{2}x)$

27. $y = \dfrac{e^{x+3}}{e^3 - 1} + \dfrac{e^{2x}}{1 - e^3}$

29. No solution

31. $y = e^{-2x}(2 \cos 3x - e^{\pi} \sin 3x)$

33. (b) $\lambda = n^2\pi^2/L^2$, n a positive integer; $y = C \sin(n\pi x/L)$

SOLUTIONS

1. The auxiliary equation is $r^2 - 6r + 8 = 0 \;\Rightarrow\; (r-4)(r-2) = 0 \;\Rightarrow\; r = 4, r = 2$. Then by (8) the general solution is $y = c_1e^{4x} + c_2e^{2x}$.

2. The auxiliary equation is $r^2 - 4r + 8 = 0 \;\Rightarrow\; r = 2 \pm 2i$. Then by (11) the general solution is $y = e^{2x}(c_1 \cos 2x + c_2 \sin 2x)$.

3. The auxiliary equation is $r^2 + 8r + 41 = 0 \;\Rightarrow\; r = -4 \pm 5i$. Then by (11) the general solution is $y = e^{-4x}(c_1 \cos 5x + c_2 \sin 5x)$.

4. The auxiliary equation is $2r^2 - r - 1 = (2r+1)(r-1) = 0 \;\Rightarrow\; r = 1, r = -\frac{1}{2}$. Then the general solution is $y = c_1e^{x} + c_2e^{-x/2}$.

5. The auxiliary equation is $r^2 - 2r + 1 = (r-1)^2 = 0 \;\Rightarrow\; r = 1$. Then by (10), the general solution is $y = c_1e^{x} + c_2xe^{x}$.

6. The auxiliary equation is $3r^2 - 5r = r(3r-5) = 0 \;\Rightarrow\; r = 0, r = \frac{5}{3}$, so $y = c_1 + c_2e^{5x/3}$.

7. The auxiliary equation is $4r^2 + 1 = 0 \;\Rightarrow\; r = \pm\frac{1}{2}i$, so $y = c_1 \cos\left(\frac{1}{2}x\right) + c_2 \sin\left(\frac{1}{2}x\right)$.

8. The auxiliary equation is $16r^2 + 24r + 9 = (4r+3)^2 = 0 \;\Rightarrow\; r = -\frac{3}{4}$, so $y = c_1e^{-3x/4} + c_2xe^{-3x/4}$.

9. The auxiliary equation is $4r^2 + r = r(4r+1) = 0 \;\Rightarrow\; r = 0, r = -\frac{1}{4}$, so $y = c_1 + c_2e^{-x/4}$.

10. The auxiliary equation is $9r^2 + 4 = 0 \;\Rightarrow\; r = \pm\frac{2}{3}i$, so $y = c_1 \cos\left(\frac{2}{3}x\right) + c_2 \sin\left(\frac{2}{3}x\right)$.

11. The auxiliary equation is $r^2 - 2r - 1 = 0 \;\Rightarrow\; r = 1 \pm \sqrt{2}$, so $y = c_1e^{\left(1+\sqrt{2}\right)t} + c_2e^{\left(1-\sqrt{2}\right)t}$.

12. The auxiliary equation is $r^2 - 6r + 4 = 0 \;\Rightarrow\; r = 3 \pm \sqrt{5}$, so $y = c_1e^{\left(3+\sqrt{5}\right)t} + c_2e^{\left(3-\sqrt{5}\right)t}$.

13. The auxiliary equation is $r^2 + r + 1 = 0 \;\Rightarrow\; r = -\frac{1}{2} \pm \frac{\sqrt{3}}{2}i$, so $y = e^{-t/2}\left[c_1 \cos\left(\frac{\sqrt{3}}{2}t\right) + c_2 \sin\left(\frac{\sqrt{3}}{2}t\right)\right]$.

14. $6r^2 - r - 2 = (2r+1)(3r-2) = 0$ so $y = c_1e^{-x/2} + c_2e^{2x/3}$. The solutions $(c_1, c_2) = (0, 1)$, $(1, 0)$, $(1, 2)$, $(-2, 1)$ are shown. Each solution consists of a single continuous curve that approaches either 0 or $\pm\infty$ as $x \to \pm\infty$.

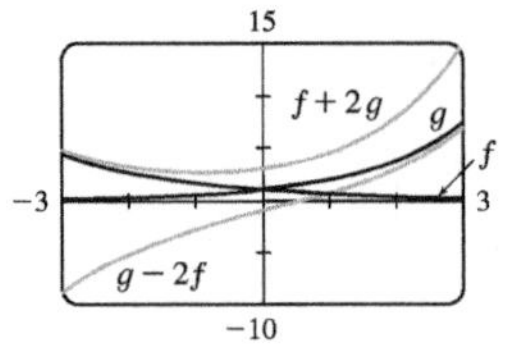

15. $r^2 - 8r + 16 = (r-4)^2 = 0$ so $y = c_1e^{4x} + c_2xe^{4x}$. The graphs are all asymptotic to the x-axis as $x \to -\infty$, and as $x \to \infty$ the solutions tend to $\pm\infty$.

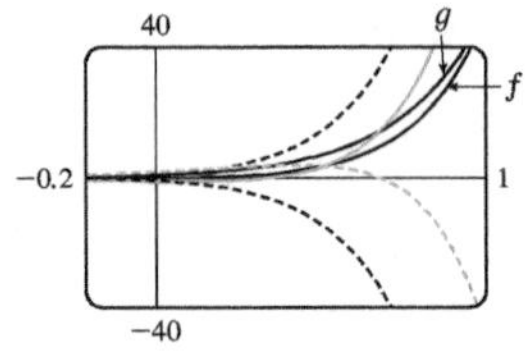

16. $r^2 - 2r + 5 = 0 \;\Rightarrow\; r = 1 \pm 2i$ and the solution is $y = e^{x}(c_1 \cos 2x + c_2 \sin 2x)$. Graphs for $(c_1, c_2) = (1, 0), (0, 1), (1, -1), (-1, 2)$ are shown. The solutions are all asymptotic to the x-axis as $x \to -\infty$ and they all oscillate. The amplitudes of the oscillations become arbitrarily large as $x \to \infty$ and arbitrarily small as $x \to -\infty$.

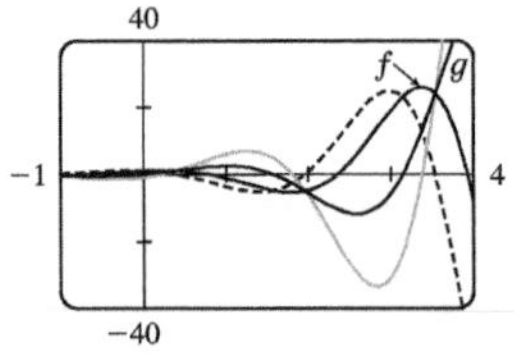

17. $2r^2 + 5r + 3 = (2r+3)(r+1) = 0$, so $r = -\frac{3}{2}, r = -1$ and the general solution is $y = c_1e^{-3x/2} + c_2e^{-x}$. Then $y(0) = 3 \;\Rightarrow\; c_1 + c_2 = 3$ and $y'(0) = -4 \;\Rightarrow\; -\frac{3}{2}c_1 - c_2 = -4$, so $c_1 = 2$ and $c_2 = 1$. Thus the solution to the initial-value problem is $y = 2e^{-3x/2} + e^{-x}$.

18. $r^2+3=0 \Rightarrow r=\pm\sqrt{3}i$ and the general solution is $y=e^{0x}\left(c_1\cos(\sqrt{3}\,x)+c_2\sin(\sqrt{3}\,x)\right)=c_1\cos(\sqrt{3}\,x)+c_2\sin(\sqrt{3}\,x)$. Then $y(0)=1 \Rightarrow c_1=1$ and $y'(0)=3 \Rightarrow c_2=\sqrt{3}$, so the solution to the initial-value problem is $y=\cos(\sqrt{3}\,x)+\sqrt{3}\sin(\sqrt{3}\,x)$.

19. $4r^2-4r+1=(2r-1)^2=0 \Rightarrow r=\frac{1}{2}$ and the general solution is $y=c_1e^{x/2}+c_2xe^{x/2}$. Then $y(0)=1 \Rightarrow c_1=1$ and $y'(0)=-1.5 \Rightarrow \frac{1}{2}c_1+c_2=-1.5$, so $c_2=-2$ and the solution to the initial-value problem is $y=e^{x/2}-2xe^{x/2}$.

20. $2r^2+5r-3=(2r-1)(r+3)=0 \Rightarrow r=\frac{1}{2}, r=-3$ and the general solution is $y=c_1e^{x/2}+c_2e^{-3x}$. Then $1=y(0)=c_1+c_2$ and $4=y'(0)=\frac{1}{2}c_1-3c_2$ so $c_1=2, c_2=-1$ and the solution to the initial-value problem is $y=2e^{x/2}-e^{-3x}$.

21. $r^2+16=0 \Rightarrow r=\pm4i$ and the general solution is $y=e^{0x}(c_1\cos 4x+c_2\sin 4x)=c_1\cos 4x+c_2\sin 4x$. Then $y\left(\frac{\pi}{4}\right)=-3 \Rightarrow -c_1=-3 \Rightarrow c_1=3$ and $y'\left(\frac{\pi}{4}\right)=4 \Rightarrow -4c_2=4 \Rightarrow c_2=-1$, so the solution to the initial-value problem is $y=3\cos 4x-\sin 4x$.

22. $r^2-2r+5=0 \Rightarrow r=1\pm2i$ and the general solution is $y=e^x(c_1\cos 2x+c_2\sin 2x)$. Then $0=y(\pi)=e^\pi(c_1+0) \Rightarrow c_1=0$ and $2=y'(\pi)=(c_1+2c_2)e^\pi \Rightarrow c_2=1/e^\pi$ and the solution to the initial-value problem is $y=\dfrac{e^x}{e^\pi}\sin 2x=e^{x-\pi}\sin 2x$.

23. $r^2+2r+2=0 \Rightarrow r=-1\pm i$ and the general solution is $y=e^{-x}(c_1\cos x+c_2\sin x)$. Then $2=y(0)=c_1$ and $1=y'(0)=c_2-c_1 \Rightarrow c_2=3$ and the solution to the initial-value problem is $y=e^{-x}(2\cos x+3\sin x)$.

24. $r^2+12r+36=(r+6)^2=0 \Rightarrow r=-6$ and the general solution is $y=c_1e^{-6x}+c_2xe^{-6x}$. Then $0=y(1)=c_1e^{-6}+c_2e^{-6} \Rightarrow c_1+c_2=0$ and $1=y'(1)=-6c_1e^{-6}-5c_2e^{-6} \Rightarrow 6c_1+5c_2=-e^6$, so $c_1=-e^6$ and $c_2=e^6$. The solution to the initial-value problem is $y=-e^6e^{-6x}+e^6xe^{-6x}=(x-1)e^{6-6x}$.

25. $4r^2+1=0 \Rightarrow r=\pm\frac{1}{2}i$ and the general solution is $y=c_1\cos\left(\frac{1}{2}x\right)+c_2\sin\left(\frac{1}{2}x\right)$. Then $3=y(0)=c_1$ and $-4=y(\pi)=c_2$, so the solution of the boundary-value problem is $y=3\cos\left(\frac{1}{2}x\right)-4\sin\left(\frac{1}{2}x\right)$.

26. $r^2+2r=r(2+r)=0 \Rightarrow r=0, r=-2$ and the general solution is $y=c_1+c_2e^{-2x}$. Then $1=y(0)=c_1+c_2$ and $2=y(1)=c_1+c_2e^{-2}$ so $c_2=\dfrac{e^2}{1-e^2}$, $c_1=\dfrac{1-2e^2}{1-e^2}$. The solution of the boundary-value problem is $y=\dfrac{1-2e^2}{1-e^2}+\dfrac{e^2}{1-e^2}\cdot e^{-2x}$.

27. $r^2-3r+2=(r-2)(r-1)=0 \Rightarrow r=1, r=2$ and the general solution is $y=c_1e^x+c_2e^{2x}$. Then $1=y(0)=c_1+c_2$ and $0=y(3)=c_1e^3+c_2e^6$ so $c_2=1/(1-e^3)$ and $c_1=e^3/(e^3-1)$. The solution of the boundary-value problem is $y=\dfrac{e^{x+3}}{e^3-1}+\dfrac{e^{2x}}{1-e^3}$.

28. $r^2+100=0 \Rightarrow r=\pm10i$ and the general solution is $y=c_1\cos 10x+c_2\sin 10x$. But $2=y(0)=c_1$ and $5=y(\pi)=c_1$, so there is no solution.

29. $r^2-6r+25=0 \Rightarrow r=3\pm4i$ and the general solution is $y=e^{3x}(c_1\cos 4x+c_2\sin 4x)$. But $1=y(0)=c_1$ and $2=y(\pi)=c_1e^{3\pi} \Rightarrow c_1=2/e^{3\pi}$, so there is no solution.

30. $r^2-6r+9=(r-3)^2=0 \Rightarrow r=3$ and the general solution is $y=c_1e^{3x}+c_2xe^{3x}$. Then $1=y(0)=c_1$ and $0=y(1)=c_1e^3+c_2e^3 \Rightarrow c_2=-1$. The solution of the boundary-value problem is $y=e^{3x}-xe^{3x}$.

31. $r^2+4r+13=0 \Rightarrow r=-2\pm3i$ and the general solution is $y=e^{-2x}(c_1\cos 3x+c_2\sin 3x)$. But $2=y(0)=c_1$ and $1=y\left(\frac{\pi}{2}\right)=e^{-\pi}(-c_2)$, so the solution to the boundary-value problem is $y=e^{-2x}(2\cos 3x-e^\pi\sin 3x)$.

32. $9r^2-18r+10=0 \Rightarrow r=1\pm\frac{1}{3}i$ and the general solution is $y=e^x\left(c_1\cos\frac{x}{3}+c_2\sin\frac{x}{3}\right)$. Then $0=y(0)=c_1$ and $1=y(\pi)=e^\pi\left(\frac{1}{2}c_1+\frac{\sqrt{3}}{2}c_2\right) \Rightarrow c_2=\dfrac{2}{\sqrt{3}\,e^\pi}$. The solution of the boundary-value problem is $y=\dfrac{2e^x}{\sqrt{3}\,e^\pi}\sin\left(\dfrac{x}{3}\right)=\dfrac{2}{\sqrt{3}}e^{x-\pi}\sin\left(\dfrac{x}{3}\right)$.

33. (a) *Case 1* ($\lambda = 0$): $y'' + \lambda y = 0 \;\Rightarrow\; y'' = 0$ which has an auxiliary equation $r^2 = 0 \;\Rightarrow\; r = 0 \;\Rightarrow$ $y = c_1 + c_2 x$ where $y(0) = 0$ and $y(L) = 0$. Thus, $0 = y(0) = c_1$ and $0 = y(L) = c_2 L \;\Rightarrow\; c_1 = c_2 = 0$. Thus, $y = 0$.

Case 2 ($\lambda < 0$): $y'' + \lambda y = 0$ has auxiliary equation $r^2 = -\lambda \;\Rightarrow\; r = \pm\sqrt{-\lambda}$ (distinct and real since $\lambda < 0$) $\Rightarrow\; y = c_1 e^{\sqrt{-\lambda}x} + c_2 e^{-\sqrt{-\lambda}x}$ where $y(0) = 0$ and $y(L) = 0$. Thus, $0 = y(0) = c_1 + c_2$ (∗) and $0 = y(L) = c_1 e^{\sqrt{-\lambda}L} + c_2 e^{-\sqrt{-\lambda}L}$ (†).

Multiplying (∗) by $e^{\sqrt{-\lambda}L}$ and subtracting (†) gives $c_2\left(e^{\sqrt{-\lambda}L} - e^{-\sqrt{-\lambda}L}\right) = 0 \;\Rightarrow\; c_2 = 0$ and thus $c_1 = 0$ from (∗). Thus, $y = 0$ for the cases $\lambda = 0$ and $\lambda < 0$.

(b) $y'' + \lambda y = 0$ has an auxiliary equation $r^2 + \lambda = 0 \;\Rightarrow\; r = \pm i\sqrt{\lambda} \;\Rightarrow\; y = c_1 \cos\sqrt{\lambda}\,x + c_2 \sin\sqrt{\lambda}\,x$ where $y(0) = 0$ and $y(L) = 0$. Thus, $0 = y(0) = c_1$ and $0 = y(L) = c_2 \sin\sqrt{\lambda}L$ since $c_1 = 0$. Since we cannot have a trivial solution, $c_2 \neq 0$ and thus $\sin\sqrt{\lambda}\,L = 0 \;\Rightarrow\; \sqrt{\lambda}\,L = n\pi$ where n is an integer $\Rightarrow\; \lambda = n^2\pi^2/L^2$ and $y = c_2 \sin(n\pi x/L)$ where n is an integer.

34. The auxiliary equation is $ar^2 + br + c = 0$. If $b^2 - 4ac > 0$, then any solution is of the form $y(x) = c_1 e^{r_1 x} + c_2 e^{r_2 x}$ where $r_1 = \dfrac{-b + \sqrt{b^2 - 4ac}}{2a}$ and $r_2 = \dfrac{-b - \sqrt{b^2 - 4ac}}{2a}$. But a, b, and c are all positive so both r_1 and r_2 are negative and $\lim_{x\to\infty} y(x) = 0$. If $b^2 - 4ac = 0$, then any solution is of the form $y(x) = c_1 e^{rx} + c_2 x e^{rx}$ where $r = -b/(2a) < 0$ since a, b are positive. Hence $\lim_{x\to\infty} y(x) = 0$. Finally if $b^2 - 4ac < 0$, then any solution is of the form $y(x) = e^{\alpha x}(c_1 \cos\beta x + c_2 \sin\beta x)$ where $\alpha = -b/(2a) < 0$ since a and b are positive. Thus $\lim_{x\to\infty} y(x) = 0$.